Essentials of Anatomy and Physiology

Fourth Edition

Rod R. Seeley
Idaho State University

Trent D. Stephens
Idaho State University

Philip Tate
Phoenix College

McGraw Hill

Boston   Burr Ridge, IL   Dubuque, IA   Madison, WI   New York   San Francisco   St. Louis
Bangkok   Bogotá   Caracas   Kuala Lumpur   Lisbon   London   Madrid   Mexico City
Milan   Montreal   New Del   Sydney   Taipei   Toronto

McGraw-Hill Higher Education

*A Division of The **McGraw-Hill** Companies*

ESSENTIALS OF ANATOMY AND PHYSIOLOGY, FOURTH EDITION

Published by McGraw-Hill, a business unit of The McGraw-Hill Companies, Inc., 1221 Avenue of the Americas, New York, NY 10020. Copyright © 2002, 1999, 1996, 1991 by The McGraw-Hill Companies, Inc. All rights reserved. No part of this publication may be reproduced or distributed in any form or by any means, or stored in a database or retrieval system, without the prior written consent of The McGraw-Hill Companies, Inc., including, but not limited to, in any network or other electronic storage or transmission, or broadcast for distance learning.

Some ancillaries, including electronic and print components, may not be available to customers outside the United States.

This book is printed on acid-free paper.

1 2 3 4 5 6 7 8 9 0 VNH/VNH 0 9 8 7 6 5 4 3 2 1

ISBN 0–07–027260–3
ISBN 0–07–112264–8 (ISE)

Sponsoring editor: *Martin J. Lange*
Developmental editor: *Kristine A. Queck*
Senior development manager: *Kristine Tibbetts*
Marketing manager: *Michelle Watnick*
Project manager: *Jill R. Peter*
Production supervisor: *Laura Fuller*
Designer: *K. Wayne Harms*
Cover designer: *Nathan Bahls*
Cover image: *PhotoDisc*
Photo research coordinator: *John C. Leland*
Photo research: *Alexandra Truitt & Jerry Marshall www.pictureresearching.com*
Senior supplement producer: *Stacy A. Patch*
Media technology senior producer: *Barbara R. Block*
Compositor: *GTS Graphics, Inc.*
Typeface: *10/12 Garamond*
Printer: *Von Hoffmann Press, Inc.*

The credits section for this book begins on page 616 and is considered an extension of the copyright page.

Library of Congress Cataloging-in-Publication Data

Seeley, Rod R.
    Essentials of anatomy and physiology / Rod R. Seeley, Trent D. Stephens, Philip Tate. — 4th ed.
       p.   cm.
    Includes index.
    ISBN 0–07–027260–3
    1. Human physiology. 2. Human anatomy. I. Stephens, Trent D. II. Tate, Philip. III. Title.

    QP34.5 .S418   2002
    612–dc21
                            2001018731
                            CIP

INTERNATIONAL EDITION ISBN 0–07–112264–8
Copyright © 2002. Exclusive rights by The McGraw-Hill Companies, Inc., for manufacture and export. This book cannot be re-exported from the country to which it is sold by McGraw-Hill. The International Edition is not available in North America.

www.mhhe.com

Brief Contents

Appendices

Contents

About the Authors

Rod R. Seeley   Professor of Physiology, Idaho State University

With a B.S. in zoology from Idaho State University and an M.S. and Ph.D. in zoology from Utah State University, Rod Seeley has built a solid reputation as a widely published author of journal and feature articles, a popular public lecturer, and an award-winning instructor. Very much involved in the methods and mechanisms that help students learn, he contributes to this text his teaching expertise and proven ability to communicate effectively in any medium.

Trent D. Stephens   Professor of Anatomy and Embryology, Idaho State University

An award-winning educator, Trent Stephens teaches human anatomy, neuroanatomy, and embryology. His skill as a biological illustrator has greatly influenced every illustration in this text. With B.S. and M.S. degrees in zoology from Brigham Young University and a Ph.D. in anatomy from the University of Pennsylvania, Trent Stephens has also published numerous scientific papers and books. His students continually rate him highly on their evaluations—you will too!

Philip Tate   Instructor of Anatomy and Physiology, Phoenix College

From the community college to the private 4-year college, Phil Tate has taught anatomy and physiology to all levels of students: nursing and allied health, physical education, and biology majors. At San Diego State University, Phil earned B.S. degrees in both mathematics and zoology and an M.S. in ecology. He earned his doctorate in biological education from Idaho State University.

Student Preface

Human anatomy and physiology courses present exciting challenges. A basic knowledge of the structure and function of cells, organs, and organ systems is necessary to understand how life is maintained, how we can survive changes, and how to predict the consequences of malfunctions. Nearly everyone is interested in knowing more about the human body. For example, most people are eager to learn about the structure and function of the heart, especially when someone they know has problems such as coronary artery disease, heart attacks, heart failure, or damaged heart valves. Others want to know more about the reproductive systems, perhaps as background information when fertility problems arise. This information is also helpful to those who try to pursue a healthy life style, critically evaluate information presented in advertisements, or understand information presented to them by health care professionals. It is clear that future health care professionals must have a solid understanding of the structure and function of the body so they can provide care for patients. Whether a student intends to become a health professional or simply an informed citizen, understanding the basic structure and function of organs and organ systems is an important place to begin.

Essentials of Anatomy and Physiology is designed to help you develop a solid, basic understanding of anatomy and physiology without presenting an overwhelming amount of detail. Great care has been taken to select the most important terms and carefully describe the anatomy of cells, organs, and organ systems. This textbook provides clear and accurate descriptions of anatomical structures, explanations of how each structure works, and examples of how body structures work together to maintain life. To emphasize the basic concepts of anatomy and physiology, we have provided explanations of how the systems respond to events such as aging, changes in physical activity, and disease. We have included elements in the text that encourage you to remember how structures work, and to use the information to analyze and predict responses to a variety of changes. For example, enough information is presented to allow you to understand the normal structure and function of the heart and how the heart responds when a person exercises, or to predict the consequences of many conditions, such as blood loss or blood transfusions. The approach is both relevant and exciting. Critical thinking exercises have been included to emphasize the relevancy of the information and to help you develop a working knowledge of the subject.

Chapter Structure and Learning Aids

Knowing the format of the chapters in a text will help you understand the learning aids available to you. A "Visual Guide" to the book follows this preface. It shows the structure of a chapter and calls attention to features designed to aid your learning. This information will help you plan the approach you use to study and how to evaluate your understanding of the information before you take exams. For example, reviewing the objectives listed at the beginning of each chapter allows you to understand what instructors will expect you to know. Answering the Content Review questions at the end of each chapter will help you determine whether you know the major concepts presented in the chapters. The Predict questions are designed to help you learn how to logically predict outcomes by applying the material presented in the chapters. Answers to these questions are included in the text to help you follow the logic used to answer them correctly. The Develop Your Reasoning Skills questions at the end of each chapter are designed to help you further learn to think critically and apply the knowledge gained from reading the chapter.

Art Program

Tremendous effort has been dedicated to developing exceptional illustrations for this text. Drawings have been painstakingly crafted and refined so they represent anatomical structures and physiological processes with utmost clarity and accuracy. Photographs have been carefully selected to complement the illustrations and support the text discussions. A special series of figures has been developed to concisely show how structures are controlled to maintain homeostasis. All of the illustrations and photographs in the text are visually appealing and intellectually stimulating. They are designed to provide concrete, visual reinforcement of the topics discussed throughout the text. Careful examination of each figure will greatly assist you in fully understanding the concepts of anatomy and physiology.

Supplements

This book is just one part of a large multimedia package of learning tools. *The Essentials of Anatomy and Physiology* Online Learning Center is your gateway to an enriching interactive study environment. You can order additional study aids—including anatomy atlases, flashcards, coloring guides, and instructional CD-ROMs—by calling the McGraw-Hill Customer Service Center at 800-338-3987. The "Visual Guide" that follows this preface offers a preview of some of the exciting multimedia products that can be used in conjunction with *Essentials of Anatomy and Physiology* . A complete listing of the supplemental materials available for use with this text is provided on page xviii.

E-mail us!

We have written this text to help students learn anatomy and physiology. We greatly enjoy and benefit from correspondence with students. It is helpful to know what you find to be most useful in the text and also what still needs further clarification. We are interested in improving the text and your constructive comments are both helpful and appreciated. If you have difficulty understanding a concept presented in the text, contact us via the Message Board located on the Online Learning Center at www.mhhe.com/biosci/ap/seeleyessentials4e/student/olc/message.mhtml/. We would be delighted to help you. The process of explaining difficult concepts to students can lead to better ways to present the material. Your suggestion may well result in improvements to future editions of the text.

Visual Guide

Learning Aids

Chapter Objectives

Each chapter begins with a series of objectives that emphasize important facts, topics, and concepts to be covered.

Key Terms

All key terms in the chapter are listed and defined on the opening page. Pronunciation guides are provided for complex words, and a term's derivation or origin is given when knowing the original meaning is instructionally helpful. Within the chapter, key terms are set in boldface. They are also gathered in the glossary at the end of the book.

Predict

Placed throughout every chapter, these innovative critical thinking exercises are designed to develop problem-solving skills. Based on information covered in the adjacent narrative, Predict questions challenge students to apply new concepts as they solve a problem. Answers are given at the end of each chapter.

Did You Know?

These boxed sidebars provide relevant and interesting examples to enhance the background of students who plan to pursue health-related careers.

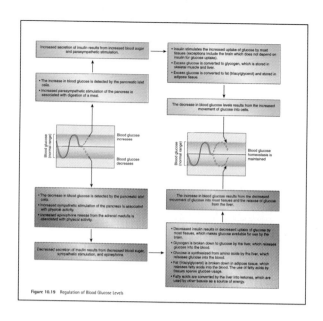

Homeostasis Figures

These specialized figures illustrate the mechanisms of homeostasis by summarizing the functions of a system and the means by which that system regulates a parameter within a narrow range of values.

Clinical Focus

These in-depth boxed essays explore relevant topics of clinical interest. Subjects covered include pathologies, current research, sports medicine, exercise physiology, pharmacology, and clinical applications.

Systems Pathology

These modified case studies explore a specific disorder or condition related to a particular body system. In addition to a case scenario and background information about the subject condition, every Systems Pathology box includes a Predict question and a System Interactions table that summarizes how the condition profiled impacts each body system.

Summary

The integumentary system consists of the skin, hair, glands, and nails.

Functions of the Integumentary System

The integumentary system separates and protects us from the external environment. Other functions include sensation, vitamin D production, temperature regulation, and excretion of small amounts of waste products.

Hypodermis

• The hypodermis is loose connective tissue that attaches the skin to underlying tissues.
• About half of the body's fat is stored in the hypodermis.

Skin

Dermis

• The dermis is dense connective tissue.
• Collagen and elastic fibers provide structural strength, and the blood vessels of the papillae supply the epidermis with nutrients.

Epidermis

• The epidermis is stratified squamous epithelium divided into strata. Cells are produced in the stratum basale.
  The stratum corneum is many layers of dead, squamous cells containing hard keratin. The most superficial layers are sloughed.
• Keratinization is the transformation of stratum basale cells into stratum corneum cells.
  Structural strength results from keratin inside the cells and from desmosomes, which hold the cells together.
  Permeability characteristics result from lipids surrounding the cells.

Skin Color

• Melanocytes produce melanin, which is responsible for different racial skin colors. Melanin production is determined genetically but can be modified by hormones and ultraviolet light (tanning).
• Carotene, a plant pigment ingested as a source of vitamin A, can cause the skin to appear yellowish.
• Scattering of light by collagen produces a bluish color.
• Increased blood flow produces a red skin color, whereas a decreased blood flow causes a pale skin color. Decreased blood oxygen results in the blue color of cyanosis.

Accessory Skin Structures

Hair

• Hairs are columns of dead, keratinized epithelial cells. Each hair consists of a shaft (above the skin), root (below the skin), and hair bulb (site of hair cell formation).
• Hairs have a growth phase and a resting phase.

Muscles

• Contraction of the arrector pili, which are smooth muscles, causes hair to "stand on end" and produces "goose flesh."

Glands

• Sebaceous glands produce sebum, which oils the hair and the surface of the skin.

• Merocrine sweat glands produce sweat, which cools the body.
• Apocrine sweat glands produce an organic secretion that can be broken down by bacteria to cause body odor.

Nails

• The nail consists of the nail body and nail root.
• The nail matrix produces the nail, which is stratum corneum containing hard keratin.

Physiology of the Integumentary System

Protection

• The skin prevents the entry of microorganisms, acts as a permeability barrier, and provides protection against abrasion and ultraviolet light.

Sensation

• The skin contains sensory receptors for pain, heat, cold, and pressure.

Vitamin D Production

• Ultraviolet light stimulates the production of a precursor molecule in the skin that is modified by the liver and kidneys into vitamin D.
• Vitamin D increases calcium uptake in the intestines.

Temperature Regulation

• Through dilation and constriction of blood vessels, the skin controls heat loss from the body.
• Evaporation of sweat cools the body.

Excretion

• Skin glands remove small amounts of waste products but are not important in excretion.

Effects of Aging on the Integumentary System

• Blood flow to the skin is reduced, the skin becomes thinner, and elasticity is lost.
• Sweat and sebaceous glands are less active, and the number of melanocytes decreases.

The Integumentary System as a Diagnostic Aid

• The integumentary system is easily observed and often reflects events occurring in other parts of the body (e.g., cyanosis, jaundice, rashes).

Burns

• Partial-thickness burns damage only the epidermis (first-degree burns) or the epidermis and the dermis (second-degree burns).
• Full-thickness burns (third-degree burns) destroy the epidermis, dermis, and usually underlying tissues.

Skin Cancer

• Basal cell carcinoma involves the cells of the stratum basale and is readily treatable.
• Squamous cell carcinoma involves the cells immediately superficial to the stratum basale and can metastasize.
• Malignant melanoma involves melanocytes, can metastasize, and is often fatal.

Chapter Summary

This summary outline briefly states the important facts and concepts covered in each chapter to provide a convenient "big picture" of the chapter content.

Content Review

1. Name the components of the integumentary system.
2. What type of tissue is the hypodermis, and what are its functions?
3. What type of tissue is the dermis? What is responsible for its structural strength? How does the dermis supply the epidermis with blood?
4. What kind of tissue is the epidermis? In which stratum of the epidermis are new cells formed? From which stratum are they sloughed?
5. Define "keratinization." What structural changes does keratinization produce to make the skin resistant to abrasion and water loss?
6. Name the cells that produce melanin. What happens to the melanin after it is produced? What is the function of melanin?
7. Describe the factors that determine the amount of melanin produced in the skin.
8. How do melanin, carotene, collagen, and blood affect skin color?
9. Define the "root," "shaft," and "hair bulb" of a hair. What kind of cells are found in a hair?
10. What is a hair follicle? Why is it important in the repair of skin?
11. What part of a hair is the site of hair growth? What are the stages of hair growth?

12. What happens when the arrector pili of the skin contract?
13. What secretion is produced by the sebaceous glands? What is the function of the secretion?
14. Which glands of the skin are responsible for cooling the body? Which glands are involved in producing body odor?
15. Name the parts of a nail. Where are the cells that make up the nail produced, and what kind of cells make up a nail? What is the lunula? Describe nail growth.
16. How does the integumentary system provide protection?
17. List the types of sensations detected by receptors in the skin.
18. Describe the production of vitamin D by the body. What is the function of vitamin D?
19. How does the integumentary system assist in the regulation of body temperature?
20. Name the substances excreted by skin glands. Is the skin an important site of excretion?
21. What changes occur in the skin as a result of aging?
22. Why is the skin a useful diagnostic aid? Give three examples of how the skin functions as a diagnostic aid.
23. Define the different categories of burns. How is repair accomplished after each type?
24. What is the most common cause of skin cancer? Describe three types of skin cancer and the risks of each type.

Content Review

These questions systematically review the chapter content by requiring students to summarize or restate the content in their own words. Answering these questions helps students determine whether they have mastered the important points presented in the chapter.

Develop Your Reasoning Skills

1. A woman has stretch marks on her abdomen, yet she states that she has never been pregnant. Is this possible?
2. Harry Fastfeet, a white man, jogs on a cool day. What color would you expect his skin to be (a) after going outside and just before starting to run, (b) during the run, and (c) 5 minutes after the run?
3. Given what you know about the cause of acne, propose some ways to prevent or treat the disorder.

4. Consider the following statement: Dark-skinned children are more susceptible to rickets (insufficient calcium in the bones) than fair-skinned children. Defend or refute this statement.
5. Pulling on hair can be quite painful, yet cutting hair is not painful. Explain.

Develop Your Reasoning Skills

These innovative critical thinking exercises require the application of chapter content to new situations. They utilize chapter concepts to provide additional practice in problem solving.

Answers to Predict Questions

1. p. xx. Because the permeability barrier is composed mainly of lipids surrounding the epidermal cells, substances that are lipid-soluble can easily diffuse through the barrier. This fact is used as a basis for administering some medications through the skin. On the other hand, water-soluble substances have difficulty diffusing through the skin. The lipid barrier of the skin prevents water loss from the body.
2. p. xx. (a) The lips are pinker or redder than the palms of the hand. Several explanations for this are possible. There could be more blood vessels in the lips, there could be

increased blood flow in the lips, or the blood vessels could be easier to see through the epidermis of the lips. The last possibility actually explains most of the difference in color between the lips and palms. The epidermis of the lips is thinner and not as heavily keratinized as that of the palms. In addition, the dermal papillae containing the blood vessels in the lips are "high" and closer to the surface.
(b) A person who does manual labor has a thicker stratum corneum (and possibly calluses) than a person who does not perform manual labor. The thicker epidermis masks the underlying blood vessels, and the palms do not

appear as pink. In addition, carotene accumulating in the lipids of the stratum corneum might give the palms a yellowish cast.
(c) The posterior surface of the forearm appears darker because of the tanning effect of ultraviolet light from the sun. The posterior surface of the forearm is usually exposed to more sunlight than the anterior surface of the forearm.
3. p. xx. The story is impossible. Hair color results from melanin that is added to the hair in the hair bulb as the hair grows. The hair itself is dead. To turn white, the hair must grow out without the addition of melanin. This,

Answers to Predict Questions

Predict questions are answered at the end of each chapter so students can evaluate their own responses and understand the logic used to arrive at the correct answer.

Online Learning Center

The Online Learning Center (OLC) that accompanies this text is found at www.mhhe.com/seeleyessentials. This online resource offers an extensive array of learning tools that are tailored to coincide with each chapter of the text.

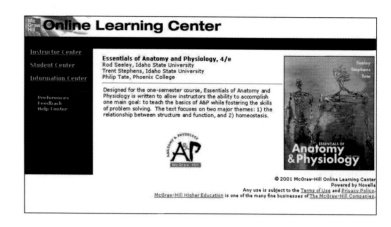

Learning Activities

Among the activities awaiting you at the OLC are chapter quizzes, crossword puzzles, art labeling exercises, vocabulary flashcards, and animation-based activities. In addition, the OLC offers numerous case studies and clinical applications, cutting-edge online reference materials, and links to related anatomy and physiology Internet sites.

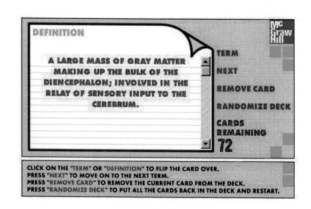

Premium Study Tools

Logging on to the OLC gives you access to premium McGraw-Hill interactive study tools like the Essential Study Partner and BioCourse.com.

Essential Study Partner

This interactive study tool contains hundreds of animations and learning activities designed to help you grasp complex concepts. Interactive diagrams and quizzes make learning anatomy and physiology stimulating and fun.

BioCourse.com

This online forum provides a wealth of information and learning opportunities for students of the life sciences. Keep abreast of breaking news by clicking the latest scientific headlines from the New York Times or links to prominent journals in the *Briefing Room*. Visit the *Student Center* to ask a question on the discussion boards, brush up on test-taking tips, or perform job and internship searches. Conduct a virtual laboratory experiment at *BioLabs*, or head to *The Quad* to browse the vast array of rich, multimedia content specific to your course. BioCourse.com is the place where science comes to life!

Instructor Preface

We have been teaching Anatomy and Physiology and related courses for many years. We have also explored the literature and carried out objective investigations in our classes to help us understand how students learn. This extensive experience has allowed us to develop a picture of what we believe works to help anatomy and physiology students learn effectively. We have used this information and the feedback from hundreds of reviewers, who also teach anatomy and physiology, to develop *Essentials of Anatomy and Physiology*. The professionals at McGraw-Hill have provided tremendous encouragement and support in this process. Their expertise and commitment to excellence has helped us develop this exceptional learning aid for your students.

Intended Audience

This one-semester text is intended to provide an introduction to anatomy and physiology, with no prerequisite knowledge in chemistry, physics, or cell biology expected. The concepts specific to these fields that are necessary for understanding anatomy and physiology are presented in the text. This book strikes a well-contrived balance of anatomy and physiology. Some texts emphasize anatomy at the expense of physiology, or present physiological facts without providing adequate information to allow students to understand them. We have tried to provide a solid background in anatomy that supports a comprehensive treatment of physiology. Clearly, knowledge of anatomy is required for students to understand how structures function.

When teaching beginning students, it is important not to obscure the "big picture" with an overwhelming deluge of detail. An introductory-level text must provide enough information to allow students to solve basic problems without including volumes of non-essential facts. It is our goal to present, in the text and illustrations, basic content at an appropriate level and in a way that fosters the development of problem-solving skills that emphasize the practical application of concepts to real-life situations.

Themes

As in previous editions of *Essentials of Anatomy and Physiology,* we emphasize the relationship between structure and function and homeostasis. Just as the structure of a hammer makes it well suited for the function of pounding nails, the structure of specific cells, tissues, and organs within the body allows them to perform their specific functions effectively. For example, the structure of proteins and their arrangement in muscle cells makes the contraction of muscle possible, and bone cells surround themselves with a mineralized matrix that provides strength and support.

Homeostasis is necessary for the survival of the human body. This book emphasizes the importance of mechanisms that maintain homeostasis. Because failure of these mechanisms also illustrates how they work, examples of pathological conditions resulting in dysfunction, disease, and possibly death are presented. Changes in response to physical activity and aging are also included to illustrate how homeostatic mechanisms work. Consideration of pathology, exercise, and aging adds relevance and interest, makes the material more meaningful, and enhances the background of students who plan to pursue health-related careers.

Essentials of Anatomy and Physiology also delivers a strong emphasis on critical thinking. Critical thinking exercises are interwoven throughout the text to help students use the information they have learned and to appreciate the relevance of the information in real-life situations. The numerous examples and questions in the text are used to help students learn to think critically. It is not possible to memorize how all organs and organ systems respond to all types of stimuli. However, it is very possible to learn the basic structure and function of cells, organs, and organ systems and then use that knowledge to predict responses to many different types of stimuli, including those that result from exercise, aging, and disease.

New in the Fourth Edition

Each new edition causes one to think furiously about what changes should be made to improve the text. Because new information is steadily discovered by thousands of researchers, it is important to determine what new information and what changes should be included in the text. For example, molecular techniques have led to a better understanding of the way molecules released from some cells bind to molecules in the membranes of other cells and stimulate a response. This information clarifies our understanding of how nerve cells communicate with other nerve cells and with muscle cells to produce a specific response. It makes it easier to understand how hormones and other extracellular signal molecules affect the activities of target cells. Simply increasing the amount of information in a text in response to new discoveries is not always necessary. Frequently, the new information makes concepts clearer and more easily explained. The topics we chose to expand upon in light of new information, clarify based on reviewer feedback, or add for depth of coverage are listed below:

- Chapter 2—Information about the chemical structure of phospholipids and steroids has been added.
- Chapter 3—A clearer description of the structure of the cell membrane, additional information about the function of the smooth endoplasmic reticulum, and new information about peroxisomes and production of mitochondria has been presented. Information about cystic fibrosis has been added to emphasize the importance of small changes in genetic material, their potential effects on protein structure, and their dramatic consequences.
- Chapter 4—New histology figures have been added to make the categorization of epithelial tissues and connective tissues clearer, and a more thorough description of dense collagenous connective tissue has been added.
- Chapter 5—The most current information about nutrition and the integumentary system has been added, as well as new findings regarding the effects of different ultraviolet light (UVA and UVB) on the skin and their potential for causing skin cancer.
- Chapter 7—Current information about slow-twitch and fast-twitch muscle fibers and the impact of exercise on them is presented, and muscle tables have been updated to more thoroughly describe skeletal muscle anatomy.
- Chapter 8—New sections on the knee-jerk and withdrawal reflexes have been added, along with additional information on spinal cord injury and treatment and current information about treatments for Parkinson's disease, strokes, and Alzheimer's disease.
- Chapter 10—New information on receptors, both intracellular and membrane bound, clarifies understanding of how cells communicate and how extracellular signal molecules regulate the activities of cells. A more thorough explanation of prostaglandins presents the subcategories of eicosanoid compounds.
- Chapter 11—A clearer explanation of platelet plug formation and factors that control prothrombin time are presented. The term "erythrocyte" has been replaced with "red blood cell" throughout the book to make the terminology more commonplace and more consistent with the use of terms in clinical settings.
- Chapter 12—Updated information on action potentials in cardiac muscle and the effect of plasma calcium and potassium levels on cardiac muscle function is presented. In addition, there is new information on the heart rate and the effect of exercise on cardiac output.
- Chapter 14—Updated information on the size of the thymus in people of various ages and on immunotherapy for breast cancer has been included.
- Chapter 15—Information on the vital capacity of the lung in different groups of people has been expanded.
- Chapter 16—Important clinical information pertaining to pathologies of the digestive system such as hiatal hernia, hypertrophic pyloric stenosis, appendicitis, inflammatory bowel disease, Crohn's disease, ulcerative colitis, and irritable bowel syndrome has been added.
- Chapter 17—Current information is presented on recommended daily allowances (RDA), daily values, and other nutritional recommendations.
- Chapter 18—Explanations of filtration pressure and reabsorption have been further clarified.
- Chapter 20—New information about ATP production with aging, mitochondrial DNA and mutations in the mitochondrial DNA, and tumor suppression genes is presented.

Creative efforts can improve explanations and illustrations, which in turn leads to better organization of concepts and better explanations of functions. Finding ways to improve explanations and creating examples to illustrate them takes a great deal of time. For the fourth edition, we focused much of our attention on refining concept explanations in the text and furnishing examples to reinforce them.

Hundreds of illustrations have been changed in this edition. Some of the illustrations are new and many have been modified. In each case the new illustration provides a better visual representation of the structure or physiological mechanism it aims to display. We have worked hard to coordinate colors throughout the text so that muscles, bones, and other structures are the same color in each illustration. Minimizing color variation from one piece of art to the next makes it easier for students to see continuity between the figures. Vast improvements have also been made in the placement of the illustrations in the text. To make it easier for students to refer to a figure while reading the text, we have labored to place each illustration close to the text material that describes it without creating a book that is too long.

It goes without saying that we have worked hard to eliminate distortions or errors in the text. We have considered all reviewer comments carefully and have analyzed each paragraph in each chapter with the goal of making the text as accurate as it can be. We have spent countless hours reviewing the literature, checking the use of terms, and at times visiting the histology or anatomy lab to make sure that information in the text is accurate.

Systematic Presentation and Pedagogy

Essentials of Anatomy and Physiology is designed to help students learn in a systematic fashion. Explanations are based on a conceptual framework that allows students to tie together individual pieces of information. Simple facts are presented first, and explanations are developed in a logical sequence. Throughout the text discussions, we introduce and define key terms, including pronunciations and etymologies when necessary. To further explain and visually supplement the text discussions, we carefully incorporate clear and accurate illustrations that emphasize the functions of structures. Finally, to reinforce the explanations, clear and relevant examples are presented to help students understand how structures function under a variety of common conditions.

Learning Aids
A variety of pedagogical devices have been installed throughout the text to help students make the most of the systematically organized content. Important terms and their definitions are presented at the beginning of every chapter. Reviewing the definitions before reading the chapter allows students to more easily remember and understand them. The objectives at the beginning of the chapter help students understand what they should gain from reading it. Short essays titled Did You Know? provide interesting and relevant points such as a historical presentation of the use of cadavers, the importance of research using non-human organisms in the discovery of new information, and misconceptions held to be true at times in the past. Clinical Focus boxes explore clinical topics related to the text discussion. The Predict questions placed adjacent to related material throughout the text are intended to help students apply new information or use it to understand how mechanisms work. At the end of every chapter, a detailed summary helps students review the content presented in the text. Content Review questions help students check if they have learned the content presented in the chapter, while Develop Your Reasoning Skills questions require students to apply the information or use it to understand how mechanisms work.

At the end of the book is a series of appendices that offer students easy access to information regarding measurements, laboratory values, scientific notation, solution concentration, and pH values. Following the appendices is a helpful glossary that gathers definitions and pronunciations of important terms found throughout the text. In many cases the etymology of the term, especially when it is not clear from the structure of the word, is presented to help students remember the term. Understanding the meaning of word roots is extremely helpful to students who are challenged by having to learn a large vocabulary. The glossary also indicates the page in the text where each term is introduced.

Critical Thinking Exercises
At best, some anatomy and physiology texts include a few "thought" questions that, for the most part, involve a restatement or a summary of content. Yet once students understand the material well enough to state it in their own words, it only seems logical for them to proceed to the next step—that is, to apply the knowledge to hypothetical situations. To encourage students to engage in critical thinking activities, this text features two sets of problem-solving questions in every chapter. Predict questions and Develop Your Reasoning Skills exercises provide students with an opportunity as well as a challenge, because we believe the simple assumption that practice in solving problems greatly enhances critical thinking.

Information is presented at a level that is sufficiently simple to avoid unnecessary confusion, but complete enough so that students can learn to use the information to successfully predict the consequences of many hypothetical situations. Content Review questions are provided to help students know if they have learned the basic terminology, facts, and concepts. Predict questions throughout the chapters and Develop Your Reasoning Skills questions at the end of the chapters are presented to encourage students to learn to think critically. Answers and explanations for the Predict questions are included in the text. The explanations illustrate the methods used to solve problems and provide a model for the development of problem-solving skills. When students are exposed to the reasoning used to correctly solve a problem, they are more likely to be able to successfully apply that reasoning to future problems. The acquisition of problem-solving skills is necessary for a complete understanding of anatomy and physiology; it is fun; and it makes it possible for the student to deal with the many problems that occur as part of professional and everyday life.

Clinical Information
This text provides clinical examples to promote interest and demonstrate relevance, but clinical information is used primarily to illustrate the application of basic knowledge. Even though clinical information emphasizes how relevant knowledge of anatomy and physiology is, it is not an end in itself. In some texts, mere clinical descriptions, lists of medical terminology, or brief explanations of pathologies represent a significant portion of the material, but little effort is made to demonstrate how this wealth of background knowledge can be utilized. The ability to apply information to solve a problem is a skill that will always be an asset for students, even after knowledge learned today is no longer current. We encourage students using *Essentials of Anatomy and Physiology* to think critically with the clinical knowledge they have gained.

Organization and Content

The order of chapters in the text is fairly traditional and is similar to that found in many other texts at this level. However, the content of the chapters and the organization of the information within each chapter is, in many ways, unique. The content in this text is organized in what we feel is the best framework for helping students develop a working knowledge of the subject matter. Although the chapters build on one another, and can be taught effectively in the sequence in which they are presented, care has been taken to make chapters sufficiently complete to allow them to be covered in a different order as well.

Major Themes of Anatomy and Physiology Chapter 1 presents major themes in anatomy and physiology, and the definitions and subcategories of anatomy and physiology. It also illustrates the hierarchy of organization of human structures and the basic characteristics of life. Chapter 1 emphasizes that humans are composed of trillions of cells, carry out metabolism, respond to stimuli, grow, differentiate, and reproduce. The concept of homeostasis is illustrated through discussion and example, and the related concepts of feedback control—both positive and negative—and their consequences are presented. Homeostasis figures are introduced, and this model is used throughout the text to illustrate how systems function to maintain a constant internal environment. The terminology used to describe directional references, planes, body regions, body cavities, and serous membranes is presented in Chapter 1 and is applied consistently throughout the remainder of the book.

Chemistry Chapter 2 presents the essential concepts in chemistry that are necessary for understanding the concepts of anatomy and physiology presented in this text. Students who have taken a chemistry class may be able to skip this chapter, but most students are likely to benefit from reading it. General terms like matter, mass, and weight are defined. The concepts of elements and atoms are introduced and basic atomic structure is presented. The basic behavior of electrons and the principles of ionic, covalent, and hydrogen bonding are described. Definitions of molecules and compounds, and some characteristics of their behavior are presented. Major characteristics of chemical reactions are described. Energy relationships of chemical reactions, and the rates of chemical reactions are explained. Acids, bases, the pH scale, inorganic chemistry, and organic chemistry are defined. The characteristics of important organic chemicals such as carbohydrates, lipids, proteins, and nucleic acids are described and the functions of enzymes are presented.

Cell Structures and Their Functions Chapter 3 introduces essential information about the cell. A list of cell functions and a brief description of cell structure are presented. The structure and function of membranes and organelles are introduced. Movement through the cell membrane, osmosis, filtration, and mediated transport mechanisms are described. Cell metabolism and the organelles involved and protein synthesis are explained. The roles of DNA and RNA in transcription and translation are emphasized. Cell division (mitosis) and meiosis are described, and the importance of cell differentiation is also presented.

Tissues, Glands, and Membranes Chapter 4 defines tissues and the four primary tissue types, with emphasis on their functional characteristics. Major categories of epithelial, connective, muscle, and nervous tissue are described and illustrated with example figures. Categories of membranes and their locations are presented. Inflammation and tissue repair are described.

Support and Movement Chapters 5, 6, and 7 describe the integumentary, skeletal, and muscular systems. Chapter 5 presents the functions of the integumentary system. The structure of the hypodermis and skin, including the epidermis and dermis are described, as are accessory structures of the skin such as hair, glands, and nails. The role of the skin in sensations, vitamin D production, temperature regulation, and excretion is explained. Aging, burns, skin cancer and other pathologies are described. Chapter 6 presents the structure and functions of bones. Types of bone are identified based on both shape and histology, and bone growth and repair are emphasized. The anatomy of the appendicular and axial skeleton is described, summarized in tables, and presented in figures. Articulations, or joints, are classified and examples of the joints are described, with emphasis on synovial joints. Chapter 7 describes the microscopic structure of muscle tissue and the processes of contraction and relaxation. This chapter also introduces membrane potentials, action potentials, and basic physiological characteristics of skeletal muscle. The anatomy of the major skeletal muscles of the body is described, presented in tables, and illustrated. Smooth and cardiac muscle are also introduced, but more briefly than skeletal muscle. These muscle types are described in later chapters in more detail.

Systems of Integration and Control Chapters 8, 9, and 10 present the nervous and endocrine systems. Chapter 8 introduces the basic functions and divisions of the nervous system. The cells of the nervous system are described and membrane potentials and action potentials are explained. Unlike many texts, enough information is presented to allow students to understand the role of the resting membrane potential and factors that affect action potentials. The structure and function of the synapse are presented, as well as the mechanisms by which neurotransmitters influence postsynaptic neurons. Neuronal interactions are illustrated in the presentation of functions accomplished by reflexes. Chapter 8 also introduces neuronal circuits and the structure and function of the major components of the brain and spinal cord. The peripheral nervous system and its subdivisions are defined, and the structural and functional characteristics of the autonomic nervous system are presented. A variety of clinical examples are presented in this chapter to help students understand how the components of the nervous system involved in each pathology function. Chapter 9 describes the functions of sensory organs and provides adequate information to allow students to understand how sensory organs work and the consequences of abnormalities that affect the sensory organs or pathways that transmit and integrate sensory information. Pain is described in enough detail so students can understand its functions, as well as some techniques used to modulate pain sensations. Care has been taken to present the special senses of olfaction, taste, vision, hearing, and balance. The objective, as in the remainder of the text, is to present enough information about the structure and function of organs involved to allow students to understand how they work and predict how they respond to stimuli. Examples are provided, including clinical examples. Chapter 10 introduces the basic principles of the endocrine system and describes the major endocrine organs and the role they play in the control of functions. Characteristics of chemical signals and the means by which they interact with target cells are described. Molecular biology has provided information that makes it easier to understand how chemical signals produce responses in specific cells. The endocrine glands, the hormones secreted by the endocrine glands, and the effects of hormones on their target tissues are described. The mechanisms that control hormone secretion are emphasized, and the consequences of reduced secretion or over-secretion of hormones are presented.

Systems of Regulation and Maintenance Chapter 11 describes the anatomy and physiology of blood, Chapter 12 describes the anatomy and physiology of the heart, Chapter 13 presents the anatomy and physiology of blood vessels and circulation, and Chapter 14 presents the anatomy and physiology of the lymphatic system and organs involved in the immune response. The basic anatomy of structures is exceptionally well illustrated. Without providing overwhelming detail, a clear picture of the functions of the circulatory system is presented. The coverage of the regulation of the circulatory system is exceptional, and no other text presents the same concise and complete picture. It is exciting and convenient for students to develop the ability to predict responses of the circulatory system to changes and to pathologies.

Chapter 15 describes the anatomy and physiology of the respiratory system, Chapter 16 describes the anatomy and physiology of the digestive system, Chapter 17 describes nutrition, metabolism, and body temperature regulation. Chapter 18 presents the urinary system and fluid balance. These chapters aim to help students develop the ability to understand how these systems work to maintain homeostasis. The pattern of describing and illustrating the functions and structures of these systems and the mechanisms that control them is repeated throughout these chapters. Consistent emphasis on these themes helps students understand changes that occur in response to a variety of stimuli and pathologies and fosters the ability to predict changes in response to stimuli. Care has been taken to provide adequate information to help students develop analytical and predictive abilities without an overwhelming amount of detail. The essential information is described in the text and figures have been developed to clearly illustrate the functions and regulatory mechanisms specific to each system.

Reproduction and Development Chapter 19 describes and illustrates the anatomy and physiology of the male and female reproductive systems, and Chapter 20 provides basic information about development, heredity, and aging. The basics of sexual reproduction are presented and the roles of meiosis and differentiation of male and female reproductive structures are explained. Control mechanisms are emphasized, and the roles they play in the development of sperm and oocytes, the maintenance of these cells, and how reproductive structures bring these cells together and result in fertilization are explored. Puberty, reproductive cycles in adults, pregnancy, parturition, and lactation are presented. The basic mechanisms of heredity and development are also presented. Finally, appropriate for the last chapter, Chapter 20 presents many of the basic changes that occur in humans as they age.

Teaching and Learning Supplements

There is much more to *Essentials of Anatomy and Physiology* than this book. Numerous study and teaching aids round out the complete package. Students can order supplemental study materials by contacting the McGraw-Hill Customer Service Department at 800-338-3987. Instructors can obtain teaching aids by calling the Customer Service Department or contacting your McGraw-Hill sales representative.

Online Learning Center The Online Learning Center (OLC) at www.mhhe.com/ seeleyessentials offers an extensive array of learning and teaching tools. This website includes chapter-specific quizzes and web links, clinical applications, interactive activities, art labeling exercises, case studies, and more. Teaching resources at the instructor site include image and animations libraries, technology resources, clinical applications, case studies, and the Online Instructor's Manual for *Essentials of Anatomy and Physiology.*

Essential Study Partner for Anatomy and Physiology
This exclusive interactive study tool is accessed via the Online Learning Center. It contains 120 animations and more than 800 learning activities to help students grasp complex concepts. Interactive diagrams and quizzes make learning stimulating and fun.

BioCourse.com Available through the Online Learning Center, BioCourse.com delivers rich, interactive content to fortify the learning and teaching experience in the life sciences. In addition to over ten thousand animations, images, case studies and video presentations, discussion boards and laboratory exercises foster collaboration and infinite learning and teaching opportunities. Biocourse.com contains these specific areas:

The Faculty Club gives new and experienced instructors access to a variety of resources to help increase their effectiveness in lecture, discover groups of instructors with similar interests, and find information on teaching techniques and pedagogy. A comprehensive search feature allows instructors to search for information using a variety of criteria.

The Student Center allows students the opportunity to search BioCourse for information specific to the course area they are studying, or by using specific topics or keywords. Information is also available for many aspects of student life including tips for studying and test taking, surviving the first year of college, and job and internship searches.

BioLabs Laboratory instructors often face a special set of challenges. BioLabs helps address those challenges by providing laboratory instructors and coordinators with a source for basic information on suppliers, best practices, professional organizations and lab exchanges.

Briefing Room is where to go for current news in the life sciences. News feeds from the New York Times, links to prominent journals, commentaries from popular McGraw-Hill authors, and XanEdu journal search service are just a few of the resources you will find here.

The Quad utilizes a powerful indexing and searching tool to provide the user with a guided review of specific course content. Information is available from a variety of McGraw-Hill sources including textbook material, Essential Study Partner modules, Online Learning Centers, and images from Visual Resource Libraries.

R&D Center is the opportunity to see what new textbooks, animations, and simulations we're working on and to send us your feedback. You can also learn about other opportunities to review as well as submit ideas for new projects.

Laboratory Manual Written by Kevin Patton of St. Charles County Community College, this manual divides the material typically covered in anatomy and physiology labs into 42 subunits. Selection of the subunits and the sequence of their use permits the design of a laboratory course that is integrated with the emphasis and sequence of the lecture material. Basic content is introduced first, and gradually more complex activities are developed. This laboratory manual also contains coloring exercises, boxed hints, safety alerts, separate lab reports, and a full-color histology minireference.

Instructor's Manual for the Laboratory Manual This online manual is housed within the instructor OLC. It provides all answers to the lab report questions, suggestions on how to use various exercises, materials lists, helpful hints, reagent recipes, and more.

Transparencies The set of transparency acetates that accompanies the text includes 250 full-color images identified by the authors as the most useful figures to incorporate in lecture presentations.

Instructor's Manual Accessed via the Online Learning Center, the Instructor's Manual by Margaret Weck of St. Louis College of Pharmacy includes supplemental topics, teaching strategies, and demonstration ideas for your lectures. This manual also provides a listing of relevant transparencies for each text chapter and answers to the Develop Your Reasoning Skills questions.

Test Item File The Test Item File contains multiple choice, matching, true/false, and essay questions specifically designed to complement each chapter of the text. Instructors using WebCT, Blackboard, or PageOut can access the Test Item File online.

Microtest Microtest is a computerized test generator free upon request to qualified adopters. The test generator contains the complete Test Item File on CD-ROM. Requires no programming experience and is designed to work on both Windows and Macintosh platforms.

PageOut™

PageOut is McGraw-Hill's exclusive tool for creating your own website for your A & P course. It requires no knowledge of coding. Simply type your course information into the templates provided. PageOut is hosted by McGraw-Hill. In addition to the materials specifically designed to accompany *Essentials of Anatomy and Physiology*, McGraw-Hill offers the following supplemental resources to enrich the study and instruction of anatomy and physiology.

Anatomy and Physiology Laboratory Manual-Fetal Pig by Terry R. Martin, Kishwaukee College. Provides excellent full-color photos of the dissected fetal pig with corresponding labeled art. It includes World Wide Web activities for many chapters.

Web-Based Cat Dissection Review for Human Anatomy and Physiology by John Waters, Pennsylvania State University. This online multimedia program contains vivid, high-quality labeled cat dissection photographs. The program helps students easily identify and review the corresponding structures and functions between the cat and the human body.

Dynamic Human Version 2.0 A set of two interactive CD-ROMs that cover each body system and demonstrate clinical concepts, histology, and physiology with animated three-dimensional and other images.

Interactive Histology CD-ROM by Bruce Wingerd and Paul Paolini, San Diego State University. This CD contains 135 full-color, high-resolution LM images and 35 SEM images of selected tissue sections typically studied in A&P. Each image has labels that can be clicked on or off, has full explanatory legends, offers views at two magnifications, and has links to study questions. The CD also has a glossary with pronunciation guides.

Life Science Animation YRL 2.0 Contains over 200 animations of major biological concepts and processes such as the sliding filament mechanism, active transport, genetic transcription and translation, and other topics that may be difficult for students to visualize.

Life Science Animations 3D Videotape Contains 42 key biological processes that are narrated and animated in vibrant full color with dynamic three-dimensional graphics.

Life Science Animations (LSA) videotape series Contains 53 animations on five VHS videocassettes; Chemistry, The Cell, and Energetics; Cell Division, Heredity, Genetics, Reproduction, and Development; Animal Biology No. 1; Animal Biology No. 2; and Plant Biology, Evolution, and Ecology. Another available videotape is Physiological Concepts of Life Science.

Atlas to Human Anatomy by Dennis Strete, McLennan Community College and Christopher H. Creek This atlas, takes a systems approach with references to regional anatomy, thereby making it a great complement to your regular course structure, as well as to your laboratory.

Atlas of the Skeletal Muscles, third edition, by Robert and Judith Stone, Suffolk County Community College A guide to the structure and function of human skeletal muscles. The illustrations help students locate muscles and understand their actions.

Laboratory Atlas of Anatomy and Physiology, third edition, by Eder et al. A full-color atlas containing histology, human skeletal anatomy, human muscular anatomy, dissections, and reference tables.

Coloring Guide to Anatomy and Physiology by Robert and Judith Stone, Suffolk County Community College. This supplemental text provides a thorough review of anatomical and physiological concepts and emphasizes learning through the process of color association.

Acknowledgments

No modern textbook is solely the work of the authors. To adequately acknowledge the support of loved ones is not possible. They have had the patience and understanding to tolerate our frustrations and absence, and they have been willing to provide assistance and undying encouragement. We also wish to express our gratitude to the staff of McGraw-Hill for their help and encouragement. We sincerely appreciate Marty Lange, Kris Tibbetts, and Kris Queck for their hours of work, suggestions, and tremendous patience and encouragement. We also thank Project Manager Jill Peter and Photo Editor John Leland for the many hours spent turning manuscript into a book. Sincere thanks also goes to Barb Block, who managed the production of the Online Learning Center that accompanies the book. The McGraw-Hill employees with whom we have worked are excellent professionals. They have been consistently helpful and their efforts are appreciated. Their commitment to this project has clearly been more than simply a job to them.

We also thank the many illustrators who worked on the development and execution of the illustration program for the fourth edition of *Essentials of Anatomy and Physiology*. The art program for this text represents a monumental effort, and we appreciate their contribution to the overall appearance and pedagogical value of the illustrations.

Finally, we sincerely thank the reviewers and the teachers who have provided us with excellent constructive criticism. The remuneration they received represents only a token payment for their efforts. To conscientiously review a textbook requires a true commitment and dedication to excellence in teaching. Their helpful criticism and suggestions for improvement were significant contributions that we greatly appreciate. Their names follow.

Rod Seeley
Trent Stephens
Phil Tate

Reviewers

Laurie M. Bradley
Hudson Valley Community College

John R. Capeheart
University of Houston—Downtown

Steven B. Chandler
Florida A & M University

John William Davis
Benedictine College

Larry DeLay
Waubonsee Community College

Mary Ann De Michele-Sweet
Carlow College

Danielle Desroches
William Paterson University

James DeWeese
Solano Community College

Inge Eley
Hudson Valley Community College

Barbara J. Engebretsen
Wayne State College

Beth Erviti
Greenfield Community College

Bradley J. Fillmore
Idaho State University

Joyce A. Foster
State Fair Community College

Daniel Gong
Seattle Central Community College

Brent M. Graves
Northern Michigan University

James Hesson
Black Hills State University

Geoffrey Jowett
Savannah College of Art and Design

William Kleinelp
Middlesex County College

Billie S. Lane
Chattanooga State Technical Community College

Michael A. Lawson
Missouri Southern State College

Steven W. Lewis
Penn Valley Community College

Joyce Morgenroth
Cornell University

John Olson
Villanova University

Amy Griffin Ouchley
University of Louisiana–Monroe

Michael A. Palladino
Monmouth University

Robert Reeder
Concordia University

Donald Rodd
University of Evansville

Jane Rudolph
Salt Lake Community College

Brian R. Shmaefsky
Kingwood College

Michael E. Smith
Valdosta State University

Rick Stewart
Fresno City College

Jake N. Stickelmeyer
North Seattle Community College

Jeff Taylor
North Central State College

Jeffrey E. Thompson
Hudson Valley Community College

Brian Wisenden
Minnesota State University Moorhead

Edward J. Zalisko
Blackburn College

Chapter One

Introduction to the Human Body

anatomical position
(an'ă-tom'i-kăl) Position in which a person is standing erect with the feet forward, arms hanging to the sides, and the palms of the hands facing forward.

anatomy
(ă-nat'ŏ-mē) [Gr. *ana*, apart + *tome*, a cutting] Scientific discipline that investigates the structure of the body.

frontal plane
Plane separating the body into anterior and posterior portions; also called a coronal plane.

homeostasis
(hō'mē-ō-stā'sis) [Gr. *homoio*, like + *stasis*, a standing] Existence and maintenance of a relatively constant environment within the body with respect to functions and the composition of fluids and tissues.

mesentery
(mes'en-ter-ē) [Gr. *mesos*, middle + *enteron*, intestine] Double layer of peritoneum extending from the abdominal wall to the abdominopelvic organs; conveys blood vessels and nerves to abdominopelvic organs; holds and supports abdominopelvic organs.

negative feedback
Mechanism by which any deviation from an ideal normal value or set point is resisted or negated; returns a parameter to its normal range and thereby maintains homeostasis.

physiology
(fiz-ē-ol'ŏ-jē) [Gr. *physis*, nature + *logos*, study] Scientific discipline that deals with the processes or functions of living things.

positive feedback
Mechanism by which any deviation from an ideal normal value or set point is made greater.

sagittal plane
(saj'i-tăl) [L. *sagitta*, the flight of an arrow] Plane running vertically through the body and dividing it into right and left parts.

serous membrane
(sēr'ŭs) Thin sheet consisting of epithelium and connective tissue that lines cavities not opening to the outside of the body; does not contain glands but does secrete serous fluid.

tissue
(tish'ū) [L. *texo*, to weave] Collection of cells with similar structure and function and the substances between the cells.

transverse plane
(trans-vers') Plane separating the body into superior and inferior parts.

Objectives

After reading this chapter, you should be able to:

1. Explain the importance of understanding the relationship between structure and function.

2. Define anatomy and physiology.

3. Describe seven levels of organization of the body, and give the major characteristics of each level.

4. List 11 organ systems and give the major functions of each.

5. List six characteristics of life.

6. Define homeostasis and explain why it is important.

7. Diagram a negative-feedback mechanism and a positive-feedback mechanism, and describe their relationships to homeostasis.

8. Describe a person in the anatomical position.

9. Define the directional terms for the human body, and use them to locate specific body structures.

10. Name and describe the three major planes of the body and an organ.

11. Define the regions and parts of the body.

12. Describe the major trunk cavities.

13. Describe the serous membranes, and give their functions.

Human anatomy and physiology is the study of the structure and function of the human body. The human body consists of many intricate parts with coordinated functions that are maintained by a complex system of checks and balances. The coordinated function of all the parts of the human body allows us to detect stimuli, such as observing a sunset; respond to stimuli, such as removing a hand from a hot object; perform mental functions, such as remembering and thinking; among many other functions.

The study of human anatomy and physiology is important for those who plan a career in the health sciences, because a sound knowledge of structure and function is necessary for health professionals to perform their duties. Understanding anatomy and physiology also prepares us to evaluate recommended treatments, critically review advertisements and reports in the popular literature, and rationally discuss the human body with health professionals and nonprofessionals.

Knowledge of the structure and function of the human body allows us to understand how the body responds to a stimulus. For example, eating a candy bar results in an increase in blood sugar (the stimulus). Knowledge of the pancreas allows us to predict that the pancreas will secrete insulin (the response). Insulin moves into blood vessels and is transported to cells, where it increases the movement of sugar from the blood into the cells, providing them with a source of energy. As glucose moves into cells, blood sugar levels decrease.

Knowledge of human anatomy and physiology also provides the basis for understanding disease. In one type of diabetes mellitus, for example, the pancreas does not secrete adequate amounts of insulin. Without adequate insulin, not enough sugar moves into cells, which deprives them of a needed source of energy, and they therefore malfunction.

Anatomy

Anatomy (ă-nat′ŏ-mē) is the scientific discipline that investigates the structure of the body. The word "anatomy" means to dissect, or cut apart and separate, the parts of the body for study. Anatomy covers a wide range of studies, including the structure of body parts, their microscopic organization, and the processes by which they develop. In addition, anatomy examines the relationship between the structure of a body part and its function. Just as the structure of a hammer makes it well suited for pounding nails, the structure of body parts allows them to perform specific functions effectively. For example, bones can provide strength and support because bone cells surround themselves with a hard, mineralized substance. Understanding the relationship between structure and function makes it easier to understand and appreciate anatomy.

Systemic anatomy is the study of the body by systems and is the approach taken in this and most other introductory textbooks. Examples of systems are the circulatory, nervous, skeletal, and muscular systems.

Regional anatomy is the study of the organization of the body by areas. Within each region, such as the head, abdomen, or arm, all systems are studied simultaneously. It is the approach taken in most medical and dental schools.

Surface anatomy is the study of external features, such as bony projections, which serve as landmarks for locating deeper structures (for examples of external landmarks, see chapters 6 and 7). Anatomical imaging involves the use of x-rays, ultrasound, magnetic resonance imaging (MRI), and other technologies to create pictures of internal structures. Both surface anatomy and anatomical imaging provide important information useful in diagnosing disease.

Did You Know?

For much of history, public sentiment made it difficult for anatomists to obtain human bodies for dissection. In the early 1800s, the benefits of human dissection for training physicians had become very apparent, and the need for cadavers increased beyond the ability to acquire them legally. Thus arose the resurrectionists, or body snatchers. For a fee and no questions asked, they removed bodies from graves and provided them to medical schools. Because the bodies were not easy to obtain and were not always in the best condition, two enterprising men named William Burke and William Hare went one step further. Over a period of time, they murdered 17 people and sold their bodies to a medical school. When discovered, Hare testified against Burke and went free. Burke was convicted, hanged, and publicly dissected. Discovery of Burke's activities so outraged the public that sensible laws regulating the acquisition of cadavers were soon passed, and this dark chapter in the history of anatomy was closed.

Physiology

Physiology (fiz-ē-ol′ō-jē, meaning the study of nature) is the scientific discipline that deals with the processes or functions of living things. It is important in physiology to recognize structures as dynamic rather than static, or unchanging. The major goals of physiology are (1) to understand and predict the body's responses to stimuli, and (2) to understand how the body maintains conditions within a narrow range of values in the presence of a continually changing environment.

Physiology is divided according to (1) the organisms involved or (2) the levels of organization within a given organism. Human physiology is the study of a specific organism, the human, whereas cellular and systemic physiology are examples of physiology that emphasize specific organizational levels.

Structural and Functional Organization

The body can be studied at seven structural levels: chemical, organelle, cell, tissue, organ, organ system, and organism (figure 1.1).

Figure 1.1   Levels of Organization

Seven levels of organization for the human body are the chemical, organelle, cell, tissue, organ, organ system, and organism.

Chemical

The structural and functional characteristics of all organisms are determined by their chemical makeup. The **chemical** level of organization involves interactions among atoms and their combinations into molecules. The function of a molecule is related intimately to its structure. For example, collagen molecules are strong, ropelike fibers that give skin structural strength and flexibility. With old age, the structure of collagen changes, and the skin becomes fragile and is torn more easily. A brief overview of chemistry is presented in chapter 2.

Organelle

An **organelle** (or′gă-nel) is a small structure contained within a cell that performs one or more specific functions. For example, the nucleus is an organelle containing the cell's hereditary information. Organelles are discussed in chapter 3.

Cell

Cells are the basic living units of all plants and animals. Although cell types differ in structure and function, they have many characteristics in common. Knowledge of these characteristics and their variations is essential to a basic understanding of anatomy and physiology. The cell is discussed in chapter 3.

Tissue

A group of cells with similar structure and function plus the extracellular substances located between them is a **tissue** (tish′ū). The many tissues that make up the body are classified into four primary tissue types: epithelial, connective, muscle, and nervous. Tissues are discussed in chapter 4.

Organ

Organs (ōr′gănz) are composed of two or more tissue types that together perform one or more common functions. The skin, stomach, eye, and heart are examples of organs.

Organ System

An **organ system** is a group of organs classified as a unit because of a common function or set of functions. In this text the body is considered to have 11 major organ systems: integumentary, skeletal, muscular, nervous, endocrine, cardiovascular, lymphatic, respiratory, digestive, urinary, and reproductive (figure 1.2).

The coordinated activity of the organ systems is necessary for normal function. For example, the digestive system takes in and processes food, which is carried by the blood of the cardiovascular system to the cells of the other systems. These cells use the food and produce waste products that are carried by the blood to the kidneys of the urinary system, which functions to remove waste products from the blood. Because the organ systems are so interrelated, dysfunction of one organ system can have profound effects on other systems. For example, a heart attack can result in inadequate circulation of blood. Consequently, the organs of other systems, such as the brain and kidneys, can malfunction. Throughout this text, the interactions of the organ systems is considered in Systems Pathology essays.

Organism

An **organism** is any living thing considered as a whole, whether composed of one cell, such as a bacterium, or trillions of cells, such as a human. The human organism is a complex of organ systems that are mutually dependent on one another.

Characteristics of Life

Humans are organisms and have many characteristics in common with other organisms. The most important common feature of all organisms is life. Essential characteristics of life are organization, metabolism, responsiveness, growth, differentiation, and reproduction.

1. **Organization** is the condition in which the parts of an organism have specific relationships to each other and the parts interact to perform specific functions. Living things are highly organized. All organisms are composed of one or more cells. Cells, in turn, are composed of

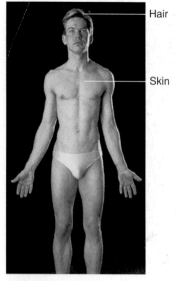

Integumentary System
Provides protection, regulates temperature, prevents water loss, and produces vitamin D precursors. Consists of skin, hair, nails, and sweat glands.

Hair
Skin

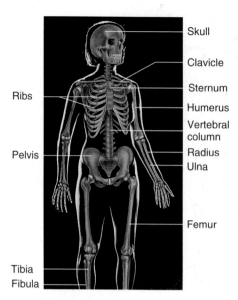

Skull
Clavicle
Sternum
Humerus
Vertebral column
Radius
Ulna
Femur
Ribs
Pelvis
Tibia
Fibula

Skeletal System
Provides protection and support, allows body movements, produces blood cells, and stores minerals and fat. Consists of bones, associated cartilages, and joints.

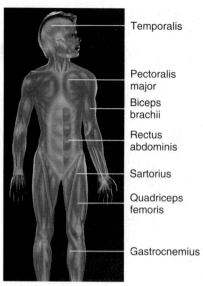

Temporalis
Pectoralis major
Biceps brachii
Rectus abdominis
Sartorius
Quadriceps femoris
Gastrocnemius

Muscular System
Produces body movements, maintains posture, and produces body heat. Consists of muscles attached to the skeleton.

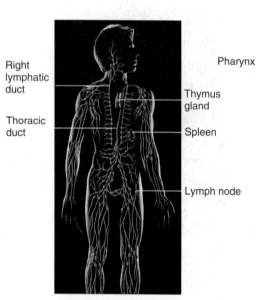

Right lymphatic duct
Thoracic duct
Thymus gland
Spleen
Lymph node

Lymphatic System
Removes foreign substances from the blood and lymph, combats disease, maintains tissue fluid balance, and absorbs fats from the digestive tract. Consists of the lymph vessels, lymph nodes, and other lymph organs.

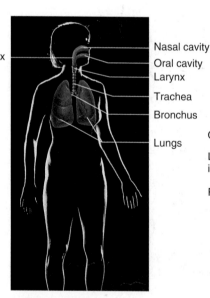

Pharynx
Nasal cavity
Oral cavity
Larynx
Trachea
Bronchus
Lungs

Respiratory System
Exchanges oxygen and carbon dioxide between the blood and air and regulates blood pH. Consists of the lungs and respiratory passages.

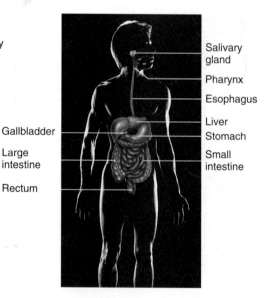

Gallbladder
Large intestine
Rectum
Salivary gland
Pharynx
Esophagus
Liver
Stomach
Small intestine

Digestive System
Performs the mechanical and chemical processes of digestion, absorption of nutrients, and elimination of wastes. Consists of the mouth, esophagus, stomach, intestines, and accessory organs.

Figure 1.2 Organ Systems of the Body

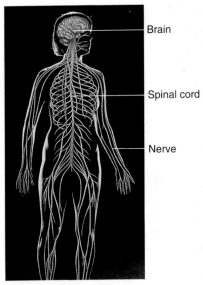

Nervous System
A major regulatory system that detects sensations and controls movements, physiological processes, and intellectual functions. Consists of the brain, spinal cord, nerves, and sensory receptors.

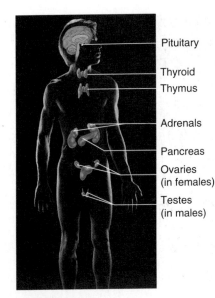

Endocrine System
A major regulatory system that influences metabolism, growth, reproduction, and many other functions. Consists of glands, such as the pituitary, that secrete hormones.

Cardiovascular System
Transports nutrients, waste products, gases, and hormones throughout the body; plays a role in the immune response and the regulation of body temperature. Consists of the heart, blood vessels, and blood.

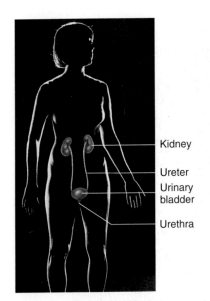

Urinary System
Removes waste products from the blood and regulates blood pH, ion balance, and water balance. Consists of the kidneys, urinary bladder, and ducts that carry urine.

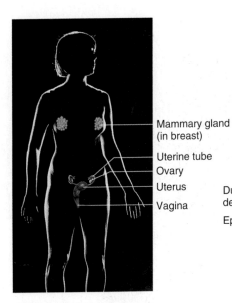

Female Reproductive System
Produces oocytes and is the site of fertilization and fetal development; produces milk for the newborn; produces hormones that influence sexual functions and behaviors. Consists of the ovaries, vagina, uterus, mammary glands, and associated structures.

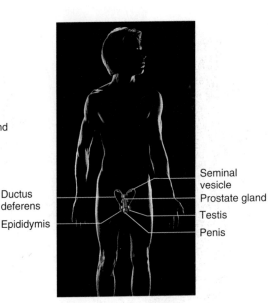

Male Reproductive System
Produces and transfers sperm cells to the female and produces hormones that influence sexual functions and behaviors. Consists of the testes, accessory structures, ducts, and penis.

Figure 1.2 *(continued)*

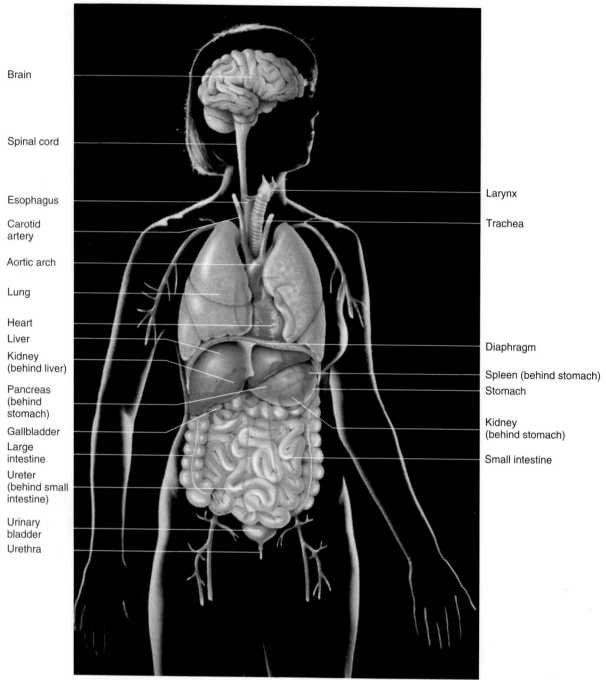

Brain

Spinal cord

Esophagus

Carotid artery

Aortic arch

Lung

Heart
Liver
Kidney (behind liver)

Pancreas (behind stomach)

Gallbladder

Large intestine

Ureter (behind small intestine)

Urinary bladder
Urethra

Larynx

Trachea

Diaphragm

Spleen (behind stomach)
Stomach

Kidney (behind stomach)

Small intestine

The relationship of different organ systems to one another.

Figure 1.2   *(continued)*

highly specialized organelles, which depend on the precise functions of large molecules. Disruption of this organized state can result in loss of functions and death.

2. **Metabolism** (mĕ-tab′ō-lizm) is the ability to use energy to perform vital functions, such as growth, movement, and reproduction. Plants can capture energy from sunlight, and humans obtain energy from food.

3. **Responsiveness** is the ability of an organism to sense changes in the environment and make the adjustments that help maintain its life. Responses include movement toward food or water and away from danger or poor environmental conditions. Organisms can also make adjustments that maintain their internal environment. For example, if body temperature increases in a hot environment, sweat glands produce sweat, which can lower body temperature back toward normal levels.

4. **Growth** results in an increase in size of all or part of the organism. It can result from an increase in cell number, cell size, or the amount of substance surrounding cells. For example, bones become larger as the number of bone cells increases and they surround themselves with bone matrix.

5. **Differentiation** consists of changes in cell structure and function from generalized to specialized. For example, following fertilization, generalized cells specialize to become specific cell types, such as skin, bone, muscle, or nerve cells. These differential cells form the tissues and organs.

6. **Reproduction** is the formation of new cells or new organisms. Without reproduction of cells, growth and tissue repair are impossible. Without reproduction of the organism, the species becomes extinct.

Homeostasis

Homeostasis (hō′mē-ō-stā′sis) is the existence and maintenance of a relatively constant environment within the body. Each cell of the body is surrounded by a small amount of fluid, and the normal functions of each cell depend on the maintenance of its fluid environment within a narrow range of conditions, including temperature, volume, and chemical content. These conditions are called **variables** because their values can change. For example, body temperature is a variable that can increase in a hot environment or decrease in a cold environment.

Homeostatic mechanisms, such as sweating or shivering, normally maintain body temperature near an ideal normal value, or **set point** (figure 1.3). Note that these mechanisms are not able to maintain body temperature precisely at the set point. Instead, body temperature increases and decreases slightly around the set point, producing a **normal range** of values. As long as body temperatures remain within this normal range, homeostasis is maintained.

The organ systems help control the internal environment so that it remains relatively constant. For example, the digestive, respiratory, circulatory, and urinary systems function together so that each cell in the body receives adequate oxygen and nutrients and so that waste products do not accumulate to a toxic level. If the fluid surrounding cells deviates from homeostasis, the cells do not function normally and may even die. Disruption of homeostasis results in disease and sometimes death.

Negative Feedback

Most systems of the body are regulated by **negative-feedback mechanisms**, which function to maintain homeostasis. "Negative" means that any deviation from the set point is made smaller or is resisted. Negative feedback does not prevent variation but maintains variation within a normal range.

The maintenance of normal blood pressure is an example of a negative-feedback mechanism. Normal blood pressure is important because it is responsible for moving blood from the heart to tissues. The blood supplies the tissues with oxygen and nutrients and removes waste products. Thus normal blood pressure is required to ensure that tissue homeostasis is maintained.

Many negative-feedback mechanisms, such as the one maintaining normal blood pressure, have three components: (1) a **receptor** (rē-sep′tŏr, rē-sep′tōr) monitors the value of a variable such as blood pressure; (2) a **control center**, such as part of the brain, establishes the set point around which the variable is maintained; and (3) an **effector** (ē-fek′tŏr), such as the heart, can change the value of the variable. Blood pressure depends in part on contraction (beating) of the heart: as heart rate increases, blood pressure increases, and as heart rate decreases, blood pressure decreases.

The receptors that monitor blood pressure are located within large blood vessels near the heart. If blood pressure increases slightly, the receptors detect the increased blood pressure and send that information to the control center in the brain. The control center causes heart rate to decrease, resulting in a decrease in blood pressure. If blood pressure decreases slightly, the receptors inform the control center, which increases heart rate, producing an increase in blood pressure. As a result, blood pressure is maintained with a normal range (figure 1.4).

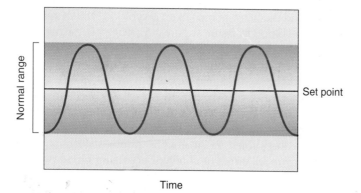

Figure 1.3   Homeostasis

Homeostasis is the maintenance of a variable, such as body temperature, around an ideal normal value, or set point. The value of the variable fluctuates around the set point, establishing a normal range of values.

1	P R E D I C T

Donating a pint of blood reduces blood volume, which results in a decrease in blood pressure (just as air pressure in a tire decreases as air is let out of the tire). What effect does donating blood have on heart rate? What would happen if a negative-feedback mechanism did not return the value of some parameter such as blood pressure to its normal range?

✔ *Answer on page 18*

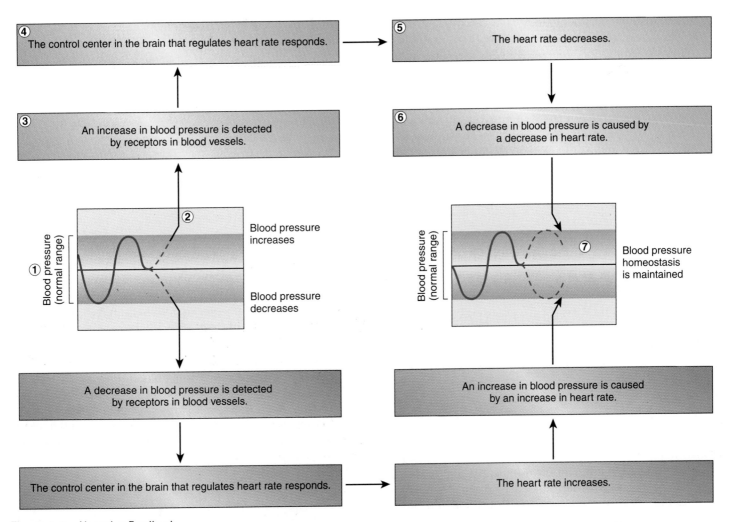

④ The control center in the brain that regulates heart rate responds.

⑤ The heart rate decreases.

③ An increase in blood pressure is detected by receptors in blood vessels.

⑥ A decrease in blood pressure is caused by a decrease in heart rate.

Blood pressure (normal range)

② Blood pressure increases

Blood pressure decreases

①

Blood pressure (normal range)

⑦ Blood pressure homeostasis is maintained

A decrease in blood pressure is detected by receptors in blood vessels.

An increase in blood pressure is caused by an increase in heart rate.

The control center in the brain that regulates heart rate responds.

The heart rate increases.

Figure 1.4   Negative Feedback

Throughout the text, all homeostasis figures have the same format as in figure 1.4. The changes caused by an increase of a variable outside the normal range are shown in the green boxes, and the changes caused by a decrease are shown in the red boxes. To help you learn how to interpret homeostasis figures, some of the steps in this figure are numbered: (1) Blood pressure is within its normal range. (2) Blood pressure increases and is outside the normal range. (3) The increase in blood pressure is detected by receptors. (4) The blood pressure control center responds to the change in blood pressure detected by the receptors. (5) The control center causes heart rate to decrease. (6) The decrease in heart rate causes blood pressure to decrease. (7) Blood pressure returns to its normal range and homeostasis is maintained. Follow the responses to a decrease in blood pressure outside its normal range by following the red boxes.

Positive Feedback

Positive-feedback mechanisms are *not* homeostatic and are rare in healthy individuals. "Positive" implies that when a deviation from a normal value occurs, the response of the system is to make the deviation even greater. Positive feedback therefore usually creates a cycle leading away from homeostasis and in some cases results in death.

Inadequate delivery of blood to cardiac (heart) muscle is an example of positive feedback. Contraction of cardiac muscle generates blood pressure and moves blood through blood vessels to tissues. A system of blood vessels on the outside of the heart provides cardiac muscle with a blood supply sufficient to allow normal contractions to occur. In effect, the heart pumps blood to itself. Just as with other tissues, blood pressure must be maintained to ensure adequate delivery of blood to cardiac muscle. Following extreme blood loss, blood pressure decreases to the point at which the delivery of blood to cardiac muscle is inadequate. As a result, cardiac muscle homeostasis is disrupted, and cardiac muscle does not

function normally. The heart pumps less blood, which causes the blood pressure to drop even further. The additional decrease in blood pressure causes less blood delivery to cardiac muscle, and the heart pumps even less blood, which again decreases the blood pressure (figure 1.5). The process continues until the blood pressure is too low to sustain the cardiac muscle, the heart stops beating, and death results.

Following a moderate amount of blood loss (e.g., after donating a pint of blood), negative-feedback mechanisms result in an increase in heart rate that restores blood pressure. If blood loss is severe, however, negative-feedback mechanisms may not be able to maintain homeostasis, and the positive-feedback effect of an ever-decreasing blood pressure can develop.

Circumstances in which negative-feedback mechanisms are not adequate to maintain homeostasis illustrate a basic principle. Many disease states result from failure of negative-feedback mechanisms to maintain homeostasis. The purpose of medical therapy is to overcome illness by aiding negative-feedback mechanisms. For example, a trans-

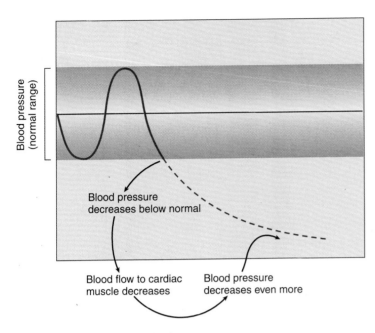

Figure 1.5   Positive Feedback

A large decrease in blood pressure causes decreased blood flow to the heart. The heart is unable to pump enough blood to maintain blood pressure or adequate blood flow to the heart muscle. Thus, the ability of the heart to pump decreases further, and blood pressure decreases even more.

fusion reverses a constantly decreasing blood pressure and restores homeostasis.

A few positive-feedback mechanisms do operate in the body under normal conditions, but in all cases they are eventually limited in some way. Birth is an example of a normally occurring positive-feedback mechanism. Near the end of pregnancy, the uterus is stretched by the baby's large size. This stretching, especially around the opening of the uterus, stimulates contractions of the uterine muscles. The uterine contractions push the baby against the opening of the uterus, stretching it further. This stimulates additional contractions that result in additional stretching. This positive-feedback se-

Did You Know?

The idea that the body maintains a balance (homeostasis) can be traced back to ancient Greece. It was believed that the body supported four juices, or humors: the red juice of blood, the yellow juice of bile, the white juice secreted from the nose and lungs, and the black juice in the pancreas. It was also thought that health resulted from a proper balance of these juices and that disease was caused by an excess of one of them. Normally the body would attempt to heal itself by expelling the excess juice. An example was thought to be the expulsion of mucus from the nose of a person with a cold. This led to the practice of bloodletting to restore the body's normal balance of juices. Tragically, in the eighteenth and nineteenth centuries, bloodletting went to extremes. When bloodletting did not result in improvement of the patient, it was taken as evidence that not enough blood had been removed to restore a healthy balance of the body's juices. The obvious solution was to let more blood, undoubtedly causing many deaths. Eventually the failure of this approach became obvious, and the practice was abandoned. Fortunately, we now understand more about how the body maintains homeostasis.

2   P R E D I C T

Is the sensation of thirst associated with a negative- or a positive-feedback mechanism? Explain. (*Hint:* What is being regulated when one becomes thirsty?)

✔ *Answer on page 18*

quence ends only when the baby is delivered from the uterus and the stretching stimulus is eliminated.

Terminology and the Body Plan

When you begin to study anatomy and physiology, the number of new words may seem overwhelming. Learning is easier and more interesting if you pay attention to the origin, or **etymology** (et′ĕ-mol′o-jē), of new words. Most of the terms are derived from Latin or Greek and are descriptive in the original languages. For example, anterior in Latin means "to go before." The anterior surface of the body is therefore the surface of the body that goes before when we are walking.

Words are often modified by adding a prefix or suffix. The suffix "-itis" means an inflammation; so appendicitis is an inflammation of the appendix. As new terms are introduced in this text, their meanings are often explained. The glossary and the list of word roots, prefixes, and suffixes on the inside front and back covers of the textbook also provide additional information about the new terms.

Directional Terms

Directional terms refer to the body in the anatomical position, regardless of its actual position. The term **anatomical** (an′ă-tom′i-kăl) **position** refers to a person standing erect with the feet forward, arms hanging to the sides, and the palms of the hands facing forward. In human anatomy, the term above is replaced by **superior**, below by **inferior**, front by **anterior**, and back by **posterior**. Directional terms are used to describe the position of structures in relation to other structures or body parts. For example, the neck is superior to the chest but inferior to the head. Important directional terms are presented in table 1.1 and are illustrated in figure 1.6.

3   P R E D I C T

Provide the correct directional term for the following statement. When a boy is standing on his head, his nose is _____ to his mouth.

✔ *Answer on page 18*

Planes

At times it is conceptually useful to discuss the body in reference to a series of planes (imaginary flat surfaces) passing through it (figure 1.7). Sectioning the body is a way to "look inside" and observe the body's structures. A **sagittal** (saj′i-tăl) **plane** runs vertically through the body and separates it into right and left parts. The word sagittal literally means "the flight of an arrow" and refers to the way the body would be split by an arrow passing anteriorly to posteriorly. If the plane divides

Table 1.1   Directional Terms for Humans

Terms	Etymology*	Definition†	Example
Right		Toward the body's right side	The right ear
Left		Toward the body's left side	The left ear
Inferior	L, lower	A structure below another	The nose is inferior to the forehead
Superior	L, higher	A structure above another	The mouth is superior to the chin
Anterior	L, to go before	Toward the front of the body	The teeth are anterior to the throat
Posterior	L. *posterus*, following	Toward the back of the body	The brain is posterior to the eyes
Dorsal	L. *dorsum*, back	Toward the back (synonymous with posterior)	The spine is dorsal to the breastbone
Ventral	L. *venter*, belly	Toward the belly (synonymous with anterior)	The navel is ventral to the spine
Proximal	L. *proximus*, nearest	Closer to the point of attachment to the body than another structure	The elbow is proximal to the wrist
Distal	L. *di + sto*, to be distant	Farther from the point of attachment to the body than another structure	The knee is distal to the hip
Lateral	L. *latus*, side	Away from the midline of the body	The nipple is lateral to the breastbone
Medial	L. *medialis*, middle	Toward the middle or midline of the body	The bridge of the nose is medial to the eye
Superficial	L. *superficialis*, surface	Toward or on the surface	The skin is superficial to muscle
Deep	O.E. *deop*, deep	Away from the surface, internal	The lungs are deep to the ribs

*Origin and meaning of the word: L, Latin; O.E., Old English
†All directional terms refer to a human in the anatomical position.

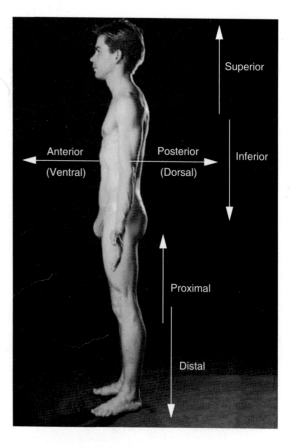

Figure 1.6   Directional Terms

All directional terms are in relation to a person in the anatomical position: a person standing with the feet and palms of the hands facing forward, with the thumbs to the outside.

Cerebrum

Cerebellum
Brainstem — Nasal septum

Spinal cord — Tongue
— Pharynx (throat)
Vertebral column

— Trachea

(b) **Midsagittal section of the head**

Midsagittal plane

Sagittal plane

Transverse, or horizontal, plane

Frontal, or coronal, plane

(a)

Skin
Fat
Hip muscle

Coxa (hip bone)

Femur (thigh bone)

Thigh muscles

(c) **Frontal section through the right hip**

Liver — Stomach
— Large intestine
— Spleen
Kidney — Vertebra
— Kidney
Spinal cord

(d) **Transverse section through the abdomen**

Figure 1.7   Planes of Section of the Body

(a) In the center of the illustration, planes of section through the whole body are indicated by "glass" sheets. Actual sections through the head *(b)*, hip *(c)* and abdomen *(d)* are also shown.

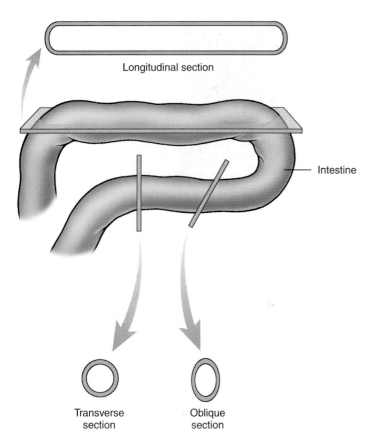

Longitudinal section

Intestine

Transverse section

Oblique section

Figure 1.8 Planes of Section of an Organ

In the center of the illustration, planes of section through the intestine are indicated by "glass" sheets. The views of the intestine after sectioning are also shown. Although the intestine is basically a tube, the sections appear quite different in shape.

the body into equal right and left halves, it is a **midsagittal** (mid′saj′i-tăl) **plane**. A **transverse** (trans-vers′), or **horizontal, plane** runs parallel to the surface of the ground and divides the body into superior and inferior parts. A **frontal,** or **coronal** (kŏr′ŏ-năl, kō-rō′nal), **plane** runs vertically from right to left and divides the body into anterior and posterior parts.

Organs are often sectioned to reveal their internal structure (figure 1.8). A cut through the long axis of the organ is a **longitudinal section**, and a cut at a right angle to the long axis is a **transverse,** or **cross, section**. If a cut is made across the long axis at other than a right angle, it is called an **oblique section**.

Body Parts and Regions

A number of terms are used when referring to different regions or parts of the body (figure 1.9). The upper limb is divided into the arm, forearm, wrist, and hand. The **arm** extends from the shoulder to the elbow, and the **forearm** extends from the elbow to the wrist. The lower limb is divided into the thigh, leg, ankle, and foot. The **thigh** extends from the hip to the knee, and the **leg** extends from the knee to the ankle. Note that, contrary to popular usage, the terms arm and leg refer to only a part of the respective limb.

The central region of the body consists of the **head, neck,** and **trunk**. The trunk can be divided into the **thorax** (chest), **abdomen** (region between the thorax and pelvis), and **pelvis** (the inferior end of the trunk associated with the hips).

The abdomen is often subdivided superficially into four **quadrants** by two imaginary lines—one horizontal and one vertical—that intersect at the navel (figure 1.10*a*). The quadrants formed are the right upper, left upper, right lower, and left lower quadrants. In addition to these quadrants, the abdomen is sometimes subdivided into nine **regions** by four imaginary lines—two horizontal and two vertical. These four lines create an imaginary tic-tac-toe figure on the abdomen, resulting in nine regions: epigastric (ep-i-gas′trik), right and left hypochondriac (hī-pō-kon′drē-ak), umbilical (ŭm-bil′i-kăl), right and left lumbar (lŭm′bar), hypogastric (hī-pō-gas′trik), and right and left iliac (il′ē-ak) (figure 1.10*b*). The quadrants or regions are used by clinicians as reference points for locating the underlying organs. For example, the appendix is located in the right lower quadrant, and the pain of an acute appendicitis is usually felt there.

---

4 **P R E D I C T**

Using figures 1.2 (p. 6) and 1.10*a*, determine in which quadrant each of the following organs is located: spleen, gallbladder, kidneys, most of the stomach, and most of the liver.

✔ *Answer on page 18*

Body Cavities

The body contains many cavities, such as the nasal, cranial, and abdominal cavities. Some of these cavities open to the outside of the body, and some do not. Introductory anatomy and physiology textbooks sometimes describe a dorsal cavity, in which the brain and spinal cord are found, and a ventral body cavity, which contains all the trunk cavities. The concept of a dorsal cavity is not described in medical-level works on anatomy and therefore is not emphasized here. Discussion in this chapter is limited to the major trunk cavities that do not open to the outside.

The trunk contains three large cavities: the thoracic cavity, the abdominal cavity, and the pelvic cavity (figure 1.11). The **thoracic cavity** is surrounded by the rib cage and is separated from the abdominal cavity by the muscular diaphragm. It is divided into right and left parts by a median structure called the **mediastinum** (me′dē-as-tī′nŭm; wall). The mediastinum is a partition containing the heart, thymus gland, trachea, esophagus, and other structures. The two lungs are located on either side of the mediastinum.

The **abdominal cavity** is bounded primarily by the abdominal muscles and contains the stomach, intestines, liver, spleen, pancreas, and kidneys. The **pelvic** (pel′vik) **cavity** is a small space enclosed by the bones of the pelvis and contains the urinary bladder, part of the large intestine, and the internal reproductive organs. The abdominal and pelvic cavities are not physically separated and sometimes are called the **abdominopelvic** (ab-dom′i-nō-pel′vik) **cavity**.

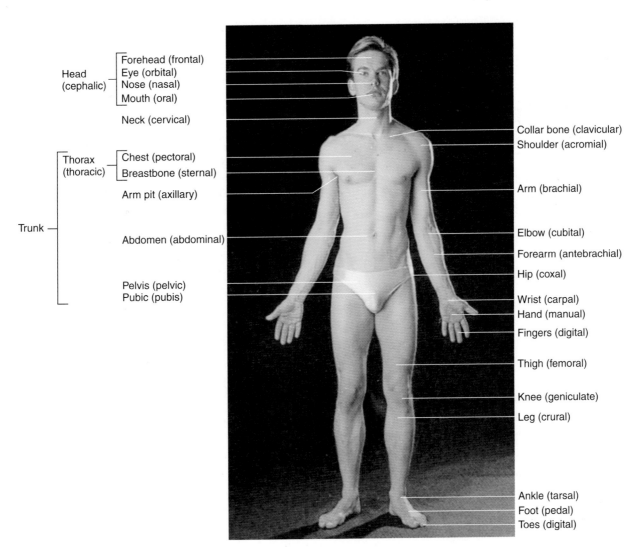

Head (cephalic)
- Forehead (frontal)
- Eye (orbital)
- Nose (nasal)
- Mouth (oral)

Neck (cervical)

Thorax (thoracic)
- Chest (pectoral)
- Breastbone (sternal)

Arm pit (axillary)

Trunk

Abdomen (abdominal)

Pelvis (pelvic)
Pubic (pubis)

Collar bone (clavicular)
Shoulder (acromial)

Arm (brachial)

Elbow (cubital)
Forearm (antebrachial)
Hip (coxal)
Wrist (carpal)
Hand (manual)
Fingers (digital)

Thigh (femoral)

Knee (geniculate)
Leg (crural)

Ankle (tarsal)
Foot (pedal)
Toes (digital)

Figure 1.9 Body Parts
The common names and anatomical terms (in parentheses) are indicated for some parts of the body.

Serous Membranes

Serous (sēr′ŭs) **membranes** line the trunk cavities and cover the organs of these cavities. To understand the relationship between serous membranes and an organ, imagine an inflated balloon into which a fist has been pushed. The inner balloon wall in contact with the fist (organ) represents the **visceral** (vis′er-ăl; organ) **serous membrane**, and the outer part of the balloon wall represents the **parietal** (pă-rī′ĕ-tăl; wall) **serous membrane** (figure 1.12). The cavity or space between the visceral and parietal serous membranes is normally filled with a thin, lubricating film of serous fluid produced by the membranes. As an organ rubs against another organ or against the body wall, the serous fluid and smooth serous membranes function to reduce friction.

The thoracic cavity contains three serous membrane-lined cavities: a pericardial cavity and two pleural cavities. The **pericardial** (per-i-kar′dē-ăl) **cavity** surrounds the heart (figure 1.13a). The heart is covered by the visceral pericardium and is contained within a connective tissue sac that is lined with the parietal pericardium. The pericardial cavity, which contains

pericardial fluid, is located between the visceral and parietal pericardia.

Each lung is surrounded by a **pleural** (ploor′ăl) **cavity** and is covered by visceral pleura (figure 1.13b). The inner surface of the thoracic wall is lined by the parietal pleura. The pleural cavity is located between the visceral and parietal pleurae and contains pleural fluid.

The abdominopelvic cavity contains a serous membrane-lined cavity called the **peritoneal** (per′i-tō-nē′ăl) **cavity** (figure 1.13c). Many of the organs of the abdominopelvic cavity are covered by visceral peritoneum, and the wall of the abdominopelvic cavity is lined with parietal peritoneum. The peritoneal cavity is located between the visceral and parietal peritoneum and contains peritoneal fluid.

Did You Know?

The serous membranes can become inflamed—usually as a result of an infection. **Pericarditis** (per′i-kar-dī′tis) is inflammation of the pericardium, **pleurisy** (ploor′i-sē) is inflammation of the pleura, and **peritonitis** (per′i-tō-nī′tis) is inflammation of the peritoneum.

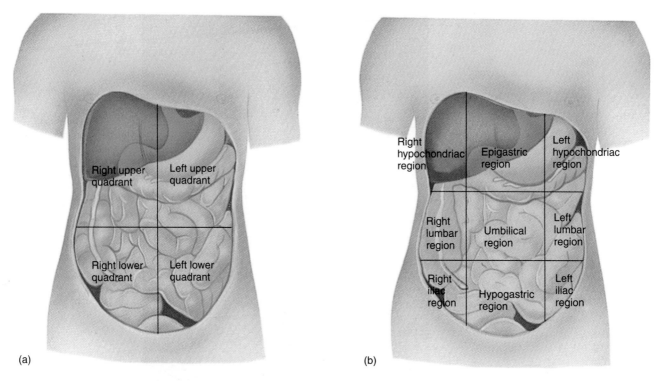

(a)

(b)

Figure 1.10   Subdivisions of the Abdomen

Lines are superimposed over internal organs to demonstrate the relationship of the organs to the subdivisions. (*a*) Abdominal quadrants consist of four subdivisions. (*b*) Abdominal regions consist of nine subdivisions.

(a)

(b)

Figure 1.11   Trunk Cavities

(*a*) Anterior view showing the major trunk cavities. The diaphragm separates the thoracic cavity from the abdominal cavity. The mediastinum, which includes the heart, divides the thoracic cavity. (*b*) Sagittal view of the trunk cavities. The dashed line shows the division between the abdominal and pelvic cavities. The mediastinum has been removed to show the thoracic cavity.

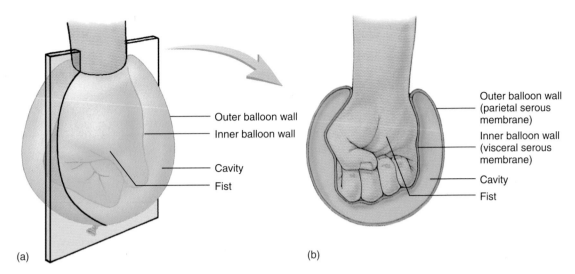

Figure 1.12   Serous Membranes

(a) Fist pushing into a balloon. A "glass" sheet indicates the location of a cross section through the balloon. (b) Interior view produced by the cross section in (a). The fist represents an organ and the walls of the balloon the serous membranes. The inner wall of the balloon represents a visceral serous membrane in contact with the fist (organ). The outer wall of the balloon represents a parietal serous membrane.

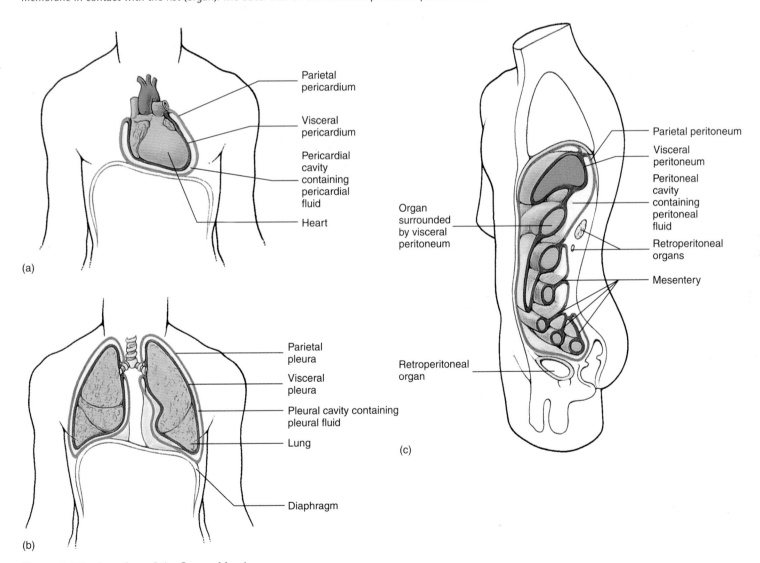

Figure 1.13   Location of the Serous Membranes

(a) Frontal section showing the pericardial membranes and pericardial cavity. (b) Frontal section showing the pleural membranes and pleural cavities. (c) Sagittal section through the abdominopelvic cavity showing the peritoneum, peritoneal cavity, mesenteries, and retroperitoneal organs.

The parietal peritoneum is connected to the visceral peritoneum of many abdominopelvic organs by a double-layered membrane called a **mesentery** (mes′en-ter-ē) (figure 1.13c). The mesenteries anchor the organs to the body wall and provide a pathway for nerves and blood vessels to reach the organs. Other abdominopelvic organs are more closely attached to the body wall and do not have mesenteries. They are covered by the parietal peritoneum and are said to be **retroperitoneal** (re′trō-per′i-tō-nē′ăl; behind the peritoneum). The retroperitoneal organs include the kidneys, adrenal glands, pancreas, portions of the intestines, and the urinary bladder (see figure 1.13c).

5   P R E D I C T

Explain how an organ can be located within the abdominopelvic cavity but not be within the peritoneal cavity.

✔ *Answer on page 18*

Summary

A knowledge of anatomy and physiology can be used to predict the body's responses to stimuli when healthy or diseased.

Anatomy

- Anatomy is the study of the structures of the body.
- Systemic anatomy is the study of the body by organ systems. Regional anatomy is the study of the body by areas.
- Surface anatomy uses superficial structures to locate deeper structures, and anatomical imaging is a noninvasive method for examining deep structures.

Physiology

- Physiology is the study of the processes and functions of the body.

Structural and Functional Organization

- The human body can be organized into seven levels: chemical (atoms and molecules), organelle (small structures within cells), cell, tissue (groups of cells with similar structure and structure), organ (two or more tissues that perform one or more common functions), organ system (groups of organs with common functions), and organism.
- The 11 organ systems are the integumentary, skeletal, muscular, nervous, endocrine, cardiovascular, lymphatic, respiratory, digestive, urinary, and reproductive systems (see figure 1.2).

Characteristics of Life

- The characteristics of life include organization, metabolism, responsiveness, growth, differentiation, and reproduction.

Homeostasis

- Homeostasis is the condition in which body functions, fluids, and other factors of the internal environment are maintained within a range of values suitable to support life.
- Negative-feedback mechanisms operate to maintain homeostasis.
- Positive-feedback mechanisms make deviations from normal even greater. Although a few positive-feedback mechanisms normally exist in the body, most positive-feedback mechanisms are harmful.

Terminology and the Body Plan
Directional Terms

- A human standing erect with the feet forward, arms hanging to the sides, and palms facing forward is in the anatomical position.
- Directional terms always refer to the anatomical position, regardless of the body's actual position (see table 1.1).

Planes

- A sagittal plane divides the body into left and right parts, a transverse plane divides the body into superior and inferior parts, and a frontal plane divides the body into anterior and posterior parts.
- A longitudinal section divides an organ along its long axis, a transverse section cuts an organ at a right angle to the long axis, and an oblique section cuts across the long axis at an angle other than a right angle.

Body Regions

- The body can be divided into the limbs, head, neck, and trunk.
- The abdomen can be divided superficially into four quadrants or nine regions that are useful for locating internal organs or describing the location of a pain.

Body Cavities

- The thoracic cavity is bounded by the ribs and the diaphragm. The mediastinum divides the thoracic cavity into two parts.
- The abdominal cavity is bounded by the diaphragm and the abdominal muscles.
- The pelvic cavity is surrounded by the pelvic bones.

Serous Membranes

- The trunk cavities are lined by serous membranes. The parietal part of a serous membrane lines the wall of the cavity, and the visceral part covers the internal organs.
- The serous membranes secrete fluid that fills the space between the parietal and visceral membranes. The serous membranes protect organs from friction.
- The pericardial membrane surrounds the heart, the pleural membranes surround the lungs, and the peritoneal membranes line the abdominopelvic cavity and cover its organs.
- Mesenteries are parts of the peritoneum that hold the abdominal organs in place and provide a passageway for blood vessels and nerves to organs.
- Retroperitoneal organs are found "behind" the parietal peritoneum. The kidneys, urinary bladder, and pancreas are examples of retroperitoneal organs.

Content Review

1. Define anatomy, surface anatomy, anatomical imaging, and physiology.
2. List seven structural levels at which the body can be studied conceptually.
3. Define tissue. What are the four primary tissue types?
4. Define organ and organ system. What are the 11 organ systems of the body and their functions?
5. Name six characteristics of life.
6. What does the term homeostasis mean? If a deviation from homeostasis occurs, what kind of mechanism restores homeostasis?
7. Describe a negative-feedback mechanism in terms of receptor, control center, and effector. Give an example of a negative-feedback mechanism.
8. Define positive feedback. Why are positive-feedback mechanisms generally harmful? Give an example of a harmful and a beneficial positive-feedback mechanism.
9. Why is knowledge of the etymology of anatomical and physiological terms useful?
10. What is the anatomical position? Why is it important to remember the anatomical position when using directional terms?
11. Define and give an example of the following directional terms: inferior, superior, anterior, posterior, dorsal, ventral, proximal, distal, lateral, medial, superficial, and deep.
12. Define the sagittal, midsagittal, transverse, and frontal planes of the body.
13. Define the longitudinal, transverse, and oblique sections of an organ.
14. List the subdivisions of the upper limb, lower limb, and trunk.
15. Describe the four-quadrant and nine-region methods of subdividing the abdominal region. What is the purpose of these methods?
16. Define the following cavities: thoracic, abdominal, pelvic, and abdominopelvic. What is the mediastinum?
17. What is the difference between the visceral and parietal layers of a serous membrane? What function do serous membranes perform?
18. Name the serous membranes associated with the lungs, heart, and abdominopelvic organs.
19. Define mesentery. What does the term retroperitoneal mean? Give an example of a retroperitoneal organ.

Develop Your Reasoning Skills

1. A male has lost blood as a result of a gunshot wound. Even though bleeding has been stopped, his blood pressure is low and dropping and his heart rate is elevated. Following a blood transfusion, his blood pressure increases and his heart rate decreases. Which of the following statement(s) is (are) consistent with these observations?
   a. Negative-feedback mechanisms can be inadequate without medical intervention.
   b. The transfusion interrupted a positive-feedback mechanism.
   c. The increased heart rate after the gunshot wound and before the transfusion is a result of a positive-feedback mechanism.
   d. a and b
   e. a, b, and c
2. During physical exercise, respiration rate increases. Two students are discussing the mechanisms involved: Student A claims they are positive-feedback mechanisms, and student B claims they are negative-feedback mechanisms. Do you agree with student A or student B, and why?
3. Complete the following statements using the correct directional terms for a human being.
   a. The navel is _____ to the nose.
   b. The heart is _____ to the breastbone (sternum).
   c. The forearm is _____ to the arm.
   d. The ear is _____ to the eye.
4. Describe in as many directional terms as you can the relationship between your kneecap and your heel.
5. The esophagus is a muscular tube that connects the pharynx (throat) to the stomach. In which quadrant and region is the esophagus located? In which quadrant and region is the urinary bladder located?
6. During pregnancy, which would increase more in size, the mother's abdominal or pelvic cavity? Explain.
7. A bullet enters the left side of a male, passes through the left lung, and lodges in the heart. Name in order the serous membranes and their cavities through which the bullet passes.

Answers to Predict Questions

1. p. 7 Donating a pint of blood results in a decrease in blood pressure. Negative-feedback mechanisms, such as an increase in heart rate, return blood pressure toward a normal value. When a negative-feedback mechanism fails to return a value to its normal level, the value can continue to deviate from its normal range. Homeostasis is not maintained in this situation, and the person's health or life can be threatened.

2. p. 9 The thirst sensation is associated with a decrease in body fluid levels. The thirst mechanism causes the person to drink fluids, which returns the fluid level to normal. Thirst is therefore a sensation involved in negative-feedback control of body fluids.

3. p. 9 When a boy is standing on his head, his nose is superior to his mouth. Remember that directional terms refer to a person in the anatomical position and not to the body's current position.

4. p. 12 The spleen is in the left upper quadrant, the gallbladder is in the right upper quadrant, the left kidney is in the left upper quadrant, the right kidney is in the right upper quadrant, the stomach is mostly in the left upper quadrant, and the liver is mostly in the right upper quadrant.

5. p. 16 There are two ways. First, the visceral peritoneum wraps around organs. Thus the peritoneal cavity surrounds the organ, but the organ is not inside the peritoneal cavity. The peritoneal cavity contains only peritoneal fluid. Second, retroperitoneal organs are in the abdominopelvic cavity, but they are between the wall of the abdominopelvic cavity and the parietal peritoneal membrane.

Chapter Two

The Chemistry of Life

acid
(as′id) Any substance that is a proton donor; or any substance that releases hydrogen ions.

atom
(at′ŏm) [Gr. *atomos*, indivisible, uncut] Smallest particle into which an element can be divided using chemical methods; composed of neutrons, protons, and electrons.

base
Any substance that is a proton acceptor; or any substance that binds to hydrogen ions.

buffer
(bŭf′er) A chemical that resists changes in pH when either an acid or a base is added to a solution containing the buffer.

covalent bond
(kō-vāl′ent) Chemical bond that is formed when two atoms share one or more pairs of electrons.

electron
(ē-lek′tron) Negatively charged particle found around the nucleus of atoms.

enzyme
(en′zīm) [Gr. *en*, in + *zyme*, leaven] A protein molecule that increases the rate of a chemical reaction without being permanently altered.

ion
(ī′on) Atom or group of atoms carrying an electrical charge because of the loss or gain of one or more electrons.

ionic (ī-on′ik) **bond**
Chemical bond resulting from the attraction between ions of opposite charges.

molecule
(mol′ĕ-kūl) Two or more atoms chemically combined to form a structure that behaves as an independent unit.

neutron
(noo′tron) [L. *neuter*, neither] Electrically neutral particle found in the nuclei of atoms.

proton
(prō′ton) [Gr. *protos*, first] Positively charged particle found in the nuclei of atoms.

Objectives

After reading this chapter, you should be able to:

1. Define matter, mass, and weight.
2. Define element and atom.
3. Name the subatomic particles of an atom, and describe how they are organized.
4. Describe two types of chemical bonds.
5. Define hydrogen bond, and explain its importance.
6. Distinguish between a molecule and a compound.
7. Describe the process of dissociation.
8. Using symbols, explain synthesis, decomposition, and exchange reactions.
9. Explain how reversible reactions produce chemical equilibrium.
10. Distinguish between chemical reactions that release or take in energy.
11. List the factors that affect the rate of chemical reactions.
12. Describe the pH scale and its relationship to acidity and alkalinity.
13. Explain why buffers are important.
14. List the properties of water that make it important for living organisms.
15. Describe four important types of organic molecules and their functions.
16. Explain how enzymes work.

A basic knowledge of chemistry—the scientific discipline that deals with the composition and structure of substances and with the reactions they undergo—is essential for understanding anatomy and physiology, because all of the structures of the body are composed of chemicals and all of the functions of the body result from chemical reactions. For example, the generation of nerve impulses and the physiological processes of digestion, muscle contraction, and metabolism can all be described in chemical terms. Many abnormal conditions and their treatments can also be explained in chemical terms, even though their symptoms appear as malfunctions in organ systems. For example, Parkinson's disease, one symptom of which is uncontrolled shaking movements, results from a shortage of a chemical called dopamine in certain nerve cells of the brain. It is treated by giving patients another chemical that is converted to dopamine by brain cells.

This chapter outlines some basic chemical principles and emphasizes the relationship of these principles to living organisms. It is not a comprehensive review of chemistry, but it does review some of the basic chemical principles that make anatomy and physiology more understandable. You should refer to this chapter when chemical phenomena are discussed later in the text.

Basic Chemistry
Matter, Mass, and Weight

All living and nonliving things are composed of **matter**, which is anything that occupies space and has mass. **Mass** is the amount of matter in an object, and **weight** is the gravitational force acting on an object of a given mass. For example, the weight of an apple results from the force of gravity "pulling" on the apple's mass.

1   P R E D I C T

The difference between mass and weight can be illustrated by considering an astronaut. How would an astronaut's mass and weight in outer space compare with his mass and weight on the earth's surface?

✔ *Answer on page 40*

The international unit for mass is the **kilogram (kg)**, which is the mass of a platinum–iridium cylinder kept at the International Bureau of Weights and Measurements in France. The mass of all other objects is compared with this cylinder. For example, a 2.2-lb lead weight, or 1 liter (L) (1.06 qt) of water, each have a mass of approximately 1 kg. An object with 1/1000 the mass of the standard kilogram cylinder is defined to have a mass of 1 **gram (g)**.

Chemists use a balance to determine the mass of objects. Although we commonly refer to weighing an object on a balance, we actually are "massing" the object because the balance compares objects of unknown mass with objects of known mass. When the unknown and known masses are ex-

actly balanced, the gravitational pull of earth on both of them is the same. Thus, the effect of gravity on the unknown mass is counteracted by the effect of gravity on the known mass. A balance produces the same results at sea level as on a mountaintop because it does not matter if the gravitational pull is strong or weak. It only matters that the effect of gravity on both the unknown and known masses is the same.

Elements and Atoms

An **element** is the simplest type of matter with unique chemical properties. As of March 1996, 112 elements are known. A list of the elements commonly found in the human body is given in table 2.1. About 96% of the weight of the body results from the elements oxygen, carbon, hydrogen, and nitrogen.

An **atom** (at′ŏm) is the smallest particle of an element that has the chemical characteristics of that element. An element is composed of atoms of only one kind. For example, the element carbon is composed of only carbon atoms, and the element oxygen is composed of only oxygen atoms.

An element, or an atom of that element, often is represented by a symbol. Usually the first letter or letters of the element's name are used—for example, C for carbon, H for hydrogen, Ca for calcium, and Cl for chlorine. Occasionally the symbol is taken from the Latin, Greek, or Arabic name for the element—for example, Na from the Latin word *natrium* is the symbol for sodium.

Atomic Structure

The characteristics of living and nonliving matter result from the structure, organization, and behavior of atoms. Neutrons, protons, and electrons are the three major types of subatomic particles that form atoms. **Neutrons** (noo′tronz) have no electrical charge, **protons** (prō′tonz) have positive charges, and **electrons** (ē-lek′tronz) have negative charges. The positive charge of a proton is equal in magnitude to the negative charge of an electron. Because the numbers of protons and electrons in atoms are equal, the individual charges cancel each other, and atoms are electrically neutral.

Protons and neutrons form the **nucleus** of the atom, and electrons are located around the nucleus (figure 2.1). The nucleus accounts for 99.97% of an atom's mass, but only 1 ten-trillionth of its volume. Most of the volume of an atom is occupied by the electrons. Although it is impossible to know precisely where any given electron is located at any particular moment, the region where electrons are most likely to be found can be represented by an **electron cloud** (see figure 2.1). The darker the color in each small volume of the diagram, the greater the likelihood of finding an electron there at any given moment.

The **atomic number** of an element is equal to the number of protons in each atom, and because the number of electrons and protons is equal, the atomic number also indicates the number of electrons. Each element is uniquely defined by

Table 2.1   Some Common Elements

Element	Symbol	Atomic Number	Percent in Human Body by Weight	Percent in Human Body by Number of Atoms
Hydrogen	H	1	9.5	63.0
Carbon	C	6	18.5	9.5
Nitrogen	N	7	3.3	1.4
Oxygen	O	8	65.0	25.5
Sodium	Na	11	0.2	0.3
Phosphorus	P	15	1.0	0.22
Sulfur	S	16	0.3	0.05
Chlorine	Cl	17	0.2	0.03
Potassium	K	19	0.4	0.06
Calcium	Ca	20	1.5	0.31
Iron	Fe	26	Trace	Trace
Iodine	I	53	Trace	Trace

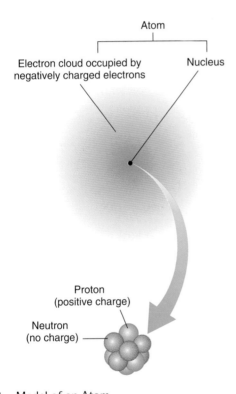

Figure 2.1   Model of an Atom

The tiny, dense nucleus consists of positively charged protons and uncharged neutrons. Most of the volume of an atom is occupied by rapidly moving, negatively charged electrons, which can be represented as an electron cloud. The probable location of an electron is indicated by the number of dots in the electron cloud. The darker the color in each small part of the electron cloud, the more likely the electron is located there.

the number of protons in the atoms of that element. For example, only hydrogen atoms have one proton, only carbon atoms have six protons, and only oxygen atoms have eight protons (figure 2.2; see table 2.1).

Electrons and Chemical Bonding

The chemical behavior of an atom is determined largely by its outermost electrons. **Chemical bonding** occurs when the outermost electrons are transferred or shared between atoms. Two major types of chemical bonding are ionic and covalent bonding.

Ionic Bonding

An atom is electrically neutral because it has an equal number of protons and electrons. If an atom loses or gains electrons, the number of protons and electrons are no longer equal, and a charged particle called an **ion** (ī'on) is formed. After an atom loses an electron, it has one more proton than it has electrons and is positively charged. For example, a sodium atom (Na) can lose an electron to become a positively charged sodium ion (Na^+) (figure 2.3*a*). After an atom gains an electron, it has one more electron than it has protons and is negatively charged. For example, a chlorine atom (Cl) can accept an electron to become a negatively charged chloride ion (Cl^-). Because oppositely charged ions are attracted to each other, positively charged ions tend to remain close to negatively charged ions, which is called **ionic** (ī-on′ik) **bonding**. Thus, Na^+ and Cl^- ions are held together by ionic bonding to form an array of ions called sodium chloride, or table salt (figure 2.3*b*).

Ions are denoted by using the symbol of the atom from which the ion was formed. The charge of the ion is indicated by a superscripted plus (+) or minus (−) sign. For example, a sodium ion is Na^+, and a chloride ion is Cl^-. If more than one electron has been lost or gained, a number is used with the plus or minus sign. Thus Ca^{2+} is a calcium ion formed by the loss of two electrons. Some ions commonly found in the body are listed in table 2.2.

2	P R E D I C T

If an iron (Fe) atom loses three electrons, what is the charge of the resulting ion? Write the symbol for this ion.

✔ *Answer on page 40*

Covalent Bonding

Covalent bonding results when atoms share one or more pairs of electrons. The resulting combination of atoms is called a molecule. An example is the covalent bond between two hy-

Figure 2.2   Hydrogen, Carbon, and Oxygen Atoms

Within the nucleus, the number of positively charged protons (p^+) and uncharged neutrons (n^0) is indicated. The negatively charged electrons (e^-) are around the nucleus. Atoms are electrically neutral because the number of protons and electrons within atoms are equal.

Figure 2.3   Ionic Bonding

(*a*) A sodium atom loses an electron to become a positively charged ion, and a chlorine atom gains an electron to become a negatively charged ion. The attraction between the oppositely charged ions results in ionic bonding and the formation of sodium chloride. (*b*) The sodium and chlorine ions are organized to form a cube-shaped array. (*c*) Photomicrograph of salt crystals reflects the cubic arrangement of the ions.

Table 2.2   Important Ions

Common Ions	Symbol	Function
Calcium	Ca^{2+}	Component of bones and teeth, necessary for blood clotting and muscle contraction
Sodium	Na^+	Helps maintain membrane potentials (electrical charge differences across a membrane) and water balance
Potassium	K^+	Helps maintain membrane potentials
Hydrogen	H^+	Helps maintain acid–base balance
Hydroxide	OH^-	Helps maintain acid–base balance
Chloride	Cl^-	Helps maintain acid–base balance
Bicarbonate	HCO_3^-	Helps maintain acid–base balance
Ammonium	NH_4^+	Helps maintain acid–base balance
Phosphate	PO_4^{3-}	Component of bone and teeth, involved in energy exchange and acid–base balance
Iron	Fe^{2+}	Necessary for red blood cell formation and function
Magnesium	Mg^{2+}	Necessary for enzymes

No interaction between the two hydrogen atoms because they are too far apart.

The positively charged nucleus of each hydrogen atom begins to attract the electron of the other.

A covalent bond is formed when the electrons are shared between the nuclei because the electrons are equally attracted to each nucleus.

Figure 2.4   Covalent Bonding

drogen atoms to form a hydrogen molecule (figure 2.4). Each hydrogen atom has one electron. As the atoms get closer together, the positively charged nucleus of each atom begins to attract the electron of the other atom. At an optimal distance, the two nuclei mutually attract the two electrons, and each electron is shared by both nuclei. The two hydrogen atoms are now held together by a covalent bond.

When an electron pair is shared between two atoms, a **single covalent bond** results. A single covalent bond can be represented by a single line between the symbols of the atoms involved (for example, H—H). A **double covalent bond** results when two atoms share two pairs of electrons. When a carbon atom combines with two oxygen atoms to form carbon dioxide, two double covalent bonds are formed. Double covalent bonds are indicated by a double line between the atoms (O=C=O).

Two hydrogen atoms can share their electrons with an oxygen atom to form a water molecule (figure 2.5). The hydrogen atoms do not share the electrons equally with the oxygen atom, however, and the electrons tend to spend more time around the oxygen atom than around the hydrogen atoms. This unequal sharing of electrons is called a **polar covalent bond**, because the unequal sharing of electrons results in one end (pole) of the molecule having a small electrical charge opposite to that of the other end. Molecules with this asymmetrical electrical charge are called **polar molecules**, whereas molecules with a symmetrical electrical charge are called **nonpolar molecules**.

Hydrogen Bonds

A polar molecule has positive and negative "ends" that can be weakly attracted to ions or to the "ends" of other polar molecules. Although this attraction is called a **hydrogen bond**, it is much weaker than ionic or covalent bonds. For example, the positively charged hydrogen of one water molecule is weakly attracted to a negatively charged oxygen of another water molecule (figure 2.6). Thus, the water molecules are held together by hydrogen bonds.

Hydrogen bonds also play an important role in determining the shape of complex molecules because the hydrogen bonds between different polar parts of a single large molecule hold the molecule in its normal three-dimensional shape (see the sections on Proteins and Nucleic Acids on p. 34).

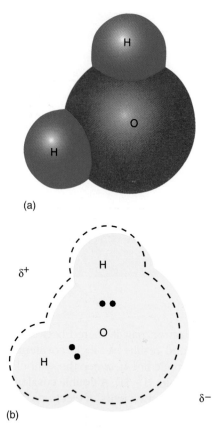

(a)

(b)

δ^+

δ^-

Figure 2.5 Polar Covalent Bonding

(*a*) Water molecule formed when two hydrogen atoms form covalent bonds with an oxygen atom. (*b*) Electron pairs (indicated by dots) are shared between the hydrogen atoms and oxygen. The dashed line indicates the position of the electron cloud if the electrons were shared equally between the hydrogen and oxygen atoms. The electrons are shared unequally, however, as shown by the electron cloud (yellow) not coinciding with the dashed outline. Consequently, the oxygen side of the molecule has a slight negative charge (indicated by δ^-) and the hydrogen side of the molecule has a slight positive charge (indicated by δ^+).

Molecules and Compounds

A **molecule** (mol′ĕ-kūl) is formed when two or more atoms chemically combine to form a structure that behaves as an independent unit. The atoms that combine to form a molecule can be of the same type, such as two hydrogen atoms combining to form a hydrogen molecule. More typically, a molecule consists of two or more different types of atoms such as two hydrogen atoms and an oxygen atom forming water. Thus, a glass of water consists of a collection of individual water molecules positioned next to one another.

A **compound** (kom′pownd) is a substance composed of two or more *different* types of atoms that are chemically combined. Not all molecules are compounds. For example, a hydrogen molecule is not a compound because it does not consist of different types of atoms. Most molecules, however, are covalent compounds. Atoms joined by covalent bonding form molecules because the atoms form distinct units as a re-

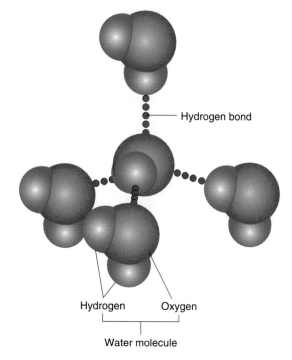

Hydrogen bond

Hydrogen

Oxygen

Water molecule

Figure 2.6 Hydrogen Bonds

The positive hydrogen part of one water molecule forms a hydrogen bond with the negative oxygen part of another water molecule. As a result, hydrogen bonds hold the water molecules together.

sult of the joining of the atoms to one another by a pair of shared electrons. For example, a water molecule is a covalent compound.

On the other hand, ionic compounds are not molecules because the ions are held together by the force of attraction between opposite charges. A piece of sodium chloride does not consist of individual sodium chloride molecules positioned next to one another. Instead, it is an organized array of individual Na^+ ions and individual Cl^- ions in which each charged ion is surrounded by several ions of the opposite charge (see figure 2.3*b*). Sodium chloride is an example of a substance that is a compound but not a molecule.

Molecules and compounds can be represented by the symbols of the atoms forming the molecule or compound plus subscripts denoting the number of each type of atom. For example, glucose (a sugar) can be represented as $C_6H_{12}O_6$, indicating that glucose has 6 carbon, 12 hydrogen, and 6 oxygen atoms.

Dissociation

When ionic compounds dissolve in water, their ions **dissociate** (di-sō′sē-āt′), or separate, from each other because the positively charged ions are attracted to the negative ends of the water molecules, and the negatively charged ions are attracted to the positive ends of the water molecules. For example, when sodium chloride dissociates in water, the Na^+

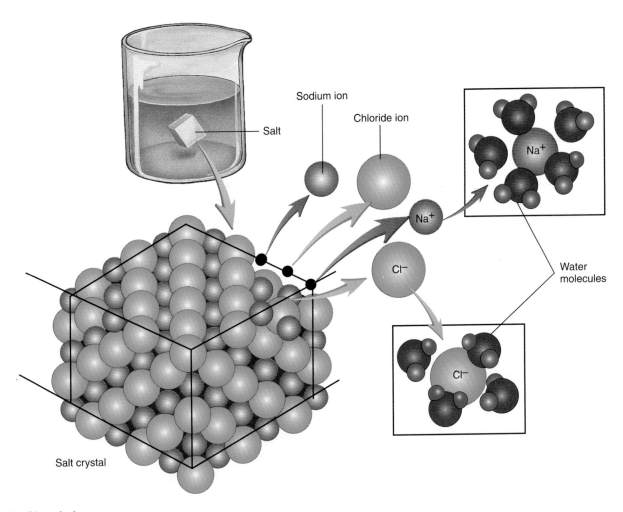

Figure 2.7   Dissociation

Sodium chloride (table salt) dissociating in water. The positively charged sodium ions (Na$^+$) are attracted to the negative oxygen (red) end of the water molecule, and the negatively charged chlorine ions (Cl$^-$) are attracted to the positive hydrogen (blue) end of the water molecule.

and Cl$^-$ ions separate, and water molecules surround and isolate the ions, keeping them in solution (figure 2.7).

When molecules dissolve in water, the molecules usually remain intact even though they are surrounded by water molecules. Thus, in a glucose solution, glucose molecules are surrounded by water molecules.

Did You Know?

Ions that dissociate in water are sometimes called **electrolytes** (ē-lek′trō-lītz) because they have the capacity to conduct an electrical current, which is the flow of charged particles. An electrocardiogram (ECG) is a recording of electrical currents produced by the heart. These currents can be detected by electrodes on the surface of the body because the ions in the body fluids conduct electrical currents.

Chemical Reactions

In a **chemical reaction**, atoms, ions, molecules, or compounds interact either to form or to break chemical bonds. The substances that enter into a chemical reaction are called the **re-** actants, and the substances that result from the chemical reaction are called the **products**.

Classification of Chemical Reactions

For our purposes, chemical reactions can be classified as synthesis, decomposition, or exchange reactions.

Synthesis Reactions

When two or more reactants combine to form a larger, more complex product, the process is called a **synthesis reaction**. This can be represented symbolically as follows:

$$A + B \rightarrow AB$$

Examples of synthesis reactions include the synthesis of the complex molecules of the human body from the basic "building blocks" obtained in food and the synthesis of **adenosine triphosphate (ATP)** (ă-den′ō-sēn trī-fos′fāt) molecules. In ATP, A stands for adenosine, T stands for tri- (or three), and

Clinical Focus   Clinical Applications of Atomic Particles

Protons, neutrons, and electrons are responsible for the chemical properties of atoms. They also have other properties that can be useful in a clinical setting. For example, some of these properties have enabled the development of methods for examining the inside of the body.

Isotopes (ī'sō-tōpz) are two or more forms of the same element that have the same number of protons and electrons but a different number of neutrons. For example, hydrogen has no neutrons, and its isotope deuterium has one. Water made with deuterium is called heavy water because of the weight of the "extra" neutron. Because isotopes of the same atom have the same number of electrons, they are very similar in their chemical behavior. The nuclei of some isotopes are stable and do not change. Radioactive isotopes, however, have unstable nuclei that lose neutrons or protons. Several different kinds of radiation can be produced when neutrons and protons, or the products formed by their breakdown, are released from the nucleus of the isotope.

The radiation given off by some radioactive isotopes can penetrate and destroy tissues. Rapidly dividing cells are more sensitive to radiation than are slowly dividing cells. Radiation is used to treat cancerous (malignant) tumors because cancer cells divide rapidly. If the treatment is effective, few healthy cells are destroyed, but the cancerous cells are killed.

Radioactive isotopes also are used in diagnosis. The radiation can be detected, and the movement of the radioactive isotopes throughout the body can be traced. For example, the thyroid gland normally takes up iodine and uses it in the formation of thyroid hormones. Radioactive iodine can be used to determine if iodine uptake is normal in the thyroid gland.

Radiation can be produced in ways other than changing the nucleus of atoms. X-rays are a type of radiation formed when electrons lose energy by moving from a higher energy state to a lower one. X-rays are used in examination of bones to determine if they are broken, and of teeth to see if they have caries (cavities). Mammograms, which are low-energy radiographs (x-ray films) of the breast, can be used to detect tumors because the tumors are slightly denser than normal tissue.

Computers can be used to analyze a series of radiographs, each made at a slightly different body location. The picture of each radiographic "slice" through the body is assembled by the computer to form a three-dimensional image. A **computed tomography** (tō-mog'rǎ-fē) **(CT) scan** is an example of this technique (figure A). CT scans are used to detect tumors and other abnormalities in the body.

Magnetic resonance imaging (MRI) is another method for looking into the body (figure B). The patient is placed into a very powerful magnetic field, which aligns the hydrogen nuclei. Radiowaves given off by the hydrogen nuclei are monitored, and the data are used by a computer to make an image of the body. Because MRI detects hydrogen, it is very effective for visualizing soft tissues that contain a lot of water. MRI technology is used to detect tumors and other abnormalities in the body.

Figure A   CT Scan
CT scan of a patient with a cerebral hemorrhage (arrow).

Figure B   MRI
MRI of the same patient with a cerebral hemorrhage (arrow).

P stands for a phosphate group (PO_4^{3-}). Thus, ATP consists of adenosine and three phosphate groups. ATP is synthesized when adenosine diphosphate (ADP), which has two (di-) phosphate groups, combines with a phosphate group to form the larger ATP molecule. The phosphate group that reacts with ADP is often denoted as P_i, where the "i" indicates that the phosphate group is associated with an inorganic substance (see the section on Inorganic Chemistry on p. 30).

$$A\text{-}P\text{-}P \quad + \quad P_i \quad \rightarrow \quad A\text{-}P\text{-}P\text{-}P$$
$$(ADP) \qquad (phosphate \qquad (ATP)$$
$$group)$$

Decomposition Reactions

In a **decomposition reaction**, reactants are broken down into smaller, less complex products. A decomposition reaction is the reverse of a synthesis reaction and can be represented in this way:

$$AB \rightarrow A + B$$

Examples of decomposition reactions include the breakdown of food molecules into basic building blocks, and the breakdown of ATP to ADP and a phosphate group.

$$A\text{-}P\text{-}P\text{-}P \quad \rightarrow \quad A\text{-}P\text{-}P \quad + \quad P_i$$
$$(ATP) \qquad (ADP) \qquad (phosphate group)$$

Exchange Reactions

An **exchange reaction** is a combination of a decomposition and a synthesis reaction. In decomposition, reactants are broken down. In synthesis, the products of the decomposition reaction are combined. The symbolic representation of an exchange reaction is:

$$AB + CD \rightarrow AC + BD$$

The reaction of hydrochloric acid (HCl) with sodium hydroxide (NaOH) to form table salt (NaCl) and water (H_2O) is an exchange reaction.

$$HCl + NaOH \rightarrow NaCl + H_2O$$

Reversible Reactions

In a **reversible reaction**, the reaction can proceed from reactants to products and from products to reactants. When the rate of product formation is equal to the rate of reactant formation, the reaction is said to be at **equilibrium**. At equilibrium the amount of the reactants and products relative to each other tends to remain constant.

The following analogy may help to clarify the concept of reversible reactions and equilibrium. Imagine a trough containing water. The trough is divided into two compartments by a partition, but the partition contains holes that allow water to move freely between the compartments. Because water can move in either direction, this is like a reversible reaction. Let the amount of water in the left compartment represent the amount of reactant, and the amount of water in the right compartment represent the amount of product. At equilibrium, the amount of reactant relative to the amount of product in each compartment is always the same because the partition allows water to pass between the two compartments until the level of water is the same in both compartments. For example, if the amount of reactant is increased by adding water to the left compartment, water flows from the left compartment through the partition to the right compartment until the level of water is the same in both. Thus, the amounts of reactant and product are once again equal. Unlike this analogy, however, the amount of reactants relative to the products in most reversible reactions is not one to one. Depending on the specific reversible reaction, there can be one part reactant to two parts product, two parts products to one part reactant, or many other possibilities.

An important reversible reaction in the human body is the reaction between carbon dioxide (CO_2) and water (H_2O) to form hydrogen ions (H^+) and bicarbonate ions (HCO_3^-) (The reversibility of the reaction is indicated by two arrows pointing in opposite directions):

$$CO_2 + H_2O \rightleftarrows H^+ + HCO_3^-$$

If carbon dioxide is added to water, the amount of carbon dioxide relative to the amount of hydrogen ions increases. The reaction of carbon dioxide with water produces more hydrogen ions, however, and the amount of carbon dioxide relative to the amount of hydrogen ions returns to equilibrium. Conversely, adding hydrogen ions to the water results in the formation of more carbon dioxide, and the equilibrium is restored.

Maintaining a constant level of hydrogen ions in body fluids is necessary for the nervous system to function properly. This level can be maintained, in part, by controlling blood carbon dioxide levels. For example, slowing the respiration rate causes blood carbon dioxide levels to increase, which in turn causes an increase in hydrogen ion concentration in the blood.

3   P R E D I C T

If the respiration rate increases, carbon dioxide is removed from the blood. What effect does this have on blood hydrogen ion levels?

✔ *Answer on page 40*

Energy and Chemical Reactions

Energy, unlike matter, does not occupy space and has no mass. **Energy** is defined as the capacity to do **work**, that is, to move matter. Energy can be subdivided into potential energy and kinetic energy. **Potential energy** is stored energy that could do work but is not doing so. For example, a coiled spring has potential energy. It could push against an object and move the object, but as long as the spring does not uncoil, no work is accomplished. **Kinetic** (ki-net′ik) **energy** is energy caused by the movement of an object and is the form of energy that actually does work. An uncoiling spring pushing an object causing it to move is an example. When potential energy is released, it becomes kinetic energy, thus doing work.

According to the law of conservation of energy, energy is neither created nor destroyed. One type of energy can be changed into another, however. For example, as a moving object slows down and comes to rest, its kinetic energy is converted into heat energy by friction.

The **chemical energy** of a substance results from the relative positions and interactions among its charged subatomic particles. Consider two balls attached by a relaxed spring. In order to push the balls together and compress the spring, energy must be put into this system. As the spring is compressed, potential energy increases. When the compressed spring expands, potential energy decreases. Similarly charged particles, such as two negatively charged electrons or two positively charged nuclei, repel each other. As similarly charged particles move closer together, their potential energy increases, much like compression of a spring, and as they move farther apart, their potential energy decreases. Chemical bonding is a form of potential energy because of the charges and positions of the subatomic particles bound together.

Chemical reactions are important because of the products they form and the energy changes that result as the relative position of subatomic particles changes. If the products of a chemical reaction contain less potential energy than the reactants, energy is released. For example, food molecules contain more potential energy than waste products. The difference in potential energy between food and waste products is used by living systems for many activities, such as growth, repair, movement, and heat production, as the potential energy in the food molecules changes into other forms of energy.

Figure 2.8 Energy and Chemical Reactions

In each figure the upper shelf represents a higher energy level with more potential energy, and the lower shelf represents a lower energy level with less potential energy. (*a*) Reaction in which energy is released as a result of the breakdown of ATP. (*b*) Reaction in which the input of energy is required for the synthesis of ATP.

An example of a reaction that releases energy is the breakdown of ATP to ADP and a phosphate group (figure 2.8*a*). The phosphate group is attached to the ADP molecule by a covalent bond, which has potential energy. After the breakdown of ATP, some of that energy is released as heat and some is available for use by cells.

$$\text{ATP} \rightarrow \text{ADP} + \text{P}_i + \text{Heat} + \text{Energy (e.g., for synthesis reactions and muscle contractions)}$$

ATP is called the energy currency of the cell because almost all of the chemical reactions of the cell that require energy use ATP as the energy source.

4	P R E D I C T

Why does body temperature increase during exercise?

✔ *Answer on page 40*

Energy must be added from another source if the products of a chemical reaction contain more energy than the reactants (figure 2.8*b*). The energy released during the breakdown of food molecules is the source of energy for this kind of reaction in the body. The energy from food molecules is used to synthesize molecules such as ATP, fats, and proteins.

$$\text{ADP} + \text{P}_i + \text{Energy (from food molecules)} \rightarrow \text{ATP}$$

Did You Know?

The energy that makes almost all life on earth possible ultimately comes from the sun. In the process of photosynthesis, plants capture the energy in sunlight and convert it into chemical bonds in glucose. The plants and the organisms that eat plants use the energy from glucose to form ATP. The energy from the breakdown of ATP fuels the chemical reactions of life.

Rate of Chemical Reactions

The rate at which a chemical reaction proceeds is influenced by several factors, including how easily the substances react with one another, their concentrations, the temperature, and the presence of a catalyst.

Reactants

Reactants differ from one another in their ability to undergo chemical reactions. For example, iron corrodes much more rapidly than does stainless steel. For this reason, during its recent refurbishment the iron bars forming the skeleton of the Statue of Liberty were replaced with stainless steel bars.

Concentration

Within limits, the greater the concentration of reactants, the greater the rate at which a chemical reaction will occur because, as the concentration increases, the reacting molecules are more likely to come into contact with one another. For example, the normal concentration of oxygen inside cells enables it to come into contact with other molecules, producing the chemical reactions necessary for life. If the oxygen concentration decreases, the rates of chemical reactions decrease. This decrease may impair cell function and even result in cell death.

Temperature

The rate of chemical reactions also increases when the temperature is increased. When a person has a fever of only a few degrees, reactions occur throughout the body at a faster rate. The result is increased activity in most organ systems, such as increased heart and respiratory rates. When body temperature drops, the rate of reactions decreases. The clumsy movement of very cold fingers results largely from the reduced rate of chemical reactions in cold muscle tissue.

Catalysts

At normal body temperatures, most chemical reactions would take place too slowly to sustain life if it were not for the body's catalysts. A **catalyst** (kat′ă-list) is a substance that increases the rate of a chemical reaction, without itself being permanently changed or depleted. An **enzyme** (en′zīm) is a protein molecule that acts as a catalyst. Many of the chemical reactions that occur in the body require enzymes. Enzymes are considered in greater detail later in the section on Proteins (see p. 34).

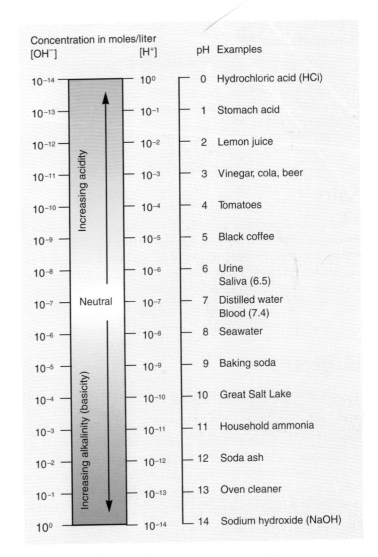

Figure 2.9   The pH Scale

A pH of 7.0 is considered to be neutral. Solutions with a pH value of less than 7.0 are acidic; and the lower the value, the more acidic the solution. Solutions with a pH value greater than 7.0 are basic, or alkaline; and the higher the value, the more basic the solution. Representative fluids and their approximate pH values are listed.

Acids and Bases

An **acid** is a proton donor. Because a hydrogen atom without its electron is a proton, any substance that releases hydrogen ions in water is an acid. For example, hydrochloric acid (HCl) in the stomach forms hydrogen (H^+) ions and chloride (Cl^-) ions:

$$HCl \rightarrow H^+ + Cl^-$$

A **base** is a proton acceptor. For example, sodium hydroxide (NaOH) forms sodium ions (Na^+) and hydroxide ions (OH^-). It is a base because the hydroxide ion is a proton acceptor that binds with a hydrogen ion to form water.

$$NaOH \rightarrow Na^+ + OH^-$$
$$H^+$$
$$H_2O$$

The pH Scale

The **pH scale** (figure 2.9), which ranges from 0 to 14, indicates the hydrogen ion concentration of a solution. Pure water is defined as a neutral solution. A **neutral solution** has an equal number of hydrogen ions and hydroxide ions and has a pH of 7.0. An **acidic solution** has a pH less than 7.0 and has a greater concentration of hydrogen ions than hydroxide ions. An **alkaline** (al′kă-līn), or **basic, solution** has a pH greater than 7.0 and has fewer hydrogen ions than hydroxide ions. As the pH value becomes smaller, the solution is more acidic; as the pH value becomes larger, the solution is more basic.

The symbol pH stands for the power (p) of hydrogen ion (H^+) concentration. The power is a factor of 10, which means that a change in the pH of a solution by one pH unit represents a 10-fold change in the hydrogen ion concentration. For example, a solution of pH 6.0 has 10 times more hydrogen ions than a solution with a pH of 7.0. Thus small changes in pH represent large changes in hydrogen ion concentration. See appendixes D and E for more information on solutions and pH.

Salts

A **salt** is a compound consisting of a positive ion other than a hydrogen ion and a negative ion other than a hydroxide ion. Salts are formed by the reaction of an acid and a base. For example, hydrochloric acid combines with sodium hydroxide to form the salt sodium chloride.

$$\begin{array}{ccccccc} \text{HCl} & + & \text{NaOH} & \rightarrow & \text{NaCl} & + & \text{H}_2\text{O} \\ \text{(acid)} & & \text{(base)} & & \text{(salt)} & & \text{(water)} \end{array}$$

Buffers

The chemical behavior of many molecules changes as the pH of the solution in which they are dissolved changes. The survival of an organism depends on its ability to regulate body fluid pH within a narrow range. One way normal body fluid pH is maintained is through the use of buffers. A **buffer** (bŭf'er), is a chemical that resists changes in pH when either an acid or a base is added to a solution containing the buffer. When an acid is added to a buffered solution, the buffer binds to the hydrogen ions, preventing them from causing a decrease in the pH of the solution (figure 2.10).

5   **P R E D I C T**

If a base is added to a solution, would the pH of the solution increase or decrease? If the solution is buffered, what response from the buffer prevents the change in pH?

✔ *Answer on page 40*

Inorganic Chemistry

Originally it was believed that inorganic substances were those that came from nonliving sources and organic substances were those extracted from living organisms. As the science of chemistry developed, however, it became apparent that organic substances could be manufactured in the laboratory. As defined currently, **inorganic chemistry** deals with those substances that do not contain carbon, whereas **organic chemistry** is the study of carbon-containing substances. These definitions have a few exceptions. For example, carbon dioxide and carbon monoxide are classified as inorganic molecules, even though they contain carbon.

Oxygen and Carbon Dioxide

Oxygen (O_2) is an inorganic molecule consisting of two oxygen atoms bound together by a double covalent bond. About

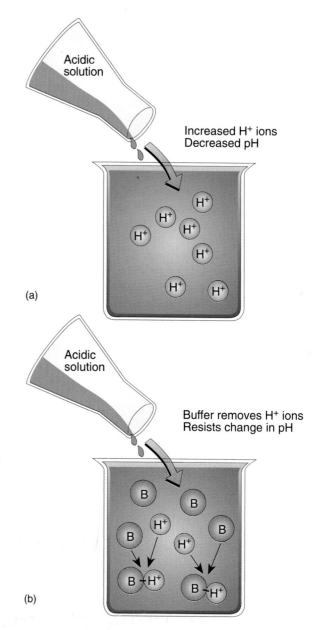

(a)

(b)

Figure 2.10 Buffers

(*a*) The addition of an acid to a nonbuffered solution results in an increase of hydrogen ions and a decrease in pH. (*b*) The addition of an acid to a buffered solution results in a much smaller change in pH. The added hydrogen ions bind to the buffer (symbolized by the letter "B").

21% of the gas in the atmosphere is oxygen, and it is essential for most living organisms. Oxygen is required by humans in the final step of a series of chemical reactions in which energy is extracted from food molecules (see chapters 3 and 17).

Carbon dioxide (CO_2) consists of one carbon atom bound by double covalent bonds to two oxygen atoms. Carbon dioxide is produced when organic molecules such as glucose are metabolized within the cells of the body (see chapters 3 and 17). Once carbon dioxide is produced, it is eliminated from the cell as a metabolic by-product, transferred to the lungs by the blood, and exhaled during respiration. If carbon dioxide is allowed to accumulate within cells, it becomes toxic.

Water

Water (H_2O) is an inorganic molecule that consists of one atom of oxygen joined by polar covalent bonds to two atoms of hydrogen. It has many important properties for living organisms.

1. *Stabilizing body temperature.* Water can absorb large amounts of heat and remain at a stable temperature. Blood, which is mostly water, can transfer heat effectively from deep within the body to the body's surface. Blood is warmed deep in the body and then flows to the surface, where the heat is released. In addition, water evaporation in the form of sweat results in significant heat loss from the body.
2. *Protection.* Water is an effective lubricant. For example, tears protect the surface of the eye from the rubbing of the eyelids. Water also forms a fluid cushion around organs that helps to protect them from damage. The cerebrospinal fluid that surrounds the brain is an example.
3. *Chemical reactions.* Most of the chemical reactions necessary for life do not take place unless the reacting molecules are dissolved in water. For example, sodium chloride must dissociate in water into Na^+ and Cl^- ions before they can react with other ions. Water also directly participates in many chemical reactions. For example, during the digestion of food, large molecules and water react to form smaller molecules.
4. *Transport.* Many substances dissolve in water and can be moved from place to place as the water moves. For example, blood transports nutrients, gases, and waste products within the body.

Organic Chemistry

The ability of carbon to form covalent bonds with other atoms makes possible the formation of the large, diverse, complicated molecules necessary for life. A series of carbon atoms bound together by covalent bonds constitute the "backbone" of many large molecules. Variation in the length of the carbon chains and the combination of atoms bound to the carbon backbone allow the formation of a wide variety of molecules. For example, some protein molecules have thousands of carbon atoms bound by covalent bonds to one another or to other atoms such as nitrogen, sulfur, hydrogen, and oxygen.

The four major groups of organic molecules essential to living organisms are carbohydrates, lipids, proteins, and nucleic acids. Each of these groups has specific structural and functional characteristics (table 2.3).

Table 2.3 Important Organic Molecules and Their Functions

Molecule	Elements	Building Blocks	Function	Examples
Carbohydrate	C, H, O	Monosaccharides	Energy	Monosaccharides can be used as energy sources. Glycogen (polysaccharide) is an energy storage molecule.
Lipid	C, H, O (P, N in some)	Glycerol and fatty acids (for fats)	Energy	Fats can be stored and broken down later for energy; per unit of weight fats yield twice as much energy as carbohydrates.
			Structure	Phospholipids and cholesterol are important components of cell membranes.
			Regulation	Steroid hormones regulate many physiological processes (e.g., estrogen and testosterone are responsible for many of the differences between males and females).
Protein	C, H, O, N (S in most)	Amino acids	Regulation	Enzymes control the rate of chemical reactions. Hormones regulate many physiological processes (e.g., insulin affects glucose transport into cells).
			Structure	Collagen fibers form a structural framework in many parts of the body.
			Energy	Proteins can be broken down for energy; per unit of weight they yield the same energy as carbohydrates.
			Contraction	Actin and myosin in muscle are responsible for muscle contraction.
			Transport	Hemoglobin transports oxygen in the blood.
			Protection	Antibodies and complement protect against microorganisms and other foreign substances.
Nucleic acid	C, H, O, N, P	Nucleotides	Regulation	DNA directs the activities of the cell.
			Heredity	Genes are pieces of DNA that can be passed from one generation to the next generation.
			Protein synthesis	RNA is involved in protein synthesis.

Carbohydrates

Carbohydrates are composed of carbon, hydrogen, and oxygen atoms. In most carbohydrates, for each carbon atom there are two hydrogen atoms and one oxygen atom. Note that the ratio of hydrogen atoms to oxygen atoms is two to one, the same as in water. They are called carbohydrates because each carbon (carbo) is combined with the same atoms that form a water molecule (hydrated). For example, the chemical formula for glucose is $C_6H_{12}O_6$.

The smallest carbohydrates are **monosaccharides** (mon-ō-sak′ă-rīdz; one sugar) or simple sugars. Glucose (blood sugar) and fructose (fruit sugar) are important monosaccharide energy sources for many of the body's cells. Larger carbohydrates are formed by chemically binding monosaccharides together. For this reason, monosaccharides are considered the building blocks of carbohydrates. **Disaccharides** (dī-sak′ă-rīdz; two sugars) are formed when two monosaccharides join. For example, glucose and fructose combine to form the disaccharide sucrose (table sugar) (figure 2.11*a*). **Polysaccharides** (pol-ē-sak′ă-rīdz; many sugars) consist of many monosaccharides bound in long chains. Glycogen, or animal starch, is a polysaccharide of glucose (figure 2.11*b*). When cells containing glycogen need energy, the glycogen is broken down into individual glucose molecules, which can be used as energy sources. Plant starch, also a polysaccharide of glucose, can be ingested and broken down into glucose. Cellulose, another polysaccharide of glucose, is an important structural component of plant cell walls. Humans cannot digest cellulose, however, and it is eliminated in the feces, where the cellulose fibers provide bulk.

Lipids

Lipids are substances that dissolve in nonpolar solvents, such as alcohol or acetone, but not in polar solvents, such as wa-

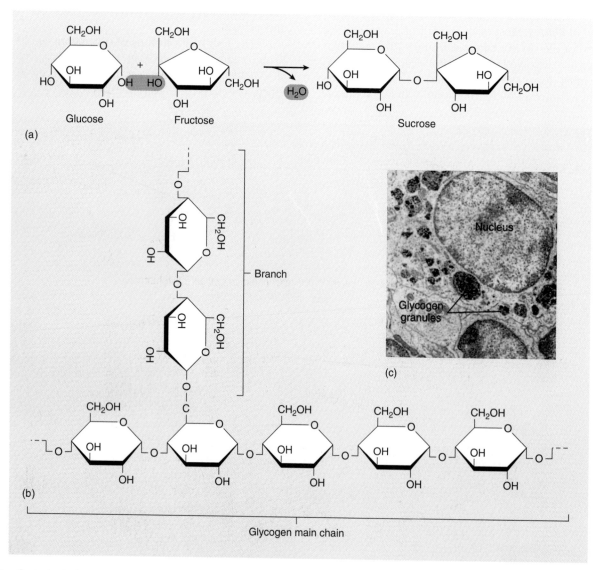

Figure 2.11 Carbohydrates

(*a*) Glucose and fructose are monosaccharides that combine to form the disaccharide sucrose. (*b*) Glycogen is a polysaccharide formed by combining many glucose molecules. (*c*) The photomicrograph shows glycogen granules in a liver cell.

ter. Lipids are composed mainly of carbon, hydrogen, and oxygen; but other elements such as phosphorus and nitrogen are minor components of some lipids. Lipids contain a lower proportion of oxygen to carbon than do carbohydrates.

Fats, phospholipids, and steroids are examples of lipids. **Fats** are important energy storage molecules; they also pad and insulate the body. The building blocks of fats are **glycerol** (glis'er-ol) and **fatty acids** (figure 2.12). Glycerol is a three-carbon molecule with a **hydroxyl** (hī-drok'sil) **group** (−OH) attached to each carbon atom, and fatty acids consist of a carbon chain with a **carboxyl** (kar-bok'sil) **group** attached at one end. A carboxyl group consists of both an oxygen atom and a hydroxyl group attached to a carbon atom (−COOH). The carboxyl

group is responsible for the acidic nature of the molecule because it releases hydrogen ions into solution. **Triacylglycerols** (trī-as'il-glis'er-olz), which are also called **triglycerides** (trī-glis'er-īdz), are the most common type of fat molecules. Triacylglycerols have three fatty acids bound to a glycerol molecule.

Fatty acids differ from one another according to the length and degree of saturation of their carbon chains. Most naturally occurring fatty acids contain 14 to 18 carbon atoms. A fatty acid is **saturated** if it contains only single covalent bonds between the carbon atoms. The carbon chain is **unsaturated** if it has one or more double covalent bonds (figure 2.13). Unsaturated fats are believed to be the best type of fats for human consumption,

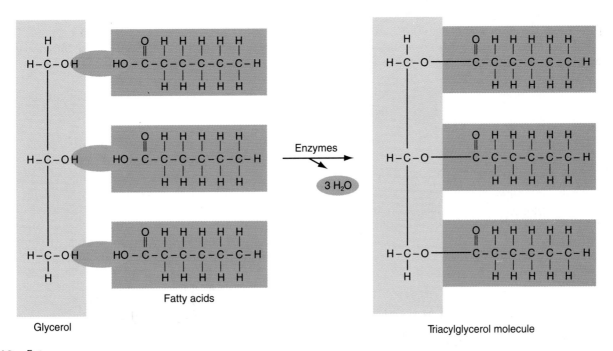

Figure 2.12   Fats
Glycerol and three fatty acids combine to form a triacylglycerol molecule, the most common type of fat in humans.

Figure 2.13   Saturated and Unsaturated Fatty Acids
(*a*) Palmitic acid is saturated, having only single covalent bonds between carbon atoms (indicated by single lines). (*b*) Linolenic acid is unsaturated, having some double covalent bonds between carbon atoms (indicated by double lines).

because saturated fats may contribute more to the development of atherosclerosis, a disease of blood vessels.

Phospholipids are similar to triacylglycerols, except that one of the fatty acids bound to the glycerol is replaced by a molecule containing phosphate. They are polar at the end of the molecule to which the phosphate is bound and nonpolar at the other end. The polar end of the molecule is attracted to water, and the nonpolar end is repelled by water. Phospholipids are important structural components of cell membranes (see chapter 3).

Steroids are composed of carbon atoms bound together into four ringlike structures. Important steroid molecules include cholesterol, bile salts, estrogen, progesterone, and testosterone. Cholesterol is an important steroid because other molecules are synthesized from it. For example, bile salts, which increase fat absorption in the intestines, are derived from cholesterol, as are the reproductive hormones estrogen, progesterone, and testosterone. In addition, cholesterol is an important component of cell membranes. Although high levels of cholesterol in the blood increase the risk of cardiovascular disease, a certain amount of cholesterol is vital for normal function.

Proteins

All **proteins** contain carbon, hydrogen, oxygen, and nitrogen, and most have some sulfur. The building blocks of proteins are **amino** (ă-mē′nō) **acids**, which are organic acids containing an **amine** (ă-mēn′) **group** ($-NH_2$) and a carboxyl group (figure 2.14). There are 20 basic types of amino acids. Humans can synthesize 12 of these from simple organic molecules, but the remaining 8 "essential amino acids" must be obtained in the diet.

Although there are only 20 amino acids, they can combine to form numerous types of proteins with unique structures and functions. Different proteins have different kinds and numbers of amino acids arranged to form a chain of amino acids (see figure 2.14). Hydrogen bonds between amino acids in the chain cause it to fold or coil to assume a specific three-dimensional shape (see figure 2.14). The ability of proteins to perform their functions depends on their shape. If the hydrogen bonds that maintain the shape of the protein are broken, the protein becomes nonfunctional. This change in shape is called **denaturation**, and it can be caused by abnormally high temperatures or changes in pH.

Proteins perform many important functions. For example, enzymes are proteins that regulate the rate of chemical reactions, structural proteins provide the framework for many of the body's tissues, and muscles contain proteins that are responsible for muscle contraction.

Enzymes

An **enzyme** (en′zīm) is a protein catalyst that increases the rate at which a chemical reaction proceeds without the enzyme being permanently changed. Enzymes increase the rate of chemical reactions by lowering the **activation energy**, which is the energy necessary to start a chemical reaction. For example, heat in the form of a spark is required to start the reaction between oxygen and gasoline. Most of the chemical reactions that occur in the body have high activation energies, which are decreased by enzymes (figure 2.15). The lowered activation energies enable reactions to proceed at rates that sustain life.

Consider this analogy, in which paper clips represent amino acids and your hands represent enzymes. Paper clips in a box only occasionally join together. Using your hands, however, a chain of paper clips can be rapidly formed. In a similar fashion, enzymes can quickly join amino acids into a chain, forming a protein. With an enzyme, the rate of a chemical reaction can take place more than a million times faster than without the enzyme.

The three-dimensional shape of enzymes is critical for their normal function. According to the **lock-and-key model** of enzyme action, the shape of an enzyme and that of the reactants allow the enzyme to bind easily to the reactants. Bringing the reactants very close to one another reduces the activation energy for the reaction. Because the enzyme and the reactants must fit together, enzymes are very specific for the reactions they control, and each enzyme controls only one type of chemical reaction. After the reaction takes place, the enzyme is released and can be used again (figure 2.16).

The chemical events of the body are regulated primarily by mechanisms that control either the concentration or activity of enzymes. The rate at which enzymes are produced in cells or whether the enzymes are in an active or inactive form determines the rate of each chemical reaction.

Nucleic Acids

Nucleic (noo-klē′ik) **acids** are large molecules composed of carbon, hydrogen, oxygen, nitrogen, and phosphorus. The building blocks of nucleic acids are **nucleotides** (noo′klē-ō-tīdz), which are organic molecules containing a five-carbon sugar, a nitrogen base, and a phosphate group (figure 2.17).

Deoxyribonucleic (dē-oks′ē-rī′bō-noo-klē′ik) **acid (DNA)** is called the genetic, or hereditary, material of the cell. Copies of DNA are transferred from one generation of cells to the next generation. DNA contains the information that determines the structure of proteins. The nucleotides of DNA contain the sugar deoxyribose, and they form two strands that coil around each other to form a twisted ladderlike structure called a double helix. DNA molecules are associated with histone proteins to form **chromatin** (krō′ma-tin). The proteins are involved with regulating DNA function. For most of the life of a cell, chromatin is organized as a string of beads. During cell division, however, the chromatin condenses into structures called **chromosomes** (krō′mō-sōmz). DNA, chromatin, and chromosomes are considered in greater detail in chapter 3.

Ribonucleic (rī′bō-noo-klē′ik) **acid (RNA)** is a single strand of nucleotides that contains the sugar ribose. Three different types of RNA are involved in protein synthesis (see chapter 3).

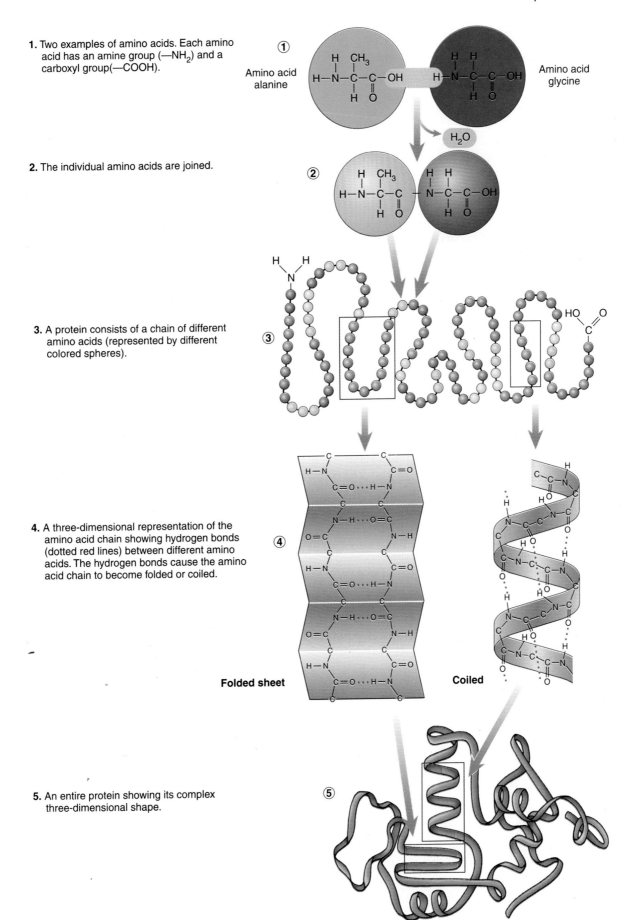

1. Two examples of amino acids. Each amino acid has an amine group (—NH₂) and a carboxyl group(—COOH).

2. The individual amino acids are joined.

3. A protein consists of a chain of different amino acids (represented by different colored spheres).

4. A three-dimensional representation of the amino acid chain showing hydrogen bonds (dotted red lines) between different amino acids. The hydrogen bonds cause the amino acid chain to become folded or coiled.

5. An entire protein showing its complex three-dimensional shape.

Figure 2.14   Proteins

(a)

ATP $\longrightarrow$ ADP + P$_i$ + Energy

(b)

Enzyme
ATP $\longrightarrow$ ADP + P$_i$ + Energy

Figure 2.15 Activation Energy and Enzymes

(a) Activation energy is needed to change ATP to ADP. The upper shelf represents a higher energy state, and the lower shelf represents a lower energy state. The "wall" extending above the upper shelf represents the activation energy. Even though energy is released when ATP is converted to ADP, the activation energy "wall" must be overcome before the reaction can proceed. (b) The enzyme lowers the activation energy, making it easier for the reaction to proceed.

Figure 2.16 Enzyme Action

The enzyme brings two reacting molecules together. This is possible because the reacting molecules "fit" the shape of the enzyme (lock-and-key model). After the reaction, the unaltered enzyme can be used again.

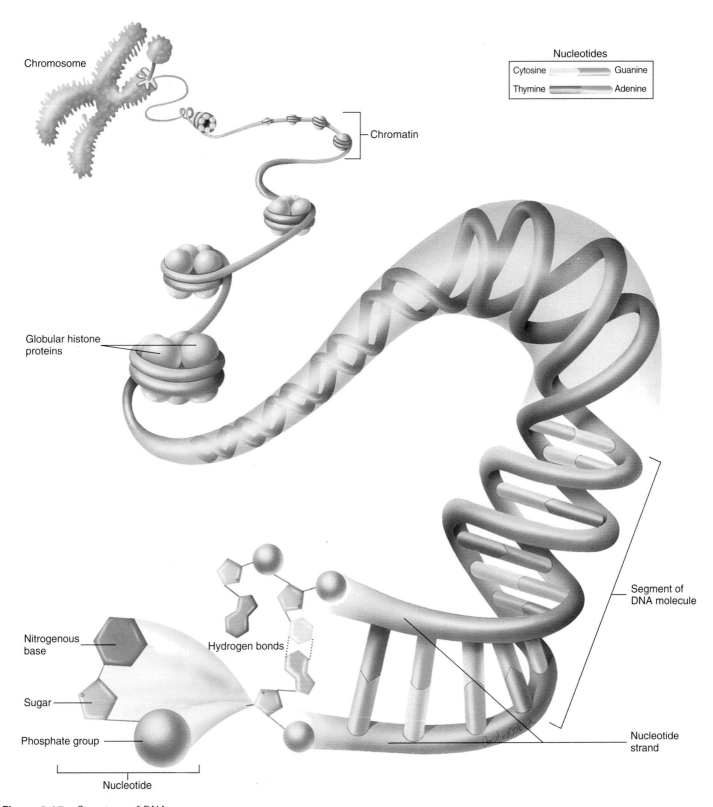

Chromosome

Nucleotides

| Cytosine | | Guanine |
| Thymine | | Adenine |

Chromatin

Globular histone proteins

Segment of DNA molecule

Nitrogenous base

Hydrogen bonds

Sugar

Phosphate group

Nucleotide strand

Nucleotide

Figure 2.17 Structure of DNA

Nucleotides join to form the two nucleotide strands of DNA. The nucleotides of one strand are joined by hydrogen bonds (dotted red lines) to the nucleotides of the other strand to form a DNA molecule. Associated with the DNA molecule are histone proteins. Usually the DNA molecule and its associated proteins are stretched out, resembling a string of beads, and is called chromatin. During cell division the chromatin condenses to form bodies within cells called chromosomes.

Summary

Chemistry is the study of the composition and structure of substances and the reactions they undergo.

Basic Chemistry

Matter, Mass, and Weight

- Matter is anything that occupies space.
- Mass is the amount of matter in an object, and weight results from the gravitational attraction between earth and matter.

Elements and Atoms

- An element is the simplest type of matter with unique chemical and physical properties.
- An atom is the smallest particle of an element that has the chemical characteristics of that element. An element is composed of only one kind of atom.

Atomic Structure

- Atoms consist of neutrons, positively charged protons, and negatively charged electrons.
- Atoms are electrically neutral because the number of protons in atoms equals the number of electrons.
- Protons and neutrons are found in the nucleus, and electrons, which are located around the nucleus, can be represented by an electron cloud.
- The atomic number is the unique number of protons in each atom of an element.

Electrons and Chemical Bonding

- Ionic bonding results when an electron is transferred from one atom to another.
- Covalent bonding results when a pair of electrons are shared between atoms. A polar covalent bond is an unequal sharing of electron pairs.

Hydrogen Bonds

- A hydrogen bond is the weak attraction that occurs between the oppositely charged regions of polar molecules. Hydrogen bonds are important in determining the three-dimensional structure of large molecules.

Molecules and Compounds

- A molecule is two or more atoms chemically combined to form a structure that behaves as an independent unit.
- A compound is two or more different types of atoms chemically combined. A compound can be a molecule (covalent compound) or an organized array of ions (ionic compound).

Dissociation

- Dissociation is the separation of ions in an ionic compound by polar water molecules.

Chemical Reactions

Classification of Chemical Reactions

- A synthesis reaction is the combination of reactants to form a new, larger product.
- A decomposition reaction is the breakdown of larger reactants into smaller products.

- An exchange reaction is a decomposition reaction, in which reactants are broken down, and a synthesis reaction, in which the products of the decomposition reaction combine.

Reversible Reactions

- In a reversible reaction, the reactants can form products, or the products can form reactants.
- The amount of reactants relative to products is constant at equilibrium.

Energy and Chemical Reactions

- Energy is the capacity to do work. Potential energy is stored energy that could do work, and kinetic energy does work by causing the movement of an object.
- Energy can be neither created nor destroyed, but one type of energy can be changed into another.
- Energy exists in chemical bonds as potential energy.
- Energy is released in chemical reactions when the products contain less potential energy than the reactants. The energy can be lost as heat, be used to synthesize molecules, or can do work.
- Energy is absorbed in reactions when the products contain more potential energy than the reactants.

Rate of Chemical Reactions

- The rate of chemical reactions increases when the concentration of the reactants increases, temperature increases, or a catalyst is present.
- A catalyst (enzyme) increases the rate of chemical reactions without being altered permanently.

Acids and Bases

- Acids are proton (hydrogen ion) donors, and bases are proton acceptors.

The pH Scale

- A neutral solution has an equal number of hydrogen ions and hydroxide ions and a pH of 7.0.
- An acidic solution has more hydrogen ions than hydroxide ions and a pH of less than 7.0.
- A basic solution has fewer hydrogen ions than hydroxide ions and a pH greater than 7.0.

Salts

- A salt is formed when an acid reacts with a base.

Buffers

- Buffers are chemicals that resist changes in pH when acids or bases are added.

Inorganic Chemistry

- Inorganic chemistry is mostly concerned with non-carbon-containing substances, but does include such carbon-containing substances as carbon dioxide and carbon monoxide.

Oxygen and Carbon Dioxide

- Oxygen is involved with the extraction of energy from food molecules.

- Carbon dioxide is a by-product of the breakdown of food molecules.

Water

- Water stabilizes body temperature.
- Water provides protection by acting as a lubricant or cushion.
- Water is necessary for many chemical reactions.
- Water transports many substances.

Organic Chemistry

- Organic molecules contain carbon atoms bound together by covalent bonds.

Carbohydrates

- Carbohydrates provide the body with energy.
- Monosaccharides are the building blocks that form more complex carbohydrates, such as disaccharides and polysaccharides.

Lipids

- Lipids provide energy (fats), are structural components (phospholipids), and regulate physiological processes (steroids).

- The building blocks of triacylglycerols (fats) are glycerol and fatty acids.

Proteins

- Proteins regulate chemical reactions (enzymes), are structural components, and cause muscle contraction.
- The building blocks of proteins are amino acids.
- Denaturation of proteins disrupts hydrogen bonds, which changes the shape of proteins and makes them nonfunctional.
- Enzymes are specific, bind to reactants according to the lock-and-key model, and function by lowering activation energy.

Nucleic Acids

- Nucleic acids include DNA, the genetic material, and RNA, which is involved in protein synthesis.
- The building blocks of nucleic acids are nucleotides, which consist of a sugar (deoxyribose or ribose), a nitrogen base, and a phosphate group.

Content Review

1. Define chemistry. Why is an understanding of chemistry important?
2. Define matter. What is the difference between mass and weight?
3. Define element and atom. How many different kinds of atoms are found in a specific element?
4. List the components of an atom, and explain how they are organized to form an atom. Compare the charges of the subatomic particles.
5. Distinguish between ionic, covalent, polar covalent, and hydrogen bonds. Define ion.
6. What is the difference between a molecule and a compound?
7. What happens to ionic and covalent compounds when they dissolve in water?
8. Define chemical reaction. Describe synthesis, decomposition, and exchange reactions, giving an example of each.
9. What is meant by the equilibrium condition in a reversible reaction?
10. Define potential and kinetic energy.
11. Give an example of a chemical reaction that releases energy and an example of a chemical reaction that requires the input of energy.
12. Name three ways that the rate of chemical reactions can be increased.
13. What is an acid and what is a base? Describe the pH scale.
14. Define salt. What is a buffer, and why are buffers important?
15. Distinguish between inorganic and organic chemistry.
16. Why is oxygen necessary for human life? Where does the carbon dioxide we breathe out come from?
17. List four functions that water performs in the human body.
18. Name the four major types of organic molecules. Give a function for each.
19. Describe the action of enzymes in terms of activation energy and the lock-and-key model.

Develop Your Reasoning Skills

1. If an atom of iodine (I) gains an electron, what is the charge of the resulting ion? Write the symbol for this ion.
2. For each of the following chemical equations, determine if a synthesis reaction, a decomposition reaction, an exchange reaction, or dissociation has taken place:
   a. $HCl \rightarrow H^+ + Cl^-$
   b. Glucose + Fructose $\rightarrow$ Sucrose (table sugar)
   c. $NaHCO_3 + HCl \rightarrow H_2CO_3 + NaCl$
   d. $2 H_2O \rightarrow 2 H_2 + O_2$
3. In terms of the energy in chemical bonds, explain why eating food is necessary for increasing muscle mass.
4. Given that the hydrogen ion concentration in a solution is based on the following reversible reaction:

$$CO_2 + H_2O \rightleftarrows H^+ + HCO_3^-$$

What happens to the pH of the solution when $NaHCO_3$ (sodium bicarbonate) is added to the solution? (*Hint:* The sodium bicarbonate dissociates to form Na^+ and HCO_3^- ions.)
5. A mixture of chemicals is warmed slightly. As a consequence, although little heat is added, the solution becomes very hot. Explain what happens to make the solution hot.
6. Two solutions, when mixed together at room temperature, produce a chemical reaction. When the solutions are boiled, however, and allowed to cool to room temperature before mixing, no chemical reaction takes place. Explain.

Answers to Predict Questions

1. p. 20 The mass (amount of matter) of the astronaut on the surface of earth and in outer space does not change. In outer space, where the force of gravity from earth is very small, the astronaut is "weightless" compared with his weight on earth's surface.

2. p. 22 Because atoms are electrically neutral, the iron (Fe) atom has the same number of protons and electrons. The loss of three electrons results in an iron ion that has three more protons than electrons and therefore a charge of +3. The correct symbol is Fe^{3+}.

3. p. 27 Carbon dioxide and water are in equilibrium with hydrogen ions and bicarbonate ions. A decrease in carbon dioxide causes some hydrogen ions to react with bicarbonate ions to form carbon dioxide and water. Consequently, the hydrogen ion concentration decreases.

4. p. 28 During exercise, muscle contractions increase. This requires the release of potential energy during chemical reactions. For example, the potential energy in the phosphate bond of ATP is released when ATP is broken down into ADP and P_i. Some of the energy is used to drive muscle contractions, and some of it is released as heat. Because the rate of these reactions increases during exercise, more heat is produced than when at rest, and body temperature increases.

5. p. 30 Note that buffers take up H^+ ions when an acid is added to a buffered solution. It is reasonable to expect a buffer to release H^+ ions when a base is added to a buffered solution. The released H^+ ions can combine with the base to prevent an increase in pH. For example, H^+ ions can combine with OH^- ions to form water.

Chapter Three

Cell Structures and Their Functions

active transport
Carrier-mediated process that requires ATP and can move substances against a concentration gradient.

cell membrane
[plasma (plaz′mă) membrane] Outermost component of the cell, surrounding and binding the rest of the cell contents.

diffusion
(di-fū′zhŭn) [L. *diffundo*, to pour in different directions] Tendency for solute molecules to move from an area of higher concentration to an area of lower concentration in a solution.

endoplasmic reticulum (ER)
(en′dō-plas′mik re-tik′ū-lŭm) [*endo* + Gr. *plastos*, formed] Membranous network inside the cytoplasm; rough ER has ribosomes attached to the surface; smooth ER does not.

facilitated diffusion
(fă-sil′i-tā-tĭd di-fū′zhŭn) Carrier-mediated process that does not require ATP and moves substances into or out of cells from a higher to a lower concentration.

Golgi apparatus
(gōl′jē) Stacks of flattened, membrane-bound sacks that collect, modify, package, and distribute proteins and lipids.

meiosis
(mī-ō′sis)[Gr., a lessening] Process of cell division that results in gametes. Consists of two cell divisions that result in four cells, each of which contains half the number of chromosomes as the parent cell.

mitochondrion, pl. mitochondria
(mī′tō-kon′drē-on, mī′tō-kon′drē-ă) [Gr. *mitos*, thread + *chandros*, granule] Small, bean-shaped or rod-shaped structures in the cytoplasm that are sites of ATP production.

mitosis
(mī-tō′sis) [Gr., thread] Division of the nucleus. Process of cell division that results in two daughter cells with exactly the same number and type of chromosomes as the parent cell.

nucleus, pl. nuclei
(noo′klē-ŭs, noo′klē-ī) [L., inside of a thing] Cell organelle containing most of the cell's genetic material.

osmosis
(os-mō′sis) [Gr. *osmos*, thrusting or an impulsion] Diffusion of solvent (water) through a selectively permeable membrane from a region of higher water concentration to one of lower water concentration.

ribosome
(rī′bō-sōm) Small, spherical, cytoplasmic organelle where protein synthesis occurs.

Objectives

After reading this chapter, you should be able to:

1. Describe the structure of the cell membrane.
2. Describe the structure and function of the nucleus and nucleoli.
3. Compare the structure and function of rough and smooth endoplasmic reticulum.
4. Describe the roles of the Golgi apparatuses and secretory vesicles in secretion.
5. Explain the role of lysosomes in digesting material taken into cells by phagocytosis.
6. Describe the structure and function of mitochondria.
7. Compare the structure and function of cilia, flagella, and microvilli.
8. List four ways by which substances cross the cell membrane.
9. Explain the role of osmosis and that of osmotic pressure in controlling the movement of water across the cell membrane. Compare hypotonic, isotonic, and hypertonic solutions.
10. Define "mediated transport," and compare the processes of facilitated diffusion, active transport, and secondary active transport.
11. Describe endocytosis and exocytosis.
12. Describe the process of protein synthesis.
13. Explain what is accomplished during mitosis and meiosis.
14. Define "differentiation," and explain how it occurs.

The cell is the basic living unit of all organisms. The simplest organisms consist of a single cell, whereas humans are composed of trillions of cells. If each of these cells was about the size of a standard brick, we could build a colossal structure in the shape of a human over 5½ miles (10 km) high! Obviously, there are many differences between a cell and a brick. Cells are much smaller than bricks: An average-sized cell is one fifth the size of the smallest dot you can make on a sheet of paper with a sharp pencil! In spite of their extremely small size, cells are complex living structures.

Cells of the human body have many characteristics in common. However, most cells are also specialized to perform specific functions. The human body is made up of populations of these specialized cells. Communication and coordination between these populations are critical for a complex organism, such as a human, to survive.

The study of cells is an important link between the study of chemistry in chapter 2 and tissues in chapter 4. A knowledge of chemistry makes it possible to understand cells because cells are composed of molecules that are responsible for many of the characteristics of cells. Cells, in turn, determine the form and functions of the tissues of the body. It is also important to understand that a great many diseases and other human disorders have a cellular basis. This chapter considers the structure of cells and how cells perform the activities necessary for life.

Functions of the Cell

The main functions of the cell include

1. *Basic unit of life*. The cell is the smallest part to which an organism can be reduced that still retains the characteristics of life.
2. *Protection and support*. Cells produce and secrete various molecules that provide protection and support of the body. For example, bone cells are surrounded by a mineralized material, making bone a hard tissue that protects the brain and other organs and that supports the weight of the body.
3. *Movement*. All the movements of the body occur because of molecules located within specific cells such as muscle cells.
4. *Communication*. Cells produce and receive chemical and electrical signals that allow them to communicate with one another. For example, nerve cells communicate with one another and with muscle cells, causing them to contract.
5. *Cell metabolism and energy release*. The chemical reactions that occur within cells are referred to collectively as cell metabolism. Energy released during metabolism is used for cell activities, such as the synthesis of new molecules, muscle contraction, and heat production, which helps maintain body temperature.
6. *Inheritance*. Each cell contains a copy of the genetic information of the individual. Specialized cells are responsible for transmitting that genetic information to the next generation.

Cell Structure

Each cell is a highly organized unit. Within cells, specialized structures called **organelles** (or′gă-nelz, "little organs") perform specific functions (figure 3.1 and table 3.1). The nucleus is an organelle containing the cell's genetic material. The living material surrounding the nucleus is called **cytoplasm** (sī′tō-plazm), which contains many other types of organelles. The cytoplasm is enclosed by the cell, or plasma, membrane.

The number and type of organelles within each cell determine the cell's specific structure and functions. For example, cells secreting large amounts of protein contain well-developed organelles that synthesize and secrete protein, whereas muscle cells have organelles that enable the cells to contract. The following sections describe the structure and main functions of the major organelles found in cells.

Cell Membrane

The **cell membrane**, or **plasma** (plaz′mă) **membrane**, is the outermost component of a cell. The cell membrane encloses the cytoplasm and forms the boundary between material inside the cell and material outside it. Substances outside the cell are called **extracellular substances**, and substances inside the cell are called **intracellular substances**. The cell membrane encloses the cell, supports the cell contents, is a selective barrier that determines what moves into and out of the cell, and plays a role in communication between cells.

The major molecules that make up the cell membrane are phospholipids and proteins. In addition, the membrane contains other molecules, such as cholesterol, carbohydrates, water, and ions. The phospholipids form a double layer of molecules. The polar, phosphate-containing ends of the phospholipids are hydrophilic (water loving) and therefore face the water inside and outside the cell. The nonpolar, fatty acid ends of the phospholipids are hydrophobic (water fearing) and therefore face away from the water on either side of the membrane, toward the center of the double layer of phospholipids (figure 3.2). The double layer of phospholipids forms a lipid barrier between the inside and outside of the cell.

Studies of the arrangement of molecules in the cell membrane have given rise to a model of its structure called the **fluid mosaic model**. The double layer of phospholipid molecules has a liquid quality. Cholesterol within the membrane gives it added strength and flexibility. Protein molecules "float" among the phospholipid molecules and, in some cases, may extend from the inner to the outer surface of the cell membrane. Carbohydrates may be bound to some protein molecules, modifying their functions. The proteins function as membrane channels, carrier molecules, receptor molecules, enzymes, or structural supports in the membrane. **Membrane channels** and **carrier molecules** are involved with the movement of substances through the cell membrane. **Receptor molecules** are part of an intercellular communication system that enables coordination of the activities of cells. For example, a nerve cell can release a chemical messenger that moves to a muscle cell and temporarily binds to its receptor. The binding acts as a signal that triggers a response such as contraction of the muscle cell.

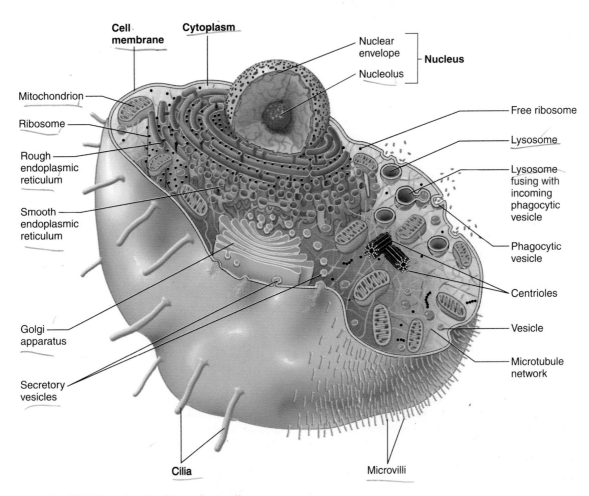

Figure 3.1   Generalized Cell Showing the Major Organelles

No single cell contains all organelle types. In addition, some kinds of cells contain many organelles of one type, and another kind of cell contains very few.

Table 3.1	Organelles and Their Locations and Functions
Organelles	**Location and Function(s)**
Nucleus	Usually near center of the cell; contains genetic material of cell (DNA) and nucleoli; site of ribosome and messenger RNA synthesis
Nucleolus	In the nucleus; site of ribosomal RNA and ribosomal protein synthesis
Rough endoplasmic reticulum (rough ER)	In cytoplasm; many ribosomes attached to ER; site of protein synthesis
Smooth endoplasmic reticulum (smooth ER)	In cytoplasm; site of lipid synthesis
Golgi apparatus	In cytoplasm; modifies protein structure and packages proteins in secretory vesicles
Secretory vesicle	In cytoplasm; contains materials produced in the cell; formed by the Golgi apparatus; secreted by exocytosis
Lysosome	In cytoplasm; contains enzymes that digest material taken into the cell
Mitochondrion	In cytoplasm; site of aerobic respiration and the major site of ATP synthesis
Microtubule	In cytoplasm; supports cytoplasm; assists in cell division and forms components of cilia and flagella
Cilia	On cell surface with many on each cell; cilia move substances over surface of certain cells
Flagella	On sperm cell surface with one per cell; propels the sperm cells
Microvilli	Extensions of cell surface with many on each cell; increase surface area of certain cells

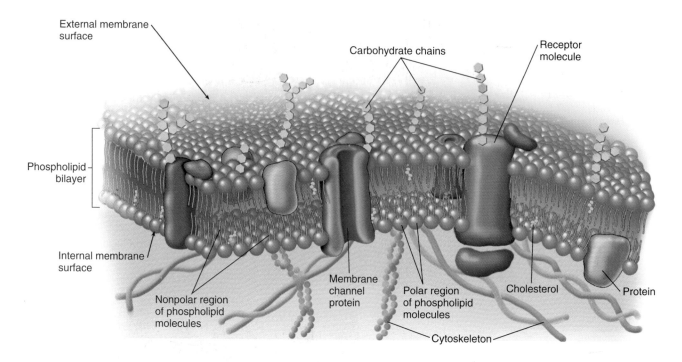

Figure 3.2 The Cell Membrane

The cell membrane is composed of a double layer of phospholipid molecules with proteins "floating" in the membrane. The nonpolar end of each phospholipid molecule is directed toward the center of the membrane, and the polar end of each phospholipid molecule is directed toward the water environment either outside or inside the cell. Cholesterol molecules are interspersed among the phospholipid molecules. Groups of proteins can form membrane channels, carrier molecules, receptor molecules, enzymes, or structural supports.

Nucleus

The **nucleus** (noo'klē-ŭs) is a large organelle usually located near the center of the cell (see figure 3.1). All cells of the body have a nucleus at some point in their life cycle, although some cells, such as red blood cells, lose their nuclei as they mature. Other cells, such as osteoclasts (a type of bone cell) and skeletal muscle cells, contain more than one nucleus.

The nucleus is bounded by a **nuclear envelope**, which consists of outer and inner membranes with a narrow space between them (figure 3.3). At many points on the surface of the nucleus, the inner and outer membranes come together to form **nuclear pores**, through which materials can pass into or out of the nucleus.

The nucleus contains loosely coiled fibers called **chromatin** consisting of deoxyribonucleic acid (DNA) and proteins (see figures 2.17 and 3.3*b*). During cell division, the chromatin fibers become more tightly coiled to form the 23 pairs of **chromosomes** (krō'mō-sōmz) characteristic of human cells (see the section on Cell Division on p. 59). The genes that influence the structural and functional features of every individual are made up of DNA molecules. The DNA molecules store information that allows the genes to determine the structure of proteins.

Nucleoli and Ribosomes

Nucleoli (noo-klē'ō-lī) number from one to four per nucleus. They are rounded, dense, well-defined nuclear bodies with no surrounding membrane (see figure 3.3). The subunits of ribosomes are formed within a nucleolus. Proteins produced in the cytoplasm move through the nuclear pores into the nucleus and to the nucleolus. These proteins are joined to **ribosomal ribonucleic** (rī'bō-noo-klē'ik) **acid (rRNA)**, produced within the nucleolus, to form large and small ribosomal subunits (figure 3.4). The ribosomal subunits then move from the nucleus through the nuclear pores into the cytoplasm, where one large and one small subunit join to form a ribosome.

Ribosomes (rī'bō-sōmz) are the organelles where proteins are produced (see section on Protein Synthesis on p. 56). Free ribosomes are not attached to any other organelles in the cytoplasm, whereas other ribosomes are attached to a membrane called the endoplasmic reticulum.

Rough and Smooth Endoplasmic Reticulum

The **endoplasmic reticulum** (en'dō-plas'mik re-tik'ū-lŭm) **(ER)** is a series of membranes that extends from the outer nuclear membrane into the cytoplasm (figure 3.5). **Rough ER** is ER with ribosomes attached to it. A large amount of rough ER in a cell indicates that it is synthesizing large amounts of protein for export from the cell. On the other hand, ER without ribosomes is called **smooth ER**. Smooth ER is a site for lipid synthesis in cells. Smooth ER also participates in detoxification of chemicals within the cell. In skeletal muscle cells, the smooth ER stores calcium ions.

Figure 3.3   The Nucleus

(*a*) The nuclear envelope consists of inner and outer membranes that become fused at the nuclear pores. The nucleolus is a condensed region of the nucleus not bounded by a membrane and consisting mostly of RNA and protein. (*b*) Transmission electron micrograph of the nucleus. (*c*) Scanning electron micrograph showing the inner surface of the nuclear envelope and the nuclear pores.

The Golgi Apparatus

The **Golgi** (gol'jē) **apparatus** (named for Camillo Golgi [1843–1926], an Italian histologist) consists of closely packed stacks of curved, membrane-bound sacs (figure 3.6). It collects, modifies, packages, and distributes proteins and lipids manufactured by the ER. For example, proteins produced at the ribosomes enter the Golgi apparatus from the ER. In some cases, the Golgi apparatus chemically modifies the proteins by attaching carbohydrate or lipid molecules to them. The proteins then are packaged into membrane sacs that pinch off from the margins of the Golgi apparatus (see section on Secretory Vesicles below). The Golgi apparatus is present in larger numbers and is most highly developed in cells that secrete protein, such as the cells of the salivary glands or the pancreas.

Secretory Vesicles

A **vesicle** (ves'i-kl) is a small, membrane-bound sac that transports or stores materials within cells. **Secretory vesicles** pinch off from the Golgi apparatus and move to the surface of the cell (see figure 3.6). Their membranes then fuse with the cell membrane, and the contents of the vesicles are released to the exterior of the cell. In many cells, secretory vesicles accumulate in the cytoplasm and are released to the exterior when the cell receives a signal. For example, secretory vesicles containing the hormone insulin remain in the cytoplasm of pancreatic cells until rising blood levels of glucose act as a stimulus for their release.

Lysosomes

Lysosomes (lī'sō-sōmz) (see figure 3.1) are membrane-bound vesicles formed from the Golgi apparatus. They contain a variety of enzymes that function as intracellular digestive systems. Particulate material taken into a cell is contained within vesicles that fuse with lysosomes. The enzymes within the lysosomes break down the ingested materials. For example, white blood cells take up bacteria, which the enzymes within lysosomes destroy. Also, when tissues are damaged, ruptured lysosomes within the damaged cells release their enzymes and digest both healthy and damaged cells. The released enzymes are responsible for part of the resulting inflammation (see chapter 4).

1. Ribosomal proteins, produced in the cytoplasm, are transported through nuclear pores into the nucleolus.

2. Ribosomal ribonucleic acid (rRNA), produced in the nucleolus, is assembled with ribosomal proteins to form small and large ribosomal subunits.

3. The small and large ribosomal subunits leave the nucleolus and the nucleus through nuclear pores.

4. The small and large subunits, now in the cytoplasm, combine with one another to form ribosomes.

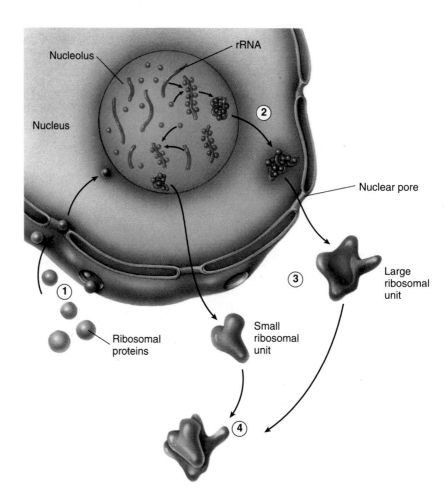

Figure 3.4 Production of Ribosomes

Figure 3.5 The Endoplasmic Reticulum

The outer membrane of the nuclear envelope is continuous with the endoplasmic reticulum (ER). Rough ER has ribosomes attached to its membrane, and smooth ER has no ribosomes attached to it. Some cells contain predominantly smooth ER, and others contain predominantly rough ER.

Did You Know?

Some diseases result from nonfunctional lysosomal enzymes. For example, **Pompe's disease** results from the inability of lysosomal enzymes to break down the carbohydrate glycogen produced in certain cells. Glycogen accumulates in large amounts in the heart, liver, and skeletal muscles. Glycogen accumulation in the heart muscle cells often leads to heart failure. **Lipid storage disorders** are often hereditary and are characterized by the accumulation of large amounts of lipid in phagocytic cells. These cells take up the lipid by phagocytosis, but they lack the enzymes required to break down the lipid droplets. Symptoms include enlargement of the spleen and liver and replacement of bone marrow by lipid-filled phagocytes.

Peroxisomes

Peroxisomes (per-ok'si-sōmz) are small, membrane-bound vesicles containing enzymes that break down fatty acids and amino acids. Hydrogen peroxide (H_2O_2), which can be toxic to the cell, is a by-product of that breakdown. Peroxisomes also contain an enzyme that breaks down hydrogen peroxide to water and oxygen. Cells that are active in detoxification, such as liver and kidney cells, have many peroxisomes.

Mitochondria

Mitochondria (mī′tō-kon′drē-ă; sing. mitochondrion) are small, bean-shaped or rod-shaped organelles with inner and outer membranes separated by a space (figure 3.7 and see figure 3.1). The outer membranes have a smooth contour, but the inner membranes have numerous infoldings called **cristae** (kris′tē), which project like shelves into the interior of the mitochondria.

Mitochondria are the major sites of adenosine triphosphate (ATP) production within cells. ATP is the major energy source for most chemical reactions within the cell, and cells with a large energy requirement have more mitochondria than cells that require less energy. Mitochondria carry out aerobic respiration (discussed in greater detail in the section Cell Metabolism on p. 54) in which oxygen is required to allow the reactions that produce ATP to proceed. Cells that carry out extensive active transport, which is described on p. 54, contain many mitochondria, and, when muscles enlarge as a result of exercise, the mitochondria increase in number within the muscle cells and provide the additional ATP required for muscle contraction.

Increases in the number of mitochondria result from the division of preexisting mitochondria. The information for making some mitochondrial proteins and for mitochondrial division is contained in a unique type of DNA within the mitochondria. This DNA is more like bacterial DNA than that of the cell's nucleus.

Cytoskeleton

The **cytoskeleton** (sī-tō-skel′ĕ-ton) consists of proteins that support the cell, hold organelles in place, and enable the cell to change shape. The cytoskeleton consists of microtubules, microfilaments, and intermediate filaments (figure 3.8).

Microtubules are hollow structures formed from protein subunits that perform a variety of roles, such as helping to provide support to the cytoplasm of cells, assisting in the process of cell division, and forming essential components of certain organelles such as cilia and flagella.

Microfilaments are small fibrils formed from protein subunits that structurally support the cytoplasm. Some microfilaments are involved with cell movements. For example, microfilaments in muscle cells enable the cells to shorten or contract.

Intermediate filaments are fibrils formed from protein subunits that are smaller in diameter than microtubules but larger in diameter than microfilaments. They provide mechanical support to the cell.

Cilia, Flagella, and Microvilli

Cilia (sĭl′ē-ă) project from the surface of cells, are capable of moving (see figure 3.1), and vary in number from none to thousands per cell. Cilia have a cylindrical shape, contain specialized microtubules, and are enclosed by the cell membrane.

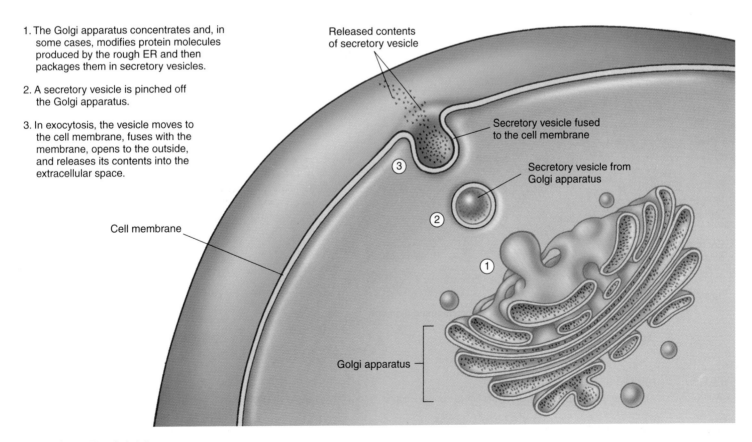

1. The Golgi apparatus concentrates and, in some cases, modifies protein molecules produced by the rough ER and then packages them in secretory vesicles.

2. A secretory vesicle is pinched off the Golgi apparatus.

3. In exocytosis, the vesicle moves to the cell membrane, fuses with the membrane, opens to the outside, and releases its contents into the extracellular space.

Released contents of secretory vesicle

Secretory vesicle fused to the cell membrane

Secretory vesicle from Golgi apparatus

Cell membrane

Golgi apparatus

Figure 3.6   The Golgi Apparatus

Figure 3.7 Mitochondria

(*a*) Typical mitochondrion structure. (*b*) Electron micrograph of mitochondria in longitudinal and cross sections.

Cilia are numerous on surface cells that line the respiratory tract. Their coordinated movement moves mucus, in which dust particles are embedded, upward and away from the lungs. This action helps keep the lungs clear of debris.

Flagella (flă-jel′ă) have a structure similar to that of cilia but are much longer, and usually occur only one per cell. Sperm cells each have one flagellum, which functions to propel the sperm cell.

Microvilli (mī′krō-vil′ī) are specialized extensions of the cell membrane that are supported by microfilaments (see figure 3.1), but they do not actively move like cilia and flagella. Microvilli are numerous on cells that have them and function

to increase the surface area of those cells. They are abundant on the surface of cells that line the intestine, kidney, and other areas in which absorption is an important function.

1	P R E D I C T

List the organelles that are common in cells that (a) synthesize and secrete proteins, (b) actively transport substances into cells, and (c) ingest foreign substances. Explain the function of each organelle you list.

✔ *Answer on page 70*

Figure 3.8 Cytoskeleton

(*a*) Microtubules, microfilaments, and intermediate filaments form the cytoskeleton. (*b*) Scanning electron micrograph of the cytoskeleton.

Whole-Cell Activity

To understand how a cell functions, the interactions between the organelles must be considered. For example, the transport of many food molecules into the cell requires ATP and cell membrane proteins. Most ATP is produced by mitochondria. The production of cell membrane proteins requires amino acids that are transported into the cell across the cell membrane by transport proteins. Information contained in DNA within the nucleus determines which amino acids are combined at ribosomes to form proteins. The mutual interdependence of cellular organelles is coordinated to maintain homeostasis within the cell and the entire body. The following sections, Movement Through the Cell Membrane, Cell Metabolism, Protein Synthesis, and Cell Division, illustrate the interactions of organelles that result in a functioning cell.

Movement Through the Cell Membrane

The cell membrane is **selectively permeable**, allowing some substances, but not others, to pass into or out of the cell. Intracellular material has a different composition from extracellular material, and the survival of cells depends on maintaining the difference. Substances such as enzymes, glycogen, and potassium ions are found at higher concentrations intracellularly; and sodium, calcium, and chloride ions are found in greater concentrations extracellularly. In addition, nutrients must enter cells continually, and waste products must exit. Because of the permeability characteristics of the cell membrane and its ability to transport certain molecules, cells are able to maintain proper intracellular concentrations of molecules. Rupture of the membrane, alteration of its permeability characteristics, or inhibition of transport processes can disrupt the normal intracellular concentration of molecules and lead to cell death.

Molecules can pass through the cell membrane in four ways:

1. *Directly through the phospholipid membrane.* Molecules that are soluble in lipids, such as oxygen, carbon dioxide, and steroids, pass through the cell membrane readily by dissolving in the lipid bilayer. The phospholipid bilayer acts as a barrier to most substances that are not lipid-soluble; but certain small, non-lipid-soluble molecules, such as water, and urea, can diffuse between the phospholipid molecules of the cell membrane.

2. *Membrane channels.* Cell membrane **channels**, consisting of large protein molecules, extend from one surface of the cell membrane to the other (see figure 3.2). There are several channel types, each of which allows only certain molecules to pass through it. The size, shape, and charge of molecules determines whether they can pass through each kind of channel.

For example, sodium ions pass through sodium channels, and potassium and chloride ions pass through potassium and chloride channels, respectively. Rapid movement of water across the cell membrane apparently occurs through membrane channels.

3. *Carrier molecules.* Large polar molecules that are not lipid-soluble, such as glucose and amino acids, cannot pass through the cell membrane in significant amounts unless they are transported by special carrier molecules. Substances that are transported across the cell membrane by carrier molecules are said to be transported by **carrier-mediated processes**. The **carrier molecules** are proteins that extend from one side of the cell membrane to the other. They bind to molecules to be transported and move them across the cell membrane. Each carrier molecule transports a specific type of molecule. For example, carrier molecules that transport glucose across the cell membrane do not transport amino acids, and carrier molecules that transport amino acids do not transport glucose.

4. *Vesicles.* Large non-lipid-soluble molecules, small pieces of matter, and even whole cells can be transported across the cell membrane in a vesicle, which is a membrane-bound sac. Because of the fluid nature of membranes, the vesicle and the cell membrane can fuse, allowing the contents of the vesicle to cross the cell membrane.

Diffusion

A **solution** is a solid, liquid, or gas and consists of one or more substances called **solutes** dissolved in the predominant solid, liquid, or gas, which is called the **solvent**. Diffusion can be viewed as the tendency for solutes, such as ions or molecules, to move from an area of higher concentration to an area of lower concentration in solution (figure 3.9a and b, and table 3.2). Examples of diffusion are the movement and distribution of smoke or perfume throughout a room in which there are no air currents, or that of a dye throughout a beaker of still water.

Diffusion is a product of the constant random motion of all solutes in a solution. More solute particles occur in an area of higher concentration than in one of lower concentration. Because particles move randomly, the chances are greater that solute particles will move from the higher toward the lower concentration than from a lower to higher concentration. At equilibrium, the net movement of solutes stops, although random motion continues, and the movement of solutes in any one direction is balanced by an equal movement in the opposite direction (figure 3.9c).

A **concentration gradient** is a measure of the difference in the concentration of a solute in a solvent between two points. For a given distance between two points, the concentration gradient is equal to the higher concentration minus the lower concentration of a solute. Movement down, or with, a

Concentration
gradient for red
molecules

Concentration
gradient for blue
molecules

(a) One solution (red balls representing one type of solute molecule) is layered onto a second solution (blue balls represent a second type of solute molecule). There is a concentration gradient for the red molecules from the red solution into the blue solution because there are no red molecules in the blue solution. There is also a concentration gradient for the blue molecules from the blue solution into the red solution because there are no blue molecules in the red solution.

(b) Red molecules move down their concentration gradient into the blue solution (red arrow), and the blue molecules move down their concentration gradient into the red solution (blue arrow).

(c) Red and blue molecules are distributed evenly throughout the solution. Even though the red and blue solute molecules continue to move randomly, an equilibrium exists, and no net movement occurs because no concentration gradient exists.

Figure 3.9 Diffusion

Table 3.2 Types and Characteristics of Movement Across Cell Membranes

Type	Transport	Requires ATP	Examples
Diffusion	With the concentration gradient through the lipid portion of the cell membrane or through membrane channels	No	Oxygen, carbon dioxide, chloride ions, and urea
Osmosis	With the concentration gradient (for water) through the lipid portion of the cell membrane or through membrane channels	No	Water
Filtration	Movement of liquid and substances by pressure through a partition containing holes	No	In the kidneys, filtration of everything in blood except proteins and blood cells
Facilitated diffusion	With the concentration gradient by carrier molecules	No	Glucose in most cells
Active transport	Against the concentration gradient* by carrier molecules	Yes	Sodium, potassium, calcium, and hydrogen ions; amino acids
Secondary active transport	Against the concentration gradient by carrier molecules; the energy for secondary active transport of one substance comes from the concentration gradient of another	Yes	Glucose, amino acids
Endocytosis	Movement into cells by vesicles	Yes	Ingestion of particles by phagocytosis and liquids by pinocytosis
Exocytosis	Movement out of cells by vesicles	Yes	Secretion of proteins

*Active transport normally moves substances against their concentration gradient, but it can also move substances with their concentration gradient.

Clinical Focus   Relationships Between Cell Structure and Cell Function

Each cell is well adapted for the functions it performs, and the abundance of organelles in each cell reflects the function of the cell. For example, epithelial cells that line the larger-diameter respiratory passages secrete mucus and transport it toward the throat, where it is either swallowed or expelled from the body by coughing. Particles of dust and other debris suspended in the air become trapped in the mucus. The production and transport of mucus from the respiratory passages function to keep these passages clean. Cells of the respiratory system have abundant rough ER, Golgi apparatuses, secretory vesicles, and cilia. The ribosomes on the rough ER are the sites where proteins, a major component of mucus, are produced. The Golgi apparatuses package the proteins and other components of mucus into secretory vesicles, which move to the surface of the epithelial cells. The contents of the secretory vesicles are released onto the surface of the epithelial cells. Cilia on the cell surface then propel the mucus toward the throat.

In people who smoke, the prolonged exposure of the respiratory epithelium to the irritation of tobacco smoke causes the respiratory epithelial cells to change in structure and function. The cells flatten and form several layers of epithelial cells. These flattened epithelial cells no longer contain abundant rough ER, Golgi apparatuses, secretory vesicles, or cilia. The respiratory epithelium is adapted to protect the underlying cells from irritation, but once altered by smoking it can no longer function to secrete mucus and transport it toward the throat to clean the respiratory passages. Extensive replacement of normal epithelial cells in respiratory passages is associated with chronic inflammation of the respiratory passages (bronchitis), which is common in people who smoke heavily.

concentration gradient, describes the diffusion of solutes from a higher toward a lower concentration of solutes. Movement up, or against, a concentration gradient, describes the movement of solutes from a lower toward a higher concentration of solutes. This second type of movement does not occur by diffusion and requires energy to move solutes against their concentration gradient. The concentration gradient is said to be steeper when the concentration gradient is large.

Diffusion is an important means of transporting substances through the extracellular and intracellular fluids in the body. In addition, substances that can pass either through the lipid layers of the cell membrane or through membrane channels diffuse through the cell membrane. Some nutrients enter and some waste products leave the cell by diffusion. The normal intracellular concentrations of many substances depend on diffusion. For example, if the extracellular concentration of oxygen is reduced, not enough oxygen diffuses into the cell, and normal cell function cannot occur.

2   PREDICT

Urea is a toxic waste produced inside liver cells. It diffuses from those cells into the blood and is eliminated from the body by the kidneys. What would happen to the intracellular and extracellular concentration of urea if the kidneys stopped functioning?

✔ *Answer on page 70*

Osmosis

Osmosis (os-mō′sis) is the diffusion of water (a solvent) across a selectively permeable membrane, such as the cell membrane, from a region of higher water concentration to one of lower water concentration (see table 3.2). Osmosis is important to cells because large volume changes caused by water movement can disrupt normal cell functions. Osmosis occurs when the cell membrane is either less permeable or not permeable to solutes *and* a concentration gradient for water exists across the cell membrane. Water diffuses from a solution with a higher concentration of water across the cell membrane into a solution with a lower water concentration. The ability to predict the direction of water movement depends on knowing which solution on either side of a membrane has the highest water concentration.

The concentration of a solution, however, is not expressed in terms of water, but in terms of solute concentration. For example, if sugar solution A is twice as concentrated as sugar solution B, then solution A has twice as much sugar (solute) as solution B. As the concentration of a solution increases, the amount of water (solvent) proportionately decreases. Thus water diffuses from the less concentrated solution, which has fewer solute molecules and more water molecules, into the more concentrated solution with more solute molecules and fewer water molecules.

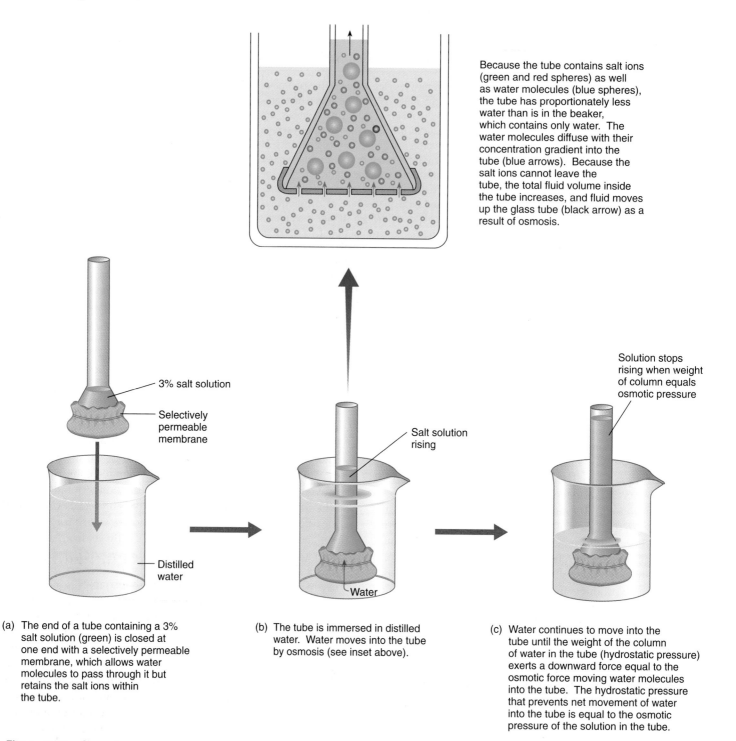

Because the tube contains salt ions (green and red spheres) as well as water molecules (blue spheres), the tube has proportionately less water than is in the beaker, which contains only water. The water molecules diffuse with their concentration gradient into the tube (blue arrows). Because the salt ions cannot leave the tube, the total fluid volume inside the tube increases, and fluid moves up the glass tube (black arrow) as a result of osmosis.

3% salt solution

Selectively permeable membrane

Distilled water

Salt solution rising

Water

Solution stops rising when weight of column equals osmotic pressure

(a) The end of a tube containing a 3% salt solution (green) is closed at one end with a selectively permeable membrane, which allows water molecules to pass through it but retains the salt ions within the tube.

(b) The tube is immersed in distilled water. Water moves into the tube by osmosis (see inset above).

(c) Water continues to move into the tube until the weight of the column of water in the tube (hydrostatic pressure) exerts a downward force equal to the osmotic force moving water molecules into the tube. The hydrostatic pressure that prevents net movement of water into the tube is equal to the osmotic pressure of the solution in the tube.

Figure 3.10 Osmosis

Osmotic pressure is the force required to prevent the movement of water across a selectively permeable membrane. Thus osmotic pressure is a measure of the tendency of water to move by osmosis across a selectively permeable membrane. It can be measured by placing a solution into a tube that is closed at one end by a selectively permeable membrane and immersing the tube in distilled water (figure 3.10a). Water molecules move by osmosis through the membrane into the tube, forcing the solution to move up the tube (figure 3.10b). As the solution rises, its weight produces **hydrostatic**

pressure (figure 3.10c), which moves water out of the tube back into the distilled water surrounding the tube. Net movement of water into the tube stops when the hydrostatic pressure in the tube causes water to move out of the tube at the same rate that it diffuses into the tube by osmosis. The osmotic pressure of the solution in the tube is equal to the hydrostatic pressure that prevents net movement of water into the tube.

The greater the concentration of a solution, the greater its osmotic pressure, and the greater the tendency for water to move into the solution. This occurs because water moves from

Red blood cell

H_2O

Hypotonic solution

Isotonic solution

Hypertonic solution

(a) A hypotonic solution with a low solute concentration results in swelling (blue arrows) and lysis (puff of white in the lower left part of the cell) of a red blood cell placed into the solution.

(b) An isotonic solution with a concentration of solutes equal to that inside the cell results in a normally shaped red blood cell. Water moves into and out of the cell in equilibrium (blue arrows), but there is no net water movement.

(c) A hypertonic solution, with a high solute concentration, causes shrinkage (crenation) of the red blood cell as water moves out of the cell and into the hypertonic solution (blue arrows).

Figure 3.11   Effects of Hypotonic, Isotonic, and Hypertonic Solutions on Red Blood Cells

less concentrated solutions (less solute, more water) into more concentrated solutions (more solute, less water). The greater the concentration of a solution (the less water it has), the greater the tendency for water to move into the solution, and the greater the osmotic pressure must be to prevent that movement.

Cells will either swell, remain unchanged, or shrink when placed into a solution. When a cell is placed into a **hypotonic** (hī′pō-ton′ik) solution, the solution usually has a lower concentration of solutes and a higher concentration of water than the cytoplasm of the cell. Water moves by osmosis into the cell, causing it to swell. If the cell swells enough, it can rupture, a process called **lysis** (lī′sis) (figure 3.11a). When a cell is immersed in an **isotonic** (ī′sō-ton′ik) solution, the concentrations of various solutes and water are the same on both sides of the cell membrane. The cell therefore neither shrinks nor swells (figure 3.11b). When a cell is immersed in a **hypertonic** (hī′per-ton′ik) solution, the solution usually has a higher concentration of solutes and a lower concentration of water than the cytoplasm of the cell. Water moves by osmosis from the cell into the hypertonic solution, resulting in cell shrinkage, or **crenation** (krē-nā′shŭn) (figure 3.11c). Solutions injected into the circulatory system or into tissues must be isotonic because swelling or shrinking disrupts the normal function of cells and can lead to cell death.

Filtration

Filtration is the movement of fluid through a partition containing small holes (see table 3.2). The fluid movement results from the pressure or weight of the fluid pushing against the partition. The fluid and substances small enough to pass through the holes move through the partition, but substances larger than the holes do not pass through it. For example, in

a car, oil but not dirt particles passes through an oil filter. In the body, filtration occurs in the kidneys as a step in urine production. Blood pressure moves fluid from the blood through a partition, or filtration membrane. Water, ions, and small molecules pass through the filtration membrane as a step in urine formation, whereas larger substances, such as proteins and blood cells, remain in the blood (see chapter 18).

Mediated Transport Mechanisms

Many nutrient molecules, such as amino acids and glucose, cannot enter the cell by the process of diffusion, and many substances, such as proteins, produced in cells cannot leave the cell by diffusion. Carrier molecules within the cell membrane are involved in **carrier-mediated transport mechanisms**, which function to move large, water-soluble molecules or electrically charged ions across the cell membrane. After a molecule to be transported binds to a carrier molecule on one side of the membrane, the three-dimensional shape of the carrier molecule changes, and the transported molecule is moved to the opposite side of the cell membrane (figure 3.12). The transported molecule is then released by the carrier molecule, which resumes its original shape and is available to transport another molecule. There are three kinds of mediated transport: facilitated diffusion, active transport, and secondary active transport.

Facilitated Diffusion

Facilitated diffusion is a mediated transport process that moves substances into or out of cells from a higher to a lower concentration (see table 3.2). Because movement is with the concentration gradient, metabolic energy in the form of ATP is not required.

3   PREDICT

The transport of glucose into most cells occurs by facilitated diffusion. Because diffusion occurs from a higher to a lower concentration, glucose cannot accumulate within these cells at a higher concentration than is found outside the cell. Once glucose enters a cell, it is rapidly converted to other molecules, such as glucose phosphate or glycogen. What effect does this conversion have on the ability of the cell to transport glucose?

✔ *Answer on page 70*

Active Transport

Active transport is a carrier-mediated process that moves substances from regions of lower concentration to ones of higher concentration against a concentration gradient (see table 3.2). Consequently, active transport processes accumulate substances on one side of the cell membrane at concentrations many times greater than those on the other side. Active transport requires energy in the form of ATP, and if ATP is not available, active transport stops. Examples of active transport include the movement of amino acids from the small intestine into the blood.

In some cases, the active transport mechanism can exchange one substance for another. For example, the **sodium–potassium exchange pump** moves sodium ions out of cells and potassium ions into cells (figure 3.13). The result is a higher concentration of sodium ions outside the cell and a higher concentration of potassium ions inside the cell. The concentration gradients for sodium and potassium ions, established by the sodium–potassium exchange pump, are essential in maintaining the resting membrane potential (see chapter 8).

Cystic fibrosis is a genetic disorder that affects the active transport of chlorine ions into cells. This disorder is discussed in the *Systems Pathology* essay on p. 66.

Secondary Active Transport

Secondary active transport involves the active transport of one substance, such as an ion, out of a cell, establishing a concentration gradient. The diffusion of the substance back into the cell, down its concentration gradient, provides the energy to transport a different substance, such as glucose, into the cell (figure 3.14).

Endocytosis and Exocytosis

Endocytosis (en'dō-sī-tō'sis) is the uptake of material through the cell membrane by the formation of a membrane-bound sac called a vesicle (see table 3.2). The two types of endocytosis are phagocytosis and pinocytosis.

Phagocytosis (fag'ō-sī-tō'sis) means "cell eating" and applies to endocytosis when solid particles are ingested. A part of the cell membrane extends around a particle and fuses so that the particle is surrounded by the membrane. That part of the membrane then "pinches off" to form a vesicle containing the particle. The vesicle is within the cytoplasm of the cell, and the cell membrane is left intact (figure 3.15). White blood cells and some other cell types phagocytize bacteria, cell debris, and foreign particles. Phagocytosis is an important means by which white blood cells take up and destroy harmful substances that have entered the body.

Pinocytosis (pin'ō-sī-tō'sis) means "cell drinking." It is distinguished from phagocytosis in that much smaller vesicles are formed, they contain liquid rather than particles, and the cell membrane invaginates to form the vesicles that are taken into the cell. Pinocytosis is a common transport mechanism and occurs in certain kidney cells, epithelial cells of the intestine, liver cells, and cells that line capillaries.

In some cells, secretions accumulate within vesicles. These secretory vesicles then move to the cell membrane, where the vesicle membrane fuses with the cell membrane, and the content of the vesicle is eliminated from the cell (see figure 3.6). This process is called **exocytosis** (ek'sō-sī-tō'sis) (figure 3.16 and see table 3.2). Secretion of digestive enzymes by the pancreas, of mucus by the salivary glands, and of milk from the mammary glands are examples of exocytosis. In many respects the process is similar to that of endocytosis, but it occurs in an opposite direction. Endocytosis results in the uptake of materials by cells, and exocytosis in the release of materials from cells. Both endocytosis and exocytosis require energy in the form of ATP to form vesicles.

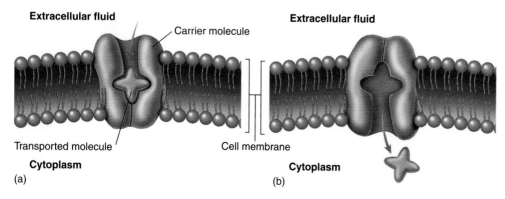

Figure 3.12   Mediated Transport Mechanism

(*a*) A molecule binds to a protein carrier molecule on one side of the cell membrane. (*b*) The carrier molecule changes shape and releases the molecule on the other side of the cell membrane.

Cell Metabolism

Cell metabolism is the sum of all the chemical reactions in the cell (figure 3.17). The breakdown of food molecules releases energy that is used to synthesize ATP (see chapter 17). When ATP is broken down, energy is released which can be used to drive other chemical reactions or processes such as active transport. The breakdown of the sugar glucose, such as the sugar from a candy bar, by a series of reactions within the cytoplasm

Extracellular fluid

1. Three sodium ions (Na^+) and adenosine triphosphate (ATP) bind to the carrier molecule.

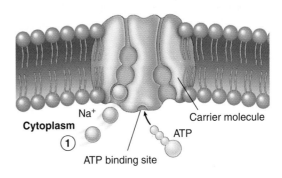

2. The ATP breaks down to adenosine diphosphate (ADP) and a phosphate (P) and releases energy.

3. The carrier molecule changes shape, and the sodium ions are transported across the membrane.

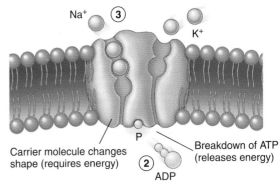

4. The sodium ions diffuse away from the carrier molecule.

5. Two potassium ions (K^+) bind to the carrier molecule.

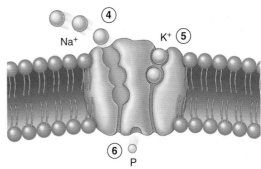

6. The phosphate is released.

7. The carrier molecule changes shape, transporting potassium ions across the membrane, and the potassium ions diffuse away from the carrier molecule. The carrier molecule can again bind to sodium ions and ATP.

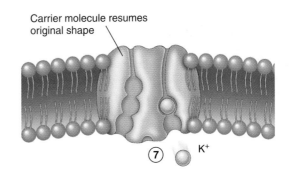

Figure 3.13   Sodium–Potassium Exchange Pump

of a cell is called **glycolysis** (glī-kol′i-sis). Glucose is converted to pyruvic acid, which can enter alternative biochemical pathways, depending on oxygen availability.

Aerobic (ār-ō′bik) **respiration** occurs when oxygen is available. Pyruvic acid molecules enter mitochondria and, through a series of chemical reactions, called the citric acid cycle and the electron-transport chain, are converted to carbon dioxide and water. Aerobic respiration can produce 36 to 38 ATP molecules from each glucose molecule. Aerobic respiration requires oxygen because the last reaction in the series is the combination of oxygen with hydrogen to form water. If this reaction does not take place, the reactions immediately preceding it do not occur either. This explains why breathing oxygen is necessary for animal life: without oxygen, aerobic respiration is inhibited, and the cells do not produce enough ATP to sustain life. During aerobic respiration,

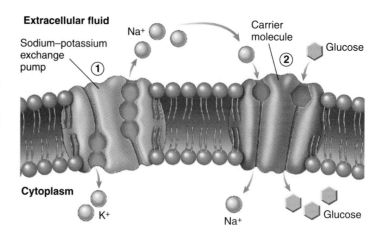

1. A sodium–potassium exchange pump maintains a concentration of sodium ions that is higher outside the cell than inside.

2. The sodium ions diffuse back into the cell by facilitated diffusion, assisted by a carrier molecule that also facilitates the diffusion of glucose. The diffusing sodium ions provide energy that can be used to move glucose against its concentration gradient.

Figure 3.14 Secondary Active Transport

the carbon atoms of food molecules are broken down to carbon dioxide. Thus, the carbon dioxide humans breathe out comes from the food they eat.

Anaerobic respiration occurs without oxygen and includes the conversion of pyruvic acid to lactic acid. There is a net production of two ATP molecules for each glucose molecule. Anaerobic respiration does not produce as much ATP as aerobic respiration, but it allows cells to function for short periods when oxygen levels are too low for aerobic respiration to provide all the needed ATP. For example, during intense exercise, when aerobic respiration has depleted the oxygen supply, anaerobic respiration can provide additional ATP.

Protein Synthesis

DNA contains the information that directs protein synthesis. The proteins produced in a cell are structural components inside the cell, structural proteins secreted to the outside of the cell, and enzymes that regulate chemical reactions in the cell. DNA influences the structural and functional characteristics of the entire organism because it directs protein synthesis. Whether an individual has blue eyes, brown hair, or other inherited traits is determined ultimately by DNA.

A DNA molecule consists of nucleotides joined together to form two nucleotide strands (see figure 2.17). The two strands are connected and resemble a ladder that is twisted around its long axis. The nucleotides function as chemical "letters" that form chemical "words." A **gene** is a sequence of nucleotides (making a word) providing a chemical set of instructions for making a specific protein. Each DNA molecule contains many different genes.

Recall from chapter 2 that proteins consist of amino acids. The unique structural and functional characteristics of different proteins are determined by the kinds, numbers, and arrangement of their amino acids. The nucleotide sequence of a gene determines the amino acid sequence of a specific protein.

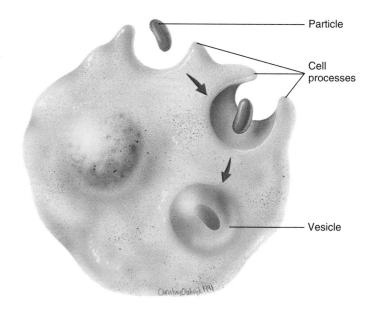

Figure 3.15 Phagocytosis

Cell processes extend from the cell and surround the particle to be taken into the cell by phagocytosis. The cell processes surround the particle and fuse to form a vesicle that contains the particle. The vesicle then is internalized within the cell.

DNA directs the production of proteins in two steps—transcription and translation—which can be illustrated with an analogy. Suppose a chef wants a recipe that is found only in a reference book in the library. Because the book cannot be checked out, the chef makes a copy, or **transcription**, of the recipe. Later, in the kitchen the information contained in the copied recipe is used to prepare a meal. The changing of something from one form to another (from recipe to meal) is called **translation**.

In terms of this analogy, DNA (the reference book) contains many genes (recipes) for making different proteins (meals). DNA, however, is too large a molecule to pass through the nuclear pores to go to the ribosomes (kitchen) where the

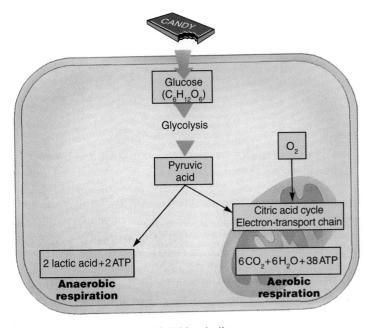

(a)

(b)

Figure 3.16 Exocytosis

(*a*) Secretory products accumulate within vesicles whose membranes fuse with the cell membrane, releasing the contents of the vesicles to the cell surface. (*b*) Electron micrograph of exocytosis.

Figure 3.17 Overview of Cell Metabolism

Aerobic respiration requires oxygen and produces more ATP per glucose molecule than does anaerobic metabolism.

copy is used to construct a protein by means of translation. Of course, the actual ingredients are needed to turn a recipe into a meal. The ingredients necessary to synthesize a protein are amino acids. Specialized molecules, called **transfer RNA (tRNA)**, carry the amino acids to the ribosome (figure 3.18).

In summary, the synthesis of proteins involves transcription—making a copy of part of the information in DNA (a gene), and translation—converting that copied information into a protein. The details of transcription and translation are considered next.

Transcription

The events leading to protein synthesis begin in the nucleus. DNA determines the structure of mRNA through transcription. The double strands of a DNA segment separate, and DNA nucleotides pair with RNA nucleotides (figure 3.19). Each nucleotide of DNA contains one of the following organic bases: thymine, adenine, cytosine, or guanine; and each nucleotide of mRNA contains uracil, adenine, cytosine, or guanine. The number and sequence of nucleotides in the DNA determine the number and sequence of nucleotides in the mRNA because DNA nucleotides only pair with specific RNA nucleotides: DNA's thymine with RNA's adenine, DNA's adenine with RNA's uracil, DNA's cytosine with RNA's guanine, and DNA's guanine with RNA's cytosine.

After the DNA nucleotides pair up with the RNA nucleotides, an enzyme catalyzes reactions that form chemical bonds between the RNA nucleotides to form a long mRNA segment. Once the mRNA segment has been transcribed, portions of the mRNA molecule can be removed, or two or more mRNA molecules can be combined.

proteins (the meal) are prepared. Just as the reference book stays in the library, DNA remains in the nucleus. Through transcription therefore the cell makes a copy of the information in DNA necessary to make a particular protein. The copy, which is called **messenger RNA (mRNA)**, travels from the nucleus to the ribosomes in the cytoplasm, where the information in the

1. DNA contains the information necessary to produce proteins.
2. Transcription of DNA results in mRNA, which is a copy of the information in DNA needed to make a protein.
3. The mRNA leaves the nucleus and goes to a ribosome.
4. Amino acids, the building blocks of proteins, are carried to the ribosome by tRNAs.
5. In the process of translation, the information contained in mRNA is used to determine the number, kinds, and arrangement of amino acids in the protein.

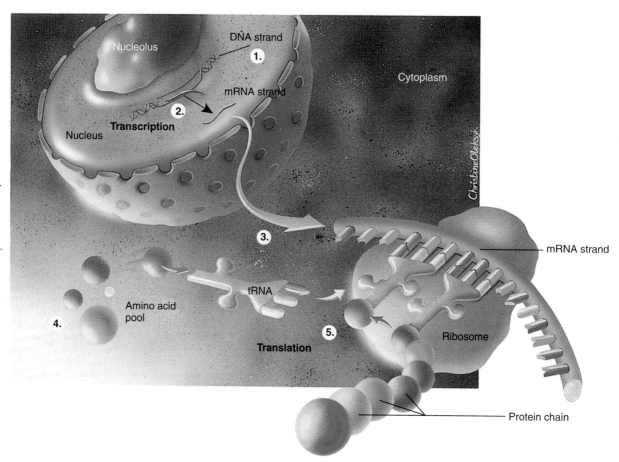

Figure 3.18 Overview of Protein Synthesis

Translation

Translation, the synthesis of proteins based on the information in mRNA, occurs at ribosomes. The mRNA molecules produced by transcription pass through the nuclear pores to the ribosomes. The information in mRNA is carried in groups of three nucleotides called **codons**, which code for specific amino acids. For example, the nucleotide sequence uracil, cytosine, and adenine (UCA) of mRNA codes for the amino acid serine. There are 64 possible mRNA codons, but only 20 amino acids are in proteins. As a result, more than one codon can code for the same amino acid. For example, CGA, CGG, CGT, and CGC code for the amino acid alanine, and UUU and UAC code for phenylalanine. Some codons do not code for amino acids but perform other functions. For example, UAA acts as a signal for stopping the production of a protein.

Protein synthesis requires two types of RNA in addition to mRNA: tRNA and **ribosomal RNA (rRNA)**. There is one type of tRNA for each mRNA codon. A series of three nucleotides of each tRNA molecule, the **anticodon**, pairs with the codon of the mRNA. Another part of each tRNA molecule binds to a specific amino acid. For example, the tRNA that pairs with the

UUU codon of mRNA has the anticodon AAA and binds only to the amino acid phenylalanine.

The ribosomes, which consist of ribosomal RNA and proteins, align mRNA with tRNA molecules so that the anticodons of tRNAs pair with the codons of mRNA while the mRNA is attached to a ribosome (figure 3.20). The amino acids bound to the tRNAs are then joined to one another by an enzyme associated with the ribosome. The enzyme causes the formation of a chemical bond, called a **peptide bond**, between the adjacent amino acids to form a **polypeptide chain**, consisting of many amino acids bound together by peptide bonds. The polypeptide chain then becomes folded to form the three-dimensional structure of the protein molecule. A protein can consist of a single polypeptide chain or two or more polypeptide chains that are joined after each chain is produced on separate ribosomes.

4 · **P R E D I C T**

Explain how changing one nucleotide within a DNA molecule of a cell could change the structure of a protein produced by the cell.

✔ *Answer on page 70*

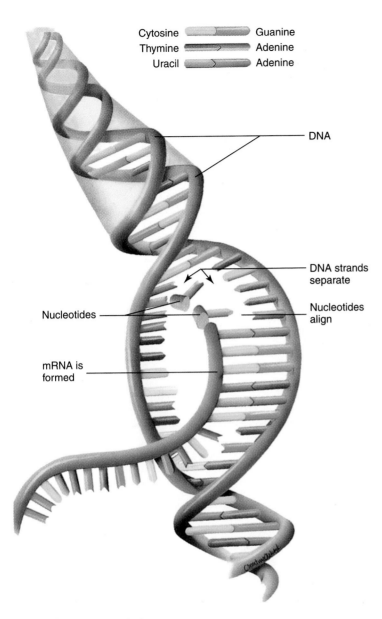

Cytosine ▭▭▭ Guanine
Thymine ▭▭▭ Adenine
Uracil ▭▭▭ Adenine

DNA

DNA strands separate

Nucleotides align

Nucleotides

mRNA is formed

Figure 3.19 Transcription

Formation of mRNA by transcription of DNA chains in the cell nucleus. A segment of the DNA chain is opened, and RNA polymerase (an enzyme) assembles nucleotides into mRNA according to the base pair combinations shown in the inset. Thus the sequence of nucleotides in DNA determines the sequence of nucleotides in mRNA. As nucleotides are added, an mRNA chain is formed.

Cell Division

Cell division is the formation of two daughter cells from a single parent cell. The new cells necessary for growth and tissue repair are formed through mitosis, and the sex cells necessary for reproduction are formed through meiosis.

During mitosis and meiosis the DNA within the parent cell is distributed to the daughter cells. The DNA is found within chromosomes. Each cell of the human body, except

for sex cells, contains 46 chromosomes. Sex cells have half the number of chromosomes as other cells (see the section on Meiosis on p. 61). The 46 chromosomes are called a **diploid** (dip′loyd) number of chromosomes and are organized to form 23 pairs of chromosomes. Of the 23 pairs, one pair is the sex chromosomes, which consist of two **X chromosomes** if the person is a female or an X chromosome and a **Y chromosome** if the person is a male. The remaining 22 pairs of chromosomes are called **autosomes** (aw′tō-sōmz). The combination of sex chromosomes determines the individual's sex, and the autosomes determine most other characteristics.

Mitosis

All cells of the body, except those that give rise to sex cells, divide by **mitosis** (mī-tō′sis). Mitosis involves two steps: (1) the genetic material within a cell is **replicated**, or duplicated, and (2) the cell divides to form two daughter cells with the same amount and type of DNA as the parent cell. Because DNA determines the structure and function of cells, the daughter cells, which have the same DNA as the parent cell, can have the same structure and perform the same functions as the parent cell.

The period between active cell divisions is called **interphase**, during which DNA is replicated. The two strands of DNA separate from each other, and each strand serves as a template for the production of a new strand of DNA (figure 3.21). Nucleotides found in the DNA of a template strand pair with nucleotides that are subsequently joined by enzymes to form a new strand of DNA. The sequence of nucleotides in the DNA template determines the sequence of nucleotides in the new strand of DNA because adenine pairs with thymine, and cytosine pairs with guanine. The new strand of DNA combines with the template strand to form a double strand of DNA.

At the end of interphase, each cell has two complete sets of genetic material. The DNA is dispersed throughout the nucleus as thin threads called **chromatin** (krō′mă-tin) (figure 3.22*a*).

Mitosis follows interphase. For convenience, mitosis is divided into four stages. Although each stage represents major events, the process of mitosis is continuous. Learning each of the stages is helpful, but the most important concept to understand is how each of the two cells produced by mitosis obtains the same number and type of chromosomes as the parent cell. There are four stages in mitosis:

1. *Prophase.* During **prophase** (figure 3.22*b*), the chromatin condenses to form visible chromosomes. After interphase, each chromosome is made up of two separate but genetically identical strands of chromatin called **chromatids** (krō′mă-tidz), which are linked at one point by a specialized region called the **centromere** (sen′trō-mēr). Replication of the genetic material during interphase results in the two identical

1. To start protein synthesis a ribosome binds to mRNA. The ribosome also has two binding sites for tRNA, one of which is occupied by a tRNA with its amino acid. Note that the codon of mRNA and the anticodon of tRNA are aligned and joined. The other tRNA binding site is open.

2. By occupying the open tRNA binding site the next tRNA is properly aligned with mRNA and with the other tRNA.

3. An enzyme within the ribosome catalyzes a synthesis reaction to form a peptide bond between the amino acids. Note that the amino acids are now associated with only one of the tRNAs.

4. The ribosome shifts position by three nucleotides. The tRNA without the amino acid is released from the ribosome, and the tRNA with the amino acids takes its position. A tRNA binding site is left open by the shift. Additional amino acids can be added by repeating steps 2 through 4. Eventually a stop codon in the mRNA ends the production of the protein, which is released from the ribosome.

5. This is an overview of protein synthesis.

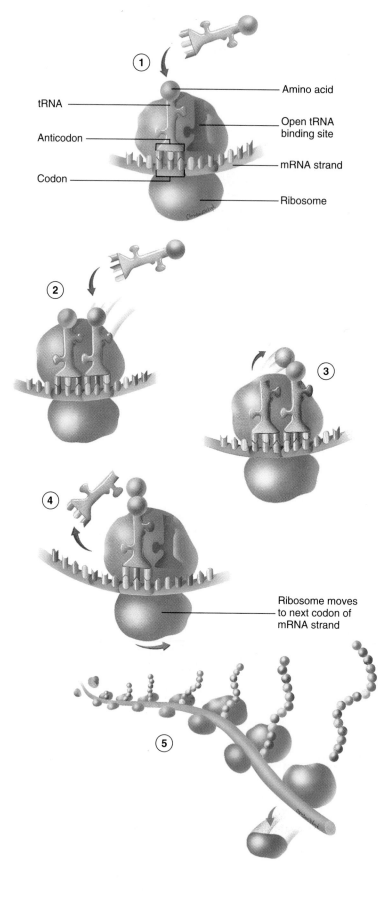

Figure 3.20 Translation of mRNA to Produce a Protein

chromatids of each chromosome. Also during prophase, microtubules called **spindle fibers** extend from the **centrioles** (sen'trē-ōlz) to the centromeres (see figures 3.1 and 3.22*b*). Centrioles are small organelles that divide and migrate to each pole of the cell. In late prophase, the nucleolus and nuclear envelope disappear.

2. *Metaphase.* In **metaphase** (figure 3.22*c*), the chromosomes align near the center of the cell.

3. *Anaphase.* At the beginning of **anaphase** (figure 3.22*d*), the centromeres separate. When this happens, each chromatid is then referred to as a chromosome. Thus, when the centromeres divide, the chromosome number doubles to form two identical sets of 46 chromosomes.

Each of the two sets of 46 chromosomes is moved by the spindle fibers toward the centriole at one of the poles of the cell. At the end of anaphase, each set of chromosomes has reached an opposite pole of the cell, and the cytoplasm begins to divide.

4. *Telophase.* During **telophase** (figure 3.22*e*), the chromosomes in each of the daughter cells become organized to form two separate nuclei. The chromosomes begin to unravel and resemble the genetic material during interphase.

Following telophase, the cytoplasm of the two cells completes division, and two separate daughter cells are produced (figure 3.22*f*).

Meiosis

The formation of all body cells, except for sex cells, occurs by mitosis. Sex cells are formed by **meiosis** (mī-ō'sis), a process in which the nucleus of a sex cell precursor cell undergoes two divisions, resulting in (1) four nuclei, each containing half as many chromosomes as the parent cell and (2) one chromosome from each of the chromosome pairs. The daughter cells that are produced differentiate into **gametes** (gam'ētz), or **sex cells**. The sex cells are **sperm cells** in males and **oocytes** (ō'ō-sītz) in females (see chapter 19). Each gamete has a **haploid** (hap'loyd) number of chromosomes, which is half the number of chromosomes found in other body cells. The haploid number of chromosomes in humans is 23 chromosomes. Sperm cells have 22 autosomal chromosomes and either an X or Y chromosome, and oocytes contain 22 autosomal chromosomes and an X chromosome. During **fertilization**, when a sperm cell fuses with an oocyte, the normal number of 46 chromosomes, in 23 pairs, is reestablished.

Meiosis involves two divisions. The first division during meiosis is divided into four stages: prophase I, metaphase I, anaphase I, and telophase I (figure 3.23). As in prophase of mitosis, during prophase I of meiosis the nuclear envelope degenerates, spindle fibers form, and the already duplicated chromosomes become visible. Each chromosome consists of two chromatids joined by a centromere. In prophase I, however, the members of each pair of chromosomes lie close together. Because each chromosome consists of two chromatids, the four chromatids of a chromosome pair is called a **tetrad**. In metaphase I the tetrads align near the center of the cell, and in anaphase I each pair of chromosomes separates and moves toward opposite poles of the cell. For each pair of

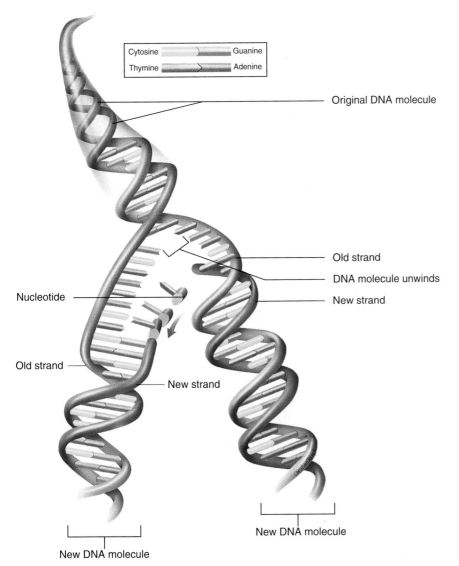

Figure 3.21   Replication of DNA

The strands of DNA separate from each other, and each strand functions as a template for the production of a new strand. The base-pairing relationship between nucleotides (see inset) determines the sequence of nucleotides in the newly formed strand. Two identical molecules of DNA are produced, each with one new strand and one old, template strand of the original DNA molecule.

(a) **Interphase** is the time between cell divisions. DNA is found as thin threads of chromatin in the nucleus. DNA replication occurs during interphase.

Nucleus

Chromatin

(b) In **prophase**, the chromatin condenses into chromosomes. Each chromosome consists of two chromatids joined at the centromere. The centrioles move to the opposite ends of the cell, and the nucleolus and the nuclear envelope disappear.

Centriole

Centromere

Chromatid

Chromatid

Chromosome

(c) In **metaphase**, the chromosomes align in the center of the cell in association with the spindle fibers.

Spindle fiber

(d) In **anaphase**, the chromatids separate to form two sets of identical chromosomes. The chromosomes, assisted by the spindle fibers, move toward the centrioles at each end of the cell.

Centriole

Identical chromosomes

(e) In **telophase**, the chromosomes disperse, the nuclear envelopes and the nucleoli form, and the cytoplasm begins to divide to form two cells.

Nucleoli

Nuclear envelope

(f) Mitosis is complete, and a new interphase begins. The chromosomes have unraveled to become chromatin. Cell division has produced two daughter cells, each with DNA that is identical to the DNA parent cell.

Figure 3.22   Mitosis

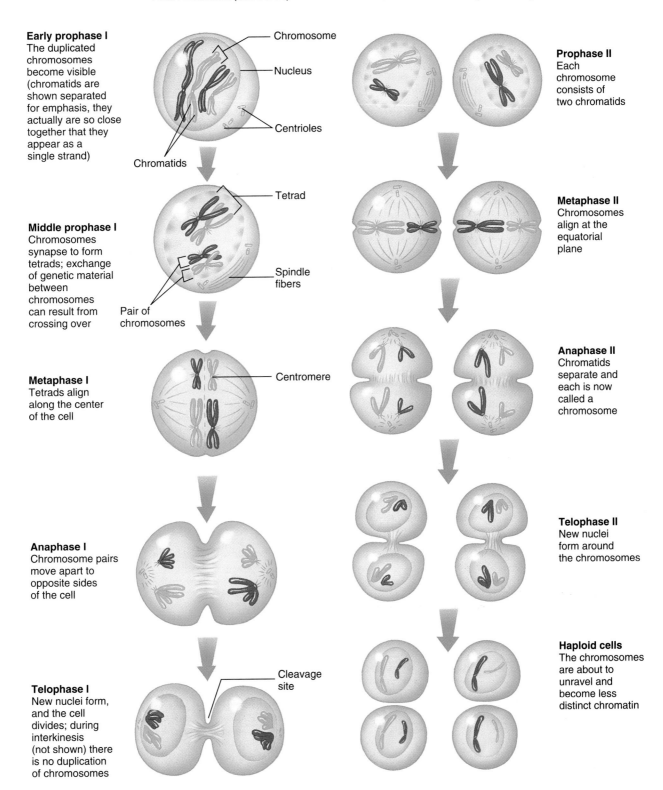

FIRST DIVISION (MEIOSIS I)

SECOND DIVISION (MEIOSIS II)

Early prophase I
The duplicated chromosomes become visible (chromatids are shown separated for emphasis, they actually are so close together that they appear as a single strand)

Chromosome

Nucleus

Centrioles

Chromatids

Prophase II
Each chromosome consists of two chromatids

Middle prophase I
Chromosomes synapse to form tetrads; exchange of genetic material between chromosomes can result from crossing over

Tetrad

Spindle fibers

Pair of chromosomes

Metaphase II
Chromosomes align at the equatorial plane

Metaphase I
Tetrads align along the center of the cell

Centromere

Anaphase II
Chromatids separate and each is now called a chromosome

Anaphase I
Chromosome pairs move apart to opposite sides of the cell

Telophase II
New nuclei form around the chromosomes

Telophase I
New nuclei form, and the cell divides; during interkinesis (not shown) there is no duplication of chromosomes

Cleavage site

Haploid cells
The chromosomes are about to unravel and become less distinct chromatin

Figure 3.23   Meiosis

chromosomes, one daughter cell receives one member of the pair, and the other daughter cell receives the other member. Thus each daughter cell has 23 chromosomes, and each of the chromosomes is composed of two chromatids. Telophase I is similar to telophase of mitosis, producing two daughter cells.

Interkinesis (in'ter-ki-nē'sis) is the period of time between the first and second meiotic divisions. Replication of DNA does not take place during interkinesis.

The second meiotic division also has four stages: prophase II, metaphase II, anaphase II, and telophase II. These stages occur much as they do in mitosis, except that 23 chromosomes result instead of 46. The chromosomes align near the center of the cell in metaphase II, and their chromatids split apart in anaphase II. The chromatids are now called chromosomes, and each new cell receives 23 chromosomes.

In addition to reducing the number of chromosomes in a cell from 46 to 23, meiosis also dramatically increases genetic diversity for two reasons:

1. *Crossing over.* When tetrads are formed, some of the chromatids can break apart, and part of one chromatid can be exchanged for part of another. This exchange is called **crossing over.** As a result, chromatids with different DNA content are formed.
2. *Random distribution.* For any given person, one member of each chromosome pair is derived from the person's father, and the other member from the person's mother. When that person produces sex cells, during metaphase of the first meiotic division, the chromosomes align randomly, and when they split apart, each daughter cell receives some of the father's and some of the mother's chromosomes. How many of the father's or mother's chromosomes each sex cell receives is determined by chance, which is called **random distribution** of the chromosomes.

With crossing over and random distribution of chromosomes, the possible number of gametes with different genetic makeup is practically unlimited. When the different gametes of two individuals unite, it is virtually certain that the resulting genetic makeup has never before occurred and will never occur again. Table 3.3 contrasts mitosis and meiosis.

Differentiation

A new individual begins when a sperm cell and oocyte unite to form a single cell. The trillions of cells that ultimately make up the body of an adult stem from that single cell. Therefore all the cells in an individual's body contain the same complement of DNA that encodes all of the genetic information for that individual. Not all cells look and function alike, even though the genetic information contained in them is identical. Bone cells, for example, do not look like or function as fat cells or red blood cells.

The process by which cells are developed with specialized structures and functions is called **differentiation.** The single cell formed during fertilization divides by mitosis to form two cells, which divide to form four cells, and so on. The cells continue to divide until there are thousands of cells, which differentiate and give rise to the different cell types.

During differentiation of a cell, some portions of DNA are active, but others are inactive. The active and inactive sections of DNA differ with each cell type. The portion of DNA that is responsible for the structure and function of a bone cell is different from that responsible for the structure and function of a fat cell. Differentiation, then, results from the selective activation and inactivation of segments of DNA. The mechanisms that determine which portions of DNA are active in any one cell type are not fully understood, but the resulting differentiation produces the many cell types that function together to make a person. Eventually, as cells differentiate and mature, the rate at which they divide slows or even stops.

Did You Know?

Through the process of differentiation, cells become specialized to certain functions and are no longer capable of producing an entire organism if isolated. Over 30 years ago, however, it was demonstrated in frogs that if the nucleus is removed from a differentiated cell and is transferred to an oocyte with the nucleus removed, a complete, normal frog can develop from that oocyte. This process, called **cloning,** demonstrated that during differentiation, genetic information is not irrevocably lost. Because mammalian oocytes are considerably smaller than frog oocytes, cloning of mammalian cells has been technically much more difficult. Dr. Ian Wilmut and his colleagues at the Roslin Institute in Edinburgh, Scotland, overcame those technical difficulties in 1996, when they successfully cloned the first mammal, a sheep. Since that time, several other mammalian species have been cloned.

Did You Know?

Apoptosis (ăp'op-tō'sis) or **programmed cell death** is a normal process by which cell numbers within various tissues are adjusted and controlled. During development, extra tissue is removed by apoptosis, such as cells between the developing fingers and toes, to fine-tune the contours of the developing fetus. The number of cells in most adult tissues is maintained at a specific level. Apoptosis eliminates excess cells produced by proliferation within some adult tissues to maintain a constant number of cells within the tissue. Damaged or potentially dangerous cells, virus-infected cells, and potential cancer cells are also eliminated by apoptosis.

Apoptosis is regulated by specific genes. The proteins coded for by those genes initiate events within the cell that ultimately lead to the cell's death. As apoptosis begins, the chromatin within the nucleus condenses and fragments. This is followed by fragmentation of the nucleus and finally by death and fragmentation of the cell. The cell fragments are cleaned up by specialized cells called macrophages.

Table 3.3   Comparison of Mitosis and Meiosis

Feature	Mitosis	Meiosis
Time of DNA replication	Interphase	Interphase
Number of cell divisions	One	Two; there is no replication of DNA between the two meiotic divisions
Cells produced	Two daughter cells genetically identical to the parent cell; each daughter cell has the diploid number of chromosomes.	Gametes, each different from the parent cell and each other; the gametes have the haploid number of chromosomes; in males, four gametes (sperm cells); in females, 1 gamete (oocyte) and two or three polar bodies
Function	New cells are formed during growth or tissue repair; new cells have identical DNA and can perform the same functions as the parent cells	Gametes are produced for reproduction; during fertilization the haploid number of chromosomes in each gamete unites to restore the diploid number typical of most cells; genetic variability is increased because of crossing over and random distribution of chromosomes

Did You Know?

A **tumor** (too'mōr; a swelling) is any swelling that occurs within the body, usually involving cell proliferation. A tumor can be either **malignant** (mă-lig'nănt, meaning with malice or intent to cause harm), able to spread and become worse, or **benign** (bē-nīn', meaning kind), not inclined to spread and not likely to become worse.

Cancer (kan'ser) refers to a malignant, spreading tumor and the illness that results from such a tumor. Benign tumors are usually less dangerous than malignant tumors, but they can cause problems. As a benign tumor enlarges, it can compress surrounding tissues and impair their functions. In some cases (e.g., brain tumors), the results can be death.

Malignant tumors can spread by local growth and expansion or by metastasis (mĕ-tas'tă-sis, meaning moving to another place), which results from tumor cells separating from the main neoplasm and being carried by the lymphatic or circulatory system to a new site, where a second tumor forms.

Cancers lack the normal growth control that is exhibited by most other adult tissues. Cancer results when a cell or group of cells, for some reason, breaks away from the normal control of growth and differentiation. This breaking loose involves the genetic machinery and can be induced by viruses, environmental toxins, and other causes.

The illness associated with cancer usually occurs as the tumor invades and destroys the healthy surrounding tissues, eliminating their functions.

Promising anticancer therapies are being developed in which cells responsible for immune responses can be stimulated to recognize tumor cells and destroy them. A major advantage in such anticancer treatments is that the cells of the immune system can specifically attack the tumor cells and not other, healthy tissues. Other therapies currently under investigation include techniques to starve a tumor to death by cutting off its blood supply. Drugs that can inhibit blood vessel development are currently under investigation.

5   P R E D I C T

Cancer cells divide continuously. The normal mechanisms that regulate whether cell division occurs or ceases do not function properly in cancer cells. Cancer cells, such as breast cancer cells, do not look like normal, mature cells. Explain.

✔ *Answer on page 70*

Systems Pathology
cystic fibrosis

CYSTIC FIBROSIS

Tim S. is a 5-year-old white male. He is small for his age and has had frequent bouts of pulmonary infections all his life. Tim always seemed to have a "runny nose." None of the infections were very serious, mostly just irritating. This time, however, his congestion became so extreme that he was unable to breathe and was rushed to the hospital. There, a series of tests demonstrated that Tim suffered from cystic fibrosis.

Cystic fibrosis is a genetic disorder that occurs at a rate of approximately one per 2000 births and currently affects 33,000 people in the United States. It is the most common lethal genetic disorder among whites. The diagnosis is based on the existence of recurrent respiratory disease, increased sodium in the sweat, and high levels of unabsorbed fats in the stool. Approximately 98% of all cases of cystic fibrosis are diagnosed before the patient is 18 years old.

At the molecular level, cystic fibrosis results from an abnormality in chloride ion channels. There are three types of cystic fibrosis: (1) In about 70% of cases, a defective channel protein fails to reach the cell membrane from its site of production inside the cell. (2) In the second group, the channel protein is incorporated into the cell membrane but fails to bind ATP. (3) In the final category, the channel protein is incorporated into the cell membrane and ATP is bound to the channel protein, but the channel does not open. The result of any of these defects is that chloride ions do not exit cells at a normal rate.

Normally, as chloride ions move out of cells lining tubes, such as ducts or respiratory passages in the body, water follows by osmosis. In cystic fibrosis, chloride ions do not exit these cells at normal rates and, therefore less water moves into the tubes. With less water present, the mucus produced by cells lining those tubes is thick and cannot be readily moved over the surface of the cells by their cilia. As a result, the tubes become clogged with mucus, and much of their normal function is lost.

The most critical effects of cystic fibrosis, accounting for 90% of the deaths, are on the respiratory system. Cystic fibrosis also affects the secretory cells lining ducts of the pancreas, sweat glands, and salivary glands.

In normal lungs, a thin fluid layer of mucus is moved by ciliated cells. In people with cystic fibrosis, the viscous mucus resists movement by cilia and accumulates in the lung passages. The mucus accumulation obstructs the passageways and increases the likelihood of infections. This results in chronic airflow obstruction, difficulty in breathing, and recurrent respiratory infections. Chronic coughing occurs as the affected person attempts to remove the mucus.

Cystic fibrosis was once fatal during early childhood, but many patients are now surviving into young adulthood because of modern medical treatment. Currently, approximately 80% of people with cystic fibrosis live past age 20. Pulmonary therapy consists of supporting and enhancing existing respiratory functions, and infections are treated with antibiotics.

The buildup of thick mucus in the pancreatic and hepatic ducts blocks them so that pancreatic digestive enzymes and bile salts are prevented from reaching the small intestine. As a result, fats and fat-soluble vitamins, which require bile salts for absorption, and which cannot be adequately digested without pancreatic enzymes, are not taken up by intestinal cells in normal amounts. The patient suffers from deficiencies of vitamins A, D, E, and K, which result in conditions such as night blindness, skin disorders, rickets, and excessive bleeding. Therapy includes administering the missing vitamins to the patient and reducing dietary fat intake.

Future treatments could include the development of drugs that correct or assist chloride ion transport. Alternatively, cystic fibrosis may some day be cured through gene therapy; that is, inserting a functional copy of the defective gene into the cells of people with the disease.

6	P R E D I C T

Predict the effect of cystic fibrosis on the concentrations of chloride ions inside and outside the cell. In normal muscle and nerve cells at rest, many potassium ion channels are open and potassium ions tend to flow out of the cell down their concentration gradient. How is this flow of potassium ions affected in cells of people with cystic fibrosis?

✔ *Answer on page 70*

System	Interactions
Integumentary	Cystic fibrosis is characterized by increased perspiration with abnormally high quantities of sodium in the sweat which can lead to decreased blood sodium levels. A number of skin rashes and other disorders can develop as a result of the abnormal perspiration.
Nervous	Night blindness can develop as a result of vitamin A deficiency caused by insufficient absorption of the vitamin in the digestive tract.
Endocrine	Diabetes mellitus resulting from decreased production of the hormone insulin may develop because blockage of the pancreatic duct by mucus results in pancreatic digestive enzymes, retained within the pancreas, destroying the pancreatic tissues (pancreatic islets), which produce insulin.
Cardiovascular	Fragile blood vessels can develop, resulting in excessive bleeding. Decreased blood clotting results from insufficient vitamin K absorption from the digestive tract. Erythrocyte (red blood cell) membranes become fragile because of inadequate vitamin E absorption.
Respiratory	The respiratory passages become clogged with viscous mucus, which blocks the airways and inhibits respiration. Recurrent respiratory infections also occur. Decreased airflow into and out of the lungs results in reduced oxygen flow to the tissues. Respiratory complications account for most deaths.
Digestive	Pancreatic ducts and ducts from the liver and salivary glands are blocked with thick mucus. Fats and the fat-soluble vitamins, A, D, E, and K, are poorly absorbed. Deficiencies in fat-soluble vitamins result that affect many other systems. The intestine can become impacted with dehydrated stool. Gallstones can form in the gallbladder or liver ducts.
Reproductive	Reproductive ability is greatly decreased. In 95% of males with cystic fibrosis, there is an absence of living sperm cells in the semen. Viscous secretions in the male or female reproductive tracts decrease fertility.

Summary

Cell Structure and Function

- Cells are highly organized units composed of living material.
- The nucleus contains genetic material, and cytoplasm is living material outside the nucleus.

Cell Membrane

- The cell membrane forms the outer boundary of the cell. It determines what enters and leaves the cell.
- The cell membrane is composed of a double layer of lipid molecules in which proteins float. The proteins function as membrane channels, carrier molecules, receptor molecules, enzymes, and structural components of the membrane.

Nucleus

- The nuclear envelope consists of two separate membranes with nuclear pores.
- DNA and associated proteins are found inside the nucleus as chromatin. DNA is the hereditary material of the cell and controls the activities of the cell.

Nucleoli and Ribosomes

- Nucleoli consist of RNA and proteins and are the sites of ribosomal subunit assembly.
- Ribosomes are the sites of protein synthesis.

Rough and Smooth Endoplasmic Reticulum

- Rough ER is ER with ribosomes attached. It is a major site of protein synthesis.
- Smooth ER does not have ribosomes attached and is a major site of lipid synthesis.

The Golgi Apparatus

- The Golgi apparatus is a series of closely packed membrane sacs that function to collect, modify, package, and distribute proteins and lipids produced by the ER.

Secretory Vesicles

- Secretory vesicles are membrane-bound sacs that carry substances from the Golgi apparatus to the cell membrane, where the vesicle contents are released.

Lysosomes

- Membrane-bound sacs containing enzymes are called lysosomes. Within the cell the lysosomes break down phagocytized material.

Mitochondria

- Mitochondria are the major sites of ATP production, which cells use as an energy source. Mitochondria carry out aerobic respiration (requires oxygen).

Cytoskeleton

- The cytoskeleton supports the cytoplasm and organelles and is involved with cell movements.
- The cytoskeleton is composed of microtubules, microfilaments, and intermediate filaments.

Cilia, Flagella, and Microvilli

- Cilia move substances over the surface of cells.
- Flagella are much longer than cilia and propel sperm cells.
- Microvilli increase the surface area of cells and aid in absorption.

Whole-Cell Activity

- The interactions between organelles must be considered for cell function to be fully understood.

Movement Through the Cell Membrane

- Lipid-soluble molecules pass through the cell membrane readily by dissolving in the lipid portion of the membrane.
- Small molecules can pass through membrane channels.
- Large molecules that are not lipid-soluble can be transported through the membrane by carrier molecules.
- Large molecules that are not lipid-soluble, particles, and cells can be transported across the membrane by vesicles.

Diffusion

- Diffusion is the movement of a solute from an area of higher concentration to an area of lower concentration within a solvent. At equilibrium, there is a uniform distribution of molecules.
- For a given distance, a concentration gradient is equal to the higher concentration minus the lower concentration of a solute in a solution.

Osmosis

- Osmosis is the diffusion of a solvent (water) across a selectively permeable membrane.
- Osmotic pressure is a measure of the tendency of water to move across the selectively permeable membrane.
- In a hypotonic solution, cells swell (and can undergo lysis); in an isotonic solution, cells neither swell nor shrink; and in a hypertonic solution, cells shrink and undergo crenation.

Filtration

- Filtration is the passage of a solution through a partition in response to a pressure difference. Some materials in the solution do not pass through the partition.

Mediated Transport Mechanisms

- Mediated transport is the movement of a substance across a membrane by means of a carrier molecule. The substances transported tend to be large, water-soluble molecules.
- Facilitated diffusion moves substances from a higher to a lower concentration and does not require energy in the form of ATP.
- Active transport can move substances from a lower to a higher concentration and requires ATP. An exchange pump is an active transport mechanism that moves two substances in opposite directions across the cell membrane.
- Secondary active-transport uses the power of one substance moving down its concentration gradient to move another substance into the cell.

Endocytosis and Exocytosis

- Endocytosis is the movement of materials into cells by the formation of a vesicle. Phagocytosis is the movement of solid material into cells by the formation of a vesicle. Pinocytosis is similar to phagocytosis, except that the material ingested is much smaller and is in solution.
- Exocytosis is the secretion of materials from cells by vesicle formation.

Cell Metabolism

- Aerobic respiration requires oxygen and produces carbon dioxide, water, and 36 to 38 ATP molecules from a molecule of glucose.
- Anaerobic respiration does not require oxygen and produces lactic acid and two ATP molecules from a molecule of glucose.

Protein Synthesis

- Cell activity is regulated by enzymes (proteins), and DNA controls enzyme production.

Transcription

- During transcription, the sequence of nucleotides in DNA (a gene) determines the sequence of nucleotides in mRNA; the mRNA moves through the nuclear pores to ribosomes.

Translation

- During translation the sequence of codons in mRNA is used at ribosomes to produce proteins. Anticodons of tRNA bind to the codons of mRNA, and the amino acids carried by tRNA are joined to form a protein.

Cell Division
Mitosis

- Cell division that occurs by mitosis produces new cells for growth and tissue repair.
- DNA replicates during interphase, the time between cell division.
- Mitosis is divided into four stages:
  Prophase—Each chromosome consists of two chromatids joined at the centromere.
  Metaphase—Chromosomes align at the center of the cell.
  Anaphase—Chromatids separate at the centromere and migrate to opposite poles.
  Telophase—The two new nuclei assume their normal structure, and cell division is completed, producing two new daughter cells.

Meiosis

- Meiosis results in the formation of gametes (sperm cells or oocytes). Gametes have half the number (haploid number) of chromosomes that other (diploid) body cells do.
- There are two cell divisions in meiosis. Each division has four stages similar to those in mitosis.
- During meiosis the processes of crossing over within tetrads and random distribution of chromosomes increase genetic variability.

Differentiation

- Differentiation, the process by which cells develop specialized structures and functions, results from the selective activation and inactivation of DNA.

Content Review

1. Define cytoplasm and cell organelle.
2. Describe the structure of the cell membrane. What functions does it perform?
3. Describe the structure of the nucleus and nuclear envelope. Name the organelles found in the nucleus, and give their functions.
4. Where are ribosomes assembled, and what kinds of molecules are found in them?
5. What is endoplasmic reticulum? Compare the functions of rough and smooth endoplasmic reticulum.
6. Describe the Golgi apparatus, and state its function.
7. Where are secretory vesicles produced? What are their contents, and how are they released?
8. What is the function of the lysosomes?
9. Describe the structure and function of mitochondria.
10. Name the components of the cytoskeleton, and give their functions.
11. Describe the structure and function of cilia, flagella, and microvilli.
12. How do lipid-soluble molecules, small molecules that are not lipid-soluble, and large molecules that are not lipid-soluble cross the cell membrane?
13. Define solution, solute, solvent, diffusion, and concentration gradient.
14. Define osmosis and osmotic pressure.
15. What happens to cells that are placed in isotonic solutions? In hypertonic or hypotonic solutions? What are crenation and lysis?
16. Define filtration.
17. What is mediated transport? How are facilitated diffusion and active transport similar, and how are they different?
18. How does secondary active transport work?
19. Describe phagocytosis, pinocytosis, and exocytosis. What do they accomplish?
20. Describe how proteins are synthesized and how the structure of DNA determines the structure of proteins.
21. Define autosome, sex chromosome, diploid number, and haploid number.
22. How do the sex chromosomes of males and females differ?
23. Describe what happens during interphase and each phase of mitosis. What kind of tissues undergo mitosis?
24. Describe the events of meiosis. What happens during meiosis to increase genetic variability?
25. Define differentiation. In general terms, how does differentiation occur?

Develop Your Reasoning Skills

1. Suppose that a cell has the following characteristics: many mitochondria, well-developed rough ER, well-developed Golgi apparatuses, and numerous vesicles. Predict the major function of the cell. Explain how each characteristic supports your prediction.
2. Secretory vesicles fuse with the cell membrane to release their contents to the outside of the cell. In this process the membrane of the secretory vesicle becomes part of the cell membrane. Because small pieces of membrane are continually added to the cell membrane, one would expect the cell membrane to become larger and larger as secretion continues. The cell membrane stays the same size, however. Explain how this happens.
3. The body of a male was found floating in the salt water of Grand Pacific Bay, which has a concentration that is slightly greater than body fluids. When seen during an autopsy, the cells in his lung tissues were clearly swollen. Choose the most logical conclusion.
   a. He probably drowned in the bay.
   b. He may have been murdered elsewhere.
   c. He did not drown.
4. Patients with kidney failure can be kept alive by dialysis, which removes toxic waste products from the blood. In a dialysis machine, blood flows past one side of a selectively permeable dialysis membrane, and dialysis fluid flows on the other side of the membrane. Small substances, such as ions, glucose, and urea, can pass through the dialysis membrane, but larger substances, such as proteins, cannot. If you wanted to use a dialysis machine to remove only the toxic waste product urea from blood, what could you use for the dialysis fluid?
   a. A solution that is isotonic and contains only protein
   b. A solution that is isotonic and contains the same concentration of substances as blood, except for having no urea in it
   c. Distilled water
   d. Blood
5. In sickle-cell anemia a protein inside red blood cells does not function normally. Consequently, the red blood cells become sickle-shaped and plug up small blood vessels. It is known that sickle-cell anemia is hereditary and results from changing one nucleotide for a different nucleotide within the gene that is responsible for producing the protein. Explain how this change results in an abnormally functioning protein.

Answers to Predict Questions

1. p. 48 (a) Cells specialized to synthesize and secrete proteins have abundant rough ER, because this is an important site of protein synthesis. Well-developed Golgi apparatuses exist to package proteins in secretory vesicles, and numerous secretory vesicles are present.

(b) Cells highly specialized to actively transport substances into the cell have a large surface area exposed to the fluid from which substances are actively transported. Numerous mitochondria are present near the membrane across which active transport occurs.

(c) Cells highly specialized to ingest foreign substances have numerous lysosomes in their cytoplasm and evidence of vesicles containing foreign substances.

2. p. 51 Urea is produced continually by liver cells and diffuses from the cells into the blood. If the kidneys stop eliminating urea, it begins to accumulate in the blood and in the liver cells. The urea finally reaches concentrations high enough to be toxic to cells, causing cell damage followed by cell death.

3. p. 54 Glucose transported by facilitated diffusion across the cell membrane moves from a higher to a lower concentration. If glucose molecules are converted quickly to some other molecule as they enter the cell, a large concentration difference is maintained, and thus glucose transport into the cell continues proportional to the magnitude of the concentration difference.

4. p. 58 Changing a single nucleotide within a DNA molecule, also changes the nucleotide sequence of messenger RNA produced from that segment of DNA. The change in mRNA results in a different codon, and a different amino acid is placed in the amino acid chain for which the messenger RNA codes. Because a change in the amino acid sequence of a protein can change its structure, one substitution of a nucleotide in a DNA chain can result in altered protein structure and function.

5. p. 65 Cancer cells generally appear to be undifferentiated. Instead of dividing and then undergoing differentiation, they continue to divide and do not differentiate. One measure of the severity of cancer is related to the degree of differentiation the cancer cells have undergone. Those that are more differentiated divide more slowly and are less dangerous than those that differentiate little.

6. p. 66 Chloride ions do not move in normal amounts out of the cells of people with cystic fibrosis because chloride ion channels are defective. Instead, the chloride ions tend to accumulate inside the cell. Potassium ions tend to move out of muscle and nerve cells down their concentration gradient. The positively charged potassium ions, however, are attracted by the negatively charged chloride ions accumulated inside the cell. This attraction reduces the movement of potassium ions out of the cell and causes more potassium ions to accumulate inside the cell.

Chapter Four

Tissues, Glands, and Membranes

connective tissue
One of the four major tissue types; consists of cells usually surrounded by large amounts of extracellular material; holds other tissues together and supports the body.

edema
(e-dē'mǎ) [Gr. *oidema,* a swelling] Excessive accumulation of fluid in the tissues, usually causing swelling.

epithelial tissue
(ep-i-thē'lē-ǎl) One of the four major tissue types; consists of cells with a basement membrane (exceptions are lymph capillaries and liver sinusoids), little extracellular material, and no blood vessels; covers the surfaces of the body and forms glands.

extracellular matrix
(eks-trǎ-sel'ū-lǎr mā'triks) Nonliving chemical substances located between cells; often consisting of protein fibers, ground substance, and fluid.

gland
A single cell or a multicellular structure that secretes substances into the blood, into a cavity, or onto a surface.

inflammatory response
(in-flam'ǎ-tōr-ē) Complex sequence of events involving chemicals and immune system cells that results in the isolation and destruction of foreign substances, such as bacteria and dead tissues; symptoms include redness, heat, swelling, pain, and disturbance of function.

mucous membrane
(mū'kǔs) Thin sheet consisting of epithelium and connective tissue that lines cavities that open to the outside of the body; many contain mucous glands, which secrete mucus.

muscle tissue
One of the four major tissue types; consists of cells with the ability to contract; includes skeletal, cardiac, and smooth muscle.

nervous tissue
(ner'vǔs) One of the four major tissue types; consists of neurons, which have the ability to conduct action potentials, and neuroglia, which are support cells.

serous membrane
(sēr'ǔs) Thin sheet consisting of epithelium and connective tissue that lines cavities not opening to the outside of the body; does not contain glands but does secrete serous fluid.

tissue
(tish'ū) [L. *texo,* to weave] A collection of cells with similar structure and function, and the substances between the cells.

tissue repair
Substitution of viable cells for damaged or dead cells by regeneration or replacement.

Objectives

After reading this chapter, you should be able to:

1. List the characteristics of epithelial tissue.

2. Classify and give an example of the major types of epithelium.

3. Explain the function in epithelium of the following: cell layers, cell shapes, free cell surfaces, and connections between cells.

4. Define and categorize glands.

5. Describe the basis for classifying connective tissue, and give examples of each major type.

6. Name the three types of muscle, and list their functions.

7. State the functions of nervous tissue and describe a neuron.

8. List the structural and functional characteristics of mucous and serous membranes.

9. Describe the process of inflammation, and explain why inflammation protects the body.

10. Describe the major events involved in tissue repair.

A **tissue** (tish'ū) is a group of cells with similar structure and function, as well as similar extracellular substances located between the cells. The microscopic study of tissue structure is called **histology** (his-tol'ō-jē). Knowledge of tissue structure and function is important in understanding how individual cells are organized to form tissues and how tissues are organized to form organs, organ systems, and the complete organism. There is a relationship between the structure of each tissue type and its function and between the tissues in an organ and the organ's function.

Development, growth, aging, trauma, and diseases result from changes in tissues. For example, enlargement of skeletal muscles occurs because skeletal muscle cells increase in size in response to exercise. Reduced elasticity of blood vessel walls in aging people results from slowly developing changes in connective tissue, and tissue abnormalities, including cancer, result from changes in tissues that can be identified by microscopic examination.

The four basic tissue types are epithelial, connective, muscle, and nervous tissue. This chapter emphasizes epithelial and connective tissues. Muscle and nervous tissues are considered in more detail in later chapters.

Epithelial Tissue

Epithelium (ep-i-thē'lē-ŭm; pl.: epithelia, ep-i-thē'lē-ă), or **epithelial** (ep-i-thē'lē-ăl) **tissue**, is found throughout the body where it covers internal and external surfaces. It also forms most glands. Surfaces of the body include the skin on the outside of the body and the lining of cavities such as the digestive tract, respiratory passages, and blood vessels. Epithelium consists almost entirely of cells with very little extracellular matrix between them. Although there are some exceptions, most epithelia have a **free surface**, composed of a layer of epithelial cells with one surface which is not in contact with other cells, and a **basement membrane**, which attaches the epithelial cells to underlying tissues (figure 4.1). The basement membrane is made up of carbohydrates and proteins that are secreted by epithelial cells and cells of the underlying tissue. Blood vessels do not extend from the underlying tissues into epithelium, so gases and nutrients that reach the epithelium must diffuse across the basement membrane from the underlying tissues, where blood vessels are abundant. Waste products produced by the epithelial cells diffuse across the basement membrane to blood vessels.

Functions of Epithelia

The major functions of epithelia include:

1. *Protecting underlying structures.* Examples include the skin and the epithelium of the oral cavity, which protect the underlying structures from abrasion.
2. *Acting as barriers.* Epithelium prevents the movement of many substances through the epithelial layer. For example, the skin acts as a barrier to water and prevents water loss from the body. The skin is also a barrier that prevents the entry of many toxic molecules and microorganisms into the body.
3. *Permitting the passage of substances.* Epithelium allows the movement of many substances through the epithelial layer. For example, oxygen and carbon dioxide are exchanged between the air and blood by diffusion through the epithelium in the lungs.
4. *Secreting substances.* Examples include the sweat glands, mucous glands, and the enzyme-secreting portion of the pancreas.

Figure 4.1 Characteristics of Epithelium

Epithelium lining a blood vessel illustrates the following epithelial characteristics: little extracellular material between cells, a free surface, a basement membrane attaching epithelial cells to underlying tissues. Oxygen and other nutrients diffuse to epithelial cells through the basement membrane because no capillaries penetrate the basement membrane to provide a blood supply to epithelial cells from the underlying tissues.

Table 4.1   Classification of Epithelia

Number of Layers	Cell Shape
Simple (one layer)	Squamous Cuboidal Columnar
Pseudostratified (a modified form of simple epithelium)	Columnar

Stratified (more than one layer)	Squamous
	    Moist
	    Keratinized

Transitional (a type of stratified epithelium)	Roughly cuboidal or many-surfaced

5. *Absorbing substances.* The cell membranes of certain epithelial tissues contain carrier molecules (see chapter 3) that regulate the absorption of materials. For example, the epithelial cells of the intestine absorb digested food molecules, vitamins, and ions.

Classification of Epithelia

Epithelia are classified according to the number of cell layers and the shape of the cells (table 4.1). **Simple epithelium** consists of a single layer of cells. **Stratified epithelium** consists of more than one layer of epithelial cells, with some cells sitting on top of other cells. Categories of epithelium based on cell shape are **squamous** (skwā′mŭs; flat), **cuboidal** (cubelike), and **columnar** (tall and thin). In most cases, each epithelium is given two names. Examples include simple squamous, simple columnar, and stratified squamous epithelia. When epithelium is stratified, it is named according to the shape of the cells at the free surface.

Simple squamous epithelium is a single layer of thin, flat cells (figure 4.2*a*). Because substances easily pass through this thin layer of tissue, it is often found where diffusion or filtration take place. For example, the respiratory passages end as small sacs called **alveoli** (al-vē′ō-lī). The alveoli consist of simple squamous epithelium that allows oxygen from the air to diffuse into the body and carbon dioxide to diffuse out of the body into the air. Simple squamous epithelial tissue in the filtration membranes of the kidneys forms thin barriers through which small molecules, but not large ones, can pass. Small molecules and water from blood are filtered through these barriers as a major step in urine formation. Large molecules, such as proteins and blood cells, remain in the blood vessels of the kidneys.

Simple squamous epithelium also functions to prevent abrasion between organs in the thoracic and abdominopelvic cavities. The outer surfaces of the organs are covered with simple squamous epithelium that secretes a slippery fluid. The fluid lubricates the surfaces between the organs, preventing damage from friction when the organs rub against one another.

Simple cuboidal epithelium is a single layer of cubelike cells (figure 4.2*b*). These cells have a greater volume than simple squamous epithelial cells and contain more cell organelles. The organelles of simple cuboidal cells that actively transport molecules into and out of the cells include mitochondria, which produce ATP, and organelles needed to synthesize the transport proteins. Transport of molecules across a layer of simple cuboidal epithelium can also be regulated by the amount of ATP produced or by the type of transport molecules synthesized. The many kidney tubules, all having large portions of their wall composed of simple cuboidal epithelium,

Free surface
Nucleus
Basement membrane
Simple squamous epithelial cell

Capillary epithelial cells

Nucleus

(a) Simple Squamous Epithelium

Location
Lining of blood vessels, heart, lymphatic vessels, and serous membranes; alveoli (air sacs) of lungs; and kidney tubules (Bowman's capsule and thin segment of the loop of Henle).

Structure
Single layer of thin, flat cells.

Function
Diffusion, filtration, and protection against friction (secretes serous fluid).

Figure 4.2   Types of Epithelium   *(continued on next page)*

Free surface

Nucleus

Basement membrane

Simple cuboidal epithelial cell

(b) Simple Cuboidal Epithelium

Kidney

Location

Kidney tubules, glands and their ducts, choroid plexus of the brain, lining of terminal bronchioles of the lungs, and surface of the ovaries.

Structure

Single layer of cube-shaped cells; some cells have microvilli (kidney tubules) or cilia (terminal bronchioles of the lungs).

Function

Active transport and facilitated diffusion result in secretion and absorption by cells of the kidney tubules; secretion by cells of glands and choroid plexus; movement of mucus-containing particles out of the terminal bronchioles by ciliated cells.

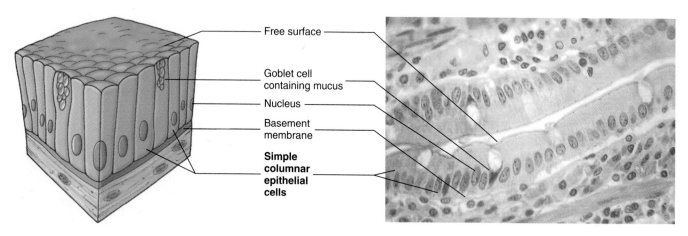

Free surface

Goblet cell containing mucus

Nucleus

Basement membrane

Simple columnar epithelial cells

(c) Simple Columnar Epithelium

Lining of stomach and intestines

Location

Lining of stomach, intestines, glands, ducts, bronchioles of lungs, auditory tubes, uterus, and uterine tubes.

Structure

Single layer of tall, narrow cells; some have microvilli (stomach, intestine, and glands) or cilia (bronchioles of lungs, auditory tubes, uterus, and uterine tubes).

Function

Secretion by cells of the stomach, intestines, and glands; absorption by cells of the intestine; movement of cilia clears mucus-containing particles from the lungs and is partially responsible for the movement of the oocyte through the uterine tube.

Figure 4.2 Types of Epithelium *(continued)*

Cilia
Free surface
Goblet cell
containing mucus
Nucleus
Basement
membrane
**Pseudostratified
columnar
epithelial cells**

(d) Pseudostratified Columnar Epithelium

Location
Lining of nasal cavity, nasal sinuses, auditory tubes, pharynx, trachea, and bronchi of lungs.

Structure
Single layer of cells; some cells are tall and thin and reach the free surface, and others do not; the nuclei of these cells are at different levels and appear stratified; the cells are almost always ciliated and are associated with goblet cells that produce mucus onto the free surface.

Function
Synthesize and secrete mucus onto the free surface and moves mucus (or fluid) that contains foreign particles over the surface of the free surface and from passages.

Trachea
Bronchus

Free surface
**Moist stratified
squamous
epithelial cells**
Nucleus
Basement
membrane

(e) Stratified Squamous Epithelium

Location
Skin; cornea; and lining of mouth, throat, esophagus, anus, and vagina.

Structure
Many layers of cells in which the basal layer is cuboidal or columnar and becomes flattened at the free surface.

Function
Protection against abrasion, barrier against infection, and prevents loss of water from the body.

Skin
Cornea
Mouth
Esophagus

Figure 4.2 Types of Epithelium *(continued on next page)*

(f) Transitional Epithelium

Location
Lining of urinary bladder, ureters, and superior urethra.

Structure
Stratified cells that appear cuboidal when the organ or tube is not stretched and squamous when the organ or tube is stretched by fluid.

Function
Accommodates fluctuations in the volume of fluid in an organ or tube; protection against the caustic effects of urine.

Figure 4.2 Types of Epithelium *(continued)*

excrete waste products into the tubules and reabsorb useful materials from the tubules as urine is formed.

Simple columnar epithelium is a single layer of tall, thin cells (figure 4.2*c*). These large cells contain organelles that enable them to perform complex functions. For example, the simple columnar epithelium of the small intestine produces and releases digestive enzymes that complete the process of digesting food. The columnar cells then absorb the digested foods by active transport, facilitated diffusion, or simple diffusion.

Pseudostratified columnar epithelium is a special type of simple epithelium (figure 4.2*d*). The prefix pseudo- means false, so this type of epithelium appears to be stratified but is not. It consists of one layer of cells, with all the cells attached to the basement membrane. There is an appearance of two or more layers of cells because some of the cells are tall and reach the free surface, whereas others are short and do not reach the free surface. Pseudostratified columnar epithelium is found lining some of the respiratory passages, such as the nasal cavity, trachea, and bronchi. Pseudostratified columnar epithelium secretes mucus, which covers its surface, and cilia located on the free surface move the mucus and the debris that accumulates in it over the surfaces of the respiratory passages and toward the exterior of the body.

Stratified squamous epithelium forms a thick epithelium because it consists of many layers of cells (figure 4.2*e*). The deepest cells are cuboidal or columnar and are capable of dividing and producing new cells. As these newly formed cells are pushed to the surface, they become flat and thin. If cells at the surface are damaged or rubbed away, they are replaced by cells formed in the deeper layers. One type of stratified squamous epithelium forms the outer layer of the skin and is called kera-

tinized stratified squamous epithelium (see chapter 5). The outer layers consist of dead stratified epithelial cells tightly bound to one another. They provide protection against abrasion, form a barrier that prevents microorganisms and toxic chemicals from entering the body, and prevent the loss of water from the body. In contrast, stratified squamous epithelium of the mouth is composed of living cells with a moist surface. It also provides protection against abrasion and acts as a mechanical barrier, preventing the entry of microorganisms into the body. Water, however, can move across it more readily than across the skin.

Transitional epithelium is a special type of stratified epithelium that can be greatly stretched (figure 4.2*f*). In the unstretched state, transitional epithelium consists of five or more layers of cuboidal or columnar cells that often are dome-shaped at the free surface. As transitional epithelium is stretched, the cells change shape to a low cuboidal or squamous shape, and the number of cell layers decreases. Transitional epithelium is found lining cavities that can expand greatly, such as the urinary bladder. It also protects underlying structures from the caustic effects of urine.

Structural and Functional Relationships

Cell Layers and Cell Shapes

The number of cell layers and the shape of the cells in a specific type of epithelium reflect the function the epithelium performs. Two important functions are controlling the passage of materials through the epithelium and protecting the underlying

tissues. Simple epithelium, with its single layer of cells, is found in organs in which the principal function is the movement of materials. Examples include diffusion of gases across the wall of the alveoli of the lungs, filtration of fluid across the filtration membranes in the kidneys, secretion in glands, and nutrient absorption in the intestines. The movement of materials through a stratified epithelium is hindered by its many layers. Stratified epithelium is well adapted for its protective function. As the outer cell layers are damaged, they are replaced by cells from deeper layers. Stratified squamous epithelium is found in areas of the body where abrasion can occur, such as in the skin, anal canal, and vagina.

Differences in function are also reflected in cell shape. Cells are normally flat and thin when the function is diffusion, such as in the alveoli of the lungs, or filtration, such as in kidney tubules. Cells with the major function of secretion or absorption are usually cuboidal or columnar. They are larger because they contain more organelles, which are responsible for the function of the cell. The stomach, for example, is lined with simple columnar epithelium. These cells contain many **secretory vesicles** (ves′i-klz) filled with **mucus** (mū′kŭs), which is a clear, viscous material. The large amounts of mucus produced by the simple columnar epithelium protect the stomach lining against the digestive enzymes and acid produced in the stomach. An ulcer, or irritation in the epithelium and underlying tissue, can develop if this protective mechanism fails. Simple cuboidal epithelial cells that secrete or absorb molecules, such as in the kidney tubules, contain many mitochondria, which produce the ATP required for active transport.

1 **P R E D I C T**

What type of epithelium would you expect to find in small blood vessels, the capillaries, which are the site of diffusion of substances between the blood and tissues? What type of epithelium would you expect to find in the ducts of the pancreas, which carry digestive enzymes to the small intestine and which produce a watery secretion? What type of epithelium would you expect to find lining the mouth?

✔ *Answer on page 94*

The shape and number of layers of epithelial cells can change if they are subjected to long-term irritation or to other abnormal conditions. People who smoke cigarettes eventually experience changes in the epithelium of the larger respiratory passages. The delicate pseudostratified columnar epithelium, which performs a cleaning function by moving mucus and debris from the passageways, is replaced by stratified squamous epithelium that is more resistant to irritation, but does not perform a cleaning function. Also, lung cancer most often results from changes in epithelial cells of the lung passageways of smokers. The changes in the structure of the cells are used to identify the cancer.

Free Cell Surfaces

Most epithelia have a free surface, which is not in contact with other cells and faces away from underlying tissues. The characteristics of the free surface reflect the functions it performs.

The free surface can be smooth, or it can have microvilli or cilia. **Smooth surfaces** reduce friction. For example, the lining of blood vessels is simple squamous epithelium with a smooth surface, which reduces friction as blood flows through the vessels. **Microvilli** are cylindrical extensions of the cell membrane that function to increase the cell surface area (see chapter 3). Normally many microvilli cover the free surface of each cell involved in absorption or secretion, such as the cells lining the small intestine. **Cilia** (see chapter 3) propel materials along the surface of cells. The nasal cavity and trachea are lined with pseudostratified columnar ciliated epithelium. Intermixed with the ciliated cells are specialized mucus-producing cells called **goblet cells** (see figure 4.2*d*). Dust and other materials are trapped in the mucus that covers the epithelium, and movement of the cilia propels the mucus with its entrapped particles to the back of the throat, where it is swallowed or coughed up. The constant movement of mucus helps to keep the respiratory passages clean.

Cell Connections

Epithelial cells are connected to one another in several ways (figure 4.3). **Tight junctions** bind adjacent cells together and

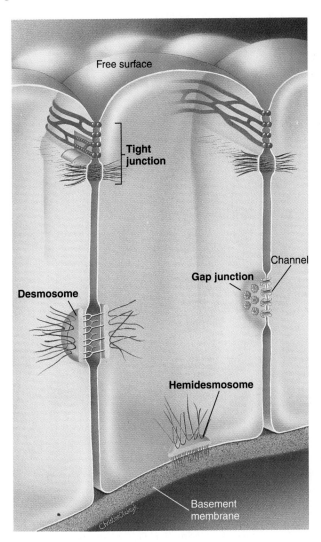

Figure 4.3 Cell Connections

form permeability barriers. Because tight junctions completely surround each cell, they prevent the passage of materials between epithelial cells. Materials that pass through the epithelial layer must pass through the cells, which can regulate what materials cross the epithelial layer. Tight junctions are found in the lining of the intestines and most other simple epithelia. **Desmosomes** (dez′mō-sōmz) are mechanical links that function to bind cells together. Modified desmosomes, called **hemidesmosomes** (hem-ē-dez′mō-sōmz), also anchor cells to the basement membrane. Many desmosomes are found in epithelia subjected to stress, such as the stratified squamous epithelium of the skin. **Gap junctions** are small channels that allow small molecules and ions to pass from one epithelial cell to an adjacent one. Most epithelial cells are connected to one another by gap junctions, and it is believed that molecules or ions moving through the gap junctions act as communication signals to coordinate the activities of the cells.

Glands

A **gland** is a multicellular structure that secretes substances onto a surface, into a cavity, or into the blood. Most glands are composed primarily of epithelium. Sometimes single goblet cells are classified as unicellular glands because they secrete mucus onto epithelial surfaces. Glands with ducts are called **exocrine** (ek′sō-krin) glands (figure 4.4). The exocrine glands can be **simple**, with ducts that have no branches, or **compound**, with ducts that have many branches. The end of a duct can be **tubular**. Some tubular glands are straight and others have coiled tubules. Some tubular glands have ends that are expanded into a saclike structure called an **acinus** (as′i-nŭs, meaning grapelike), or **alveolus** (al-vē′ō-lŭs, meaning small cavity). Secretions from exocrine glands pass through the ducts onto a surface or into an organ. For example, sweat from sweat glands and oil from sebaceous glands flow onto the skin surface.

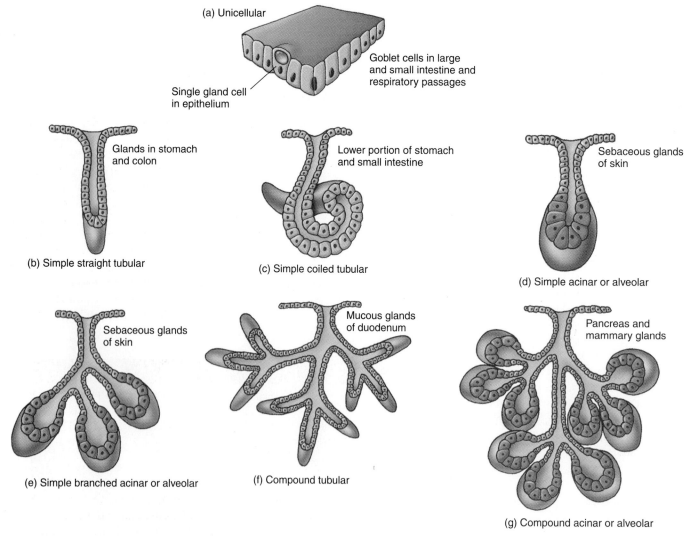

Figure 4.4 Types of Exocrine Glands

Endocrine (en'dō-krin) glands have no ducts and empty their secretions into the blood. These secretions, called **hormones** (hōr'mōnz), are carried by the blood to other parts of the body. Endocrine glands are discussed more fully in chapter 10.

Connective Tissue

Connective tissue structure is usually characterized by large amounts of extracellular materials that separate cells from one another. The extracellular material, or **extracellular matrix** (ma'triks), has three major components: (1) protein fibers, (2) ground substance consisting of nonfibrous protein and other molecules, and (3) fluid.

Three types of protein fibers help to form most connective tissues. **Collagen** (kol'lă-jen) **fibers**, which resemble microscopic ropes, are flexible but resist stretching. **Reticular** (rē-tik'ū-lăr) **fibers** are very fine, short, collagen fibers that branch to form a supporting network. **Elastic fibers** have a structure similar to coiled metal bed springs. After being stretched, elastic fibers have the ability to recoil to their original shape.

Ground substance is the shapeless background against which cells and collagen fibers are seen in the light microscope. Although ground substance appears shapeless, the molecules within the ground substance are highly structured. **Proteoglycans** (prō'tē-ō-glī'kanz) resemble the limbs of pine trees, with proteins forming the branches and polysaccharides forming the pine needles. This structure enables proteoglycans to trap large quantities of water between the polysaccharides.

Connective tissue cells are named according to their functions. **Blast** cells produce the matrix, **cyte** cells maintain it, and **clast** cells break it down for remodeling. For example, **osteoblasts** (os'tē-ō-blasts; *osteo* means bone) form bone, **osteocytes** (os'tē-ō-sītz) maintain bone, and **osteoclasts** (os'tē-ō-klasts) break down bone. Cells associated with the immune system are also found in connective tissue. **Macrophages** (mak'rō-fāg-ez) are large cells that are capable of moving about and ingesting foreign substances, including microorganisms that are found in the connective tissue. **Mast cells** are nonmotile cells that release chemicals that promote inflammation.

Functions of Connective Tissue

Connective tissues perform the following major categories of functions:

1. *Enclosing and separating.* Sheets of connective tissues form capsules around organs such as the liver and kidneys. Connective tissue also forms layers that separate tissues and organs. For example, connective tissues separate muscles, arteries, veins, and nerves from one another.
2. *Connecting tissues to one another.* For example, tendons are strong cables, or bands, of connective tissue that attach muscles to bone, and ligaments are connective tissue bands that hold bones together.

3. *Supporting and moving.* Bones of the skeletal system provide rigid support for the body, and the semirigid cartilage supports structures such as the nose, ears, and surfaces of joints. Joints between bones allow one part of the body to move relative to other parts.
4. *Storing.* Adipose tissue (fat) stores high-energy molecules, and bones store minerals such as calcium and phosphate.
5. *Cushioning and insulating.* Adipose tissue (fat) cushions and protects the tissues it surrounds and provides an insulating layer beneath the skin that helps conserve heat.
6. *Transporting.* Blood transports substances throughout the body, such as gases, nutrients, enzymes, hormones, and cells of the immune system.
7. *Protecting.* Cells of the immune system and blood provide protection against toxins and tissue injury, as well as from microorganisms. Bones protect underlying structures from injury.

Classification

The nature of the extracellular matrix determines the functional characteristics of the connective tissue and is used as a means of classifying connective tissues (table 4.2).

Matrix with Protein Fibers as the Primary Feature

Dense collagenous tissue has an extracellular matrix consisting mostly of collagen fibers (figure 4.5*a*). The few cells found in dense collagenous connective tissue are **fibroblasts** (fī'brō-blasts), which are responsible for the production of the collagen fibers. Structures made up of dense collagenous connective tissue include tendons, which attach muscles to bone; many ligaments, which attach bones to other bones; and much of the dermis of the skin, which is a layer of connective tissue under a layer of stratified squamous epithelium. **Dense elastic connective tissue** has abundant elastic fibers among collagen fibers. The elastic fibers allow the tissue to stretch and recoil. Examples include the dense elastic connective tissue of the vocal cords (figure 4.5*b*), the walls of large arteries, and elastic ligaments.

---

2   P R E D I C T

In tendons, collagen fibers are oriented parallel to the length of the tendon. In the skin, collagen fibers are oriented in many directions. What are the functional advantages of the fiber arrangements in tendons and in the skin?

✔ *Answer on page 94*

In contrast to dense connective tissue, the protein fibers in **loose**, or **areolar** (ă-rē'ō-lăr), **connective tissue** are widely separated from one another (figure 4.5*c*). Loose connective tissue is the "loose packing" material of the body, which fills

Table 4.2 Classification of Connective Tissues

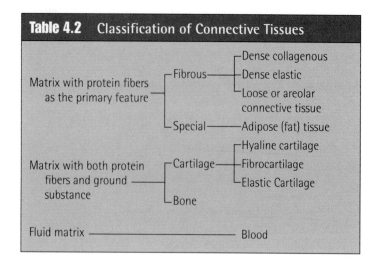

Matrix with protein fibers as the primary feature	Fibrous	Dense collagenous
		Dense elastic
		Loose or areolar connective tissue
	Special	Adipose (fat) tissue
Matrix with both protein fibers and ground substance	Cartilage	Hyaline cartilage
		Fibrocartilage
		Elastic Cartilage
	Bone	
Fluid matrix		Blood

Matrix with Both Protein Fibers and Ground Substance

Cartilage (kar′ti-lij) is composed of cartilage cells, or **chondrocytes** (kon′drō-sītz), located in spaces called **lacunae** (lă-koo′nē) within an extensive matrix (figure 4.5e). Collagen in the matrix gives cartilage flexibility and strength. Cartilage is resilient because the proteoglycans of the matrix trap water, which makes the cartilage relatively rigid and enables it to spring back after being compressed. Cartilage provides support, but, if it is bent or slightly compressed, it resumes its original shape. Cartilage heals slowly after an injury because blood vessels do not penetrate it. Thus cells and nutrients necessary for tissue repair do not easily reach the damaged area.

Hyaline (hī′ă-lin; meaning clear or glassy) **cartilage** (see figure 4.5e) is the most abundant type of cartilage and has many functions. It covers the ends of bones where bones come together to form joints. In joints, hyaline cartilage forms smooth, resilient surfaces that can withstand repeated compression. Hyaline cartilage also forms the costal cartilages, which attach the ribs to the sternum (breastbone). **Fibrocartilage** (figure 4.5f) has more collagen than does hyaline cartilage, and bundles of collagen fibers can be seen in the matrix. In addition to withstanding compression, it is able to resist pulling or tearing forces. It is found in the disks between vertebrae (bones of the back), for example. In addition to collagen and proteoglycans, **elastic cartilage** (figure 4.5g)

the spaces between organs and holds them in place. It is found around glands, muscles, and nerves, and it attaches the skin to underlying tissues.

Although **adipose** (ad′i-pōs; fat) **tissue** has a matrix with protein fibers, it is not a typical connective tissue. It has very little matrix, and the individual cells are large and closely packed together (figure 4.5d). Adipose cells are filled with lipids and function to store energy. Adipose tissue also pads and protects parts of the body and acts as a thermal insulator.

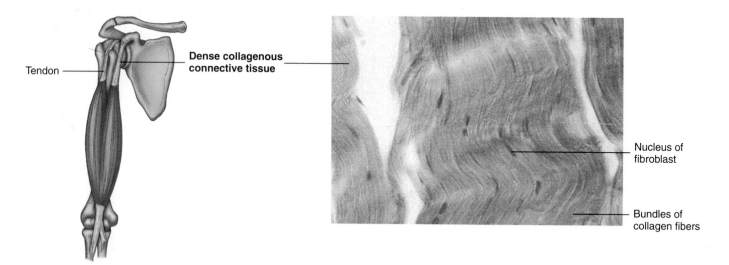

(a) Dense Collagenous Connective Tissue

Location
Tendons (attach muscle to bone), nonelastic ligaments (attach bone to bone), most of the dermis of the skin, and organ capsules.

Structure
Matrix consists almost entirely of collagen fibers produced by fibroblasts; the fibers can all be oriented in the same direction (tendons and ligaments) or in many different directions (dermis and capsules).

Function
Able to withstand great pulling forces in the direction of fiber orientation.

Figure 4.5 Connective Tissues

Vocal folds
(true vocal cords)

Dense elastic connective tissue

Vestibular fold
(false vocal cord)

Base of tongue

Nucleus of fibroblast

Elastin fibers

(b) Dense Elastic Connective Tissue

Location
Elastic ligaments between vertebrae and along the dorsal aspect of the neck, vocal folds, and in the walls of elastic arteries.

Structure
Matrix is composed of collagen and elastic fibers oriented either in the same direction (elastic ligaments and vocal folds) or in many different directions (walls of elastic arteries).

Function
Able to stretch and recoil like a rubber band with strengh in the direction of fiber orientation.

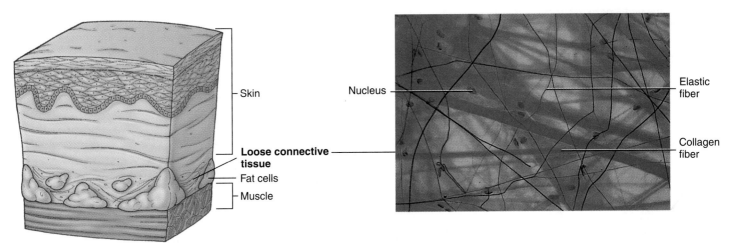

Skin

Loose connective tissue

Fat cells

Muscle

Nucleus

Elastic fiber

Collagen fiber

(c) Loose, or Areolar, Tissue

Location
Widely distributed throughout the body; it is the substance on which most epithelial tissue rests; it is the packing between glands, muscles, and nerves; it attaches the skin (dermis) to underlying tissues, and forms the superficial layer of the dermis.

Structure
Cells (fibroblasts, macrophages, and lymphocytes) within a fine network of mostly collagen fibers; the cells and fibers are seperated from one another by fluid-filled spaces; often associated with other connective tissues such as adipose tissue.

Function
Loose packing, support, and nourishment for the structures with which it is associated.

Figure 4.5   Connective Tissues *(continued on next page)*

(d) Adipose Tissue

Location
Under skin, around organs such as the heart and kidneys, in the breast, and in cavities within bones.

Structure
Little extracellular material between adipose cells; the cells are so full of lipids that the cytoplasm is pushed to the periphery of the cell.

Function
Energy storage, packing material that provides protection, and heat insulator.

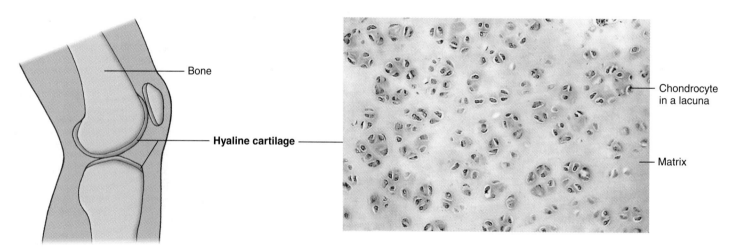

(e) Hyaline Cartilage

Location
Hyaline cartilage is found in the costal cartilages of ribs, the cartilage rings of the respiratory tract, and in the nasal cartilages; it covers the ends of bones and it is found in the growth (epiphyseal) plates of bones and the embryonic skeleton.

Structure
Solid matrix with small and evenly dispersed collagen fibers throughout the ground substance making the matrix appear transparent; chondrocytes are found within lacunae.

Function
Hyaline cartilage provides support and with some flexibility and forms smooth surfaces in joints; it is also a site of bone growth and forms most of the embryonic skeleton.

Figure 4.5 Connective Tissues *(continued)*

Vertebra

Fibrocartilage

Intervertebral disk

Chondrocyte in lacuna

Collagen fibers in matrix

(f) Fibrocartilage

Location
Fibrocartilage is found in intervertebral disks (the disks between vertebrae), the symphysis pubis (joint between the pubic bones), and the articulating cartilage of some joints (e.g., knee and temporomandibular [jaw] joints).

Structure
Similar to hyaline cartilage. The collagen fibers are more numerous than in hyaline and elastic cartilage and they are arranged in thick bundles.

Function
Fibrocartilage is somewhat flexible and capable of withstanding considerable pressure. Connects structures subjected to great pressure.

External ear

Elastic cartilage

Elastic fibers in matrix

Chondrocyte in lacuna

(g) Elastic Cartilage

Location
Elastic cartilage is found in the external ear, epiglottis, and auditory tube.

Structure
The structure of elastic cartilage is similar to hyaline cartilage, but the matrix also contains abundant elastic fibers.

Function
Elastic cartilage provides rigidity with even more flexibility than hyaline cartilage because elastin fibers return to their original shape after being stretched.

Figure 4.5   Connective Tissues *(continued on next page)*

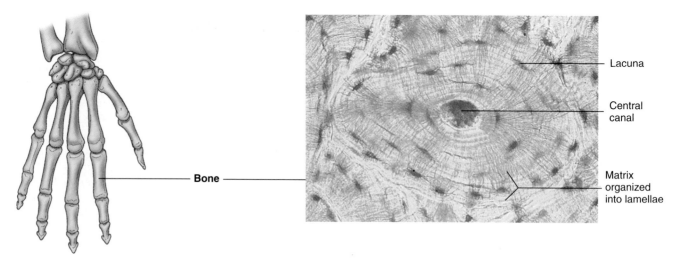

(h) Bone

Location
All the bones of the body.

Structure
Hard, mineralized matrix with osteocytes located within lacunae; the matrix is organized into layers called lamellae.

Function
Provides great strength and support and protects internal organs such as the brain.

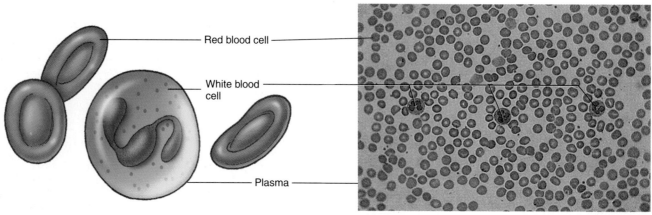

(i) Blood

Location
Within the blood vessels and heart.

Structure
Blood cells within a fluid matrix called plasma.

Function
Transports oxygen, carbon dioxide, hormones, nutrients, waste products, and other substances; protects the body from infection and is involved in temperature regulation.

Figure 4.5 Connective Tissues *(continued)*

contains elastic fibers that appear as coiled fibers among bundles of collagen fibers. Elastic cartilage is able to recoil to its original shape when bent. The external ear contains elastic cartilage.

3   P R E D I C T

A man was suspected of a gruesome murder in which an object was used to repeatedly stab and cut the victim. The police found a towel with blood and some tissue on it in the man's apartment. He claimed he scraped his hand in a fall on his stairs. After examining the towel, a piece of tissue with rigid but clear matrix and lacunae was identified. Explain why the man's story is very unlikely.

✔ *Answer on page 94*

Bone is a hard connective tissue that consists of living cells and a mineralized matrix (figure 4.5*b*). Bone cells, or **osteocytes**, are located within spaces in the matrix called lacunae. The strength and rigidity of the mineralized matrix enables bones to support and protect other tissues and organs of the body. The two types of bone, **compact** and **cancellous** (kan′sĕ-lŭs), are considered in greater detail in chapter 6.

Fluid Matrix

Blood is unique because the matrix is liquid, enabling blood cells to move through blood vessels (figure 4.5*i*). Some blood cells even leave the blood and wander into other tissues. The liquid matrix enables blood to flow rapidly through the body, carrying food, oxygen, waste products, and other materials. Blood is discussed more fully in chapter 11.

Muscle Tissue

The main characteristic of **muscle tissue** is its ability to contract, or shorten, making movement possible. Muscle contraction results from contractile proteins located within the muscle cells (see chapter 7). The length of muscle cells is greater than the diameter. Because they often resemble tiny threads, muscle cells are sometimes called **muscle fibers**.

The three types of muscle tissue are skeletal, cardiac, and smooth muscle. **Skeletal muscle** is what normally is thought of as "muscle" (figure 4.6*a*). It is the meat of animals and constitutes about 40% of a person's body weight. As the name implies, skeletal muscle attaches to the skeleton and enables body movement. It is normally under voluntary (conscious) control. Skeletal muscle cells tend to be long, cylindrical cells with several nuclei per cell. The nuclei of these cells are located near the periphery of the cell. Some skeletal muscle cells extend the length of an entire muscle. Skeletal muscle cells are **striated** (strī′āt-ed), or banded, because of the arrangement of contractile proteins within the cells (see chapter 7).

Cardiac muscle is the muscle of the heart and is responsible for pumping blood (figure 4.6*b*). It is under involuntary (unconscious) control. Cardiac muscle cells are cylindrical in shape but much shorter in length than skeletal muscle cells. Cardiac muscle cells are striated and usually have one nucleus per cell. They often are branched and connected to one another by **intercalated** (in-ter′kă-lā-ted) **disks**. The intercalated disks, which contain specialized gap junctions, are important in coordinating the contractions of the cardiac muscle cells (see chapter 12).

Smooth muscle forms the walls of hollow organs (except the heart) and also is found in the skin and the eyes (figure

Nucleus (near periphery of cell)

Skeletal muscle cell

Striations

Muscle

(a) Skeletal Muscle

Location
Attaches to bone.

Structure
Skeletal muscle cells appear striated. Cells are large, long, and cylindrical, with many nuclei located at the periphery.

Function
Movement of the body; under voluntary control.

Figure 4.6   Muscle Tissue *(continued on next page)*

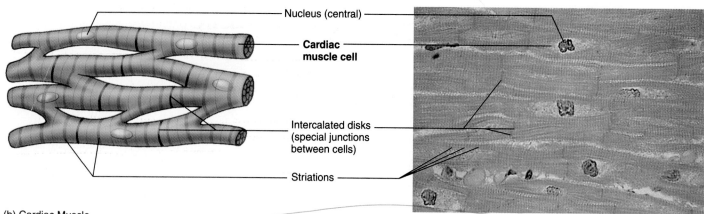

Nucleus (central)

Cardiac muscle cell

Intercalated disks (special junctions between cells)

Striations

(b) Cardiac Muscle

Location
Cardiac muscle is in the heart.

Structure
Cardiac muscle cells are cylindrical and striated and have a single, centrally located, nucleus. They are branched and connected to one another by intercalated disks.

Function
Pumps the blood and is under involuntary control.

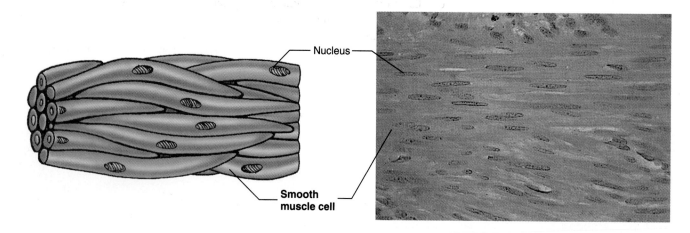

Nucleus

Smooth muscle cell

(c) Smooth Muscle

Location
Smooth muscle is in hollow organs such as the stomach and intestine.

Structure
Smooth muscle cells are tapered at each end, are not striated, and have a single nucleus.

Function
Regulates the size of organs, forces fluid through tubes, controls the amount of light entering the eye, and produces "goose flesh" in the skin and is under involuntary control.

Wall of stomach
Wall of colon

Wall of small intestine

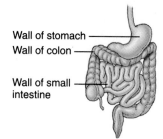

Figure 4.6 Muscle Tissue *(continued)*

4.6*c*). It is responsible for a number of functions, such as movement of food through the digestive tract and emptying of the urinary bladder. Smooth muscle is controlled involuntarily. Smooth muscle cells are tapered at each end, have a single nucleus, and are not striated.

---

4   **P R E D I C T**

Make a table that summarizes the characteristics of the three major muscle types. The muscle types should form a column at the left side of the table and the characteristics of muscle should form a row at the top of the table.

✔ *Answer on page 94*

Nervous Tissue

Nervous tissue forms the brain, spinal cord, and nerves. It is responsible for coordinating and controlling many bodily activities. For example, the conscious control of skeletal muscles and the unconscious regulation of cardiac muscle are accomplished by nervous tissue. Awareness of ourselves and the external environment, emotions, reasoning skills, and memory are other functions performed by nervous tissue. Many of these functions depend on the ability of nervous tissue cells to communicate with one another and with the cells of other tissues by electrical signals called **action potentials**.

Nervous tissue consists of neurons and support cells. The **neuron** (noor´on), or **nerve cell**, is responsible for the conduction of action potentials. It is composed of three parts (figure 4.7). The **cell body** contains the nucleus and is the site of general cell functions. **Dendrites** (den´drītz) and axons (ak´sonz) are nerve cell processes (extensions). Dendrites usually receive action potentials and conduct them toward the cell body, whereas the axon (only one per neuron) usually conducts action potentials away from the cell body. **Neuroglia** (noo-rog´lē-ă) are the support cells of the nervous system, and they function to nourish, protect, and insulate the neurons. Nervous tissue is considered in greater detail in chapter 8.

Membranes

A **membrane** is a thin sheet or layer of tissue that covers a structure or lines a cavity. Most membranes consist of epithelium and the connective tissue on which the epithelium rests. The two major categories of membranes are mucous membranes and serous membranes.

Mucous Membranes

Mucous (mū´kŭs) **membranes** consist of various kinds of epithelium resting on a thick layer of loose connective tissue. They line cavities that open to the outside of the body, such as the digestive, respiratory, excretory, and reproductive tracts. Many, but not all, mucous membranes have mucous glands, which secrete mucus. The functions of mucous membranes

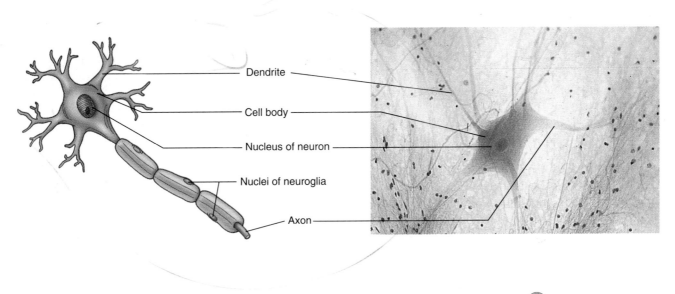

Dendrite

Cell body

Nucleus of neuron

Nuclei of neuroglia

Axon

Brain

Spinal cord

Spinal nerves

Location
Neurons are located in the brain, spinal cord, and in ganglia.

Structure
The neuron consists of dendrites, a cell body, and a long axon. Neuroglia, or support cells, surround the neurons.

Function
Neurons transmit information in the form of electrical charges that occur across the cell membrane called action potentials. Neuroglia support, protect, and form specialized sheaths around axons.

Figure 4.7   Nervous Tissue

vary, depending on their location, and include protection, absorption, and secretion. For example, the stratified squamous epithelium of the oral cavity (mouth) performs a protective function, whereas the simple columnar epithelium of the intestine absorbs nutrients and secretes digestive enzymes and mucus. Inflammation of the mucous membrane of the nasal passages caused by the common cold or allergies is called **rhinitis** (rī-nī′tis; *rhin-* refers to the nose).

Serous Membranes

Serous (sēr′ŭs) membranes consist of simple squamous epithelium resting on a delicate layer of loose connective tissue. Serous membranes line the trunk cavities and cover the organs located within these cavities (see figure 1.13). The serous membranes secrete serous fluid, which covers the surface of the membranes. The smooth surface of the epithelial cells of the serous membranes, together with the lubricating qualities of the serous fluid, combine to prevent damage from abrasion when organs in the thoracic or abdominopelvic cavities rub against one another. The serous membranes are named according to their location: the **pleural** (ploor′ăl) **membranes** are associated with the lungs, the **pericardial** (per-i-kar′dē-ăl) **membranes** are associated with the heart, and the **peritoneal** (per′i-tō-nē′ăl) **membranes** are located in the abdominopelvic cavity. When the suffix "-itis" is added to the name of a structure, it means that the structure is inflamed. **Pericarditis** (per′i-kar-dī′tis) and **peritonitis** (per′i-tō-nī′tis) are inflammations of the pericardial membranes and peritoneal membranes, respectively. **Pleurisy** (ploor′i-sē) is inflammation of the pleural membranes (see below for a description of inflammation).

Other Membranes

In addition to mucous and serous membranes, there are several other membranes in the body. The **skin**, or **cutaneous** (kū-tā′nē-ŭs; meaning skin) **membrane**, is stratified squamous epithelium and dense connective tissue (see chapter 5). Other membranes are made up of only connective tissue. **Synovial** (si-nō′vē-ăl) **membranes** line the inside of joint cavities (the space where bones come together within a movable joint), and the **periosteum** (per-ē-os′tē-ŭm) surrounds bone. These connective tissue membranes are discussed in chapter 6.

Inflammation

The **inflammatory response**, or **inflammation**, occurs when tissues are damaged (figure 4.8). For example, viruses infect epithelial cells of the upper respiratory tract to produce inflammation and the symptoms of the common cold. Also, inflammation results from the immediate and painful events that follow trauma such as closing your finger in a car door or cutting yourself with a knife. Inflammation mobilizes the body's defenses and isolates and destroys microorganisms, foreign materials, and damaged cells so that tissue repair can proceed. Inflammation produces five major symptoms: redness, heat, swelling, pain, and disturbance of function. Although unpleasant, the processes producing the symptoms are usually beneficial.

Following an injury, chemical substances called **mediators of inflammation** are released or activated in the injured tissues and adjacent blood vessels. The mediators include **histamine** (his′tă-mēn), **kinins** (kī′ninz), **prostaglandins** (pros-tă-glan′dinz), **leukotrienes** (lū-kō-trī′ēnz), and others. Some mediators cause dilation of blood vessels, which produces the symptoms of redness and heat, similar to what occurs when a person blushes. Dilation of blood vessels is beneficial because it increases the speed with which blood cells and other substances important for fighting infections and repairing the injury are brought to the injury site.

Mediators of inflammation also increase the permeability of blood vessels, allowing materials and blood cells to move out of the vessels and into the tissue, where they can deal directly with the injury. **Edema** (e-dē′mă), or swelling, of the tissues results when water, proteins, and other substances from the blood move into the tissues. One of the proteins, fibrin, forms a fibrous network that "walls off" the site of injury from the rest of the body. This mechanism can help prevent the spread of infectious agents. One type of blood cell that enters the tissues is the **neutrophil** (noo′trō-fil), a phagocytic white blood cell that fights infections by ingesting bacteria. It also ingests tissue debris, clearing the area for tissue repair. Many neutrophils are killed in this process; the mixture of dead neutrophils, other cells, and fluid that can accumulate is called **pus**.

Pain associated with inflammation is produced in several ways. Nerve cell endings are stimulated by direct damage and by some mediators of inflammation to produce pain sensations. In addition, the increased pressure in the tissue caused by edema and accumulation of pus can cause pain.

Pain, limitation of movement resulting from edema, and tissue destruction all contribute to the disturbance of function. This disturbance of function can be adaptive because it warns the person to protect the injured area from further damage.

> ### Did You Know?
>
> Sometimes the inflammatory response lasts longer or is more intense than is desirable, and drugs are used to suppress the symptoms by inhibiting the synthesis, release, or actions of the mediators of inflammation. For example, the effects of histamine released in people with hay fever are suppressed by antihistamines. Aspirin is an effective antiinflammatory agent that relieves pain by preventing the synthesis of prostaglandins.

Tissue Repair

Tissue repair, the substitution of viable cells for dead cells, can occur by regeneration or replacement. In **regeneration**, the new cells are the same type as those that were destroyed, and normal function is usually restored. In **replacement**, a new type of tissue develops that eventually causes scar production

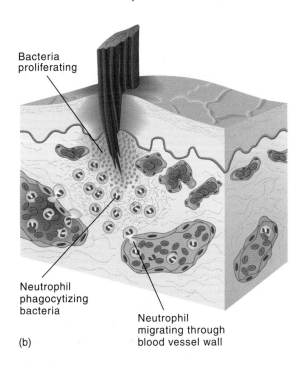

(a)

(b)

Figure 4.8   Inflammation

(*a*) A splinter in the skin causes tissue damage and introduces bacteria. Mediators of inflammation are released from injured tissues and surrounding blood vessels. Mediators of inflammation cause the blood vessels to dilate and become more permeable. This causes the skin to become red, and fluid that leaves the blood vessels causes swelling. (*b*) Neutrophils leave the vessels and arrive at the site of bacterial infection, where they begin to phagocytize the bacteria.

and the loss of some tissue function. The tissues involved and the severity of the wound determine the type of tissue repair that dominates.

Cells can be classified into three groups on the basis of their ability to divide and produce new cells. **Labile cells** continue to divide throughout life. Damage to such labile cells as the cells of the skin and mucous membranes can be repaired completely by regeneration. **Stable cells** do not actively divide after growth ceases, but they do retain the ability to divide after an injury. For example, connective tissue and glands, including the liver and pancreas, are capable of regeneration. **Permanent cells** have little or no ability to divide. Neurons and skeletal muscle cells are examples of permanent cells. If they are killed, they are usually replaced by connective tissue. Permanent cells, however, can usually recover from a limited amount of damage. For example, if the axon of a neuron is damaged, the neuron can grow a new axon. If the cell body is sufficiently damaged, however, the neuron dies and is replaced by connective tissue.

Did You Know?

A small population of "stem cells" in the brain that can divide and form new neurons has been discovered. Although mature neurons do not form additional neurons, it may be possible to develop treatments for some brain injuries that stimulate the "stem cells." A class of chemicals called growth factors has been identified that stimulate stem cells to divide and make injured neurons recover more rapidly. The new neurons may be incorporated with other functional neurons of the central nervous system.

In addition to the type of cells involved, the severity of an injury can influence whether repair is by regeneration or replacement. Generally, the more severe the injury, the greater the likelihood that repair involves replacement.

Repair of the skin is an illustration of tissue repair (figure 4.9). When the edges of a wound are close together, the wound fills with blood, and a clot forms (see chapter 11). The **clot** contains a threadlike protein, fibrin, which binds the edges of the wound together and stops the bleeding. The surface of the clot dries to form a **scab**, which seals the wound and helps to prevent infection.

An inflammatory response is activated to fight infectious agents in the wound and to help the repair process. Dilation of blood vessels brings blood cells and other substances to the injury area, and increased blood vessel permeability allows them to enter the tissue. The area is "walled off" by the fibrin, and neutrophils enter the tissue from the blood.

The epithelium at the edge of the wound undergoes regeneration and migrates under the scab while the inflammatory response proceeds. Eventually the epithelial cells from the edges meet, and the epithelium is restored. After the epithelium is repaired, the scab is sloughed off (shed).

A second type of phagocytic cell, called a **macrophage**, removes the dead neutrophils, cellular debris, and the decomposing clot. Fibroblasts from the surrounding connective tissue migrate into the area, producing collagen and other extracellular matrix components. Capillaries grow from blood vessels at the edge of the wound and revascularize the area. The result is the replacement of the clot by a delicate connective tissue called **granulation tissue**, which consists of fibroblasts, collagen, and capillaries. Eventually normal connective tissue

Blood clot

Epidermis

Blood vessel

Dermis

Subcutaneous fat

(a)

Scab

New epidermis growing into wound

Macrophages migrating to wound site

Fibroblasts migrating to wound site

(b)

New epidermis

Scab

Granulation tissue (fibroblasts proliferating)

(c)

Freshly healed epidermis

Epidermis

Subcutaneous fat

Granulation tissue being replaced with dermis

(d)

Figure 4.9 Tissue Repair

(*a*) Fresh wound cuts through the epithelium (epidermis) and underlying connective tissue (dermis), and a clot forms. (*b*) About 1 week after the injury a scab is present, and epidermis is growing into the wound. Fibroblasts and macrophages move into the deep regions of the wound. (*c*) About 2 weeks after the injury the epidermis has grown completely into the wound, and the fibroblasts have formed granulation tissue. (*d*) About 1 month after the injury the wound has closed completely, the scab has been sloughed, and the granulation tissue is being replaced by new connective tissue.

replaces the granulation tissue. Sometimes a large amount of granulation tissue persists as a scar, which at first is bright red because of the vascularization of the tissue. The scar turns from red to white as collagen accumulates and the blood vessels decrease in number.

When the wound edges are far apart, the clot may not completely close the gap, and it takes much longer for the epithelial cells to regenerate and cover the wound. With increased tissue damage, the degree of the inflammatory response is greater, there is more cell debris for the phagocytes to remove, and the risk of infection is greater. Much more

granulation tissue forms, and **wound contracture**, a result of the contraction of fibroblasts in the granulation tissue, pulls the edges of the wound closer together. Although wound contracture reduces the size of the wound and speeds healing, it can lead to disfiguring and debilitating scars.

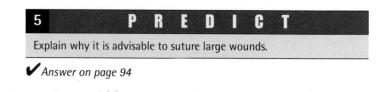

5 **P R E D I C T**

Explain why it is advisable to suture large wounds.

✔ *Answer on page 94*

Systems Pathology

cancer: malignant melanoma

CANCER: MALIGNANT MELANOMA

Ms. B. was proud of the tan she worked so hard to perfect each summer. When she was in college she noticed one of the small dark moles on her shoulder seemed to be getting larger. It was tender, appeared to be ulcerated in the center, and had developed irregular edges. Ms. B's friend, who was taking anatomy and physiology, insisted that she have a physician examine the mole. The physician quickly arranged to take a **biopsy** (bī′op-sē) of the mole and sent it to a pathology laboratory for analysis. The results confirmed that the mole was a **malignant melanoma** (mă-lig′nănt mel′ă-nō′mă). Ms. B's physician explained how tumor cells differ from normal cells, explained the major difference between benign and malignant tumors, and described the effect of malignant tumor cells on normal tissues. He then explained that the tumor must be surgically removed as soon as possible.

A **tumor** (too′mŏr) is any swelling, but modern usage has limited the term to swellings that involve neoplastic tissue. A **neoplasm** (nē′ō-plazm), meaning "new growth," refers to abnormal tissue growth resulting from cellular divisions that continue after normal cell division of the tissue has stopped or slowed considerably. A neoplasm can be **benign** (bē-nīn′) or **malignant** (mă-lig′nănt). Benign tumors do not invade and destroy surrounding healthy tissue. They may have an irregular shape, but are generally surrounded by a connective tissue capsule. Although benign tumors are less dangerous than malignant tumors, they can cause major problems when they enlarge and compress surrounding tissues. For example, benign brain tumors can compress nervous tissue, resulting in loss of brain function and even death.

The term **cancer** (kan′ser) refers to a malignant, spreading tumor and the illness that results from such a tumor. Malignant tumors normally do not have capsules and they can spread by local growth and tissue destruction into healthy surrounding tissues. The margins of malignant tumors are very irregular and inflammation is normally evident between the tumor and the normal surrounding tissues. Malignant tumors also spread to distant sites by **metastasis** (mě-tas′tă-sis), which occurs when tumor cells separate from the main mass and are carried by the lymphatic or circulatory system to a new site, where a second neoplasm is formed. The illness associated with cancer usually occurs as tumors invade and destroy healthy surrounding tissue, eliminating its function.

Malignant neoplasms lack the normal growth control that most other adult tissues have. This lack of normal control involves the genetic machinery and can be induced by viruses, environmental toxins, and other causes. Cancer therapy concentrates on trying to confine and then kill the malignant cells by killing the tissue with radiation or lasers, by removing the tumor surgically, by treating the patient with drugs that selectively kill cells undergoing division, or by stimulating the patient's immune system to destroy the tumor. **Oncology** (ong-kol′ō-jē, tumor study) is the study of cancer and its associated problems.

Malignant melanomas are malignant tumors of the skin. The malignant cells originate from pigment-producing cells of the skin called **melanocytes** (mel′ă-nō-sītz). Some factors that may contribute to the formation of malignant melanoma are genetic predisposition, solar radiation, and steroid hormone activity. A malignant melanoma normally develops in a **nevus** (nē′vŭs, pl. **nevi**, nē′vī), or mole, which is a benign neoplasm consisting of an aggregation of melanocytes. Characteristics consistent with the formation of malignant melanomas in nevi include change in color, change in size, an irregular notched margin, itching, bleeding or oozing, nodular features, scab formation, and ulceration.

Treatment of malignant melanomas with no evidence of metastasis involves surgical excision of both the primary lesion site and regional lymph nodes. Malignant melanomas are dangerous because of their ability to metastasize. They invade deeper layers of the dermis and the subcutaneous tissues. Once malignant cells enter the lymphatic and circulatory systems, they can rapidly spread to distant sites. Only 20% to 40% of patients with metastatic malignant melanoma are alive and cured 5 years after diagnosis. Different forms of malignant melanoma are classified on the basis of their structure, which, in part, determines their tendency to invade the deeper layers of the skin and metastasize to other parts of the body. Malignant melanomas that develop on the extremities have the best, head and neck lesions have the next best, and trunk lesions have the poorest rate of cure.

Most melanomas occur in the 40- to 70-year-old age group, but the frequency of malignant melanoma is increasing among those between the ages of 20 to 40 years, because of increased exposure of the skin to ultraviolet light.

---

6   P R E D I C T

A person who had sometime ago been diagnosed as having malignant melanoma, began to experience severe headaches, which increased in intensity as time passed. She also began to develop shortness of breath and a constant urge to cough. Explain how malignant melanoma could be responsible for these manifestations.

✔ *Answer on page 94*

Systems Interactions   The effect of malignant melanoma on other systems

Systems	Interactions
Muscle	Metastasis to skeletal muscle is not the most important feature. Severe atrophy of skeletal muscle and other tissues, however, can occur in advanced stages of the disease.
Circulatory	Provides a route for metastasis because cells can enter the capillaries or venules and pass to distant sites, such as the lungs and brain.
Lymphatic	Provides a route for metastasis because cells can enter lymphatic vessels and spread to lymph nodes where they initiate tumors. The lymph nodes closest to the original tumor are affected first and those more distant are affected later.
Nervous	Metastasis can result in tumors that affect the function of the nervous system. Pain, paralysis, and loss of sensations result as tumors compress and destroy nervous tissue in the brain or spinal cord. Death results when a tumor destroys or compresses an essential part of the central nervous system.
Respiratory	The lungs are common sites for metastasis. Malignant tumors destroy lung tissue and block air passageways, resulting in reduced gas exchange.
Digestive	The digestive system is a potential site for metastasis. Damage caused by malignant tumors in the liver, for example, can be life-threatening.
Urinary	The urinary system is a potential site for metastasis. Damage caused by metastatic tumors in the kidneys, can be life-threatening.
Endocrine	Endocrine organs are potential sites for metastasis and may result in the destruction of these tissues.
Reproductive	The reproductive system is a potential site for metastasis and may result in the destruction of these tissues.
Skeletal	Metastasis can result in tumors that can invade and destroy the bone marrow that produces cells of the circulatory system, such as red blood cells (erythrocytes), white blood cells (leukocytes), and platelets.

Summary

- A tissue is a group of cells with similar structure and function, as well as the extracellular substances located between the cells.
- Histology is the study of tissues.

Epithelial Tissue

- Epithelial tissue covers surfaces, usually has a basement membrane, has little extracellular material, and has no blood vessels.

Functions of Epithelia

- General functions of epithelia include protection, acting as barriers, and secretion and absorption of substances.

Classification of Epithelia

- Simple epithelium has one layer of cells, whereas stratified epithelium has more than one.
- Pseudostratified columnar epithelium is simple epithelium that appears to have two or more cell layers.
- Transitional epithelium is stratified epithelium that can be greatly stretched.

Structural and Functional Relationships

- Simple epithelium is involved with diffusion, secretion, or absorption. Stratified epithelium serves a protective role. Squamous cells function in diffusion or filtration. Cuboidal or columnar cells, which contain more organelles, secrete or absorb.
- A smooth, free surface reduces friction. Microvilli increase surface area, and cilia move materials over the cell surface.

- Desmosomes mechanically bind cells together, tight junctions form a permeability barrier, and gap junctions allow intercellular communication.
- Hemidesmosomes mechanically bind cells to the basement membrane.

Glands

- A gland is a single cell or a multicellular structure that secretes.
- Exocrine glands have ducts, and endocrine glands do not.

Connective Tissue

- Connective tissue holds cells and tissues together.
- Connective tissue has an extracellular matrix consisting of protein fibers, ground substance, and fluid.
- Collagen fibers are flexible but resist stretching, reticular fibers form a fiber network, and elastic fibers recoil.
- Blast cells form the matrix, cyte cells maintain it, and clast cells break it down.

Functions of Connective Tissue

- Connective tissues enclose and separate; connect tissues to one another; and support, store, cushion, insulate, transport, and protect.

Classification

- Connective tissue that has protein fibers as the primary feature of the extracellular matrix are dense collagenous connective tissue (tendons, many ligaments, and dermis of skin), dense

elastic connective tissue (elastic ligaments, walls of arteries), loose connective tissue ("loose packing" material of the body), and adipose tissue.
- Connective tissue that has protein fibers and ground substance as important features of the extracellular matrix are hyaline cartilage, fibrocartilage, elastic cartilage, and bone.
- Connective tissue that has a fluid matrix is blood.

Muscle Tissue
- Muscle tissue is specialized to shorten, or contract.
- The three types of muscle tissue are skeletal, cardiac, and smooth muscle.

Nervous Tissue
- Nervous tissue is specialized to conduct action potentials (electrical signals).
- Neurons conduct action potentials, and neuroglia support the neurons.

Membranes
- Mucous membranes line cavities that open to the outside of the body (digestive, respiratory, excretory, and reproductive tracts). They contain glands and secrete mucus.
- Serous membranes line trunk cavities that do not open to the outside of the body (pleural, pericardial, and peritoneal cavities). They do not contain glands but do secrete serous fluid.
- Other membranes include the cutaneous membrane (skin), synovial membranes (line joint cavities), and periosteum (around bone).

Inflammation
- The function of the inflammatory response is to isolate and destroy harmful agents.
- The inflammatory response produces five symptoms: redness, heat, swelling, pain, and disturbance of function.

Tissue Repair
- Tissue repair is the substitution of viable cells for dead cells. Labile cells divide throughout life and can undergo regeneration. Stable cells do not ordinarily divide but can regenerate if necessary. Permanent cells have little or no ability to divide. If killed, repair is by replacement.
- Tissue repair involves clot formation, inflammation, formation of granulation tissue, and the regeneration or replacement of tissues. In severe wounds, wound contracture can occur.

Content Review

1. Define tissue and histology.
2. In what areas of the body is epithelium located? What are four characteristics of epithelial tissue?
3. Explain how epithelial tissue is classified according to the number of cell layers and cell shape. What is pseudostratified columnar and transitional epithelium?
4. What kinds of functions would a single layer of epithelium be expected to perform? A stratified layer? Give an example of each.
5. Contrast the functions performed by squamous cells with those of cuboidal or columnar cells. Give an example of each.
6. What is the function of an epithelial free surface that is smooth, one that has microvilli, and one that has cilia?
7. Name the ways in which epithelial cells are connected to one another, and give the function for each way.
8. Define gland. Distinguish between an exocrine and an endocrine gland.
9. What are the three major components of the extracellular matrix of connective tissue? How are they used to classify connective tissue?
10. What are the functions of connective tissues? How does connective tissue differ from other types of tissue?
11. Explain the difference between connective tissue cells that are termed blast, cyte, and clast cells.
12. Describe dense collagenous connective tissue and dense elastic connective tissue, and give two examples.
13. How is adipose tissue different from other connective tissues? List the functions of adipose tissue.
14. Describe the components of cartilage. Give an example of hyaline cartilage, fibrocartilage, and elastic cartilage.
15. Describe the components of bone.
16. Functionally, what is unique about muscle? Which of the muscle types is under voluntary control? What tasks does each type perform?
17. Functionally, what is unique about nervous tissue? What do neurons and neuroglia accomplish? What is the difference between an axon and a dendrite?
18. Compare mucous and serous membranes according to the type of cavity they line and their secretions. Name the serous membranes associated with the lungs, heart, and abdominopelvic organs.
19. What is the function of the inflammatory response? Name the five symptoms of inflammation, and explain how each is produced.
20. Define tissue repair. What is the difference between repair by regeneration and by replacement?
21. Differentiate between labile cells, stable cells, and permanent cells. Give an example of each type. What is the significance of these cell types to tissue repair?
22. Describe the process of tissue repair when the edges of a wound are close together versus when they are far apart.

Develop Your Reasoning Skills

1. Predict what types of epithelium are likely to be found lining the trachea of a heavy smoker and a heavy smoker who stopped smoking 1 or 2 years ago.
2. The blood–brain barrier is a specialized epithelium in capillaries that prevents many materials from passing from the blood into the brain. What kind of cell connections would be expected in the blood–brain barrier?
3. One of the functions of the pancreas is to produce digestive enzymes that are secreted into the small intestine. How many cell layers and what cell shape, cell surface, and type of

cell-to-cell connections would be expected in the epithelium that is responsible for producing the digestive enzymes?

4. Some dense connective tissue has elastic fibers in addition to collagen fibers. This enables a structure to stretch and then recoil to its original shape. Examples are certain ligaments that hold together the vertebrae (bones of the back). When the back is bent (flexed), the ligaments are stretched. How does the elastic nature of these ligaments help the back to function? How are the fibers in the ligaments organized?

5. The aorta is a large blood vessel that is attached to the heart. When the heart beats, blood is ejected into the aorta, which

expands to accept the blood. The wall of the aorta is constructed with dense connective tissue that has elastic fibers. How are the fibers arranged?

6. Antihistamines block the effect of a chemical mediator, histamine, that is released during the inflammatory response. Give an example of when it could be harmful to use an antihistamine and an example of when it could be beneficial.

Answers to Predict Questions

1. p. 77   Simple squamous epithelium is found in capillaries. It promotes diffusion of gases and other substances between the blood and tissues surrounding the capillaries. Simple cuboidal epithelium is found lining the ducts of the pancreas. Simple cuboidal epithelium is adapted for secretion of substances, such as watery secretion, and tight junctions between the cells exist and function to prevent digestive enzymes from passing between the cells and out of the ducts. Stratified squamous epithelium protects against abrasion in the mouth.

2. p. 79   When a muscle contracts, the pull it exerts is transmitted along the length of its tendons. The tendons need to be very strong in that direction but not as strong in others. The collagen fibers, which are like microscopic ropes, are therefore all arranged in the same direction to maximize their strength. In the skin, collagen fibers are oriented in many directions because the skin can be pulled in many directions. The collagen fibers can be somewhat randomly oriented, or they can be

organized into alternating layers. The fibers within a layer run in the same direction, but the fibers of different layers run in different directions.

3. p. 85   The tissue found on the towel has the same characteristics as cartilage. After examining the major locations in which cartilage is found (see figure 4.5), it is very unlikely that he could have scraped his hand badly enough to cause cartilage to be torn from his hand. The presence of the cartilage on the bloody towel is an indication that he is not telling the truth and that the cartilage came from a severe wound. It is very unlikely that the man's story is true.

4. p. 87   There is more than one way to organize a table that summarizes the characteristics of the major muscle types. See the table below.

5. p. 90   Suturing large wounds brings the edges of the wounds close together. Healing is therefore more rapid, there is less danger of infections, less scar tissue is formed, and wound contracture is greatly reduced.

6. p. 91   The circulatory system and the lymphatic system are routes by which

malignant cells can spread to distant sites. Cells can enter the capillaries or venules and pass through the circulatory system to distant sites, such as the brain and lungs. Cells can also enter lymphatic vessels and spread to lymph nodes or distant sites where they initiate tumors. The lymph nodes closest to the original tumor are affected first, and those more distant are affected later.

Metastasis to the nervous system can result in tumors that affect the function of the brain. Pain, paralysis, and loss of sensation may result as tumors compress and destroy nervous tissue in the brain or spinal cord. Death results when a tumor destroys an essential part of the central nervous system.

The lungs are common sites for metastasis. Malignant tumors destroy lung tissue and block air passageways, resulting in reduced gas exchange. Irritation and inflammation of lung tissue caused by the cancer as well as the possibility of secondary infections can cause coughing.

Major Characteristics of the Three Muscle Types

Muscle Type	Nuclei in Each Cell	Location of Nuclei	Control	Cell Shape	Striated	Branching Fibers
Skeletal	Many	Peripheral	Voluntary	Long and cylindrical	Yes	No
Cardiac	One	Central	Involuntary	Branching cylinders joined by intercalated disks	Yes	Yes
Smooth	One	Central	Involuntary	Spindle-shaped cells	No	No

Chapter Five

The Integumentary System

arrector pili
(ă-rek′tōr pī′lī) [L., that which raises hair] Smooth muscle attached to the hair follicle and dermis that raises the hair by contracting.

dermis
(der′mis) [Gr. *derma*, skin] Dense connective tissue that forms the deep layer of the skin; responsible for the structural strength of the skin.

epidermis
(ep-i-derm′is) [Gr. *epi*, upon + *derma*, skin] Outer part of the skin formed of epithelial tissue that rests on the dermis; resists abrasion and forms a permeability barrier.

hair
Threadlike outgrowth of the skin consisting of columns of dead, keratinized epithelial cells.

hypodermis
(hī-pō-der′mis) [Gr. *hypo*, under + *derma*, skin] Loose connective tissue under the dermis that attaches the skin to muscle and bone.

keratinization
(ker′ă-tin-i-zā′shŭn) Production of keratin and changes in the structure and shape of epithelial cells as they move to the skin surface.

melanin
(mel′ă-nin) [Gr. *melas*, black] Brown to black pigment responsible for skin and hair color.

nail
(nāl) Thin, horny plate at the ends of the fingers and toes, consisting of several layers of dead epithelial cells containing a hard keratin.

sebaceous gland
(sē-bā′shŭs) [L. *sebum*, tallow] Gland of the skin that produces sebum; usually associated with a hair follicle.

stratum
(strat′ŭm) [L., bed cover, layer] Layer of tissue.

sweat gland
(swet) Usually a secretory organ that produces a watery secretion called sweat that is released onto the surface of the skin; some sweat glands, however, produce an organic secretion.

vitamin D
(vīt′ă-min, vī′ta-min) Fat-soluble vitamin produced after several steps from a precursor molecule in skin exposed to ultraviolet light; increases calcium and phosphate uptake in the intestine.

Objectives

After reading this chapter, you should be able to:

1. Describe the structure and function of the hypodermis, dermis, and epidermis.

2. Define epidermal strata and relate them to the process of keratinization.

3. Explain how melanin, carotene, blood, and collagen affect skin color.

4. Describe the structure of a hair and discuss the phases of hair growth.

5. Name the glands of the skin and describe the secretions they produce.

6. Describe the parts of a nail and explain how nails grow.

7. Discuss the functions of skin, hair, glands, and nails.

8. List the changes the integumentary system undergoes with age.

9. Explain how the integumentary system can be used as a diagnostic aid.

10. Classify burns on the basis of the amount of skin damage they produce.

11. Name and define the types of skin cancer.

The **integumentary system** consists of the skin and accessory structures, such as hair, nails, and glands. Integument means covering, and the integumentary system is familiar to most people because it covers the outside of the body and is easily observed. In addition, humans are concerned with the appearance of the integumentary system. Skin without blemishes is considered attractive, whereas acne is a source of embarrassment for many teenagers. The development of wrinkles and the graying or loss of hair is a sign of aging that some people find unattractive. Because of these feelings, much time, effort, and money is spent on changing the appearance of the integumentary system. For example, people apply lotion to their skin, color their hair, and trim their nails. They also try to prevent sweating with antiperspirants and reduce body odor with washing, deodorants, and perfumes.

The appearance of the integumentary system can indicate physiological imbalances in the body. Some disorders affect just the integumentary system, such as acne or warts. Disorders of other parts of the body can be reflected in the integumentary system and thus are useful for diagnosis. For example, reduced blood flow through the skin during a heart attack can cause a pale appearance, whereas increased blood flow as a result of fever can cause a flushed appearance. Also, the rashes of some diseases are characteristic, such as the rashes of measles, chickenpox, and allergic reactions. In addition, the integumentary system and the other systems often interact in complex ways in both health and disease (see Systems Pathology: Burns on p. 107).

Functions of the Integumentary System

Although we are often concerned with how the integumentary system looks, it has many important functions that go beyond appearance. The integumentary system forms the boundary between the body and the external environment, separating us from the external environment while allowing us to interact with it. Major functions of the integumentary system include:

1. *Protection.* The skin provides protection against abrasion and ultraviolet light. It also prevents the entry of microorganisms and dehydration by reducing water loss from the body.
2. *Sensation.* The integumentary system has sensory receptors that can detect heat, cold, pressure, and pain.
3. *Vitamin D production.* When exposed to ultraviolet light, the skin produces a molecule that can be transformed into vitamin D.
4. *Temperature regulation.* Body temperature is regulated by controlling blood flow through the skin and the activity of sweat glands.
5. *Excretion.* Small amounts of waste products are lost through the skin and in gland secretions.

Hypodermis

Just as a house rests on a foundation, the skin rests on the **hypodermis** (hī-pō-der′mis; under the dermis), which attaches it to underlying bone and muscle and supplies it with blood vessels and nerves (figure 5.1). The hypodermis, which is not part of the skin, is sometimes called **subcutaneous** (sŭb-koo-tā′nē-ŭs; under the skin) **tissue**. The hypodermis is loose connective tissue that contains about half the body's stored fat, although the amount and location vary with age, sex, and diet. Fat in the hypodermis functions as padding and insulation, and it is responsible for some of the differences in appearance between men and women.

Did You Know?

The hypodermis can be used to estimate total body fat. The skin and hypodermis are pinched at selected locations, and the thickness of the fold of skin and underlying hypodermis is measured. The thicker the fold, the greater the amount of total body fat. Clinically, the hypodermis is the site of subcutaneous injections.

Skin

The skin is made up of two major tissue layers. The **dermis** (der′mis; skin) is a layer of dense connective tissue, and the **epidermis** (ep-i-der′mis; upon the dermis) is a layer of epithelial tissue that rests on the dermis (see figure 5.1). If the hypodermis is the foundation on which the house rests, the dermis forms most of the house, and the epidermis is its roof.

Dermis

The dense connective tissue that makes up the dermis contains fibroblasts, fat cells, and macrophages. Compared with the hypodermis, the dermis has fewer fat cells and blood vessels. Nerve endings, hair follicles, smooth muscles, glands, and lymphatic vessels extend into the dermis (see figure 5.1).

Collagen and elastic fibers in the dermis are responsible for most of the structural strength of the skin. The collagen fibers are oriented in many different directions and can resist stretch. More collagen fibers are oriented in some directions than in others, however. This produces **cleavage**, or **tension, lines** in the skin, and the skin is most resistant to stretch along these lines (figure 5.2). It is important for surgeons to be aware of cleavage lines. An incision made across the cleavage lines is likely to gap and produce considerable scar tissue, but an incision made parallel with the lines tends to gap less and produce less scar tissue (see chapter 4). If the skin is overstretched for any reason, the dermis can be damaged, leaving lines that are visible through the epidermis. These lines, called **striae** (strī′ē), or **stretch marks**, can develop on the abdomen and breasts of a woman during pregnancy.

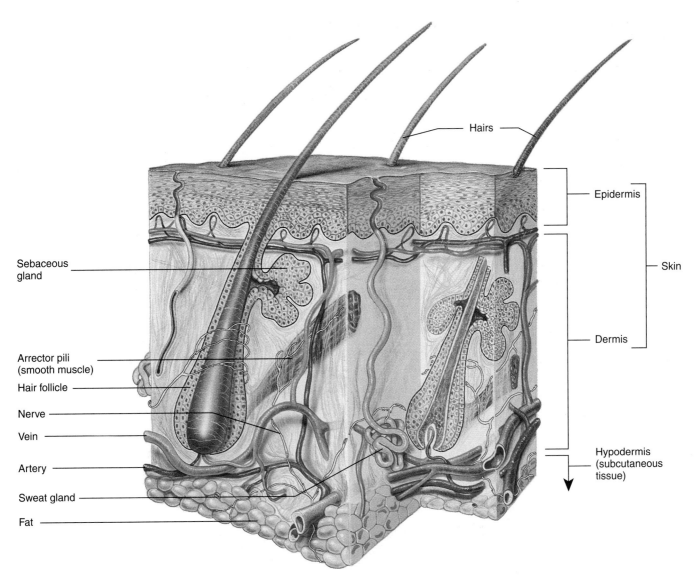

Hairs

Epidermis

Skin

Dermis

Sebaceous gland

Arrector pili (smooth muscle)

Hair follicle

Nerve

Vein

Artery

Sweat gland

Fat

Hypodermis (subcutaneous tissue)

Figure 5.1   Skin and Hypodermis

The skin, consisting of the epidermis and the dermis, is connected by the hypodermis to underlying structures. Note the accessory structures (hairs, glands, and arrector pili), some of which project into the hypodermis, and the large amount of fat in the hypodermis.

The upper part of the dermis has projections called **dermal papillae** (pă-pil′ē), which extend toward the epidermis (figure 5.3*a*). The dermal papillae contain many blood vessels that supply the overlying epidermis with nutrients, remove waste products, and aid in regulating body temperature. The dermal papillae in the palms of the hands, the soles of the feet, and the tips of the digits are in parallel, curving ridges that shape the overlying epidermis into fingerprints and footprints. The ridges increase friction and improve the grip of the hands and feet.

Did You Know?

The dermis is that part of an animal hide from which leather is made. The epidermis is removed, and the dermis is preserved by tanning. Clinically, the dermis in humans is sometimes the site of certain injections, such as the tuberculin skin test.

Epidermis

The epidermis is stratified squamous epithelium; in its deepest layers, cells are produced by mitosis. As new cells are formed, they push older cells to the surface, where they slough, or flake off. The outermost cells protect the cells underneath, and the deeper replicating cells replace cells lost from the surface. During their movement the cells change shape and chemical composition. This process is called **keratinization** (ker′ă-tin-i-zā′shŭn) because the cells become filled with the protein **keratin** (ker′ă-tin). As keratinization proceeds, epithelial cells eventually die and produce an outer layer of cells that resists abrasion and forms a permeability barrier.

Although keratinization is a continuous process, distinct layers called **strata** (stra′tă) are recognized (figure 5.3*b*). The deepest stratum, the **stratum basale** (bā′să-lē), consists of cuboidal or columnar cells that undergo mitotic divisions about every 19 days. One daughter cell becomes a

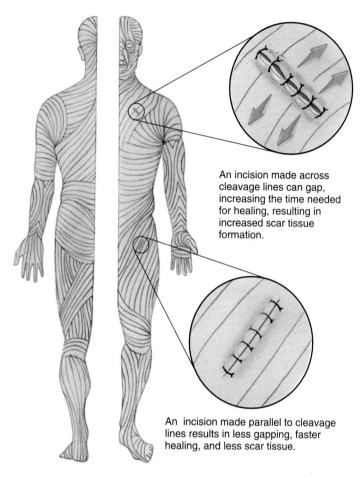

An incision made across cleavage lines can gap, increasing the time needed for healing, resulting in increased scar tissue formation.

An incision made parallel to cleavage lines results in less gapping, faster healing, and less scar tissue.

Figure 5.2 Cleavage Lines

The orientation of collagen fibers produces cleavage, or tension, lines in the skin.

(a)

Epidermis

Dermal papillae

Duct of sweat gland

Stratum corneum

Intermediate strata
Stratum basale

Dermis

Papillae

(b)

Figure 5.3 Epidermis and Dermis

(*a*) The epidermis rests on the dermis. Dermal papilla project toward the epidermis. (*b*) Photomicrograph of the epidermis resting on the dermis. Note the strata of the epidermis and the papillae of the dermis.

new stratum basale cell and can divide again. The other cell is pushed toward the surface, a journey that takes about 40 to 56 days. As cells move to the surface, changes in the cells produce intermediate strata.

The **stratum corneum** (kōr′nē-ŭm) is the most superficial strata of the epidermis. It consists of dead, squamous cells filled with the hard protein keratin. Keratin gives the stratum corneum its structural strength. The stratum corneum cells are also coated and surrounded by lipids, which help prevent fluid loss through the skin.

1 P R E D I C T

What kinds of substances could easily pass through the skin by diffusion? What kinds would have difficulty?

✔ *Answer on page 110*

The stratum corneum is composed of 25 or more layers of dead squamous cells joined by desmosomes (see chapter 4). Eventually the desmosomes break apart, and the cells are sloughed from the skin. Dandruff is an example of stratum corneum cells sloughed from the surface of the scalp. In skin subjected to friction, the number of layers in the stratum corneum greatly increases, producing a thickened area called a

callus (kal′ŭs). Over a bony prominence, the stratum corneum can thicken to form a cone-shaped structure called a **corn**.

Skin Color

Skin color is determined by pigments in the skin, by blood circulating through the skin, and by the thickness of the stratum corneum. **Melanin** (mel′ă-nin) is the term used to describe a group of pigments responsible for skin, hair, and eye color. Most melanin molecules are brown to black pigments, but some are yellowish or reddish. Melanin is believed to provide protection against ultraviolet light from the sun.

Melanin is produced by **melanocytes** (mel′ă-nō-sītz), which are irregularly shaped cells with many long processes that extend between the epithelial cells of the deep part of the epidermis (figure 5.4). The Golgi apparatuses of the melanocytes package melanin into vesicles called **melanosomes** (mel′ă-nō-sōmz), which move into the cell processes of the melanocytes. Epithelial cells phagocytize the tips of the melanocyte cell processes, thereby acquiring melanosomes.

1. Melanosomes are produced by the Golgi apparatus of the melanocyte.

2. Melanosomes move into melanocyte cell processes.

3. Epithelial cells phagocytize the tips of the melanocyte cell processes containing melanosomes.

4. The melanosomes are then within epithelial cells.

Epithelial cell

Melanocyte

Melanosomes

Nucleus

Golgi apparatus

Figure 5.4   Melanin Transfer from Melanocytes to Epithelial Cells

Melanocytes make melanin, which is packaged into melanosomes and transferred to many epithelial cells.

Although all the epithelial cells of the epidermis can contain melanin, only the melanocytes produce it.

Large amounts of melanin occur in some regions of the skin, such as freckles; moles; the genitalia; the nipples; and the pigmented, circular areas around the nipples. Other areas, such as the lips, palms of the hands, and soles of the feet, have less melanin. Racial variations in skin color are determined by the amount, kind, and distribution of melanin. All races have about the same number of melanocytes.

Melanin production is determined by genetic factors, hormones, and exposure to light. Genetic factors are responsible for the amounts of melanin produced in different races. Although many genes are responsible for skin color, a single mutation can prevent the manufacture of melanin. For example, **albinism** (al′bi-nizm) is a recessive genetic trait that causes a deficiency or absence of melanin. Albinos have fair skin, white hair, and unpigmented irises in the eyes. During pregnancy certain hormones cause an increase in melanin production in the mother, darkening the nipples, the pigmented circular areas around the nipples, and the genitalia. The cheekbones, forehead, and chest can also darken, resulting in "the mask of pregnancy," and a dark line of pigmentation can appear on the midline of the abdomen. Exposure to ultraviolet light, for example in sunlight, also stimulates melanocytes to increase melanin production. The result is a suntan.

The location of pigments and other substances in the skin affects the color produced. If a dark pigment is located in the dermis or hypodermis, light reflected off the dark pigment can be scattered by collagen fibers of the dermis to produce a blue color. The same effect produces the blue color of the sky as light is reflected from dust particles in the air. The deeper within the dermis or hypodermis any dark pigment is located, the bluer the pigment appears because of the light-scattering effect of the overlying tissue. This effect causes the blue color of tattoos, bruises, and some superficial blood vessels.

Carotene (kar′o-tēn) is a yellow pigment found in plants such as squash and carrots. Humans normally ingest carotene and use it as a source of vitamin A. Carotene is lipid-soluble, and,

when consumed, it accumulates in the lipids of the stratum corneum and in the fat cells of the dermis and hypodermis. This gives the skin a slight yellowish tint. If large amounts of carotene are consumed, the skin can become quite yellowish.

Blood flowing through the skin imparts a reddish hue, and when blood flow increases the red color intensifies. Examples include blushing, anger, and the inflammatory response. A decrease in blood flow such as occurs in shock can make the skin appear pale. A decrease in the blood oxygen content produces a bluish color called cyanosis (sī-ă-nō′sis). Birthmarks are congenital (present at birth) disorders of the blood vessels (capillaries) in the dermis.

2   P R E D I C T

Explain the differences in skin color between: (a) the palms of the hands and the lips, (b) the palms of the hands of a person who does heavy manual labor and one who does not, and (c) the anterior and posterior surfaces of the forearm.

✔ *Answer on page 110*

Accessory Skin Structures

Hair

The presence of **hair** is one of the characteristics common to all mammals. If the hair is thick and covers most of the body surface, it is called fur. In humans, some hair is found everywhere in the skin except the palms, soles, lips, nipples, parts of the genitalia, and the distal segments of the fingers and toes.

The **shaft** of the hair protrudes above the surface of the skin, whereas the **root** and **hair bulb** are below the surface (figure 5.5*a*). A hair has a hard **cortex**, which surrounds a softer center, the **medulla** (me-dool′ă). The cortex is covered by the **cuticle** (kū′ti-kl), a single layer of overlapping cells that holds the hair in the hair follicle. The **hair follicle** is an extension of the epidermis deep into the dermis, and it can

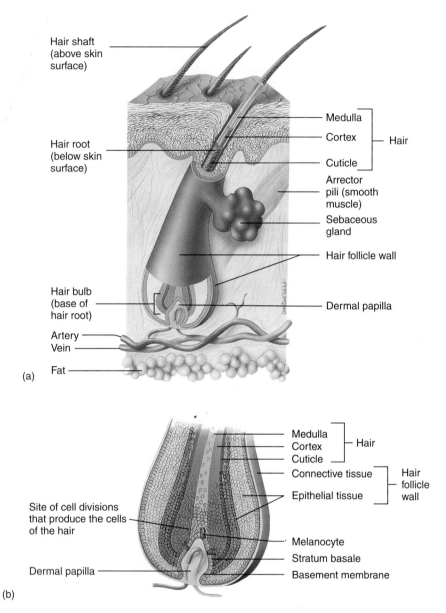

Hair shaft (above skin surface)

Hair root (below skin surface)

Hair bulb (base of hair root)

Artery
Vein

Fat

(a)

Medulla
Cortex — Hair
Cuticle

Arrector pili (smooth muscle)

Sebaceous gland

Hair follicle wall

Dermal papilla

Medulla
Cortex — Hair
Cuticle

Connective tissue
Epithelial tissue
— Hair follicle wall

Site of cell divisions that produce the cells of the hair

Melanocyte
Stratum basale
Basement membrane

Dermal papilla

(b)

Figure 5.5 Hair

(*a*) Hair within a hair follicle. (*b*) Enlargement of the hair bulb and hair follicle wall.

play an important role in tissue repair. If the surface epidermis is damaged, the epithelial cells within the hair follicle can divide and serve as a source of new epithelial cells.

Hair is produced in the hair bulb, which rests on a dermal papilla (figure 5.5*b*). Blood vessels within the papilla supply the hair bulb with the nourishment needed to produce the hair. Hair is produced in cycles. During the growth stage, it is formed by epithelial cells within the hair bulb. These cells, like the cells of the stratum basale in the skin, divide and undergo keratinization. The hair grows longer as cells are added to the base of the hair within the hair bulb. Thus the hair root and shaft consist of columns of dead keratinized epithelial cells. During the resting stage, growth stops, and the hair is held in the hair follicle. When the next growth stage begins, a new hair is formed, and the old hair falls out. The duration of each stage depends on the individual hair. Eyelashes grow for about 30 days and rest for 105 days,

whereas scalp hairs grow for 3 years and rest for 1 to 2 years. The loss of hair normally means that the hair is being replaced, because the old hair falls out of the hair follicle when the new hair begins to grow. In some men, however, a permanent loss of hair results in "pattern baldness." Although many of the hair follicles are lost, some remain and produce a very short, transparent hair, which for practical purposes is invisible. These changes occur when male sex hormones act on the hair follicles of men who have the genetic predisposition for "pattern baldness."

Hair color is determined by varying amounts and types of melanin. The production and distribution of melanin by melanocytes occurs in the hair bulb by the same method as in the skin. With age, the amount of melanin in hair can decrease, causing the hair to become faded in color, or the hair can have no melanin and be white. Gray hair is usually a mixture of unfaded, faded, and white hairs.

3   P R E D I C T

Marie Antoinette's hair supposedly turned white overnight after she heard she would be sent to the guillotine. Explain why you believe or disbelieve this story.

✔ *Answer on page 110*

Muscles

Associated with each hair follicle are smooth muscle cells, the **arrector pili** (ă-rek′tōr pī′lī) (see figure 5.5*a*). Contraction of the arrector pili causes the hair to become more perpendicular to the skin's surface, or to "stand on end," and also produces a raised area of skin called "goose flesh." In animals with fur, contraction of the arrector pili is beneficial because it increases the thickness of the fur by raising the hairs. In the cold, the thicker layer of fur traps air and becomes a better insulator. The thickened fur can also make the animal appear larger and more ferocious, which might deter an attacker. It is unlikely that humans, with their sparse amount of hair, derive any important benefit from contraction of their arrector pili.

Glands

The major glands of the skin are the **sebaceous** (sē-bā′shŭs) **glands** and the **sweat glands** (figure 5.6). Most sebaceous glands are connected by a duct to the superficial part of a hair follicle. They produce **sebum**, an oily, white substance rich in lipids. The sebum lubricates the hair and the surface of the skin, which prevents drying and protects against some bacteria.

There are two kinds of sweat glands. **Merocrine** (mer′ō-krin) **sweat glands** are located in almost every part of the skin and are most numerous in the palms and soles. They produce a secretion that is mostly water with a few salts. Merocrine sweat glands have ducts that open onto the surface of the skin through sweat pores. When the body temperature starts to rise above normal levels, the sweat glands produce sweat, which evaporates and cools the body. Sweat can also be released in the palms, soles, axillae (armpits), and other places because of emotional stress.

Did You Know?

Emotional sweating is used in lie detector (polygraph) tests because sweat gland activity usually increases when a person tells a lie. Even small amounts of sweat can be detected because the salt solution conducts electricity and lowers the electrical resistance of the skin.

Apocrine (ap′ō-krin) **sweat glands** produce a thick secretion rich in organic substances. They open into hair follicles, but only in the axillae and genitalia. Apocrine sweat glands become active at puberty because of the influence of sex hormones. The organic secretion, which is essentially odorless when released, is quickly broken down by bacteria into odiferous substances to cause what is commonly known as body odor.

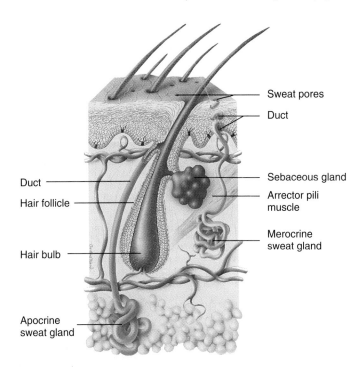

Figure 5.6   Glands of the Skin

Sebaceous and apocrine sweat glands empty into the hair follicle. Merocrine sweat glands empty onto the surface of the skin.

Nails

The distal ends of the digits of humans and other primates have nails, whereas reptiles, birds, and most mammals have claws or hooves. The **nail** is a thin plate, consisting of layers of dead stratum corneum cells that contain a very hard type of keratin. The visible part of the nail is the **nail body**, and the part of the nail covered by skin is the **nail root** (figure 5.7). The **eponychium** (ep-ō-nik′ē-ŭm), or **cuticle**, is stratum corneum that extends onto the nail body. The nail root and nail body attach to the **nail bed**, the proximal portion of which is the **nail matrix**. A small part of the nail matrix, the **lunula** (loo′noo-lă), can be seen through the nail body as a whitish, crescent-shaped area at the base of the nail. The nail grows from the nail matrix, located under the proximal end of the nail. Unlike hair, nails grow continuously and do not have a resting stage.

Physiology of the Integumentary System

Protection

The integumentary system performs many protective functions.

1. The intact skin plays an important role in preventing water loss because its lipids act as a barrier to the diffusion of water.
2. The skin prevents the entry of microorganisms and other foreign substances into the body. Secretions from skin

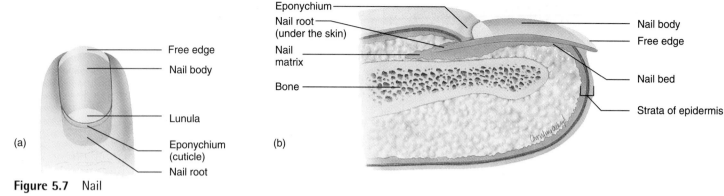

Figure 5.7 Nail

(*a*) Dorsal view. (*b*) Lateral view of a sagittal section through the nail. The stratum basale and a few layers of cells are indicated in purple. Most of the epidermis is absent from the nail bed.

glands also produce an environment unsuitable for some microorganisms.

3. The stratified squamous epithelium of the skin protects underlying structures against abrasion.
4. Melanin absorbs ultraviolet light and protects underlying structures from its damaging effects.
5. Hair provides protection in several ways: the hair on the head acts as a heat insulator, eyebrows keep sweat out of the eyes, eyelashes protect the eyes from foreign objects, and hair in the nose and ears prevents the entry of dust and other materials.
6. The nails protect the ends of the digits from damage and can be used in defense.

Sensation

The skin has receptors in the epidermis and dermis that can detect pain, heat, cold, and pressure (see chapter 8). Although hair does not have a nerve supply, movement of the hair can be detected by sensory receptors around the hair follicle.

Vitamin D Production

When the skin is exposed to ultraviolet light, a precursor molecule of **vitamin D** is formed. The precursor is carried by the blood to the liver, where it is modified, and then to the kidneys, where the precursor is modified further to form active vitamin D. If exposed to enough ultraviolet light, humans can produce all the vitamin D they need. Many people need to ingest vitamin D, however, because clothing and indoor living reduce their exposure to ultraviolet light. Fatty fish (and fish oils) and vitamin D–fortified milk are the best sources of vitamin D. Eggs, butter, and liver contain small amounts of vitamin D, but are not considered significant sources because too large a serving size is necessary to meet daily vitamin D requirements. Adequate levels of vitamin D are necessary because vitamin D stimulates calcium and phosphate uptake in the intestines. These substances are necessary for normal bone metabolism (see chapter 6) and normal muscle function (see chapter 7).

Temperature Regulation

Body temperature normally is maintained at about 37°C (98.6°F). Regulation of body temperature is important because the rate of chemical reactions within the body can be increased or decreased by changes in body temperature. Even slight changes in temperature can make enzymes operate less efficiently and disrupt the normal rates of chemical changes in the body.

Exercise, fever, or an increase in environmental temperature tend to raise body temperature. Homeostasis requires the loss of excess heat. Blood vessels (arterioles) in the dermis dilate and enable more blood to flow through the skin, thus transferring heat from deeper tissues to the skin (figure 5.8*a*), where the heat is lost by radiation (infrared energy), convection (air movement), or conduction (direct contact with an object). Sweat that spreads over the surface of the skin and evaporates also carries away heat and reduces body temperature.

If body temperature begins to drop below normal, heat can be conserved by constriction of dermal blood vessels, which reduces blood flow to the skin (figure 5.8*b*). Thus, less heat is transferred from deeper structures to the skin, and heat loss is reduced. With smaller amounts of warm blood flowing through the skin, however, the skin temperature decreases. If the skin temperature drops below about 15°C (59°F), blood vessels dilate.

4 **PREDICT**

You many have noticed that on very cold winter days peoples' noses and ears turn red. Can you explain the advantage of this response?

✔ *Answer on page 111*

Excretion

Excretion is the removal of waste products from the body. In addition to water and salts, sweat contains a small amount of waste products such as urea, uric acid, and ammonia. Even though large amounts of sweat can be lost from the body, the sweat glands do not play a significant role in the excretion of waste products.

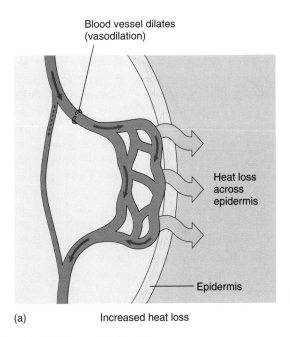

Blood vessel dilates
(vasodilation)

Heat loss
across
epidermis

Epidermis

(a)   Increased heat loss

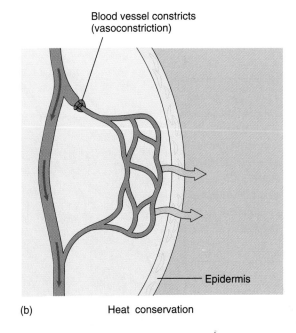

Blood vessel constricts
(vasoconstriction)

Epidermis

(b)   Heat conservation

Figure 5.8   Heat Exchange in the Skin

(*a*) Blood vessels in the dermis dilate (vasodilate), allowing more blood to flow through the blood vessels close to the surface, where heat is lost from the body. (*b*) Blood vessels in the dermis constrict (vasoconstrict), reducing blood flow and heat loss.

Effects of Aging on the Integumentary System

As the body ages, the skin is more easily damaged because the epidermis thins and the amount of collagen in the dermis decreases. Skin infections are more likely and repair of the skin occurs more slowly. A decrease in the number of elastic fibers in the dermis and loss of fat from the hypodermis cause the skin to sag and wrinkle. A decrease in the activity of sweat glands and a decrease in the blood supply to the dermis result in a poor ability to regulate body temperature. The skin becomes drier as sebaceous gland activity decreases. The number of melanocytes generally decreases, but in some areas, the number of melanocytes increases to produce **age spots**. Note that age spots are different from **freckles**, which are caused by increased melanin production. Gray or white hair also results because of a decrease in or a lack of melanin production. Skin that is exposed to sunlight shows signs of aging more rapidly than nonexposed skin, so avoiding overexposure to sunlight and using sun blockers is advisable.

The Integumentary System as a Diagnostic Aid

The integumentary system is useful in diagnosis because it is observed easily and often reflects events occurring in other parts of the body. For example, **cyanosis** (sī-ă-nō′sis), a bluish color caused by decreased blood oxygen content, is an indication of impaired circulatory or respiratory function. A yel-lowish skin color, **jaundice** (jawn′dis), can occur when the liver is damaged by a disease such as viral hepatitis. Normally the liver secretes bile pigments, which are products of the breakdown of worn-out red blood cells, into the intestine. Bile pigments are yellow, and their buildup in the blood and tissues can indicate an impairment of liver function.

Rashes and lesions in the skin can be symptoms of problems elsewhere in the body. For example, scarlet fever results from a bacterial infection in the throat. The bacteria in the throat release a toxin into the blood that causes a pink–red rash in the skin. The development of a rash can also indicate an allergic reaction to foods or drugs such as penicillin.

The condition of the skin, hair, and nails is affected by nutritional status. In vitamin A deficiency the skin produces excess keratin and assumes a characteristic sandpaper texture, whereas in iron-deficiency anemia the nails lose their normal contour and become flat or concave (spoon-shaped).

Hair concentrates many substances that can be detected by laboratory analysis, and comparison of a patient's hair to a "normal" hair can be useful in certain diagnoses. For examples, lead poisoning results in high levels of lead in the hair. The use of hair analysis as a screening test to determine the general health or nutritional status of an individual is unreliable, however.

Burns

Burns are classified according to the depth of the burn (figure 5.9). In **partial-thickness burns** some part of the stratum basale remains viable, and regeneration of the epidermis occurs from within the burn area as well as from the edges of

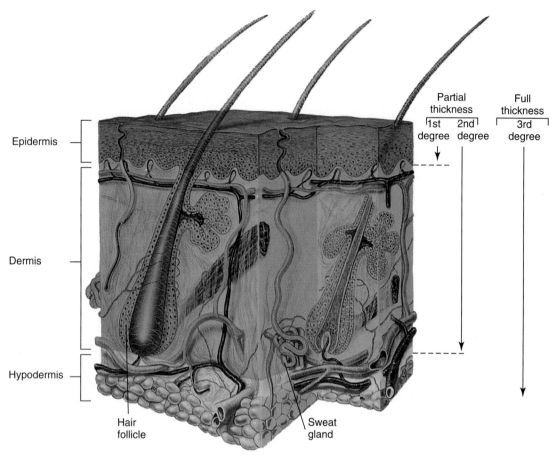

Epidermis

Dermis

Hypodermis

Partial thickness
1st degree 2nd degree

Full thickness
3rd degree

Hair follicle

Sweat gland

Figure 5.9 Burns

Parts of the skin damaged by different types of burns are shown. Partial-thickness burns are subdivided into first-degree burns (damage to only the epidermis) and second-degree burns (damage to the epidermis and part of the dermis). Full-thickness, or third-degree, burns destroy the epidermis, dermis, and sometimes deeper tissues.

the burn. Partial-thickness burns are divided into first- and second-degree burns.

First-degree burns involve only the epidermis and are red and painful, and slight **edema** (e-dē′mă), or swelling, can be present. They can be caused by sunburn or brief exposure to hot or cold objects, and they heal without scarring in about a week.

Second-degree burns damage the epidermis and the dermis. If there is minimal dermal damage, symptoms include redness, pain, edema, and blisters. Healing takes about 2 weeks, and there is no scarring. If the burn goes deep into the dermis, however, the wound appears red, tan, or white; can take several months to heal; and might scar. In all second-degree burns, the epidermis regenerates from epithelial tissue in hair follicles and sweat glands, as well as from the edges of the wound.

In **full-thickness**, or **third-degree**, **burns** the epidermis and the dermis are completely destroyed, and recovery occurs from the edges of the burn wound. Third-degree burns often

are surrounded by areas of first- and second-degree burns. Although the first- and second-degree burn areas are painful, the region of third-degree burn is usually painless because sensory receptors in the epidermis and dermis have been destroyed. Third-degree burns appear white, tan, brown, black, or deep cherry red.

Deep partial-thickness and full-thickness burns take a long time to heal, and they form scar tissue with disfiguring and debilitating wound contracture. To prevent these complications and to speed healing, skin grafts are often performed. In a split skin graft the epidermis and part of the dermis are removed from another part of the body and placed over the burn. Interstitial fluid from the burn nourishes the graft until blood vessels grow into the graft and supply it with nourishment. Meanwhile, the donor tissue produces new epidermis from epithelial tissue in the hair follicles and sweat glands in the same manner as in superficial second-degree burns.

Skin Cancer

Skin cancer is the most common type of cancer. Although chemicals and radiation (x-rays) are known to induce cancer, the development of skin cancer most often is associated with exposure to ultraviolet (UV) light from the sun. Consequently, most skin cancers develop on the face, neck, or hands.

Basal cell carcinoma (kar-si-nō′mă), the most frequent skin cancer, begins with cells in the stratum basale and extends into the dermis to produce an open ulcer (figure 5.10*a*). Surgical removal or radiation therapy cures this type of cancer. Fortunately there is little danger that this type of cancer will spread, or **metastasize** (mě-tas′tă-sīz), to other areas of the body. **Squamous cell carcinoma** develops from cells immediately superficial to the stratum basale. Normally these cells undergo little or no cell division. In squamous cell carcinoma, however, the cells continue to divide as they produce keratin. Typically the result is a nodular, keratinized tumor confined to the epidermis (figure 5.10*b*). If untreated, the tumor can invade the dermis, metastasize, and cause death. **Malignant melanoma** (mel′ă-nō′mă) is a rare form of skin cancer that arises from melanocytes, usually in a preexisting mole. A mole is an aggregation, or "nest," of melanocytes. The melanoma can appear as a large, flat, spreading lesion or as a deeply pigmented nodule (figure 5.10*c*). Metastasis is common, and unless diagnosed and treated early in development, this cancer is often fatal.

Limiting exposure to the sun and using sunscreens can reduce the likelihood of developing skin cancer. Some concern over the use of sunscreens, however, has recently arisen because of the different types of UV radiation they can block. Exposure to UVB can cause sunburn and is associated with the development of basal cell and squamous cell carcinomas. The development of malignant melanoma is associated with exposure to UVA. Sunscreens that block primarily UVB allow longer exposure to the sun without sunburning, but thereby increase exposure to UVA and the possible development of malignant melanoma. Use of sunscreens that effectively block UVB and UVA is advisable.

(a)

(b)

(c)

Figure 5.10   Cancer of the Skin

(*a*) Basal cell carcinoma. (*b*) Squamous cell carcinoma. (*c*) Malignant melanoma.

Clinical Focus Disease of the Skin

Bacterial Infections

Acne (ak'nē) is a disorder of the hair follicles and sebaceous glands. Four factors are believed to be involved: hormones, sebum, abnormal keratinization, and the bacterium *Propionibacterium acnes*. The lesions begin with the overproduction of epidermal cells in the hair follicle. These cells are shed from the wall of the hair follicle, and they stick to one another to form a mass of cells mixed with sebum that blocks the hair follicle. During puberty, hormones, especially testosterone, stimulate the sebaceous glands, and sebum production increases. Because both the adrenal glands and the testes produce testosterone, the effect is seen in males and females. An accumulation of sebum behind the blockage produces a whitehead. A blackhead develops when the accumulating mass of cells and sebum pushes through the opening of the hair follicle. Although there is general agreement that dirt is not responsible for the black color, the exact cause of the black color in blackheads is disputed. A pimple results if the wall of the hair follicle ruptures, forming an entry into the surrounding tissue. *P. acnes* and other bacteria stimulate an inflammatory response that results in the formation of a red pimple filled with pus. If tissue damage is extensive, scarring occurs.

Impetigo (im-pe-tī'gō) is a skin disease caused by *Staphylococcus aureus*. It usually affects children, producing small blisters containing pus that easily rupture to form a thick, yellowish crust. The bacteria are transmitted by direct contact (touching) and enter the skin through abrasions or small breaks in the skin.

Decubitis (dē-kū'bi-tŭs) ulcers, also known as bedsores or pressure sores, can develop in people who are bedridden or confined to a wheelchair. The weight of the body, especially in areas over bony projections such as the hip bones and heels, compresses tissue and reduces circulation. The lack of blood flow results in the destruction of the hypodermis and the skin. After the skin dies, bacteria gain entry to produce an infected ulcer.

Viral Infections

Interestingly, many of the viruses that cause skin diseases do not enter the body through the skin. Instead, the viruses enter through the respiratory system, where they reside and multiply for about 2 weeks. Then they are carried by the blood to the skin where they cause lesions. Examples are rubeola, rubella, and chickenpox. Rubeola (rū-bē'ō-lă; measles) can become dangerous because it can develop into pneumonia, or the virus can invade the brain and cause damage. Rubella (rū-bel'ă; German measles) is a mild disease but can prove dangerous if contracted during pregnancy. The virus can cross the placenta and damage the fetus, resulting in deafness, cataracts, heart defects, mental retardation, or death. Chickenpox is a mild disease if contracted during childhood. Herpes zoster (zos'ter), or shingles, is a disease caused by the chickenpox virus that occurs after the childhood infection. The virus remains dormant within nerve cells. Trauma, stress, or another illness somehow activates the virus, which moves through the nerve to the skin, where it causes very painful lesions along the nerve's pathway.

Cold sores, or fever blisters, are caused by the herpes (her'pēz) simplex I virus, which is related to the chickenpox virus. The initial infection usually does not produce symptoms. Dormant viruses can become active, however, and produce lesions in the skin around the mouth and in the mucous membrane of the mouth. The virus is transmitted by oral or respiratory routes. The herpes simplex II virus is transmitted by sexual contact and produces genital lesions, referred to as genital herpes.

Warts are uncontrolled growths of the epidermis caused by the human *Papillomavirus*. Usually the growths are benign and disappear spontaneously, or they can be removed by a variety of techniques. The viruses are transmitted to the skin by direct contact with contaminated objects or an infected person. They can also be spread by scratching.

Ringworm

Ringworm is a fungal infection that produces patchy scaling and an inflammatory response in the skin. The lesions are often circular with a raised edge and in ancient times were thought to be caused by worms. Several species of fungus cause ringworm in humans, and they usually are described by their location on the body. Ringworm in the scalp is called ringworm, ringworm of the groin is called jock itch, and ringworm of the feet is called athlete's foot.

Eczema and Dermatitis

Eczema (ek'zĕ-mă, eg-zē'mă) and dermatitis (der-mă-tī'tis) are terms that describe inflammatory conditions of the skin. Causes of the inflammation can be allergy; infection; poor circulation; or exposure to physical factors, such as chemicals, heat, cold, or sunlight.

Psoriasis

Psoriasis (sō-rī'ă-sis) is characterized by increased cell division in the stratum basale, abnormal keratin production, and elongation of the dermal papillae toward the skin surface. The result is a thicker-than-normal stratum corneum that sloughs to produce large, silvery scales. If the scales are scraped away, bleeding occurs from the blood vessels at the top of the dermal papillae. Evidence suggests that the disease has a genetic component and that the immune system stimulates the increased cell divisions. Psoriasis is a chronic disease that can be controlled with drugs and phototherapy (UV light), but as yet has no cure.

Systems Pathology

BURNS

Mr. S is a 23-year-old man who had difficulty falling asleep at night. He often stayed up late watching TV or reading until he fell asleep. Mr. S was also a chain smoker. One night he took several sleeping pills. Unfortunately, he fell asleep before putting out his cigarette, which started a fire. As a result, Mr. S was severely burned, receiving full-thickness and partial-thickness burns (figure A*a*). He was rushed to the emergency room and was eventually transferred to a burn unit.

For the first day after his accident, his condition was critical because he went into shock. Administration of large volumes of intravenous fluid stabilized his condition. As part of his treatment, Mr. S was also given a high-protein, high-calorie diet.

A week later, dead tissue was removed from the most serious burns (figure A*b*), and a skin graft was performed. Despite the use of topical antimicrobial drugs and sterile bandages, however, some of the burns became infected. An additional complication was the development of a venous thrombosis in his leg.

Although the burns were painful and the treatment was prolonged, Mr. S made a full recovery. He no longer smokes.

Background Information

When large areas of skin are severely burned, systemic effects are produced that can be life-threatening. Within minutes of a major burn injury, there is increased permeability of capillaries, which are the small blood vessels in which fluid, gases, nutrients, and waste products are normally exchanged between the blood and tissues. This increased permeability occurs at the burn site and throughout the body. As a result, fluid and ions are lost from the burn wound and into tissue spaces. The loss of fluid decreases blood volume, which decreases the ability of the heart to pump blood. The resulting decrease in blood delivery to tissues can cause tissue damage, shock, and even death. Treatment consists of administering intravenous fluid at a faster rate than it leaks out of the capillaries. Although this can reverse the shock and prevent death, fluid continues to leak into tissue spaces, causing pronounced edema of the tissues.

Typically, after 24 hours, capillary permeability returns to normal, and the amount of intravenous fluid administered can be greatly decreased. How burns result in capillary permeability changes is not well understood. It is clear that following a burn, immunological and metabolic changes occur that affect not only capillaries, but the rest of the body as well. For example, mediators of inflammation (see chapter 4), which are

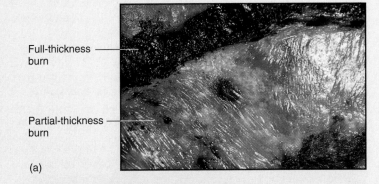

Full-thickness burn

Partial-thickness burn

(a)

(b)

Figure A   Burn Victim
(*a*) Partial and full-thickness burns. (*b*) Patient in a burn unit.

released in response to the tissue damage, contribute to changes in capillary permeability throughout the body.

Substances released from the burn may also play a role in causing cells to function abnormally. Burn injuries result in an almost immediate hypermetabolic state that persists until wound closure. Two other factors contributing to the increased metabolism are (1) a resetting of the temperature control center in the brain to a higher temperature and (2) hormones released by the endocrine system (e.g., epinephrine and norepinephrine from the adrenal glands increase cell metabolism). Compared with a normal body temperature of approximately 37°C (98.6°F), a body temperature of 38.5°C (101.3°F) is typical in burn patients, despite the higher loss of water by evaporation from the burn.

In severe burns, the increased metabolic rate can result in weight loss as great as 30% to 40% of the patient's preburn weight. To help compensate, caloric intake may double or even triple. In addition, the need for protein, which is necessary for tissue repair, is greater.

The skin normally maintains homeostasis by preventing the entry of microorganisms. Because burns damage and even completely destroy the skin, microorganisms can cause infections. For this reason, burn patients are maintained in an aseptic environment, which attempts to prevent the entry of microorganisms into the wound. They are also given antimicrobial drugs, which kill microorganisms or suppress their growth. **Debridement** (dā-brēd-mon′), the removal of dead tissue from the burn, helps to prevent infections by cleaning the wound and removing tissue in which infections could develop. Skin grafts, performed within a week of the injury, also prevent infections by closing the wound and preventing the entry of microorganisms.

Despite these efforts, however, infections are still the major cause of death of burn victims. Depression of the immune system during the first or second week after the injury contributes to the high infection rate. The thermally altered tissue is recognized as a foreign substance that can stimulate the immune system. As a result, the immune system is overwhelmed as immune system cells become less effective and production of the chemicals that normally provide resistance to infections decreases (see chapter 14). The greater the magnitude of the burn, the greater the depression of the immune system, and the greater the risk of infection.

Venous thrombosis (throm-bō′sis), the development of a clot in a vein, is also a complication of burns. Blood normally forms a clot when exposed to damaged tissue, such as at a burn site, but the clot can also block blood flow, resulting in tissue destruction. In addition, the concentration of chemicals in the blood that cause clotting increases for two reasons: loss of fluid from the burn and the increased release of clotting factors from the liver.

5	P R E D I C T

When Mr. S is first admitted to the burn unit, the nurses carefully monitor his urine output. Why does that make sense in light of his injuries?

✔ *Answer on page 111*

System Interactions

System	Interactions
Skeletal	Red bone marrow replaces red blood cells (erythrocytes) destroyed in the burnt skin.
Muscular	Loss of muscle mass resulting from the hypermetabolic state caused by the burn.
Nervous	Pain is sensed in the partial-thickness burns. The temperature-regulatory center in the brain is set to a higher temperature, contributing to increased body temperature. Abnormal K^+ concentrations disturb normal nervous system activity: elevated levels are caused by release of K^+ from damaged cells; low levels can be caused by rapid loss of these ions in fluid from the burn.
Endocrine	Increased secretion of epinephrine and norepinephrine from the adrenal glands in response to the injury contributes to increased body temperature by increasing metabolism.
Cardiovascular	Increased capillary permeability causes decreased blood volume, resulting in decreased blood delivery to tissues, edema, and shock. The pumping effectiveness of the heart is impaired by ion imbalance and substances released from the burn. Increased blood clotting causes venous thrombosis. Preferential delivery of blood to the injury promotes healing.
Lymphatic and Immune	Increased inflammation in response to tissue damage. Later, depression of the immune system can result in infections.
Respiratory	Airway obstruction can result from edema. An increased respiration rate is caused by increased metabolism and lactic acid buildup.
Digestive	Decreased blood delivery as a result of the burn causes degeneration of the intestinal lining and liver. Bacteria from the intestine can cause systemic infections. The liver releases blood-clotting factors in response to the injury. Increased nutrients necessary to support increased metabolism and for repair of the integumentary system are absorbed.
Urinary	The kidneys compensate for the increased fluid loss caused by the burn by greatly reducing or even stopping urine production. Decreased blood volume causes decreased blood flow to the kidneys, which reduces urine output, but can cause kidney tissue damage. Hemoglobin, released from red blood cells damaged in the burnt skin, can interfere with urine production in the kidneys.

Summary

The integumentary system consists of the skin, hair, glands, and nails.

Functions of the Integumentary System

The integumentary system separates and protects us from the external environment. Other functions include sensation, vitamin D production, temperature regulation, and excretion of small amounts of waste products.

Hypodermis

- The hypodermis is loose connective tissue that attaches the skin to underlying tissues.
- About half of the body's fat is stored in the hypodermis.

Skin

Dermis

- The dermis is dense connective tissue.
- Collagen and elastic fibers provide structural strength, and the blood vessels of the papillae supply the epidermis with nutrients.

Epidermis

- The epidermis is stratified squamous epithelium divided into strata.
  Cells are produced in the stratum basale.
  The stratum corneum is many layers of dead, squamous cells containing keratin. The most superficial layers are sloughed.
- Keratinization is the transformation of stratum basale cells into stratum corneum cells.
  Structural strength results from keratin inside the cells and from desmosomes, which hold the cells together.
  Permeability characteristics result from lipids surrounding the cells.

Skin Color

- Melanocytes produce melanin, which is responsible for different racial skin colors. Melanin production is determined genetically but can be modified by hormones and ultraviolet light (tanning).
- Carotene, a plant pigment ingested as a source of vitamin A, can cause the skin to appear yellowish.
- Scattering of light by collagen produces a bluish color.
- Increased blood flow produces a red skin color, whereas a decreased blood flow causes a pale skin color. Decreased blood oxygen results in the blue color of cyanosis.

Accessory Skin Structures

Hair

- Hairs are columns of dead, keratinized epithelial cells. Each hair consists of a shaft (above the skin), root (below the skin), and hair bulb (site of hair cell formation).
- Hairs have a growth phase and a resting phase.

Muscles

- Contraction of the arrector pili, which are smooth muscles, causes hair to "stand on end" and produces "goose flesh."

Glands

- Sebaceous glands produce sebum, which oils the hair and the surface of the skin.

- Merocrine sweat glands produce sweat, which cools the body.
- Apocrine sweat glands produce an organic secretion that can be broken down by bacteria to cause body odor.

Nails

- The nail consists of the nail body and nail root.
- The nail matrix produces the nail, which is stratum corneum containing hard keratin.

Physiology of the Integumentary System

Protection

- The skin prevents the entry of microorganisms, acts as a permeability barrier, and provides protection against abrasion and ultraviolet light.

Sensation

- The skin contains sensory receptors for pain, heat, cold, and pressure.

Vitamin D Production

- Ultraviolet light stimulates the production of a precursor molecule in the skin that is modified by the liver and kidneys into vitamin D.
- Vitamin D increases calcium uptake in the intestines.

Temperature Regulation

- Through dilation and constriction of blood vessels, the skin controls heat loss from the body.
- Evaporation of sweat cools the body.

Excretion

- Skin glands remove small amounts of waste products but are not important in excretion.

Effects of Aging on the Integumentary System

- Blood flow to the skin is reduced, the skin becomes thinner, and elasticity is lost.
- Sweat and sebaceous glands are less active, and the number of melanocytes decreases.

The Integumentary System as a Diagnostic Aid

- The integumentary system is easily observed and often reflects events occurring in other parts of the body (e.g., cyanosis, jaundice, rashes).

Burns

- Partial-thickness burns damage only the epidermis (first-degree burn) or the epidermis and the dermis (second-degree burn).
- Full-thickness burns (third-degree burns) destroy the epidermis, dermis, and usually underlying tissues.

Skin Cancer

- Basal cell carcinoma involves the cells of the stratum basale and is readily treatable.
- Squamous cell carcinoma involves the cells immediately superficial to the stratum basale and can metastasize.
- Malignant melanoma involves melanocytes, can metastasize, and is often fatal.

Content Review

1. Name the components of the integumentary system.
2. What type of tissue is the hypodermis, and what are its functions?
3. What type of tissue is the dermis? What is responsible for its structural strength? How does the dermis supply the epidermis with blood?
4. What kind of tissue is the epidermis? In which stratum of the epidermis are new cells formed? From which stratum are they sloughed?
5. Define "keratinization." What structural changes does keratinization produce to make the skin resistant to abrasion and water loss?
6. Name the cells that produce melanin. What happens to the melanin after it is produced? What is the function of melanin?
7. Describe the factors that determine the amount of melanin produced in the skin.
8. How do melanin, carotene, collagen, and blood affect skin color?
9. Define the "root," "shaft," and "hair bulb" of a hair. What kind of cells are found in a hair?
10. What is a hair follicle? Why is it important in the repair of skin?
11. What part of a hair is the site of hair growth? What are the stages of hair growth?
12. What happens when the arrector pili of the skin contract?
13. What secretion is produced by the sebaceous glands? What is the function of the secretion?
14. Which glands of the skin are responsible for cooling the body? Which glands are involved in producing body odor?
15. Name the parts of a nail. Where are the cells that make up the nail produced, and what kind of cells make up a nail? What is the lunula? Describe nail growth.
16. How does the integumentary system provide protection?
17. List the types of sensations detected by receptors in the skin.
18. Describe the production of vitamin D by the body. What is the function of vitamin D?
19. How does the integumentary system assist in the regulation of body temperature?
20. Name the substances excreted by skin glands. Is the skin an important site of excretion?
21. What changes occur in the skin as a result of aging?
22. Why is the skin a useful diagnostic aid? Give three examples of how the skin functions as a diagnostic aid.
23. Define the different categories of burns. How is repair accomplished after each type?
24. What is the most common cause of skin cancer? Describe three types of skin cancer and the risks of each type.

Develop Your Reasoning Skills

1. A woman has stretch marks on her abdomen, yet she states that she has never been pregnant. Is this possible?
2. Harry Fastfeet, a white man, jogs on a cool day. What color would you expect his skin to be (a) after going outside and just before starting to run, (b) during the run, and (c) 5 minutes after the run?
3. Given what you know about the cause of acne, propose some ways to prevent or treat the disorder.
4. Consider the following statement: Dark-skinned children are more susceptible to rickets (insufficient calcium in the bones) than fair-skinned children. Defend or refute this statement.
5. Pulling on hair can be quite painful, yet cutting hair is not painful. Explain.

Answers to Predict Questions

1. p. 98   Because the permeability barrier is composed mainly of lipids surrounding the epidermal cells, substances that are lipid-soluble can easily diffuse through the barrier. This fact is used as a basis for administering some medications through the skin. On the other hand, water-soluble substances have difficulty diffusing through the skin. The lipid barrier of the skin prevents water loss from the body.

2. p. 99   (a) The lips are pinker or redder than the palms of the hand. Several explanations for this are possible. There could be more blood vessels in the lips, there could be increased blood flow in the lips, or the blood vessels could be easier to see through the epidermis of the lips. The last possibility actually explains most of the difference in color between the lips and palms. The epidermis of the lips is thinner and not as heavily keratinized as that of the palms. In addition, the dermal papillae containing the blood vessels in the lips are "high" and closer to the surface.

(b) A person who does manual labor has a thicker stratum corneum (and possibly calluses) than a person who does not perform manual labor. The thicker epidermis masks the underlying blood vessels, and the palms do not appear as pink. In addition, carotene accumulating in the lipids of the stratum corneum might give the palms a yellowish cast.

(c) The posterior surface of the forearm appears darker because of the tanning effect of ultraviolet light from the sun. The posterior surface of the forearm is usually exposed to more sunlight than the anterior surface of the forearm.

3. p. 101   The story is impossible. Hair color results from melanin that is added to the hair in the hair bulb as the hair grows. The hair itself is dead. To turn white, the hair must grow out without the addition of melanin. This,

Answers to Predict Questions

of course, takes considerably more time than one night.

4. p. 102   On cold days, skin blood vessels of the ears and nose can dilate, bringing warm blood to the ears and nose, thus preventing tissue damage from the cold. The increased blood flow makes the ears and nose appear red.

5. p. 108   Reducing water loss is one of the normal functions of the skin. Loss of or damage to the skin can greatly increase water loss. In addition, burning large areas of the skin results in increased capillary permeability and additional loss of fluid from the burn into tissue spaces. The loss of fluid reduces blood volume, which results in reduced blood flow to the kidneys. Consequently, urine output by the kidneys decreases, which reduces fluid loss and thereby helps compensate for the fluid loss caused by the burn. The reduced blood flow to the kidneys can cause tissue damage, however. To counteract this effect, during the first 24 hours following the injury part of the treatment for burn victims is the administration of large volumes of fluid. But, how much fluid should be given? The amount of fluid given should be sufficient to match that lost plus enough to prevent kidney damage and allow the kidneys to function. Urine output is therefore monitored. If it is too low, more fluid is administered, and if it is too high, less fluid is administered. An adult receiving intravenous fluids should produce 30 to 50 mL of urine per hour, and children should produce 1 mL/kg of body weight per hour.

Chapter Six

The Skeletal System: Bones and Joints

articulation
A place where two bones come together; a joint.

cancellous bone
(kan'sĕ-lŭs) Bone with a latticelike appearance; spongy bone.

compact bone
Bone that is denser and has fewer spaces than cancellous bone.

endochondral ossification
Growth of cartilage, which is then replaced by bone.

foramen
(fō-rā'men) A hole; referring to a hole or opening in a bone.

girdle
A belt or zone; the bony region where the limbs attach to the body.

osteon
(os'tē-on) A single central canal, with its contents, and the associated concentric lamellae and osteocytes surrounding it; also called a Haversian system.

lamella
(lă-mel'ă) A thin sheet or layer of bone.

matrix
Noncellular substance surrounding the cells of connective tissue.

ossification
(os'i-fi-kā'shŭn) Bone formation.

paranasal sinus
Air-filled cavity within certain skull bones that connects to the nasal cavity; located in the frontal, maxillary, sphenoid, and ethmoid bones.

synovial fluid
(si-nō'vē-ăl) [G. *syn*, together + *oon*, egg] A somewhat slippery, viscous substance serving as a lubricant in movable joints, tendon sheaths, and bursae; produced by the synovial membranes.

trabecula
(tră-bek'ū-lă) [G., beam] A beam or plate of cancellous bone.

Objectives

After reading this chapter, you should be able to:

1. List and describe the components of the skeletal system.

2. Describe the components of the connective tissue matrix and state the function of each.

3. Describe the structure of compact and cancellous bone.

4. Outline the process of bone ossification, growth, remodeling, and repair.

5. Describe the main features of the skull as seen from the lateral, frontal, internal, and inferior views.

6. Describe the shape of the vertebral column and list its divisions. Describe the general features of each vertebra and the differences among vertebrae from each region of the vertebral column.

7. List the bones of the thoracic cage, including the three types of ribs.

8. Name and describe the bones of the pectoral girdle and upper limb.

9. Name and describe the bones of the pelvic girdle and lower limb.

10. List and describe the various types of joints.

11. Describe the major types of joint movement.

Sitting, standing, walking, picking up a pencil, and taking a breath all involve the skeletal system (figure 6.1). Without the skeletal system to support our bodies, we would have no rigid framework to support the soft tissues of the body and no system of levers so critical for movement. The skeletal system consists of bones and their associated connective tissues, including cartilage, tendons, and ligaments. The term skeleton is derived from a Greek word meaning dried. Despite this concept of the skeleton as dry, and nonliving, the skeletal system actually consists of dynamic, living tissues that are capable of growth, adapt to stress, and undergo repair after injury.

Functions of the Skeletal System

1. *Bone.* **Bone** is the most rigid component of the skeletal system.
   a. *Support.* Bone provides a rigid framework that supports the soft tissues of the body and maintains the body's shape.
   b. *Protection.* Bones protect internal organs that are critical to survival, such as the brain, lungs, and heart.
   c. *Lever system.* Bones provide a system of levers on which muscles act to produce body movements.
   d. *Mineral storage.* The matrix of bone contains abundant stores of minerals, which can be drawn upon by other tissues as needed.
   e. *Blood cell formation.* Blood cells are produced in the marrow of many bones.
2. *Cartilage.* **Cartilage** (kar′ti-lij) is somewhat rigid but more flexible than bone, and its functions reflect these characteristics.
   a. *Model for bone growth.* Cartilage is abundant in the embryo and the fetus, where it provides a model from which most of the adult bones develop. Cartilage is a major site of skeletal growth in the embryo, fetus, and child.
   b. *Smooth joint surfaces.* In the adult, the surfaces of bones within movable joints are covered with cartilage, which provides a smooth cushion between adjacent bones.
   c. *Support.* Cartilage also provides a firm, yet flexible support within certain structures, such as the nose, external ears, ribs, and trachea.
3. *Tendons and ligaments form attachments.* Tendons and ligaments are strong bands of fibrous connective tissue. **Tendons** attach muscles to bones, and **ligaments** attach bones to bones.

Connective Tissue

Bone, cartilage, tendons, and ligaments are connective tissues. In connective tissues the extracellular matrix is largely responsible for their characteristics. The characteristics of the extracellular matrix are determined by the types and relative

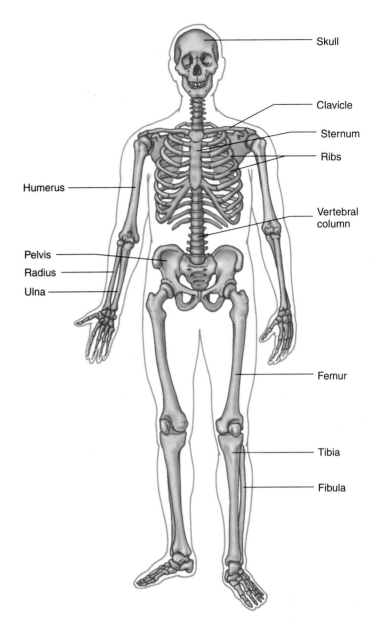

Figure 6.1 The Skeletal System

quantities of the molecules it contains, such as collagen, proteoglycan (ground substance), and other organic molecules, as well as water and minerals. **Collagen** (kol′lă-jen) is a tough, ropelike protein. **Proteoglycans** (prō′tē-ō-glī′kanz) are large molecules consisting of polysaccharides attached to core proteins, much like the needles of a pine are attached to the tree's branches. The proteoglycans form large aggregates, much like pine branches combine to form a whole tree. Proteoglycans can attract and retain large amounts of water between their polysaccharide "needles."

The extracellular matrix of tendons and ligaments contains large amounts of collagen fibers, making these structures very tough, like ropes or cables. The extracellular matrix of cartilage contains collagen and proteoglycans. Collagen makes cartilage tough, whereas the water-filled proteoglycans make it smooth and resilient. As a result, cartilage is relatively rigid, but springs back to its original shape if it is bent or slightly compressed, and it is an excellent shock absorber.

The extracellular matrix of bone contains collagen and minerals, including calcium and phosphate. The matrix resembles reinforced concrete. The ropelike collagen fibers, like the reinforcing steel bars of reinforced concrete, lend flexible strength to the bone. The mineral component, like the concrete part of reinforced concrete, gives the bone compression (weight-bearing) strength. Most of the mineral in bone is in the form of calcium phosphate crystals called **hydroxyapatite** (hī-drok′sē-ap-ă-tīt).

---

1   P R E D I C T

What would a bone be like if all the mineral were removed? What would it be like if all the collagen were removed?

✔ *Answer on page 151*

General Features of Bone

There are four types of bone, based on their shape: long, short, flat, and irregular. **Long bones** are longer than they are wide. Most of the bones of the upper and lower limbs are long bones. **Short bones** are approximately as broad as they are long, such as the bones of the wrist and ankle. **Flat bones** have a relatively thin, flattened shape. Examples of flat bones are certain skull bones, ribs, scapulae (shoulder blades), and the sternum. **Irregular bones** include the vertebrae and facial bones, with shapes that do not fit readily into the other three categories.

Each long bone consists of a central shaft, called the **diaphysis** (dī-af′i-sis), and two ends, each called an **epiphysis** (e-pif′i-sis) (figure 6.2*a* and *b*). A thin layer of **articular** (ar-tik′ū-lăr; joint) **cartilage** covers the ends of the epiphyses where the bone articulates with other bones. A long bone that is still growing has an **epiphyseal plate**, or **growth plate**, composed of cartilage, between each epiphysis and the diaphysis (see figure 6.2*a*). The epiphyseal plate is the site of growth in bone length. When bone growth stops, the cartilage of each epiphyseal plate is replaced by bone and is called an **epiphyseal line** (see figure 6.2*b*).

Bones contain cavities such as the large **medullary cavity** in the diaphysis (see figure 6.2), as well as smaller cavities in the epiphyses of long bones and in the interior of other bones. These spaces are filled with either yellow or red marrow. **Marrow** is the soft tissue in the medullary cavities of the bone. **Yellow marrow** consists mostly of fat. **Red marrow** consists of blood-forming cells and is the only site of blood formation in adults (see chapter 11). Children's bones have proportionately more red marrow than do adult bones. As a person ages, red marrow is mostly replaced by yellow marrow. In adults, red marrow is confined to the bones in the central axis of the body and in the most proximal epiphyses of the limbs.

Most of the outer surface of bone is covered by dense connective tissue called the **periosteum** (per-ē-os′tē-ŭm), which contains blood vessels and nerves (see figure 6.2). The surface of the medullary cavity is lined with a thinner connective tissue membrane, the **endosteum** (en-dos′tē-ŭm). The periosteum and endosteum contain **osteoblasts** (os′tē-ō-blastz;

bone-forming cells), which function in the formation of bone, as well as in the repair and remodeling of bone.

Bone is formed in thin sheets of extracellular matrix called **lamellae** (lă-mel′ē), with bone cells, called **osteocytes** (os′tē-ō-sītz), located between the lamellae (figure 6.3). The osteocytes are located within spaces called **lacunae** (lă-koo′nē). Cell processes extend from the osteocytes across the extracellular matrix of the lamellae within tiny canals called **canaliculi** (kan-ă-lik′ū-lī).

There are two major types of bone, based on their histological structure. **Compact bone** is mostly solid matrix and cells. **Cancellous** (kan′sĕ-lŭs) **bone** consists of a lacy network of bone with many small, marrow-filled spaces.

Compact Bone

Compact bone (figure 6.3*a*) forms the diaphysis of long bones and the thinner surfaces of all other bones. Most of the lamellae of compact bone are organized into sets of concentric rings, with each set surrounding a **central**, or **Haversian** (ha-ver′shan), **canal**. Blood vessels that run parallel to the long axis of the bone are contained within the central canals. Each central canal, with the lamellae and osteocytes surrounding it, is called an **osteon** (os′tē-on), or **Haversian system**. Each osteon, seen in cross section, looks like a microscopic target, with the central canal as the "bull's eye" (figure 6.3*b*). Osteocytes, located in lacunae, are connected to one another by cell processes in canaliculi. The canaliculi give the osteon the appearance of having tiny cracks in the lamellae.

Osteocytes receive nutrients and eliminate wastes through blood vessels in the compact bone. Blood vessels in the periosteum and endosteum supply blood to blood vessels in the central canals. Nutrients leave the blood vessels of the central canals and diffuse to the osteocytes through the canaliculi. Waste products diffuse in the opposite direction.

Cancellous Bone

Cancellous (spongy) bone (see figures 6.2*b* and 6.4) is located in the epiphyses of long bones, and it forms the center of all other bones. It consists of delicate interconnecting rods or plates of bone called **trabeculae** (tră-bek′ū-lē; beam), which resemble the beams or scaffolding of a building (figure 6.4*a*). Like scaffolding, the trabeculae add strength to a bone without the added weight that would be present if the bone were solid mineralized matrix. The spaces between the trabeculae are filled with marrow. Each trabecula consists of several lamellae with osteocytes between the lamellae (figure 6.4*b*). Usually no blood vessels penetrate the trabeculae, and the trabeculae have no central canals. Nutrients exit vessels in the marrow and pass by diffusion through canaliculi to the osteocytes of the trabeculae.

Bone Ossification

Ossification (os′i-fi-kā′shŭn) is the formation of bone by osteoblasts. It involves the synthesis of an organic matrix

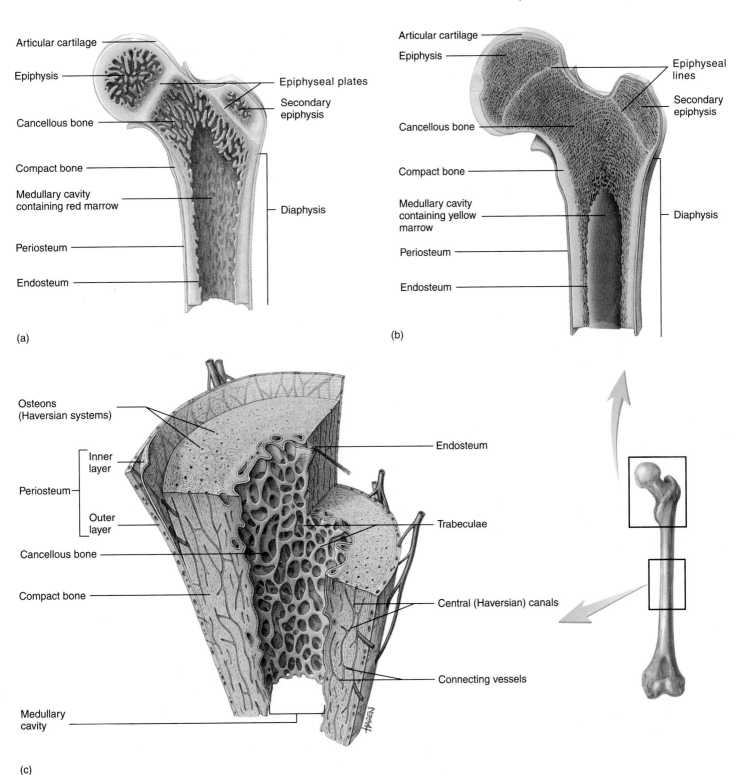

Figure 6.2   A Long Bone

(*a*) Frontal section through the end of a young long bone (femur). (*b*) Frontal section through the end of an adult long bone (femur). (*c*) Internal features of a part of a long bone.

containing collagen and proteoglycans and the addition of hydroxyapatite crystals to the matrix. After an osteoblast becomes completely surrounded by bone matrix, it becomes a mature bone cell, or osteocyte. Bones develop in the fetus by two processes, each involving the formation of bone matrix on preexisting connective tissue (figure 6.5). Bone formation that occurs within connective tissue membranes is intramembranous ossification, and bone formation that occurs inside cartilage is endochondral ossification. Both types of bone formation result in compact and cancellous bone.

115

Osteon (Haversian system)

Lamellae between osteons

Blood vessels within a central canal

Osteocytes in lacunae

(a)   Connecting vessel

Lamellae on surface of the bone

Concentric rings of lamellae

Periosteum

Concentric rings of lamellae in an osteon

Canaliculi

Central canal

Lacunae

(b)

Figure 6.3   Compact Bone

(*a*) Fine structure of compact bone. (*b*) Photomicrograph of compact bone.

Intramembranous (in′tră-mem′brā-nŭs) **ossification** occurs when osteoblasts begin to produce bone in connective tissue membranes. This occurs primarily in the bones of the skull. Osteoblasts line up on the surface of connective tissue fibers and begin depositing bone matrix to form trabeculae. The process begins in areas called **ossification centers** (see figure 6.5), and the trabeculae radiate out from the centers. Usually two or more ossification centers exist in each flat skull bone, and the skull bones result from fusion of these centers as they enlarge. The trabeculae are constantly remodeled after their initial formation, and they may enlarge or be replaced by compact bone.

The bones at the base of the skull and most of the remaining skeletal system develop through the process of **endochondral ossification** from cartilage models, which have the general shape of the mature bone (figure 6.6*a*). During endochondral ossification, cartilage cells, called **chondrocytes**, increase in number, hypertrophy (enlarge), and die; and the cartilage matrix becomes calcified, forming an ossification center. As this process is occurring in the center of the cartilage model, blood vessels accumulate in the perichondrium. The presence of blood vessels in the outer surface of future bone causes some of the unspecified

connective tissue cells on the surface to become osteoblasts. These osteoblasts then produce a collar of bone around part of the outer surface of the diaphysis, and the perichondrium becomes periosteum in that area (figure 6.6*b*). Blood vessels also grow into the center of the diaphyses, stimulating ossification to occur. The center part of the diaphysis, where bone first begins to appear, is called the **primary ossification center**. Osteoblasts invade spaces in the center of the bone left by the dying cartilage cells, some of the calcified cartilage matrix is removed by cells called **osteoclasts** (os′tē-ō-klastz; bone-eating cells), and the osteoblasts line up on the remaining calcified matrix and begin to form bone lamellae. As the bone develops it is constantly remodeled. A medullary cavity forms in the center of the diaphysis as osteoclasts remove bone and calcified cartilage, which are replaced by bone marrow (figure 6.6*c* and *d*). Later, **secondary ossification centers** form in the epiphyses (figure 6.6*e* and *f*).

Bone Growth

All bone growth occurs by the apposition of new bone lamellae onto existing bone or other connective tissue. As osteoblasts deposit new bone matrix on the surface of bones

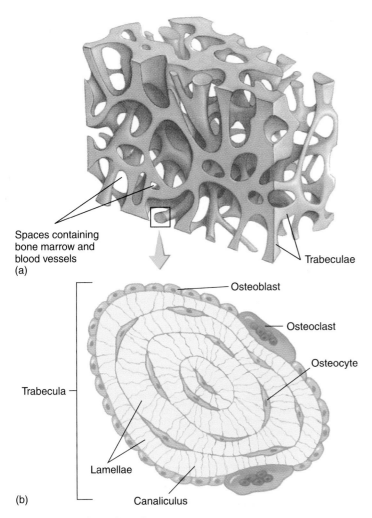

Spaces containing
bone marrow and
blood vessels
(a)

Trabeculae

Osteoblast

Osteoclast

Osteocyte

Trabecula

Lamellae

(b)

Canaliculus

Figure 6.4   Cancellous Bone

(*a*) Trabeculae (beams of bone) are separated by spaces, which in life are filled with marrow. (*b*) Transverse section of a trabecula.

between the periosteum and the existing bone matrix, the bone increases in width or diameter. Growth in the length of a bone, which is the major source of increased height in the individual, occurs in the epiphyseal plate (figure 6.7). Chondrocytes increase in number within the proliferating zone of the epiphyseal plate. They line up in columns parallel to the long axis of the bone, causing elongation of the bone, and then hypertrophy and die. The cartilage matrix is calcified. Much of the cartilage that forms around the hypertrophied cells is removed by osteoclasts, and the dying chondrocytes are replaced by osteoblasts. The osteoblasts start forming bone by depositing bone lamellae on the surface of the calcified cartilage. This process produces a zone of ossification on the diaphyseal side of the epiphyseal plate.

2   P R E D I C T

Describe the appearance of an adult if endochondral growth did not occur in the long bones during childhood.

✔ *Answer on page 151*

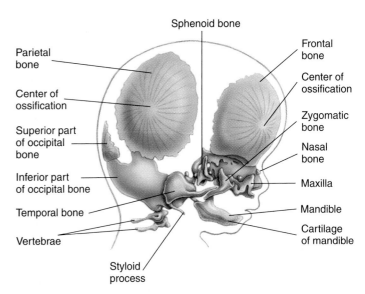

Sphenoid bone

Parietal bone

Frontal bone

Center of ossification

Center of ossification

Superior part of occipital bone

Zygomatic bone

Inferior part of occipital bone

Nasal bone

Temporal bone

Maxilla

Vertebrae

Mandible

Styloid process

Cartilage of mandible

Figure 6.5   Bone Formation in a 12-Week-Old Fetus

Intramembranous ossification occurs at ossification centers in the flat bones of the skull (yellow). Endochondral ossification occurs in the bones forming the inferior part of the skull (blue).

Bone Remodeling

Bone remodeling involves the removal of existing bone by osteoclasts and the deposition of new bone by osteoblasts. Bone remodeling occurs in all bone. Remodeling of newly formed bone in the epiphyseal plate is involved in bone growth. It is responsible for changes in bone shape, the adjustment of bone to stress, bone repair, and calcium ion regulation in the body fluids. A long bone increases in length and diameter by apposition of new bone on the outer surface and by growth at the epiphyseal plate. At the same time, bone is removed from the inner, medullary surface of the bone. Consequently, as the bone diameter increases, the thickness of the compact bone surrounding the medullary cavity tends to remain fairly constant. If the size of the medullary cavity did not also increase as bone size increased, the bone would become thick and very heavy.

Bone is the major storage site for calcium in the body. Blood calcium levels must be maintained within narrow limits for functions such as action potential conduction and muscle contraction to occur normally. Calcium is removed from bones when blood calcium levels decrease, and it is deposited when dietary calcium is adequate. This removal and deposition is under hormonal control (see chapter 10).

If too much bone is deposited, the bones become thick or have abnormal spurs or lumps that can interfere with normal function. Too little bone formation or too much bone removal weakens the bones and makes them susceptible to fracture.

Bone Repair

When a bone is broken, blood vessels in the bone are also damaged. The vessels bleed, and a clot forms in the damaged area (figure 6.8*a*). Two to three days after the injury, blood vessels and cells from surrounding tissues begin to invade the

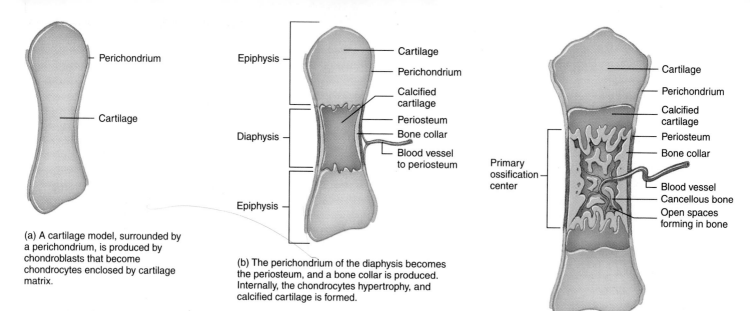

(a) A cartilage model, surrounded by a perichondrium, is produced by chondroblasts that become chondrocytes enclosed by cartilage matrix.

Perichondrium

Cartilage

(b) The perichondrium of the diaphysis becomes the periosteum, and a bone collar is produced. Internally, the chondrocytes hypertrophy, and calcified cartilage is formed.

Epiphysis

Diaphysis

Epiphysis

Cartilage
Perichondrium
Calcified cartilage
Periosteum
Bone collar
Blood vessel to periosteum

Cartilage
Perichondrium
Calcified cartilage
Periosteum
Bone collar
Blood vessel
Cancellous bone
Open spaces forming in bone

Primary ossification center

(c) A primary ossification center forms as blood vessels and osteoblasts invade the calcified cartilage. The osteoblasts lay down bone matrix, forming cancellous bone.

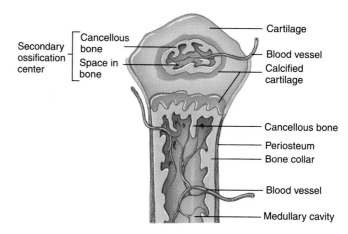

Cartilage
Calcified cartilage
Perichondrium
Calcified cartilage
Periosteum
Bone collar
Blood vessel
Medullary cavity

(d) The process of bone collar formation, cartilage calcification, and cancellous bone production continues. Calcified cartilage begins to form in the epiphysis. A medullary cavity begins to form in the center of the diaphysis.

Secondary ossification center

Cancellous bone
Space in bone

Cartilage
Blood vessel
Calcified cartilage

Cancellous bone
Periosteum
Bone collar

Blood vessel

Medullary cavity

(e) Secondary ossification centers form in the epiphyses of long bones.

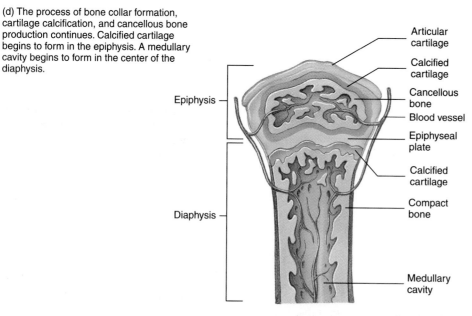

Epiphysis

Diaphysis

Articular cartilage
Calcified cartilage
Cancellous bone
Blood vessel
Epiphyseal plate
Calcified cartilage
Compact bone

Medullary cavity

(f) The original cartilage model is almost completely ossified. Unossified cartilage becomes the epiphyseal plate and the articular cartilage over the articular (joint) surface at the ends of the bone.

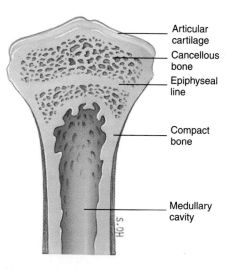

Articular cartilage
Cancellous bone
Epiphyseal line

Compact bone

Medullary cavity

(g) Mature bone in which the epiphyseal plate has become the epiphyseal line and all the cartilage in the epiphysis, except the articular cartilage, has become bone.

Figure 6.6 Endochondral Ossification of a Long Bone

Epiphyseal side

Epiphyseal
plate

1. Chondrocytes in the resting zone
   do not divide.

2. New cartilage is produced on the
   epiphyseal side of the plate as the
   chondrocytes divide and form stacks
   of cells.

3. Chondrocytes mature and enlarge.

4. Matrix is calcified and chondrocytes
   die.

5. The cartilage on the diaphyseal side
   of the plate is replaced by bone.

(1) Zone of
resting
cartilage

(2) Proliferating
zone

(3) Zone of
hypertrophy

(4) Calcified
cartilage

(5) Ossification
zone

Diaphyseal side

(a)

(b)

Length of bone
increases.

Epiphyseal
plate

Chondrocytes
divide and enlarge.

Thickness of
epiphyseal plate
remains unchanged.

Calcified cartilage
is replaced by bone.

Bone is added
to diaphysis.

Bone of
diaphysis

(c)

Figure 6.7   Endochondral Bone Growth

(*a*) Location of the epiphyseal plate in a long bone. (*b*) Photomicrograph of an epiphyseal plate, demonstrating the zones of proliferation and hypertrophy and the areas of calcification and ossification. (*c*) As the chondrocytes of the epiphyseal plate divide and align in columns, there is an expansion of cartilage toward the epiphysis, and the bone elongates. At the same time, the older cartilage is calcified and then replaced by bone, which is, in turn, remodeled, resulting in expansion of the medullary cavity of the diaphysis. The net result is an epiphyseal plate that remains uniform in thickness through time but that is constantly moving toward the epiphysis, resulting in elongation of the bone.

clot. Some of these cells produce a fibrous network of connective tissue between the broken bones, which holds the bone fragments together and fills the gap between the fragments. Other cells produce islets of cartilage in the fibrous network. The zone of tissue repair between the two bone fragments is called a **callus** (figure 6.8*b*).

Osteoblasts enter the callus and begin forming cancellous bone (figure 6.8*c*). Cancellous bone formation in the cal-

lus is usually complete 4 to 6 weeks after the injury. Immobilization of the bone is critical up to this time, because movement can refracture the delicate new matrix. Subsequently, the cancellous bone is slowly remodeled to form compact and cancellous bone, and the repair is complete (figure 6.8*d*). Total healing of the fracture may require several months. If bone healing occurs properly, the healed region can be even stronger than the adjacent bone.

Figure 6.8   Bone Repair

(*a*) When a bone is broken, a clot forms in the damaged area. (*b*) Blood vessels and cells invade the clot and produce a fibrous network and cartilage between the broken bones, called a callus. (*c*) Osteoblasts enter the callus and begin forming cancellous bone. (*d*) The cancellous bone is slowly remodeled to form compact and cancellous bone, and the repair is complete.

Clinical Focus   Bone Fractures

Bone fractures (figure A) can be classified as **open,** or **compound,** if the bone protrudes through the skin, and **closed,** or **simple,** if the skin is not perforated. If the fracture totally separates the two bone fragments, it is called **complete;** if it doesn't, it is called **incomplete.**

An incomplete fracture that occurs on the convex side of the curve of a bone is called a **green-stick fracture.** A **comminuted** (kom′i-nū-ted) fracture is one in which the bone breaks into more than two fragments. Fractures can also be classified according to

the direction of the fracture line as **linear** (parallel to the long axis), **transverse** (at right angles to the long axis), or **oblique** (at an angle other than a right angle to the long axis).

Figure A   Bone Fractures

Although immobilization is critical during the early stages of bone healing, complete immobilization is not good for the muscles and joints, or even for the bone itself. Not long ago, it was common practice to completely immobilize a bone for as long as 10 weeks. It is now known that, if a bone is immobilized for as little as 2 weeks, the muscles associated with that bone may lose as much as half their strength. Furthermore, if a bone is completely immobilized, it is not subjected to the normal mechanical stresses that help it to form. Bone matrix is reabsorbed, and the strength of the bone decreases. In experimental animals, complete immobilization of the back for 1 month resulted in up to a threefold decrease in vertebral compression strength. Modern therapy attempts to balance bone immobilization with enough exercise to minimize muscle and bone atrophy and to maintain joint mobility. These goals are accomplished by limiting the amount of time a cast is left on the patient, and by employing "walking casts," which allow some movement.

General Considerations of Bone Anatomy

It is traditional to list 206 bones in the average adult skeleton (table 6.1 and figure 6.9), although the actual number varies from person to person and decreases with age as some bones become fused.

Several common terms are used to describe the features of bones (table 6.2). For example, a hole in a bone is called a **foramen** (fō-rā′men; pl.: foramina, fō-rā′min-ă). A foramen usually exists in a bone because some structure, such as a nerve or blood vessel, passes through the bone at that point. If the hole is elongated into a tunnellike passage through the bone, it is called a **canal** or a **meatus** (mē-ā′tus). A depression in a bone is called a **fossa** (fos′ă). A lump on a bone is called

Clinical Focus   Skeletal Disorders

Growth and Developmental Disorders

Giantism (jī′an-tizm) is a condition of abnormally increased size that usually involves excessive endochondral growth at the epiphyseal plates of long bones. **Dwarfism,** the condition in which a person is abnormally small, is often the result of improper growth in the epiphyseal plates (figure B).

Osteogenesis imperfecta (os′tē-ō-jen′ĕ-sis im-per-fek′tă), a group of genetic disorders producing very brittle bones that are easily fractured, occurs because insufficient collagen is formed to properly strengthen the bones. Prenatal fractures of the limbs often occur in the fetus. These fractures usually heal in poor alignment, causing the limbs to appear bent and shortened.

Rickets (rik′ets) is a condition involving growth retardation resulting from nutritional deficiencies either in minerals (calcium and phosphate, necessary for normal ossification) or in vitamin D (necessary for calcium and phosphate absorption). The condition results in bones that are soft, weak, and easily broken. Rickets most often occurs in children who receive inadequate amounts of sunlight (necessary for vitamin D production by the body) and whose diets are deficient in vitamin D.

Bacterial Infections

Osteomyelitis (os′tē-ō-mī-e-lī′tis) is bone inflammation that often results from bacterial infection, and it can lead to complete destruction of the bone. **Staphylococcus** (staf′i-lō-kok′ŭs) (staph) infections, introduced into the body through wounds, are the most common cause of osteomyelitis. Tuberculosis is primarily a lung disease, but it can also affect bones. Because of milk pasteurization and other improvements in hygiene, tuberculosis became rare in the United States. Because tuberculosis can be a complication in AIDS and because a drug-resistant form of tuberculosis has emerged, tuberculosis has once more become a clinical problem in the United States.

Tumors

There are many types of bone **tumors** with a wide range of resultant bone defects. Tumors may be benign or malignant. Malignant bone tumors may metastasize (spread) to other parts of the body or may result from metastasizing tumors elsewhere.

Decalcification

Osteomalacia (os′tē-ō-mă-lā′shē-ă), or the softening of bones, results from calcium depletion from bones. If the body has an unusual need for calcium (e.g., during pregnancy when fetal growth requires large amounts of calcium), it may be removed from the mother's bones, which consequently soften and weaken. Osteomalacia is sometimes called adult rickets and can result from vitamin D deficiency.

Osteoporosis (os′tē-ō-pō-rō′sis), or porous bone, results from reduction in the overall quantity of bone tissue (see Systems Pathology: Osteoporosis on p. 148).

Figure B   Giant and Dwarf (both are adults)

Table 6.1 Number of Named Bones Listed by Category

Bones		Number	Bones	Number
AXIAL SKELETON			**APPENDICULAR SKELETON**	
Skull			*Pectoral Girdle*	
Cranial vault			Scapula	2
Paired	Parietal	2	Clavicle	2
	Temporal	2	*Upper Limb*	
Unpaired	Frontal	1	Humerus	2
	Occipital	1	Ulna	2
	Sphenoid	1	Radius	2
	Ethmoid	1	Carpals	16
Face			Metacarpals	10
Paired	Maxilla	2	Phalanges	28
	Zygomatic	2	TOTAL GIRDLE AND UPPER LIMB	64
	Palatine	2	*Pelvic Girdle*	
	Nasal	2	Coxa	2
	Lacrimal	2	*Lower Limb*	
	Inferior nasal concha	2	Femur	2
Unpaired	Mandible	1	Tibia	2
	Vomer	1	Fibula	2
Auditory ossicles	Malleus	2	Patella	2
	Incus	2	Tarsals	14
	Stapes	2	Metatarsals	10
	TOTAL SKULL	28	Phalanges	28
Hyoid		1	TOTAL GIRDLE AND LOWER LIMB	62
			TOTAL APPENDICULAR SKELETON	126
Vertebral Column			**TOTAL BONES**	206
Cervical vertebrae		7		
Thoracic vertebrae		12		
Lumbar vertebrae		5		
Sacrum		1		
Coccyx		1		
	TOTAL VERTEBRAL COLUMN	26		
Thoracic Cage				
Ribs		24		
Sternum (3 parts, sometimes considered 3 bones)		1		
	TOTAL THORACIC CAGE	25		
	TOTAL AXIAL SKELETON	80		

a **tubercle** (too'ber-kl), or **tuberosity** (too'ber-os'i-tē), and a projection from a bone is called a **process**. Most tubercles and processes are sites of muscle attachment on the bone. Increased muscle pull, such as when a person lifts weights to build up muscle mass, can increase the size of some tubercles. The smooth, rounded end of a bone, where it forms an articulation (a joint) with another bone, is called a **condyle** (kon'dīl).

Axial Skeleton

The axial skeleton is divided into the skull, the vertebral column, and the thoracic cage.

Skull

The bones of the skull (see table 6.1) are divided into two groups: those of the cranial vault and those of the face. The **cranial vault**, or **braincase**, consists of 8 bones that immediately surround and protect the brain; the 14 **facial bones** form the structure of the face. Thirteen of the facial bones are rather solidly connected to form the bulk of the face. The mandible, the fourteenth bone, forms a freely movable articulation with the rest of the skull. There are also 3 auditory ossicles (os'i-klz) in each middle ear (6 total) to bring the total number of bones in the skull to 28.

The **hyoid** (hī'oyd) bone is not part of the skull but is attached to the skull and larynx by muscles and ligaments. It

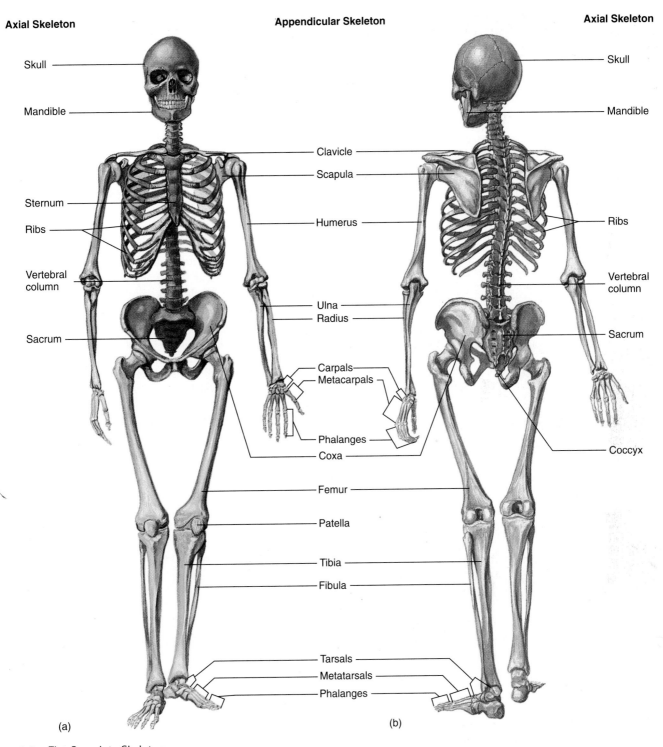

Axial Skeleton

Skull

Mandible

Sternum

Ribs

Vertebral
column

Sacrum

Appendicular Skeleton

Clavicle

Scapula

Humerus

Ulna

Radius

Carpals

Metacarpals

Phalanges

Coxa

Femur

Patella

Tibia

Fibula

Tarsals

Metatarsals

Phalanges

Axial Skeleton

Skull

Mandible

Ribs

Vertebral
column

Sacrum

Coccyx

(a)

(b)

Figure 6.9 The Complete Skeleton

(The skeleton is not in the anatomical position) (*a*) Anterior view. (*b*) Posterior view.

serves as the attachment point for several important neck and tongue muscles (the hyoid bone and associated muscles can be seen in figure 7.16).

Many students studying anatomy never see the separate, individual bones of the skull. Even if they do, it makes more sense from a functional, or clinical, perspective to study most of the bones as they appear together in the intact skull. Many

of the anatomical features of the skull cannot be fully appreciated by examining the separate bones. For example, several ridges on the skull cross more than one bone, and several foramina are located between bones rather than within a single bone. For these reasons, it is more relevant to think of the skull, excluding the mandible, as a single unit. The major features of the intact skull are therefore described from four views.

Table 6.2 General Anatomical Terms for Various Features of Bones

Term	Description
Major Features	
Body, shaft	Main portion
Head	Enlarged (often rounded) end
Neck	Constricted area between head and body
Condyle	Smooth, rounded articular surface
Facet	Small, flattened articular surface
Crest	Prominent ridge
Process	Prominent projection
Tubercle or tuberosity	Knob or enlargement
Trochanter	Large tuberosity found only on the proximal femur
Epicondyle	Enlargement near or above a condyle
Openings or Depressions	
Foramen	Hole
Canal, meatus	Tunnel
Fissure	Cleft
Sinus	Cavity
Fossa	Depression

Lateral View

The **parietal** (pă-rī′ĕ-tăl; wall) and **temporal** (tem′pŏ-răl; the term refers to time; the hairs of the temples turn white, indicating the passage of time) **bones** form a large portion of the side of the head (figure 6.10). These two bones join each other on the side of the head at the **squamous** (skwā′mŭs) **suture**. A suture is a joint uniting bones of the skull. Anteriorly, the parietal bone is joined to the **frontal** (forehead) **bone** by the **coronal** (kōr′ō-năl) **suture**, and posteriorly it is joined to the **occipital** (ok-sip′i-tăl; back of the head) bone by the **lambdoid** (lam′doyd; shaped like the Greek letter lambda, λ) **suture**. A prominent feature of the temporal bone is a large opening, the **external auditory meatus** (mē-ā′tus), a canal that enables sound waves to reach the eardrum. The **mastoid** (mas′toyd; resembling a breast) **process** of the temporal bone can be seen and felt as a prominent lump just posterior to the ear. Important neck muscles involved in rotation of the head attach to the mastoid process.

Part of the **sphenoid** (sfē′noyd; wedge-shaped) **bone** can be seen immediately anterior to the temporal bone. Although it appears to be two small, paired bones on either side of the skull, the sphenoid bone is actually a single bone that extends completely across the skull. It resembles a butterfly, with its body in the center of the skull and its wings extending to the sides of the skull. Anterior to the sphenoid bone is the **zygomatic** (zī-gō-mat′ik; yoke) **bone**, or cheek bone, which can be easily felt. The **zygomatic arch**, which consists of joined processes from the temporal and zygomatic bones, forms a

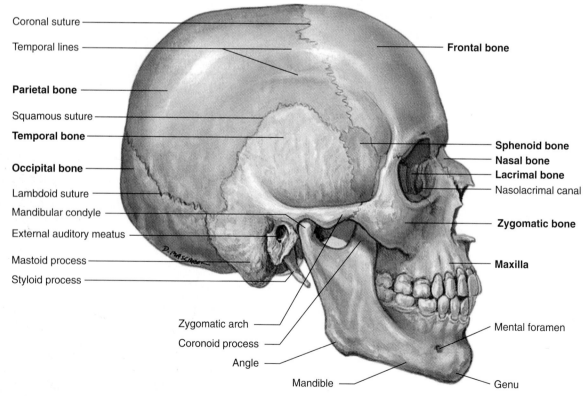

Figure 6.10 Lateral View of the Skull

Viewed from the right side.

bridge across the side of the face and provides a major attachment site for a muscle moving the mandible.

The **maxilla** (mak-sil′ă) forms the upper jaw, and the **mandible** (man′di-bl) forms the lower jaw. The maxilla articulates by sutures to the temporal bone. The maxilla contains the superior set of teeth, and the mandible contains the inferior teeth.

Frontal View

The major structures seen from the frontal view are the frontal bone, the zygomatic bones, the maxillae, and the mandible (figure 6.11*a*). The teeth are very prominent in this view. Many bones of the face can be easily felt through the skin (figure 6.11*b*).

From this view, the most prominent openings into the skull are the **orbits** (ōr′bitz) (eye sockets) and the **nasal cavity**. The orbits are cone-shaped fossae, so named because of the rotation of the eyes within them. The bones of the orbits provide both protection for the eyes and attachment points for the muscles that move the eyes. The orbit is a good example of why it is valuable to study the skull as an intact structure. No fewer than seven bones come together to form the orbit, and, for the most part, the contribution of each bone to the orbit cannot be appreciated when the bones are examined individually.

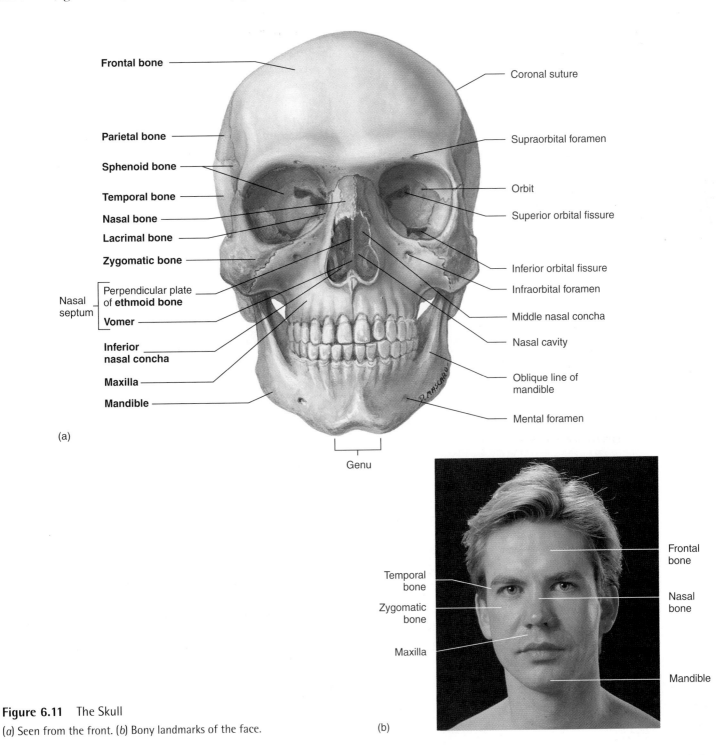

Figure 6.11   The Skull

(*a*) Seen from the front. (*b*) Bony landmarks of the face.

Each orbit (see figure 6.11*a*) has several openings through which structures communicate with other cavities. The largest of these are the **superior** and **inferior orbital fissures**. They provide openings through which nerves and blood vessels communicate with the orbit or pass to the face. The optic nerve, for the sense of vision, passes from the eye through the **optic foramen** and enters the cranial vault. The **nasolacrimal** (nā-zō-lak′ri-măl) **canal** (see figure 6.10) passes from the orbit into the nasal cavity. It contains a duct that carries tears from the eyes to the nasal cavity. A small **lacrimal** (lak′ri-măl; tear) bone can be seen in the orbit just above the opening of this canal (see figure 6.10).

3   P R E D I C T

Why does your nose run when you cry?

✔ *Answer on page 151*

The nasal cavity is divided into right and left halves by a **nasal septum** (sep′tŭm; wall) (see figure 6.11*a*). The bony part of the nasal septum consists primarily of the **vomer** (vō′mer; shaped like a plowshare) inferiorly and the **perpendicular plate** of the **ethmoid** (eth′moyd; sieve-shaped) **bone** superiorly. The anterior part of the nasal septum is formed by cartilage.

The external part of the nose is formed mostly of cartilage. The bridge of the nose is formed by the **nasal bones**.

Each of the lateral walls of the nasal cavity has three bony shelves, the **nasal conchae** (kon′kē; resembling a conch shell). The inferior nasal concha is a separate bone, and the middle and superior conchae are projections from the ethmoid bone. The conchae function to increase the surface area in the nasal cavity. The increased surface area of the overlying epithelium facilitates moistening and warming of the air inhaled through the nose (see chapter 15).

Several of the bones associated with the nasal cavity have large cavities within them, called the **paranasal** (par-ă-nā′săl) **sinuses** (figure 6.12), which open into the nasal cavity. The sinuses decrease the weight of the skull and act as resonating chambers during voice production. Compare the normal voice to the voice of a person who has a cold and whose sinuses are "stopped up." The sinuses are named for the bones where they are located and include the frontal, maxillary, ethmoidal, and sphenoidal sinuses.

The skull has additional sinuses, the **mastoid air cells**, which are located inside the mastoid processes of the temporal bone. These air cells open into the middle ear instead of into the nasal cavity. An auditory tube connects the middle ear to the throat.

Interior of the Cranial Vault

When the floor of the cranial vault is viewed from above with the roof cut away (figure 6.13), it can be divided roughly into three

(a)

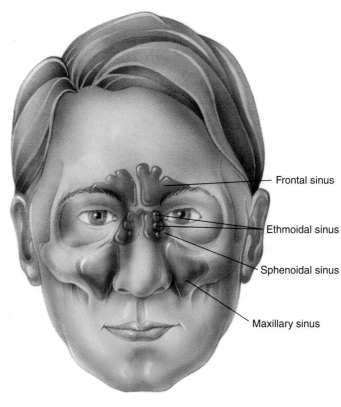

(b)

Figure 6.12   The Paranasal Sinuses

(*a*) Lateral view. (*b*) Anterior view.

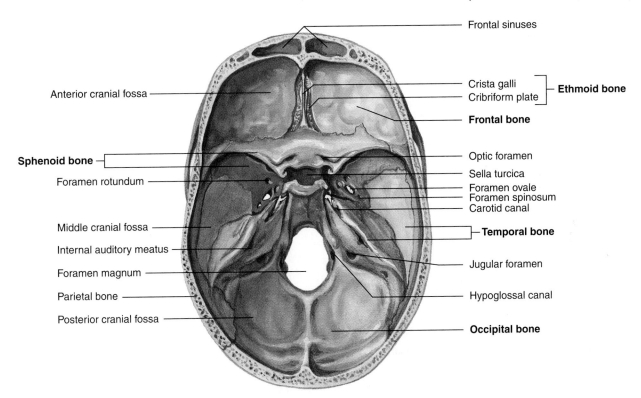

Frontal sinuses

Crista galli
Cribriform plate   **Ethmoid bone**

Frontal bone

Anterior cranial fossa

Optic foramen

Sphenoid bone

Sella turcica
Foramen ovale
Foramen spinosum
Carotid canal

Foramen rotundum

Middle cranial fossa

Temporal bone

Internal auditory meatus

Jugular foramen

Foramen magnum

Parietal bone

Hypoglossal canal

Posterior cranial fossa

Occipital bone

Figure 6.13   Floor of the Cranial Vault
The roof of the skull has been removed, and the floor is viewed from above.

cranial fossae (anterior, middle, and posterior), which are formed as the developing skull conforms to the shape of the brain. The bones forming the floor of the cranial vault, from anterior to posterior, are the frontal, ethmoid, sphenoid, temporal, and occipital. Several foramina can be seen in the floor of the middle fossa (see figure 6.13). These allow passage of nerves and blood vessels through the skull. The large **foramen magnum**, through which the spinal cord joins the brain, is located in the posterior fossa. The central region of the sphenoid bone is modified into a structure resembling a saddle, the **sella turcica** (sel′ă tŭr′sĭ-kă; Turkish saddle), which is occupied by the pituitary gland.

Base of Skull Seen from Below

Many of the same foramina that can be seen in the interior of the skull also can be seen in the base of the skull, when seen from below, with the mandible removed (figure 6.14). Other specialized structures, such as processes for muscle attachments, can also be seen. The foramen magnum is located in the occipital bone near the center of the skull base. **Occipital condyles** (ok-sip′i-tăl kon′dīlz), the smooth points of articulation between the skull and the vertebral column, are located beside the foramen magnum.

Two long, pointed **styloid** (stī′loyd; stylus or pen-shaped) **processes** project from the inferior surface of the temporal bone. Muscles involved in movement of the tongue, the hyoid bone, and the pharynx (throat) originate from this process. The **mandibular fossa**, where the mandible articulates with the temporal bone, is anterior to the mastoid process.

The **hard palate** (pal′ăt) forms the floor of the nasal cavity and the roof of the mouth. The anterior two thirds are formed by the maxillae, and the posterior one third by the **palatine** (pal′ă-tīn) **bones**. The connective tissue and muscles that make up the **soft palate** extend posteriorly from the hard or bony palate. The hard and soft palates function to separate the nasal cavity and nasopharynx (upper part of the throat) from the mouth, enabling us to chew and breathe at the same time.

Vertebral Column

The **vertebral column**, or backbone, is the central axis of the skeleton, extending from the base of the skull to slightly past the end of the pelvis. It usually consists of 26 individual bones, grouped into five regions (figure 6.15; see table 6.1): 7 **cervical** (ser′vi-kal) **vertebrae** (ver′tĕ-brē), 12 **thoracic** (thō-ras′ik) **vertebrae**, 5 **lumbar** (lŭm′bar) **vertebrae**, 1 **sacral** (sā′krăl) **bone**, and 1 **coccygeal** (kok-sij′ē-ăl) **bone**. The adult vertebral column has four major curvatures (see figure 6.15). The cervical region curves anteriorly, the thoracic region curves posteriorly, the lumbar region curves anteriorly, and the sacral and coccygeal regions together curve posteriorly.

The vertebral column performs the following five major functions: (1) supports the weight of the head and trunk; (2) protects the spinal cord; (3) allows spinal nerves to exit the spinal cord; (4) provides a site for muscle attachment; and (5) permits movement of the head and trunk.

Incisive fossa
Maxilla
Palatine foramen
Inferior orbital fissure
Pterygoid hamulus
Sphenoid bone
Foramen ovale
Foramen spinosum
External auditory meatus
Jugular foramen
Occipital condyle
Foramen magnum
Palatine process of maxillary bone
Horizontal plate of palatine bone
} Hard palate
Zygomatic bone
Lateral pterygoid plate
Vomer
Styloid process
Mandibular fossa
Carotid canal
Mastoid process
Temporal bone
Occipital bone
Nuchal lines

Figure 6.14 Base of the Skull
Viewed from below, mandible removed.

> **Did You Know?**
>
> Abnormal vertebral curvatures are not uncommon. **Kyphosis** (kī-fō′sis; hunchback) is an abnormal posterior curvature of the spine, mostly in the upper thoracic region, resulting in a hunchback condition. **Lordosis** (lōr-dō′sis; curving forward) is an abnormal anterior curvature of the spine, mainly in the lumbar region, resulting in a swayback condition. **Scoliosis** (skō-lē-ō′sis) is an abnormal lateral curvature of the spine.

Each vertebra consists of a body, an arch, and various processes (figure 6.16). The weight-bearing portion of each vertebra is the **body**. The **vertebral arch** surrounds a large opening called the **vertebral foramen**. The vertebral foramina of all the vertebrae form the **vertebral canal**, where the spinal cord is located. The vertebral canal protects the spinal cord from injury. Each vertebral arch consists of two **pedicles** (ped′ĭ-klz; feet), which extend from the body to the transverse process of each vertebra, and two **laminae** (lam′i-nē; thin plates), which extend from the transverse processes to the spinous process. A **transverse process** extends laterally from each side of the arch, between the pedicle and lamina, and a single **spinous process** projects dorsally from where the two laminae meet.

The spinous processes can be seen and felt as a series of lumps down the midline of the back (the spinous processes can be seen in figure 6.21). The transverse and spinous processes provide attachment sites for muscles that move the vertebral column. Spinal nerves exit the spinal cord through the **intervertebral foramina**, which are formed by notches in the pedicles of adjacent vertebrae (see figure 6.15). Each vertebra has a superior and inferior **articular process** where the vertebrae articulate with each other. Each articular process has a smooth "little face" called an **articular facet** (fas′et).

The vertebrae are separated by **intervertebral disks** (see figure 6.15), which are formed by dense fibrous connective tissue.

Regional Differences in Vertebrae

The **cervical vertebrae** (figure 6.17a to c) have very small bodies, except for the atlas, which has no body. Each of the transverse processes has a transverse foramen through which the vertebral arteries pass toward the brain. Several of the cervical vertebrae also have partly split spinous processes. The first cervical vertebra (figure 6.17a) is called the **atlas** because it holds up the head, as Atlas in classical mythology held up the world. Movement between the atlas and the occipital bone is

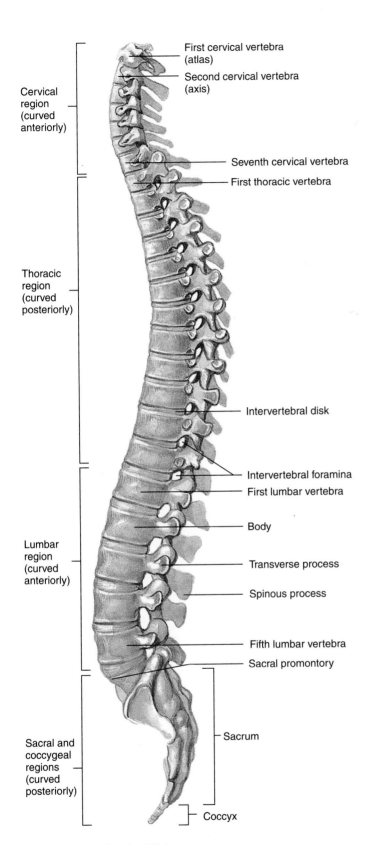

Figure 6.15 Vertebral Column
Viewed from the left side.

Cervical region (curved anteriorly)

First cervical vertebra (atlas)
Second cervical vertebra (axis)
Seventh cervical vertebra
First thoracic vertebra

Thoracic region (curved posteriorly)

Intervertebral disk

Intervertebral foramina
First lumbar vertebra
Body
Transverse process
Spinous process

Lumbar region (curved anteriorly)

Fifth lumbar vertebra
Sacral promontory

Sacrum

Sacral and coccygeal regions (curved posteriorly)

Coccyx

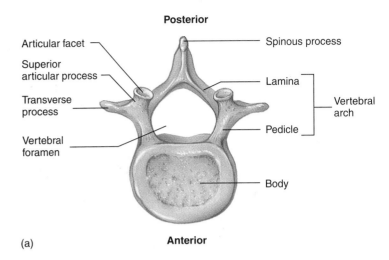

Posterior

Articular facet
Superior articular process
Transverse process
Vertebral foramen

Spinous process
Lamina
Pedicle
Body

Vertebral arch

(a)

Anterior

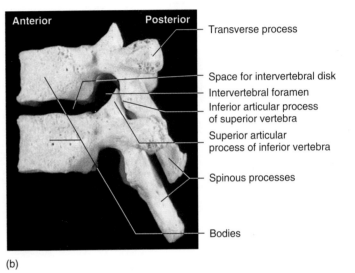

Anterior
Posterior
Transverse process
Space for intervertebral disk
Intervertebral foramen
Inferior articular process of superior vertebra
Superior articular process of inferior vertebra
Spinous processes
Bodies

(b)

Figure 6.16 Vertebrae

(*a*) A typical vertebra seen from a superior view. (*b*) Photograph of two thoracic vertebrae from a lateral view.

responsible for a "yes" motion of the head. It also allows a slight tilting of the head from side to side. The second cervical vertebra (figure 6.17*b*) is called the **axis** because a considerable amount of rotation occurs at this vertebra, as in shaking the head "no." This rotation occurs around a process called the **dens** (denz), which extends superiorly from the axis.

The **thoracic vertebrae** (figure 6.17*d*) possess long, thin spinous processes that are directed inferiorly. The thoracic vertebrae also have extra articular facets on their lateral surfaces that articulate with the ribs.

The **lumbar vertebrae** (figure 6.17*e*) have large, thick bodies and heavy, rectangular transverse and spinous processes. The superior articular facets of the lumbar vertebrae face medially, whereas the inferior articular facets face laterally. This arrangement tends to "lock" adjacent lumbar vertebrae together, giving the lumbar part of the vertebral column more strength. The articular facets in other regions of the vertebral column have a more "open" position, allowing for more rotational movement but less stability than in the lumbar region.

Figure 6.17 Regional Differences in Vertebrae

(*a*) Atlas (first cervical vertebra), superior view. (*b*) Axis (second cervical vertebra), superior view. (*c*) Another cervical vertebra, superior view. (*d*) Thoracic vertebra, superior view. (*e*) Lumbar vertebra, superior view.

Did You Know?

Because the cervical vertebrae are relatively delicate and have small bodies, dislocations and fractures are more common in this area than in other regions of the vertebral column. Because the lumbar vertebrae have massive bodies and carry a large amount of weight, ruptured intervertebral disks are more common in this area than in other regions of the column. Each intervertebral disk is made up of a ring of fibrous connective tissue with a softer center of semifluid tissue. The weight of the body may compress the disk, causing the fibrous ring to bulge or even break. This allows the vertebrae to come close together and compress the nerves exiting the intervertebral foramina. The coccyx is easily broken in falls during which a person sits down hard on a solid surface. Also, a mother's coccyx may be fractured during childbirth.

The five sacral vertebrae are fused into a single bone called the **sacrum** (figure 6.18). The spinous processes of the first four sacral vertebrae form the **median sacral crest**. The spinous process of the fifth vertebra does not form, leaving a **sacral hiatus** (hī-ā′tŭs) at the inferior end of the sacrum, which is often the site of "caudal" anesthetic injections given just before childbirth. The anterior edge of the body of the first sacral vertebra bulges to form the **sacral promontory** (prom′on-tō-rē) (see figure 6.15), a landmark that can be felt during a vaginal examination. It is used as a reference point during measurement to determine if the pelvic openings are large enough to allow for normal vaginal delivery of a baby.

The **coccyx** (kok′siks; shaped like a cuckoo's bill), or tailbone, usually consists of four more-or-less fused vertebrae.

The vertebrae of the coccyx do not have the typical structure of most other vertebrae. They consist of extremely reduced vertebral bodies, without the foramina or processes, usually fused into a single bone.

Thoracic Cage

The **thoracic cage**, or **rib cage**, protects the vital organs within the thorax and prevents the collapse of the thorax during respiration. It consists of the thoracic vertebrae, the ribs with their associated cartilages, and the sternum.

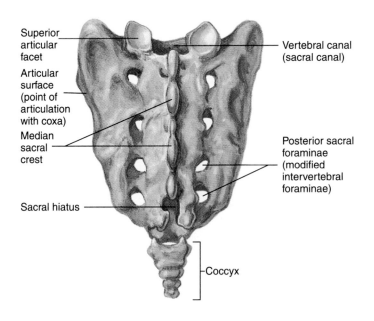

Figure 6.18   Posterior View of the Sacrum and Coccyx

Ribs and Costal Cartilages

The 12 pairs of ribs (figure 6.19) can be divided into true and false ribs. The superior seven pairs, called the **true ribs**, attach directly to the sternum by means of costal cartilages. The inferior five pairs, called **false ribs**, do not attach directly to the sternum. Three pairs, ribs 8 through 10, attach to the sternum by a common cartilage; two pairs, ribs 11 and 12, called the **floating ribs**, do not attach to the sternum.

Sternum

The **sternum** (ster′nŭm), or the breastbone (see figure 6.19), is divided into three parts: the **manubrium** (mă-nū′brē-ŭm; handle), the **body**, and the **xiphoid** (zif′oyd or zī′foyd; sword) **process**. The sternum resembles a sword, with the manubrium forming the handle, the body forming the blade, and the xiphoid process forming the tip. At the superior end of the sternum, a depression, called the **jugular notch**, is located between the ends of the clavicles where they articulate with the sternum. A slight elevation, called the **sternal angle**, can be felt at the junction of the manubrium and the body of the sternum. This junction is an important landmark because it identifies the location of the second rib. This identification allows the ribs to be counted and, for example, allows location of the apex of the heart, which is located between the fifth and sixth ribs.

The xiphoid process is another important landmark of the sternum. During cardiopulmonary resuscitation (CPR), it is very important to place the hands over the body of the sternum rather than over the xiphoid process. If the hands are placed over the xiphoid process, the pressure applied during CPR could break the xiphoid process and drive it into an underlying abdominal organ such as the liver, causing internal bleeding.

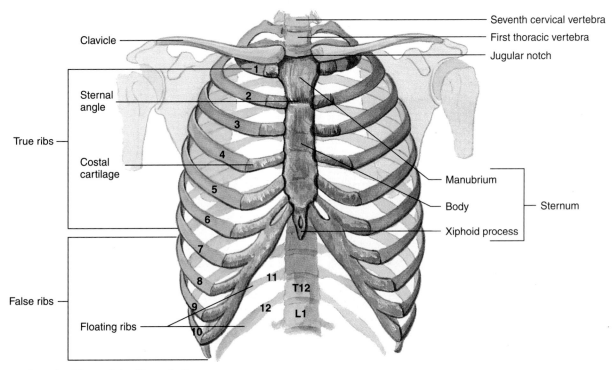

Figure 6.19   Anterior View of the Thoracic Cage

Appendicular Skeleton

The **appendicular** (ap'en-dik'ū-lăr) skeleton consists of the bones of the upper and lower limbs, as well as the girdles, which attach the limbs to the axial skeleton.

Pectoral Girdle

The **pectoral** (pek'tŏ-răl), or **shoulder**, **girdle** consists of four bones, two scapulae and two clavicles, which attach the upper limb to the body: the **scapula** (skap'ū-lă), or **shoulder blade** (figures 6.20 and 6.21; also see figure 6.9), and the **clavicle** (klav'i-kl), or **collarbone** (see figure 6.9a). The scapula is a flat, triangular bone with three large fossae, where muscles extending to the arm are attached. A fourth fossa, the **glenoid** (glen'oyd) **fossa**, is where the head of the humerus connects to the scapula. A ridge, called the **spine**, runs across the posterior surface of the scapula. A projection, called the **acromion** (ă-krō'mē-on) **process**, extends from the scapular spine to form the point of the shoulder. The clavicle articulates with the scapula at the acromion process. The proximal end of the clavicle is attached to the sternum, providing the only bony attachment of the scapula to the remainder of the skeleton. The **coracoid** (kōr'ă-koyd) **process** curves below the clavicle and provides attachment for arm and chest muscles.

Upper Limb

The upper limb consists of the bones of the arm, forearm, wrist, and hand (see figure 6.9).

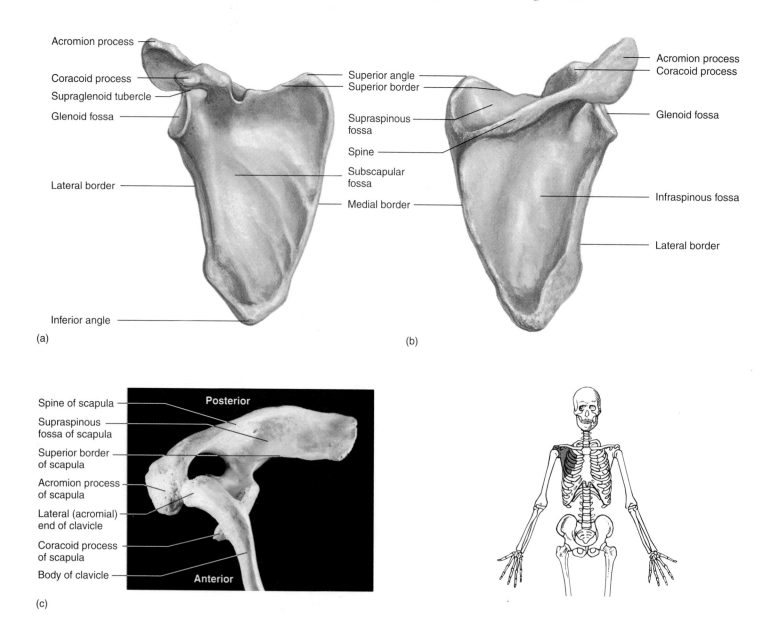

Figure 6.20 Bones of the Right Scapula

(a) Anterior view. (b) Posterior view. (c) Photograph of the right scapula and clavicle from a superior view, showing the relationship between the distal end of the clavicle and the acromion process of the scapula.

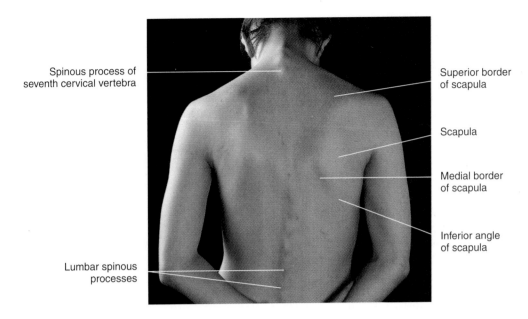

Spinous process of
seventh cervical vertebra

Superior border
of scapula

Scapula

Medial border
of scapula

Inferior angle
of scapula

Lumbar spinous
processes

Figure 6.21   Bones of the Back

Surface anatomy showing bones of the posterior vertebral column and scapula.

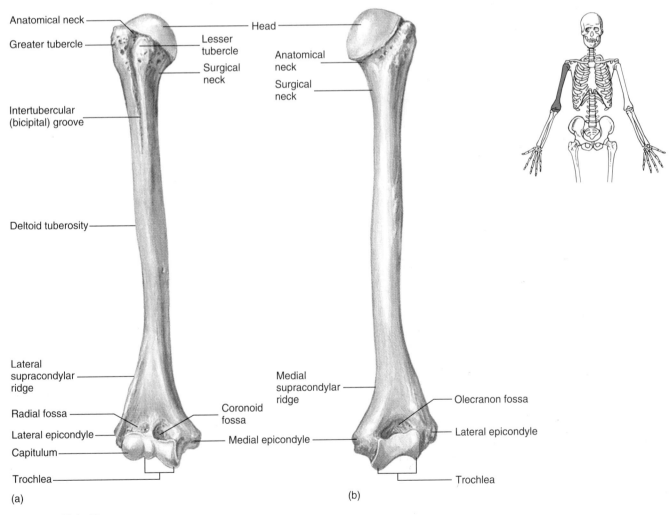

Anatomical neck

Greater tubercle

Head

Lesser
tubercle

Surgical
neck

Anatomical
neck

Surgical
neck

Intertubercular
(bicipital) groove

Deltoid tuberosity

Lateral
supracondylar
ridge

Medial
supracondylar
ridge

Olecranon fossa

Radial fossa

Coronoid
fossa

Lateral epicondyle

Lateral epicondyle

Capitulum

Medial epicondyle

Trochlea

Trochlea

(a)

(b)

Figure 6.22   Right Humerus

(*a*) Anterior view. (*b*) Posterior view.

Arm

The **arm** is the region between the shoulder and the elbow and contains the **humerus** (hū′mer-ŭs) (figure 6.22). The proximal end of the humerus has a smooth, rounded **head**, which attaches the humerus to the scapula at the glenoid fossa. Around the edge of the humeral head is the anatomical neck. This neck is not easily accessible if the proximal end of the humerus must be removed and replaced. A more accessible site for surgical removal is at the surgical neck, located at the proximal end of the humeral shaft. Lateral to the head are two tubercles, a **greater tubercle** and a **lesser tubercle**. Muscles originating on the scapula attach to the greater and lesser tubercles and hold the humerus to the scapula. Approximately one-third of the way down the shaft of the humerus, on the lateral surface, is the **deltoid tuberosity**, where the deltoid muscle attaches. The distal end of the humerus is modified into specialized condyles that connect the humerus to the forearm bones. **Epicondyles** (ep′i-kon′dīlz) on the distal end of the humerus, just lateral to the condyles, provide attachment sites for forearm muscles.

Did You Know?

The size of the deltoid tuberosity can increase as the result of frequent and powerful pull from the deltoid muscle. For example, in bodybuilders, the deltoid muscle and the deltoid tuberosity enlarge substantially. Anthropologists, examining ancient human remains, can use the presence of enlarged deltoid tuberosities as evidence that a person was engaged in lifting heavy objects during life. If the humerus of a person exhibits an unusually large deltoid tuberosity for her age, it may indicate, in some societies, that she was a slave and was required to lift heavy loads.

Forearm

The **forearm** has two bones, the **ulna** (ŭl′nă) on the medial side of the forearm (the side with the little finger) and the **radius** on the lateral (thumb) side (figure 6.23). The proximal end of the ulna forms a **semilunar notch** that fits tightly over the end of the humerus, forming most of the elbow joint. Just proximal to the semilunar notch is an extension of the ulna, called the **olecranon** (ō-lek′ră-non; elbow) **process**, which can be felt as the point of the elbow (the olecranon process is shown in figure 6.25). Just distal to the semilunar notch is a **coronoid** (kōr′ŏ-noyd) **process**, which helps complete the "grip" of the ulna on the distal end of the humerus. The distal end of the ulna forms a head, which articulates with the bones of the wrist, and a **styloid process** is located on its medial side. The ulnar head can be seen as a prominent lump on the posterior ulnar side of the wrist. The proximal end of the radius has a head by which the radius articulates with both the humerus and the ulna. The radius does not attach as firmly to the humerus as does the ulna. The radial head rotates against the humerus and ulna. Just distal to the radial head is a **radial tuberosity**, where one of the arm muscles, the biceps brachii, attaches. The distal end of the radius articulates with the wrist bones. A styloid process is located on the lateral side of the distal end of the radius. The radial and ulnar styloid processes provide attachments for ligaments of the wrist.

Figure 6.23 Right Ulna and Radius
Anterior view.

Wrist

The **wrist** is a relatively short region between the forearm and hand and is composed of eight **carpal** (kar′păl) bones (figure 6.24). These eight bones are the scaphoid (skaf′oyd), lunate (lū′nāt), triquetrum (trī-kwē′trŭm), pisiform (pis′i-fōrm), trapezium (tra-pē′zē-ŭm), trapezoid (trap′ĕ-zoyd), capitate (kap′i-tāt), and hamate (ha′māt). The eight carpal bones are arranged in two rows of four bones each and form a slight curvature that is concave anteriorly and convex posteriorly.

Did You Know?

The bones and ligaments on the anterior side of the wrist form a **carpal tunnel,** which does not have much "give." Tendons and nerves pass from the forearm through the carpal tunnel to the hand. Fluid and connective tissue can accumulate in the carpal tunnel as a result of inflammation associated with overuse or trauma. The inflammation can also cause the tendons in the carpal tunnel to enlarge. The accumulated fluid and enlarged tendons can apply pressure to a major nerve passing through the tunnel. The pressure on this nerve causes **carpal tunnel syndrome,** which consists of tingling, burning, and numbness in the hand.

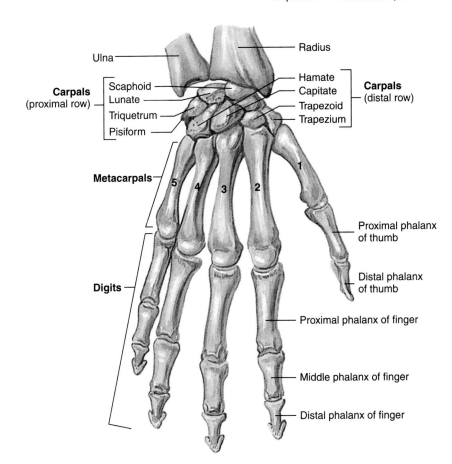

Figure 6.24 Right Wrist and Hand
Posterior view.

Hand

Five **metacarpals** (met′ă-kar′pălz; after the carpals) are attached to the carpal bones and form the bony framework of the hand (see figure 6.24). The metacarpals are aligned with the five **digits**: the thumb and fingers. They are numbered 1 to 5 from the thumb to the little finger. The ends, or heads, of the five metacarpals, associated with the thumb and fingers, form the knuckles (figure 6.25). Each finger consists of three small bones called **phalanges** (fă-lan′jēz; sing., phalanx, fă′langks; the Greek phalanx is a wedge of soldiers holding their spears, tips outward, in front of them). The phalanges of each finger are called proximal, middle, and distal, according to their position in the digit. The thumb has two phalanges, proximal and distal. The digits are also numbered 1 to 5, starting from the thumb.

Figure 6.25 Left Upper Limb
Surface anatomy.

Figure 6.26 Anterior View of the Pelvis

Pelvic Girdle

The **pelvic girdle**, or **pelvis** (figure 6.26), is the place where the lower limbs attach to the body. The pelvis is a ring of bones formed by the sacrum and two **coxae** (kok'sē). The sacrum forms part of the pelvis but is also part of the axial skeleton. Each coxa (figure 6.27) is formed by three bones fused to one another to form a single bone. The **ilium** (il'ē-ŭm; groin) is the most superior, the **ischium** (is'kē-ŭm; hip) is inferior and posterior, and the **pubis** (pū'bis; refers to the genital hair) is inferior and anterior. An **iliac crest** can be seen along the superior margin of each ilium, and an **anterior superior iliac spine**, an important hip landmark, is located at the anterior end of the iliac crest. The coxae join each other anteriorly at the **pubic** (pū'bik) **symphysis** and join the sacrum posteriorly at the **sacroiliac** (sā-krō-il'ē-ak) **joints**. (See figure 6.26) The **acetabulum** (as-ĕ-tab'ū-lŭm, vinegar cup) is the socket of the hip joint. The **obturator** (ob'too-rā-tŏr) **foramen** is the large hole in each coxa that is closed off by muscles and other structures.

The male pelvis can be distinguished from the female pelvis in that the male pelvis is usually larger and more massive, but the female pelvis tends to be broader (figure 6.28 and table 6.3). Both the inlet and outlet of the female pelvis are larger than those of the male pelvis, and the subpubic angle is greater in the female (figure 6.28a and b). The increased size of these openings helps accommodate the fetus during childbirth. The **pelvic inlet** is formed by the pelvic brim and the sacral promontory. The **pelvic outlet** is bounded by the ischial spines, the pubic symphysis, and the coccyx (figure 6.28c).

Lower Limb

The lower limb consists of the bones of the thigh, leg, ankle, and foot.

Thigh

The **thigh** (figure 6.29a and b) is the region between the hip and the knee. It contains a single bone called the **femur**. The **head** of the femur articulates with the acetabulum of the coxa; and the **condyles**, at the distal end of the femur, articulate with the tibia. **Epicondyles**, located medial and lateral to the condyles, provide points of muscle attachment. The femur can be distinguished from the humerus by its long neck located between the head and the **trochanters** (trō'kan-terz; runners). The trochanters are points of muscle attachment. The **patella** (pa-tel'ă), or kneecap (figure 6.29c), is located within the major tendon of the anterior thigh muscles and enables the tendon to turn the corner over the knee.

> ### Did You Know?
>
> A "broken hip" usually is a break of the femoral neck. A broken hip is difficult to repair and often requires pinning to hold the femoral head to the shaft. A major complication can occur if the blood vessels between the femoral head and the acetabulum are damaged. If this occurs, the femoral head may degenerate from lack of nourishment.

Leg

The **leg** (figure 6.30) is the region between the knee and the ankle. It contains two bones, called the **tibia** (tib'ē-ă; shin bone) and the **fibula** (fib'ū-lă; resembling a clasp or buckle). The tibia is the larger of the two and supports most of the weight in the leg. The rounded condyles of the femur rest on the flat **condyles** on the proximal end of the tibia. Just distal to the condyles of the tibia, on its anterior surface, is the **tibial tuberosity**, where the muscles of the anterior thigh

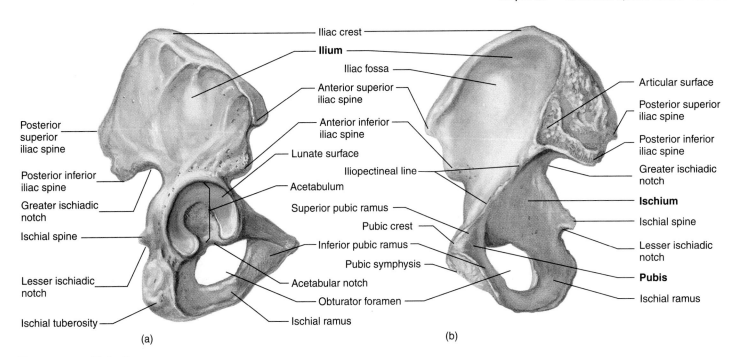

Figure 6.27   Right Coxa

(a) Lateral view. (b) Medial view.

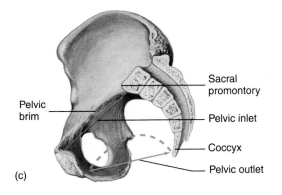

Figure 6.28   Comparison of the Male and Female Pelvis

(a) Male. The pelvic inlet (red dashed line), which is labeled and outlet (blue dashed line) are small, and the subpubic angle is less than 90 degrees. (b) Female. The pelvic inlet (red dashed line) and outlet (blue dashed line), which is labeled are larger, and the subpubic angle is 90 degrees or greater (see table 6.3). (c) Midsagittal section through the pelvis to show the pelvic inlet (red arrow and red dashed line) and outlet (blue arrow and blue dashed line).

Table 6.3	Differences Between Male and Female Pelvis
Area	**Description of Difference**
General	Female pelvis somewhat lighter in weight and wider laterally, but shorter superiorly to inferiorly and less funnel-shaped; less obvious muscle attachment points in female than in male
Sacrum	Broader in female, with the inferior portion directed more posteriorly; the sacral promontory projects less anteriorly in female
Pelvic inlet	Heart-shaped in male; oval in female
Pelvic outlet	Broader and more shallow in female
Subpubic angle	Less than 90 degrees in male; 90 degrees or more in female
Ilium	More shallow and flared laterally in female
Ischial spines	Farther apart in female
Ischial tuberosities	Turned laterally in female and medially in male (not shown in figure 6.27)

Head
Greater trochanter
Neck
Fovea capitis
Head
Greater trochanter
Neck
Lesser trochanter
Body (shaft) of femur
Body (shaft) of femur
Medial epicondyle
Lateral epicondyle
Patellar groove
(a)
Medial epicondyle
Lateral epicondyle
Lateral condyle
Medial condyle
(b)
Anterior surface
(c)

Figure 6.29 The Right Femur and Patella

(*a*) Anterior view of the femur. (*b*) Posterior view of the femur. (*c*) Anterior view of the patella.

attach. The fibula does not articulate with the femur but attaches by its head to the proximal end of the tibia. The distal ends of the tibia and fibula unite to form a partial socket that articulates with a bone of the ankle (the talus). A prominence can be seen on each side of the ankle (these are shown in figure 6.31). These are the medial **malleolus** (mal-ē′ō-lŭs; a hammer or mallet) of the tibia and the lateral malleolus of the fibula.

Ankle

The **ankle** consists of seven **tarsal** (tar′săl; the sole of the foot) bones (figure 6.31). The tarsal bones are the **talus** (tā′lŭs), **calcaneus** (kal-kā′nē-ŭs), **cuboid** (kū′boyd), and **navicular** (nă-vik′yū-lăr); and the medial, intermediate, and

lateral **cuneiforms** (kū′nē-i-fōrmz). The talus (ankle bone) articulates with the tibia and fibula to form the ankle joint, and the calcaneus forms the heel (figure 6.32).

Foot

The **metatarsals** (met′ă-tar′sălz) and **phalanges** of the foot are arranged and numbered in a manner very similar to the metacarpals and phalanges of the hand (see figure 6.31). The metatarsals are somewhat longer than the metacarpals, whereas the phalanges of the foot are considerably shorter than those of the hand. The heads formed at the distal ends of the metatarsals make up the ball of the foot. There are two primary **arches** in the foot, formed by the positions of the tarsals and the metatarsals, and held in place by

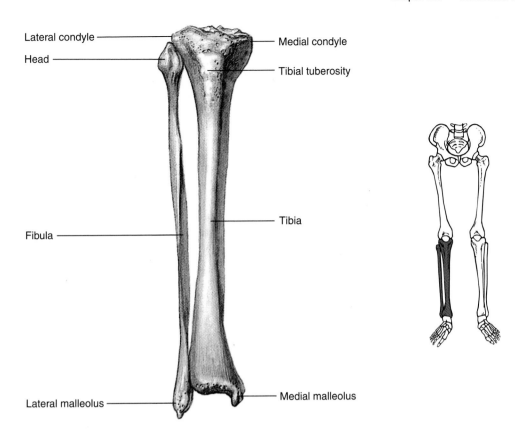

Figure 6.30   Right Tibia and Fibula
Anterior view.

ligaments. A longitudinal arch extends from the heel to the ball of the foot, and a transverse arch extends across the foot. The arches function similarly to the springs of a car, allowing the foot to give and spring back.

Articulations

An **articulation**, or joint, is a place where two bones come together. A joint is usually considered movable, but that is not always the case. Many joints exhibit limited movement, and others are completely, or almost completely, immovable.

One method of classifying joints is a functional classification, based on the degree of motion at each joint and includes the terms **synarthrosis** (sin′ar-thrō′sis; nonmovable joint), **amphiarthrosis** (am′fi-ar-thrō′sis; slightly movable joint), and **diarthrosis** (dī-ar-thrō′sis; freely movable joint). Functional classification is somewhat restrictive and is not used in this text. Another method of classifying joints is a structural classification. Joints are classified according to the major connective tissue type that binds the bones together and according to whether there is a fluid-filled joint capsule. The three major structural classes of joints are fibrous, cartilaginous, and synovial. The structural classification with its various subclasses allows for a more precise classification and thus is used in this text.

Fibrous Joints

Fibrous joints consist of two bones that are united by fibrous tissue and that exhibit little or no movement. Joints in this group are further classified on the basis of structure as sutures, syndesmoses, or gomphoses. **Sutures** (soo′choorz) are fibrous joints between the bones of the skull. In a newborn, some parts of the sutures are quite wide and are called **fontanels** (fon′tă-nelz′), or soft spots (figure 6.33). They allow flexibility in the skull during the birth process, as well as growth of the head after birth. **Syndesmoses** (sin′dez-mō′sēz) are fibrous joints in which the bones are separated by some distance and are held together by ligaments. An example is the fibrous membrane connecting most of the distal parts of the radius and ulna. **Gomphoses** (gom-fō′sēz) consist of pegs fitted into sockets and held in place by ligaments. The joint between a tooth and its socket is a gomphosis.

Cartilaginous Joints

Cartilaginous joints unite two bones by means of cartilage. Only slight movement can occur at these joints. Examples are the cartilage in the epiphyseal plates of growing long bones and the cartilages between the ribs and sternum. The cartilage of some cartilaginous joints, where much strain is placed on the joint, may be reinforced by the presence of additional collagen fibers. This type of cartilage, called **fibrocartilage** (see chapter 4), forms joints such as the intervertebral disks.

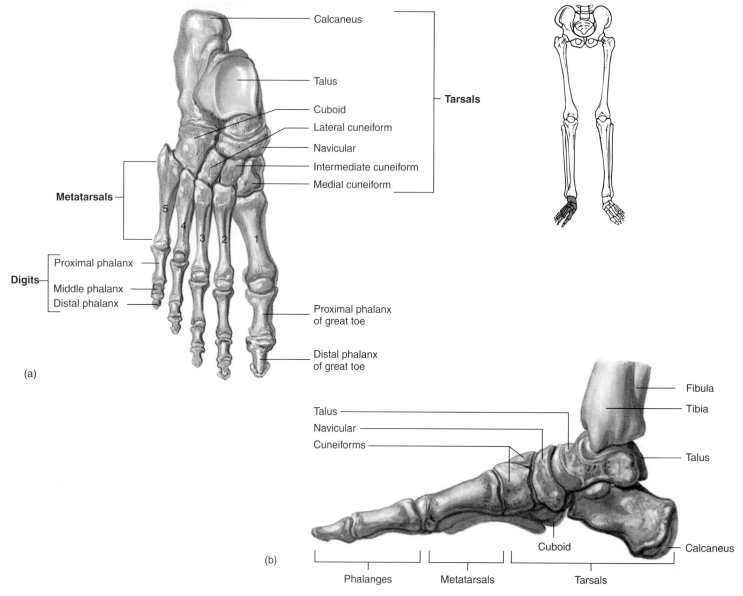

Tarsals

Calcaneus

Talus

Cuboid

Lateral cuneiform

Navicular

Intermediate cuneiform

Medial cuneiform

Metatarsals

5

4

3   2   1

Digits

Proximal phalanx

Middle phalanx

Distal phalanx

Proximal phalanx
of great toe

Distal phalanx
of great toe

(a)

Talus

Navicular

Cuneiforms

Fibula

Tibia

Talus

Cuboid

Calcaneus

(b)

Phalanges   Metatarsals   Tarsals

Figure 6.31 Bones of the Right Foot

(*a*) Superior view. (*b*) Medial view.

Medial condyle

Calcaneus

Lateral malleolus

Patella

Head of fibula

Tibial tuberosity

Medial malleolus

Lateral condyle

Figure 6.32 The Lower Limbs

Surface anatomy.

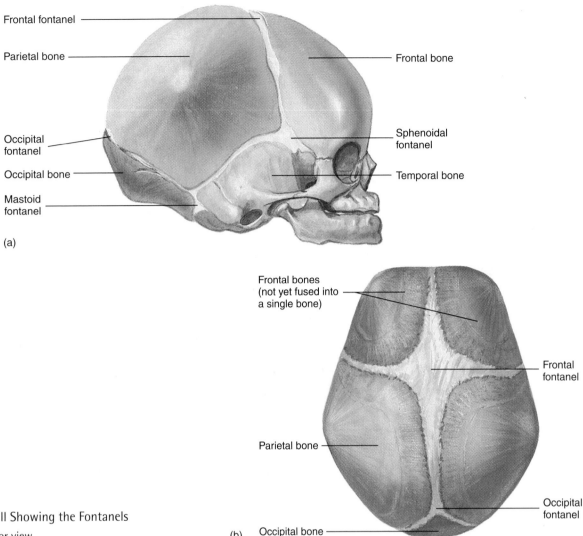

Frontal fontanel

Parietal bone

Frontal bone

Occipital
fontanel

Sphenoidal
fontanel

Occipital bone

Temporal bone

Mastoid
fontanel

(a)

Frontal bones
(not yet fused into
a single bone)

Frontal
fontanel

Parietal bone

Occipital
fontanel

Occipital bone

(b)

Figure 6.33   Fetal Skull Showing the Fontanels
(*a*) Lateral view. (*b*) Superior view.

Synovial Joints

Synovial (si-nō′vē-ăl; G. *syn,* together + *oon,* egg) **joints** are freely movable joints that contain **synovial fluid** in a cavity surrounding the ends of articulating bones. Most joints that unite the bones of the appendicular skeleton are large, synovial joints, whereas many of the joints that unite the bones of the axial skeleton are not. This pattern reflects the greater mobility of the appendicular skeleton compared with the axial skeleton.

Several features of synovial joints are important to their function (figure 6.34). The articular surfaces of bones within synovial joints are covered with a thin layer of **articular cartilage**, which provides a smooth surface where the bones meet. The **joint cavity** is filled with synovial fluid. The cavity is enclosed by a **joint capsule**, which helps hold the bones together and, at the same time, allows for movement. Portions of the joint capsule may be thickened to form ligaments. In addition, ligaments and tendons outside the joint capsule contribute to the strength of the joint.

A **synovial membrane** lines the joint cavity everywhere except over the articular cartilage. The membrane produces synovial fluid, which is a complex mixture of polysaccharides, proteins, fat, and cells. Synovial fluid forms a thin lubricating film covering the surfaces of the joint. In certain synovial joints, the synovial membrane may extend as a pocket or sac, called a **bursa** (ber′să; pocket). Bursae are located between structures that rub together, such as where a tendon crosses a bone; they function to reduce friction, which could damage the structures involved. Inflammation of a bursa, often resulting from abrasion, is called a **bursitis**. A synovial membrane may extend as a **tendon sheath** along some tendons associated with joints (see figure 6.34).

Types of Synovial Joints

Synovial joints are classified according to the shape of the adjoining articular surfaces (figure 6.35). **Plane,** or **gliding, joints** consist of two opposed flat surfaces that glide over each other. Examples of these joints are the articular facets

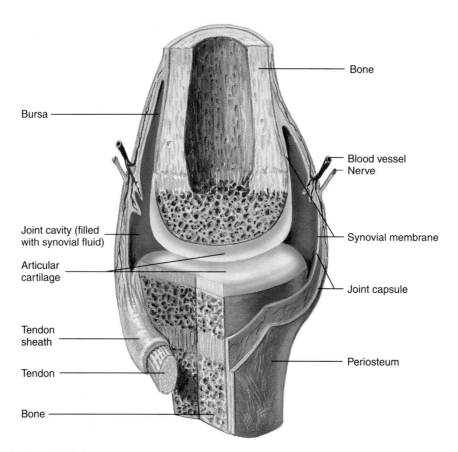

Figure 6.34 Structure of a Synovial Joint

between vertebrae. **Saddle joints** consist of two saddle-shaped articulating surfaces oriented at right angles to each other. Movement in these joints can occur in two planes. The joint between the metatarsal and proximal phalanx of the thumb is a saddle joint. **Hinge joints** permit movement in one plane only. They consist of a convex cylinder of one bone applied to a corresponding concavity of the other bone. Examples are the elbow, knee, and finger joints (figure 6.36*a*). The flat condylar surface of the knee joint is modified into a concave surface by shock-absorbing fibrocartilage pads, called **menisci** (mĕ-nis′sī). **Pivot joints** restrict movement to rotation around a single axis. Each pivot joint consists of a cylindrical bony process that rotates within a ring composed partly of bone and partly of ligament. The rotation that occurs between the axis and atlas when shaking the head "no" is an example. The articulation between the proximal ends of the ulna and radius is also a pivot joint.

Ball-and-socket joints consist of a ball (head) at the end of one bone and a socket in an adjacent bone into which a portion of the ball fits. This type of joint allows a wide range of movement in almost any direction. Examples are the shoulder and hip joints (figure 6.36*b* and *c*). **Ellipsoid** (ē-lip′soyd), or **condyloid**, (kon′di-loyd) **joints** are elongated ball-and-socket joints. The shape of the joint limits its range of movement nearly to a hinge motion, but in two planes. The joint between the occipital condyles of the skull and the atlas of the vertebral column and the joints between the metacarpals and phalanges are examples of ellipsoid joints.

> **Did You Know?**
>
> A sprain results when the bones of a joint are forcefully pulled apart and the ligaments around the joint are pulled or torn. A separation exists when the bones remain apart after an injury to a joint. A dislocation is when the end of one bone is pulled out of the socket in a ball-and-socket, ellipsoid, or pivot joint.

Types of Movement

The types of movement occurring at a given joint are related to the structure of that joint. Some joints are limited to only one type of movement, whereas others permit movement in several directions. All the movements are described relative to the anatomical position. Because most movements are accompanied by movements in the opposite direction, they are listed in pairs (figure 6.37).

There are a number of ways to define **flexion** and **extension**, but in each case there are exceptions to the definition. The literal definition is to bend and straighten, respectively. We have chosen to use a definition with more utility and fewer exceptions. Flexion moves a part of the body in the anterior or ventral direction. Extension moves a part in a posterior or dorsal direction (figure 6.37*a* and *b*). An exception is the knee, in which flexion moves the leg in a posterior direction and extension moves it in an anterior direction.

Class and Example of Joint	Structures Joined	Movement
Plane		
Acromioclavicular	Acromion process of scapula and clavicle	Slight
Carpometacarpal	Carpals and metacarpals two through five	Multiple axes as a group
Costovertebral	Ribs and vertebrae	Slight
Intercarpal	Between carpals	Slight
Intermetatarsal	Between metatarsals	Slight
Intertarsal	Between tarsals	Slight
Intervertebral	Between articular processes of adjacent vertebrae	Slight
Sacroiliac	Between sacrum and coxa (complex joint with several planes and synchondroses)	Slight
Tarsometatarsal	Tarsals and metatarsals	Slight
Saddle		
Carpometacarpal pollicis	Carpal and metacarpal of thumb	Two axes
Intercarpal	Between carpals	Slight
Sternoclavicular	Manubrium of sternum and clavicle	Slight
Hinge		
Cubital (elbow)	Humerus, ulna, and radius	One axis
Genu (knee)	Femur and tibia	One axis
Interphalangeal	Between phalanges	One axis
Talocrural (ankle)	Talus, tibia, and fibula	Multiple axes, one predominates
Pivot		
Medial atlantoaxial	Atlas and axis	Rotation
Proximal radioulnar	Radius and ulna	Rotation
Distal radioulnar	Radius and ulna	Rotation
Ball-and-Socket		
Coxal (hip)	Coxa and femur	Multiple axes
Humeral (shoulder)	Scapula and humerus	Multiple axes
Ellipsoid		
Atlantooccipital	Atlas and occipital bone	Two axes
Metacarpopha-langeal (knuckles)	Metacarpals and phalanges	Mostly one axis
Metatarsopha-langeal (ball of foot)	Metatarsals and phalanges	Mostly one axis
Radiocarpal (wrist)	Radius and carpals	Multiple axes
Temporomandibular	Mandible and temporal bone	Multiple axes, one predominates

Plane

Saddle

Hinge

Pivot

Ball-and-socket

Elipsoid

Figure 6.35   Types of Synovial Joints

Figure 6.36 Three Selected Joints

(a) Sagittal section through the right knee joint. (b) Frontal section through the right shoulder. (c) Frontal section through the right hip joint.

(a)

(b)

(c)

(d)

(e)

Figure 6.37   Selected Movements *(continued on next page)*

(*a*) Flexion and extension of the elbow. (*b*) Flexion and extension of the neck. (*c*) Abduction and adduction of the fingers. (*d*) Pronation and supination of the forearm. (*e*) Medial and lateral rotation of the humerus.

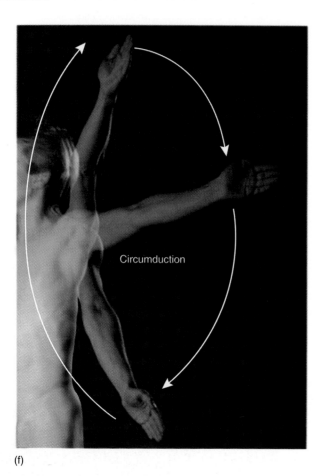

Circumduction

(f)

Figure 6.37 Selected Movements *(continued)*
(*f*) Circumduction of the shoulder.

Movement of the foot toward the plantar surface, such as when standing on the toes, is commonly called **plantar flexion**. Movement of the foot toward the shin, such as when walking on the heels, is called **dorsiflexion**.

Did You Know?

Hyperextension is usually defined as an abnormal, forced extension of a joint beyond its normal range of motion. For example, if a person falls and attempts to break the fall by putting out his hand, the force of the fall directed into the hand and wrist may cause hyperextension of the wrist, which may result in sprained joints or broken bones. Some health professionals, however, define hyperextension as the normal movement of a structure into the space posterior to the anatomical position.

Abduction (ab-dŭk′shun; to take away) is movement away from the midline; **adduction** (to bring together) is movement toward the midline (figure 6.37*c*). Moving the legs away from the midline of the body, as in the outward movement of "jumping jacks," is abduction, and bringing the legs back together is adduction.

Pronation (prō-nā′shun) and **supination** (soo′pi-nā′shun) are best described with the elbow flexed at a 90-degree angle. When the elbow is flexed, pronation is rotation of the forearm so that the palm is down, and supination is rotation of the forearm so that the palm faces up (figure 6.37*d*).

Eversion (ē-ver′zhŭn) is turning the foot so that the plantar surface (bottom of the foot) faces laterally; **inversion** (in-ver′zhŭn) is turning the foot so that the plantar surface faces medially.

Rotation is the turning of a structure around its long axis (figure 6.37*e*), as in shaking the head "no." Rotation of the arm can best be demonstrated with the elbow flexed, so that rotation is not confused with supination and pronation of the forearm. With the elbow flexed, medial rotation of the arm brings the forearm against the anterior surface of the abdomen, and lateral rotation moves it away from the body.

Protraction (prō-trak′shun) is a movement in which a structure, such as the mandible, glides anteriorly. In **retraction** (rē-trak′shun), the structure glides posteriorly.

Elevation is movement of a structure in a superior direction. Closing the mouth involves elevation of the mandible. **Depression** is movement of a structure in an inferior direction. Opening the mouth involves depression of the mandible.

Excursion is the movement of a structure to one side or the other, such as in moving the mandible from side to side.

Opposition is a movement unique to the thumb and little finger. It occurs when the tips of the thumb and little finger are brought toward each other across the palm of the hand. The thumb can also oppose the other digits. **Reposition** returns the digits to the anatomical position.

Circumduction (ser-kŭm-dŭk′shun) occurs at freely movable joints such as the shoulder. In circumduction, the arm moves so that it describes a cone with the shoulder joint at the apex (figure 6.37*f*).

Most movements that occur in the course of normal activities are combinations of movements. A complex movement can be described by naming the individual movements involved.

4 P R E D I C T

What combination of movements is required at the shoulder and elbow joints for a person to perform a crawl stroke in swimming?

✔ *Answer on page 151*

Clinical Focus   Joint Disorders

Arthritis

Arthritis (ar-thrī'tis) (figure C), the inflammation of a joint, is the most common and best known of the joint disorders, affecting 10% of the world's population. There are more than 100 different types of arthritis, which differ in their cause and progress. Causes include infectious agents, metabolic disorders, trauma, and immune disorders.

Rheumatoid (rū'mă-toyd) **arthritis** affects about 3% of all women and about 1% of all men in the United States. It is a general connective tissue disorder that affects the skin, vessels, lungs, and other organs, but it is most pronounced in the joints. It is severely disabling and most commonly destroys small joints such as those in the hands and feet. The initial cause is unknown but may involve a transient infection or an autoimmune disease, which is an immune reaction against one's own tissues. There may also be a genetic predisposition to this disease. In rheumatoid arthritis, the synovial membrane and associated connective tissue cells proliferate, forming a pannus (clothlike layer) in the joint capsule, which can grow into the articulating surfaces of the bones, destroying the articular cartilage. In advanced stages, the bones forming the joint may become fused.

Degenerative Joint Disease

Degenerative joint disease (DJD), also called **osteoarthritis** (os'tē-ō-ar-thrī'tis), results from the gradual "wear and tear" of a joint that occurs with advancing age. Slowed metabolic rates with increased age also seem to contribute to DJD. It is very common in older individuals and affects 85% of all people in the United States over the age of 70. It tends to occur in the weight-bearing joints such as the knees and is more common in overweight individuals. Mild exercise retards joint degeneration and enhances mobility.

Gout

Gout (gowt) is caused by an increase in uric acid in the body. Uric acid is a waste product, which can accumulate as crystals in various tissues, including the kidneys and joint capsules. Gout is more common in males than in females.

Frequently, only one or two joints are affected. The most commonly affected joints (85% of the cases) are the base of the great toe and other foot and leg joints. Any joint may ultimately be involved, and damage to the kidneys from crystal formation occurs in almost all advanced cases.

Bursitis and Bunions

Bursitis (ber-sī'tis) is the inflammation of a bursa. The bursae around the shoulders and elbows are common sites of bursitis. A **bunion** (bun'yun) is a bursitis that develops over the joint at the base of the great toe. Bunions are frequently irritated by shoes that are too tight and that rub on them.

Joint Replacement

As a result of recent advancements in biomedical technology, many joints of the body can now be replaced by artificial joints. **Joint replacement,** or **arthroplasty** (ar'thrō-plas-tē), was developed in the late 1950s. It is used in patients with joint disorders to eliminate unbearable pain and to increase joint mobility. Degenerative joint disease is the leading disease requiring joint replacement, accounting for two thirds of the patients. Rheumatoid arthritis accounts for more than half the remaining cases.

Artificial joints usually are composed of metal (e.g., stainless steel, titanium alloys, or cobalt-chrome alloys) in combination with modern plastics (e.g., high-density polyethylene, silicone rubber, or elastomer). The bone of the articular area is removed on one side (hemireplacement) or both sides (total replacement) of the joint, and the artificial articular structures are attached to the bone. The smooth metal surface rubbing against the smooth plastic surface provides a low-friction contact with a range of movement that depends on the design.

(a)

(b)

Figure C   Rheumatoid Arthritis
(*a*) Photograph of hands with rheumatoid arthritis.
(*b*) Roentgenogram of the same hands.

Systems Pathology
Osteoporosis

OSTEOPOROSIS

Mrs. B is a 65-year-old woman. She has smoked heavily for 50 years. She does not exercise, seldom goes outside, has a poor diet, and is slightly underweight. While attending a family picnic, Mrs. B tripped on a lawn sprinkler and fell. She was unable to stand because of severe hip pain, so she was rushed to the hospital where a radiograph revealed a fracture in the neck of her femur (figure D*a*) and that she had osteoporosis (figure D*b*).

Because of the location of the fracture and the osteoporosis, Mrs. B's orthopedic surgeon suggested that she should undergo hip replacement surgery. Mrs. B had a successful hip transplant and then began physical therapy. She was also placed on a diet and exercise program designed to improve the strength of her bones. In addition she was prescribed estrogen and Alendronate (see following discussion) therapy and was advised to quit smoking.

Background Information

Osteoporosis, or porous bone, results from reduction in the overall quantity of bone matrix. It occurs when the rate of bone reabsorption exceeds the rate of bone formation. The loss of bone mass makes bones so porous and weakened that they become deformed and prone to fracture. The occurrence of osteoporosis increases with age. In both men and women, bone mass starts to decrease at about age 40, and continually decreases thereafter. Women can eventually lose approximately one-half, and men one-quarter, of their cancellous bone. Osteoporosis is 2.5 times more common in women than in men.

In postmenopausal women, the decreased production of the female sex hormone, estrogen, can cause osteoporosis. The degeneration occurs mostly in cancellous bone, especially in the vertebrae of the spine and the bones of the forearm. Collapse of the vertebrae can cause a decrease in height or, in more severe cases, produce kyphosis in the upper back.

Conditions that result in decreased estrogen other than menopause can also cause osteoporosis. Examples include removal of the ovaries before menopause, extreme exercise to the point of amenorrhea (lack of menstrual flow), anorexia nervosa (self starvation), and cigarette smoking.

In males, reduction in testosterone levels can cause loss of bone tissue. Decreasing testosterone levels are usually less of a problem for men than decreasing estrogen levels are for women for two reasons. First, because males have denser

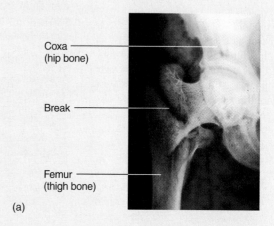

Coxa (hip bone)

Break

Femur (thigh bone)

(a)

(b)   Normal   Osteoporotic
        bone   bone

Figure D   Osteoporosis
(*a*) Radiograph of a broken hip. A "broken hip" is usually a break in the femur in the hip region (in this case, the break is at the base of the neck). (*b*) Photomicrograph of normal bone and osteoporotic bone.

bones than females, loss of some bone tissue has less of an effect. Second, testosterone levels generally don't decrease significantly until after age 65, and even then the rate of decrease is often slow.

Inadequate dietary intake or absorption of calcium can contribute to osteoporosis. Absorption of calcium from the small intestine decreases with age, and individuals with osteoporosis often have insufficient intake of calcium, vitamin D, and vitamin C. Drugs that interfere with calcium uptake or use can also increase the risk of osteoporosis.

Finally, osteoporosis can result from inadequate exercise or disuse caused by fractures or paralysis. Significant amounts of bone are lost after 8 weeks of immobilization.

Treatments for osteoporosis are designed to reduce bone loss or increase bone formation (or both). Increased dietary calcium and vitamin D can increase calcium uptake and promote bone formation. Daily doses of 1000 to 1500 mg of calcium and 800 IU (20 μg) of vitamin D are recommended. Exercise, such as walking or using light weights, also appears to be effective not only in reducing bone loss, but in increasing bone mass.

In postmenopausal women, estrogen replacement therapy decreases osteoclast activity, which reduces bone loss, but does not result in an increase in bone mass because osteoclast activity still exceeds osteoblast activity. Calcitonin (Miacalcin), which inhibits osteoclast activity, is now available as a nasal spray. Calcitonin can be used to treat osteoporosis in men and women and has been shown to produce a slight increase in bone mass. Alendronate (Fosamax) belongs to a class of drugs called bisphosphonates. Bisphosphonates bind to hydroxyapatite and inhibit bone resorption by osteoclasts. Alendronate increases bone mass and reduces fracture rates even more effectively than calcitonin. Slow-releasing sodium fluoride (Slow Fluoride) in combination with calcium citrate (Citracal) also appear to increase bone mass.

Early diagnosis of osteoporosis can lead to more preventative treatments. Instruments that measure the absorption of photons (particles of light) by bone are currently used, of which dual-energy x-ray absorptiometry (DEXA) is considered the best.

5   P R E D I C T

What advice should Mrs. B give to her granddaughter so that the granddaughter will be less likely to develop osteoporosis when she is Mrs. B's age?

✔ *Answer on page 151*

Systems Interactions

System	Interactions
Integumentary	Mrs. B has little exposure to the sun because of her indoor lifestyle, resulting in little vitamin D production and decreased calcium absorption.
Muscular	Mrs. B's muscle atrophy and weakness made it difficult for her to maintain her balance. Thus she was more likely to fall and injure herself. Following the surgery, her physical therapy placed stress on her bones and improved her muscular strength.
Nervous	Pain sensations following the injury and during her rehabilitation help to prevent further injury.
Endocrine	Calcitonin is being used to treat osteoporosis.
Cardiovascular	Blood clotting following the injury starts the process of tissue repair. Blood cells are carried to the injury site to fight infections and remove cell debris. Blood vessels grow into the recovering tissue, providing nutrients and removing waste products.
Lymphatic and Immune	Immune cells resist possible infection following surgery, such as hip-replacement surgery, and release chemicals that promote tissue repair.
Respiratory	Excessive smoking lowers estrogen levels, which increases bone loss.
Digestive	Inadequate calcium and vitamin D in the diet can contribute to inadequate calcium absorption by the digestive system and osteoporosis.
Reproductive	Decreased estrogen following menopause contributed to her osteoporosis.

Summary

The skeletal system consists of bone, cartilage, tendons, and ligaments.

Functions of the Skeletal System

- Bones support the body, protect internal organs, provide levers on which muscles act, store minerals, and produce blood cells.
- Cartilage provides a model for bone formation and growth, provides a smooth cushion between adjacent bones, and provides firm, flexible support.
- Tendons attach muscles to bones, and ligaments attach bones to bones.

Connective Tissue

- Connective tissue consists of matrix and the cells that produce matrix.
- Varying amounts of collagen, proteoglycan, and mineral in the matrix determine the characteristics of the connective tissue.

General Features of Bone

- Long bones consist of a diaphysis (shaft), epiphyses (ends), and epiphyseal (growth) plates. The diaphysis contains a medullary cavity, and the end of the epiphysis is covered by articular cartilage.

Compact Bone

- Compact bone tissue consists of osteons.
- Osteons consist of osteocytes organized into lamellae surrounding central canals.

Cancellous Bone

- Cancellous bone tissue consists of trabeculae without central canals.

Bone Ossification

- Bone ossification is either intramembranous or endochondral.
- Intramembranous ossification occurs within connective tissue membranes.
- Endochondral ossification occurs within cartilage.

Bone Growth

- Bone growth occurs by apposition. Bone elongation occurs at the epiphyseal plate as chondrocytes proliferate, hypertrophy, die, and are replaced by bone.

Bone Remodeling

- Bone remodeling consists of removal of existing bone by osteoclasts and deposition of new bone by osteoblasts.

Bone Repair

- During bone repair, cells move into the damaged area and form a callus, which is replaced by bone.

General Considerations of Bone Anatomy

- There are 206 bones.

Axial Skeleton

- The axial skeleton includes the skull, vertebral column, and thoracic cage.

Skull

- The skull consists of 28 bones: 8 cranial vault bones, 14 facial bones, and 6 auditory ossicles.
- From a lateral view, the parietal, temporal, and sphenoid bones can be seen.
- From a frontal view, the orbits and nasal cavity can be seen, as well as associated bones and structures, such as the frontal bone, zygomatic bone, maxilla, and mandible.
- The interior of the cranial vault contains three fossae with several foramina.
- Seen from below, the base of the skull reveals numerous foramina and other structures, such as processes for muscle attachment.

Vertebral Column

- The vertebral column contains 7 cervical, 12 thoracic, and 5 lumbar vertebrae, plus 1 sacral and 1 coccygeal bone.
- Each vertebra consists of a body, an arch, and processes.
- Regional differences in vertebrae are as follows: cervical vertebrae have transverse foramina; thoracic vertebrae have long spinous processes and attachment sites for the ribs; lumbar vertebrae have rectangular transverse and spinous processes, and the position of their facets limit rotation; the sacrum is a single, fused bone; the coccyx is four or fewer fused vertebrae.

Thoracic Cage

- The thoracic cage consists of thoracic vertebrae, ribs, and sternum.
- There are 12 pairs of ribs: 7 true and 5 false (two of the false ribs are also called floating ribs).

- The sternum consists of the manubrium, body, and xiphoid process.

Appendicular Skeleton

- The appendicular skeleton consists of the bones of the upper and lower limbs and their girdles.

Pectoral Girdle

- The pectoral girdle includes the scapula and clavicle.

Upper Limb

- The upper limb consists of the arm (humerus), forearm (ulna and radius), wrist (eight carpal bones), and hand (five metacarpals, three phalanges in each finger, and two phalanges in the thumb).

Pelvic Girdle

- The pelvic girdle is made up of the sacrum and two coxae. Each coxa consists of an ilium, ischium, and pubis.

Lower Limb

- The lower limb includes the thigh (femur), leg (tibia and fibula), ankle (seven tarsals), and foot (metatarsals and phalanges, similar to the bones in the hand).

Articulations

- An articulation is a place where bones come together.

Fibrous Joints

- Fibrous joints consist of bones united by fibrous connective tissue. They allow little or no movement.

Cartilaginous Joints

- Cartilaginous joints consist of bones united by cartilage, and they exhibit slight movement.

Synovial Joints

- Synovial joints consist of articular cartilage over the uniting bones, a joint cavity lined by a synovial membrane and containing synovial fluid, and a joint capsule. They are highly movable joints.
- Synovial joints can be classified as plane, saddle, hinge, pivot, ball-and-socket, or ellipsoid.

Types of Movement

- The major types of movement include flexion/extension, abduction/adduction, pronation/supination, eversion/inversion, rotation, protraction/retraction, elevation/depression, excursion, opposition/reposition, and circumduction.

Content Review

1. The skeletal system consists of what connective tissues? List the functions of these tissues.
2. Name the major types of fibers and molecules found in the extracellular matrix of the skeletal system. How do they contribute to the functions of tendons, ligaments, cartilage, and bones?
3. Define the terms diaphysis, epiphysis, epiphyseal plate, medullary cavity, articular cartilage, periosteum, and endosteum.
4. Describe the structure of compact bone. How do nutrients reach the osteocytes in compact bone?
5. Describe the structure of cancellous bone. What are trabeculae?

6. Define and describe intramembranous and endochondral ossification.
7. How does bone grow? How do long bones grow in length?
8. What is accomplished by bone remodeling? How does bone repair occur?
9. Define the axial skeleton and the appendicular skeleton.
10. Name the bones of the cranial vault and the face.
11. Give the locations of the paranasal sinuses. What are their functions?
12. What is the function of the hard palate?
13. Through what foramen does the brain connect to the spinal cord?
14. How do the vertebrae protect the spinal cord? Where do spinal nerves exit the vertebral column?
15. Name and give the number of each type of vertebra. Describe the characteristics that distinguish the different types of vertebrae from one another.
16. What is the function of the thoracic cage? Name the parts of the sternum. Distinguish true, false, and floating ribs.

17. Name the bones that make up the pectoral girdle, arm, forearm, wrist, and hand. How many phalanges are in each finger and in the thumb?
18. Define the pelvis. What bones fuse to form each coxa? Where and with what bones do the coxae articulate?
19. Name the bones of the thigh, leg, ankle, and foot.
20. Define the term articulation, or joint. Name and describe the differences between the three major classes of joints.
21. Describe the structure of a synovial joint. How do the different parts of the joint function to permit joint movement?
22. On what basis are synovial joints classified? Describe the different types of synovial joints, and give examples of each. What movements do each type of joint allow?
23. Describe and give examples of flexion/extension, abduction/adduction, and supination/pronation.

Develop Your Reasoning Skills

1. A 12-year-old boy fell while playing basketball. The physician explained that the head (epiphysis) of the femur was separated from the shaft (diaphysis). Although the bone was set properly, by the time the boy was 16 it was apparent that the injured lower limb was shorter than the normal one. Explain why this difference occurred.
2. Justin Time leaped from his hotel room to avoid burning to death in a fire. If he landed on his heels, what bone was likely to fracture? Unfortunately for Justin, a 240-pound fireman, Hefty Stomper, ran by and stepped heavily on the distal part of Justin's foot (not the toes). What bones now could be broken?
3. One day while shopping, Ms. Wantta Bargain picked up her 3-year-old son, Somm, by his right wrist and lifted him into a shopping cart. She heard a clicking sound and Somm immediately began to cry and hold his elbow. Given that lifting the child caused a separation at the elbow, which is more likely: separation of the radius and humerus or separation of the ulna and humerus?
4. Why are women knock-kneed more commonly than men?

Answers to Predict Questions

1. p. 114 If all the mineral is removed, the bone becomes so flexible that it can be tied into a knot. This can be accomplished by soaking a bone in vinegar (a weak acid) for an extended time. The bone will not be rigid enough to support weight.

   If all the collagen is removed, the bone becomes very brittle and can be easily broken. Because of collagen loss, the bones of many older people break easily.
2. p. 117 If endochondral bone growth fails to occur, the bone is normal in diameter (or even greater in diameter than normal) but much shorter than normal. This is the condition seen in one type of dwarfism, in which the head and trunk are normal in size, but the long bones of the limbs are very short.

3. p. 126 Tears are produced in lacrimal glands in the superior lateral corner of the orbit. The tears run across the surface of the eye and enter the duct that passes through the nasolacrimal canal to the nasal cavity. The extra moisture in the nasal cavity causes a "runny nose."
4. p. 146 Just before the swimmer begins the power stroke, the arm is flexed and medially rotated, and the forearm is extended and pronated. During the power stroke, the arm is powerfully extended, slightly abducted, and medially rotated. During the recovery stroke, the arm is circumducted, laterally rotated, and flexed in preparation for the next stroke. The forearm is flexed during the first part of the recovery stroke and extended during the last part.

5. p. 149 Taking in adequate calcium and vitamin D through the digestive system during adulthood increases calcium absorption from the small intestine. The increased calcium is used to increase bone mass. The greater the bone mass before the onset of osteoporosis, the greater the tolerance for bone loss later in life. For this reason it is important for adults, especially women in their 20s and 30s, to ingest adequate amounts of calcium. Exercising the muscular system places stress on bone, which also increases bone density. The granddaughter should not smoke because this reduces estrogen levels. Following menopause, estrogen replacement therapy can reduce bone loss.

Chapter Seven

The Muscular System

aerobic respiration
(ār-ō'bik) Metabolism in the presence of oxygen.

anaerobic respiration
(an-ār-ō'bik) Metabolism in the absence of oxygen.

antagonist
(an-tag'ŏ-nist) A muscle that works in opposition to another muscle.

insertion
(in-ser'shŭn) The more movable attachment point of a muscle.

isometric contraction
(ī-sō-met'rik) Muscle contraction in which the length of the muscle does not change, but the amount of tension increases.

isotonic contraction
(ī-sō-ton'ik) Muscle contraction in which the amount of tension is constant and the muscle shortens.

motor unit
A single motor neuron and all the skeletal muscle fibers it innervates.

muscle twitch
Contraction of an entire muscle in response to a stimulus that causes an action potential in one or more muscle fibers.

myofibril
(mī-ō-fī'bril) A fine, longitudinal fibril of skeletal muscle, consisting of sarcomeres and composed of thick (myosin) and thin (actin) myofilaments placed end to end.

myofilament
(mī-ō-fil'ă-ment) An ultramicroscopic protein thread that helps form myofibrils in skeletal muscle. Thin myofilaments are composed of actin, and thick myofilaments are composed of myosin.

neuromuscular junction
(noo-rō-mŭs'kū-lăr) The synaptic junction between a nerve axon and a muscle fiber.

origin
(or'i-jin) The less movable attachment point of a muscle.

oxygen debt
(ok'sē-jen) The amount of oxygen required to convert the lactic acid produced during anaerobic respiration to glucose and to replenish creatine phosphate stores.

sarcomere
(sar'kō-mēr) [Gr. *sarco*, flesh, muscle + *meros*, part] The part of a myofibril formed of actin and myosin myofilaments, extending from Z disk to Z disk; the structural and functional unit of a muscle.

sliding filament mechanism
The mechanism by which muscle contraction occurs wherein actin and myosin myofilaments slide past one another.

synergist
(sin'er-jist) A muscle that works with another muscle to cause a movement.

Objectives

After reading this chapter, you should be able to:

1. Describe the microscopic structure of a muscle and produce diagrams that illustrate the arrangement of myofilaments, myofibrils, and sarcomeres.

2. Describe the events that result in muscle contraction and relaxation in response to an action potential in a motor neuron.

3. Distinguish between aerobic and anaerobic muscle contraction.

4. Distinguish between fast-twitch and slow-twitch muscles and explain the function for which each type is best adapted.

5. Distinguish among skeletal, smooth, and cardiac muscle.

6. Define the following terms and give an example of each: origin, insertion, synergist, antagonist, and prime mover.

7. Describe various facial expressions and list the major muscles causing each.

8. Describe mastication, tongue movement, and swallowing and list the muscles or groups of muscles involved in each.

9. Describe the muscles of the trunk and the actions they accomplish.

10. Describe the movements of the arm, forearm, and hand and list the muscle groups involved in each movement.

11. Describe the movements of the thigh, leg, and foot and list the muscle groups involved in each movement.

As a runner rounds the last corner of the track and sprints for the finish line, her arms and legs are pumping to reach her maximum speed. Her heart is beating rapidly and her breathing is rapid, deep, and regular. Blood is shunted away from digestive organs, and a greater volume is delivered to skeletal muscles to maximize the oxygen supply to them. These actions are accomplished by muscle tissue, the most abundant tissue of the body, and one of the most adaptable. The runner crosses the finish line in first place. Is she a "born runner" or could almost anyone become a world-class runner with the right training and discipline?

You don't have to be running for the muscular system to be at work. Even when you aren't "moving," postural muscles keep you sitting or standing upright, respiratory muscles keep you breathing, the heart continually pumps blood to all parts of the body, and blood vessels constrict or relax to direct blood to organs where it is needed.

Functions of the Muscular System

Movement within the body is accomplished by cilia or flagella on the surface of certain cells, by the force of gravity, or by the contraction of muscles. Most of the body's movement, from the beating of the heart to running a marathon, results from muscle contraction. As described in chapter 4, there are three types of muscle tissue: skeletal, cardiac, and smooth. This chapter deals primarily with the structure and function of skeletal muscle; cardiac and smooth muscle are described briefly. Most skeletal muscles are attached to bones, are typically under conscious control, and are responsible for most body movements (figure 7.1). The major functions of the muscular system are

1. *Body movement.* Contraction of skeletal muscles is responsible for the overall movements of the body, such as walking, running, or manipulating objects with the hands.
2. *Maintenance of posture.* Skeletal muscles constantly maintain tone, which keeps us sitting or standing erect.
3. *Respiration.* Muscles of the thorax are responsible for the movements necessary for respiration.
4. *Production of body heat.* When skeletal muscles contract, heat is given off as a by-product. This released heat is critical to the maintenance of body temperature.
5. *Communication.* Skeletal muscles are involved in all aspects of communication, such as speaking, writing, typing, gesturing, and facial expression.
6. *Constriction of organs and vessels.* The contraction of smooth muscle within the walls of internal organs and vessels causes constriction of those structures. This constriction can help propel and mix food and water in the digestive tract, propel secretions from organs, and regulate blood flow through vessels.

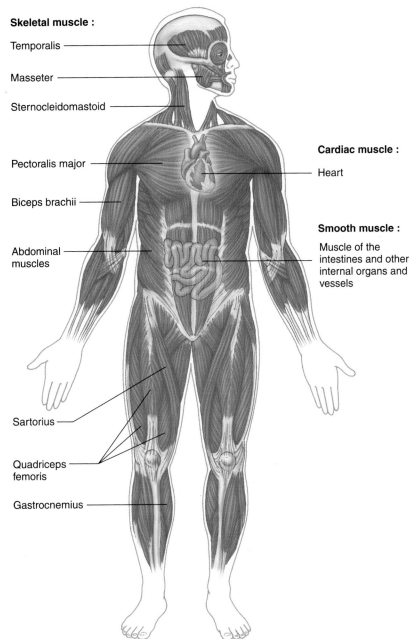

Figure 7.1

The Muscular System

7. *Heart beat.* The contraction of cardiac muscle causes the heart to beat, propelling blood to all parts of the body.

Characteristics of Skeletal Muscle

Skeletal muscle, with its associated connective tissue, constitutes approximately 40% of body weight. Skeletal muscle is so named because most skeletal muscles are attached to the skeletal system. It is also called **striated muscle** because of the transverse bands or striations that can be seen in the muscle under the microscope. It is responsible for locomotion, facial expressions, posture, and other body movements. In addition to these features, the metabolism that occurs in the large mass of muscle tissue of the body produces heat essential for the maintenance of normal body temperature.

Skeletal muscle has four major functional characteristics: contractility, excitability, extensibility, and elasticity.

1. **Contractility** (kon-trak-til′i-tē) is the ability of skeletal muscle to shorten with force. When skeletal muscles contract, they cause movement of the structures to which they are attached. Skeletal muscles shorten forcefully during contraction, but they lengthen passively. Either gravity or the contraction of an opposing muscle produces a force that pulls on the shortened muscle, causing it to lengthen.
2. **Excitability** (ek-sĭ′tă-bil′i-tē) is the capacity of skeletal muscle to respond to a stimulus. Normally skeletal muscle contracts as a result of stimulation by nerves.
3. **Extensibility** (eks-ten′sĭ-bil′i-tē) means that skeletal muscles can be stretched. After a contraction, skeletal muscles can be stretched to their normal resting length and beyond to a limited degree.
4. **Elasticity** (ĕ-las-tis′i-tē) is the ability of skeletal muscles to recoil to their original resting length after they have been stretched.

Structure

Each skeletal muscle is surrounded by a connective tissue sheath called the **epimysium** (ep-i-mis′ē-ŭm), or **fascia** (fash′ē-ă) (figure 7.2a). A muscle is composed of numerous visible bundles called **muscle fasciculi** (fă-sik′ū-lī), which are surrounded by loose connective tissue called the **perimysium** (per′i-mis′ē-ŭm). Each fasciculus is composed of several **muscle cells** or **muscle fibers** (figure 7.2b). Each muscle fiber is a single cylindrical cell that contains several nuclei located at the periphery of the muscle fiber. The largest, longest human muscle cells are up to 30 cm long and 0.15 mm in diameter. Such giant cells may contain several thousand nuclei. Each muscle fiber is surrounded by loose connective tissue, called **endomysium** (en′dō-mis′ē-ŭm).

Muscle contraction is much easier to understand when we understand the structure of a muscle cell. The cytoplasm of each muscle fiber, called the **sarcoplasm** (sar′kō-plazm; *sarco* is Greek meaning muscle), contains numerous myofibrils (figure 7.2c). Each **myofibril** (mī-ō-fī′bril) is a threadlike structure that extends from one end of the muscle fiber to the other. Myofibrils consist of two major kinds of protein fibers: actin and myosin myofilaments (figure 7.2d). **Actin myofilaments** (ak′tin mī-ō-fil′ă-ments), or thin myofilaments, resemble two minute strands of pearls twisted together (figure 7.2e). **Troponin** (trō′pō-nin) molecules are attached at specific intervals along the actin myofilaments and provide calcium-binding sites on the actin myofilament. **Tropomyosin** (trō-pō-mī′ō-sin) filaments are located along the groove between the twisted strands of actin myofilament subunits. These filaments expose attachment sites on the actin myofilament when calcium is bound to troponin, and they cover attachment sites on the actin myofilament

when calcium is not bound to troponin. **Myosin** (mī′ō-sin) **myofilaments**, or thick myofilaments, resemble bundles of minute golf clubs (figure 7.2f). The part of the myosin molecule that resembles golf club heads can bind to the exposed attachment sites on the actin myofilaments.

The actin and myosin myofilaments are arranged into highly ordered repeating units along the myofibril called **sarcomeres** (sar′kō-mērz) (see figures 7.2c and d). The sarcomere is the basic structural and functional unit of skeletal muscle, because it is the smallest portion of skeletal muscle capable of contracting. Each sarcomere extends from one Z disk to another Z disk. Each **Z disk** is a network of protein fibers forming an attachment site for actin myofilaments.

The arrangement of the actin and myosin myofilaments gives the myofibril a banded appearance. A light **I band**, which consists only of actin myofilaments, spans each Z disk and ends at the myosin myofilaments (figure 7.3, and see figure 7.2d). A darker, central region in each sarcomere, called an **A band**, extends the length of the myosin myofilaments. The actin and myosin myofilaments overlap for some distance at both ends of the A band. In the center of each sarcomere is a second light zone, called the **H zone**, which consists only of myosin myofilaments. The myosin myofilaments are anchored in the center of the sarcomere at a dark-staining band, called the **M line**. The alternating I bands and A bands of the sarcomeres are responsible for the striations seen in skeletal muscle fibers observed through the microscope (see figure 7.3).

The cell membrane of the muscle fiber is called the **sarcolemma** (sar′kō-lem′ă) (see figure 7.2b). The multiple nuclei of the muscle fiber are located just deep to the sarcolemma. The sarcolemma has along its surface many tubelike invaginations called **transverse**, or **T tubules**, which are located at regular intervals along the muscle fiber and wrap around sarcomeres where the actin and myosin myofilaments overlap. The T tubules are associated with a highly organized, smooth endoplasmic reticulum called the **sarcoplasmic reticulum** (re-tik′ū-lŭm). T tubules connect the sarcolemma to the sarcoplasmic reticulum. The sarcoplasmic reticulum has a relatively high concentration of calcium ions, which play a major role in muscle contractions.

Membrane Potentials

Muscle fibers, like other cells of the body, have electrical properties. This section describes the electrical properties of skeletal muscle fibers and later sections illustrate their role in contraction.

The outside of most cell membranes is positively charged compared with the inside of the cell membrane (figure 7.4a and b). The charge difference, called the **resting membrane potential**, develops for two reasons: (1) the concentration of potassium ions inside the cell membrane is higher than that outside the cell membrane, and (2) the cell membrane is more permeable to potassium ions than it is to other ions, including negatively charged ions located inside

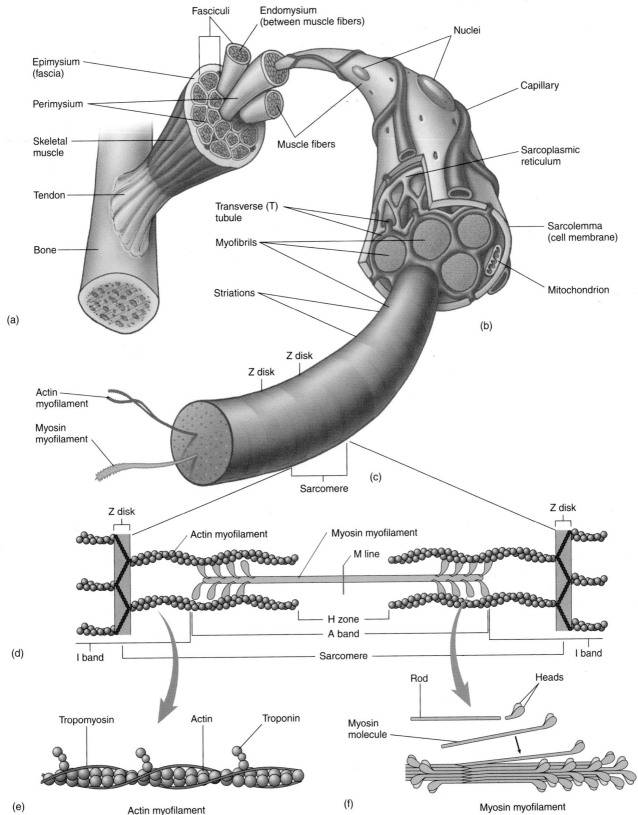

Figure 7.2 Parts of a Muscle

(a) Part of a muscle attached by a tendon to a bone. A muscle is composed of muscle fasciculi, each surrounded by perimysium. The fasciculi are composed of bundles of individual muscle fibers (muscle cells), each surrounded by endomysium. (b) Enlargement of one muscle fiber. The muscle fiber contains several myofibrils. (c) A myofibril extended out the end of the muscle fiber. The banding patterns of the sarcomeres are shown in the myofibril. (d) A single sarcomere from a myofibril, which is composed of actin myofilaments and myosin myofilaments. The Z disk anchors the actin myofilaments and the M line anchors the myosin myofilaments. The A band is the length of the myosin myofilaments, the H zone is the area where only myosin myofilaments occur, with no overlapping actin myofilaments, and the I band is the area where only actin myofilaments occur with no overlapping myosin myofilaments. (e) Actin myofilaments are made up of actin, troponin, and tropomyosin molecules. (f) Myosin myofilaments are made up of myosin molecules.

(a)

Nucleus

Striations

Skeletal muscle fiber

Sarcomere

M line

Myofibrils

H zone

Z disk

Mitochondria

A band

I band

Figure 7.3 Skeletal Muscle

(*a*) Light micrograph showing the striations in each muscle fiber. (*b*) Electron micrograph of skeletal muscle, and a much higher magnification than seen in part *a*. Several sarcomeres are shown in a muscle fiber.

(b)

the cell. This occurs because potassium ion channels are open, whereas other ion channels, such as those for sodium ions, are closed.

A few potassium ions are able to diffuse down their concentration gradient from inside to just outside the cell membrane. Negatively charged ions cannot diffuse through the cell membrane with the potassium ions because the cell membrane is less permeable to the negatively charged ions. Because potassium ions are positively charged, their movement from inside the cell to the outside causes the outside of the cell membrane to become positively charged compared to the inside of the cell membrane.

Potassium ions only diffuse down their concentration gradient until the charge difference across the cell membrane is great enough to prevent any additional diffusion of potassium ions out of the cell. The resting membrane potential is in equilibrium because the tendency for potassium ions to diffuse out of the cell is opposed by the negative charge inside the cell, which tends to attract the positively charged potassium ions back into the cell (see figures 7.4*a* and *b*).

When a muscle cell or nerve cell is stimulated, sodium ion channels open, and the membrane becomes very permeable to sodium ions for a brief time (figure 7.4*c*). The

sodium ion concentration is much greater outside the cell than inside, and, therefore, a few positively charged sodium ions quickly diffuse down their concentration gradient into the cell, causing the inside of the cell membrane to become more positive. This change is called **depolarization**. The sodium ion channels then close and additional potassium ion channels open (figure 7.4*d*). The cell membrane then quickly becomes less permeable to sodium ions, and the permeability of the membrane to potassium ions increases, allowing a few potassium ions to diffuse out of the cell. The additional potassium ion channels then close as the charge across the cell membrane returns to its resting condition (return to figure 7.4*a*). The change back to the resting membrane potential is called **repolarization**. The rapid depolarization and repolarization of the cell membrane is called an **action potential**. In a muscle fiber, an action potential results in muscle contraction.

The sodium–potassium exchange pump transports potassium ions from outside the cell to the inside and transports sodium ions from inside the cell to the outside (see chapter 3). The active transport of potassium and sodium ions restores the normal, resting concentrations of ions on either side of the cell membrane, thus maintaining the resting membrane potential.

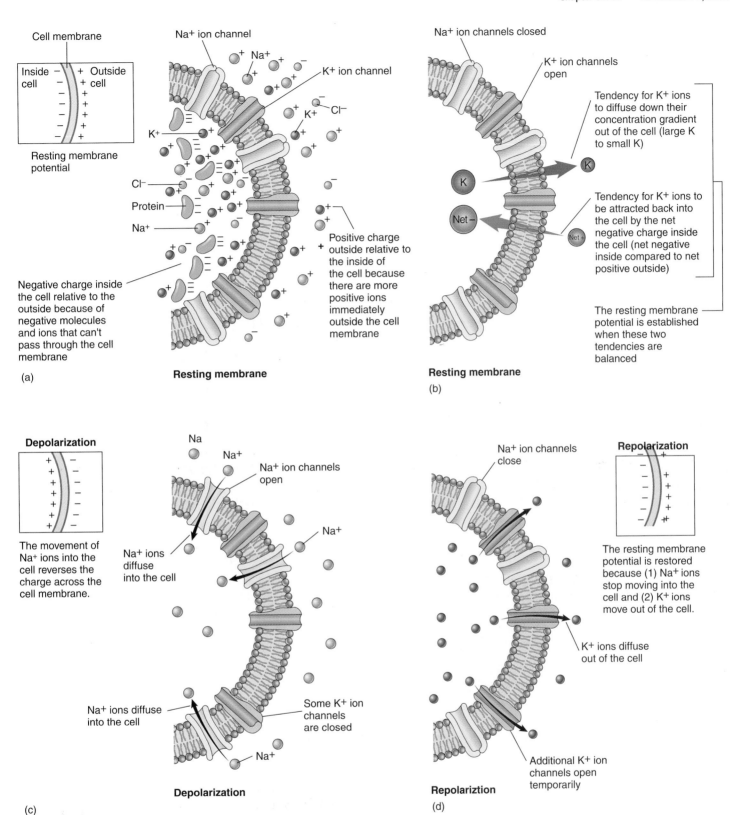

Cell membrane

Inside − | + Outside
cell − | + cell
− | +
− | +
− | +
− | +

Resting membrane potential

Na+ ion channel

+ Na+ +
+
+ K+ ion channel

K+ − Cl−
+

K+
+
Cl−
Protein
Na+

Negative charge inside the cell relative to the outside because of negative molecules and ions that can't pass through the cell membrane

Positive charge outside relative to the inside of the cell because there are more positive ions immediately outside the cell membrane

(a)   **Resting membrane**

Na+ ion channels closed

K+ ion channels open

Tendency for K+ ions to diffuse down their concentration gradient out of the cell (large K to small K)

K

Net −

Net +

Tendency for K+ ions to be attracted back into the cell by the net negative charge inside the cell (net negative inside compared to net positive outside)

The resting membrane potential is established when these two tendencies are balanced

Resting membrane

(b)

Depolarization

+ | −
+ | −
+ | −
+ | −
+ | −
+ | −
+ | −

The movement of Na+ ions into the cell reverses the charge across the cell membrane.

Na
Na+
Na+ ion channels open

Na+ ions diffuse into the cell

Na+

Na+ ions diffuse into the cell

Some K+ ion channels are closed

Na+

Depolarization

(c)

Na+ ion channels close

Repolarization

− | +
− | +
− | +
− | +
− | +
− | +

The resting membrane potential is restored because (1) Na+ ions stop moving into the cell and (2) K+ ions move out of the cell.

K+ ions diffuse out of the cell

Additional K+ ion channels open temporarily

Repolariztion

(d)

Figure 7.4   Resting Membrane Potential and Action Potential

(*a*) Resting membrane. (*b*) During the resting membrane potential a net positive charge occurs outside the cell because the concentration of potassium ions inside the cell is greater than that outside the cell and the cell membrane is permeable to potassium ions. This permeability results because potassium ion channels are open, whereas sodium ion channels are closed. Potassium ions diffuse down their concentration gradient from the inside to the outside of the cell. (*c*) During the depolarization phase of an action potential, sodium ion channels open, potassium ion channels close, and sodium ions diffuse down their concentration gradient into the cell. (*d*) During the repolarization phase of an action potential, sodium ion channels close, more potassium ion channels reopen, and potassium ions diffuse down their concentration gradient out of the cell. This process reestablishes the resting membrane potential.

Nerve Supply

Skeletal muscle fibers do not contract unless they are stimulated by motor neurons. This section describes how neurons stimulate skeletal muscle fibers.

Motor neurons are nerve cells that carry action potentials to skeletal muscle fibers. Axons of these neurons enter muscles and send out branches to several muscle fibers. Each branch forms a junction with a muscle fiber, called a **neuromuscular junction**, or **synapse** (sin'aps) (figure 7.5*a*). The term synapse is a more general term; it refers to the cell-to-cell junction between a nerve cell and either another nerve cell or an effector cell, such as a muscle or gland cell. Neuromuscular junctions are located near the center of a muscle fiber. A single motor neuron and all the skeletal muscle fibers it innervates are called a **motor unit** (see figure 7.5*a*). A motor unit in a small, precisely controlled muscle may have only one or a few muscle fibers per unit, whereas the motor units of large thigh muscles may have as many as 1000 muscle fibers per unit. Many motor units constitute a single muscle. The strength of a given muscle contraction is determined by the number of motor units contracting in the muscle.

A neuromuscular junction is formed by enlarged axon terminals resting in indentations of the muscle fiber's cell membrane (figure 7.5*b*). An enlarged axon terminal is the **presynaptic terminal**, the space between the presynaptic terminal and the muscle fiber is the **synaptic cleft**, and the muscle fiber membrane is the **postsynaptic membrane**. Each presynaptic terminal contains many small vesicles, called **synaptic vesicles**. These vesicles contain **acetylcholine** (as-e-til-kō'lēn, ACH), which functions as a **neurotransmitter**, a molecule released by a presynaptic cell that stimulates or inhibits a postsynaptic cell.

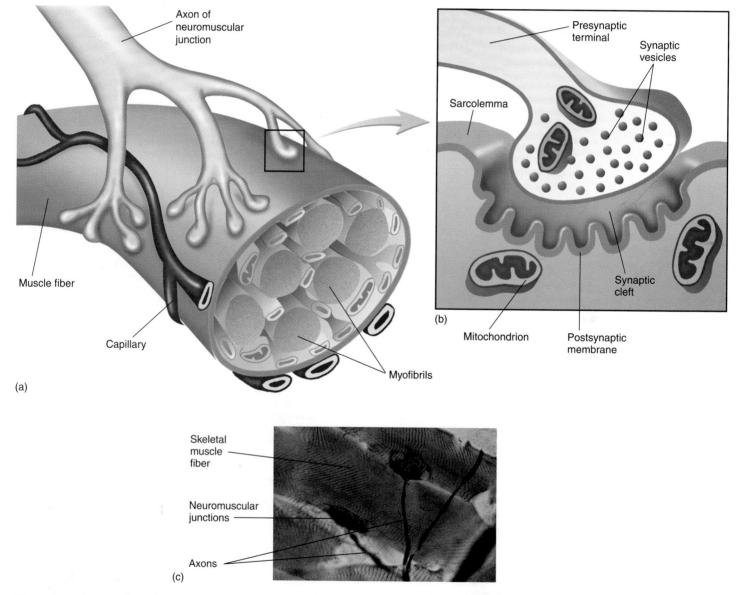

Figure 7.5 Innervation of a Motor Unit and Muscle Fiber

(*a*) A muscle fiber with the branch of a motor neuron and its neuromuscular junctions. (*b*) An enlarged cross section of one neuromuscular junction. (*c*) Photomicrograph of two axons and their neuromuscular junctions.

When an action potential reaches the presynaptic terminal, it causes the synaptic vesicles to release acetylcholine into the synaptic cleft by exocytosis (figure 7.6). The acetylcholine diffuses across the synaptic cleft and binds to acetylcholine receptor molecules on the sodium ion channels in the muscle fiber cell membrane. The combination of acetylcholine with its receptor opens sodium ion channels and therefore causes an increase in the permeability of the cell membrane to sodium ions. The resulting influx of sodium ions into the muscle fiber initiates an action potential in the muscle fiber, which causes it to contract. The acetylcholine released into the synaptic cleft between the neuron and muscle fiber is rapidly broken down by an enzyme, **acetylcholinesterase** (as′e-til-kō-lin-es′ter-ās). This enzymatic breakdown ensures that one action potential in the neuron yields only one action potential in the skeletal muscle fibers of that motor unit, and only one contraction of each muscle fiber.

Did You Know?

Anything that affects the production, release, or degradation of acetylcholine or its ability to bind to its receptor on the muscle cell membrane can affect the transmission of action potentials across the neuromuscular junction. Some insecticides bind to and inhibit acetylcholinesterase. Consequently, acetylcholine accumulates in the synaptic cleft and acts as a constant stimulus to the muscle fiber. The insects die, partly because their respiratory muscles contract and cannot relax or because they keep contracting until they fatigue and can no longer contract. Other poisons, such as **curare** (koo-rǎ′rē), the poison originally used by South American Indians in poison arrows, bind to the acetylcholine receptors on the muscle cell membrane and prevent acetylcholine from binding to them. The muscle fibers cannot therefore be stimulated by acetylcholine and do not contract, resulting in paralysis.

1. Action potentials arriving at the presynaptic terminal cause synaptic vesicles to bind to the cell membrane.

2. Synaptic vesicles release acetylcholine into the synaptic cleft by exocytosis.

3. Acetylcholine diffuses across the synaptic cleft.

4. Acetylcholine binds to acetylcholine receptors on sodium ion channels in the muscle cell membrane.

5. The combination of acetylcholine with its receptor opens sodium ion channels and causes an increase in the permeability of the muscle cell membrane to sodium ions.

Presynaptic terminal

Synaptic vesicle

Synaptic cleft

Postsynaptic membrane

Neurotransmitter (acetylcholine)

Na$^+$ ions

Neurotransmitter (acetylcholine) bound to receptor opens Na$^+$ ion channel

Figure 7.6   The Synapse

Neurotransmitters are released from synaptic vesicles in the presynaptic terminal in response to an action potential. The neurotransmitters diffuse across the synaptic cleft and bind to receptors on the postsynaptic cell membrane, causing a stimulation or inhibition of action potentials in the postsynaptic cell.

Muscle Contraction

Contraction of skeletal muscle tissue occurs as actin and myosin myofilaments slide past one another, causing the sarcomeres to shorten. Shortening of the sarcomeres causes muscles to shorten. The sliding of actin myofilaments past myosin myofilaments during contraction is called the **sliding filament mechanism** of muscle contraction. The H zones and I bands shorten during contraction, but the A bands do not change in length (figure 7.7).

Action potentials produced in skeletal muscle fibers travel along the sarcolemma and the T tubules (table 7.1). The action potentials cause the membranes of the sarcoplasmic reticulum to become more permeable to calcium ions, and calcium ions diffuse into the sarcoplasm. The calcium ions bind to troponin molecules attached to the actin myofilaments (figure 7.8). This binding causes tropomyosin filaments to move, exposing attachment sites on the actin myofilament. The exposed attachment sites on the actin myofilament bind to the heads of the myosin myofilaments to form **cross-bridges** between the actin and myosin myofilaments.

Energy for muscle contraction is supplied to the muscles in the form of adenosine triphosphate (ATP), a high-energy molecule produced from the energy that is released during the metabolism of food (see chapters 3 and 17). The energy in ATP is released as it is broken down to adenosine diphosphate (ADP) and phosphate (P). During muscle contraction, the energy released from ATP is briefly stored in the myosin head. This energy is used to bend the heads of the myosin myofilaments toward the center of the sarcomere, forcing the actin myofilaments to slide over the surface of the myosin myofilaments. In the process, ADP and P are released from the myosin heads.

As a new ATP molecule attaches to the head of the myosin molecule, the cross-bridge is released, the ATP is broken down to ADP and P, which both remain bound to the myosin head, and the myosin head is restored to its original position, where it can attach to the next actin subunit. As long as calcium remains attached to troponin, and as long as ATP remains available, the cycle of cross-bridge formation, movement, and release is repeated (see table 7.1). A new ATP must bind to myosin before the cross-bridge can be released. When ATP is not available after a person dies, the cross-bridges that have formed are not released, causing muscles to become rigid. This condition is called **rigor mortis** (rig′er mōr′tis).

Part of the energy from ATP involved in muscle contraction is required for the formation and movement of the cross-bridges, and part is released as heat. The heat released during muscle contraction increases body temperature, and a person becomes warmer during exercise. Shivering, a type of generalized muscle contraction, is one of the body's mechanisms for dealing with cold. The muscle movement involved in shivering produces heat, which raises the body temperature.

Muscle relaxation occurs as calcium ions are actively transported back into the sarcoplasmic reticulum (a process that requires ATP). As a consequence, the attachment sites on the actin molecules are once again covered by tropomyosin so that cross-bridges cannot reform.

Table 7.1 **Summary of Skeletal Muscle Contraction (see figures 7.6 and 7.7)**

1. An action potential travels along an axon to a neuromuscular junction.

2. Acetylcholine is released from the synaptic vesicles of the neuron.

3. Acetylcholine diffuses across the synaptic cleft and binds to receptor molecules in the muscle cell membrane.

4. Sodium ions diffuse into the muscle cell, initiating an action potential in the muscle cell. The action potentials travel along the sarcolemma and T tubules to the sarcoplasmic reticulum.

5. Calcium ions are released from the sarcoplasmic reticulum.

6. Calcium ions bind to troponin, associated with actin myofilaments. The binding causes tropomyosin to move into the actin groove, which exposes myosin attachment sites.

7. The heads of myosin myofilaments attach to the actin myofilaments, forming cross-bridges.

8. The heads of the myosin myofilaments bend, causing the actin myofilaments to slide over the surface of the myosin myofilaments.

9. Muscle contraction requires energy. ATP, bound to the myosin heads, is broken down, releasing energy to myosin heads, which is used to supply the energy for movement.

10. Another ATP binds to the myosin head, causing it to release the actin myofilament and the myosin bends back to its resting position.

11. As long as calcium remains attached to the troponin, and as long as ATP remains available, the muscle continues to contract and steps 7 through 10 are repeated.

1	**P R E D I C T**

Predict the consequences of having the following conditions develop in a muscle in response to a stimulus: (a) inadequate ATP is present in the muscle fiber before a stimulus is applied; (b) adequate ATP is present within the muscle fiber, but action potentials occur at a frequency so great that calcium ions are not transported back into the sarcoplasmic reticulum between individual action potentials.

✔ *Answer on page 192*

Muscle Twitch, Tetanus, and Recruitment

A **muscle twitch** is a contraction of an entire muscle in response to a stimulus that causes an action potential in one or more muscle fibers (figure 7.9). A muscle fiber does not respond to a stimulus unless the stimulus strength reaches a level called **threshold**, which is sufficient to produce an action potential in a muscle fiber. In response to an action potential, a muscle fiber contracts maximally. This phenomenon is called the **all-or-none response**.

The time between application of the stimulus to a motor neuron and the beginning of contraction is the **lag phase**. The time of contraction is the **contraction phase**. Relaxation of the muscle occurs immediately after the all-or-none contraction phase. The time during which the muscle relaxes is the **relaxation phase**.

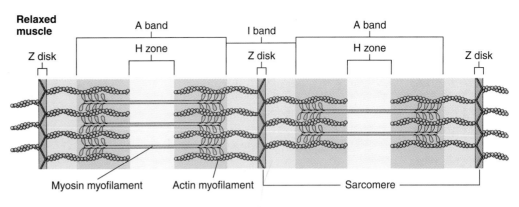

1. Actin and myosin myofilaments in a relaxed muscle (right) and a contracted muscle (#4 below) are the same length. Myofilaments do not change length during muscle contraction.

2. During contraction, actin myofilaments at each end of the sarcomere slide past the myosin myofilaments toward each other. As a result, the Z disks are brought closer together, and the sarcomere shortens.

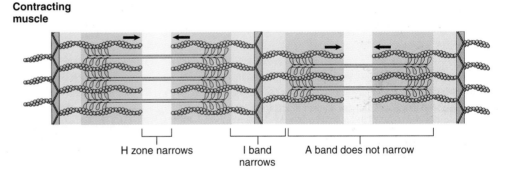

3. As the actin myofilaments slide over the myosin myofilaments, the H zones (yellow) and the I bands (blue) narrow. The A bands, which are equal to the length to the myosin myofilaments, do not narrow, because the length of the myosin myofilaments does not change.

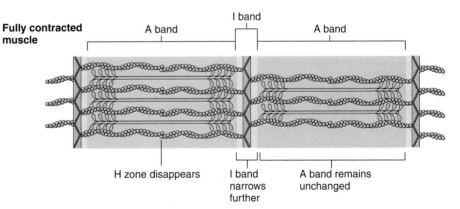

4. In a fully contracted muscle, the ends of the actin myofilaments overlap and the H zone disappears.

Figure 7.7   Sarcomere Shortening

Note that the I bands (blue) shorten, but the A bands (pink) do not. The H zone (yellow) narrows or even disappears as the actin myofilaments meet at the center of the sarcomere.

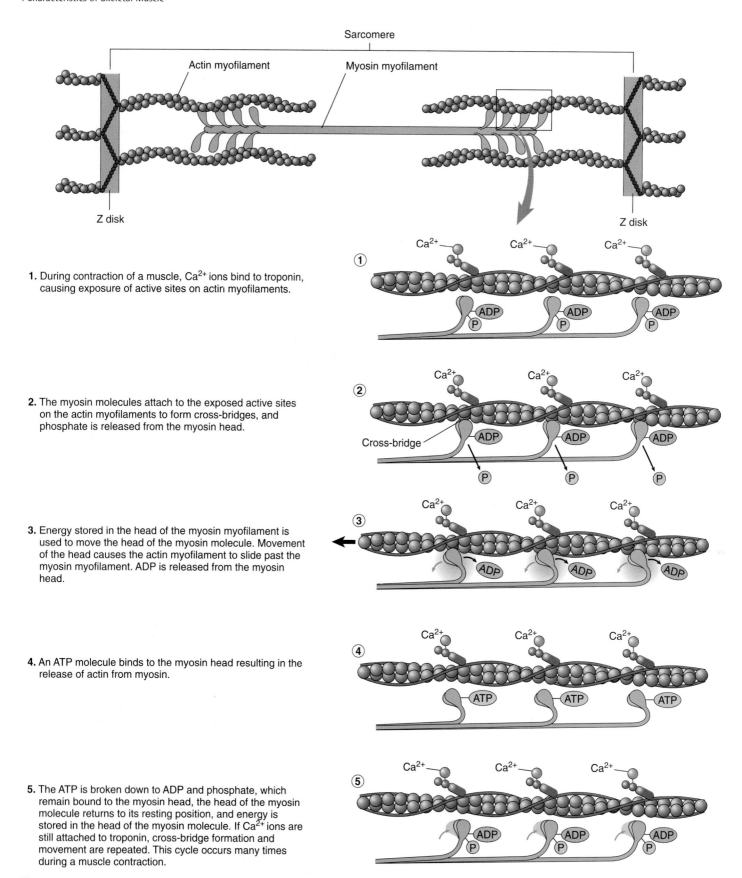

1. During contraction of a muscle, Ca^{2+} ions bind to troponin, causing exposure of active sites on actin myofilaments.

2. The myosin molecules attach to the exposed active sites on the actin myofilaments to form cross-bridges, and phosphate is released from the myosin head.

3. Energy stored in the head of the myosin myofilament is used to move the head of the myosin molecule. Movement of the head causes the actin myofilament to slide past the myosin myofilament. ADP is released from the myosin head.

4. An ATP molecule binds to the myosin head resulting in the release of actin from myosin.

5. The ATP is broken down to ADP and phosphate, which remain bound to the myosin head, the head of the myosin molecule returns to its resting position, and energy is stored in the head of the myosin molecule. If Ca^{2+} ions are still attached to troponin, cross-bridge formation and movement are repeated. This cycle occurs many times during a muscle contraction.

Figure 7.8 Breakdown of ATP and Cross-Bridge Movement During Muscle Contraction

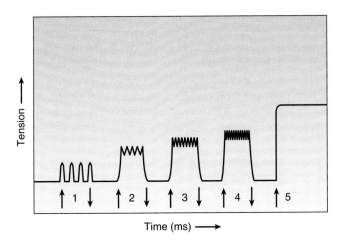

Figure 7.9   Phases of a Muscle Twitch

Hypothetical muscle twitch in a single muscle fiber. There is a short lag phase after stimulus application, followed by a contraction phase and a relaxation phase.

If successive stimuli are given to a muscle, successive twitches occur (figure 7.10, 1). As the stimulus frequency increases, muscle twitches may occur so frequently that the muscle does not have enough time to fully relax before another twitch begins (figure 7.10, 2–4). If the stimulus frequency increases even more, no relaxation occurs between muscle twitches (figure 7.10, 5). When the muscle remains contracted between stimuli without relaxing, the condition is called **tetanus**.

A small contraction force in a muscle is produced when only a few of its motor units are stimulated, each contracting in an all-or-none fashion. Stimulation of more motor units produces a greater contraction force because more motor units

Figure 7.10   Muscle Twitch—Multiple Stimuli

Multiple stimuli result in multiple twitches (1). More frequent stimuli do not allow complete relaxation between twitches so that the individual twitches seem to fuse together (2, 3, and 4). With even greater stimulus frequency (5), no relaxation can be seen between twitches, and the muscle remains continually contracted (tetanus).

are contracting. This increase in the number of motor units being activated is called **recruitment**. For example, the biceps brachii is an arm muscle that flexes the forearm. The amount of force required by the biceps to lift a 1-pound weight held in the hand is not great, and therefore only a few motor units in the biceps are recruited for the task. Lifting a 10-pound weight, however, requires more force, and therefore more motor units are recruited. Maximum force is produced in a given muscle when all the motor units of that muscle are stimulated (recruited).

If all the motor units in a muscle were stimulated simultaneously, a quick, jerking motion would occur. Because the motor units are recruited gradually so that some are stimulated and held in tetanus while additional motor units are recruited, slow, smooth, sustained contractions occur. Smooth relaxation of muscle occurs because some motor units are held in tetanus while other motor units relax.

Energy Requirements for Muscle Contraction

The ATP required to provide energy for muscle contraction is produced primarily in numerous mitochondria located within the muscle fiber sarcoplasm between the myofibrils. Even in resting muscle fibers, fairly large amounts of ATP are required for cell maintenance. It is therefore necessary for muscle fibers to constantly produce ATP.

Muscle fibers cannot easily stockpile ATP in preparation for periods of activity. The muscle fibers, however, can store another high-energy molecule, **creatine** (krē′ă-tēn) **phosphate**. Creatine phosphate provides a means of storing energy that can be used rapidly to maintain an adequate amount of ATP in the contracting muscle fiber. During periods of inactivity, as excess ATP is produced in the muscle fiber, the energy contained in the ATP is used to synthesize creatine phosphate. During periods of activity, the reserves of ATP existing in the cell are used first, and then the energy stored in creatine phosphate is accessed quickly to produce ATP, which is used in muscle contraction (figure 7.11).

ATP is produced by both anaerobic and aerobic cellular respiration (see chapter 17 for details). **Anaerobic respiration,** which occurs in the absence of oxygen, results in the breakdown of glucose to yield ATP and lactic acid. **Aerobic respiration** requires oxygen and breaks down glucose to produce ATP, carbon dioxide, and water. Anaerobic respiration occurs in the cytoplasm of cells, whereas most of aerobic metabolism occurs in the mitochondria. Cells with a high metabolic rate, such as muscle fibers, which depend on large amounts of oxygen and carry out primarily aerobic metabolism, contain large numbers of mitochondria. Aerobic respiration is much more efficient than anaerobic respiration. The metabolism of a glucose molecule by aerobic respiration theoretically can produce approximately 18 times as much ATP as is produced by anaerobic respiration. In addition, aerobic respiration can use a greater variety of nutrient molecules to produce ATP than can anaerobic respiration. For example, aerobic respiration can use fatty acids to generate ATP.

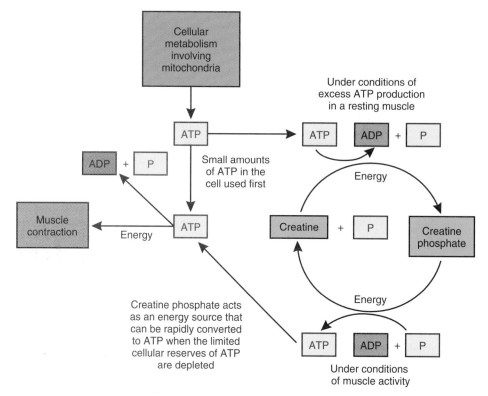

Figure 7.11 Fate of ATP in a Resting and Active Muscle

When excess ATP is produced in a resting muscle cell, part of that ATP can be used to produce creatine phosphate. When the muscle is active, creatine phosphate is a quickly available source of ATP.

Although aerobic respiration produces more ATP molecules than anaerobic respiration for each glucose molecule metabolized, anaerobic respiration can occur faster and is important when oxygen availability limits aerobic respiration. By using many glucose molecules, anaerobic respiration can rapidly produce much ATP, but anaerobic respiration can proceed for only a short time. Lactic acid is an end product of anaerobic respiration. Some of the lactic acid can diffuse out of the muscle fiber into the blood, but some remains in the muscle fibers. Lactic acid can irritate muscle fibers, causing short-term pain. Muscle pain that lasts for several days, however, indicates mechanical injury to the muscle.

Resting muscles or muscles undergoing long-term exercise, such as during long-distance running, depend primarily on aerobic respiration for ATP synthesis. Although some glucose is used as an energy source, fatty acids are a more important energy source during both sustained exercise and resting conditions. During short periods of intense exercise such as in sprinting, ATP is used up more quickly than it can be produced by aerobic respiration. Once the ATP reserves begin to decrease, the energy stored in creatine phosphate is used to maintain ATP levels in the contracting muscle fiber. Once the creatine phosphate stores are depleted, anaerobic respiration predominates. Anaerobic respiration rapidly metabolizes available glucose to provide enough ATP to support intense muscle contraction for up to 2 to 3 minutes. During intense exercise, glycogen stored in muscle fibers can be broken down to glucose, which can then be used to produce more ATP. Anaerobic metabolism is ultimately limited by depletion of glucose and a buildup of lactic acid within the muscle fiber.

After intense exercise, the respiration rate and volume remain elevated for a time, even though the muscles are no longer actively contracting. This increased respiration provides the oxygen to pay back the oxygen debt. The *oxygen debt* or *excess post exercise oxygen consumption* is the amount of oxygen needed in chemical reactions that occur to (1) convert lactic acid to glucose, (2) replenish the depleted ATP and creatine phosphate stores in muscle fibers, and (3) replenish oxygen stores in the lungs, blood, and muscles. After the lactic acid produced by anaerobic respiration is converted to glucose and creatine phosphate levels are restored, respiration rate returns to normal. The magnitude of the oxygen debt depends on the intensity of the exercise, the length of time it was sustained, and the physical condition of the individual. The metabolic capacity of an individual in poor physical condition is much lower than that of a well-trained athlete. With exercise and training, a person's ability to carry out both aerobic and anaerobic activities is enhanced.

2   P R E D I C T

After a 10-mile run with a sprint at the end, a runner continues to breathe heavily for a time. Indicate the type of metabolism that is producing energy during the run, during the sprint, and after the run.

✔ *Answer on page 192*

Muscle fatigue results when ATP is used during muscle contraction faster than it can be produced in the muscle fibers and lactic acid builds up faster than it can be removed. As a consequence, ATP falls to levels too low for muscle fibers to produce their maximum force of contraction, and contractions become weaker and weaker. Under conditions of extreme muscular fatigue, muscles may become incapable of either contracting or relaxing. This condition, called **physiological contracture**, occurs when there is too little ATP to bind to myosin myofilaments. Because binding of ATP to the myosin heads is necessary for cross-bridge release between the actin and myosin, the cross-bridges between the actin and myosin myofilaments cannot be broken, and the muscle cannot relax.

The most common type of fatigue, **psychological fatigue**, involves the central nervous system rather than the muscles themselves. The muscles are still capable of contracting, but the individual "perceives" that additional muscle contraction is impossible. A burst of activity in a tired athlete in response to spectator encouragement is an example of how psychological fatigue can be overcome.

Types of Muscle Contractions

Muscle contractions are classified as either isometric or isotonic. In **isometric** (equal distance) **contractions**, the amount of tension increases during the contraction process, but the length of the muscle does not change. Isometric contractions are responsible for the constant length of the postural muscles of the body, such as the muscles of the back. On the other hand, in **isotonic** (equal tension) **contractions**, the amount of tension produced by the muscle is constant during contraction, but the length of the muscle decreases. Movements of the arms or fingers are predominantly isotonic contractions. Most muscle contractions are a combination of isometric and isotonic contractions in which the muscles shorten some distance and the degree of tension increases.

Concentric (kon-sen'trik) **contractions** are isotonic contractions in which muscle tension increases as the muscle shortens. This is the most common type of muscle contraction. **Eccentric** (ek-sen'trik) **contractions** are isotonic contractions in which tension is maintained as the muscle lengthens. Eccentric contractions are used when a person lets a heavy weight down slowly. Substantial force is produced in muscles during eccentric contractions, and muscle injuries can occur from repetitive eccentric contractions, such as when a person runs downhill.

Muscle Tone

Muscle tone refers to the constant tension produced by muscles of the body over long periods of time. Muscle tone is responsible for keeping the back and legs straight, the head held in an upright position, and the abdomen from bulging. Muscle tone depends on a small percentage of all the motor units in a muscle being stimulated at any point in time, causing their muscle fibers to contract isometrically and out of phase with one another.

Slow and Fast Fibers

Muscle fibers are sometimes classified as either fast-twitch or slow-twitch muscle fibers. This classification is based on differences in the rod portion of the myosin myofilament (see figure 7.2). Slow-twitch fibers contain type I myosin as the predominant or even exclusive type. Fast-twitch fibers contain either type IIa or IIx myosin myofilaments. Each of these three myosin types is the product of a different myosin gene. Fast-twitch muscle fibers, also called type II muscle fibers, contract quickly and fatigue quickly, whereas slow-twitch muscle fibers, also called type I muscle fibers, contract more slowly and are more resistant to fatigue. Type IIx fibers can contract 10 times as fast as type I fibers and type IIa fibers contract at an intermediate speed. Fast-twitch muscles have larger stores of glycogen and are well adapted to performing anaerobic metabolism, whereas slow-twitch muscles contain more mitochondria and are better suited for aerobic metabolism.

The white meat of a chicken's breast is composed mainly of fast-twitch fibers. The muscles are adapted to contract rapidly for a short time but fatigue quickly. Chickens normally do not fly long distances. They spend most of their time walking. Ducks, on the other hand, fly for much longer periods and over greater distances. The red, or dark, meat of a chicken's leg or a duck's breast is composed of slow-twitch fibers. The darker appearance is due partly to a richer blood supply and partly to the presence of **myoglobin**, which stores oxygen temporarily. Myoglobin can continue to release oxygen in a muscle, even when a sustained contraction has interrupted the continuous flow of blood.

Humans exhibit no clear separation of slow-twitch and fast-twitch muscle fibers in individual muscles. Most muscles have both types of fibers, although the number of each type varies in a given muscle. The large postural muscles contain more slow-twitch fibers, whereas muscles of the upper limb contain more fast-twitch fibers. People who are good sprinters have a greater percentage of fast-twitch, type II muscle fibers in their lower limbs, whereas good long-distance runners have a higher percentage of slow-twitch, type I fibers. Athletes who are able to perform a variety of anaerobic and aerobic exercises tend to have a more balanced mixture of fast-twitch and slow-twitch muscle fibers.

Did You Know?

Average, healthy, active adults have roughly equal numbers of slow- and fast-twitch fibers in their muscles and over 3 times as many type IIa as type IIx fibers. A world-class sprinter may have over 80% type II fibers, with type IIa slightly predominating. A world-class endurance athlete, on the other hand, may have 95% type I fibers. The ratio of muscle fiber types in world-class sprinters or endurance athletes apparently has a large hereditary component but can be considerably influenced by training. Exercise increases the vascularity of muscles, increases the number of mitochondria per muscle fiber, and causes enlargement of muscle fibers by increasing the number of myofibrils and myofilaments. With weight training, type IIx myofilaments can be replaced by type IIa myofilaments as muscles enlarge. Muscle nuclei quit expressing type IIx genes and begin expressing type IIa. If the exercise stops, the type IIa genes turn off and the type IIx genes turn back on. Vigorous exercise programs can cause a limited number of type I myofilaments to be replaced by type IIa myofilaments. No study has as yet shown the reverse: replacement of type IIa or IIx myofilaments by type I myofilaments. If such replacement occurs, it takes place over a long period of time.

The number of cells in a skeletal muscle remains relatively constant following birth. Enlargement of muscles after birth is therefore primarily the result of an increase in the size of the existing muscle fibers. As people age, however, the number of muscle fibers actually decreases, and new ones cannot be added.

Smooth Muscle and Cardiac Muscle

Smooth muscle cells are small and spindle-shaped, usually with one nucleus per cell (table 7.2). They contain less actin and myosin than do skeletal muscle cells, and the myofilaments are not organized into sarcomeres. As a result, smooth muscle cells are not striated. Smooth muscle cells contract more slowly than skeletal muscle cells and do not develop an oxygen debt. The resting membrane potential of some smooth muscle cells fluctuates between slow depolarization and repolarization phases. As a result, smooth muscle cells can periodically and spontaneously reach threshold, resulting in the generation of action potentials that cause the smooth muscle cells to contract. The resulting periodic spontaneous contraction of smooth muscle is called **autorhythmicity**. Smooth muscle is under involuntary control, whereas skeletal muscle is under voluntary motor control.

Some hormones, such as those that function on the digestive system, can stimulate smooth muscle to contract.

Smooth muscle cells are organized to form layers. Most of those cells have gap junctions, specialized cell-to-cell contacts (see chapter 4), that allow action potentials to spread rapidly to all the smooth muscle cells in a given tissue. Thus all the smooth muscle cells tend to function as a unit and contract at the same time.

Cardiac muscle shares some characteristics with both smooth and skeletal muscle (see table 7.2). Cardiac muscle cells are long, striated, and branching, with usually only one nucleus per cell. The actin and myosin myofilaments are organized into sarcomeres, but the distribution of myofilaments is not as uniform as in skeletal muscle. As a result, cardiac muscle cells are striated, but not as distinctly striated as skeletal muscle. The rate of cardiac muscle contraction is between that of smooth and skeletal muscle. Cardiac muscle contraction is autorhythmic. Cardiac muscle does not develop an oxygen debt and does not fatigue. Cardiac muscle cells are connected to one another by **intercalated** (in-ter′kă-lā-ted) **disks**. Intercalated disks are specialized structures that include tight junctions and gap junctions and that facilitate action potential conduction between the cells. This cell-to-cell connection allows cardiac muscle cells to function as a unit. As with smooth muscle, cardiac muscle is under involuntary control and is influenced by hormones, such as epinephrine.

Clinical Focus Disorders and Other Conditions of Muscle Tissue

Cramps

Cramps are painful, spastic contractions of muscle that are usually the result of an irritation within a muscle. Local inflammation from buildup of lactic acid or connective tissue inflammation can cause contraction of muscle fibers surrounding the irritated region.

Hypertrophy and Atrophy

Exercise causes muscular hypertrophy (hī-per′trō-fē), which is an enlargement of a muscle resulting from an increase in the number of myofibrils within muscle fibers. Muscle hypertrophy is greater in males than in females, mainly because of greater concentrations of the male sex hormone, testosterone, in males. Disuse of muscle results in muscular atrophy (at′rō-fē), which is a decrease in muscle size because of a decrease in myofilaments within muscle fibers. Severe atrophy involves the permanent loss of skeletal muscle fibers and the replacement of those fibers by connective tissue. Immobility resulting from damage to

the nervous system or casting a broken limb leads to muscular atrophy. If the nerve supply to a muscle is severed, the muscle becomes flaccid (having no tone) and atrophies.

Muscular Dystrophy

Muscular dystrophy (dis′trō-fē) refers to a group of inherited muscle disorders in which skeletal muscle tissue degenerates and the person experiences progressive weakness. The disorders are characterized by the progressive degeneration of muscle fibers leading to atrophy and their eventual replacement by fat and other connective tissue.

Duchenne (dū-shān′) muscular dystrophy is described in the Systems Pathology on p. 189.

Myotonic (mī-ō-ton′ik) muscular dystrophy is characterized by the failure of muscles to relax following a forceful contraction, as well as by muscular weakness. The disorder is inherited as a dominant trait in both males and females and occurs in about 1 in every 20,000 births. The disorder progresses slowly,

usually affecting the face and neck muscles first and affecting the hands most severely.

Myasthenia Gravis

Myasthenia (mī-as-thē′nē-ă) gravis, which usually begins in the face, is a muscular weakness not accompanied by atrophy. It is a chronic, progressive disease resulting from the destruction of acetylcholine receptors in the neuromuscular junction. Abnormal antibodies that bind to and destroy acetylcholine receptors can be identified in many people who have myasthenia gravis. Because of the decrease in the number of acetylcholine receptors, the efficiency of neuronal stimulation of muscle fibers decreases, and the muscle is weaker as a result.

Tendinitis

As the name implies, tendinitis (ten-di-nī′tis) is an inflammation of a tendon or its attachment point. It usually occurs in athletes who overtax the muscle to which the tendon is attached.

Table 7.2   Comparison of Muscle Types

Feature	Skeletal Muscle	Cardiac Muscle	Smooth Muscle
Location	Attached to bone	Heart	Wall of hollow organs, blood vessels, and glands
Appearance			
Cell shape	Long, cylindrical	Branched	Spindle-shaped
Nucleus	Multiple, peripheral	Usually single, central	Single, central
Special features		Intercalated disks	Cell–cell attachments
Striations	Yes	Yes	No
Autorhythmic	No	Yes	Yes
Control	Voluntary	Involuntary	Involuntary
Function	Move the whole body	Heart contraction to propel blood through the body	Compression of organs, ducts, tubes, etc.

Skeletal Muscle Anatomy

General Principles

Most muscles extend from one bone to another and cross at least one joint. Muscle contraction causes most body movements by pulling one of the bones toward the other across the movable joint. Some muscles are not attached to bone at both ends. For example, some facial muscles attach to the skin, which moves as the muscles contract.

The two points of attachment of each muscle are its origin and insertion. At these attachment points, the muscle is connected to the bone by a **tendon**. Some broad, sheetlike tendons are called **aponeuroses** (ap′ō-noo-rō′sēz). The **origin**, also called the **head**, is the most stationary end of the muscle. The **insertion** is the end of the muscle attached to the bone undergoing the greatest movement. The part of the muscle between the origin and the insertion is the **belly** (figure 7.12). Some muscles, such as the biceps brachii with two heads and the triceps brachii with three heads, have multiple origins, or heads.

Muscles tend to function together to accomplish specific movements. For example, the deltoid, biceps brachii, and pectoralis major all help flex the arm. Furthermore, many muscles are members of more than one group, depending on the type of movement being considered. For example, the anterior part of the deltoid muscle functions with the flexors of the arm, whereas the posterior part functions with the extensors of the arm. Muscles that work together to cause movement are **synergists** (sin′er-jistz), and a muscle working in opposition to another muscle is called an **antagonist** (an-tag′ō-nist). The brachialis and biceps brachii are synergists in flexing the forearm; the triceps brachii is the antagonist and extends the forearm. Among a group of synergists, if one muscle plays the major role in accomplishing the desired movement, it is the **prime mover**. The brachialis is the prime mover in flexing the forearm. **Fixators** are muscles that hold one bone in place relative to the body while a usually more distal bone is moved. The muscles of the scapula act as fixators to hold the scapula in place while other muscles contract to move the humerus.

Figure 7.12   Muscle Attachment

Muscles are attached to bones by tendons. The biceps brachii has two heads that originate on the scapula. The biceps tendon inserts onto the radial tuberosity and onto nearby connective tissue.

Facial muscles

Deltoid

Biceps brachii

Linea alba

Brachioradialis

Retinaculum

Adductor longus

Gracilis

Sartorius

Patellar tendon

Patella

Gastrocnemius

Soleus

Sternocleidomastoid

Trapezius

Pectoralis major

Serratus anterior

Rectus abdominis

External abdominal oblique

Flexors of wrist and fingers

Tensor fasciae latae

Vastus lateralis

Rectus femoris

Vastus intermedius (deep to the rectus femoris and not visible in figure)

Vastus medialis

Quadriceps femoris

Tibialis anterior

Extensor digitorum longus

Fibularis longus

Fibularis brevis

Retinaculum

Figure 7.13(a) The Muscular System
Anterior view.

Nomenclature

Most muscles have names that are descriptive (figure 7.13). Some muscles are named according to their location, such as the pectoralis (chest) muscles in the chest; some according to their origin and insertion, such as the brachioradialis (L. *brachio,* arm) muscle, which extends from the arm to the radius;

some according to the number of heads, such as the biceps (*bi,* two; *ceps,* head) brachii, which has two heads; or some according to their function, such as the flexor digitorum, which flexes the digits (fingers). Other muscles are named according to their size, such as vastus, which means large; their shape, such as deltoid, which means triangular; or the orientation of their fasciculi, such as rectus, which means straight.

Sternocleidomastoid

Seventh cervical vertebra

Infraspinatus

Teres minor

Teres major

Triceps brachii

Extensors
of the wrist
and fingers

Hamstring
muscles

Semitendinosus

Biceps femoris

Semimembranosus

Fibularis longus

Fibularis brevis

Trapezius

Deltoid

Latissimus dorsi

External abdominal
oblique

Gluteus medius

Gluteus maximus

Adductor magnus

Lateral fascia

Gracilis

Gastrocnemius

Soleus

Calcaneal tendon
(Achilles tendon)

Figure 7.13(b)   The Muscular System (*continued*)
Posterior view.

Recognizing the descriptive nature of muscle names makes learning those names much easier. The most superficial muscles are shown in figure 7.13. Examining surface anatomy can be a great advantage to the anatomy student in gaining a better understanding of muscle anatomy. We have pointed out some of the muscles of the upper and lower limbs that can be seen on the surface of the body. Some muscles are especially well developed in bodybuilders (figure 7.14).

Figure 7.14   Bodybuilders

Name as many muscles as you can from the photos. Compare these photos with the labeled muscles in figure 7.13.

Did You Know?

Once considered a sport only for men, **bodybuilding** currently is enjoyed by thousands of women as well. Participants in this sport combine specific weight training and diet to develop maximum muscle mass and minimum body fat. Their major goal is to develop a well-balanced, complete physique. Bodybuilding requires knowledge of exercises that develop all muscles and necessitates consistent and rigorous training. Exercising the appropriate muscles to the proper degree is required to develop a well-proportioned body.

Vigorous weight training can double or triple the size of a muscle. The cardiorespiratory fitness of bodybuilders is similar to that of other well-trained athletes. This fitness has not always been present in bodybuilders, but it can now be attributed to modern bodybuilding techniques that include aerobic exercise and running, along with "pumping iron."

Photographs of bodybuilders can be used to identify the surface anatomy of muscles that cannot be seen easily in untrained people (see figure 7.14).

Muscles of the Head and Neck

The muscles of the head and neck include those involved in facial expression, mastication (chewing), movement of the tongue, swallowing, voice production, eye movements, and movements of the head and neck.

Facial Expression

Several muscles act on the skin around the eyes and eyebrows (table 7.3 and figure 7.15). The **occipitofrontalis** (ok-sip'i-tō-frŭn-tā'lis) raises the eyebrows. The **orbicularis oculi** (ōr-bik'ū-lā'ris ok'ū-lī) closes the eyelids and causes "crow's feet" wrinkles in the skin at the lateral corners of the eyes.

Table 7.3   Muscles of Facial Expression (see figure 7.15)

Muscle	Origin	Insertion	Action
Buccinator (buk's ĭ-nā'tōr) (figures 7.15a and b)	Maxilla and mandible	Orbicularis oris at angle of mouth	Retracts angle of mouth; flattens cheek
Depressor anguli oris (dē-pres'ōr an'gū-lī ōr'ŭs) (figures 7.15a and b)	Lower border of mandible	Lip near angle of mouth	Depresses angle of mouth
Levator labii superioris (le-vă'ter lā'bē-ī soo-pēr'ē-ōr'is) (figures 7.15a and b)	Maxilla	Skin and orbicularis oris of upper lip	Elevates upper lip
Occipitofrontalis (ok-sip'i-tō-frŭn'tā'lis) (figures 7.15a and b)	Occipital bone	Skin of eyebrow and nose	Moves scalp; elevates eyebrows
Orbicularis oculi (ōr-bik'ū-lā'ris ok'ū-lī) (figures 7.15a and b)	Maxilla and frontal bones	Circles orbit and inserts near origin	Closes eye
Orbicularis oris (ōr-bik'ū-lā'ris ōr'is) (figures 7.15a and b)	Nasal septum, maxilla, and mandible	Fascia and other muscles of lips	Closes lip
Zygomaticus major (zī'gō-mat'i-kŭs) (figures 7.15a and b)	Zygomatic bone	Angle of mouth	Elevates and abducts upper lip
Zygomaticus minor (zī'gō-mat'i-kŭs) (figures 7.15a and b)	Zygomatic bone	Orbicularis oris of upper lip	Elevates and abducts upper lip

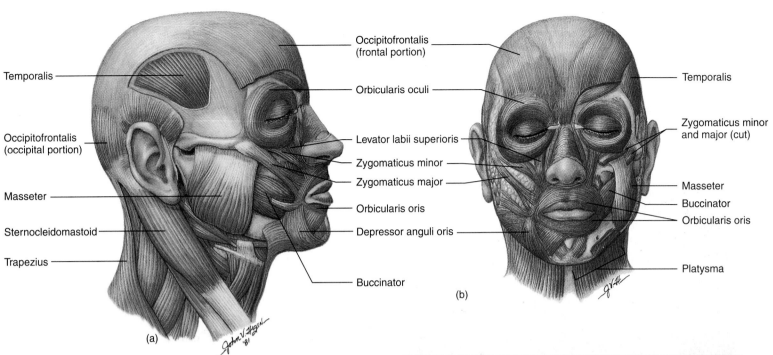

Figure 7.15 Muscles of Facial Expression
(*a*) Lateral view. (*b*) Anterior view.

Several other muscles function in moving the lips and the skin surrounding the mouth (see figure 7.15). The **orbicularis oris** (ōr′is) and **buccinator** (buk′sĭ-nā′tōr), the kissing muscles, pucker the mouth. The buccinator also flattens the cheeks as in whistling or blowing a trumpet and is therefore sometimes called the trumpeter's muscle. Smiling is accomplished primarily by the **zygomaticus** (zī′gō′-mat′i-kŭs) muscles. Sneering is accomplished by the **levator labii superioris** (le-vā′ter lā′bē-ī soo-pēr′ē-ōr-is), and frowning or pouting largely by the **depressor anguli oris** (dē-pres′ŏr an′gū-lī ōr′ŭs).

Mastication

The four pairs of muscles of chewing, or **mastication** (mas-ti-kā-shŭn), are some of the strongest muscles of the body (table 7.4). The **temporalis** (tem′pŏ-rā′lis) and **masseter** (mă-sē′ter) muscles (see figure 7.15) can be easily seen and felt on the side of the head during mastication. The **pterygoid** (ter′ĭ-goyd) muscles, consisting of two pairs, are deep to the mandible.

Table 7.4 Muscles of Mastication (see figure 7.15)			
Muscle	**Origin**	**Insertion**	**Action**
Temporalis (tem′pŏ-rā′lis) (figures 7.15*a* and *b*)	Temporal fossa	Anterior portion of mandibular ramus and coronoid process	Elevates and retracts mandible; involved in excursion
Masseter (mă-sē′ter) (figures 7.15*a* and *b*)	Zygomatic arch	Lateral side of mandibular ramus	Elevates and protracts mandible; involved in excursion
Lateral pterygoid (ter′i-goyd) (Not shown in illustration)	Lateral pterygoid plate and greater wing of sphenoid	Condylar process of mandible and articular disk	Protracts and depresses mandible; involved in excursion
Medial pterygoid (Not shown in illustration)	Lateral pterygoid plate of sphenoid and tuberosity of maxilla	Medial surface of mandible	Protracts and elevates mandible; involved in excursion

Tongue and Swallowing Muscles

The tongue is very important in mastication and speech. It moves food around in the mouth, and with the buccinator muscle, holds the food in place while the teeth grind the food. The tongue pushes food up to the palate and back toward the pharynx to initiate swallowing. The tongue consists of a mass of **intrinsic muscles**, which are located entirely within the tongue and function to change its shape. The **extrinsic muscles** are located outside the tongue but are attached to and move the tongue (figure 7.16 and table 7.5).

Swallowing involves a number of structures and their associated muscles, including the hyoid muscles, soft palate, pharynx (throat), and larynx (voice box). The **hyoid** (hī′oyd) **muscles** are divided into a suprahyoid group (superior to the hyoid bone) and an infrahyoid group (inferior to the hyoid) (see table 7.16 and figure 7.5). When the suprahyoid muscles hold the hyoid bone in place from above, the infrahyoid muscles can elevate the larynx. To observe this effect, place your hand on your larynx (Adam's apple) and swallow.

The muscles of the soft palate close the posterior opening to the nasal cavity during swallowing, preventing food and liquid from entering the nasal cavity. Swallowing is accomplished by elevation of the pharynx and larynx, followed by constriction of the pharynx. The **pharyngeal** (fă-rin′jē-ăl) **elevators** elevate the pharynx, and the **pharyngeal constrictors** constrict the pharynx from superior to inferior, forcing the food into the esophagus. Pharyngeal muscles also open the auditory tube, which connects the middle ear with the pharynx. Opening the auditory tube equalizes the pressure between the middle ear and the atmosphere. This is why it is sometimes helpful to chew gum or swallow when ascending or descending a mountain in a car or changing altitude in an airplane.

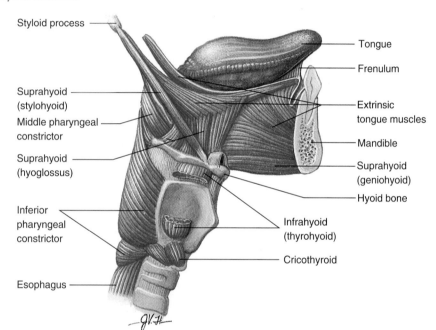

Figure 7.16 Tongue and Swallowing Muscles
Muscles of the tongue, hyoid, pharynx, and larynx as seen from the right.

Table 7.5 Tongue and Swallowing Muscles (see figure 7.16)

Muscle	Origin	Insertion	Action
Tongue muscles			
Intrinsic (Not shown)	Inside tongue	Inside tongue	Changes shape of tongue
Extrinsic (figure 7.16)	Bones around oral cavity or soft palate	Onto tongue	Moves the tongue
Hyoid muscles			
Suprahyoid (e.g., geniohyoid, stylohyoid, and hyoglossus) (figure 7.16)	Base of skull, mandible	Hyoid bone	Elevates or stabilizes hyoid
Infrahyoid (e.g., thyrohyoid) (figure 7.16)	Sternum, larynx	Hyoid bone	Depresses or stabilizes hyoid
Soft palate (Not shown)	Skull or soft palate	Palate, tongue, or pharynx	Moves soft palate, tongue, or pharynx
Pharyngeal muscles			
Elevators (Not shown)	Soft palate and auditory tube	Pharynx	Elevate pharynx
Constrictors (superior, not shown) (middle and inferior) (figure 7.16)	Larynx and hyoid	Pharynx	Constrict pharynx

Neck Muscles

The deep neck muscles (figure 7.17 and table 7.6) include neck flexors, located along the anterior surfaces of the vertebral bodies, and neck extensors, which are located posteriorly. Rotation and abduction of the head are accomplished by lateral and posterior neck muscles. The **sternocleidomastoid** (ster′nō-klī′dō-mas′toyd) muscle (see figure 7.15a), the prime mover of the lateral muscle group, is easily seen on the anterior and lateral sides of the neck. Contraction of only one sternocleidomastoid muscle causes rotation of the head. Contraction of both sternocleidomastoids results in flexion of the neck or extension of the head, depending on what other neck muscles are doing. **Torticollis** (tōr′ti-kol′is, a twisted neck), or wry neck, may result from injury to one of the sternocleidomastoid muscles. It is sometimes caused by damage to a baby's neck muscles during a difficult birth and usually can be corrected by exercising the muscle.

4   P R E D I C T

Shortening of the right sternocleidomastoid muscle rotates the head in which direction?

✔ *Answer on page 192*

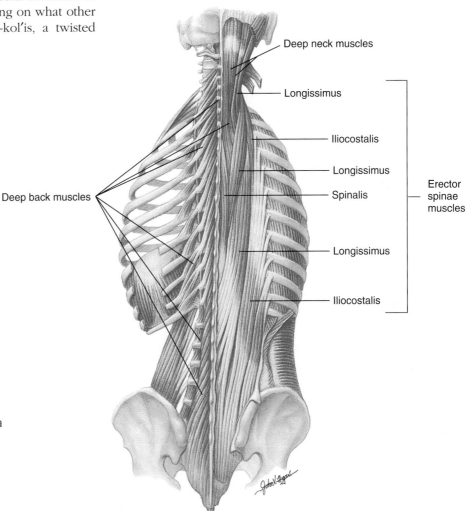

Deep neck muscles

Longissimus

Iliocostalis

Longissimus

Spinalis

Erector spinae muscles

Longissimus

Iliocostalis

Deep back muscles

Figure 7.17   Muscles of the Back, Seen from a Posterior View

The upper limb, shoulder girdle, and associated muscles have been removed.

Table 7.6 Neck Muscles (see figures 7.13, 7.15, 7.17, and 7.21)			
Muscle	Origin	Insertion	Action
Deep neck muscles			
Flexors (Not shown)	Anterior side of vertebrae	Base of skull	Flex head and neck
Extensors (figures 7.17, 7.21a)	Posterior side of vertebrae	Base of skull	Extend head and neck
Sternocleidomastoid (ster′nō-klī′dō-mas′toyd) (figures 7.13a,b; 7.15a; 7.21a)	Manubrium of sternum and medial part of clavicle	Mastoid process and nuchal line of skull	Individually rotate head, together flex neck or extend head
Trapezius (tra-pē′zē-ŭs) (figures 7.13 a,b; 7.15a; 7.21a)	Posterior surface of skull and upper vertebral column (C7–T12)	Clavicle, acromion process and scapular spine	Extends head and neck

Trunk Muscles

Trunk muscles include those that move the vertebral column, those of the thorax and abdominal wall, and those of the pelvic floor.

Muscles Moving the Vertebral Column

In humans, the back muscles are very strong to maintain erect posture. The **erector spinae** (ē-rek′tōr spī′nē) group of muscles on each side of the back are the muscles primarily responsible for keeping the back straight and the body erect (table 7.7 and see figure 7.17). **Deep back muscles**, located between the spinous and transverse processes of adjacent vertebrae, are responsible for several movements of the vertebral column such as extension, abduction, and rotation.

Thoracic Muscles

The muscles of the thorax (figure 7.18 and table 7.8) are involved almost entirely in the process of breathing. The **external intercostals** (in′ter-kos′tŭlz) elevate the ribs during inspiration. The **internal intercostals** contract during forced expiration, depressing the ribs.

The major movement produced in the thorax during quiet breathing, however, is accomplished by the dome-shaped **diaphragm** (dī′ă-fram). When it contracts, the dome is flattened, causing the volume of the thoracic cavity to increase and resulting in inspiration.

Abdominal Wall Muscles

The muscles of the anterior abdominal wall (figure 7.19 and table 7.9) flex and rotate the vertebral column, compress the abdominal cavity, and hold in and protect the abdominal organs. In a relatively muscular person with little fat, a vertical indentation, extending from the sternum through the navel to the pubis, is visible. This tendinous area of the abdominal wall, called the **linea alba** (lin′ē-ă al′bă, white line), consists of white connective tissue rather than muscle. On each side of the linea alba is the **rectus abdominis** (rek′tŭs ab-dom′ĭ-nis) muscle. **Tendinous intersections** cross the rectus abdominis at three or more locations, causing the abdominal wall of a well-muscled lean person to appear segmented. Lateral to the rectus abdominis are three layers of muscle. From superficial to deep, these muscles are the **external abdominal oblique**, **internal abdominal oblique**, and **transversus abdominis** (trans-ver′sŭs ab-dom′in-is) muscles. The fasciculi of these three muscle layers are oriented in different directions to one another. When these muscles contract, they flex and rotate the vertebral column or compress the abdominal contents.

Table 7.7	Muscles Acting on the Vertebral Column (see figure 7.17)		
Muscle	**Origin**	**Insertion**	**Action**
Superficial			
Erector spinae (ĕ-rek′tōr spī′nē) (divides into three columns Ilicostalis (il′ē-ō-kos-tā′lis) (figure 7.17)	sacrium, ilium, vertebrae, and ribs	Ribs, vertebrae, and skull	Extends vertebral column
Longissimus (lon-gis′i-m̆us) (figure 7.17)			
Spinalis (spī-nā′lis) (figure 7.17)			
Deep back muscles (figure 7.17)	Vertebrae	Vertebrae	Extend vertebral column and help bend vertebral column laterally

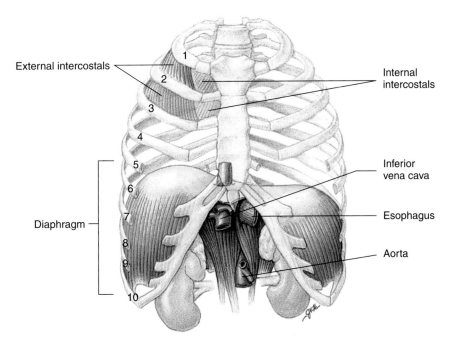

Figure 7.18   Muscles of the Thorax, Anterior View

Selected intercostal muscles and the diaphragm are shown.

Table 7.8	Muscles of the Thorax (see figures 7.18 and 7.21)		
Muscle	**Origin**	**Insertion**	**Action**
External intercostals (in'ter-kos'tŭlz) (figures 7.18; 7.21b)	Inferior edge of each rib	Superior edge of next rib below origin	Inspiration; elevates ribs
Internal intercostals (in'ter-kos'tŭlz) (figures 7.18; 7.21b)	Superior edge of each rib	Inferior edge of next rib above origin	Forced expiration; depresses ribs
Diaphragm (dī'ă-fram) (figure 7.18)	Interior ribs, sternum, and lumbar vertebrae	Central tendon of diaphragm	Inspiration; depresses floor of thorax

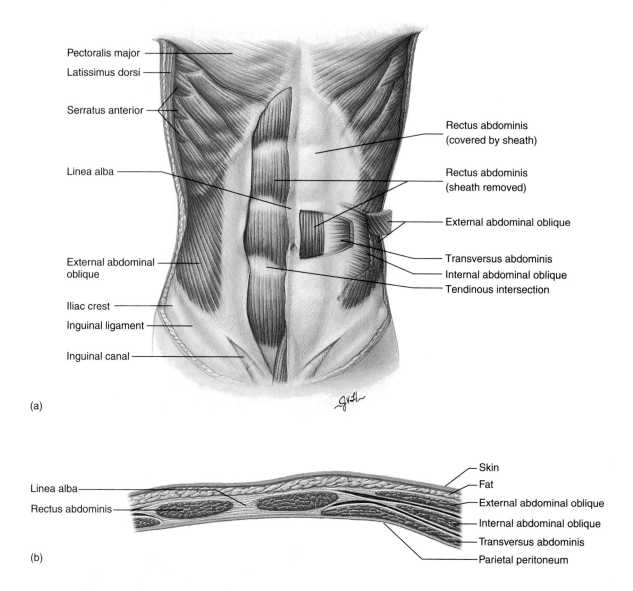

Figure 7.19   Muscles of the Anterior Abdominal Wall

(*a*) Anterior view. (*b*) Cross section.

Table 7.9	Muscles of the Abdominal Wall (see figures 7.13, 7.19, 7.21)		
Muscle	**Origin**	**Insertion**	**Action**
Rectus abdominis (rek'tŭs ab-dom'i-nis) (figures 7.13*a*; 7.19)	Pubic crest and symphysis pubis	Xiphoid process and inferior ribs	Flexes vertebral column; compresses abdomen
External abdominal oblique (figures 7.13*a*; 7.19, 7.21*c*)	Ribs 5 to 12	Iliac crest, inguinal ligament, and fascia of rectus abdominis	Compresses abdomen; flexes and rotates vertebral column
Internal abdominal oblique (figures 7.19; 7.21*c*)	Iliac crest, inguinal ligament, and lumbar fascia	Ribs 10 to 12 and fascia of rectus abdominis	Compresses abdomen; flexes and rotates vertebral column
Transversus abdominis (trans-ver'sŭs ab-dom'in-is) (figure 7.19)	Seventh to twelfth costal cartilages, lumbar fascia, iliac crest, and inguinal ligament	Xiphoid process, fascia of rectus abdominis, and pubic tubercle	Compresses abdomen

Pelvic Floor and Perineal Muscles

The pelvis is a ring of bone with an inferior opening that is closed by a muscular floor through which the anus and the openings of the urinary tract and reproductive tract penetrate. Most of the **pelvic floor**, also referred to as the **pelvic diaphragm**, is formed by the **levator ani** (le-vā′ter ā′nī) muscle. The area inferior to the pelvic floor is the **perineum** (per′i-nē′ŭm), which contains a number of muscles associated with the male or female reproductive structures (figure 7.20 and table 7.10). Several of these muscles help regulate urination and defecation.

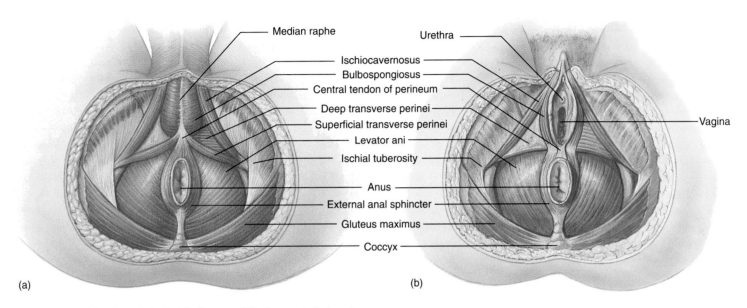

Figure 7.20   Muscles of the Pelvic Floor and Perineum. Inferior view.
(*a*) Male (*b*) Female.

Table 7.10 Muscles of the Pelvic Floor and Perineum (see Figure 7.20)			
Muscle	**Origin**	**Insertion**	**Action**
Bulbospongiosus (bul′bō-spŭn′jē-ō′sŭs) (figures 7.20*a* and *b*)	Male—central tendon of perineum and median raphe of penis	Dorsal surface of penis and bulb of penis	Constricts urethra; erects penis
	Female—central tendon of perineum	Base of clitoris	Erects clitoris
Ischiocavernosus (ish′ē-ō-kav′er-nō′sŭs) (figures 7.20*a* and *b*)	Ischial ramus	Corpus cavernosum	Compresses base of penis or clitoris
Levator ani (le′vā-ter ā′nī) (figures 7.20*a* and *b*)	Posterior pubis and ischial spine	Sacrum and coccyx	Elevates anus; supports pelvic viscera
External anal sphincter figures 7.20*a* and *b*)	Coccyx	Central tendon of perineum	Keeps orifice of anal canal closed
Transverse perinei (pĕr′i-nē′ī)			
Deep (figures 7.20*a* and *b*)	Ischial ramus	Midline connective tissue	Supports pelvic floor
Superficial (figures 7.20*a* and *b*)	Ischial ramus	Central tendon of perineum	Fixes central tendon

Upper Limb Muscles

The muscles of the upper limb include those that attach the limb and girdle to the body and those that are in the arm, forearm, and hand.

Scapular Movements

The connection of the upper limb to the body is accomplished primarily by muscles. The muscles that attach the scapula to the thorax and move the scapula include the trapezius (tra-pē′zē-ŭs), **levator scapulae** (le-vā′ter skap′ū-lē), **rhomboids** (rom′boydz), **serratus** (ser-ā′tŭs) **anterior,** and **pectoralis** (pek′tō-ra′lis) **minor** (figure 7.21 and table 7.11). These muscles act as fixators to hold the scapula firmly in position when the muscles of the arm contract. The scapular muscles also move the scapula into different positions, thereby increasing the range of movement of the upper limb. The trapezius forms the upper line from each shoulder to the neck, and the origin of the serratus anterior from the first eight or nine ribs can be seen along the lateral thorax.

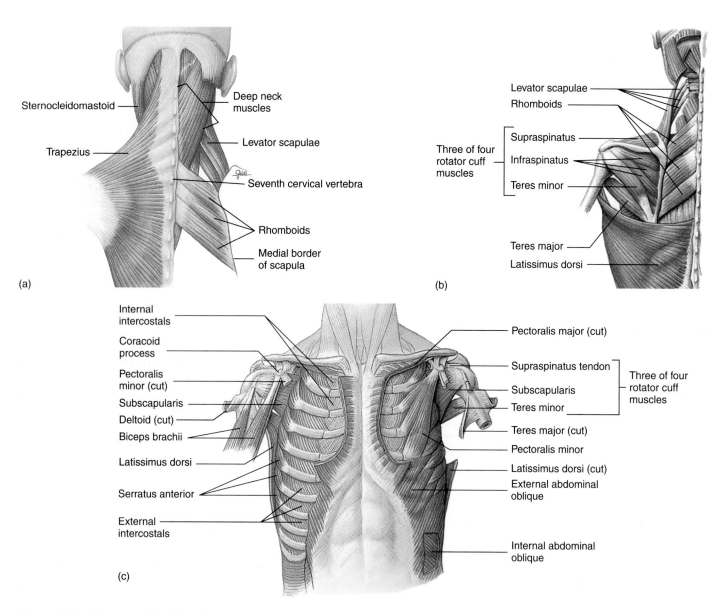

Figure 7.21   Muscles of the Shoulder

(a) Posterior view of the neck and upper shoulder. The left side shows the superficial muscles. On the right, the superficial muscles are removed to show the deep muscles. (b) Posterior view of the thoracic region, with the trapezius and deltoid muscles removed. (c) Anterior view of the thoracic region.

Table 7.11 Muscles Acting on the Scapula (see Figure 7.21)

Muscle	Origin	Insertion	Action
Levator scapulae (le-vă′ter skap′ū-lē) (figure 7.21a and b)	C1–C4	Superior angle of scapula	Elevates, retracts, and rotates scapula; laterally flexes neck
Pectoralis minor (pek′tō-ra′lis) (figure 7.21c)	Third to fifth ribs	Coracoid process of scapula	Depresses scapula or elevates ribs
Rhomboids (rom′boydz) Major (figure 7.21a and c)	T1–T4	Medial border of scapula	Retracts, rotates, and fixes scapula
Minor (figure 7.21a and c)	T1–T4	Medial border of scapula	Retracts, slightly elevates, rotates, and fixes scapula
Serratus anterior (ser-ā′tŭs) (figures 7.13a; 7.19a; 7.21c; 7.22a)	First to ninth ribs	Medial border of scapula	Rotates and protracts scapula; elevates ribs
Trapezius (tra-pē′zē-ŭs) (figures 7.13a and b; 7.21a)	Posterior surface of skull and C7–T12	Clavicle, acromion process, and scapular spine	Elevates, depresses, retracts, rotates, and fixes scapula; extends neck

Arm Movements

The arm is attached to the thorax by the **pectoralis major** and **latissimus dorsi** (lă-tis′i-mŭs dōr′sī) muscles (figure 7.22a and table 7.12; see figure 7.21c). The pectoralis major adducts and flexes the arm. It can also extend the arm from a flexed position. The latissimus dorsi medially rotates, adducts, and powerfully extends the arm. Because a swimmer uses these three motions during the power stroke of the crawl, the latissimus dorsi is often called the swimmer's muscle.

Another group of four muscles, called the **rotator cuff muscles**, attaches the humerus to the scapula and forms a cuff or cap over the proximal humerus (see table 7.12 and figure 7.21b and c). A rotator cuff injury involves damage to one or more of these muscles or their tendons. The **deltoid** (del′toyd) muscle attaches the humerus to the scapula and clavicle and is the major abductor of the upper limb. The pectoralis major forms the upper chest, and the deltoid forms the rounded mass of the shoulder (see figure 7.24). The deltoid is a common site for administering injections.

Forearm Movements

The arm can be divided into anterior and posterior compartments. The **triceps brachii** (trī′seps brā′kē-ī), the primary extensor of the forearm, occupies the posterior compartment (figure 7.22b and table 7.13). The anterior compartment is occupied mostly by the **biceps** (bī′seps) **brachii** and the **brachialis** (brā′kē-ăl-is), the primary flexors of the forearm. The **brachioradialis** (brā′kē-ō-rā′dē-al′is), which is actually a posterior forearm muscle, helps flex the forearm.

Supination and Pronation

Supination of the forearm, or turning the flexed forearm so that the palm is up, is accomplished by the **supinator** (soo′pi-nā-ter) (see table 7.13; figure 7.23 and table 7.14) and the biceps brachii, which tends to supinate the forearm while flexing it. Pronation, turning the forearm so that the palm is down, is a function of two **pronator** (prō-nā′ter) muscles.

Wrist and Finger Movements

The 20 muscles of the forearm can also be divided into anterior and posterior groups. Only a few of these muscles, the most superficial, are listed in table 7.14 and are illustrated in figure 7.23. Most of the anterior forearm muscles are responsible for flexion of the wrist and fingers, whereas most of the posterior forearm muscles cause extension. A strong band of fibrous connective tissue, the **retinaculum** (ret-i-nak′ū-lŭm, bracelet) (see figure 7.23b), covers the flexor and extensor tendons and holds them in place around the wrist so that they do not "bowstring" during muscle contraction.

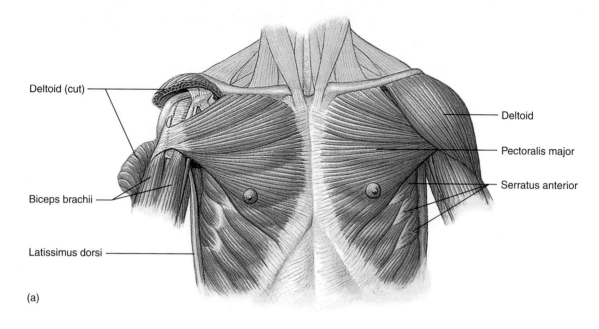

Deltoid (cut)

Biceps brachii

Latissimus dorsi

Deltoid

Pectoralis major

Serratus anterior

(a)

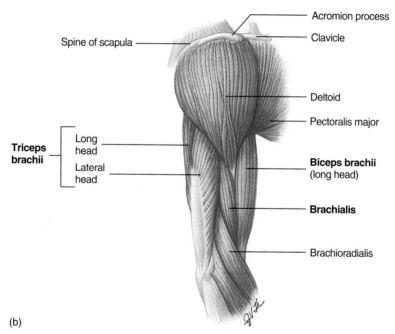

Spine of scapula

Acromion process

Clavicle

Deltoid

Pectoralis major

Triceps brachii
Long head
Lateral head

Biceps brachii
(long head)

Brachialis

Brachioradialis

(b)

Figure 7.22 Muscles of the Anterior Shoulder and Arm

(*a*) Anterior view of the shoulder and chest. (*b*) Lateral view of the arm.

The **flexor carpi** (kar′pī; wrist) muscles flex the wrist, and the **extensor carpi** muscles extend the wrist. The tendons of the wrist extensors are visible on the posterior surface of the forearm (figure 7.24). The tendon of the flexor carpi radialis is used as a landmark for locating the radial pulse. Flexion of the fingers is the function of the **flexor digitorum** (dij′i-tōr′ŭm; flexor of the digits, or fingers). Extension of the fingers is accomplished by the **extensor digitorum**. The tendons of this muscle are very visible on the dorsal surface of the hand (see figure 7.24). The thumb has

its own set of flexors, extensors, adductors, and abductors. The little finger also has some similar muscles.

Did You Know?

Forceful extension of the wrist repeated over time such as occurs in a tennis backhand may result in inflammation and pain where the extensor muscles attach to the lateral humeral epicondyle, which is the common point of origin for most extensors of the wrist and hand. This condition is sometimes referred to as "tennis elbow."

Table 7.12   Arm Movements (see figures 7.13, 7.21, and 7.22)

Muscle	Origin	Insertion	Action
Deltoid (del'toyd) (figures 7.13a and b; 7.22a and b; 7.24)	Clavicle, acromion process, and scapular spine	Deltoid tuberosity	Abducts, flexes, extends, and medially and laterally rotates arm
Latissimus dorsi (lă-tis'i-mŭs dōr'sī) (figures 7.13b; 7.19a; 7.21c and 7.22a)	T7–L5, sacrum and iliac crest	Medial crest of intertubercular groove	Adducts, medially rotates, and extends arms
Pectoralis major (pek'tō-rā'lis) (figures 7.13a; 7.19a; 7.22a and b)	Clavicle, sternum, and abdominal muscles	Lateral crest of intertubercular groove	Adducts, flexes, and medially rotates arm; extends arm from flexed position
Teres major (ter'ēz) (figures 7.13b; 7.21b and c)	Lateral border of scapula	Medial crest of intertubercular groove	Adducts, extends, and medially rotates arm
Rotator cuff			
Infraspinatus (in'fră-spī-nā'tŭs) (figures 7.13b; 7.21b)	Infraspinous fossa of scapula	Greater tubercle of humerus	Extends and laterally rotates arm
Subscapularis (sŭb'skap-ū-lār'is) (figure 7.21c)	Subscapular fossa of scapula	Lesser tubercle of humerus	Extends and medially rotates arm
Supraspinatus (sŭ'pră-spī-nā'tŭs) (figure 7.21b and c)	Supraspinous fossa of scapula	Greater tubercle of humerus	Abducts arm
Teres minor (te'rēz) (figures 7.13b; 7.21b and c)	Lateral border of scapula	Greater tubercle of humerus	Adducts, extends, and laterally rotates arm

Table 7.13   Arm Muscles (see figures 7.13, 7.22, and 7.24)

Muscle	Origin	Insertion	Action
Arm			
Biceps brachii (bī'seps brā'kē-ī) (figures 7.13a; 7.21c; 7.22a and b; 7.24)	Long head—supraglenoid tubercle; Short head—coracoid process	Radial tuberosity	Flexes arm and supinates forearm; flexes arm
Brachialis (brā'kē-al'is) (figures 7.22b; 7.24)	Humerus	Coronoid process of ulna	Flexes forearm
Triceps brachii (trī'seps brā'kē-ī) (figures 7.13b; 7.22b; 7.24)	Long head—lateral border of scapula; Lateral head—lateral and posterior surface of humerus; Medial head—posterior humerus	Olecranon process of ulna	Extends forearm; extends and adducts arm

Nineteen muscles, called **intrinsic hand muscles**, are located within the hand. **Interossei** (in'ter-os'ē-ī) muscles, located between the metacarpals, are responsible for abduction and adduction of the fingers. Other intrinsic hand muscles are responsible for many other movements of the thumb and fingers. These muscles account for the masses at the base of the thumb and little finger and the fleshy region between the metacarpals of the thumb and index finger.

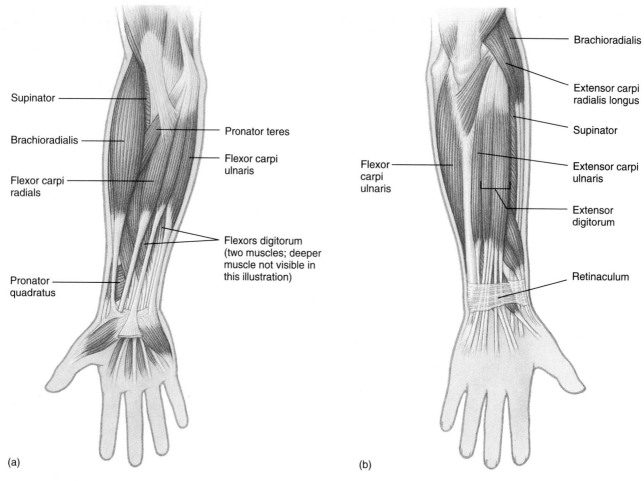

Supinator

Brachioradialis

Flexor carpi radials

Pronator quadratus

Pronator teres

Flexor carpi ulnaris

Flexors digitorum (two muscles; deeper muscle not visible in this illustration)

(a)

Brachioradialis

Extensor carpi radialis longus

Supinator

Extensor carpi ulnaris

Extensor digitorum

Retinaculum

Flexor carpi ulnaris

(b)

Figure 7.23 Muscles of the Forearm

(a) Anterior view. The flexor retinaculum has been removed. (b) Posterior view.

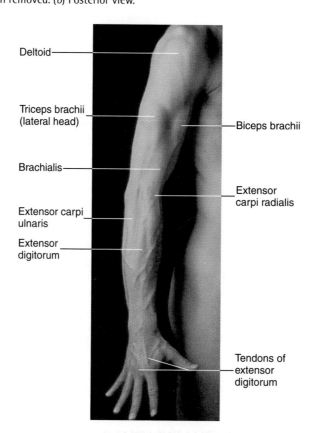

Deltoid

Triceps brachii (lateral head)

Brachialis

Extensor carpi ulnaris

Extensor digitorum

Biceps brachii

Extensor carpi radialis

Tendons of extensor digitorum

Figure 7.24 Surface Anatomy of the Right Upper Limb

Table 7.14   Forearm Muscles (see figure 7.23)

Muscle	Origin	Insertion	Action
Anterior Forearm			
Flexor carpi radialis (kar′pī rā′dē-a-lĭs) (figure 7.23a)	Medial epicondyle of humerus	Second and third metacarpals	Flexes and abducts wrist
Flexor carpi ulnaris (kar′pī ŭl-nār′is) (figure 7.23a)	Medial epicondyle of humerus and ulna	Pisiform	Flexes and adducts wrist
Flexor digitorum			
Profundus (dij′i-tōr′ŭm prō-fŭn′dŭs) (not shown)	Ulna	Distal phalanges of digits 2 through 5	Flexes fingers and wrist
Superficialis (sū′per-fish′ē-a′lis) (figure 7.23a)	Medial epicondyle of humerus, coronoid process, and radius	Middle phalanges of digits 2 through 5	Flexes fingers and wrist
Pronator			
Quadratus (prō′nā-tōr kwah-drā′tŭs) (figure 7.23a)	Distal ulna	Distal radius	Pronates forearm
Teres (prō′nā-tōr te′rēz) (figure 7.23a)	Medial epicondyle of humerus and coronoid process of ulna	Radius	Pronates forearm
Posterior Forearm			
Brachioradialis (brā′kē-ō-rā′dē-a′lis) (figure 7.23a and b)	Lateral supracondylar ridge of humerus	Styloid process of radius	Flexes forearm
Extensor carpi			
Radialis brevis (kar′pī rā′dē-a-lis brev′is) (not shown)	Lateral epicondyle of humerus	Base of third metacarpal	Extends and abducts wrist
Radials longus (lon′gus) (figure 7.23b)	Lateral supracondylar ridge of humerus	Base of second metacarpal	Extends and abducts wrist
Extensor carpi ulnaris (kar′pī ŭl-nār′is) (figure 7.23b)	Lateral epicondyle of humerus and ulna	Base of fith metacarpal	Extends and adducts wrist
Extensor digitorum (dij′i-tōr′ŭm) (figure 7.23b)	Lateral epicondyle of humerus	Bases of phalanges of digits 2 through 5	Extends fingers and wrist
Supinator (sū′pi-nā′tōr) (figure 7.23b)	Lateral epicondyle of humerus and ulna	Radius	Supinates forearm

Lower Limb Muscles

The muslces of the lower limb include those located in the hip, thigh, leg, and foot.

Thigh Movements

Several hip muscles originate on the coxa and insert onto the femur (table 7.15 and figure 7.25). The anterior muscle, the **iliopsoas** (il′ē-ō-sō′ŭs), flexes the thigh (figure 7.25a). The posterior and lateral hip muscles consist of the **gluteal** muscles and the tensor fascia latae (figure 7.25a and b). The **tensor fascia latae** (ten′sōr fa′shē-ă la′tē′) is so named because it tenses the lateral fascia, a thick band of connective tissue on the lateral side of the thigh, and by so doing, it can abduct the thigh. The **gluteus** (glū′tē-ŭs) **maximus** contributes most of the mass that can be seen as the buttocks, and the **gluteus medius**, a common site for injections, creates a smaller mass just superior and lateral to the maximus (see figure 7.27b). The gluteus maximus functions optimally to extend the thigh when the thigh is flexed at a 45-degree angle.

Table 7.15   Muscles Moving the Thigh (see figure 7.25)

Muscle	Origin	Insertion	Action
Iliopsoas (il′ē-ō-sō′ŭs) (figure 7.25a)	Iliac fossa and vertebrae T12–L5	Lesser trochanter of femur and hip capsule	Flexes and medially rotates thigh
Gluteus maximus (glū′tē-ŭs mak′si-mŭs) (figure 7.25b)	Ilium, sacrum, and coccyx	Gluteal tuberosity of femur and lateral fascia of thigh	Extends, abducts, and laterally rotates thigh
Gluteus medius (glū′tē-ŭs mē′dē-ŭs (figure 7.25b)	Ilium	Greater trochanter of femur	Abducts and medially rotates thigh
Gluteus minimus (glū′tē-ŭs min′i-mŭs) (not shown)	Ilium	Greater trochanter of femur	Abducts and medially rotates thigh
Tensor fasciae latae (ten′sōr fa′shē-ē-la′tē) (figure 7.25a)	Anterior superior iliac spine	Through lateral fascia of thigh to lateral condyle of tibia	Tenses lateral fascia; flexes, abducts, and medially rotates thigh

In addition to the hip muscles, some of the muscles located in the thigh also attach to the coxa and can cause movement of the thigh. There are three groups of thigh muscles: the anterior thigh muscles, which flex the thigh; the posterior thigh muscles, which extend the thigh; and the medial thigh muscles, which adduct the thigh.

5   P R E D I C T

Consider the sprinter's stance and the bicyclist's racing posture, and explain why these postures are used by these athletes.

✔ *Answer on page 192*

Leg Movements

The anterior thigh muscles are the **quadriceps femoris** (kwah′dri-seps fe-mōr′is, four muscles) and the **sartorius** (sar-tōr′ē-ŭs) (table 7.16; see figures 7.25a and 7.27a). The quadriceps femoris muscles are the primary extensors of the leg. They have a common insertion, the patellar tendon, on and around the patella. The patellar ligament is an extension of the patellar tendon onto the tibial tuberosity. The patellar ligament is tapped with a rubber hammer when testing the knee-jerk reflex in a physical examination. One of the quadriceps muscles, the vastus lateralis, is often used as an intermuscular injection site. The sartorius, the longest muscle in the body, is called the "tailor's muscle" because it flexes the thigh and leg and rotates the thigh laterally for sitting cross-legged, as tailors used to sit while sewing.

The posterior thigh muscles are called **hamstring muscles**, and they are responsible for flexing the leg (see table 7.16 and figures 7.13b and 7.25c). Their tendons are easily felt and seen on the medial and lateral posterior aspect of a slightly bent knee (see figure 7.27b). The hamstrings were so named because these tendons in hogs or pigs could be used to suspend hams during curing. Animals such as wolves often bring down their prey by biting through the hamstrings, thus preventing the prey animal from running. "To hamstring" someone is therefore to render them helpless. A "pulled hamstring" consists of tearing one or more of these muscles or their tendons, usually where the tendons attach to the coxa.

The medial thigh muscles, the **adductor** (a′dŭk-ter) **muscles**, are involved, as the name implies, primarily in adduction of the thigh (see table 7.16).

Ankle and Toe Movements

The 13 muscles in the leg, with tendons extending into the foot, can be divided into three groups: anterior, posterior, and lateral. As with the forearm, only the most superficial muscles are illustrated in figure 7.26 and are listed in table 7.17. The anterior muscles (figure 7.26a) are extensor muscles involved in dorsiflexion (extension) of the foot and extension of the toes.

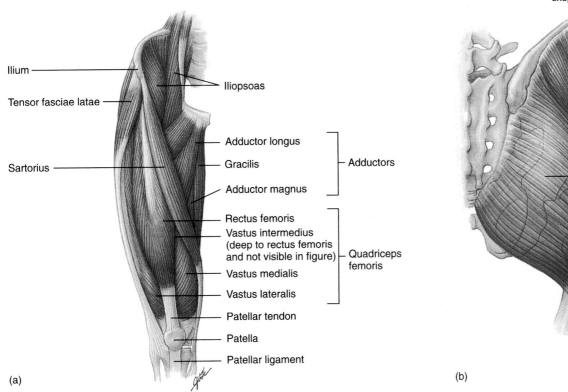

Ilium

Tensor fasciae latae

Sartorius

Iliopsoas

Adductor longus

Gracilis — Adductors

Adductor magnus

Rectus femoris

Vastus intermedius
(deep to rectus femoris
and not visible in figure) — Quadriceps
femoris

Vastus medialis

Vastus lateralis

Patellar tendon

Patella

Patellar ligament

(a)

Gluteus medius

Gluteus maximus

(b)

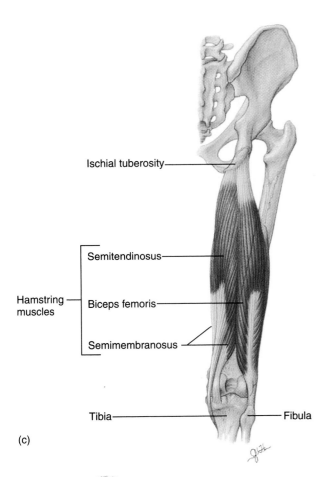

Ischial tuberosity

Semitendinosus

Hamstring
muscles

Biceps femoris

Semimembranosus

Tibia   Fibula

(c)

Figure 7.25 Muscles of the Hip and Thigh

(*a*) Anterior view. The vastus intermedius is labeled on the figure to allow
for a complete listing of the quadriceps femoris muscles, but the muscle
lies deep to the rectus femoris and cannot be seen in the figure.
(*b*) Posterior view, hip muscles. (*c*) Posterior view, thigh muscles.

The superficial muscles of the posterior compartment of
the leg (figure 7.26*b*), the **gastrocnemius** (gas'trok-nē'mē-ŭs)
and **soleus** (sō'lē-ŭs), form the bulge of the calf (posterior leg;
figure 7.26*b*). They join to form the common **calcaneal** (kal-
kā'nē-ăl), or **Achilles, tendon.** These muscles are flexors and
are involved in plantar flexion (flexion) of the foot. The deep
muscles of the posterior compartment plantar flex and invert
the foot and flex the toes.

Did You Know?

The Achilles tendon derives its name from a hero of Greek
mythology. As a baby, Achilles was dipped into magic water that
made him invulnerable to harm everywhere it touched his skin. His
mother, however, holding him by the back of his heel, overlooked
submerging his heel under the water. Consequently, his heel was
vulnerable and proved to be his undoing; he was shot in the heel
with an arrow at the battle of Troy and died. Thus, saying that
someone has an "Achilles heel" means that the person has a weak
spot that can be attacked.

The lateral muscles of the leg, called the **fibularis** (fib-ū-
lā'ris) **muscles** (figure 7.26*c*), are primarily everters (turning
the lateral side of the foot outward) of the foot, but they also
aid in plantar flexion.

The 20 muscles located within the foot, called the **intrinsic foot muscles,** flex, extend, abduct, and adduct the toes.
They are arranged in a manner similar to the intrinsic muscles of the hand.

Table 7.16 Leg Movements (see figures 7.13, 7.25, and 7.27)

Muscle	Origin	Insertion	Action
Anterior Compartment			
Quadriceps femoris (kwah'dri-seps fem'ō-ris)			
Rectus femoris (rek'tŭs fem'ō-ris) (figures 7.13a; 7.25a; 7.27a)	Ilium	Tibial tuberosity via patellar tendon	Extends leg; flexes thigh
Vastus lateralis (vas'tus lat-er-ā'lis) (figures 7.13a; 7.25a; 7.27a and b)	Femur	Tibial tuberosity via patellar tendon	Extends leg
Vastus medialis (vas'tus mē'dē-ā'lis) (figures 7.13a; 7.25a; 7.27a)	Femur	Tibial tuberosity via patellar tendon	Extends leg
Vastus intermedius (vas'tŭs in'ter-mē'dē-ŭs) (figures 7.13a; 7.25a)	Femur	Tibial tuberosity via patellar tendon	Extends leg
Sartorius (sar-tōr'ē-ŭs) (figures 7.13a; 7.25a; 7.27a)	Anterior superior iliac spine	Medial side of tibial tuberosity	Flexes and laterally rotates thigh
Medial Compartment			
Adductor longus (a'dŭk-ter lon'gŭs) (figures 7.13a; 7.25a)	Pubis	Femur	Adducts, flexes, and laterally rotates thigh
Adductor magnus (a'dŭk-ter mag'nŭs) (figures 7.13b; 7.25a)	Pubis and ischium	Femur	Adducts, extends, and laterally rotates thigh
Gracilis (gras'i-lis) (figures 7.13a, b and b; 7.25a)	Pubis near symphysis	Tibia	Adducts thigh; flexes leg
Posterior Compartment (Hamstring Muscles)			
Biceps femoris (bi'seps fem'ō-ris) (figures 7.13b; 7.25c)	Long head–ischial tuberosity; Short head–femur	Head of fibula	Flexes and laterally rotates leg; extends thigh
Semimembranosus (se'mē-mem'bră-nō'sŭs) (figures 7.13b; 7.25c)	Ischial tuberosity	Medial condyle of tibia and collateral ligament	Flexes and medially rotates leg; tenses capsule of knee joint; extends thigh
Semitendinosus (se'mē-ten'di-nō'sŭs) (figures 7.13b; 7.25c)	Ischial tuberosity	Tibia	Flexes and medially rotates leg; extends thigh

Figure 7.26 Superficial Muscles of the Leg

(a) Anterior view. (b) Posterior view. (c) Lateral view.

Table 7.17   Muscles of the Leg Acting on the Leg, Ankle, and Foot (see figures 7.13 and 7.26)

Muscle	Origin	Insertion	Action
Anterior Compartment			
Extensor digitorum longus (dij'i-tōr'ŭm lon'gŭs) (figures 7.13a; 7.26a and c)	Lateral condyle of tibia and fibula	Four tendons to phalanges of four lateral toes	Extends four lateral toes; dorsiflexes and everts foot
Extensor hallicus longus (hal'i-sis lon'gŭs) (figure 7.26a)	Middle fibula and interosseous membrane	Distal phalanx of great toe	Extends great toe; dorsiflexes and inverts foot
Tibialis anterior (tib'ē-a'lis) (figures 7.13a; 7.26a and c)	Tibia and interosseous membrane	Medical cuneiform and first metatarsal	Dorsiflexes and inverts foot
Fibularis tertius (peroneus tertius) (per'ō-nē'ŭs ter'shē-ŭs) (figure 7.26a and c)	Fibula and interosseous membrane	Fifth metatarsal	Dorsiflexes and everts foot
Posterior Compartment			
Superficial			
Gastrocnemius (gas'trok-nē'mē-ŭs) (figures 7.13b; 7.26b and c)	Medial and lateral condyles of femur	Through calcaneal (Achilles) tendon to calcaneus	Plantar flexes foot; flexes leg
Soleus (sō'lē-ŭs) (figures 7.13b; 7.26b and c)	Fibula and tibia	Through calcaneal tendon to calcaneus	Plantar flexes foot
Deep			
Flexor digitorum longus (dij'i-tōr'ŭm lon'gŭs) (not shown)	Tibia	Four tendons to distal phalanges of four lateral toes	Flexes four lateral toes; plantar flexes and inverts foot
Flexor hallucis longus (hal'i-sis lon'gŭs) (not shown)	Fibula	Distal phalanx of great toe	Flexes great toe; plantar flexes and inverts foot
Tibialis posterior (tib'ē-a'lis) (not shown)	Tibia, interosseous membrane, and fibula	Navicular, cuneiforms, cuboid, and second through fourth metatarsals	Plantar flexes and inverts foot
Lateral Compartment			
Fibularis brevis (peroneus brevis) (fib-ū-lā'ris brev'is) (figure 7.26c)	Fibula	Fifth metatarsal	Everts and plantar flexes foot
Fibularis longus (peroneus longus) (fib-ū-lā'ris lon'gŭs) (figure 7.26c)	Fibula	Medial cuneiform and first metatarsal	Everts and plantar flexes foot

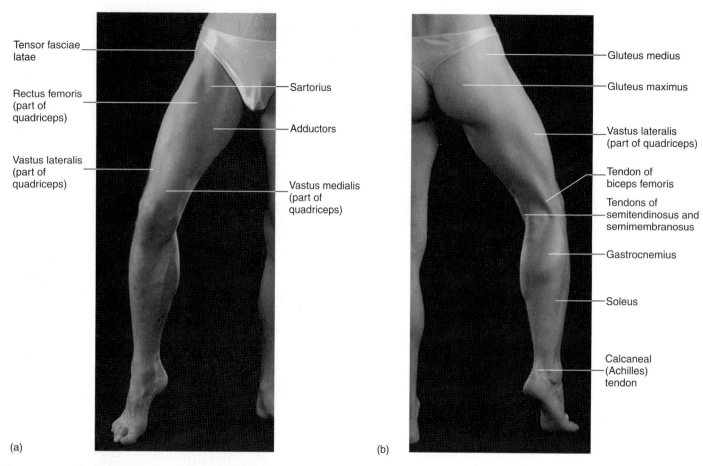

Tensor fasciae latae

Rectus femoris (part of quadriceps)

Vastus lateralis (part of quadriceps)

Sartorius

Adductors

Vastus medialis (part of quadriceps)

Gluteus medius

Gluteus maximus

Vastus lateralis (part of quadriceps)

Tendon of biceps femoris

Tendons of semitendinosus and semimembranosus

Gastrocnemius

Soleus

Calcaneal (Achilles) tendon

(a)

(b)

Figure 7.27 Surface Anatomy of the Lower Limb
(*a*) Anterior view. (*b*) Posterior view.

Systems Pathology

muscular dystrophy

DUCHENNE MUSCULAR DYSTROPHY

A couple became concerned about their 3-year-old boy when they noticed that he was much weaker than other boys his age and the differences appeared to become more obvious as time passed. He had difficulty sitting, standing, and walking. He seemed clumsy and he fell often. He had difficulty climbing stairs, and he often got from a sitting position on the floor to a standing position by using his hands and arms to climb up his legs. His muscles appeared to be poorly developed. The couple took their son to a physician to have him examined. After several tests, they were informed that their son had Duchenne muscular dystrophy.

Background Information

Duchenne muscular dystrophy (DMD) is usually identified in children at around 3 years of age when the parents notice slow motor development with progressive weakness and muscle wasting (figure A). Typically, muscular weakness begins in the pelvic girdle, causing a waddling gait. Rising from the floor by "climbing up the legs" is characteristic and is caused by weakness of the lumbar and gluteal muscles. Within 3 to 5 years, muscles of the shoulder girdle become involved. Wasting of the muscles and their replacement with connective tissue contribute to muscular atrophy and deformity of the skeleton. People with DMD are usually unable to walk by 10 to 12 years of age, and few live beyond 20 years of age. There is no effective treatment to prevent the progressive deterioration of muscles in DMD.

Duchenne muscular dystrophy results from an abnormal gene located on the X chromosome and is therefore a sex-linked (X-linked) condition. The disease affects 1 in 3000 boys. Although the gene is carried by females, DMD affects males almost exclusively. The DMD gene is responsible for producing a protein called **dystrophin**, which plays a role in attaching myofibrils to and regulating the activity of other proteins in the cell membrane. Dystrophin is thought to protect muscle cells against mechanical stress in the normal individual. In DMD, part of the gene is missing, and the protein it produces malfunctions, resulting in progressive muscular weakness.

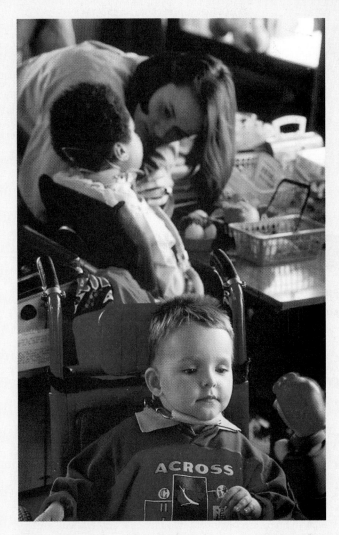

Figure A   Child with Duchenne Muscular Dystrophy

6   **P R E D I C T**

A 15-year-old boy with DMD developed pulmonary edema and then pneumonia. His physician diagnosed the condition in the following way: the pulmonary edema was the result of heart failure and the increased fluid in the lungs acted as a site where bacteria invaded and grew. The fact that the boy could not breathe deeply or cough effectively made the condition worse. Explain why a 15-year-old with this condition might develop heart failure and ineffective respiratory movements.

✔ *Answer on page 192*

System Interactions

System	Interactions
Skeletal	Replacement of muscles by connective tissue results in shortened, inflexible muscles that result in severe deformities of the skeletal system. Curvature of the spinal column can be so severe that normal respiratory movements cannot be carried out. Deformities of the limbs also occur as a result of shortened muscles.
Nervous	Some degree of mental retardation occurs in a large percentage of cases.
Cardiovascular	Cardiac muscle is affected by DMD. Consequently, heart failure occurs in a large number of people with this condition in its advanced stages. Death caused by cardiac failure usually occurs before age 20. Cardiac involvement becomes serious in as high as 95% of cases.
Lymphatic	There are no obvious direct effects on the lymphatic system, but phagocytosis of muscle fibers is accomplished mainly by macrophages.
Respiratory	Deformity of the thorax and increasing weakness of the respiratory muscles results in inadequate respiratory movements and an increase in respiratory infections such as pneumonia. Inadequate respiratory movements because of weak respiratory muscles is a major factor in many deaths.
Digestive	Smooth muscle tissue is also influenced by muscular dystrophy. The reduced ability of smooth muscle to contract can result in abnormalities of the digestive system such as an enlarged colon diameter, a twisting of the intestine resulting in increased intestinal obstruction, cramping, and reduced absorption of nutrients.
Urinary	Reduced smooth muscle function and being confined to a wheelchair increase the frequency of urinary tract infections.

Summary

Functions of the Muscular System

- The skeletal system functions to constrict organs and vessels, pump blood, cause respiration, produce body movement, maintain posture, produce movements involved in communication, and produce body heat.

Characteristics of Skeletal Muscle

- Skeletal muscle has contractility, excitability, extensibility, and elasticity.

Structure

- Each skeletal muscle fiber is a single cell containing numerous myofibrils.
- Myofibrils are composed of actin and myosin myofilaments.
- Sarcomeres are joined end to end to form myofibrils.
- Muscle fibers are organized into fasciculi, and fasciculi are organized into muscles by associated connective tissue.

Membrane Potentials

- Cell membranes have a relative positive charge on the outside and a relative negative charge inside.
- Action potentials are a brief reversal of the membrane charge.

Nerve Supply

- Motor neurons carry action potentials to skeletal muscles, where the neuron and muscle fibers form neuromuscular junctions.
- Neurons release acetylcholine, which binds to receptors on muscle cell membranes, stimulates an action potential in the muscle cell, and causes the muscle to contract.

Muscle Contraction

- Action potentials travel along T tubules to the sarcoplasmic reticulum, where they cause the release of calcium ions.
- Calcium ions, released from the sarcoplasmic reticulum, bind to the actin myofilaments, exposing attachment sites.
- Myosin forms cross-bridges with the exposed actin attachment sites.
- The myosin molecules bend, causing the actin molecules to slide past; this is the sliding filament mechanism. This process requires ATP breakdown.
- A muscle twitch is an all-or-none response to an action potential that exceeds the threshold; it consists of a lag phase, contraction phase, and relaxation phase.
- Tetanus occurs when stimuli occur so rapidly that a muscle does not relax between twitches.
- Small contraction forces are generated when small numbers of motor units are recruited, and greater contraction forces are generated when large numbers of motor units are recruited.
- Energy is produced by anaerobic (without oxygen) and aerobic (with oxygen) respiration.
- After intense exercise, the rate of aerobic metabolism remains elevated to repay the oxygen debt.
- Muscles contract either isometrically (tension increases, but muscle length stays the same) or isotonically (tension remains the same, but muscle length decreases).
- Muscle tone consists of a small percentage of muscle fibers contracting isometrically and is responsible for posture.
- Muscles contain a combination of slow-twitch and fast-twitch fibers.
- Slow-twitch fibers are better suited for aerobic metabolism, and fast-twitch fibers are adapted for anaerobic metabolism.
- Sprinters have more fast-twitch fibers, whereas distance runners have more slow-twitch fibers.

Smooth Muscle and Cardiac Muscle

- Smooth muscle is not striated, contracts more slowly than skeletal muscle, is autorhythmic, and is under involuntary control.
- Cardiac muscle is striated, has intercalated disks, is autorhythmic, and is under involuntary control.

Skeletal Muscle Anatomy

General Principles

- Most muscles have an origin on one bone and an insertion onto another and cross at least one joint.
- Muscles working together are synergists; muscles working in opposition are antagonists.
- A prime mover is the one muscle of a synergistic group that is primarily responsible for the movement.

Nomenclature

- Muscles are named according to location, origin and insertion, number of heads, or function.

Muscles of the Head and Neck

- Muscles of facial expression are associated primarily with the mouth and eyes.
- Four pairs of muscles are involved in mastication.
- Tongue movements involve intrinsic and extrinsic muscles.
- Swallowing involves suprahyoid and infrahyoid muscles, plus muscles of the soft palate, pharynx, and larynx.
- Neck muscles move the head.

Trunk Muscles

- Erector spinae muscles hold the body erect.
- Intercostal muscles and the diaphragm are involved in breathing.
- Muscles of the abdominal wall flex and rotate the vertebral column, compress the abdominal cavity, and hold in and protect the abdominal organs.
- Muscles form the floor of the pelvis.

Upper Limb Muscles

- The upper limb is attached to the body primarily by muscles.
- Arm movements are accomplished by pectoral, rotator cuff, and deltoid muscles.
- The forearm is flexed and extended by anterior and posterior arm muscles, respectively.
- Supination and pronation of the forearm are accomplished by supinators and pronators in the forearm.
- Movements of the wrist and fingers are accomplished by most of the 20 forearm muscles and 19 intrinsic muscles in the hand.

Lower Limb Muscles

- Hip muscles flex, extend, and abduct the thigh.
- Thigh muscles flex, extend, and adduct the thigh. They also flex and extend the leg.
- Muscles of the leg and foot are similar to those of the forearm and hand.

Content Review

1. Define contractility, excitability, extensibility, and elasticity.
2. List the connective tissue layers associated with muscles.
3. What are fasciculi?
4. What is a muscle fiber?
5. Describe the composition of a myofibril.
6. Describe the structure of actin and myosin myofilaments.
7. What is a sarcomere?
8. Describe the resting membrane potential and how it is produced.
9. Describe the production of an action potential.
10. What is a neuromuscular junction? What happens there?
11. Describe the sliding filament mechanism of muscle contraction.
12. Explain how an action potential results in a muscle contraction.
13. Define muscle twitch, tetanus, and recruitment.
14. Describe the two ways energy is produced in skeletal muscle.
15. Compare isometric, isotonic, concentric, and eccentric contraction.
16. What is muscle tone?
17. Compare slow-twitch and fast-twitch muscle fibers.
18. How do smooth muscles and cardiac muscles differ from skeletal muscles?
19. Define origin, insertion, synergist, antagonist, and prime mover.
20. Describe the muscles of facial expression.
21. What is mastication? What muscles are involved?
22. What are intrinsic and extrinsic tongue muscles?
23. What muscles are involved in swallowing?
24. What muscles are involved in respiration?
25. Describe the functions of the muscles of the anterior abdominal wall.
26. What is primarily responsible for attaching the upper limb to the body?
27. Describe, by muscle groups, movements of the arm, forearm, and hand.
28. Describe, by muscle groups, movements of the thigh, leg, and foot.

Develop Your Reasoning Skills

1. Harvey Leche milked cows by hand each morning before school. One morning he overslept and had to hurry to get to school on time. As he was milking the cows as fast as he could, his hands became very tired, and then for a short time he could neither release his grip nor squeeze harder. Explain what happened.

2. A researcher was investigating the fast-twitch versus slow-twitch composition of muscle tissue in the gastrocnemius muscle (in the calf of the leg) of athletes. Describe the general differences this researcher would see when comparing the muscles from athletes who were outstanding in the following events: 100-m dash, weight lifting, the 10,000-m run.

3. Describe an exercise routine that would build up each of the following groups of muscles: anterior arm, posterior arm, anterior forearm, anterior thigh, posterior leg, and abdomen.

4. Sherri Speedster started a 100-m dash but fell to the ground in pain. Examination of her right lower limb revealed the following symptoms: the leg was held in a slightly flexed position, but she could not flex it voluntarily; she could extend the leg with difficulty, but this caused her considerable pain; and there was considerable pain and bulging of the muscles in the posterior thigh. Explain the nature of her injury.

Answers to Predict Questions

1. p. 160 (a) If ATP levels are low in a muscle fiber before stimulation, the force of contraction is reduced because there is insufficient ATP for all motor units to contract.
(b) If action potentials occur at a frequency so great that calcium is not transported back into the sarcoplasmic reticulum between individual action potentials the muscle does not relax.

2. p. 164 During a 10-mile run, aerobic metabolism is the primary source of ATP production for muscle contraction. Anaerobic metabolism provides the short (15–20 s) burst of energy for the sprint at the finish. After the race, aerobic metabolism is elevated for a time to repay the oxygen debt, causing the heavy breathing after the race.

3. p. 171 Raising eyebrows—occipitofrontalis; winking—orbicularis oculi; whistling—orbicularis oris and buccinator; smiling—zygomaticus; frowning—depressor anguli oris; sneering—levator labii superioris.

4. p. 173 Shortening the right sternocleidomastoid muscle rotates the head to the left and also slightly elevates the chin.

5. p. 184 In the sprinter's stance and the bicyclist's racing posture, the thigh is flexed at a 45-degree angle because at that angle the gluteus maximus functions at its maximum in extending the thigh, thus providing maximum force.

6. p. 189 DMD affects the muscles of respiration and causes deformity of the thoracic cavity. The reduced capacity of muscle tissue to contract is one factor that reduces the ability to breathe deeply or cough effectively. In addition, the thoracic cavity can become severely deformed because of the replacement of skeletal muscle with connective tissue. The deformity can reduce the ability to breathe deeply. In addition, DMD can affect the muscle of the heart and cause heart failure.

Chapter Eight

The Nervous System

action potential
The all-or-none change in membrane potential in an excitable tissue that is propagated as an electrical signal.

cerebellum
(ser-e-bel′ŭm) [L., little brain] A part of the brain attached to the brainstem and important in maintaining muscle tone, balance, and coordination of movements.

cerebrum
(ser′ĕ-brŭm, sĕ-rē′brŭm) [L., brain] The largest part of the brain, consisting of two hemispheres and including the cortex, nerve tracts, and basal nuclei.

diencephalon
(dī-en-sef′ă-lon) [Gr., dia, through; enkephalon, brain] Part of the brain inferior to and nearly surrounded by the cerebrum, and connecting posteriorly and inferiorly to the brainstem.

ganglion
(gang′glē-on) [Gr., knot] A group of neuron cell bodies in the peripheral nervous system.

medulla oblongata
(me-dool′ă ob′long-gah′tă) Inferior portion of the brainstem that connects the spinal cord with the brain. Contains nuclei of cranial nerves plus autonomic control centers for functions such as heart rate and respiration.

meninges
(mĕ-nin′jēz) [Gr., membrane] The three connective tissue membranes that surround and protect the brain and spinal cord.

neuroglia
(noo-rog′lē-ă) [Gr. neuro, nerve + glia, glue] One of five types of cells that play a support role in the nervous system; also called glia.

neuron
(noor′on) [Gr., nerve] A nerve cell.

neurotransmitter
(noor′ō-trans-mit′er)) [Gr. neuro, nerve; L. tramitto, to send across] A chemical that is released by a presynaptic cell into the synaptic cleft and acts on the postsynaptic cell.

synapse
(sin′aps) [Gr. syn, together + haptein, to clasp] Junction between a nerve cell and another nerve cell, muscle cell, or gland cell.

Objectives

After reading this chapter, you should be able to:

1. List the divisions of the nervous system and describe the characteristics of each.
2. Describe the structure of neurons and the function of their components. Describe the location, structure, and general function of neuroglial cells.
3. Define and describe the structure of a nerve, nerve tract, nucleus, and ganglion.
4. Explain what a resting membrane potential is and how an action potential is generated and propagated.
5. Describe the structure and function of a synapse.
6. List the parts of a reflex arc and describe its function.
7. List the parts of the brainstem and diencephalon and give their functions.
8. Describe the major functional areas of the cerebral cortex and explain their interactions.
9. Describe sensory, short-term, and long-term memory.
10. Describe the major functions of the basal nuclei, limbic system, and cerebellum.
11. List the major ascending and descending pathways of the spinal cord.
12. Describe the three meningeal layers surrounding the central nervous system, the four ventricles of the brain, and the origin and circulation of the cerebrospinal fluid.
13. List the various types of cranial nerves and give a brief description of their functions.
14. Define the term plexus and describe the three primary plexuses, including their branches.
15. Contrast the structure of the autonomic nervous system and the somatic motor nervous system. Name the two divisions of the autonomic nervous system and describe the differences between them.

A man is walking down a street on a beautiful autumn day, enjoying the warmth of the sun. He passes a produce stand and decides that a big, juicy apple would taste wonderful. He sees just the right one and picks it up. At the register, he reaches into his pocket, feels the coins there, and pulls out a few. He counts out the right change and puts the rest back into his pocket. He walks on down the street and takes a big bite of the apple. He feels the apple's juicy crispness in his mouth and savors its tart-sweet flavor. Life is wonderful. All of these sensations, actions, and emotions are monitored and controlled by the nervous system, which consists of the brain, spinal cord, nerves, and sensory receptors.

Functions of the Nervous System

The nervous system is involved in some way in every body function. Some of the major functions of the nervous system are:

1. *Sensory input.* Sensory receptors monitor numerous external and internal stimuli, such as touch, temperature, taste, smell, sound, blood pressure, and body position. Action potentials from the sensory receptors travel along nerves to the spinal cord and brain, where they are interpreted.
2. *Integration.* The brain and spinal cord are the major organs for processing sensory input and initiating responses. The input may produce an immediate response, may be stored as memory, or may be ignored.
3. *Homeostasis.* The nervous system plays an important role in the maintenance of homeostasis. This function depends on the ability of the nervous system to detect, interpret, and respond to changes in internal and external conditions. The nervous system can stimulate or inhibit the activities of other systems to help maintain homeostasis.
4. *Mental activity.* The brain is the center of mental activity, including consciousness, memory, and thinking.
5. *Control of skeletal muscles.* Skeletal muscles normally contract only when stimulated by the nervous system. Thus, through the control of skeletal muscle, the nervous system controls the major movements of the body.

Divisions of the Nervous System

The nervous system can be divided into the central and the peripheral nervous systems (figure 8.1). The **central nervous system (CNS)** consists of the brain and spinal cord. The brain has several regions, which will be discussed later in this chapter. The **peripheral nervous system (PNS)** consists of nerves and ganglia, which lie outside the CNS.

The PNS has two subdivisions: The **afferent** (af'er-ent) **division** conducts action potentials from sensory receptors to the CNS (figure 8.2). The neurons that transmit action potentials from the periphery to the CNS are **afferent neurons.** The **efferent division** conducts action potentials from the CNS to effector organs such as muscles and glands. The neurons that transmit action potentials from the CNS toward the periphery are **efferent** (ef'er-ent) **neurons.**

The efferent division can be further subdivided into the **somatic** (sō-mat'ik) **motor nervous system,** which transmits action potentials from the CNS to skeletal muscles, and the **autonomic** (aw-tō-nom'ik) **nervous system (ANS),** which transmits action potentials from the CNS to cardiac muscle, smooth muscle, and glands. The autonomic nervous system, in turn, is divided into sympathetic and parasympathetic portions. The **sympathetic** (sim-pă-thet'ik) **division** prepares the person for physical activity, whereas the **parasympathetic** (par-ă-sim-pa-thet'ik) **division** activates functions such as digestion that are normally associated with the body at rest.

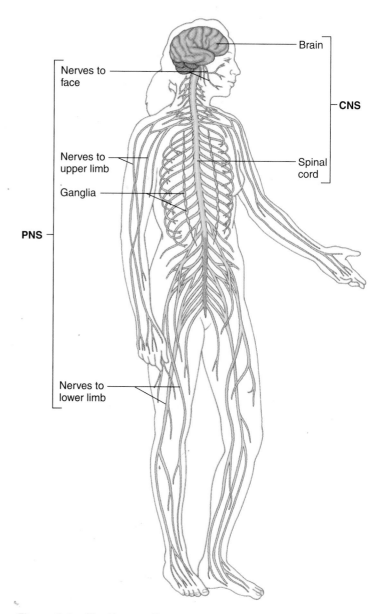

Figure 8.1 The Nervous System

The central nervous system (CNS) consists of the brain and spinal cord. The peripheral nervous system (PNS) consists of nerves and ganglia.

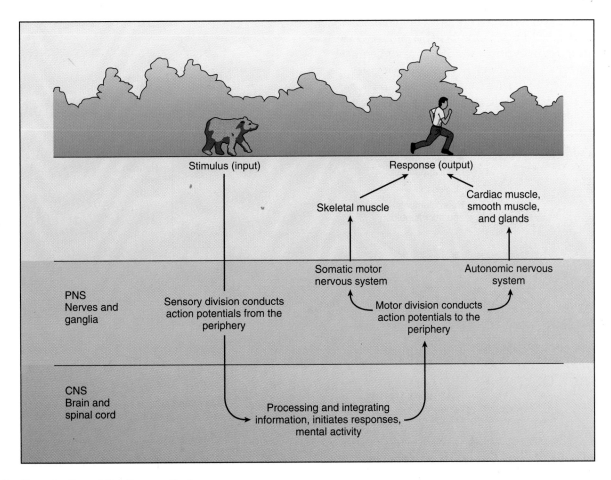

Figure 8.2   Organization of the Nervous System

The afferent division of the peripheral nervous system (PNS) detects stimuli and conducts action potentials to the central nervous system (CNS). The CNS interprets incoming action potentials and initiates action potentials that are conducted through the efferent division to produce a response. The efferent division is divided into the somatic motor nervous system and autonomic nervous system.

Cells of the Nervous System

Cells of the nervous system are neurons and neuroglia.

Neurons

Neurons (noor′onz), or **nerve cells** (figure 8.3), receive stimuli and transmit action potentials to other neurons or to effector organs. Each neuron consists of a cell body and two types of processes: dendrites and axons.

Each neuron cell body contains a single nucleus. As with any other cell, the nucleus of the neuron is the source of information for protein synthesis. If an axon, which is one of the neuron cell processes, is separated from the cell body, it dies because it has no connection to the nucleus, and no protein synthesis occurs in the axon. Extensive rough endoplasmic reticulum (rough ER) and Golgi apparatus surround the nucleus. Large numbers of neurofilaments (intermediate filaments) and microtubules course through the cytoplasm in all directions and separate the rough ER into distinct areas in the cell body. The areas of rough ER concentration, when stained with a specific dye appear as microscopic granules called **Nissl** (nis′l) **bodies.**

Dendrites (den′drītz, trees) are short, often highly branching cytoplasmic extensions that are tapered from their bases at the neuron cell body to their tips. Most dendrites are extensions of the neuron cell body, but dendritelike structures also project from the peripheral ends of some afferent axons. Dendrites usually function to receive information from other neurons or sensory receptors and transmit the information toward the neuron cell body.

An **axon** is a long cell process extending from the neuron cell body. Each axon has a constant diameter and may vary in length from a few millimeters to more than a meter. Axons of efferent neurons conduct action potentials away from the CNS and axons of afferent neurons conduct action potentials toward the CNS. Axons also conduct action potentials from one part of the brain or spinal cord to another part. Each efferent neuron has a single axon that extends from the CNS toward a target tissue. An axon may remain a single structure or may branch to form **collateral** (ko-lat′er-ăl) **axons.** Axons are surrounded by neuroglia, some of which form a highly specialized insulating layer of cells called the myelin sheath (described in more detail on p. 198).

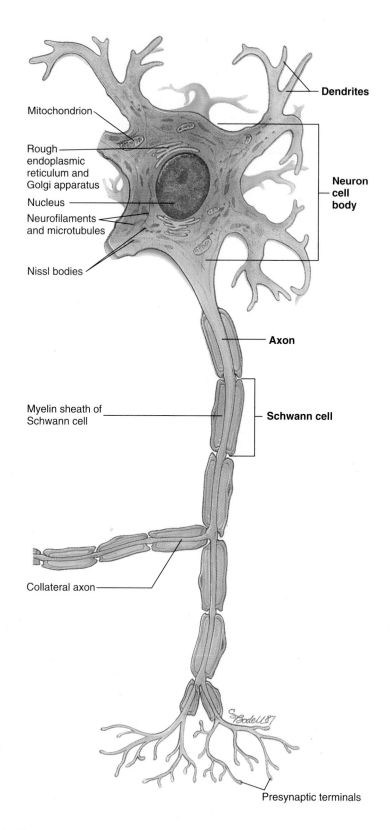

Dendrites

Mitochondrion

Rough
endoplasmic
reticulum and
Golgi apparatus

Neuron
cell
body

Nucleus

Neurofilaments
and microtubules

Nissl bodies

Axon

Myelin sheath of
Schwann cell

Schwann cell

Collateral axon

Presynaptic terminals

Figure 8.3 Structural Features of a Neuron

Neurons, or nerve cells, consist of dendrites, a cell body, and an axon. The neuron shown has several dendrites and one axon, with a collateral branch.

Types of Neurons

Three categories of neurons exist on the basis of their shape: multipolar neurons, bipolar neurons, and unipolar neurons (figure 8.4 and table 8.1). **Multipolar neurons** have many dendrites and a single axon. Most of the neurons within the CNS, including nearly all efferent neurons, are multipolar. **Bipolar neurons** have two processes: one dendrite and one axon. Bipolar neurons are located in some sensory organs, such as in the retina of the eye and in the nasal cavity. Most other afferent neurons are unipolar. **Unipolar neurons** have a single process extending from the cell body. This process divides into two processes a short distance from the cell body. One process extends to the periphery, and the other process extends to the CNS. The two extensions function as a single axon with small dendritelike extensions at the

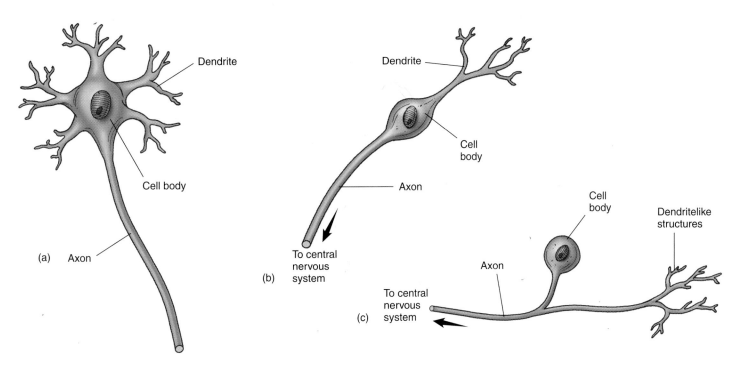

Figure 8.4   Types of Neurons
(a) Multipolar neuron. (b) Bipolar neuron. (c) Unipolar neuron.

Table 8.1	Cells of the Nervous System (see figures 8.4 and 8.5)	
Cell Type	**Description**	**Function**
Neuron		
Multipolar	Several dendrites and one axon	Most efferent neurons and most CNS neurons
Bipolar	One dendrite and one axon	Found in special sense organs such as the eye and the nose
Unipolar	A neuron with a single axon	Most afferent neurons
Neuroglia		
Astrocytes	Star-shaped	Provide structural support; form a layer around blood vessels, contribute to blood–brain barrier
Ependymal cells	Squamous epithelial-like	Line ventricles of brain, circulate cerebrospinal fluid (CSF); some form choroid plexuses, which produce CSF
Microglia	Small mobile cells	Protect CNS from infection; become phagocytic in response to inflammation
Oligodendrocytes	Cell with processes that can surround several axons	Cell processes form myelin sheaths around axons, or enclose unmyelinated axons, in the CNS
Schwann cells	Single cells surrounding axons	Form myelin sheaths around axons, or enclose unmyelinated axons in the PNS

periphery. The axon receives sensory information at the periphery and transmits that information in the form of action potentials to the CNS.

Neuroglia

Neuroglia (noo-rog′lē-ă, nerve glue), or **glial** (glī′ăl or glē′ăl) **cells**, are the nonneuronal cells of the CNS and PNS. Neuroglia are far more numerous than neurons. Most neuroglia retain the ability to divide, whereas most neurons do not. There are five types of neuroglia. **Astrocytes** (as′trō-sītz) serve as the major supporting tissue in the CNS and participate with the blood vessel endothelium to form a permeability barrier, called the **blood–brain barrier**, between the blood and the neurons. **Ependymal** (ep-en′di-măl) cells line the fluid-filled cavities (ventricles and canals) within the CNS. Some ependymal cells produce cerebrospinal fluid, and others, with cilia on the surface, help move it through the CNS. **Microglia** (mī-krog′lē-ă) help remove bacteria and cell debris from the CNS. **Oligodendrocytes** (ol′i-gō-den′drō-sītz; cells with many dendritic processes) in the CNS and **Schwann cells** in the PNS surround axons (figure 8.5; see table 8.1). Schwann cells are also referred to as **neurolemmocytes** (noor-ō-lem′ō-sītz).

Myelin Sheaths

Axons are surrounded by the cell processes of oligodendrocytes in the CNS and Schwann cells in the PNS (see figure 8.5). **Unmyelinated axons** rest in indentations of the oligodendrocytes in the CNS and the Schwann cells in the PNS (figure 8.6a). **Myelinated axons** have specialized sheaths, called **myelin sheaths**, wrapped around them. Each oligodendrocyte process or Schwann cell repeatedly wraps around a segment of an axon to form a series of tightly wrapped cell membranes. A typical small nerve usually contains more unmyelinated than myelinated axons. Myelin is an excellent insulator, which prevents almost all ion flow through the cell membrane. Gaps in the myelin sheath, called **nodes of Ranvier** (ron′vē-ā), can be seen about every millimeter between the oligodendrocyte segments or between individual Schwann cells (figure 8.6b). At the nodes of Ranvier, ions flow easily between the extracellular fluid and the axon, and action potentials can develop.

Organization of Nervous Tissue

Groups of neuron cell bodies and their dendrites form **gray matter**. Gray matter on the surface of the brain is called the **cortex**, and clusters of gray matter located deeper within the brain are called **nuclei**. In the PNS, a cluster of neuron cell bodies is called a **ganglion** (gang′glē-on; pl. ganglia, a swelling or knot). Bundles of parallel axons with their myelin sheaths are whitish in color and are called **white matter**. White matter of the CNS forms conduction **pathways**, or **nerve tracts**, which propagate action potentials from one area in the CNS to another. In the PNS, bundles of axons and their connective tissue sheaths are called **nerves**.

Propagation of Action Potentials
Membrane Potentials and Action Potentials

Cells exhibit electrical properties. The outside of most cell membranes is positively charged compared with the inside of the cell membrane, which is negatively charged (as discussed in chapter 7). This charge difference across the membrane of an unstimulated cell is called the **resting membrane potential**. The cell is said to be polarized. The outside of the cell membrane can be thought of as the positive pole of a battery, and the inside as the negative pole. Thus a small voltage difference, or potential, can be measured across the resting cell membrane.

The resting membrane potential results from differences in the concentration of ions across the cell membrane and the permeability characteristics of the cell membrane. There is a higher concentration of sodium ions (Na^+) outside the cell membrane than inside and a higher concentration of potassium ions (K^+) inside the cell membrane than outside (figure 8.7a). The concentration of sodium ions outside the cell membrane and of potassium ions inside is maintained by the **sodium–potassium exchange pump**, which actively transports potassium into and sodium out of the cell (figure 8.7b). The sodium–potassium exchange pump has little direct effect on the resting membrane potential or action potential.

When a cell is at rest, some potassium **ion channels** are open and sodium ion channels are not. The cell membrane is therefore more permeable to potassium ions than to sodium ions (figure 8.8). This allows a few potassium ions to diffuse down their concentration gradient out of the cell, carrying their positive charges with them. Larger molecules, such as proteins, which are negatively charged, are too large to diffuse out of the cell. As positive potassium ions leave the cell, the charge inside the cell becomes more negative. The molecules inside the cell with negative charges tend to attract the positive potassium ions back into the cell. A point of equilibrium is reached at which the tendency for potassium ions to move down their concentration gradient out of the cell is balanced by the negative charge within the cell, which tends to attract the potassium ions back into the cell. This point of potassium ion equilibrium is the point at which the resting membrane potential is established and there is no more net potassium ion movement out of the cell. At equilibrium, there is a net positive charge outside the cell and a net negative charge inside the cell.

Muscle and nerve cells are **excitable**. When a stimulus is applied to a muscle cell or nerve cell, some sodium channels open for a very brief time, and sodium ions diffuse quickly into the cell (figure 8.9a). The positively charged sodium ions entering the cell cause the inside of the cell membrane to become more positive, a change called **depolarization**. This depolarization results in a **local potential**. If the threshold is not reached, the sodium ion channels close again, and the local potential disappears without being conducted along the nerve cell membrane. If enough sodium ions enter the cell so that the local potential reaches a **threshold** value, this threshold depolarization causes many more sodium channels to open.

Foot processes

Cilia

Astrocyte

Capillary

(a)

(b)

Ependymal cells

Microglial cell

(c)

Neuron cell body

Axon

Myelin sheath of Schwann cell

Node of Ranvier

Oligodendrocyte

(d)

Axon

Myelin sheath

Nucleus of Schwann cell

Myelin sheath

(e)

Axon

Figure 8.5 Types of Neuroglia

(a) Astrocytes, with foot processes surrounding a blood capillary.
(b) Ependymal cells, with cilia extending from the surfaces. (c) Microglia.
(d) Oligodendrocyte, forming a myelin sheath around parts of three
axons within the CNS. (e) Schwann cell forming part of the myelin
sheath of an axon in the PNS.

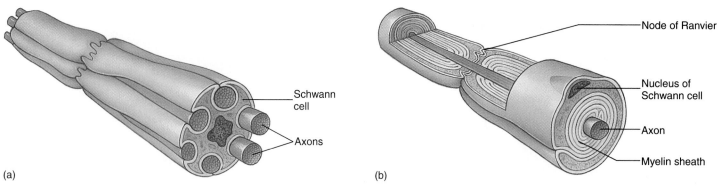

Figure 8.6 Comparison of Myelinated and Unmyelinated Axons

(*a*) Unmyelinated axons. Several axons are surrounded by the cytoplasm of a single Schwann cell. (*b*) Myelinated axon. A Schwann cell forming the myelin sheath is wrapped completely around a single axon.

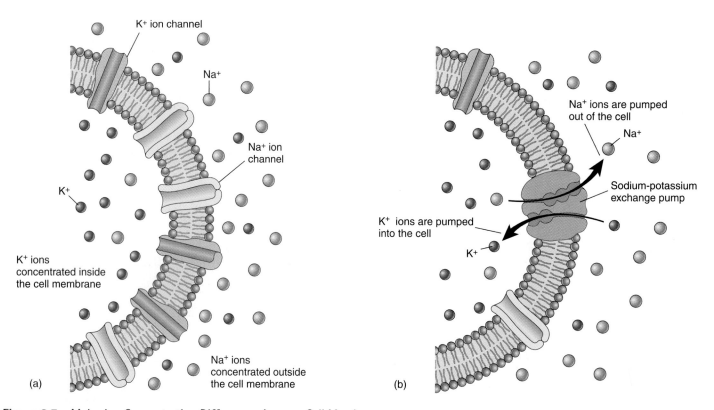

Figure 8.7 Major Ion Concentration Differences Across a Cell Membrane

(*a*) There is a higher concentration of potassium ions (K$^+$) inside the cell and a higher concentration of sodium ions (Na$^+$) outside the cell. (*b*) The sodium–potassium exchange pump moves sodium ions out of the cell in exchange for potassium ions that move into the cell.

As more sodium ions enter the cell, depolarization occurs until there is a brief reversal of charge across the membrane, and the inside of the cell membrane becomes positive relative to the outside of the cell membrane. This is called the **depolarization phase**. The charge reversal causes sodium channels to close and potassium channels to open. Sodium ions then stop entering the cell, and potassium ions leave the cell (figure 8.9*b*). This returns the cell membrane to its resting membrane potential, a change called the **repolarization phase**. The depolarization and repolarization phases constitute an **action potential**. (figure 8.10). The elevated permeability to potassium

lasts only a very short time. The sodium–potassium exchange pump slowly restores the ion distribution to the concentrations of the resting membrane potential.

Action potentials occur in an **all-or-none** fashion, that is, if threshold is reached, the charge reversal is complete; if the threshold is not reached, no action potential occurs. Action potentials in a given cell type are all of the same magnitude, that is, the amount of charge reversal is always the same. Stronger stimuli produce a greater frequency of action potentials but do not increase the size of each action potential.

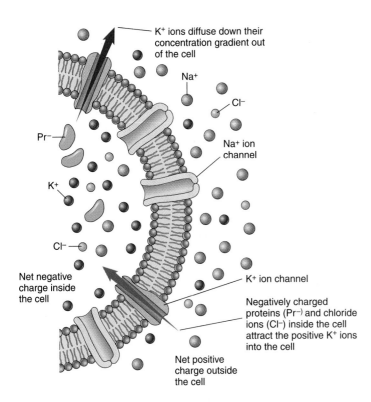

Figure 8.8   Ion Channels and Ion Concentrations Across a Cell Membrane

Concentrations of sodium ions (Na$^+$), potassium ions (K$^+$), chloride ions (Cl$^-$), and negatively charged proteins across the cell membrane are represented. Some potassium ion channels are open but sodium ion channels are not. As a result, potassium ions (K$^+$) diffuse out of the cell down their concentration gradient. The membrane is not permeable to the negatively charged proteins inside the cell. The tendency for the potassium ions to diffuse to the outside of the cell down their concentration gradient is opposed by the tendency for the positively charged potassium ions to be attracted back into the cell by the negatively charged proteins inside the cell.

Action potentials are conducted slowly in unmyelinated axons and more rapidly in myelinated axons. In unmyelinated axons, an action potential in one part of a cell membrane stimulates an adjacent part of the cell membrane to produce an action potential. By this means, the action potential is conducted along the entire axon cell membrane (figure 8.11*a*). In myelinated axons, an action potential at one node of Ranvier causes an electrical current to flow through the surrounding extracellular fluid and through the cytoplasm of the axon to the next node, stimulating that node of Ranvier to produce an action potential. By this means action potentials "jump" from one node of Ranvier to the next along the length of the axon (figure 8.11*b*). This type of action potential conduction is called **saltatory** (sal′tă-tōr-ē, to leap) **conduction.** Saltatory conduction greatly increases the conduction velocity because the nodes of Ranvier make it unnecessary for action potentials to be produced at every point along the cell membrane. Action potential conduction in a myelinated fiber is like a grasshopper jumping, whereas in an unmyelinated axon it is like a grasshopper walking.

(a) **Depolarization phase:** The stimulus causes sodium ion channels to open. Sodium ions then diffuse down their concentration gradient into the cell, causing depolarization of the cell membrane (red line in graph).

(b) **Repolarization phase:** The sodium ion channels close and additional potassium ion channels open. Potassium ions then diffuse down their concentration gradient out of the cell, causing repolarization of the cell membrane (red line in graph).

Figure 8.9   Effect of a Stimulus Causing a Voltage Change Across the Cell Membrane

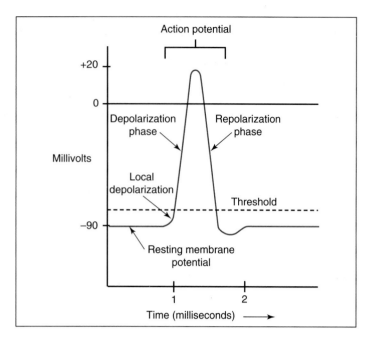

Figure 8.10 An Action Potential

The membrane potential depolarizes, or becomes more positive, during the depolarization phase and then repolarizes, or becomes more negative, during the repolarization phase. Once a local depolarization reaches threshold, an all-or-none action potential is started. During the depolarization phase, the voltage across the cell membrane changes from approximately −90 mV to approximately +20 mV. During the repolarization phase, the voltage across the cell membrane returns to −90 mV. The entire process lasts a little less than a second.

(a)

(b)

Figure 8.11 Propagation of an Action Potential

(a) An action potential in an unmyelinated nerve (represented by the orange area where a change in charge is shown across the membrane) travels along a cell membrane. An action potential in one part of the cell membrane stimulates action potentials in an adjacent part of the cell membrane. (b) Conduction of an action potential in a myelinated axon. The action potential jumps from node to node along the axon by means of electrical currents produced between the nodes.

Medium-diameter, lightly myelinated axons conduct action potentials at the rate of about 3 to 15 m/s, whereas large-diameter, heavily myelinated axons conduct action potentials at the rate of 15 to 120 m/s. In addition, several hundred times fewer ions cross the cell membrane during conduction in myelinated cells than in unmyelinated cells. Much less energy is therefore required for the sodium–potassium exchange pump to restore the ion distribution.

The Synapse

A **synapse** (sin′aps) is a junction where the axon of one neuron interacts with another neuron or an effector organ such as a muscle or gland (figure 8.12). The end of the axon forms a **presynaptic terminal**. The membrane of the dendrite or effector cell is the **postsynaptic membrane**, and the space separating the presynaptic and postsynaptic membranes is the **synaptic cleft**. Chemical substances called **neurotransmitters** (noor′ō-trans-mit′ers) are stored in **synaptic vesicles** in the presynaptic terminal. Those neurotransmitters are released by exocytosis from the presynaptic terminal in response to each action potential. The neurotransmitters diffuse across the synaptic cleft and bind to receptor molecules on the postsynaptic membrane. The binding of neurotransmitters to their receptors causes channels for sodium, potassium, or chloride ions to open or close in the postsynaptic membrane,

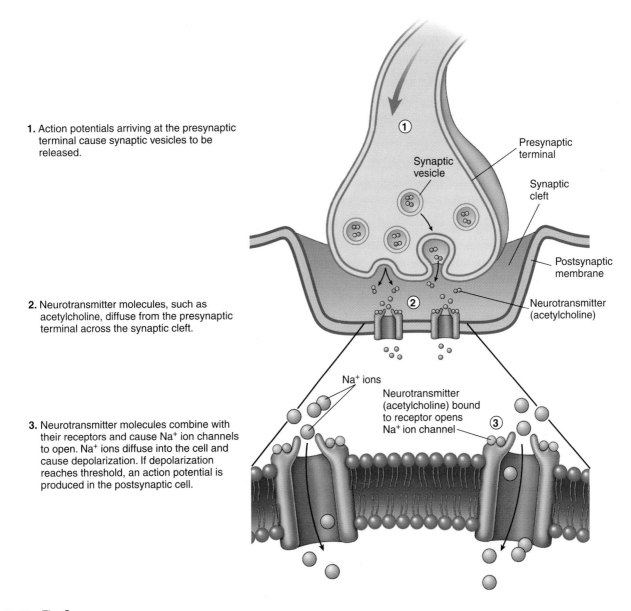

1. Action potentials arriving at the presynaptic terminal cause synaptic vesicles to be released.

2. Neurotransmitter molecules, such as acetylcholine, diffuse from the presynaptic terminal across the synaptic cleft.

3. Neurotransmitter molecules combine with their receptors and cause Na$^+$ ion channels to open. Na$^+$ ions diffuse into the cell and cause depolarization. If depolarization reaches threshold, an action potential is produced in the postsynaptic cell.

Synaptic vesicle

Presynaptic terminal

Synaptic cleft

Postsynaptic membrane

Neurotransmitter (acetylcholine)

Na$^+$ ions

Neurotransmitter (acetylcholine) bound to receptor opens Na$^+$ ion channel

Figure 8.12   The Synapse

Neurotransmitters are released from synaptic vesicles in the presynaptic terminal in response to an action potential. The neurotransmitters diffuse across the synaptic cleft and bind to receptors on the postsynaptic cell membrane, causing a stimulation or inhibition of action potentials in the postsynaptic cell.

depending on the type of neurotransmitter in the presynaptic terminal and the type of receptors on the postsynaptic membrane. The response may be either a stimulation or an inhibition of an action potential in the postsynaptic cell. For example, if sodium ion channels open, the postsynaptic cell becomes depolarized, and an action potential will occur if threshold is reached. If potassium or chloride ion channels open, the inside of the postsynaptic cell tends to become more negative, or **hyperpolarized** (hī′per-pō′lăr-ī-zed), and an action potential is inhibited from occurring.

Of the many neurotransmitter substances or suspected neurotransmitter substances, the best known are **norepinephrine** (nōr′ep-i-nef′rin) and **acetylcholine** (as′e-til-kō′lēn). Other neurotransmitters include serotonin (sĕr-ō-tō′nin), dopamine (dō′pă-mēn), γ (gamma)-aminobutyric (gam′ă ă-mē′nō-bū-tēr′ik) acid (GABA), glycine, and endorphins (en′dōr-finz). Neurotransmitter substances are rapidly broken down by enzymes or are transported back into the presynaptic terminal. Consequently, they are removed from the synaptic cleft so their effects on the postsynaptic membrane are very short term. In synapses where acetylcholine is the neurotransmitter, such as in the neuromuscular junction (see chapter 7), an enzyme called **acetylcholinesterase** (as′e-til-kō-lin-es′-ter-ās) breaks down the acetylcholine soon after it is released. No acetylcholine therefore remains in the cleft to stimulate the postsynaptic receptors and produce a second action potential, unless more acetylcholine is released from the presynaptic terminal. Norepinephrine is actively transported back into the presynaptic terminal or is broken down by other enzymes. The breakdown products are then returned to the presynaptic terminal for reuse or diffuse into the circulatory system and are carried away from the area. The release and breakdown of neurotransmitters occurs so rapidly that a neuron can be stimulated by presynaptic action potentials many times a second.

Did You Know?

Cocaine and amphetamines are strong CNS stimulants that cause elation, euphoria, psychosis, hallucinations, and paranoia. Cocaine and amphetamines also function in the PNS to increase the release and block the reuptake of norepinephrine, resulting in overstimulation of postsynaptic neurons. Symptoms include dilation of the pupils, restlessness, exaggerated reflexes, muscle spasms, tachycardia, vasoconstriction, hypertension, nausea, and vomiting. Death may occur from heart failure or respiratory failure.

Reflexes

A **reflex** is an involuntary reaction in response to a stimulus applied to the periphery and transmitted to the CNS. Reflexes allow a person to react to a stimulus more quickly than is possible if conscious thought is involved. A **reflex arc** is the neuronal pathway by which a reflex occurs. The reflex arc (figure 8.13) is the basic functional unit of the nervous system and is the smallest, simplest pathway capable of receiving a stimulus and yielding a response. A reflex arc has five basic components: (1) a **sensory receptor**; (2) an **afferent**, or **sensory**, **neuron**; (3) **association neurons**, which are neurons located between and communicating with two other neurons; (4) an efferent, or **motor, neuron**; and (5) an **effector organ**. Most reflexes involve the spinal cord or brainstem and not the higher brain centers.

The result of a reflex can be seen when a person's finger touches a hot stove. Pain receptors in the skin are stimulated by the hot stove, and action potentials are produced. Afferent neurons conduct the action potentials to the spinal cord, where they synapse with association neurons. The association neurons, in turn, synapse with efferent neurons in the spinal cord that conduct action potentials along their axons to flexor muscles in the upper limb. These muscles contract and pull the finger away from the stove. No

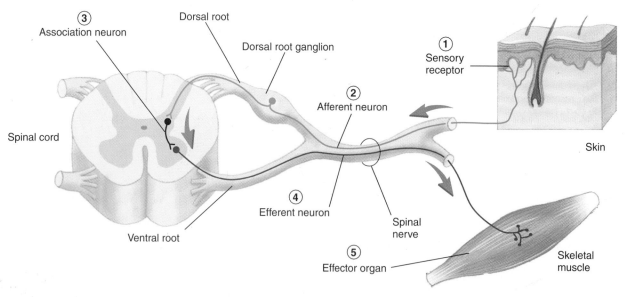

Figure 8.13 Reflex Arc

A reflex arc includes a sensory receptor (1), an afferent neuron (2), an association neuron (3), an efferent neuron (4), and an effector organ (5).

conscious thought is required for this reflex, and withdrawal of the finger from the stimulus begins before the person is consciously aware of any pain.

Knee-Jerk Reflex

The simplest reflex is the **stretch reflex**, a reflex in which muscles contract in response to a stretching force applied to them. Descending neurons within the spinal cord synapse with the neurons of the stretch reflex and modulate their activity. This activity is important in maintaining posture and in coordinating muscular activity.

The **knee-jerk reflex**, or **patellar reflex** (figure 8.14), is a classic example of the stretch reflex and is used by clinicians to determine if the higher CNS centers that normally influence this reflex are functional. When the patellar ligament is tapped, the quadriceps femoris muscle tendon and the muscles themselves are stretched. Sensory receptors within these muscles are also stretched, and the stretch reflex is activated. Consequently, contraction of the muscles extends the leg,

producing the characteristic knee-jerk response. All spinal reflexes are lost for a few weeks after a severe spinal cord injury. By about 2 weeks after injury the knee-jerk reflex returns, but it is often exaggerated. When the stretch reflex is greatly exaggerated, it indicates that the neurons within the brain or spinal cord that normally modify this reflex have been damaged.

Withdrawal Reflex

The function of the **withdrawal**, or **flexor reflex**, is to remove a limb or other body part from a painful stimulus. The sensory receptors are pain receptors (see chapter 9). Action potentials from painful stimuli are conducted by afferent neurons through the dorsal root to the spinal cord, where they synapse with excitatory association neurons, which in turn synapse with efferent neurons (figure 8.15). These neurons stimulate muscles, usually flexor muscles, that remove the limb from the source of the painful stimulus.

1. Sensory receptors in the muscle detect stretch of the muscle.

2. Afferent neurons conduct action potentials to the spinal cord.

3. Afferent neurons synapse with alpha motor neurons.

4. Stimulation of efferent neurons causes the muscle to contract and resist being stretched.

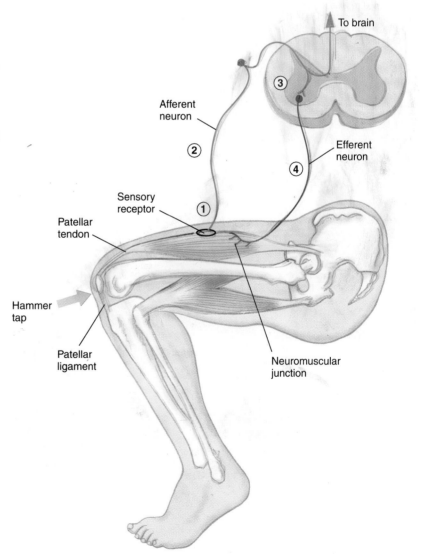

Figure 8.14   Knee-Jerk Reflex

Neuronal Circuits

Neurons are organized within the CNS to form circuits ranging from relatively simple to extremely complex. The two simplest circuits are converging and diverging circuits. **Converging circuits** have two or more neurons that synapse with the same neuron (figure 8.16a). An example of a con-

verging pathway is one involving a motor neuron in the spinal cord, which stimulates muscle contraction (figure 8.16b). Afferent fibers from pain receptors carry action potentials to the spinal cord and synapse with association neurons, which in turn synapse with a motor neuron. Neurons in the cerebral cortex, controlling conscious movement, also synapse with the same motor neuron. Both the association neurons and the

1. Pain receptors detect a painful stimulus.

2. Afferent neurons conduct action potentials to the spinal cord.

3. Afferent neurons synapse with excitatory association neurons that synapse with efferent neurons.

4. Excitation of the efferent neurons results in contraction of the flexor muscles and withdrawal of the limb from the painful stimulus.

Figure 8.15 Withdrawal Reflex

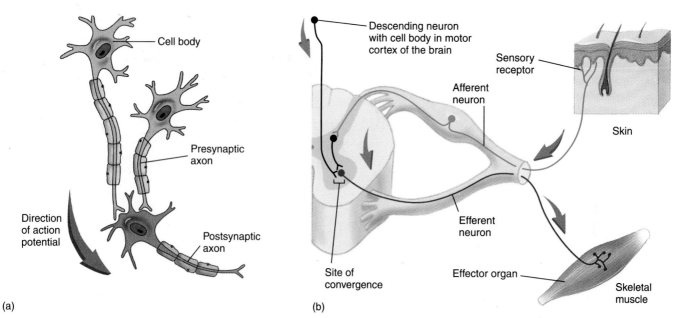

(a)

(b)

Figure 8.16 Converging Circuit

(a) General model. (b) Example of a converging circuit in the spinal cord. An afferent neuron from the periphery and a descending neuron from the brain converge on a single motor neuron.

neurons in the cerebral cortex have axons that converge onto the motor neuron, which can therefore be stimulated either through the reflex arc or by conscious thought.

In **diverging circuits**, the axon from one neuron divides and synapses with more than one other neuron (figure 8.17*a*). This allows information transmitted in one neuronal pathway to diverge into two or more pathways. An example of a diverging circuit is found in afferent neurons within the spinal cord (figure 8.17*b*). The axon of an afferent neuron carrying action potentials from pain receptors branches within the spinal cord. One branch produces a reflex response by synapsing with an association neuron, which synapses with a motor neuron, which stimulates a muscle to withdraw the injured region of the body from the source of the pain. The other branch synapses with an ascending neuron that carries action potentials to the brain, where the stimulation is interpreted as pain.

Central Nervous System

The **central nervous system** (**CNS**) consists of the brain and spinal cord. The brain is that part of the CNS housed within the cranial vault. The major regions of the brain are the brainstem, the diencephalon, the cerebrum, and the cerebellum (figure 8.18).

Brainstem

The medulla oblongata, pons, and midbrain constitute the **brainstem** (figure 8.19). The brainstem connects the spinal cord to the remainder of the brain and contains several nuclei involved in vital body functions such as the control of heart rate and breathing. Damage to small areas of the brainstem can cause death, whereas damage to relatively large areas of the cerebrum or cerebellum often do not cause death.

Medulla Oblongata

The **medulla oblongata** (ob′long-gă′tă) is the most inferior portion of the brainstem (see figure 8.19) and is continuous with the spinal cord. In addition to ascending and descending nerve tracts, the medulla oblongata contains discrete nuclei with specific functions such as regulation of heart rate and blood vessel diameter, breathing, swallowing, vomiting, coughing, sneezing, balance, and coordination.

On the anterior surface, two prominent enlargements called **pyramids** extend the length of the medulla oblongata (see figure 8.19). The pyramids consist of descending nerve tracts, which transmit action potentials from the brain to motor neurons of the spinal cord and are involved in the conscious control of skeletal muscles.

1	**P R E D I C T**

A large tumor or **hematoma** (hē-mă-tō′mă), a mass of blood which occurs as the result of bleeding into the tissues, can cause increased pressure within the skull. This pressure can force the medulla oblongata downward toward the foramen magnum of the skull. The displacement can compress the medulla oblongata and lead to death. Give two likely causes of death, and explain why they would occur.

✔ *Answer on page 235*

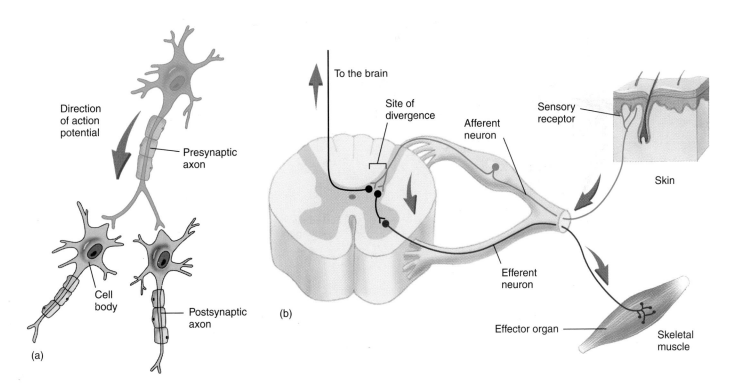

Figure 8.17   Diverging Circuit

(*a*) General model. (*b*) Example of a diverging circuit in the spinal cord. An afferent neuron from the periphery diverges and sends information to a motor neuron that sends information to the brain.

Figure 8.18 Regions of the Brain
A midsagittal section viewed from the left.

(a)   (b)

Figure 8.19 Brainstem
(*a*) Anterior view. (*b*) Posterolateral view.

Pons

Immediately superior to the medulla oblongata is the **pons**. It contains ascending and descending nerve tracts, as well as several nuclei. Some of the nuclei in the pons relay information between the cerebrum and the cerebellum. The term pons means bridge, and it describes both the structure and function of the pons. Not only is the pons a functional bridge between the cerebrum and cerebellum, but on the anterior surface, it resembles an arched footbridge (see figure 8.19*a*). Several nuclei of the medulla oblongata, described above, also extend into the lower part of the pons, so that functions such as breathing, swallowing, and balance are controlled in the lower pons, as well as in the medulla oblongata. Other nuclei in the pons control functions such as chewing and salivation.

Midbrain

The **midbrain**, just superior to the pons, is the smallest region of the brainstem (see figure 8.19*b*). The superior part of the midbrain consists of four mounds called the **colliculi** (ko-lik'ū-lī, hills). The two inferior colliculi are major relay centers for the auditory nerve pathways in the CNS. The two superior colliculi are involved in visual reflexes. Turning the head toward a tap on the shoulder, a sudden loud noise, or a bright flash of light are reflexes controlled in the superior colliculi. The midbrain contains nuclei involved in the coordination of eye movements and in the control of pupil diameter and lens shape. The midbrain also contains a black nuclear mass, called the **substantia nigra** (sŭb-stan'shē-ă nī'gră), which is part of the basal nuclei (see the section on Basal Nuclei on p. 214) and is involved in the regulation of general body movements. The rest of the midbrain consists largely of ascending pathways from the spinal cord to the cerebrum and descending motor pathways from the cerebrum to the spinal cord.

Reticular Formation

Scattered throughout the brainstem is a group of nuclei collectively called the **reticular formation**. The reticular formation is a major component of the **reticular activating system**, which plays an important role in arousing and maintaining consciousness and in regulating the sleep–wake cycle. Stimuli such as an alarm clock ringing, sudden bright lights, smelling salts, or cold water being splashed on the face can arouse consciousness. Conversely, removal of visual or auditory stimuli may lead to drowsiness or sleep. General anesthetics function by suppressing the reticular activating system. Damage to cells of the reticular formation can result in coma.

Diencephalon

The **diencephalon** (dī'en-sef'ă-lon) (figure 8.20) is the part of the brain between the brainstem and the cerebrum. Its main components are the thalamus, epithalamus, and hypothalamus.

Thalamus

The **thalamus** (thal'ă-mŭs) is by far the largest part of the diencephalon. It consists of a cluster of nuclei and is shaped somewhat like a yo-yo, with two large, lateral parts connected in the center by a small **intermediate mass** (see figure 8.20). Most sensory input that ascends through the spinal cord and brainstem projects to the thalamus, where afferent neurons synapse with thalamic neurons. Thalamic neurons, in turn, send their axons to the cerebral cortex. The thalamus also has other functions, such as influencing mood and registering an unlocalized, uncomfortable perception of pain.

Epithalamus

The **epithalamus** (ep'i-thal'ă-mŭs) is a small area superior and posterior to the thalamus (see figure 8.20). It consists of a few small nuclei that are involved in the emotional and visceral response to odors, and the pineal body. The **pineal body** (pin'ē-ăl, pinecone-shaped) is an endocrine gland that may influence the onset of puberty. It also may play a role in controlling some long-term cycles that are influenced by the light–dark cycle. The pineal body is known to influence annual behaviors such as migration in birds, as well as changes in fur color and density in some mammals (see chapter 10).

Hypothalamus

The **hypothalamus** is the most inferior part of the diencephalon and contains several small nuclei (see figure 8.20), which are very important in maintaining homeostasis. The hypothalamus plays a central role in the control of body temperature, hunger, and thirst. Sensations such as sexual pleasure, feeling relaxed and "good" after a meal, rage, and fear are related to hypothalamic functions. Emotional responses, which seem to be inappropriate to the circumstances, such as "nervous perspiration" in response to stress or feeling hungry as a result of depression, also involve the hypothalamus. A funnel-shaped stalk, the **infundibulum** (in-fŭn-dib'ū-lŭm), extends from the floor of the hypothalamus to the pituitary gland. The hypothalamus plays a major role in controlling the secretion of hormones from the pituitary gland (see chapter 10). The **mamillary** (mam'i-lār-ē) **bodies** form externally visible swellings on the posterior portion of the hypothalamus and are involved in emotional responses to odors and in memory.

Cerebrum

The **cerebrum** (ser'-ĕ-brŭm, sĕ-rē'brŭm) is the largest part of the brain (figure 8.21). It is divided into left and right hemispheres by a **longitudinal fissure**. The most conspicuous features on the surface of each hemisphere are numerous folds called **gyri** (jī'rī; sing. gyrus), which greatly increase the surface area of the cortex, and intervening grooves called **sulci** (soo'kī; sing. sulcus).

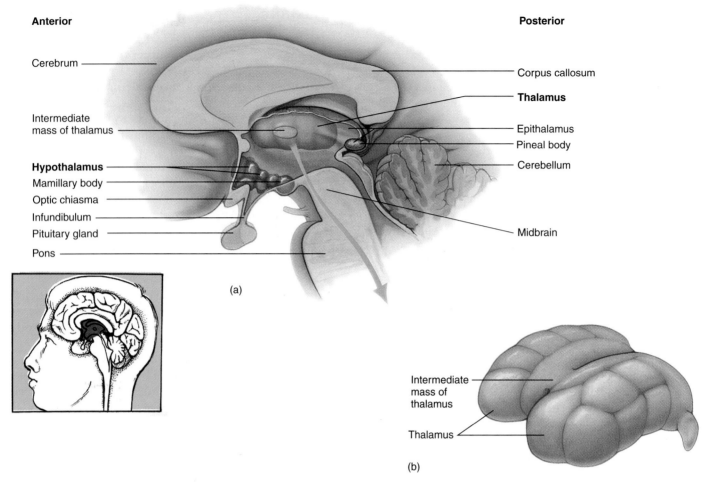

Figure 8.20 Diencephalon

(*a*) Midsagittal section of the diencephalon showing the thalamus, epithalamus, and hypothalamus. (*b*) Both halves of the thalamus as seen from a dorsolateral view with the separations between nuclei depicted by indentations on the surface.

Each cerebral hemisphere is divided into lobes (see figure 8.21), named for the skull bones overlying them. The **frontal lobe** is important in voluntary motor functions, motivation, aggression, mood, and olfactory (smell) reception. The **parietal lobe** is the principal center for the reception and evaluation of most sensory information, such as touch, pain, temperature, balance, and taste. The frontal and parietal lobes are separated by a prominent sulcus called the **central sulcus**. The **occipital lobe** functions in the reception and integration of visual input and is not distinctly separate from the other lobes. The **temporal lobe** evaluates olfactory (smell) and auditory (hearing) input and plays an important role in memory. Its anterior and inferior portions are referred to as the "psychic cortex," and they are associated with functions such as abstract thought and judgment. Most of the temporal lobe is separated from the rest of the cerebrum by a **lateral fissure**.

Functional Areas of the Cerebral Cortex

Figure 8.22 depicts a lateral view of the left cerebral cortex with some of the functional areas indicated. The terms area

and cortex are often used interchangeably for these regions of the cerebral cortex. Sensory nerve tracts project to specific regions of the cerebral cortex, called **primary sensory areas**, where sensations are perceived. The **primary somatic sensory cortex**, or **general sensory area**, is located in the parietal lobe posterior to the central sulcus. Afferent fibers carrying general sensory input, such as pain, pressure, and temperature, synapse in the thalamus, and thalamic neurons relay the information to the primary somatic sensory cortex. Afferent fibers from specific parts of the body project to specific regions of the primary somatic sensory cortex so that a topographic map of the body, with the head most inferior, exists in this part of the cerebral cortex (see figure 8.22). Other primary sensory areas include the visual cortex in the occipital lobe, the primary auditory cortex in the temporal lobe, and the taste area in the parietal lobe.

Cortical areas immediately adjacent to the primary sensory centers, called **association areas**, are involved in the process of recognition. For example, afferent action potentials originating in the retina of the eye reach the visual cortex, where the image is perceived. Action potentials then pass from the visual cortex to the visual association area, where the

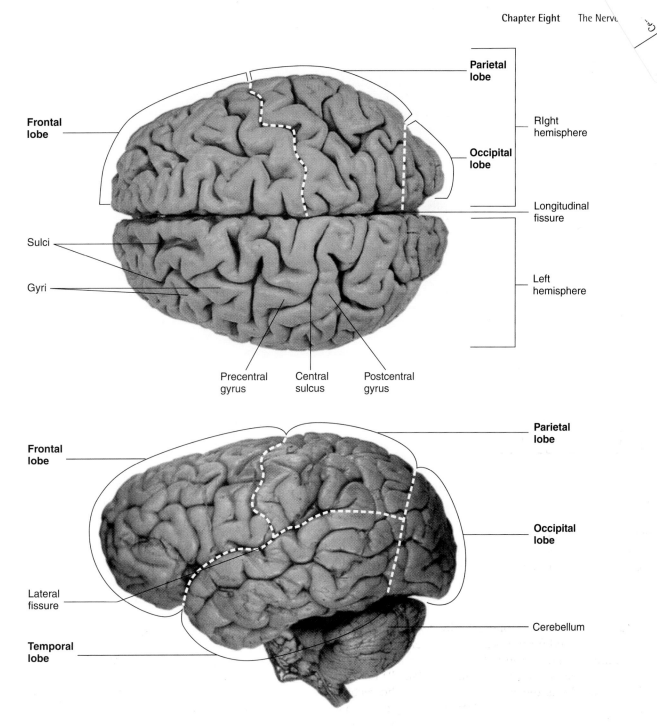

Figure 8.21 Cerebral Cortex

(*a*) Superior view of both cerebral hemispheres showing the gyri and lobes. (*b*) Lateral view of the left cerebral hemisphere showing the gyri and lobes.

present visual information is compared with past visual experience ("Have I seen this before?"). On the basis of this comparison, the visual association area "decides" whether or not the visual input is recognized and judges whether the input is significant. For example, if you pass a man walking down a street, you usually pay less attention to him if you've never seen him before than if you know him, unless some unique characteristic of the unknown person draws your attention. Other examples of association areas include the auditory association area, adjacent to the primary auditory cortex, and the somatic sensory association area, adjacent to the primary somatic sensory cortex.

The **primary motor cortex** is located in the posterior portion of the frontal lobe, directly anterior to the central sulcus (see figures 8.21 and 8.22). Efferent action potentials initiated in this region control voluntary movements of skeletal muscles. Efferent fibers project from specific regions of this cortex to specific parts of the body, so that a topographic map of the body exists in the primary motor cortex, with the head inferior, analogous to the topographic map of the primary somatic sensory cortex (see figure 8.22). The **premotor area** of the frontal lobe is the staging area where motor functions are organized before they are actually initiated in the primary motor cortex. For example, if a person decides to take a step, the

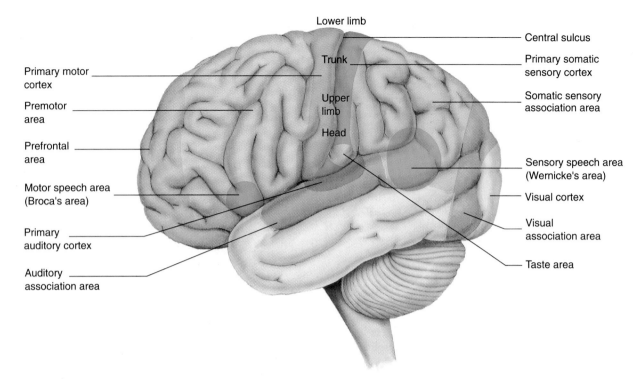

Figure 8.22   Cortical Functional Regions of the Left Hemisphere of the Cerebral Cortex

neurons of the premotor area are first stimulated, and the determination is made there as to which muscles must contract, in what order, and to what degree. Action potentials are then passed to the primary motor cortex, which actually initiates each planned movement.

The motivation and the foresight to plan and initiate movements occur in the anterior portion of the frontal lobes, the **prefrontal area**. This is a region of association cortex that is well developed only in primates, especially in humans. It is involved in motivation and regulation of emotional behavior and mood. The large size of this area in humans may account for our relatively well-developed forethought and motivation and for our emotional complexity.

Speech

In most people, the speech area is in the left cortex. Two major cortical areas are involved in speech: the **sensory speech area** (Wernicke's area), a portion of the parietal lobe, and the

motor speech area (Broca's area) in the inferior portion of the frontal lobe (see figure 8.22). Damage to these parts of the brain or to associated brain regions may result in **aphasia** (ă-fā′zē-ă), absent or defective speech or language comprehension.

To repeat a word that one hears requires the functional integrity of the following primary pathway. Action potentials from the ear reach the primary auditory cortex, where the word is perceived; the word is recognized in the auditory association area and is comprehended in portions of the sensory speech area. Action potentials representing the word are then conducted through association fibers that connect the sensory and motor speech areas. In the motor speech area, the word is formulated as it is to be repeated; action potentials then go to the premotor cortex, where the movements are programmed, and finally to the primary motor cortex, where specific movements are triggered.

Speaking a written word is somewhat similar. The information enters the visual cortex; passes to the visual association area, where it is recognized; and continues to the sensory speech area, where it is understood and formulated as it is to be spoken. From the sensory speech area it follows the same route for repeating words that one hears: through association fibers to the motor speech area, to the premotor area, and then to the primary motor cortex.

Brain Waves

Electrodes placed on a person's scalp and attached to a recording device can record the brain's electrical activity, producing an **electroencephalogram** (ē-lek′trō-en-sef′ă-lō-gram) **(EEG)** (figure 8.23). These electrodes are not positioned so that they can detect individual action potentials, but they can detect the simultaneous action potentials in large numbers of neurons. As a result, the EEG displays wavelike patterns known as **brain waves**. This electrical activity is constant, but the intensity and frequency of electrical discharge differs from time to time based on the state of brain activity. Distinct EEG patterns occur with specific brain disorders such as epileptic seizures. Neurologists use these patterns to diagnose and determine the treatment for the disorders.

Memory

Memory can be divided into at least three types: sensory, short term, and long term. **Sensory memory** is the brief retention of sensory input received by the brain while something is scanned, evaluated, and acted on. This type of memory occurs in the temporal lobe and lasts less than a second.

A given piece of data held in sensory memory can be moved within the temporal lobe from sensory memory into **short-term memory**, where information is tained for a few seconds to a few minutes. This memory is limited primarily by the number of bits of information (about seven) that can be stored at any one time. Have you ever wondered why telephone numbers are seven digits long? More bits can be stored when the numbers are grouped and separated by spaces, such as when adding an area code. When new information is presented, old information, previously stored in short-term memory, is eliminated. What happens to a telephone number you just looked up if you are distracted? If the temporal lobe is damaged, the transition from sensory to short-term memory may not occur, and the person always lives only in the present and in the more remote past, with memory already stored before the injury. This person is unable to add new memory.

Certain pieces of information are transferred from short-term to **long-term memory**, some of which may last for only a few minutes, and some of which may become permanent. Long-term memory may involve a physical change in neuron shape. A whole series of neurons, called **memory engrams** or **memory traces**, are probably involved in the long-term retention of a given piece of information, thought, or idea. Rehearsal of information assists in the transfer of information from short-term to long-term memory.

(a)

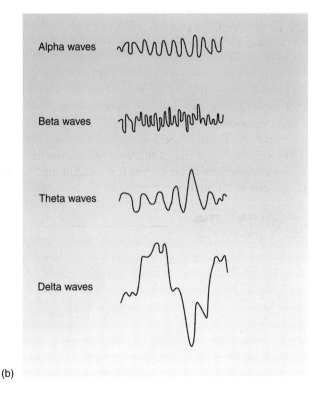

(b)

Figure 8.23   Electroencephalogram

(a) Patient with electrodes attached to his head. (b) Four electroencephalographic tracings.
1. Alpha waves, often seen in a relaxed individual with eyes closed.
2. Beta waves, typical of an alert individual.
3. Theta waves, seen in the first stage of sleep.
4. Delta waves, characteristic of deep sleep.

Right and Left Hemispheres

The right cerebral hemisphere receives sensory input from and controls muscular activity in the left half of the body. The left cerebral hemisphere receives input from and controls muscles in the right half of the body. Sensory information received by one hemisphere is shared with the other through connections between the two hemispheres called **commissures** (kom′ĭ-shūrz, a joining together). The largest of these commissures is the corpus callosum (kōr′pus kă-lō′sŭm, callous body), a broad band of nerve tracts at the base of the longitudinal fissure (see figure 8.18).

Language and perhaps other functions, such as artistic activities, are not shared equally between the two hemispheres. The left hemisphere is thought to be the more analytical hemisphere, emphasizing such skills as mathematics and speech. The right hemisphere is thought to be involved more in functions such as three-dimensional or spatial perception and musical ability.

Basal Nuclei

The **basal nuclei** are a group of functionally related nuclei (figure 8.24). Two primary nuclei are the **corpus striatum** (kōr′pŭs strī-ā′tŭm), located deep within the cerebrum, and the **substantia nigra**, a group of darkly pigmented cells located in the midbrain. The basal nuclei play an important role in posture and in planning and coordinating motor movements. Complex neural connections link the basal nuclei with the cerebral cortex. Dopamine is a neurotransmitter produced in the substantia nigra, which exerts an inhibitory influence on the corpus striatum. The major effect of the basal nuclei is to decrease muscle tone and inhibit muscular activity. Disorders of the basal nuclei, such as Parkinson's dis-

ease and cerebral palsy, result in increased muscle tone and in exaggerated, uncontrolled movements, occurring mainly when the person is trying to hold still, because of decreased basal nuclei function.

Limbic System

The olfactory cortex and certain deep cortical regions and nuclei of the cerebrum and diencephalon are grouped together under the title **limbic** (lim′bik, a boundary) **system** (figure 8.25). The limbic system responds to olfactory stimulation by initiating responses necessary for survival, such as hunger and thirst. It influences memory, emotions, visceral responses to emotions, motivation, and mood. The limbic system is connected to, and functionally associated with, the hypothalamus. Lesions in the limbic system can result in voracious appetite, increased (often perverse) sexual activity, and docility (including loss of normal fear and anger responses).

Cerebellum

Cerebellum (ser-e-bel′ŭm) means little brain (see figure 8.18). The cerebellar cortex is composed of gray matter and has gyri and sulci, but the gyri are much smaller than those of the cerebrum. Internally, the cerebellum consists of nuclei and nerve tracts. The cerebellum is involved in balance, maintenance of muscle tone, and coordination of fine motor movement. If the cerebellum is damaged, muscle tone decreases, and fine motor movements become very clumsy.

A major function of the cerebellum is that of a **comparator** (figure 8.26). Action potentials from the cerebral motor cortex descend into the spinal cord to initiate voluntary movements. Collateral branches are also sent from the motor cortex

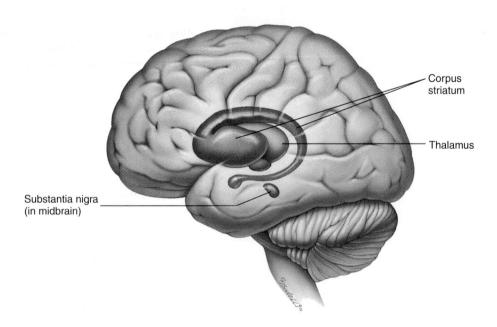

Corpus striatum

Thalamus

Substantia nigra (in midbrain)

Figure 8.24 Basal Nuclei

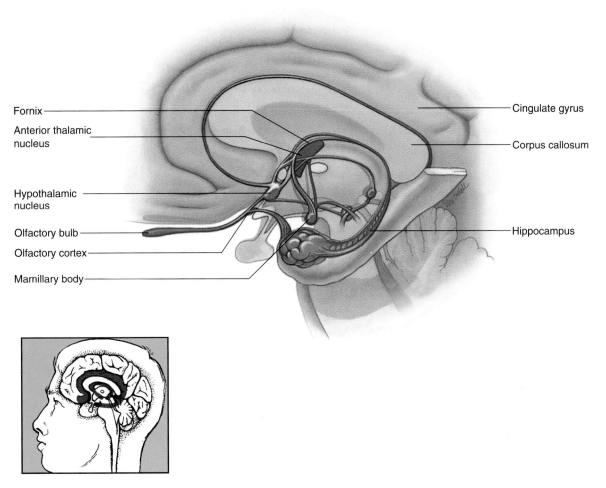

Fornix

Anterior thalamic nucleus

Hypothalamic nucleus

Olfactory bulb

Olfactory cortex

Mamillary body

Cingulate gyrus

Corpus callosum

Hippocampus

Figure 8.25   The Limbic System

The limbic system includes the olfactory cortex, the cingulate gyrus (an area of cerebral cortex on the medial side of each hemisphere), nuclei such as those of the hypothalamus and thalamus, the hippocampus (a mass of neuron cell bodies deep in the temporal lobe), and connecting nerve tracts such as the fornix.

to the cerebellum, giving information representing the intended movement. Simultaneously, action potentials from proprioceptive neurons reach the cerebellum. **Proprioceptive** (prō-prē-ō-sep′tiv) **neurons** innervate joints and tendons, providing information about the position of body parts. The cerebellum compares information about the intended movement from the motor cortex with sensory information from the moving structures. If a difference is detected, the cerebellum sends action potentials to motor neurons in the motor cortex and the spinal cord to correct the discrepancy. The result is smooth and coordinated movements. For example, if you close your eyes, the cerebellar comparator function allows you to touch your nose smoothly and easily with your finger. If the cerebellum is not functioning, your finger tends to overshoot the target. One effect of alcohol is to inhibit the function of the cerebellum. Dysfunction of the cerebellar comparator can be understood by observing the actions of someone who is drunk.

Another function of the cerebellum involves learning a motor skill such as playing the piano or riding a bicycle. When such a skill is being learned, the cerebrum is directly involved

in initiating the various movements. Once the cerebellum "learns" these skills, much of the movement can be accomplished automatically by the cerebellum.

Spinal Cord

The **spinal cord** extends from the foramen magnum at the base of the skull to the second lumbar vertebra. The cord consists of a central gray part and a peripheral white part (figure 8.27). The gray matter, seen in cross section, is shaped like the letter H, with **posterior (dorsal) horns** containing association neurons and cell processes of sensory neurons and **anterior (ventral) horns** containing motor neurons. In the thoracic and upper lumbar regions, an additional gray horn, the **lateral horn**, contains sympathetic autonomic motor neurons. Ascending axons carrying action potentials to the brain or descending axons carrying action potentials from the brain are grouped by function as **nerve pathways**, or **nerve tracts**, within the white matter of the spinal cord.

1. The motor cortex sends action potentials to motor neurons in the spinal cord.

2. Action potentials from the motor cortex inform the cerebellum of the intended movement.

3. Motor neurons in the spinal cord send action potentials to skeletal muscles, causing them to contract.

4. Proprioceptive signals from the skeletal muscles and joints to the cerebellum convey information concerning the status of the muscles and the structures being moved during contraction.

5. The cerebellum compares the information from the motor cortex to the proprioceptive information from the skeletal muscles and joints.

6. Action potentials from the cerebellum to the spinal cord modify the stimulation from the motor cortex to the motor neurons.

7. Action potentials from the cerebellum are sent to the motor cortex, which modifies its motor activity.

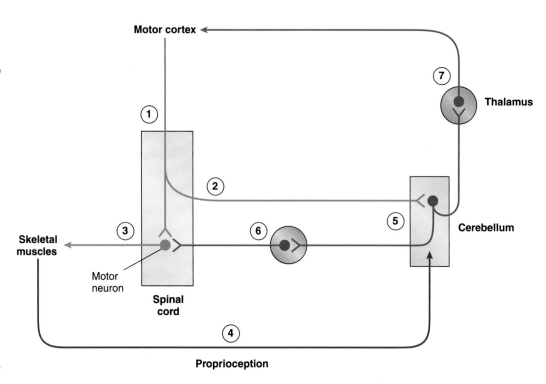

Figure 8.26   Cerebellar Comparator Function

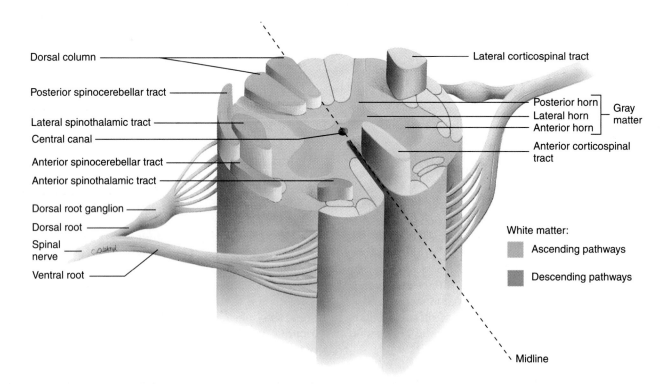

Figure 8.27   The Spinal Cord

Cross section of the spinal cord showing the horns, pathways (nerve tracts), and roots.

Dorsal (posterior) roots enter and ventral (anterior) roots exit the spinal cord. The **dorsal root** consists of afferent axons that carry action potentials to the spinal cord, and the **ventral root** consists of efferent axons that carry action potentials away from the spinal cord. The dorsal and ventral roots unite to form spinal nerves. The dorsal roots have **dorsal root ganglia**, or **spinal ganglia**, which contain the cell bodies of the afferent neurons. The axons of these neurons project into the posterior horn, where they synapse with other neurons or ascend or descend in the spinal cord.

3	P R E D I C T

Explain why the dorsal root ganglia are larger in diameter than the spinal nerves.

✔ *Answer on page 235*

Pathways

The names of most ascending (afferent, or sensory) and descending (efferent, or motor) pathways, or nerve tracts, in the CNS reflect their general function (table 8.2 and figures 8.27 to 8.29). Pathways are usually given composite names that indicate their origin and termination. The names of ascending pathways usually begin with the prefix spino-, indicating that they originate in the spinal cord. For example, a spinothalamic tract is one that originates in the spinal cord and terminates in the thalamus. The names of descending pathways usually begin with the prefix cortico-, indicating that they begin in the cerebral cortex. The corticospinal tract is a descending tract that originates in the cerebral cortex and terminates in the spinal cord.

Most ascending pathways consist of two or three neurons in sequence from the periphery to the brain. Almost all neurons relaying information to the cerebrum terminate in the

thalamus. Another neuron then relays the information from the thalamus to the cerebral cortex. The **lateral spinothalamic tract**, which transmits action potentials dealing with pain and temperature to the thalamus and on to the cerebral cortex, is an example of an ascending pathway. The **dorsal column**, which transmits action potentials dealing with touch and pressure, is another example (see figure 8.28).

The somatic motor system consists of two primary types of neurons: lower motor neurons and upper motor neurons. The cell bodies of **lower motor neurons** are in either the anterior horn of the spinal cord central gray matter or the cranial nerve nuclei of the brainstem. The axons from the lower

Table 8.2	Examples of Spinal Cord Pathways (see figures 8.27 to 8.29)
Pathway	**Function**
Ascending	
Spinothalamic	Pain, temperature, light tough, pressure, tickle, and itch sensations
Dorsal column	Proprioception, touch, deep pressure, and vibration.
Spinocerebellar	Proprioception to cerebellum
Descending	
Direct (Corticospinal)	Muscle tone and skilled movement, especially of the hands
Indirect	More unconscious control of body movements

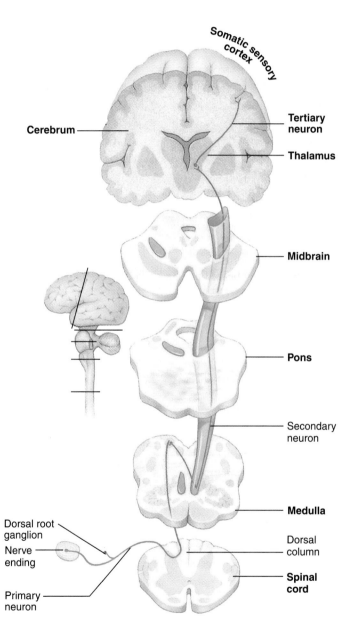

Figure 8.28 Example of an Ascending Pathway: The Dorsal Column System

This example shows the sensory pathway for touch and pressure. Information from nerve endings in the skin travels to the medulla, where it crosses to the other side of the body on its way to the primary somatic sensory cortex.

motor neurons extend through nerves to skeletal muscles. The cell bodies of **upper motor neurons** are in the motor cortex, cerebellum, and brainstem. Their axons, which compose the descending motor pathways, descend into the spinal cord or brainstem, where they synapse with lower motor neurons. Some of the descending pathways are involved in the direct, conscious control of skeletal muscles, whereas others are involved in more indirect, unconscious control. Near the inferior ends of the pyramids, most of the descending pathways involved in the conscious control of skeletal muscles cross to the opposite sides (see figure 8.29). As a result of this crossing over, the right side of the brain controls skeletal muscle on the left side of the body and vice versa.

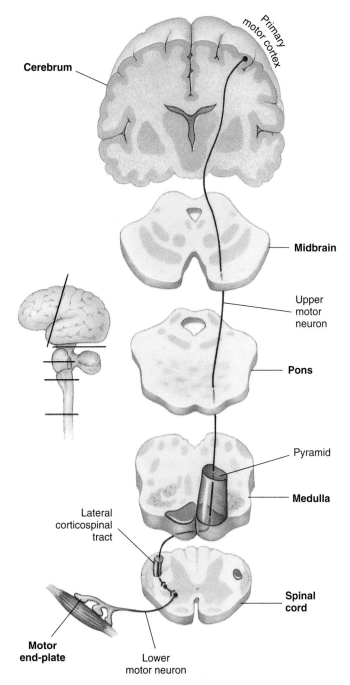

Figure 8.29 Example of a Descending Pathway: The Pyramidal System

Information controlling voluntary movement (such as turning a page) travels from the primary motor cortex to the medulla, where it crosses to the opposite side of the body before traveling in the lateral spinothalamic tract to lower motor neurons in the spinal cord.

Meninges

Three connective tissue membranes, the **meninges** (mĕ-nin′jēz) (figure 8.30), surround and protect the brain and spinal cord. The most superficial and thickest of the meninges is the **dura mater** (doo′ră mā′ter, tough mother). Folds of dura mater extend into the longitudinal fissure between the two cerebral hemispheres and between the cerebrum and cerebellum. Within these folds, the dura mater contains spaces

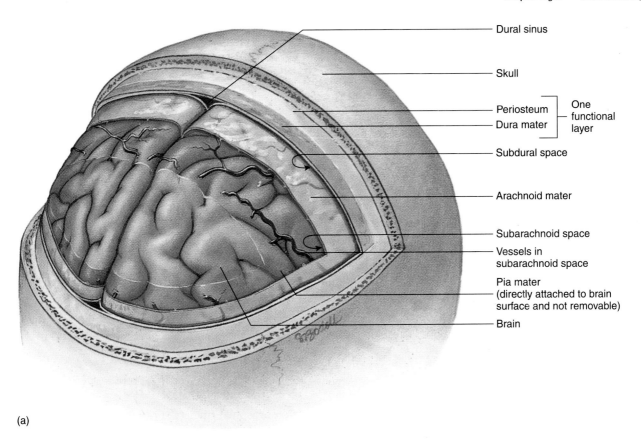

Dural sinus

Skull

Periosteum ⎤ One
          ⎥ functional
Dura mater ⎦ layer

Subdural space

Arachnoid mater

Subarachnoid space

Vessels in
subarachnoid space

Pia mater
(directly attached to brain
surface and not removable)

Brain

(a)

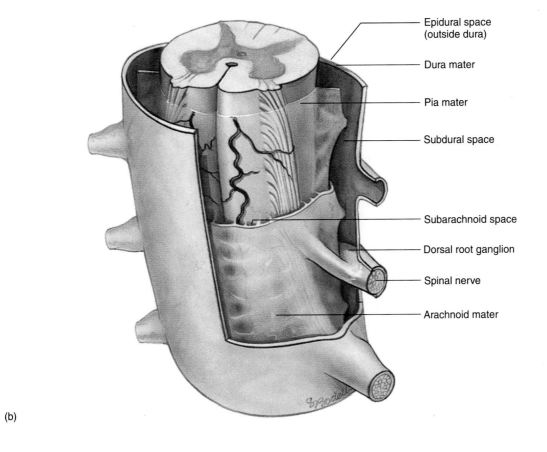

Epidural space
(outside dura)

Dura mater

Pia mater

Subdural space

Subarachnoid space

Dorsal root ganglion

Spinal nerve

Arachnoid mater

(b)

Figure 8.30   Meninges

(a) Meningeal coverings of the brain. (b) Meningeal coverings of the spinal cord.

called **dural sinuses**, which collect blood from the small veins of the brain. The dural sinuses empty into the internal jugular veins, which exit the skull.

The dura mater around the brain is tightly attached to the periosteum of the skull. The dura mater of the spinal cord is surrounded by an **epidural space** between the dura mater and the periosteum of the vertebrae (see figure 8.30*b*). Epidural anesthesia of the spinal nerves is induced by injecting anesthetics into the epidural space.

The second meningeal membrane is the very thin, wispy **arachnoid** (ă-rak′noyd; spiderlike, i.e.; cobwebs) **mater**. The third meningeal membrane, the **pia mater** (pī′ă, or pē′ă, affectionate mother), is very tightly bound to the surface of the brain and spinal cord. Between the arachnoid mater and the pia mater is the **subarachnoid space**, which is filled with cerebrospinal fluid and contains blood vessels.

Ventricles

The CNS contains fluid-filled cavities, called ventricles, that may be quite small in some areas and large in others (figure 8.31). Each cerebral hemisphere contains a relatively large cavity, called the **lateral ventricle**. The **third ventricle** is a smaller midline cavity located in the center of the diencephalon between the two halves of the thalamus and is connected by foramina (holes) to the lateral ventricles. The **fourth ventricle** is located at the base of the cerebellum and is connected to the

third ventricle by a narrow canal, called the **cerebral aqueduct**. The fourth ventricle is continuous with the **central canal** of the spinal cord. The fourth ventricle also opens into the subarachnoid space through foramina in its walls and roof.

Cerebrospinal Fluid

Cerebrospinal fluid (CSF) bathes the brain and spinal cord, providing a protective cushion around the CNS. It is produced by the **choroid** (kō′royd, lacy) **plexus**, a specialized structure made of ependymal cells, which is primarily located

Lateral ventricle: (anterior horn)

Third ventricle

Lateral ventricle: (inferior horn)

Lateral ventricle: (posterior horn)

Cerebral aqueduct

Fourth ventricle

Central canal: spinal cord

Figure 8.31 Ventricles of the Brain

Blockage of the openings in the fourth ventricle or of the cerebral aqueduct can result in accumulation of CSF in the ventricles, a condition known as **hydrocephalus.** The accumulation of fluid inside the brain ventricles causes increased pressure that dilates the ventricles and compresses the brain tissue. Compression of the nervous tissue usually results in irreversible brain damage. If the skull bones are not completely ossified when the hydrocephalus occurs, such as in a fetus or newborn, the pressure can also cause severe enlargement of the head. Hydrocephalus is treated by placing a drainage tube (shunt) from the ventricles to the abdominal cavity to eliminate the high internal pressures.

in the lateral and fourth ventricles (figure 8.32). CSF fills the brain ventricles, the central canal of the spinal cord, and the subarachnoid space. The CSF flows from the lateral ventricles into the third ventricle and then through the cerebral aqueduct into the fourth ventricle. A small amount of CSF enters the central canal of the spinal cord. The CSF exits from the fourth ventricle through small openings in its walls and roof and enters the subarachnoid space. Masses of arachnoid tissue, called **arachnoid granulations,** penetrate into the superior sagittal sinus, a dural sinus in the longitudinal fissure, and CSF passes from the subarachnoid space into the blood through these granulations.

1. Cerebrospinal fluid (CSF) is produced by the choroid plexuses of each ventricle (inset).

2. CSF from the lateral ventricles flows through foramina to the third ventricle.

3. CSF flows from the third ventricle through the cerebral aqueduct to the fourth ventricle.

4. CSF exits the fourth ventricle and enters the subarachnoid space. Some CSF enters the central canal of the spinal cord.

5. CSF flows through the subarachnoid space to the arachnoid granulations in the superior sagittal sinus where it enters the venous circulation (inset).

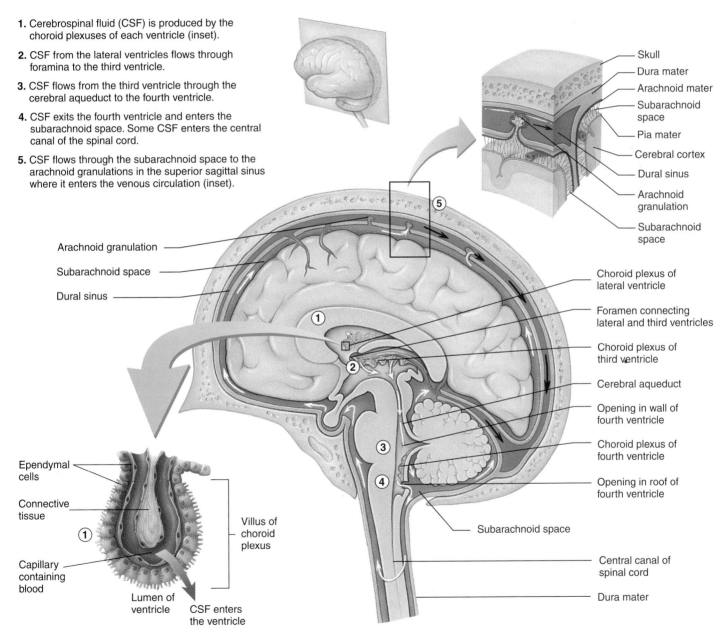

Figure 8.32   Flow of CSF

CSF flow through the ventricles and subarachnoid space is shown by white arrows. The white arrows going through the foramina in the wall and roof of the fourth ventricle depict the CSF entering the subarachnoid space. CSF passes back into the blood through the arachnoid granulations (white and black arrow), which penetrate the dural sinus. The black arrows show the direction of blood flow in the sinuses.

Clinical Focus   Central Nervous System Disorders

Infections

Encephalitis (en-sef-ă-lī′tis) is an inflammation of the brain, most often caused by a virus and less often by bacteria or other agents. A large variety of symptoms result, including fever, coma, and convulsions. Encephalitis can also result in death.

Meningitis (men-in-jī′tis) is an inflammation of the meninges. It can be caused by either a viral or a bacterial infection. Symptoms usually include stiffness in the neck, headache, and fever. In severe cases, meningitis can also cause paralysis, coma, or death.

Rabies (rā′bēz) is a viral disease transmitted by the bite of an infected animal such as a skunk, bat, or dog. The rabies virus infects the brain, salivary glands, muscles, and connective tissue. When the patient attempts to swallow, the effort can produce pharyngeal muscle spasms. Sometimes even the thought of swallowing water or the sight of water can induce the spasms. Thus the term "hydrophobia," which means the fear of water, is applied to the disease. The brain infection results in abnormal excitability, aggression, and, in the later stages, paralysis and death.

Tabes dorsalis (tā′bēz dōr-sā′lis) is a progressive disorder occurring as a result of a syphilis infection. It can occur many years after the initial infection. Tabes means a wasting away, and dorsalis refers to the dorsal roots and dorsal regions of the spinal cord. The symptoms are anesthesia and ataxia. Anesthesia is a loss of sensation resulting from damage of the dorsal roots, and ataxia is the inability to coordinate voluntary muscle activity such as walking. The inability to walk results from a loss of proprioceptive function, which is carried in the dorsal column of the cord. Eventually paralysis develops as the infection spreads.

Tetanus (tet′ă-nŭs) is a disease caused by bacteria (*Clostridium tetani*) found in soil contaminated with animal wastes. It is often introduced into the body through an open wound. The bacteria produce a potent neurotoxin that affects lower motor neurons in the spinal cord and brainstem, as well as inhibitory association neurons synapsing with those neurons. It binds to the lower motor neurons and causes them to initiate action potentials. It also blocks release of inhibitory neurotransmitters normally released from the inhibitory association neurons synapsing with the lower motor neurons. As a result, the toxin causes muscle contraction and prevents muscle relaxation, so that the body becomes rigid. The jaw muscles are affected early in the disease, locking the jaw in a closed position. For this reason, tetanus is sometimes referred to as "lockjaw." Death results from spasms in the diaphragm and other respiratory muscles.

Multiple sclerosis (sklĕ-rō′sis) (MS) is an autoimmune condition that may be initiated by a viral infection. The disease results in inflammation in areas of the brain and spinal cord. The inflammation, promoted by the immune response, results in localized brain lesions and demyelination of the brain and spinal cord. The myelin sheaths around axons become sclerotic, or hard, resulting in poor conduction of action potentials. Multiple sclerosis exhibits symptomatic periods that are separated by periods of apparent remission. With each recurrence of a symptomatic period, however, many neurons are permanently damaged. Progressive symptoms of the disease include exaggerated reflexes, tremor, nystagmus (tremorous movement of the eyes), and speech defects.

Movement Disorders

Movement disorders, or **dyskinesias** (dis-ki-nē′zē-ăz), are a group of disorders involving the basal nuclei that result in a resting tremor, as well as in brisk, jerky, purposeless movements, resembling fragments of voluntary movements. **Sydenham's chorea** (St. Vitus' dance) is a disease usually associated with a toxic or infectious disorder that apparently causes temporary dysfunction of the basal nuclei in children. **Huntington's chorea** (kōr-ē′ă) is a dominant hereditary disorder that begins in middle life and causes progressive degeneration of the basal nuclei in affected persons.

Cerebral palsy (pawl′zē) is a general term referring to defects in motor functions or coordination resulting from several types of brain damage, which may be caused by abnormal brain development or birth-related injury. Some symptoms of cerebral palsy are related to basal nuclei dysfunction, such as increased muscle tone and resting tremors. One of the features of cerebral palsy is the presence of slow, writhing, aimless movements. When the face, neck, and tongue muscles are involved, characteristics are grimacing, protrusion and writhing of the tongue, and difficulty in speaking and swallowing.

Parkinson's (par′kin-sonz) **disease**, characterized by muscular rigidity, resting tremor, a slow, shuffling gait, and general lack of movement, is caused by a lesion in another part of the basal nuclei. A resting tremor called "pill-rolling" is characteristic of Parkinson's disease and consists of circular movement of the opposed thumb and index finger tip. The increased muscular rigidity in Parkinson's disease results from defective inhibition of muscle tone by some of the basal nuclei. In this disease, dopamine, an inhibitory neurotransmitter substance, is deficient. Because dopamine cannot cross the barrier, Parkinson's disease is treated (to a limited extent) with L-dopa, a precursor to dopamine that crosses the blood–brain barrier from the capillaries of the brain into the brain tissue. However, there are long-term, negative side effects with L-dopa. As a result, other drugs, such as Ropinirole and Pramipexole, which have fewer side effects, are now being used to treat the symptoms. Parkinson's disease is also being treated by transplanting fetal cells capable of producing dopamine into the Parkinson patient. Removal of a portion of the corpus striatum, or implantation of an electrical pulse generator to stimulate specific basal nuclei, are now being used to effectively treat Parkinson's disease.

Cerebellar lesions (lĕ′zhŭnz) result in a spectrum of characteristic functional disorders that are essentially opposite of those seen in basilar nuclei dysfunctions. There is a decrease in muscle tone and a tendency to point past a mark that one tries to touch with the finger. A cerebellar tremor is an "intention tremor"; that is, the more carefully one tries to control a given movement, the greater the tremor becomes. For example, when a person with a cerebellar tremor tries to drink a glass of water, the closer the glass comes to the mouth, the shakier the movement becomes. This type of tremor is in direct contrast to basal nuclei tremors described previously, in which the resting tremor largely or completely disappears during purposeful movement.

Other Disorders

Nearly all brain **tumors** (too′mŏrz) develop from neuroglia and not from neurons. Symptoms vary widely, depending on the location of the tumor, but may include headaches, neuralgia (pain along the distribution of a peripheral nerve), paralysis, seizures, coma, and death.

Stroke is a term meaning a sudden blow, suggesting the speed with which this type of defect can occur. It is also referred to clinically as a **cerebrovascular** (ser′ĕ-brō-vas′kū-lăr or sĕ-rē′brō-vas′kū-lăr) **accident (CVA)**. A CVA may be caused by a **hemorrhage** (hem′ŏ-rij), bleeding into the tissue; by a clot, called a **thrombus** (throm′bŭs), in a blood vessel; by a piece of a clot, called an **embolism** (em′bō-lizm), that has broken loose and floats through the circulation until it reaches and blocks a small vessel; or by **vasospasm** (vā′sō-spazm), constricting the cerebral blood vessels. A hemorrhage, thrombus, embolism, or vasospasm can result in a local area of cell death, called an **infarct** (in′farkt), caused by a lack of blood supply, surrounded by an area of cells that are secondarily affected. Symptoms depend on the location of the stroke and the size of the infarct, but they may include anesthesia (a lack of feeling) or paralysis on the side of the body opposite the cerebral infarct.

Cyclin-dependent kinases (CDK) normally stimulate cell division, especially at sites of injury. In mature neurons, however, CDK causes cell death. Studies have shown that CDK is produced in the cells surrounding a cerebral infarct and that CDK inhibitors can prevent the death of these secondarily effected cells. Aspirin or warfarin treatment can help prevent strokes.

Alzheimer's (ālz′hī-merz) **disease** is a severe type of mental deterioration, or dementia, usually affecting older people, but occasionally affecting people younger than 60. It accounts for half of all dementias; the other half result from drug and alcohol abuse, infections, or strokes. Alzheimer's disease is estimated to affect 10% of all people older than 65 and nearly half of those older than 85.

Alzheimer's disease involves a general decrease in brain size that results from loss of neurons in the cerebral cortex. The gyri become more narrow, and the sulci widen. The frontal lobes and specific regions of the temporal lobes are affected most severely. Symptoms include general intellectual deficiency, memory loss, short attention span, moodiness, disorientation, and irritability.

Localized axonal enlargements, called **amyliod** (am′i-loyd) **plaques**, containing large amounts of β(beta)-amyloid protein, form in the cortex of patients with Alzheimer's disease. There is some evidence that Alzheimer's disease may have characteristics of a chronic inflammatory disease, and antiinflammatory drugs have some effect in treating the disease. Estrogen, which affects some brain functions such as emotion, memory, and cognition may be involved in the disease.

The gene for β-amyloid protein has been mapped to chromosome 21 (see chapter 20), but this gene accounts for only a small portion of the cases. It is noteworthy that people with Down syndrome, which results from having three copies of chromosome 21 (trisomy 21), exhibit the cortical and other changes associated with Alzheimer's disease.

The more common, late-onset form of the disease maps to chromosome 19. A protein, **apolipoprotein E** (ap′ō-lip-ō-prō′tēn; **apo E**), which binds β-amyloid protein has also been associated with Alzheimer's disease. This protein maps to the same part of chromosome 19 as the late-onset form of Alzheimer's. Apo E may also be involved in the regulation of yet another protein, called τ (tau), which is involved in microtubule formation inside neurons. If τ does not function properly, microtubules do not form normally, and the τ proteins become tangled within the neurons, decreasing their function. Nitric oxide production, which stimulates cerebral blood flow and memory in the brain, may help protect cerebral blood vessels and brain tissue from the toxic effects of β-amyloid protein.

Tay-Sachs (tā saks) **disease** is a hereditary lipid-storage disorder of infants that primarily affects neurons of the CNS and results in severe brain dysfunction. Symptoms include paralysis, blindness, and death, usually before age 5.

Epilepsy (ep′i-lep′sē) is actually a group of brain disorders that have seizure episodes in common. The seizure, a sudden massive neuronal discharge, can be either partial or complete, depending on the amount of brain involved and whether or not consciousness is impaired. The neuronal discharges may stimulate muscles innervated by the nerves involved, resulting in involuntary muscle contractions (i.e., convulsions).

Headaches have a variety of causes that can be grouped into two basic classes: extracranial and intracranial. Extracranial headaches can be caused by inflammation of the paranasal sinuses, dental irritations, eye disorders, or tension in the muscles moving the head and neck. Intracranial headaches may result from inflammation of the brain or meninges, ventricular enlargement, vascular changes, mechanical damage, or tumors.

Peripheral Nervous System

The **peripheral nervous system** (PNS) consists of all the neuron cell bodies and processes located outside the brain and spinal cord. The PNS collects information from numerous sources both inside and on the surface of the individual and relays it by way of afferent fibers to the CNS, where the information is evaluated. Efferent fibers in the PNS relay information from the CNS to muscles and glands in various parts of the body, regulating activity in those structures. The PNS can be classified into two parts: 12 pairs of cranial nerves and 31 pairs of spinal nerves.

Cranial Nerves

The 12 **cranial nerves** (figure 8.33) are listed in table 8.3. They are designated by Roman numerals from I to XII. There are two general categories of cranial nerve function: afferent (sensory) and efferent (motor). The motor functions of the cranial nerves are further subdivided into somatic motor and parasympathetic autonomic. Sensory functions can be divided into the special senses such as vision and the more general senses such as touch and pain in the face. Somatic motor cranial nerves innervate skeletal muscles in the head and neck. Parasympathetic cranial nerves innervate glands, smooth muscle, and cardiac muscle. Some cranial nerves are only sensory, and some are only somatic motor, whereas other cranial nerves have more than one function. Cranial nerves with both afferent and efferent functions are called mixed nerves.

Three cranial nerves—the olfactory(I), optic(II), and vestibulocochlear (VIII) nerves—are sensory only. Four other cranial nerves—the trochlear (IV), abducens (VI), spinal accessory (XI), and hypoglossal (XII) nerves—are somatic motor only.

The trigeminal nerve (V) has sensory and motor functions. It has the greatest general sensory distribution of all the cranial nerves and is the only cranial nerve supplying sensory

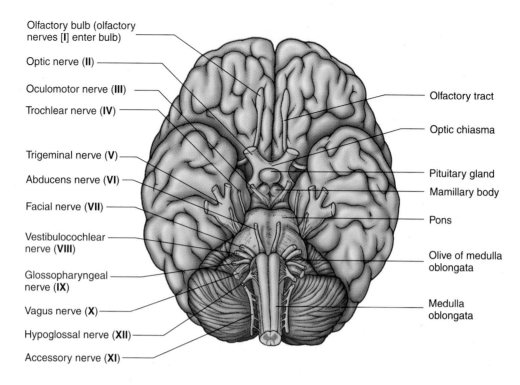

Olfactory bulb (olfactory nerves [I] enter bulb)

Optic nerve (II)

Oculomotor nerve (III)

Trochlear nerve (IV)

Trigeminal nerve (V)

Abducens nerve (VI)

Facial nerve (VII)

Vestibulocochlear nerve (VIII)

Glossopharyngeal nerve (IX)

Vagus nerve (X)

Hypoglossal nerve (XII)

Accessory nerve (XI)

Olfactory tract

Optic chiasma

Pituitary gland

Mamillary body

Pons

Olive of medulla oblongata

Medulla oblongata

Figure 8.33 Cranial Nerves
Inferior surface of the brain showing the origins of the cranial nerves.

Table 8.3	Cranial Nerves and Their Functions (see figure 8.33)			
Number	Name	General Function*	Specific Function
I	Olfactory	S	Smell
II	Optic	S	Vision
III	Oculomotor	M, P	Motor to four of six eye muscles and upper eyelid; parasympathetic: constricts pupil; thickens lens
IV	Trochlear	M	Motor to one eye muscle
V	Trigeminal	S, M	Sensory to face and teeth; motor to muscles of mastication (chewing)
VI	Abducens	M	Motor to one eye muscle
VII	Facial	S, M, P	Sensory: taste; motor to muscles of facial expression; parasympathetic to salivary and tear glands
VIII	Vestibulocochlear	S	Hearing and balance
IX	Glossopharyngeal	S, M, P	Sensory: taste and touch to back of tongue; motor to pharyngeal muscles; parasympathetic to salivary glands
X	Vagus	S, M, P	Sensory to pharynx, larynx, and viscera; motor to palate, pharynx, and larynx; parasympathetic to viscera of thorax and abdomen
XI	Accessory	M	Motor to two neck and upper back muscles
XII	Hypoglossal	M	Motor to tongue muscles

*S, sensory; M, motor; P. parasympathetic.

4   P R E D I C T

The phrenic nerve may be damaged where it descends along the neck or during open thorax or open heart surgery. Explain how damage to the right phrenic nerve affects the diaphragm. Describe the effect on the diaphragm of completely severing the spinal cord in the thoracic region (below the exit point of the phrenic nerve) versus in the upper cervical region (above the exit point of the phrenic nerve).

✔ *Answer on page 235*

Brachial Plexus

The **brachial plexus** originates from spinal nerves C5 to T1. Five major nerves emerge from the brachial plexus to supply the upper limb and shoulder. The **axillary nerve** innervates two shoulder muscles and the skin over part of the shoulder. The **radial nerve** innervates all the muscles located in the posterior arm and forearm. It innervates the skin over the posterior surface of the arm, forearm, and hand. The **musculocutaneous** (mŭs′kū-lō-kū-tā′nē-ŭs) **nerve** innervates the anterior muscles of the arm and the skin over part of the forearm. The **ulnar nerve** innervates two anterior forearm muscles and most of the intrinsic hand muscles. It also innervates the skin over the ulnar side of the hand. The ulnar nerve can be easily damaged where it passes posterior to the medial side of the elbow. The ulnar nerve at this location is called the "funny bone." The **median nerve** innervates most of the anterior forearm muscles and some of the intrinsic hand muscles. It also innervates the skin over the radial side of the hand.

Did You Know?

The radial nerve lies very close to the medial side of the humerus in the proximal part of the arm and is susceptible to damage in that area. If a person uses crutches improperly, so that the weight of the body is carried in the axilla and upper arm rather than by the hands, the top of the crutch can compress the radial nerve against the humerus. This compression can cause dysfunction of the radial nerve, resulting in paralysis of the posterior arm and forearm muscles and loss of sensation over the back of the forearm and hand. This condition is called "crutch paralysis" or "wrist drop paralysis," which describes the position of the hand with the posterior forearm muscles paralyzed. The condition is usually temporary as long as the patient begins to use the crutches correctly. The radial nerve can be permanently damaged by a fracture of the humerus in the proximal part of the arm. A sharp edge of the broken bone may cut the nerve, resulting in permanent paralysis unless the nerve is surgically repaired. Because of potential damage to the radial nerve, a broken humerus should be treated very carefully.

Lumbosacral Plexus

The **lumbosacral** (lŭm′bō-sā′krăl) **plexus** originates from spinal nerves L1 to S4. Four major nerves exit the plexus to supply the lower limb. The **obturator** (ob′tū-rā-tŏr) **nerve** innervates the muscles of the medial thigh and the skin over the same region. The **femoral nerve** innervates the anterior thigh muscles and the skin over the anterior thigh and medial side of the leg. The **tibial nerve** innervates the posterior thigh muscles, the anterior and posterior leg muscles, and most of the intrinsic foot muscles. It also innervates the skin over the sole of the foot. The **common fibular** (fib′ū-lăr) **nerve** innervates the muscles of the lateral thigh and leg and some intrinsic foot muscles. It innervates the skin over the anterior and lateral leg and the dorsal surface of the foot. The tibial and common peroneal nerves are bound together within a connective tissue sheath and together are called the **ischiadic** (is-kē-ad′ik) **nerve**. The ischiadic nerve was formerly called the **sciatic** (sī-at′ik) **nerve**, which was a degeneration of the term ischiadic.

Autonomic Nervous System

Somatic motor neuron cell bodies are located in the CNS, and their axons extend from there to skeletal muscles. Axons from autonomic motor neurons, on the other hand, do not extend all the way from the CNS to target tissues. Instead, two neurons in series extend from the CNS to the target organs. The first is called the **preganglionic neuron**, and the second is called the **postganglionic neuron**. The neurons are so named because preganglionic neurons synapse with postganglionic neurons in **autonomic ganglia** outside the CNS. Autonomic motor neurons innervate smooth muscle, cardiac muscle, and glands. Autonomic functions are controlled unconsciously.

The autonomic nervous system is composed of sympathetic and parasympathetic divisions (figure 8.36 and table 8.5). Increased activity in sympathetic neurons generally prepares the individual for physical activity, whereas parasympathetic stimulation generally activates "vegetative" functions, such as digestion, normally associated with the body at rest.

Most organs that receive autonomic motor neurons are innervated by both the parasympathetic and sympathetic divisions. Sweat glands and blood vessels, however, are innervated by sympathetic neurons almost exclusively, whereas the smooth muscles associated with the lens of the eye are innervated primarily by parasympathetic neurons. In most cases, the influence of the two autonomic divisions is opposite on structures that receive dual innervation. For example, sympathetic stimulation of the heart causes an increase in heart rate, whereas parasympathetic stimulation causes a decrease in heart rate.

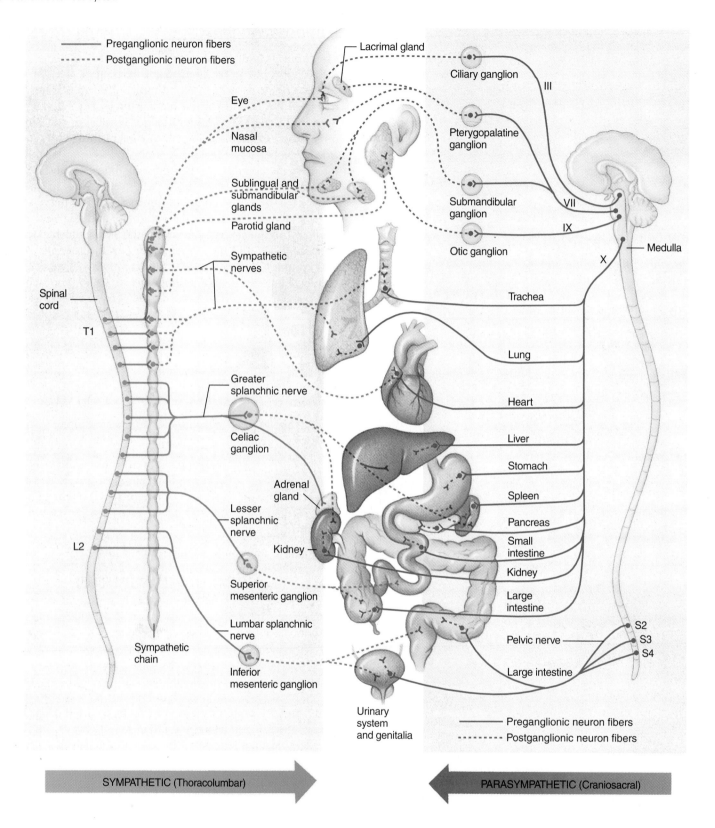

Preganglionic neuron fibers
Postganglionic neuron fibers

Lacrimal gland
Ciliary ganglion
III
Eye
Nasal mucosa
Pterygopalatine ganglion
Sublingual and submandibular glands
Parotid gland
Submandibular ganglion
VII
IX
Otic ganglion
X
Medulla
Sympathetic nerves
Spinal cord
Trachea
T1
Lung
Heart
Liver
Greater splanchnic nerve
Stomach
Celiac ganglion
Spleen
Adrenal gland
Pancreas
Lesser splanchnic nerve
Small intestine
Kidney
L2
Kidney
Large intestine
Superior mesenteric ganglion
Lumbar splanchnic nerve
S2
S3
S4
Pelvic nerve
Sympathetic chain
Large intestine
Inferior mesenteric ganglion
Urinary system and genitalia
Preganglionic neuron fibers
Postganglionic neuron fibers

SYMPATHETIC (Thoracolumbar)   PARASYMPATHETIC (Craniosacral)

Figure 8.36 Innervation of the Major Target Organs by the Autonomic Nervous System

Preganglionic fibers are indicated by solid lines, and postganglionic fibers are indicated by broken lines. The parasympathetic fibers are red, and the sympathetic fibers are blue.

Table 8.5	Autonomic Nervous System (see figure 8.36)		
Division	Location of Preganglionic Cell Body	Location of Postganglionic Cell Body	Function
Sympathetic	T1–L2	Sympathetic chain ganglia or collateral ganglia	"Fight-or-flight"; prepares the body for physical activity
Parasympathetic	Cranial nerves III, VII, IX, X; S2–S4 spinal nerves	Terminal ganglia near or embedded in the walls of target organs	Stimulates vegetative activities; slows heart and respiration rates; constricts pupil; thickens lens

Sympathetic Division

The **sympathetic division** of the autonomic nervous system prepares a person for physical activity by increasing heart rate and blood pressure, by dilating respiratory passageways, and by stimulating perspiration. The sympathetic division also stimulates the release of glucose from the liver for energy. At the same time, it inhibits digestive activities. The sympathetic division is sometimes referred to as the "fight-or-flight" system because, as it prepares the body for physical activity, it prepares the person to either stand and face a threat or leave as quickly as possible.

Cell bodies of sympathetic preganglionic neurons are in the lateral horn of the spinal cord gray matter (see figure 8.27) between the first thoracic (T1) and the second lumbar (L2) segments. The axons of the preganglionic neurons exit through ventral roots and project to either sympathetic chain ganglia or collateral ganglia. The **sympathetic chain ganglia** are connected to one another and form a chain along both sides of the spinal cord. **Collateral ganglia** are located nearer target organs and consist of the celiac, superior mesenteric, and inferior mesenteric ganglia (shown in figure 8.36). Some preganglionic neurons synapse in the sympathetic chain ganglia, but others pass through these ganglia and synapse in the collateral ganglia. Postganglionic neurons arise in the sympathetic chain ganglia or in the collateral ganglia and project to target tissues.

Parasympathetic Division

The **parasympathetic division** of the autonomic nervous system stimulates vegetative activities, such as digestion, defecation, and urination. At the same time, it slows the heart rate and respiration. It also causes the pupil of the eye to constrict and the lens to thicken.

5   P R E D I C T

List some of the responses stimulated by the autonomic nervous system in (a) a person who is extremely angry and (b) a person who has just finished eating and is now relaxing.

✔ *Answer on page 235*

Preganglionic cell bodies of the parasympathetic division are located either within brainstem nuclei of the oculomotor nerve (III), facial nerve (VII), glossopharyngeal nerve (IX), or vagus nerve (X), or within the lateral part of the central gray matter of the spinal cord in the regions giving rise to spinal nerves S2 through S4.

Axons of the preganglionic neurons extend through spinal nerves or cranial nerves to **terminal ganglia** located either near target organs in the head (see figure 8.36) or embedded in the walls of target organs in the thorax, abdomen, and pelvis. The axons of the postganglionic neurons extend a relatively short distance from the terminal ganglia to the target organ.

Autonomic Neurotransmitter Substances

All preganglionic neurons of both the sympathetic and parasympathetic divisions and all postganglionic neurons of the parasympathetic division secrete acetylcholine as a neurotransmitter. Most postganglionic neurons of the sympathetic division secrete norepinephrine, but some secrete acetylcholine. Many body functions can be stimulated or inhibited by drugs that either mimic these neurotransmitters or prevent the neurotransmitters from activating their target tissues.

Clinical Focus Peripheral Nervous System Disorders

Anesthesia, Neuritis, and Neuralgias

Anesthesia (an′es-thē′zē-ă) is the loss of sensation. It may be a pathological condition, or it may be induced temporarily to facilitate surgery or some other medical action. **Neuritis** (noo-rī′tis) is an inflammation of a nerve resulting from any one of a number of causes, including injury or infection. In motor nerves, neuritis can result in the loss of motor function. In sensory nerves, neuritis can result in anesthesia or neuralgia. **Neuralgia** is a general term meaning nerve pain. It involves severe spasms of throbbing or stabbing pain along the pathway of a nerve. Neuralgia can result from inflammation or nerve damage, or it may be of unknown cause. **Trigeminal neuralgia** involves the trigeminal nerve and consists of sharp bursts of pain in the face. **Facial palsy** involves the facial nerve and results in unilateral paralysis of the facial muscles. The affected side of the face droops because of the absence of muscle tone. **Ischiadica** (is-kē′ad-ik-ă, sciatica) is a neuralgia of the ischiadic nerve, with pain radiating down the back of the thigh and leg. The most common cause of ischiadica is a herniated lumbar disk putting pressure on the spinal nerves forming the lumbosacral plexus.

Infections

Botulism (bot′ū-lizm) is a disease caused by the toxin of the anaerobic bacterium *Clostridium botulinum*, which grows in environments such as improperly processed cans of food. The toxin blocks the release of acetylcholine in synapses. As a result, muscles cannot contract, and the person may die from respiratory or cardiac failure.

Leprosy (lep′rō-sē), or Hansen's disease, is a bacterial disease that kills the skin and other tissues, such as cells of the peripheral nervous system. Disfiguring nodules form on the body, and tissue necrosis occurs. Even though the disease can be treated with sulfone drugs, millions of people in Asia and Africa are still affected by it. Leprosy is not highly contagious and is usually transmitted from lesions or clothing of an infected person through cuts or abrasions on the skin of another. The time from infection to the appearance of symptoms may be several years. Leprosy itself is usually not fatal, but patients may die from complications.

Herpes (her′pēz) is a family of viral diseases characterized by skin lesions. The viruses apparently reside in the ganglia of sensory nerves and cause lesions along the course of the nerves. Herpes simplex I causes lesions in the area of the lips and nose. The lesions are prone to occur during times of decreased resistance, such as during a cold. For this reason they are called cold sores or fever blisters. Herpes simplex II (genital herpes) is responsible for a sexually transmitted disease causing lesions on the external genitalia. Another herpes-type virus causes chickenpox in children and shingles, also called herpes zoster, in older adults.

Poliomyelitis (pō′lē-ō-mī′ ĕlī′tis, polio) is a viral infection of the CNS, but it damages the somatic motor neurons, which extend into the PNS. Many somatic motor neurons degenerate, leaving muscles without innervation. Without stimulation from the CNS, the muscles are paralyzed, and they atrophy, or waste away.

Other Disorders

Myotonic dystrophy (mī-ō-tō′nik dis′trō-fē) is a dominant hereditary disease characterized by muscle weakness, dysfunction, and atrophy and by visual impairment as a result of nerve degeneration.

Neurofibromatosis (noor′ō-fī-brō-mă-tō′ sis) is also a genetic disorder, in which neurofibromas (benign tumors along peripheral nerve tracts) occur in early childhood and result in large skin growths, which can result in substantial disfigurement. The most famous victim of this disorder may have been the so-called "Elephant Man."

Myasthenia gravis (mī-as-thē′nē-ă gra′vis) is an autoimmune disorder in which the immune system attacks neuromuscular junctions. The receptors for acetylcholine are destroyed, which makes the neuromuscular junction less functional, resulting in muscle weakness and increased fatigability. Myasthenia gravis can eventually lead to complete muscle paralysis.

Did You Know?

Raynaud's (rā-nōz′) **disease** involves the spasmodic contraction of blood vessels in the periphery, especially in the digits, and results in pale, cold hands that are prone to ulcerations and gangrene as a result of poor circulation. This condition may be caused by exaggerated sensitivity of the blood vessels to sympathetic stimulation. Cutting the preganglionic neurons is occasionally performed to alleviate the condition. **Dysautonomia** (dis′aw-tō-nō′mē-ă) is an inherited condition involving reduced tear secretion, poor vasomotor control, dry mouth and throat, and other symptoms. It is the result of poorly controlled autonomic reflexes.

Clinical Focus Biofeedback and Meditation

Biofeedback takes advantage of electronic instruments or other techniques to monitor subconscious activities, many of which are regulated by the autonomic nervous system. Skin temperature, heart rate, and brain waves are monitored electronically. By watching the monitor and using biofeedback techniques, a person can learn to consciously reduce his heart rate and blood pressure or reduce the severity of migraine headaches.

Some people use biofeedback methods to relax by learning to reduce the heart rate or change the pattern of brain waves. The severity of peptic (stomach) ulcers, high blood pressure, anxiety, or depression can be reduced by using biofeedback techniques.

Meditation is another technique that influences autonomic functions. It is also claimed that meditation can improve one's spiritual well-being, consciousness, and holistic view of the universe. Some people find meditation techniques to be useful in reducing heart rate, blood pressure, the severity of ulcers, and other symptoms that are frequently associated with stress.

Systems Pathology
stroke

STROKE

Mr. S is approaching middle age, is somewhat overweight, and has high blood pressure. He was seated on the edge of his couch watching TV, at least most of the time, when he was not jumping to his feet and shouting at the referees for an obviously bad call. He was surrounded by empty pizza boxes, bowls of chips and salsa, empty beer cans, and full ash trays (figure A). As he cheered on his favorite team in a hotly contested big game, which they would be winning easily if it weren't for the lousy officiating, he noticed that he felt drowsy and that the television screen seemed blurry. He began to feel dizzy. As he tried to stand up, he suddenly vomited and collapsed to the floor, unconscious.

Mr. S was rushed to the local hospital where the following signs and symptoms were observed. He exhibited weakness in his limbs, especially on the right side, and ataxia, the inability to walk. He had loss of pain and temperature sensation in his right lower limb and the left side of his face. The dizziness persisted, and he appeared disoriented and lacked attentiveness. He also exhibited hoarseness and dysphagia, the inability to swallow. He had nystagmus, which is a rhythmic oscillation of the eyes. His pupils were slightly dilated, his respiration was short and shallow, and his pulse rate and blood pressure were elevated.

Background Information

Mr. S suffered a "stroke," also referred to as a **cerebrovascular accident (CVA)**. The term **stroke** describes a heterogeneous group of conditions involving death of brain tissue resulting from disruption of its vascular supply. There are two types of stroke: **hemorrhagic stroke**, results from bleeding of arteries supplying brain tissue, and **ischemic** (is-kē′mik) **stroke**, results from blockage of arteries supplying brain tissue. The blockage in ischemic stroke can result from a thrombus, which is a clot that develops in place within an artery, or an embolism, which is a plug, composed of a detached thrombus or other foreign body, such as a fat globule or gas bubble, which becomes lodged in an artery, blocking it. Mr. S was at high risk for developing a stroke. He was approaching middle age, was overweight, did not exercise enough, smoked, was under stress, and had a poor diet.

The combination of motor loss, which was seen as weakness in his limbs, and sensory loss, seen as loss of pain and temperature sensation in his left lower limb and loss of all sensation in the right side of his face, along with the ataxia,

Figure A   Sitting for a Stroke

dizziness, nystagmus, and hoarseness suggest that the stroke affected the brainstem and cerebellum. Blockage of the vertebral artery, a major artery supplying the brain, or its branches can result in what is called a lateral medullary infarction (an area of dead tissue resulting from a loss of blood supply to an area). Damage to the descending motor pathways in that area, above the medullary crossover point, results in muscle weakness. Damage to ascending pathways can result in loss of pain and temperature sensation, or other sensory modalities depending on the affected tract. Damage to cranial nerve nuclei results in the loss of pain and temperature sensation in the face, dizziness, blurred vision, nystagmus, vomiting, and hoarseness. These signs and symptoms are not observed unless the lesion is in the brainstem, where these nuclei are located. Some damage to the cerebellum, also supplied by branches of the vertebral artery, can account for the ataxia.

Drowsiness, disorientation, inattentiveness, loss of consciousness, and even seizures are generalized responses to neurological damage. Depression from neurological damage or from discouragement is also common. Slight dilation of the pupils; short, shallow respiration; and increased pulse rate and blood pressure are all signs of Mr. S's anxiety, not about the outcome of the game, but about his current condition and his immediate future. With a loss of consciousness, Mr. S would not remember the last few minutes of what he saw in the game he was watching. People in these circumstances are often worried about how they are going to deal with work tomorrow. They often have no idea that they may be permanently debilitated because the motor and sensory losses may be permanent, or that they will have a long stretch of therapy and rehabilitation ahead.

6   **P R E D I C T**

Given that Mr. S exhibited weakness in his right limbs and the loss of pain and the temperature sensation in his right lower limb and the left side of his face, state which side of the brainstem was most severely affected by the stroke. Explain your answer.

✔ *Answer on page 235*

System Interactions

System	Interactions
Integumentary	Decubitus (dē-kū′bi-tŭs) ulcers (bed sores) result from immobility because of the loss of motor function. Immobility causes compression of blood vessels in areas of the skin, which leads to death of the skin in areas supplied by those vessels.
Skeletal	Loss of bone mass, if muscles are dysfunctional for a prolonged time; in the absence of muscular activity, the bones to which those muscles are attached begin to be resorbed by osteoclasts.
Muscular	Absence of innervation because of damaged pathways or neurons leads to decreased motor function and may result in muscle atrophy.
Endocrine	Strokes in other parts of the brain could involve the hypothalamus, pineal body, or pituitary gland functions.
Cardiovascular	Risks: Phlebothrombosis (fleb′ō-throm-bō′sis, blood clot in a vein) can occur from inactivity. Edema around the brain can increase the pressure inside the skull. This increased pressure activates reflexes that increases the blood pressure. If the cardioregulatory center in the brain is damaged, death may occur rapidly because of a dramatically decreased blood pressure. Bleeding may result from the use of anticoagulants, and hypotension may result from use of antihypertensives.
Respiratory	Pneumonia may result from aspiration (fluid from the digestive tract entering the lungs when the patient vomits). Breathing may slow or stop completely if the respiratory center is damaged.
Digestive	Vomiting or dysphagia (dis-fā′jē-ă, difficulty swallowing) may occur if the brain centers controlling these functions are damaged. Hypovolemia (decreased blood volume) results from decreased fluid intake because of dysphagia; there may be a loss of bowel control.
Urinary	Motor innervation of the bladder is often affected. Urinary tract infection may result from catheter implantation or from urinary bladder distention.
Reproductive	Loss of libido (sex drive); innervation of the reproductive organs is often affected.

Summary

Functions of the Nervous System

- The functions of the nervous system are the accomplishment of mental activity, the control of homeostasis, the regulation of other systems, and the control of skeletal muscles.

Divisions of the Nervous System

- The central nervous system (CNS) consists of the brain and spinal cord, whereas the peripheral nervous system (PNS) consists of nerves and ganglia.
- The afferent division of the PNS transmits action potentials to the CNS; the efferent division carries action potentials away from the CNS.
- The somatic motor nervous system innervates skeletal muscle and is mostly under voluntary control. The autonomic nervous system innervates cardiac muscle, smooth muscle, and glands, and it is mostly under involuntary control.

- The autonomic nervous system has sympathetic and parasympathetic divisions.

Cells of the Nervous System

Neurons

- Neurons receive stimuli and transmit action potentials. Neurons consist of a cell body, dendrites, and an axon.
- Neurons are multipolar, bipolar, or unipolar.

Neuroglia

- Neuroglia are the support cells of the nervous system. They include astrocytes, microglia, ependymal cells, oligodendrocytes, and Schwann cells.

Myelin Sheaths

- Axons are either unmyelinated or myelinated.

Organization of Nervous Tissue

- Nervous tissue consists of white matter and gray matter. White matter forms nerve tracts in the CNS and nerves in the PNS. Gray matter forms the cortex and nuclei in the brain and ganglia in the PNS.

Propagation of Action Potentials

Membrane Potentials and Action Potentials

- A resting membrane potential results from the charge difference that exists across the membrane of cells.
- An action potential occurs when the charge across the cell membrane is briefly reversed.

The Synapse

- The synapse is the point of contact between two neurons or between a neuron and some other cell, such as a muscle or gland cell. An action potential arriving at the synapse causes the release of a neurotransmitter from the presynaptic terminal, which diffuses across the synaptic cleft and binds to the receptors of the postsynaptic membrane.

Reflexes

- Reflexes are the functional units of the nervous system.
- A reflex arc consists of a sensory receptor, an afferent neuron, association neurons, an efferent neuron, and an effector organ.
- The knee-jerk reflex occurs when the quadriceps femoris muscle is stretched.
- The withdrawal reflex removes a body part from a painful stimulus.

Neuronal Circuits

- Neuronal circuits are either diverging or converging.

Central Nervous System

- The CNS consists of the brain and spinal cord. The brain consists of the brainstem, diencephalon, cerebrum, and cerebellum.

Brainstem

- The brainstem contains several nuclei, as well as ascending and descending tracts.
- The medulla oblongata contains nuclei that control such activities as heart rate, breathing, swallowing, and balance.
- The pons contains relay nuclei between the cerebrum and cerebellum.
- The midbrain is involved in hearing and in visual reflexes.
- The reticular formation is scattered throughout the brainstem and is involved in maintaining consciousness and in the sleep–wake cycle.

Diencephalon

- The diencephalon consists of the thalamus (main sensory relay center), epithalamus (the pineal body may play a role in sexual maturation), and hypothalamus (important in maintaining homeostasis).

Cerebrum

- The cerebrum has two hemispheres divided into lobes. The lobes are the frontal, parietal, occipital, and temporal.
- Many CNS functions can be localized to specific areas of the cortex. Association areas are involved in the recognition of information.
- Speech involves the sensory speech area, the motor speech area, and the interactions between them and other cortical areas.
- An EEG monitors brain waves, which are a summation of the electrical activity of the brain.
- Memory consists of sensory (less than 1 s), short-term (lasting a few minutes), and long-term (permanent) memory.
- Each hemisphere controls the opposite half of the body. Commissures connect the two hemispheres. The left hemisphere is thought to be the dominant analytical hemisphere, and the right hemisphere is thought to be dominant for spatial perception and musical ability.
- The basal nuclei inhibit extraneous muscular activity.
- The limbic system is located deep within the cerebrum and is involved with the emotional and visceral response to smell, as well as other visceral functions.

Cerebellum

- The cerebellum is involved in balance and muscle coordination. Its main function is as a comparator, comparing the intended action with what is occurring and modifying the action of lower motor neurons to eliminate differences.

Spinal Cord

- The spinal cord has a central gray part organized into horns and a peripheral white part forming nerve tracts.
- Roots of spinal nerves extend out of the cord.

Pathways

- Pathways are usually given composite names that indicate their origin and termination. Almost all ascending pathways terminate in the thalamus before projecting to the cerebrum.
- The somatic motor system consists of lower and upper motor neurons.

Meninges

- Three connective tissue meninges cover the CNS: the dura mater, arachnoid mater, and pia mater.

Ventricles

- The brain and spinal cord contain fluid-filled cavities: the lateral ventricles in the cerebral hemispheres, a third ventricle in the diencephalon, a cerebral aqueduct in the midbrain, a fourth ventricle at the base of the cerebellum, and a central canal in the spinal cord.
- The fourth ventricle has openings into the subarachnoid space.

Cerebrospinal Fluid

- Cerebrospinal fluid is formed in the choroid plexuses in the ventricles, it exits through the fourth ventricle, and it reenters the blood through arachnoid granulations in the superior sagittal sinus.

Peripheral Nervous System

- The PNS consists of afferent and efferent fibers contained in spinal and cranial nerves.

Cranial Nerves

- There are 12 cranial nerves: 3 with only sensory function (S), 4 with only somatic motor function (M), 1 with motor and sensory function, 1 with somatic motor and parasympathetic (P) function, and 3 with all three functions. Four of the cranial nerves have parasympathetic function.
- The cranial nerves are: olfactory (I; S), optic (II; S), oculomotor (III; M, P), trochlear (IV; M), trigeminal (V; S, M), abducens (VI; M), facial (VII; S, M, P), vestibulocochlear (VIII; S), glossopharyngeal (IX; S, M, P), vagus (X; S, M, P), accessory (XI; M), and hypoglossal (XII; M).

Spinal Nerves

- The spinal nerves exit from the cervical, thoracic, lumbar, and sacral regions.
- The nerves are grouped into plexuses.
- The phrenic nerve, which supplies the diaphragm, is the most important branch of the cervical plexus.
- The brachial plexus supplies nerves to the upper limb.
- The lumbosacral plexus supplies nerves to the lower limb.

Autonomic Nervous System

- The autonomic nervous system contains preganglionic and postganglionic neurons.

- The autonomic nervous system has sympathetic and parasympathetic divisions.

Sympathetic Division

- The sympathetic division is involved in preparing the person for action by increasing heart rate, blood pressure, and respiration rate.
- Preganglionic cell bodies of the sympathetic division lie in the thoracic and upper lumbar regions of the spinal cord.
- Postganglionic cell bodies are located in the sympathetic chain ganglia or in collateral ganglia.

Parasympathetic Division

- The parasympathetic division is involved in vegetative activities, such as the digestion of food, defecation, and urination.
- Preganglionic cell bodies of the parasympathetic division are associated with some of the cranial and sacral nerves.
- Postganglionic cell bodies are located in terminal ganglia, located either near or within target organs.

Autonomic Neurotransmitter Substances

- All autonomic preganglionic and parasympathetic postganglionic neurons secrete acetylcholine.
- Most sympathetic postganglionic neurons secrete norepinephrine.

Content Review

1. Describe the CNS and PNS.
2. Define the afferent and efferent divisions of the PNS, and the somatic motor and autonomic nervous systems.
3. What are the functions of neurons? Name the three parts of a neuron.
4. List the three types of neurons based on their shapes.
5. Define neuroglia. Name and describe the functions of the different neuroglia.
6. What are the differences between unmyelinated and myelinated axons? Which propagates action potentials more rapidly? Why?
7. For nerve tracts, nerves, nuclei, and ganglia, name the cells or parts of cells found in each, state if they are white or gray matter, and name the part (CNS or PNS) of the nervous system in which they are found.
8. Explain the resting membrane potential and how an action potential is generated.
9. Describe the operation of the synapse, starting with an action potential in the presynaptic neuron and ending with the generation of an action potential in the postsynaptic neuron.
10. Define a reflex, and name the five components of a reflex arc and explain its operation.
11. List and describe the major types of neuronal circuits.
12. Name the four parts of the brainstem, and describe the general functions of each.
13. Name the three main components of the diencephalon, describing their functions.
14. Name the four lobes of the cerebrum, and describe the location and function of each.
15. Describe the locations in the cerebral cortex of the primary sensory areas and of their association areas. How do the association areas interact with the primary areas?
16. Describe the process required to speak a word that is seen or heard.

17. Name the three types of memory, and describe the processes that result in long-term memory.
18. Describe the function of the basal nuclei.
19. What is the function of the limbic system?
20. Describe the comparator activities of the cerebellum.
21. Describe the spinal cord gray matter. Where are sensory and motor neurons located in the gray matter?
22. Differentiate among dorsal root, ventral root, and spinal nerve. Which contain sensory fibers, and which contain motor fibers?
23. Where do the spinothalamic pathway, spinocerebellar pathway, and corticospinal pathway begin and end?
24. Distinguish between upper and lower motor neurons.
25. Name and describe the three meninges that surround the CNS.
26. Describe the production and circulation of the cerebrospinal fluid. Where does the cerebrospinal fluid return to the blood?
27. What are the three principal functional categories of the cranial nerves? List a specific function for each cranial nerve.
28. List the spinal nerves by name and number.
29. Name the main plexuses and the major nerves derived from each.
30. Define the terms preganglionic and postganglionic neuron.
31. Compare the structure of the somatic motor nervous system and the autonomic nervous system in terms of the number of neurons between the CNS and the effector organs and the types of effector organs.
32. Contrast the functions of the sympathetic and parasympathetic divisions of the autonomic nervous system.
33. What kinds of neurons (sympathetic or parasympathetic, preganglionic or postganglionic) are found in the following:
   a. Cranial nerve nuclei
   b. Lateral horn of the thoracic spinal cord gray matter
   c. Lateral portion of the sacral spinal cord gray matter
   d. Chain ganglia
   e. Ganglia in the wall of an organ

Develop Your Reasoning Skills

1. Louis Ville was accidentally struck in the head with a baseball bat. He fell to the ground unconscious. Later, when he had regained consciousness, he was unable to remember any of the events that happened during the 10 minutes before the accident. Explain.
2. A patient suffered brain damage in an automobile accident. It was suspected that the cerebellum was the part of the brain affected. On the basis of what you know about cerebellar function, how could you determine that the cerebellum was involved? What symptoms would you expect to see?
3. The left lung of a cancer patient was removed. To reduce the empty space left in the thorax after the lung was removed, the diaphragm on the left side was paralyzed to allow the abdominal viscera to push the diaphragm upward into the space. What nerve should be cut to paralyze the left half of the diaphragm?
4. Name the nerve that, if damaged, produces the following symptoms:
   a. The elbow and wrist on one side are held in a flexed position and cannot be extended.
   b. The patient is unable to extend the leg (as in kicking a ball) on one side.
5. Name the cranial nerve that, if damaged, produces the following symptoms:
   a. The patient is unable to move the tongue.
   b. The patient is unable to see out of one eye.
   c. The patient is unable to feel one side of the face.
   d. The patient is unable to move the facial muscles on one side.
   e. The pupil of one eye is dilated and does not constrict.
6. Why doesn't injury to the spinal cord at the level of C6 significantly interfere with nervous system control of the digestive system?

Answers to Predict Questions

1. p. 207 Nuclei within the medulla oblongata regulate heart rate, blood vessel diameter, breathing, swallowing, vomiting, coughing, sneezing, balance, and coordination. Even though all these functions are important, loss of some of them may not necessarily result in death. Loss of cardiovascular regulation or loss of breathing regulation, however, could result in death. Because both blood flow and respiration are vital functions, interference with either of them may remove the person's functions from the normal homeostatic range. If not corrected, the loss of homeostasis results in death. Neuronal control of breathing is more critical than cardiovascular control. Death can occur in minutes if neuronal control of respiration is lost. Neuronal control is not absolutely necessary for the heart to continue beating. Without cardiovascular regulation, however, the blood pressure is reduced, resulting in shock, which can ultimately result in death.

2. p. 212 If a person holds an object in her hand, sensations from the skin of the hand are sent to the primary somatic sensory cortex. The information is then passed to the somatic sensory association area, where the object is recognized. Action potentials then travel to the sensory speech area, where the object is given a name. From there, action potentials travel to the motor speech area, where the spoken word is initiated. Action potentials from the motor speech area travel to the premotor area and then to the primary motor cortex, where action potentials are initiated that stimulate the muscles necessary to formulate the word.

3. p. 217 Dorsal root ganglia are larger in diameter because they contain sensory neuron cell bodies, which are larger than the axons of the spinal nerves.

4. p. 227 Damage to the right phrenic nerve results in the absence of muscular contraction in the right half of the diaphragm. Because the phrenic nerves originate in the cervical region of the spinal cord, damage to the spinal cord in the thoracic region does not affect the diaphragm. Damage to the upper cervical region, however, cuts the connection between the upper and lower motor neurons. This eliminates phrenic nerve stimulation of the diaphragm and dramatically interferes with breathing. Death is likely to occur.

5. p. 229 (a) In a person who is extremely angry, the sympathetic division of the autonomic nervous system is activated, and the expected responses include increased heart rate, increased blood pressure, dilated pupils, and perspiration.
   (b) In a person who has just finished eating and is now relaxing, the parasympathetic division of the autonomic nervous system is the primary autonomic division functioning. The responses include decreased heart rate, decreased blood pressure, and increased digestive activities.

6. p. 232 The stroke was on the left side of the brainstem. Both the motor and sensory neurons to the right side of the body are located in the left cerebral cortex. At the level of the upper medulla oblongata, neither the motor or sensory pathways to the limbs have yet crossed over to the left side of the CNS. Loss of pain and temperature to the left side of the face indicates that the lesion occurred at a level where the nerve fibers from the face had entered the CNS but had not yet crossed (in the brainstem).

Chapter Nine

The Senses

ciliary body
(sil'ē-ar-ē) Structure continuous with the choroid layer of the eye at its anterior margin that contains smooth muscle cells; attached to the lens by suspensory ligaments; regulates thickness of the lens.

cochlea
(kok'lē-ă) The portion of the inner ear involved in hearing; shaped like a snail shell.

cornea
(kōr'nē-ă) Transparent, anterior part of the fibrous tunic of the eye through which light enters the eye.

cupula
(koo'poo-lă) [L. *cupa*, a tub] A gelatinous mass that overlies the hair cells of a crista ampullaris of a semicircular canal.

endolymph
(en'dō-limf) [Gr. *endo-*, inside; L. *lympha*, clear fluid] The fluid inside the membranous labyrinth of the inner ear.

iris
(ī'ris) Specialized part of the vascular tunic of the eye; the "colored" part of the eye that can be seen through the cornea; consists of smooth muscles that regulate the amount of light entering the eye.

labyrinth
(lab'i-rinth) A series of membranous and bony tunnels in the temporal bone; part of the inner ear involved in hearing and balance.

macula
(mak'u-lă) One of the sensory structures in the vestibule, consisting of hair cells and a gelatinous mass embedded with otoliths; responds to gravity.

perilymph
(per'i-limf)[Gr. *peri-*, around; L. *lympha*, clear fluid] Fluid contained between the bony labyrinth and the membranous labyrinth of the inner ear.

pupil
(pū'pĭl) Opening in the iris of the eye through which light passes.

retina
(ret'i-nă) The inner, light-sensitive tunic of the eye; nervous tunic.

sclera
(sklēr'ă) Dense, white, opaque posterior part of the fibrous tunic of the eye; white of the eye.

taste bud
Sensory structure found mostly on the tongue, which functions as a taste receptor.

tunic
(too'nik) [L., coat] An enveloping layer of the wall of the eye; the three eye tunics are the fibrous, vascular, and nervous tunics.

Objectives

After reading this chapter, you should be able to:

1. Define sensation.

2. List the sensory modalities and briefly describe each.

3. Describe olfactory neurons and explain what is known about how airborne molecules can stimulate action potentials in the olfactory nerves.

4. Outline the structure and function of a taste bud.

5. List the accessory structures of the eye and explain their functions.

6. Name the tunics of the eye, list the parts of each tunic, and give the functions of each part.

7. Explain the differences in function between the rods and cones.

8. Describe the chambers of the eye and the fluids they contain.

9. Explain how images are focused on the retina.

10. Describe the structures of the outer and middle ear, and state the function of each.

11. Describe the anatomy of the cochlea and explain how sounds are detected.

12. Explain how the structures of the vestibule and semicircular canals function in static and kinetic equilibrium.

The senses are the means by which the brain receives information about the "outside world." A **stimulus** is anything from inside or outside the body that can cause a response in a nerve, muscle, gland, or other tissue. **Sensation**, or **perception**, is the conscious awareness of stimuli received by sensory receptors. A large number of stimuli are constantly being received, but only those that are adequate to cause action potentials that reach the cerebrum can be consciously perceived. Some action potentials go to other parts of the brain, such as the cerebellum, where they help to control body functions, but they are not consciously perceived. In addition, the cerebral cortex ignores much of the sensory information that reaches it. As a result, we are consciously aware of only a small part of all the sensory information we receive. Even though sensations occur in the cerebrum, the sensation is mentally **projected** to the site of origin of the stimulus so that a sensation, such as touch, is perceived to occur, for example, in the tip of the finger, rather than in the brain.

Historically, five senses were recognized: smell, taste, sight, hearing, and touch. Today the numerous recognized senses are classified into two major groups: special and general. Senses produced by highly localized sensory organs are referred to as **special senses** and include the senses of smell, taste, sight, hearing, and balance. **General senses** are more widely distributed throughout the body and include the senses of touch, pressure, pain, temperature, vibration, itch, and proprioception (prō-prē-ō-sep'shun, the sense of movement and position of the body and limbs).

General Senses

Receptors (rē-sep'tŏrz) are sensory nerve endings in the skin and other tissues capable of responding to stimuli by developing action potentials. There are several types of receptors, each responding to a different type of stimulus. **Mechanoreceptors** (mek'ă-nō-rē-sep'tŏrz) respond to mechanical stimuli such as the bending or stretching of receptors, **chemoreceptors** (kem'ō-rē-sep'tŏrz) respond to chemicals such as odor molecules, **photoreceptors** (fō'tō-rē-sep'tŏrz) respond to light, **thermoreceptors** (ther'mō-rē-sep'tŏrz) respond to temperature changes, and **nociceptors** (nō'si-sep'tŏrs) respond to stimuli that result in the sensation of pain.

Many of the receptors for the general senses are associated with the skin (figure 9.1); others are associated with deeper structures, such as tendons, ligaments, and muscles. Receptors consist of several types of nerve endings that respond to a wide range of stimuli. Structurally the simplest and most common sensory nerve endings are **free nerve endings**, which are relatively unspecialized neuronal branches similar to dendrites. Free nerve endings are distributed throughout almost all parts of the body. Some free nerve endings respond to painful stimuli, some to temperature, some to itch, and some to movement. Temperature sensations are detected by specialized free nerve endings called **cold receptors** and **warm receptors**. Cold receptors respond to decreasing temperatures and warm receptors respond to increasing temperatures. When cold or hot temperatures become excessive, however, below 12°C (54°F) or above 47°C (117°F), respectively, neither the cold nor warm receptors function, and pain receptors are stimulated. That is why it is sometimes difficult to distinguish very cold from very warm objects touching the skin.

The remaining nerve endings (see figure 9.1) are structurally more complex than free nerve endings, and many of

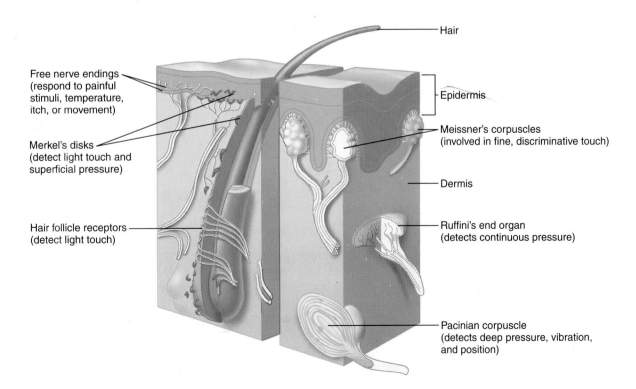

Figure 9.1 Sensory Nerve Endings in the Skin

them are enclosed by capsules. **Merkel's disks** are small, superficial nerve endings involved in detecting light touch and superficial pressure. **Hair follicle receptors**, associated with hairs, are also involved in detecting light touch. Light touch receptors are very sensitive but are not very discriminative, meaning that the point being touched cannot be precisely located. Receptors for fine, discriminative touch, called **Meissner's corpuscles**, are located just deep to the epidermis. These receptors are very specific in localizing tactile sensations. Deeper tactile receptors, called **Ruffini's end organs**, play an important role in detecting continuous pressure in the skin. The deepest receptors are the receptors associated with tendons and joints and are called **pacinian corpuscles**. These receptors relay information concerning deep pressure, vibration, and position (proprioception).

Pain

Pain is a sensation characterized by a group of unpleasant perceptual and emotional experiences. There are two types of pain sensation: (1) sharp, well-localized, pricking, or cutting pain resulting from rapidly conducted action potentials and (2) diffuse, burning, or aching pain resulting from action potentials that are propagated more slowly.

Superficial pain sensations in the skin are highly localized as a result of the simultaneous stimulation of pain receptors and tactile receptors, which help to localize the source of the pain stimuli. Deep or visceral pain sensations are not highly localized because of the absence of tactile receptors in the deeper structures. Visceral pain stimuli are normally perceived as diffuse pain.

Action potentials from pain receptors in local areas of the body can be suppressed by chemical anesthetics injected near a sensory nerve and result in reduced pain sensation. This treatment is called **local anesthesia**. Pain sensations can also be suppressed if consciousness is inhibited by chemical anesthetics that affect the reticular formation. This treatment is called **general anesthesia**.

Pain sensations can also be influenced by inherent control systems. Afferent axons from tactile receptors in the skin have collateral branches that synapse with neurons in the dorsal horn of the spinal cord. Those neurons, in turn, synapse with and inhibit the neurons in the dorsal horn that give rise to the lateral spinothalamic tract. Rubbing the skin in the area of an injury stimulates the tactile receptors, which send action potentials along the afferent axons to the spinal cord. According to the **gate control theory**, these action potentials "close the gate" and inhibit action potentials carried to the brain by the lateral spinothalamic tract. Action potentials carried by the lateral spinothalamic tract can also be inhibited by action potentials carried by descending neurons of the dorsal column system (see chapter 8). These neurons are stimulated by mental or physical activity, especially involving movement of the limbs. The descending neurons synapse with and inhibit neurons in the dorsal horn that give rise to the lateral spinothalamic tract. Vigorous mental or physical activity increases the rate of action potentials in neurons of the dorsal column and can reduce the sensation of pain.

Referred Pain

Referred pain is a painful sensation perceived to originate in a region of the body that is not the source of the pain stimulus. Most commonly, referred pain is sensed in the skin or other superficial structures when deeper structures such as internal organs are damaged or inflamed (figure 9.2). This occurs because afferent neurons from the superficial area to which the pain is referred and the neurons from the deeper, visceral area where the pain stimulation originates converge

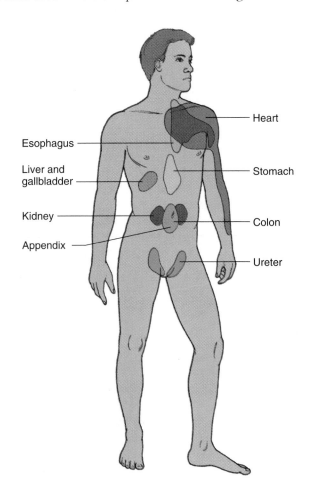

Figure 9.2 Areas of Referred Pain on the Body Surface

Pain from the indicated internal organs is referred to the surface areas shown in the figure.

onto the same ascending neurons in the spinal cord. The brain cannot distinguish between the two sources of pain stimuli, and the painful sensation is referred to the most superficial structures innervated, such as the skin.

Referred pain is clinically useful in diagnosing the actual cause of the painful stimulus. For example, heart attack victims often feel cutaneous pain radiating from the left shoulder down the arm (see figure 9.2).

1   P R E D I C T

A person has constipation that causes distention and painful cramping in the colon (part of the large intestine). What kind of pain would be experienced (local or diffuse) and where would it be perceived? Explain.

✔ *Answer on page 259*

Did You Know?

Phantom pain occurs in people who have had appendages amputated. These people may, at times, perceive intense pain in the amputated structure as if it were still there. If a sensory pathway is stimulated at any point, action potentials are initiated and propagated toward the central nervous system. Integration in the cerebral cortex results in the perception of pain that is projected to the site of the sensory receptors for that pathway, even if those sensory receptors are no longer present. A similar phenomenon can be easily demonstrated by bumping the ulnar nerve as it crosses the elbow (the funny bone). A sensation of pain is felt in the fourth and fifth digits, even though the neurons are stimulated at the elbow.

Special Senses

The sensations of smell and taste are closely related, both structurally and functionally, and are both initiated by the interaction of chemicals with sensory receptors. The sense of vision is initiated by the interaction of light with sensory receptors. Both hearing and balance function in response to the interaction of mechanical stimuli with sensory receptors. Hearing occurs in response to sound waves, and balance occurs in response to gravity or motion.

Olfaction

The sense of smell, called **olfaction** (ol-fak′shŭn), occurs in response to airborne molecules called **odors** that enter the nasal cavity (figure 9.3). **Olfactory neurons** are bipolar neurons within the olfactory epithelium lining the superior part of the nasal cavity. The dendrites of the olfactory neurons extend to the epithelial surface of the nasal cavity, and their ends are modified into bulbous enlargements. These enlargements possess long specialized cilia, which lie in a thin mucous film on the epithelial surface.

Airborne molecules become dissolved in the mucus on the surface of the epithelium and bind to receptor molecules on the membranes of the specialized cilia. The molecules must first be dissolved in fluid in order to reach the olfactory receptors. The exact nature and site of the interaction is not fully understood, but in some way the combination of airborne molecules with receptors causes the olfactory neurons to depolarize. The threshold for the detection of odors is very low, so very few molecules bound to an olfactory neuron can initiate an action potential. Once an odor molecule has become bound to a receptor, however, that receptor does not respond to another odor molecule for some time. It is unlikely that there is a different type of receptor for each of the thousands of detectable odors. It has been proposed that a wide variety of detectable odors are actually combinations of a smaller number of (perhaps as few as seven) primary odors interacting with a limited number of receptor types.

Axons from olfactory neurons form the olfactory nerves (cranial nerve I), which pass through foramina of the cribriform plate and enter the **olfactory bulb**. There they synapse with association neurons that relay action potentials to the brain through the **olfactory tracts**. Each olfactory tract terminates in an area of the brain called the **olfactory cortex**, located within the temporal and frontal lobes. Within the olfactory bulb and olfactory cortex, feedback loops occur that tend to inhibit transmission of additional action potentials stimulated by a prolonged exposure to the same odor. This feedback, plus the temporary decreased sensitivity at the level of the receptors, results in adaptation to a given odor. For example, if you enter a room that has an odor, you are aware of the odor, but you adapt to the odor and cannot smell it as well after the first few minutes. If you leave the room for some time and then reenter the room, the odor again seems more intense.

Taste

The sensory structures that detect **taste** stimuli are the **taste buds** (figure 9.4). Taste buds are oval structures located on the surface of certain **papillae** (pă-pil′ē), which are enlargements on the surface of the tongue. Taste buds are also distributed throughout other areas of the mouth and pharynx, such as on the palate, root of the tongue, and epiglottis. Each taste bud consists of two types of cells. Specialized epithelial cells form the exterior supporting capsule of the taste bud, and the interior of each bud consists of about 40 **taste cells**. Each taste cell contains hairlike processes, called **taste hairs**, that extend into a tiny opening in the epithelium, called a **taste pore**. Dissolved substances bind to receptors on the hairs and initiate action potentials that are carried by afferent neurons to the parietal lobe of the cerebral cortex.

Taste sensations from the anterior two-thirds of the tongue are carried by the facial nerve (cranial nerve VII). Taste sensations from the posterior third of the tongue are carried by the glossopharyngeal nerve (cranial nerve IX). In addition, the vagus nerve (cranial nerve X) carries some taste sensations from the root of the tongue.

Taste sensations can be divided into four basic types: sour, salty, bitter, and sweet. Even though there are only four primary taste sensations, a fairly large number of different tastes can be perceived, presumably by combining the four basic taste sensations. Many taste sensations, however, are

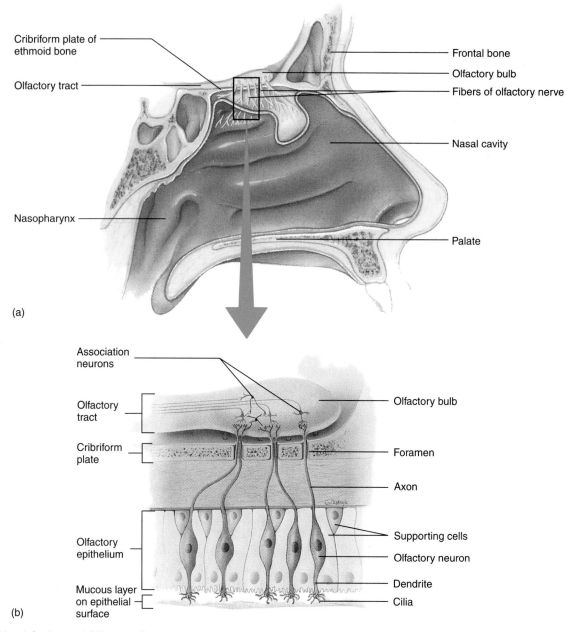

Cribriform plate of
ethmoid bone

Olfactory tract

Nasopharynx

Frontal bone

Olfactory bulb

Fibers of olfactory nerve

Nasal cavity

Palate

(a)

Association
neurons

Olfactory
tract

Cribriform
plate

Olfactory
epithelium

Mucous layer
on epithelial
surface

Olfactory bulb

Foramen

Axon

Supporting cells

Olfactory neuron

Dendrite

Cilia

(b)

Figure 9.3 Nasal Cavity and Olfactory Structures

(*a*) Sagittal view of the lateral wall of the nasal cavity, showing the location of the olfactory bulb and nerve. (*b*) Olfactory bulb and olfactory epithelium enlarged to show the olfactory neurons.

strongly influenced by olfactory sensations. This influence can be demonstrated by comparing the taste of some food before and after pinching your nose. It is easy to detect that the sense of taste is reduced while the nose is pinched.

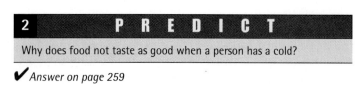

2 **P R E D I C T**

Why does food not taste as good when a person has a cold?

✔ *Answer on page 259*

Although all taste buds are able to detect all four of the basic taste sensations, each taste bud is usually most sensitive to one class of taste stimuli. The stimulus type to which each

taste bud responds most strongly is related to its position on the tongue. Taste buds at the tip of the tongue react more strongly to sweet and salty taste stimuli, taste buds at the back of the tongue react more strongly to bitter taste stimuli, and taste buds on the side of the tongue react most strongly to sour taste stimuli (see figure 9.4*a*).

Vision

The visual system includes the eyes, the accessory structures, and the afferent neurons that project to the cerebral cortex where action potentials conveying visual information are interpreted. Much of the information we obtain about the world

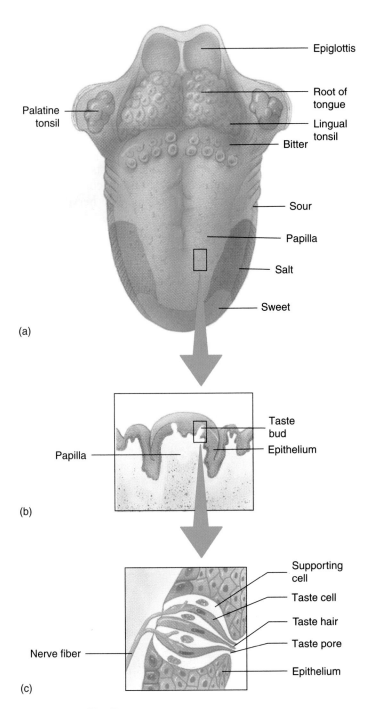

(a)

(b)

(c)

Figure 9.4   The Tongue

(a) Dorsal surface of the tongue and regions of the tongue sensitive to various tastes. (b) Section through a papilla showing the location of taste buds. (c) Enlarged view of a section through a taste bud.

around us is detected by the visual system. Our education is largely based on visual input and depends on our ability to read words and numbers. Visual input includes information about light and dark, movement, color, and hue.

Accessory Structures

Accessory structures (figure 9.5) protect, lubricate, and move the eye. They include the eyebrows, eyelids, conjunctiva, lacrimal apparatus, and extrinsic eye muscles.

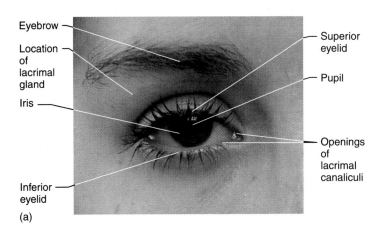

(a)

1. Tears are produced in the lacrimal gland.

2. The tears pass over the surface of the eye.

3. Tears enter the lacrimal canaliculi.

4. Tears are carried through the nasolacrimal duct.

5. Tears enter the nasal cavity from the nasolacrimal duct.

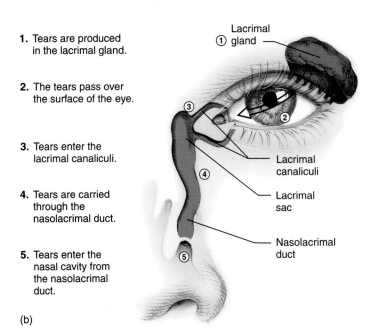

(b)

Figure 9.5   The Eye

(a) The eye with its accessory structures. (b) The lacrimal structures. Tears produced in the lacrimal gland pass over the surface of the eye (arrow) and enter the nasolacrimal duct to the nasal cavity.

Eyebrows

The **eyebrows** protect the eyes by preventing perspiration, which can irritate the eyes, from running down the forehead and into them (figure 9.5a). They also help shade the eyes from direct sunlight.

Eyelids

The **eyelids**, with their associated lashes, protect the eyes from foreign objects (see figure 9.5a). If an object suddenly approaches the eye, the eyelids protect the eye by closing and then opening quite rapidly (blink reflex). Blinking, which normally occurs about 20 times per minute, also helps to keep the eyes lubricated by spreading tears over the surface of the eye.

Conjunctiva

The **conjunctiva** (kon-jŭnk-tī′vă) is a thin, transparent mucous membrane that covers the inner surface of the eyelids and the anterior surface of the eye. Conjunctivitis is an inflammation of the conjunctiva (see the Clinical Focus: Eye Disorders on p. 249).

Lacrimal Apparatus

The **lacrimal** (lak′ri-măl) **apparatus** (figure 9.5*b*) consists of a lacrimal gland situated in the superior lateral corner of the orbit and a nasolacrimal duct and associated structures in the inferior medial corner of the orbit. The **lacrimal gland** produces tears, which pass over the anterior surface of the eye. Most of the fluid produced by the lacrimal glands evaporates from the surface of the eye, but excess tears are collected in the medial corner of the eye by small ducts called **lacrimal canaliculi** (kan-ă-lik′ū-lī). These canaliculi open into a **lacrimal sac**, an enlargement of the **nasolacrimal** (nā-zō-lak′ri-măl) **duct**, which opens into the nasal cavity. Tears serve to lubricate the eye and cleanse it. In addition, tears contain an enzyme that helps combat eye infections.

3	P R E D I C T

Explain why it is often possible to smell (or "taste") medications, such as eyedrops, that have been placed into the eyes.

✔ *Answer on page 259*

Extrinsic Eye Muscles

Movement of each eyeball is accomplished by six skeletal muscles called the **extrinsic eye muscles** (figure 9.6). Four of these muscles run more or less straight from their origins in the posterior orbit to the eye, to attach to the four quadrants of the eyeball. They are the superior, inferior, medial, and lateral **rectus muscles**. Two muscles, the superior and inferior **oblique muscles**, are placed at an angle to the long axis of the eyeball.

Anatomy of the Eye

The eyeball is a hollow, fluid-filled sphere. The sphere has a larger, posterior compartment, which makes up about five-sixths of the eye, and a much smaller anterior compartment, which makes up about one-sixth of the eye. The chambers within the eye and the fluid within each chamber are discussed on pp. 246 and 247.

The wall of the eye consists of three layers, or **tunics** (figure 9.7). The outer, or **fibrous**, tunic consists of the sclera and cornea. The middle, or **vascular**, tunic consists of the choroid, ciliary body, and iris. The inner, or **nervous**, tunic consists of the retina.

Fibrous Tunic

The **sclera** (sklēr′ă) is the firm, white, outer connective tissue layer of the posterior five-sixths of the eye. The sclera helps maintain the shape of the eye, protects the internal structure, and provides attachment sites for the extrinsic eye muscles. A small portion of the sclera can be seen as the "white of the eye."

The **cornea** (kōr′nē-ă) is the transparent, anterior sixth of the eye that permits light to enter the eye. As part of the focusing system of the eye, it also bends, or refracts, the entering light.

Did You Know?

The cornea was one of the first organs to be successfully transplanted. Several characteristics make it relatively easy to transplant: it is easily accessible and relatively easily removed, it does not have blood vessels and therefore does not require the growth of an extensive circulation into the tissue after grafting, and it is less likely to stimulate the immune system and is therefore less likely to be rejected than other tissues.

Vascular Tunic

The middle tunic of the eye is called the **vascular tunic** because it is the layer containing most of the blood vessels of the eye. The posterior portion of the vascular tunic, associated with the

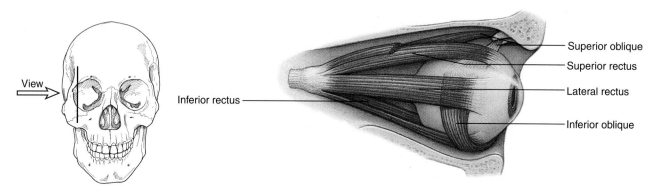

Figure 9.6 Eye Muscles

Extrinsic muscles of the right eye as seen from a lateral view with the lateral wall of the orbit removed. The medial rectus muscle cannot be seen from this view.

Anterior compartment filled with aqueous humor

Conjunctiva

Cornea

Anterior chamber

Posterior chamber

Iris

Pupil

Lens

Suspensory ligaments

Ciliary body

Posterior compartment filled with vitreous humor

Optic nerve

Retina

Choroid

Sclera

Figure 9.7   Layers and Compartments of the Eye

Sagittal section through the eye demonstrating its layers and compartments.

sclera, is the **choroid** (kō′royd). This is a very thin structure consisting of a vascular network and many melanin-containing pigment cells, so that it appears black in color. The black color absorbs light so that it is not reflected inside the eye. If light was reflected inside the eye, the reflection would interfere with vision. The interiors of cameras are black for the same reason.

Anteriorly the vascular tunic consists of the ciliary body and iris. The **ciliary** (sil′ē-ar-ē) **body** is continuous with the anterior margin of the choroid. The ciliary body contains smooth muscles called **ciliary muscles**, which attach to the perimeter of the lens by **suspensory ligaments**. The **lens** is a flexible, biconvex, transparent disc (see figure 9.7).

The **iris** is the colored part of the eye. It is attached to the anterior margin of the ciliary body, anterior to the lens. The iris is a contractile structure consisting mainly of smooth muscle that surrounds an opening called the **pupil**. Light passes through the pupil, and the iris regulates the diameter of the pupil, which controls the amount of light entering the eye. Parasympathetic stimulation from the oculomotor nerve (cranial nerve III) causes the circular smooth muscles of the iris to contract, resulting in pupillary constriction, whereas sympathetic stimulation causes radial smooth muscles of the iris to contract, resulting in pupillary dilation. As light intensity increases, the pupil constricts; as light intensity decreases, the pupil dilates.

Nervous Tunic

The **retina**, or **nervous tunic**, is the innermost tunic and it covers only the posterior five-sixths of the eye. It consists of an outer **pigmented retina** and an inner **sensory retina** (figure 9.8*a*). The pigmented retina, with the choroid, keeps light from reflecting back into the eye. The sensory retina contains photoreceptor cells, called **rods** and **cones**, which respond to light. The sensory retina also contains numerous association neurons, some of which are named in figure 9.8 and are dis-

cussed on p. 247. Over most of the retina, rods are 20 times more common than cones, with the concentration of rods increasing anteriorly. Rods are very sensitive to light and can function in very dim light, but they do not provide color vision. Cones require much more light, and they do provide color vision. There are three types of cones, each sensitive to a different color: blue, green, or red. The many colors that we can see result from various functional combinations of these three types of cones.

4   **P R E D I C T**

In dim light, colors seem to fade and objects seem to become colored as shades of gray. Explain this phenomenon.

✔ *Answer on page 259*

The outer segments of rod and cone cells are modified by numerous foldings of the cell membrane to form discs (figure 9.8*b–d*). Rod cells contain a photosensitive pigment called **rhodopsin** (rō-dop′sin), which is made up of the protein **opsin** (op′sin) in loose chemical combination with a pigment called **retinal** (ret′i-năl) (figures 9.8*e* and 9.9). Cone cells contain a slightly different photosensitive pigment. When light strikes a rod cell, retinal changes shape and loses its attachment to the opsin molecule. As a result, opsin "opens up" with a release of energy. This reaction is somewhat like a spring (opsin) being held by a trigger (retinal). This change in rhodopsin stimulates a response in the rod cell. Retinal then completely detaches from rhodopsin. Energy (ATP) is required to reattach retinal to rhodopsin and, at the same time, to return rhodopsin to the shape that it had before being stimulated by light.

Manufacture of retinal in rod cells requires vitamin A. A person with a vitamin A deficiency may have a condition

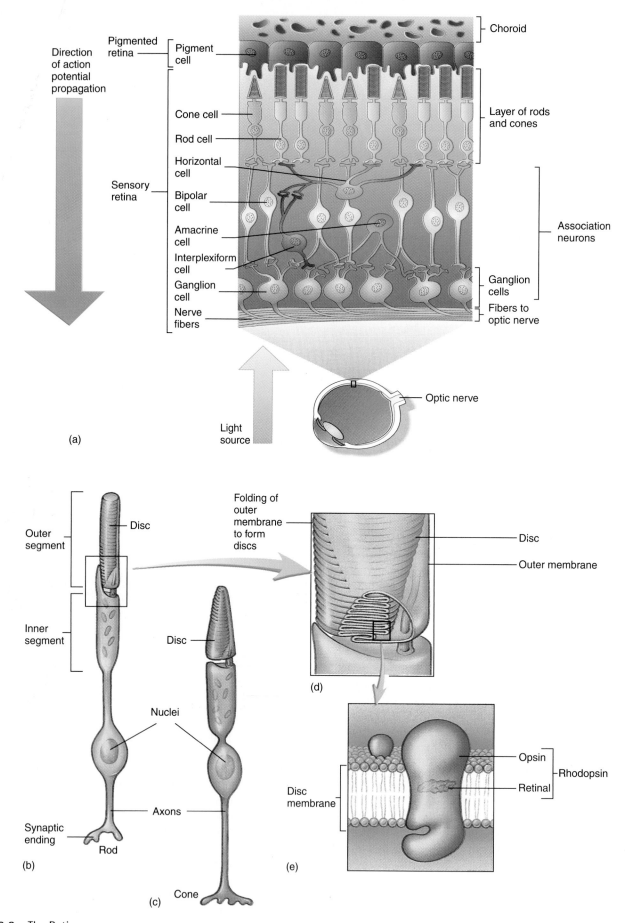

Figure 9.8 The Retina

(a) Enlarged section of the retina showing its structure. (b) Greatly enlarged view of a rod cell. (c) Greatly enlarged view of a cone cell. (d) Enlargement of a part of the rod cell to show the discs. (e) Enlargement of a disc membrane showing the position of rhodopsin.

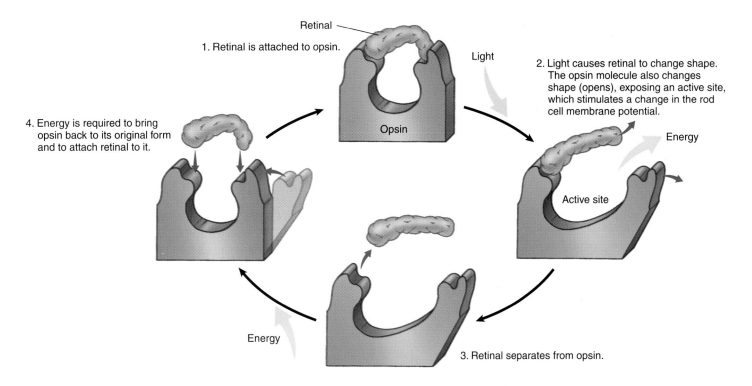

1. Retinal is attached to opsin.

Retinal

Light

2. Light causes retinal to change shape. The opsin molecule also changes shape (opens), exposing an active site, which stimulates a change in the rod cell membrane potential.

Opsin

4. Energy is required to bring opsin back to its original form and to attach retinal to it.

Energy

Active site

Energy

3. Retinal separates from opsin.

Figure 9.9   Rhodopsin Cycle

called **night blindness**, which is difficulty in seeing, especially in dim light.

The rod and cone cells synapse with bipolar cells of the sensory retina (see figure 9.8). These and the horizontal cells of the retina modify the output of the rod and cone cells. For example, this modification is involved in the sharpening of borders between objects of contrasting brightness. The bipolar and horizontal cells synapse with ganglion cells, whose axons converge at the posterior of the eye to form the **optic nerve** (cranial nerve II; see figure 9.7).

When the posterior region of the retina is examined with an ophthalmoscope (of-thal′mō-skōp), two major features can be observed: the macula lutea and the optic disc (figure 9.10). Near the center of the posterior retina is a small yellow spot called the **macula lutea** (mak′ū-lă lü′tē-ă). In the center of the macula lutea is a small pit, the **fovea** (fō′vē-ă) **centralis**. The fovea centralis is the part of the retina where light is normally focused when the eye is looking directly at an object. The photoreceptor cells are more densely packed in this part of the retina than in any other. When images are focused onto the retina, the fovea centralis is able to detect those images most clearly because of this higher concentration of photoreceptors. The fovea centralis is also the part of the retina with the highest concentration of cones.

Just medial to the macula lutea is a white spot, the **optic disc**, through which a number of fairly large blood vessels enter the eye and spread over the surface of the retina. This is also the spot at which axons from the retina meet, pass through the outer two tunics, and exit the eye as the optic nerve. The optic disc contains no photoreceptor cells and

Medial

Optic disc

Retinal vessels

Lateral

Macula lutea

Location of fovea centralis

Figure 9.10   Ophthalmoscopic View of the Retina

This view shows the posterior wall of the left eye as seen through the pupil. Notice the vessels entering the eye through the optic disc. The macula lutea, with the fovea centralis in the center, is located lateral to the optic disc.

does not respond to light; it is therefore called the **blind spot** of the eye. A small image projected onto the blind spot cannot be seen. You can demonstrate this by drawing two small dots about 2 inches apart on a card, closing one eye, and holding the card about 1 foot in front of your open eye. As you move the card toward you, focusing on one dot, the other dot seems to disappear.

Compartments of the Eye

The interior of the eye is divided into two major compartments, separated by the lens (see figure 9.7). The **anterior compartment**, between the lens and the cornea, is filled with **aqueous humor** (watery fluid), which helps maintain pressure within the eye, refracts (bends) light, and provides nutrients to the inner surface of the eye. Aqueous humor is produced by the ciliary body as a blood filtrate and is returned to the circulation through a venous ring that surrounds the cornea. Pressure within the anterior compartment resulting from the presence of aqueous humor keeps the eye inflated, much like the air in a basketball. If flow of the aqueous humor from the eye through the venous ring is blocked, the pressure in the eye increases, resulting in a condition called **glaucoma** (see the Clinical Focus: Eye Disorders on p. 249). Glaucoma can eventually lead to blindness because the fluid compresses the retina, thereby restricting blood flow through it. The anterior compartment of the eye is divided by the iris into an **anterior chamber** and a **posterior chamber**, which are continuous with each other through the pupil.

The **posterior compartment** of the eye is filled with a transparent jellylike substance, called the **vitreous** (vit′rē-ŭs) **humor**. The vitreous humor helps maintain pressure within the eye and holds the lens and the retina in place. It also functions to refract the light. Unlike the aqueous humor, the vitreous humor does not circulate.

Functions of the Complete Eye

The eye functions much like a camera. The iris allows light into the eye, which is focused by the cornea, lens, and humors onto the retina. The light striking the retina produces action potentials, that are relayed to the brain.

Light Refraction

An important characteristic of light is that it can be refracted (bent). As light passes from air to some other, denser substance, the light rays are refracted. If the surface of a lens is concave, the light rays diverge as they pass through the lens; if the surface is convex, they converge. As the light rays converge, they finally reach a point at which they cross. The crossing point is called the **focal point** (figure 9.11), and causing light to converge is called **focusing**. The focal point in the eye occurs just anterior to the retina, and the tiny image that is focused on the retina is inverted compared with the actual object.

Focusing of Images on the Retina

The cornea is a convex structure, and as light rays pass from the air through the cornea, they converge (see figure 9.11). Additional convergence occurs as light passes through the aqueous humor, lens, and vitreous humor. The greatest contrast in media density is between the air and the cornea. The greatest amount of convergence therefore occurs at that point.

The shape of the cornea and its distance from the retina are fixed, however, so that no adjustment in focus can be made by the cornea. Fine adjustments in focus are accomplished by changing the shape of the lens.

When the ciliary muscles are relaxed, the suspensory ligaments of the ciliary body maintain elastic pressure on the perimeter of the lens, keeping it relatively flat and allowing for distant vision (see figure 9.11a). When an object is brought closer than 20 feet (about 6 1/2 meters) to the eye, the ciliary muscles contract as a result of parasympathetic stimulation, pulling the ciliary body toward the lens. This reduces the tension on the suspensory ligaments of the lens and allows the lens to assume a more spherical form because of its own internal elastic nature (figure 9.11b). The spherical lens then has a more convex surface, causing greater refraction of light. This process is called **accommodation** (ă-kom′ŏ-dā′shŭn), and it enables the eye to focus on objects closer than 20 feet on the retina.

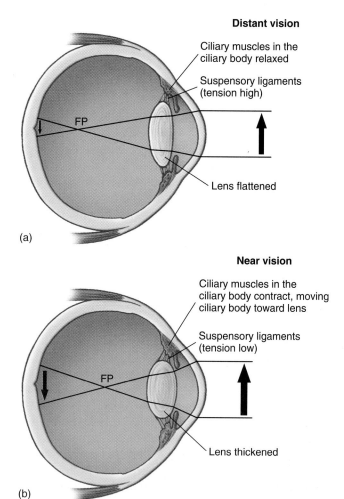

Figure 9.11 Focus and Accommodation by the Eye

The focal point (FP) is where light rays cross. (a) Distant image. The lens is flattened, and the image is focused on the retina. (b) Accommodation for near vision. The lens is more rounded, and the image is focused on the retina.

5   P R E D I C T

What changes occur, as you are driving a car, when you look down at the speedometer and then back up at the road?

✔ *Answer on page 259*

Neuronal Pathways

The **optic nerve** (figure 9.12) leaves the eye and exits the orbit through the optic foramen to enter the cranial vault. Just inside the cranial vault, the optic nerves are connected to each other at the **optic chiasm** (kī'azm). Axons from the medial part of the retina cross through the optic chiasm and project to the opposite side of the brain. Axons from the lateral part of the retina pass through the optic nerves and project to the brain on the same side of the body without crossing.

Beyond the optic chiasm, the route of the ganglionic axons is called the **optic tract** (see figure 9.12). Most of the optic tract axons terminate in the thalamus. Some axons do not terminate in the thalamus but separate from the optic tract to terminate in the superior colliculi, the center for visual reflexes. An example of a visual reflex is turning the head and eyes toward a stimulus such as a sudden noise or flash of light. Neurons from the thalamus form the fibers of the **optic radiations**, which project to the **visual cortex** in the occipital lobe (see figure 9.12).

The image seen by each eye is the **visual field** of that eye (see figure 9.12*a* and *b*). Depth perception (three-dimensional vision) requires both eyes and occurs where the two visual fields overlap (see figure 9.12*c*). Each eye sees a slightly different view of the same object. The brain then processes the two images into a three-dimensional view of the object. If only one eye is functioning, the view of the object is flat, much like viewing a photograph.

Hearing and Balance

The organs of hearing and balance are divided into three parts: external, middle, and inner ear (figure 9.13). The external ear is the part extending from the outside of the head to the eardrum. The middle ear is an air-filled chamber medial to the eardrum. The inner ear is a set of fluid-filled chambers medial to the middle ear. The external and middle ears are involved in hearing only, whereas the inner ear functions in both hearing and balance.

The Ear and Its Functions

External Ear

The **auricle** (aw'ri-kl, ear) is the fleshy part of the external ear on the outside of the head. The auricle opens into the **external auditory meatus** (mē-ā'tŭs), a passageway that leads to the eardrum. The auricle directs sound waves toward the external auditory meatus. The meatus is lined with hairs and **ceruminous** (sĕ-roo'mi-nŭs) **glands**, which produce **cerumen** (sĕroo'men), a modified sebum commonly called earwax. The hairs and cerumen help prevent foreign objects from reaching the delicate eardrum.

The **tympanic** (tim-pan'ik) **membrane**, or **eardrum**, is a thin membrane that separates the external ear from the middle ear. Sound waves reaching the tympanic membrane through the external auditory meatus cause it to vibrate.

Middle Ear

Medial to the tympanic membrane is the air-filled cavity of the middle ear. Two openings, the **oval window** and the **round window** on the medial side of the middle ear, connect the middle ear with the inner ear. The middle ear contains three **auditory ossicles** (os'i-klz, ear bones): the **malleus** (mal'ē-ŭs, hammer), **incus** (ing'kŭs, anvil), and **stapes** (stā'pēz, stirrup), which transmit vibrations from the tympanic membrane to the oval window. The malleus is attached to the medial surface of the tympanic membrane, the incus connects the malleus to the stapes, and the base of the stapes is seated in the oval window. As the vibrations are transmitted from the malleus to the stapes, the force of the vibrations is amplified about 20-fold.

There are two unblocked openings into the middle ear. One opens into the mastoid air cells in the mastoid process of the temporal bone. The other, called the **auditory tube**, or **eustachian** (ū-stā'shŭn) **tube**, opens into the pharynx and enables air pressure to be equalized between the outside air and the middle ear cavity. Unequal pressure between the middle ear and the outside environment can distort the tympanic membrane, dampen its vibrations, and make hearing difficult. Distortion of the tympanic membrane also stimulates pain fibers associated with that structure. That distortion is why, as a person changes altitude, sounds seem muffled and the tympanic membrane may become painful. These symptoms can be relieved by opening the auditory tube, allowing air to enter or exit the middle ear. Swallowing, yawning, chewing, and holding the nose and mouth shut while gently trying to force air out of the lungs are methods that can be used to open the auditory tube.

Inner Ear

The inner ear consists of interconnecting tunnels and chambers within the temporal bone, called the **bony labyrinth** (lab'i-rinth, maze). Inside the bony labyrinth is a similarly shaped but smaller set of membranous tunnels and chambers called the **membranous labyrinth** (figure 9.14*b*). The membranous

1. Each visual field is divided into a temporal and nasal half.

2. After passing through the lens, light from each half of a visual field projects to the opposite side of the retina.

3. An optic nerve consists of axons extending from the retina to the optic chiasm.

4. In the optic chiasm, axons from the nasal half of each retina cross and project to the opposite side of the brain. Axons from the temporal half of each retina do not cross.

5. An optic tract consists of axons that have passed through the optic chiasm (with or without crossing) to the thalamus.

6. The axons synapse in the lateral geniculate nuclei of the thalamus. Collateral branches of the axons in the optic tracts synapse in the superior colliculi.

7. An optic radiation consists of axons from thalamic neurons that project to the visual cortex.

8. (b) The right half of each visual field (dark green and light blue) projects to the left side of the brain, and the left half of each visual field projects to the right side of the brain (light green and dark blue).

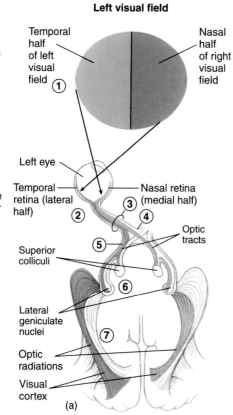

Left visual field

Temporal half of left visual field ①

Nasal half of right visual field

Left eye

Temporal retina (lateral half) ②

Nasal retina (medial half) ③ ④

Optic tracts

Superior colliculi ⑤

⑥

Lateral geniculate nuclei

⑦

Optic radiations

Visual cortex

(a)

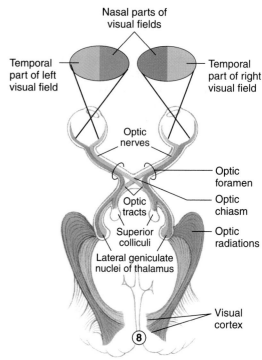

Nasal parts of visual fields

Temporal part of left visual field

Temporal part of right visual field

Optic nerves

Optic foramen

Optic tracts

Optic chiasm

Superior colliculi

Optic radiations

Lateral geniculate nuclei of thalamus

⑧

Visual cortex

(b)   Occipital lobe

Binocular

Left monocular

Right monocular

(c)

Optic nerve

Optic tract

Thalamus

Optic radiations

Visual cortex

(d)

Figure 9.12   Visual Pathways

(a) Pathways for the left eye (superior view). (b) Pathways for both eyes (superior view). (c) Overlap of the fields of vision (superior view). (d) Photograph of the visual nerves, tracts, and pathways (inferior view).

Clinical Focus   Eye Disorders

Infections

Conjunctivitis (kon-jŭnk-ti-vī′tis) is an inflammation of the conjunctiva, usually resulting from a bacterial infection. **Contagious conjunctivitis** (pinkeye) occurs primarily in children. It can be transmitted by hand contact, flies, or contaminated water, such as in swimming pools. **Neonatal gonorrheal ophthalmia** (nē-ō-nā′tăl gon-ō-rē′ăl of-thal′mē-ă) is a severe form of conjunctivitis that is contracted by an infant passing through the birth canal of a mother with gonorrhea. This infection carries a high risk of blindness. The treatment of newborn eyes with silver nitrate is effective in preventing the disease. **Chlamydial** (kla-mid′ē-ăl) **conjunctivitis** is contracted as an infant passes through the birth canal of a mother with a chlamydial infection. This infection is not affected by silver nitrate, so in many places, newborns are treated with antibiotics against both chlamydia and gonorrhea. **Trachoma** (tră-kō′mă) is the greatest single cause of blindness in the world today. The disease, also caused by chlamydia, is transmitted by hand contact, flies, or objects such as towels. It is a conjunctivitis that leads to scarring of the cornea and blindness. It is most common in arid parts of Africa and Asia.

A **chalazion** (ka-lā′zē-on) is a cyst caused by infection of the sebaceous glands along the edge of the eyelid. A **stye** (stī) is an infection of an eyelash hair follicle.

Defects of Focus

Myopia (mī-ō′pē-ă), or nearsightedness, is the ability to see close objects but not distant ones. It is a defect of the eye in which the focal point is too near to the lens and the image is focused in front of the retina when looking at distant objects (figure A*a*). Myopia is corrected by a concave lens that spreads out the light rays coming to the eye so that when the light is focused by the eye, it is focused on the retina (figure A*b*).

Hyperopia (hī-per-ō′pē-ă), or farsightedness, is the ability to see distant objects but not close ones. It is a disorder in which the focal point is too far from the lens, and the image is focused "behind" the retina when looking at a close object (figure A*c*). In hyperopia, the lens must thicken and accommodate to bring somewhat distant objects into focus, which would not be necessary for a normal eye. Closer objects cannot be brought into focus because the lens cannot thicken enough to focus the image on the retina. Hyperopia is corrected by a convex lens that causes light rays to converge as they approach the eye and to focus on the retina (figure A*d*).

Presbyopia (prez-bē-ō′pē-ă) is the decrease in the ability of the eye to accommodate for near vision. This occurs as a normal part of aging and the lens becomes less flexible. The average age of onset of presbyopia is the midforties. Presbyopia can be corrected by the use of "reading glasses" or by bifocals, which have different lenses in the top and bottom. The bottom half of a bifocal lens is more convex for a person with hyperopia to allow for near vision when the person reads, and the top half is less convex for distant vision. For a person with myopia, the bottom half of the lens is less concave to allow for near vision when the person reads, and the top half is more concave for distant vision.

Astigmatism (ă-stig′mă-tizm) is a defect in which the cornea or lens is not uniformly curved and the image is not sharply focused. Glasses may be made to adjust for

(a)   Myopia (nearsightedness)

(b)   Concave lens corrects myopia

(c)   Hyperopia (farsightedness)

(d)   Convex lens corrects hyperopia

Figure A   Visual Disorders and Their Correction by Various Lenses (FP, focal point) the abnormal curvature as long as the curvature is not too irregular. If the curvature of the cornea or lens is too irregular, the condition is difficult to correct.

Strabismus

Strabismus (stra-biz′mŭs) is a condition in which one eye or both eyes are directed medially or laterally. The condition can result from abnormally weak eye muscles.

Color Blindness

Color blindness is the absence of perception of one or more colors (figure B). There may be a complete loss of color perception or only a decrease in perception. The loss may involve perception of all three colors or of one or two colors. Most forms of color blindness occur more frequently in males and is an X-linked genetic trait (see chapter 20). In western Europe, about 8% of all males have some form of color blindness, whereas only about 1% of the females are color blind.

Blindness

Cataract (kat′ă-rakt) is the most common cause of blindness in the United States. It is a condition in which clouding of the lens occurs as the result of advancing age, infection, or trauma. Excess exposure to ultraviolet radiation may be a factor in causing cataracts, so wearing sunglasses, which reduce exposure to ultraviolet radiation, in bright sunshine is recommended. Cataracts occur to some degree in 95% of people over age 65. Surgery performed to remove a cataract involves removal of the lens. More than 400,000 cataract lenses are removed in the United States each year. In almost all cases, an artificial lens is implanted in place of the natural one. Clear vision is restored for distant vision, but the ability to accommodate for near vision is lost and glasses are required for near vision.

Glaucoma (glaw-kō′mă) is a condition involving excessive pressure buildup in the aqueous humor. Glaucoma results from an interference with normal reentry of aqueous humor into the blood or from an overproduction of aqueous humor. The increased pressure within the eye can close off the blood vessels entering the eye and may destroy the retina or optic nerve, resulting in blindness.

Diabetes mellitus (dī-ă-bē′tēz me-lī′tus) is a major cause of blindness in the United States. Diabetes can result in optic nerve degeneration, cataracts, and retinal detachment. These defects are often caused by blood vessel degeneration and hemorrhage, which are common in diabetic patients.

Retinal detachment, the separation of the sensory retina from the pigmented retina, is a relatively common problem that can result in complete blindness. If a hole or tear occurs in the retina, fluid can accumulate between the sensory and pigmented retina. As a result, the sensory retina may become detached from the pigmented retina and degenerate, resulting in loss of vision.

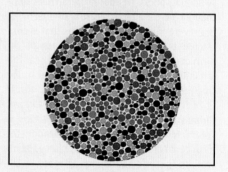

Figure B Color Blindness Charts

(*a*) A person with normal vision can see the number 74, whereas a person with red-green color blindness sees the number 21. (*b*) A person with normal vision can see the number 42. A person with red color blindness sees the number 2, and a person with green color blindness sees the number 4.

The above has been reproduced from Ishihara's Test for Colour Deficiency published by Kanehara & Co., Ltd., Tokyo, Japan. Tests for color deficiency cannot be conducted with this material. For accurate testing, the original plates should be used.

---

labyrinth is filled with a clear fluid called **endolymph** (en′dōlimf), and the space between the membranous and bony labyrinth is filled with a fluid called **perilymph** (per′i-limf). The bony labyrinth can be divided into three regions: the cochlea, vestibule, and semicircular canals. The cochlea is involved in hearing, and the vestibule and semicircular canals are involved primarily in balance.

Hearing

The **cochlea** (kok′lē-ă) (figure 9.14*a*) is shaped like a snail shell and contains a bony core shaped like a screw. The threads of this screw are called the **spiral lamina**. A Y-shaped membranous complex divides the cochlea into three portions (see figure 9.14*b*). The base of the Y is the spiral lamina. One branch of the Y is the **vestibular** (ves-tib′ū-lăr) **membrane**, and the other branch is the **basilar membrane**. The space between these membranes is called the **cochlear duct**. This complex is the membranous labyrinth, and it is filled with endolymph. If the Y is viewed lying on its right side, as in figure 9.14*b*, the space above the Y is called the **scala vestibuli** (skā′lă ves-tib′ū-

lī), and the space below the Y is called the **scala tympani** (tim-pa′nē). These two spaces are filled with perilymph. The scala vestibuli extends from the oval window to the apex of the cochlea, and the scala tympani extends from the apex to the round window. The two scalae are continuous with each other at the apex of the cochlea.

Inside the cochlear duct is a specialized structure called the **spiral organ,** or **organ of Corti** (figure 9.14*c*). The spiral organ contains specialized sensory cells called **hair cells,** which have hairlike microvilli on their surfaces (figure 9.14*c* and *d*). The hair tips are embedded within an acellular gelatinous shelf called the **tectorial** (tek-tōr′ē-ăl) **membrane,** which is attached to the spiral lamina (see figure 9.14*b* and *c*).

Hair cells have no axons of their own, but each hair cell is associated with terminals of sensory neurons, the cell bodies of which are located within the **spiral ganglion**. Afferent fibers of the sensory neurons join to form the **cochlear nerve**. This nerve joins the vestibular nerve to become the **vestibulo cochlear nerve** (cranial nerve VIII), which carries action potentials to the brain.

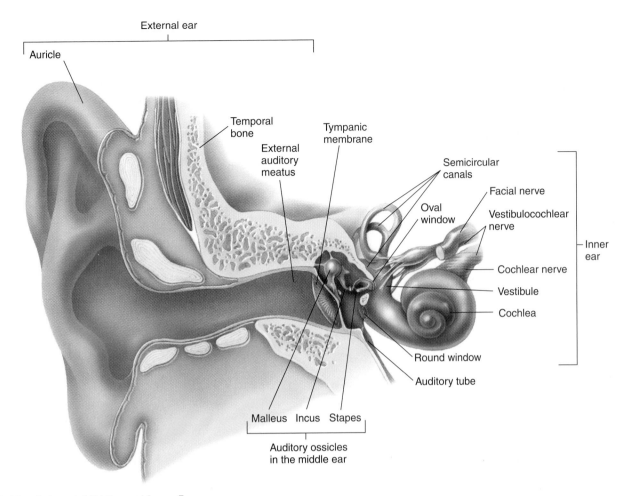

Figure 9.13   External, Middle, and Inner Ear

Sound waves are collected by the auricle and are conducted through the external auditory meatus toward the tympanic membrane (table 9.1). Sound waves strike the tympanic membrane and cause it to vibrate. This vibration causes vibration of the three ossicles of the middle ear, and by this mechanical linkage the force of vibration is amplified and transferred to the oval window (figure 9.15).

6   P R E D I C T

Why is it that when you hear a faint sound, you turn your head toward it?

✔ *Answer on page 259*

Vibrations of the base of the stapes, seated in the oval window, produce waves in the perilymph of the cochlea. The two scalae can be thought of as a continuous U-shaped tube, with the oval window at one end and the round window at the other. The vibrations of the stapes in the oval window cause movement of the perilymph, which pushes against the membrane covering the round window. This phenomenon is similar to pushing against a rubber diaphragm on one end of a fluid-filled glass tube. If the tube has a rubber diaphragm on

each end, the fluid can move. If one end of the glass tube or of the cochlear tubes were solid, no fluid movement would occur.

The waves produced in the perilymph cause displacement of the vestibular membrane. This displacement creates waves in the endolymph, within the cochlear duct, and displacement of the basilar membrane. As the basilar membrane is displaced, the hair cells, seated on the basilar membrane, move with the movements of the membrane. The microvilli of the hair cells are embedded into the tectorial membrane, which is a rigid shelf that does not move. Because one end of the microvilli move with the hair cells and their other ends are embedded into the nonmoving tectorial membrane, the microvilli bend. The bending of the microvilli causes stimulation of the hair cells, which induces action potentials in the cochlear nerves.

The basilar membrane is not uniform throughout its length. The membrane is narrower and denser near the oval window and wider and less dense near the tip of the cochlea. The various regions of the membrane can be compared to the strings in a piano (i.e., some are short and thick, and others are longer and thinner). As a result of this organization, sounds with higher **pitches** cause the basilar membrane nearer the oval window to maximally distort, whereas sounds with lower pitches cause the basilar membrane nearer the

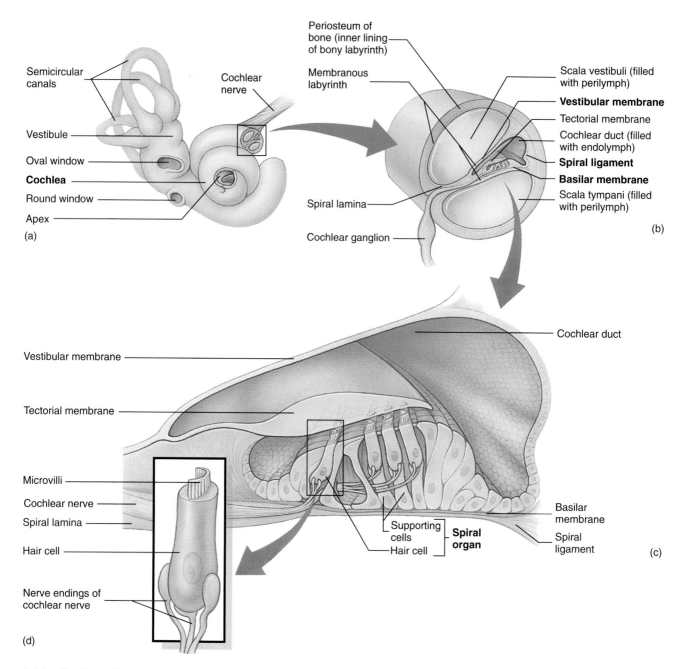

Figure 9.14 The Inner Ear

(*a*) The bony labyrinth. Windows are cut to show some internal structure. (*b*) A section through the cochlea. (*c*) An enlarged cross section of the cochlea to show the membranes, cochlear duct, and spiral organ (organ of Corti). (*d*) A single hair cell with its hairs (microvilli).

apex of the cochlea to distort maximally. Different hair cells are stimulated in each case, and, because of the differences in which hair cells are maximally stimulated, a person is able to detect variations in pitch. Sound **volume** is a function of sound wave amplitude, which causes the basilar membrane to distort more intensely and the hair cells to be stimulated more strongly.

The cochlear nerves, whose cell bodies are located in the cochlear ganglion, send axons to the **cochlear nucleus** in the brainstem. Neurons in the cochlear nucleus project to other areas of the brainstem and to the **inferior colliculus** in the midbrain. From the inferior colliculus, fibers project to the thalamus, and from there to the auditory cortex of the cerebrum.

Equilibrium

The sense of equilibrium, or balance, has two components: static equilibrium and kinetic equilibrium. **Static equilibrium** is associated with the vestibule and is involved in evaluating the position of the head relative to gravity. **Kinetic equilibrium** is associated with the semicircular canals and is involved in evaluating the change in rate of head movements.

The **vestibule** (ves′ti-bool) can be divided into two chambers: the **utricle** (ū′tri-kl) and the **saccule** (sak′ūl) (figure 9.16*a*). Each chamber contains specialized patches of epithelium called the **maculae** (mak′ū-lē), which are surrounded by endolymph (figure 9.16*b*). The maculae, like the spiral organ,

Table 9.1 Steps Involved in Hearing

1. Sound waves are collected by the auricle and conducted through the external auditory meatus to the tympanic membrane, causing it to vibrate.
2. The vibrating tympanic membrane causes the malleus, incus, and stapes to vibrate.
3. Vibration of the stapes produces waves in the perilymph of the scala vestibuli.
4. The waves of the perilymph cause displacement of the vestibular membrane, which produces simultaneous waves in the endolymph of the cochlear duct.
5. The waves in the endolymph cause the basilar membrane to be displaced.
6. As the basilar membrane is displaced, the hair cells attached to the membrane move relative to the tectorial membrane, which remains stationary.
7. The hair cell microvilli, embedded in the tectorial membrane, become bent.
8. Bending of the microvilli causes depolarization of the hair cells.
9. The hair cells induce action potentials in the cochlear neurons.
10. The action potentials generated in the cochlear neurons are conducted to the CNS.
11. The action potentials are translated in the cerebral cortex and are perceived as sound.

contain hair cells. The tips of the microvilli of these cells are embedded in a gelatinous mass weighted by **otoliths** (ō′tō-liths), particles composed of protein and calcium carbonate (figure 9.16c). The mass moves in response to gravity, bending the hair cell microvilli and initiating action potentials in the associated neurons. The action potentials from these neurons are relayed by way of the vestibulocochlear nerve (cranial nerve VIII) to the brain, where they are interpreted as a change in position of the head. For example, when a person bends over, the maculae are displaced by gravity, and the resultant action potentials provide information to the brain concerning the position of the head relative to gravity (figure 9.17).

Three **semicircular canals** are involved in kinetic equilibrium and placed at nearly right angles to one another. The placement of the semicircular canals enables a person to detect movements in essentially any direction. The base of each semicircular canal is expanded into an **ampulla** (am-pul′ă). Within each ampulla the epithelium is specialized to form a **crista ampullaris** (kris′tă am-pūl′ar′is) (figure 9.18). Each crista consists of a ridge of epithelium with a curved gelatinous mass, the **cupula** (koo′poo-lă), suspended over the crest (figure 9.18b). The cupula is structurally and functionally very similar to the maculae, except that no otoliths occur in the cupula. The hairlike processes of the crista hair cells (figure 9.18c) are embedded in the cupula. The cupula is a float

1. Sound waves strike the tympanic membrane and cause it to vibrate.
2. Vibration of the tympanic membrane causes the three bones of the middle ear to vibrate.
3. The stapes vibrates in the oval window.
4. Vibration of the stapes causes waves in the perilymph of the scala vestibuli.
5. Waves of perilymph cause displacement of the vestibular membrane and the basilar membrane. Short waves (high pitch) cause

displacement of the basilar membrane near the oval window, and longer waves (low pitch) cause displacement of the basilar membrane some distance from the oval window. Movement of the basilar membrane is detected in the hair cells of the spiral organ, which are attached to the basilar membrane.
6. Waves of perilymph in the scala vestibuli and of the endolymph in the cochlear duct are transferred to the perilymph of the scala tympani.
7. Waves in the perilymph of the scala tympani are transferred to the round window.

Figure 9.15   Effect of Sound Waves on Cochlear Structures

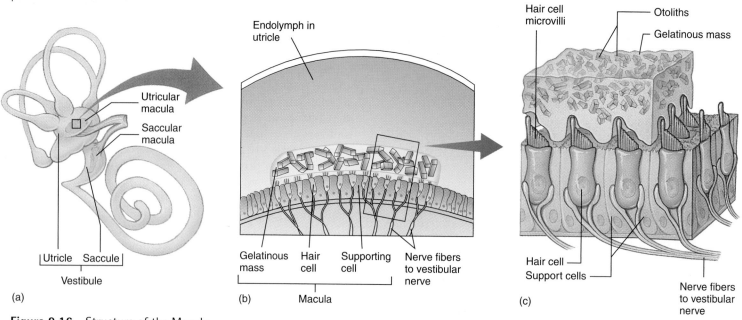

Figure 9.16 Structure of the Macula

(*a*) The location of the utricular and saccular maculae within the vestibule. (*b*) Enlarged view of a section through the utricular macula showing the otoliths. (*c*) Enlargement of that portion of part (*b*) indicated by the box. The relation between the hair cell microvilli and the gelatinous mass can be seen.

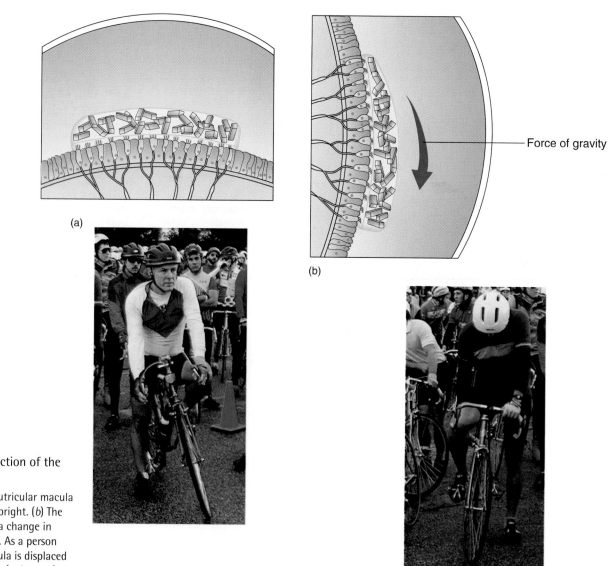

Figure 9.17 Function of the Macula

(*a*) A section of the utricular macula in a person sitting upright. (*b*) The macula responds to a change in position of the head. As a person bends over, the macula is displaced by the pull of gravity (red arrow).

that is displaced by endolymph movement within the semicircular canals (figure 9.19). As the head begins to move in a given direction, the endolymph tends to remain stationary. This difference causes the cupula to be displaced in a direction opposite to that of the movement of the head. As movement continues, the fluid "catches up." When movement of the head stops, the fluid tends to continue to move, displacing the cupula in the direction of the movement. Movement of the cupula causes the hair cell microvilli to bend, which initiates depolarization in the hair cells. This depolarization initiates action potentials in the vestibular nerves, which join the cochlear nerves and relay the information to the brain.

Clinical Focus   Ear Disorders

Deafness

Deafness can have many causes. In general, there are two categories of deafness: conduction and sensorineural (or nerve) deafness. **Conduction deafness** involves a mechanical deficiency in transmission of sound waves from the outer ear to the spiral organ. Hearing aids may help people with such hearing deficiencies by boosting the sound volume that reaches the ear. Some conduction deafness can be corrected surgically. For example, **otosclerosis** (ŏ′tō-sklē-rō′sis) is an ear disorder in which bone grows over the oval window and immobilizes the stapes. This disorder can be surgically corrected by breaking away the bony growth and the stapes. The base of the stapes, located in the oval window, is replaced by a fat pad or synthetic membrane, and the rest of the stapes is replaced by a small metal rod connected to the oval window at one end and to the incus at the other end.

Sensorineural deafness involves the spiral organ or nerve pathways and is more difficult to correct. One approach involves the direct stimulation of the cochlear nerve by action potentials. The mechanism consists of a microphone for picking up sound waves; a microelectronic processor for converting the sound into electrical signals; a transmission system for relaying the signals to the inner ear, and a long, slender electrode that is threaded into the cochlea. This electrode delivers electrical signals directly to the cochlear nerve.

Ear Infections

Infections of the middle ear, called **otitis media** (ŏ-tī′tis mē′dē-ă) are quite common in young children. These infections usually result from the spread of infection from the mucous membrane of the pharynx through the auditory tube. The symptoms of low-grade fever, lethargy, and irritability, and pulling at the ear are not often recognized by the parent as signs of middle ear infection. The infection also can cause a temporary decrease or loss of hearing because fluid buildup can dampen the tympanic membrane. In extreme cases, the infection can damage or rupture the tympanic membrane.

Chronic middle ear infections increase the chances of inner ear infections. Inner ear infections can decrease the inner ear's detection of sound and maintenance of equilibrium.

Motion Sickness

Motion sickness consists of nausea and weakness caused by continuous stimulation of the semicircular canals because of the motion occurring in a boat, automobile, or airplane.

Space Sickness

Space sickness is a balance disorder occurring in zero gravity and resulting from unfamiliar sensory input to the brain. The brain must adjust to these unusual signals, or severe symptoms such as headache and dizziness can result. Space sickness is unlike motion sickness in that motion sickness results from excessive stimulation to the brain, and space sickness results from too little stimulation as a result of weightlessness.

(a)

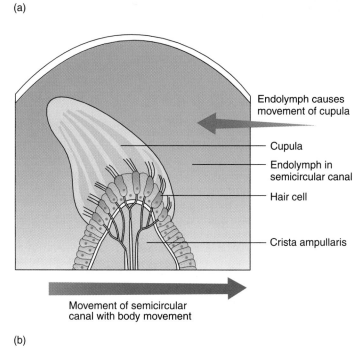

Figure 9.18 Structure of the Crista Ampullaris

(*a*) Semicircular canals showing location of the crista ampullares.
(*b*) Enlargement of a section through a crista ampullaris showing the hair cells. (*c*) Enlarged hair cell.

Figure 9.19 Function of the Crista Ampullaris

(*a*) As a person begins to tumble, the endolymph in the semicircular canals (b) tends to stay in place as the body and the crista ampullaris begin to move. As a result, the cupula is displaced by the moving endolymph (red arrow) in a direction opposite to the direction of movement (blue arrow below figure).

Summary

Sensations result only from those stimuli that reach the cerebral cortex and are consciously perceived. Senses can be defined as special or general.

General Senses

- Receptors for general senses, such as pain, temperature, touch, pressure, and proprioception, are scattered throughout the body.

Pain

- Pain is an unpleasant sensation with a fast component and a slow component.
- Pain can be "gated," referred, or phantom.

Special Senses

- Smell and taste respond to chemical stimulation, vision to light stimulation, and hearing and balance to mechanical stimulation.

Olfaction

- Olfactory neurons have enlarged distal ends with long cilia. The cilia have receptors that respond to dissolved substances in the nasal mucus.
- Axons of the olfactory neurons form the olfactory nerves, which enter the olfactory bulb. Olfactory tracts carry action potentials from the olfactory bulbs to the olfactory cortex of the brain.
- The wide range of detectable odors may result from combinations of receptor responses stimulated by only a few primary odors.

Taste

- Taste buds contain taste cells with hairs that extend into pores. Receptors on the hairs detect dissolved substances.
- There are four basic types of taste: sour, salty, bitter, and sweet.
- The facial nerves carry taste from the anterior two-thirds of the tongue, the glossopharyngeal from the posterior one-third of the tongue, and the vagus from the root of the tongue.

Vision

Accessory Structures

- The eyebrows prevent perspiration from entering the eyes.
- The eyelids protect the eyes from foreign objects.
- The conjunctiva covers the inner eyelids and the anterior surface of the eye.
- Lacrimal glands produce tears that flow across the surface of the eye. Tears lubricate and protect the eye. Excess tears pass into the nasal cavity.
- The extrinsic eye muscles move the eyeball.

Anatomy of the Eye

- The fibrous tunic is the outer layer of the eye. It consists of the sclera and cornea.
- The vascular tunic is the middle layer of the eye. It consists of the choroid, ciliary body, and iris.

- The lens is held in place by the suspensory ligaments, which are attached to the smooth muscles of the ciliary body.
- The retina (nervous tunic) is the inner layer of the eye and contains neurons sensitive to light.
- Rods are responsible for vision in low illumination (night vision).
- Cones are responsible for color vision.
- The fovea centralis has the highest concentration of cones and is the area in which images are detected most clearly.
- The optic disc, or blind spot, is where the optic nerve exits the eye and blood vessels enter.
- The anterior compartment of the eye is filled with aqueous humor, whereas the posterior compartment is filled with vitreous humor. The humors keep the eye inflated, refract light, and provide nutrients to the inner surface of the eye.

Functions of the Complete Eye

- Light passing through a concave surface diverges. Light passing through a convex surface converges.
- Converging light rays cross at the focal point and are said to be focused.
- The cornea, aqueous humor, lens, and vitreous humor all refract light. The cornea is responsible for most of the convergence, whereas the lens can adjust the focus by changing shape (accommodation).

Neuronal Pathways

- Axons pass through the optic nerves to the optic chiasm, where some cross.
- Optic tracts from the chiasm lead to the thalamus.
- Optic radiations extend from the thalamus to the visual cortex in the occipital lobe.

Hearing and Balance

The Ear and Its Functions

- The external ear consists of the auricle and the external auditory meatus.
- The middle ear connects the external and inner ear.
- The tympanic membrane (eardrum) is stretched across the external auditory meatus.
- The malleus, incus, and stapes connect the tympanic membrane to the oval window of the inner ear.
- The auditory, or eustachian, tube connects the middle ear to the pharynx and equalizes pressure. The middle ear is also connected to the mastoid air cells.
- The inner ear has three parts: the semicircular canals, the vestibule, and the cochlea.

Hearing

- The cochlea is a canal shaped like a snail's shell.
- The cochlea is divided into three compartments by the vestibular and basilar membranes.
- The spiral organ consists of hair cells that attach to the basilar and tectorial membranes.
- Sound waves are funneled by the auricle down the external auditory meatus, causing the tympanic membrane to vibrate.

- The tympanic membrane vibrations are passed along the ossicles to the oval window of the inner ear.
- Movement of the base of the stapes in the oval window causes the perilymph to move the vestibular membrane, which causes the endolymph to move the basilar membrane. Movement of the basilar membrane causes movement of the hair cells in the spiral organ and generation of action potentials, which travel along the vestibulocochlear nerve.

Equilibrium

- Static equilibrium evaluates the position of the head relative to gravity.

- Maculae, located in the vestibule, consist of hair cells with the microvilli embedded in a gelatinous mass that contains otoliths.
- The gelatinous mass moves in response to gravity.
- Kinetic equilibrium evaluates movements of the head.
- There are three semicircular canals in the inner ear, arranged perpendicular to each other. The ampulla of each semicircular canal contains a crista ampullaris, which has hair cells with microvilli embedded in a gelatinous mass, the cupula.

Content Review

1. Define stimulus and sensation.
2. List and describe the receptors associated with the general senses.
3. Explain how pain occurs and how it can be modified.
4. Define and explain referred pain and phantom pain.
5. Describe as much as is known of the process by which an airborne molecule initiates an action potential in an olfactory neuron.
6. How is the sense of taste related to the sense of smell?
7. What are the four primary tastes? Where are they concentrated in the tongue? How do they produce many different kinds of taste sensations?
8. Describe the following structures and state their functions: eyebrows, eyelids, conjunctiva, lacrimal apparatus, and extrinsic eye muscles.
9. Name the three layers (tunics) of the eye. Describe the structures composing each layer, and explain the functions of these structures.
10. Describe the two compartments of the eye, the substances that fill each compartment, and the function of the substances. Name the two chambers of the anterior compartment.

11. Describe the lens of the eye, how it is held in place, and how its shape is changed.
12. Describe the arrangement of cones and rods in the fovea centralis and in the periphery of the eye.
13. What is the blind spot of the eye, and what causes it?
14. What causes the pupil to constrict and dilate?
15. What causes light to refract? What is a focal point?
16. Define accommodation. What does accommodation accomplish?
17. Name the three regions of the ear, name the structures found in each region, and state the functions of each structure.
18. Describe the relationship between the tympanic membrane, the ear ossicles, and the oval window of the inner ear.
19. Describe the structure of the cochlea.
20. Starting with the auricle, trace sound into the inner ear to the point at which action potentials are generated in the vestibulocochlear nerve.
21. Describe the macula and its function.
22. What is the function of the semicircular canals? Describe the crista ampullaris and its mode of operation.

Develop Your Reasoning Skills

1. An elderly male with normal vision developed cataracts. He was surgically treated by removing the lenses of his eyes. What kind of glasses would be recommended to compensate for the removal of his lenses?
2. On a camping trip, Starr Gazer was admiring all the stars that could be seen in the night sky. She noticed an interesting little cluster of dim stars at the edge of her vision. When she looked directly at that part of the sky, however, she could not see the cluster. When she looked toward the stars but not directly at them, she could see them. Explain what was happening.

3. Skin divers are subject to increased pressure as they descend toward the bottom of the ocean. Sometimes this pressure can lead to damage to the ear and loss of hearing. Describe the normal mechanisms that adjust for changes in pressure, explain how the increased pressure might cause reduced hearing, and suggest some other common conditions that might interfere with pressure adjustment.
4. If a vibrating tuning fork is placed against the mastoid process of the temporal bone, the vibrations are perceived as sound, even if the external auditory meatus is plugged. Explain how this happens.

Answers to Predict Questions

1. p. 239 The pain is diffuse because deep or visceral pain, such as in the colon, is not highly localized because of the absence of tactile receptors in the deeper structures. The pain is referred to the skin over the lower central abdomen (see figure 9.2). This occurs because afferent neurons from the superficial area to which the pain is referred and the neurons from the colon, where the pain stimulation originated, converge onto the same ascending neurons in the spinal cord.

2. p. 240 Much of taste is based on olfactory function. A cold may include a stuffy nose, which decreases airflow and increases the thickness of the mucus covering the olfactory epithelium and may interfere with olfaction and thus with taste.

3. p. 242 Medications placed into the eyes can pass through the nasolacrimal duct into the nasal cavity, where their odor can be detected. Because much of our taste sensation is actually smell, the medication is perceived to have a taste.

4. p. 243 Cones are responsible for color vision, but they are not nearly as sensitive to light as the rods. Rods are much more sensitive to light, but they do not detect differences in color. In dim light, when rods rather than cones are responsible for vision, objects therefore appear only in shades of gray.

5. p. 247 While you are driving, your vision is focused out on the road, some distance in front of the car. As a result, the ciliary muscles are relaxed and the lens is relatively flat, allowing for distant vision. When you look down at the speedometer, the eye accommodates for close vision, the ciliary muscles contract, pulling the ciliary body toward the lens. This reduces the tension on the suspensory ligaments of the lens and allows the lens to assume a more spherical form. When you look back up at the road, the ciliary muscles again relax and the lens flattens, allowing for distant vision. Even though these changes occur very quickly, there is brief moment, before accommodation occurs, when you first look at the speedometer that it is out of focus. When you look back at the road, it is also briefly out of focus, as the lens changes back for distant vision.

6. p. 251 The reason that, when you hear a faint sound, you turn your head toward it is that sound waves are collected by the auricle and conducted through the external auditory meatus toward the tympanic membrane. The auricle is shaped in such a way that sound waves coming from the side and front of the head are most efficiently conducted into the external auditory meatus. Because a specific sound reaches each ear at slightly different times, a person can localize the origin of the sound. Turning the head toward the sound facilitates maximum accumulation of the sound waves by the ear. In addition, there is also a reflexive turning of the head and eyes toward a sound so that you can see what is making the sound.

Chapter Ten

The Endocrine System

endocrine

(en′dō-krin) [Gr. *endon*, inside + *krino*, to separate] Ductless gland that secretes internally, usually into the circulation.

hormone

(hōr′mōn) [Gr. *hormon*, to set into motion] A substance secreted by endocrine tissues into the blood that acts on a target tissue to produce a specific response.

hypothalamic–pituitary portal system

(hī′pō-thal′ă-mik-pi-too′i-tār-ē) A series of blood vessels that carry blood from the area of the hypothalamus to the anterior pituitary; they originate from capillary beds in the hypothalamus and terminate as a capillary bed in the anterior pituitary.

hypothalamus

(hī′pō-thal′ă-mŭs) [Gr. *hypo*, under, below + *thalamus*, bedroom] Important autonomic and endocrine control center of the brain located beneath the thalamus.

pituitary

(pi-too′i-tār-rē) or hypophysis (hī-pof′ĭ-sis) [Fr., an undergrowth] An endocrine gland attached to the hypothalamus; secretes hormones that influence the function of several other endocrine glands and tissues.

receptor molecule

(rē-sep′tŏr mol′ĕ-kūl) A molecule in the membrane or cytoplasm of cells of a target tissue to which a hormone binds. The combining of a hormone with its receptor initiates a response in the target tissue.

releasing hormone

(hōr′mōn) Hormone that is released from nerve cells of the hypothalamus and flows through the hypothalamic–pituitary portal system to the anterior pituitary; functions to regulate the secretion of hormones from the cells of the anterior pituitary gland; sometimes referred to as releasing factors.

target tissue

(tish′ū) Tissue on which a hormone acts.

Objectives

After reading this chapter, you should be able to:

1. Compare the means by which the nervous and endocrine systems regulate body functions.

2. Describe the relationship among chemical signals, receptor molecules, and receptor sites.

3. Describe how membrane-bound and intracellular receptor molecules mediate responses to intercellular chemical signals.

4. List the mechanisms by which intercellular chemical signals produce responses in their target tissues.

5. Describe the categories of intercellular chemical signals that are based on the cells from which they are released and their target cells.

6. List the major categories of hormones on the basis of their chemical structure and describe how they interact with tissues to produce a response.

7. Describe three methods of regulating the release of hormones.

8. State the location of each of the endocrine glands in the body.

9. List the hormones produced by each of the endocrine glands and describe their effects on the body.

10. Describe how the hypothalamus regulates hormone secretion from the pituitary.

11. Describe how the pituitary gland regulates the secretion of hormones from other endocrine glands.

12. Choose a hormone and use it to explain how negative feedback results in homeostasis.

Homeostasis depends on the precise regulation of the organs and organ systems of the body. The nervous and endocrine systems are the two major systems responsible for that regulation. Together they regulate and coordinate the activity of nearly all other body structures. When either the nervous or endocrine system fails to function properly, conditions can rapidly deviate from homeostasis. The nervous and endocrine systems are much like the coaches of athletic teams who direct the activities of players. When the directions are adequate, the results are generally good for the teams, but when the directions are faulty, the results are not so good.

The regulatory functions of the nervous and endocrine systems are similar in some ways, but they differ in other important ways. The nervous system controls the activity of tissues by sending action potentials along axons, which release chemical signals at their ends, near the cells they control. The endocrine system releases chemical signals into the circulatory system, which carries them to all parts of the body. The cells that can detect these chemical signals produce responses. The functions of both the nervous and endocrine systems depend on these chemical signals.

The nervous system usually acts more quickly and has short-term effects, whereas the endocrine system usually responds more slowly and has a longer-lasting effects. In general, each nervous stimulus controls a specific tissue or organ, whereas each endocrine stimulus has a more general effect on the body.

Functions of the Endocrine System

The endocrine system functions with the nervous system to regulate the many activities critical to the maintenance of homeostasis. The main functions of the endocrine system include

1. *Water balance.* The endocrine system regulates water balance by controlling the solute concentration of the blood.
2. *Uterine contractions and milk release.* The endocrine system regulates uterine contractions during delivery and stimulates milk release from the breasts in lactating females.
3. *Growth, metabolism, and tissue maturation.* The endocrine system regulates the growth of tissues, such as bone and muscle, and the rate of metabolism of most tissues, which helps maintain a normal body temperature and normal mental functions. Maturation of tissues, which results in the development of adult features and adult behavior, are also influenced by the endocrine system.
4. *Ion regulation.* The endocrine system regulates sodium, potassium, and calcium ion concentrations in the blood.
5. *Heart rate and blood pressure regulation.* The endocrine system helps regulate the heart rate and blood pressure and helps prepare the body for physical activity.
6. *Blood glucose control.* The endocrine system regulates blood glucose levels and other nutrient levels in the blood.
7. *Immune system regulation.* The endocrine system helps control the production of immune cells.
8. *Reproductive functions control.* The endocrine system controls the development and the function of the reproductive systems in males and females.

Chemical Signals

Major categories of chemical signals are presented here to allow the comparison of chemical signals of the endocrine system to other categories of chemical signals. **Chemical signals,** or **ligands** (lī′gandz), are molecules released from one location that move to another location to produce a response. **Intracellular chemical signals** are produced in one part of a cell, such as the cell membrane, and travel to another part of the same cell and bind to receptors, either in the cytoplasm or in the nucleus of the cell. **Intercellular chemical signals** are released from one cell, are carried in the intercellular fluid, and bind to their receptors, which are found in some cells, but usually not in all cells of the body.

Intercellular chemical signals can be placed into functional categories on the basis of the tissues from which they are secreted and the tissues they regulate (table 10.1).

Autocrine (aw′tō-krin) **chemical signals** are released by cells and have a local effect on the same cell type from which the chemical signals are released. Examples include prostaglandin-like chemicals released from smooth muscle cells and from platelets in response to inflammation. These chemicals cause the relaxation of blood vessel smooth muscle cells and the aggregation of platelets. As a result the blood vessels dilate and blood clots.

Chemical signals released by cells that have effects on other cell types near the cells from which they are released, without being transported in blood, are called **paracrine** (par′ă-krin) **chemical signals**. For example, a peptide called somatostatin is released by cells in the pancreas and functions locally to inhibit the secretion of insulin from other cells of the pancreas.

Hormones and neurohormones are intercellular chemical signals secreted into the circulatory system (see section, Hormones, on p. 268). They are carried in the blood to the organs they control, where they bind to receptor molecules and produce a response.

Neuromodulators and **neurotransmitters** are intercellular chemical signals, secreted by nerve cells, which play important roles in the function of the nervous system (see chapter 8).

Pheromones (fer′ō-mōnz) are chemical signals secreted into the environment that modify the behavior and the physiology of other individuals. For example, pheromones released in the urine of cats and dogs at certain times are olfactory signals that indicate fertility. Pheromones also appear to be produced by humans, although their importance is not clear. For example, pheromones produced by women can influence the length of the menstrual cycle of other women.

Table 10.1 Functional Classification of Intercellular Chemical Signals

Intercellular Chemical Signal	Description	Example	
Autocrine	Secreted by cells in a local area and influences the activity of the same cell type from which it was secreted	Prostaglandins	Autocrine chemical signal
Paracrine	Produced by a wide variety of tissues and secreted into tissue spaces; usually has a localized effect on other tissues	Histamine, prostaglandins	Paracrine chemical signal
Hormone	Secreted into the blood by specialized cells; travels some distance to target tissues; influences specific activities	Thyroid hormones, growth hormone, insulin, epinephrine, estrogen, progesterone, testosterone	Hormone
Neurohormone	Produced by neurons and functions like hormones	Oxytocin, antidiuretic hormone	Neuron / Neurohormone
Neurotransmitter or neuromodulator	Produced by neurons and secreted into extracellular spaces by presynaptic nerve terminals; travels short distances; influences postsynaptic cells	Acetylcholine, epinephrine	Neurotransmitter / Neuron
Pheromone	Secreted into the environment; modifies physiology and behavior of other individuals	Sex pheromones are released by humans and many other animals. They are released in the urine of animals, such as dogs and cats. Pheromones produced by women can influence the length of the menstrual cycles of other women.	Pheromone

Many intercellular chemical signals consistently fit one specific definition, although others do not. For example, norepinephrine functions both as a neurotransmitter substance and as a hormone; and prostaglandins function as neurotransmitters, neuromodulators, paracrine chemical signals, and autocrine chemical signals. The schemes used to classify chemicals on the basis of their functions are useful, but they do not indicate that a specific molecule always acts as the same type of chemical signal. For that reason, the study of endocrinology often includes the study of autocrine and paracrine chemical signals in addition to hormones and neurohormones.

Receptors

Chemical signals bind to proteins or glycoproteins, called **receptor molecules**, to produce a response. The portion of each receptor molecule where a chemical signal binds is a **receptor site**. The shape and chemical characteristics of each receptor site allows only a specific chemical signal to bind to it (figure 10.1). The tendency for each receptor site to bind to a specific chemical signal and not to others is called **specificity**.

Receptor Types for Intercellular Chemical Signals

There are two major types of receptor molecules that respond to an intercellular chemical signal (figure 10.2):

1. **Intracellular receptors** are located in either the cytoplasm or nucleus of the cell. Intercellular chemical signals diffuse across the cell membrane and bind to receptor sites on intracellular receptors (see figure

10.2*a*). Some intracellular receptors are enzymes. An intercellular chemical signal can bind to this kind of receptor and change the activity of the enzyme. Other intracellular receptors can bind to DNA. An intercellular chemical signal can bind to this kind of receptor and increase the synthesis of specific messenger RNA molecules. The messenger RNA then moves to the

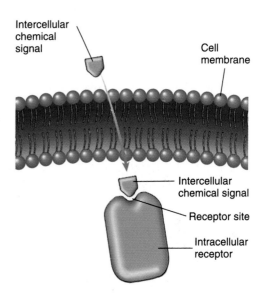

(a)

(b)

Figure 10.2   Intracellular and Membrane-Bound Receptors

(*a*) Small lipid-soluble intercellular chemical signals diffuse through the cell membrane and combine with the receptor sites of intracellular receptors. The combination of intercellular chemical signals and receptors produce a response. (*b*) Intercellular chemical signals that are large and water-soluble interact with membrane-bound receptors that extend across the cell membrane and have receptor sites exposed to the outer surface of the cell membrane. The portion of the receptor inside the cell produces the response. Membrane-bound receptors produce responses when intercellular chemical signals bind to them. There are many membrane-bound receptors and there are several mechanisms by which they can produce responses.

Figure 10.1   Receptors and Specificity of Receptor Sites

Chemical signals bind to receptor molecules. The shape and chemical characteristics of each receptor site allow only certain chemical signals to bind to it, but not others. This tendency is called specificity.

Table 10.2　Some Major Intercellular Chemical Signals, Their Source, Target Tissues, and Effects

a. Chemical Signals That Combine with Intracellular Receptors

Signal	Source	Target Tissue and Effect
Testosterone	Testis	Responsible for development of the reproductive structures and development of male secondary sexual characteristics
Progesterone	Ovary	Causes increased size of cells lining the uterus
Estrogen	Ovary	Causes increased cell division in the lining of the uterus
Aldosterone	Adrenal cortex	Increased reabsorption of Na^+ ions and increased secretion of K^+ ions in the kidney
Cortisol	Adrenal cortex	Increased breakdown of proteins and fats and increased blood levels of glucose
Triiodothyronine (T_3)	Thyroid gland	Regulate development and metabolism
1,25-dihydroxycholecalciferol	Combination of the skin, liver, and kidney	Increased reabsorption of Ca^{2+} ions in the kidney and absorption of Ca^{2+} ions in the gastrointestinal tract

b. Intercellular Chemical Signals That Bind to Membrane-Bound Receptors and Directly Control Ion Channels

Acetylcholine	Nerve endings	Skeletal muscle, smooth muscle, glands, and neurons; usually opens sodium ion channels
Serotonin	Nerve endings	Neurons; opens sodium ion channels
Glutamate	Nerve endings	Neurons; opens sodium ion channels
Glycine	Nerve endings	Neurons; opens chloride ion channels
GABA*	Nerve endings	Neurons; opens chloride ion channels

c. Intercellular Chemical Signals That Bind to Membrane-Bound Receptors That Phosphorylate Intracellular Proteins

Insulin	Pancreatic islets	Most cells; increases glucose and amino acid uptake
Growth hormone	Anterior pituitary gland	Most cells; increases protein synthesis and resists protein breakdown
Prolactin	Anterior pituitary gland	Mammary glands and ovary; increases milk production following pregnancy and helps maintain the corpus luteum
Growth factors	Various tissues	Stimulate cell division and growth in various most tissue
Some intercellular immune signal molecules	Cells of the immune system	Immune competent cells; help mediate responses of the immune system

*Abbreviations: GABA: gamma-aminobutyric acid.

cytoplasm and directs the synthesis of new proteins at the ribosome. The newly synthesized proteins produces a response (table 10.2a).

2. **Membrane-bound receptors** extend across the cell membrane, with their receptor sites on the outer surface of the cell membrane. These receptors respond to intercellular chemical signals that are large, water-soluble molecules that do not diffuse across the cell membrane. When a chemical signal binds to the receptor site of a membrane-bound receptor, the part of the receptor that extends to the inside of the cell produces a response (see figure 10.2b, table 10.2b and c). There are many membrane-bound receptors and there are several mechanisms by which they can produce responses.

Receptor Responses

When an intercellular signal binds a membrane-bound receptor, three general types of responses are possible.

1. *Receptors that directly alter membrane permeability.* Some intercellular chemical signals bind to receptor sites, and ion channels in the cell membrane open or close. The change in membrane permeability results in a change in the movement of ions across the cell membrane, which is responsible for the cell's response. For example, acetylcholine from nerve fiber endings binds to receptors that are part of the membrane channels for sodium ions. As a consequence, the sodium ion channels in skeletal muscle membranes open. Sodium ions diffuse through the open sodium ion channels into the cell to produce an action potential and contraction of the muscle fiber (figure 10.3 and table 10.2b).

2. *Receptors and G proteins.* Some intercellular chemical signals bind to receptor sites, and the result is the activation of a complex of proteins at the inner surface of the cell membrane called G proteins (figure 10.4). A G protein has alpha (α), beta (β), and gamma (γ) subunits. At the inner surface of the cell membrane, α, β, and γ subunits form a complex that binds to the inter-

(a) The sodium (Na$^+$) ion channel has receptor sites for acetylcholine. When the receptor sites are not occupied by acetylcholine, the membrane channel for Na$^+$ ions is closed.

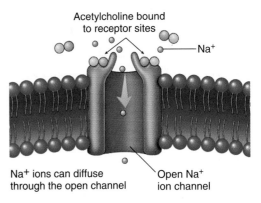

(b) Acetylcholine binds to its receptor site, which is part of the membrane channel for Na$^+$ ions, and causes the membrane channel to open. Na$^+$ ions diffuse into the cell to produce an action potential and muscle contraction. Note that each of the Na$^+$ ion channels has two receptor sites for acetylcholine.

Figure 10.3 Intercellular Chemical Signals That Directly Cause Ion Channels in the Cell Membrane to Open

(a) The membrane-bound receptor can associate with G proteins at the inner surface of the cell membrane. When the receptor site at the outside of the cell membrane is not occupied, the G proteins remain as a unit and inactive.

(b) The intercellular chemical signal binds to its receptor site on the outside of the cell membrane. The combination causes the G proteins to separate from the receptor and the alpha (α) subunit to separate from the gamma (γ) and beta (β) subunits. GTP replaces GDP on the alpha (α) subunit. The α subunit, with GTP bound to it, can activate enzymes or open membrane channels.

Figure 10.4 Membrane-Bound Receptors That Activate G Proteins

cellular portion of the receptor molecule. When an intercellular chemical signal binds to the membrane-bound receptor, the α subunit separates from the β and γ subunits. Guanosine triphosphate (GTP) then replaces guanosine diphosphate (GDP) on the subunit. The α subunit with GTP bound to it, in turn, activates enzymes that produce intracellular chemical signals. Several types of intracellular chemical signals are produced by G proteins, depending on the receptor molecule and the specific function of the G proteins present in the cell. Examples of intracellular chemical signals include **cyclic adenosine monophosphate (c AMP)**, **diacylglycerol** (dī′as-il-glis′er-ol, **DAG**), and **inosotol** (in-ō′si-tōl) **triphosphate (IP$_3$)**. These intracellular chemical

signals bind to receptor molecules in the cell and alter their activity to produce a response. In some cases the intracellular chemical signals can open or close membrane channels.

3. *Receptors that alter the activity of enzymes.* Some intercellular chemical signals bind to receptor sites, and the result is an increase or decrease in enzyme activity (figure 10.5). Because enzymes regulate the activity of chemical reactions with cells (see chapter 2), altering enzyme activity changes chemical activity, producing a cellular response. For example, increasing the activity of the enzyme responsible for the breakdown of glycogen to glucose makes glucose available as an energy source for muscle contraction (see chapter 7).

(a) The membrane-bound receptor is associated with an enzyme at the inner surface of the cell membrane. When the receptor site at the outside of the cell membrane is not occupied by an intercellular chemical signal, the enzyme remains inactive.

(b) The intercellular chemical signal binds to its receptor site on the outside of the cell membrane, and causes the enzyme at the inner surface of the cell membrane to become active.

Figure 10.5   Membrane-Bound Receptors That Control Enzyme Activity

1. A chemical signal combines with the receptor site of the membrane-bound receptor.

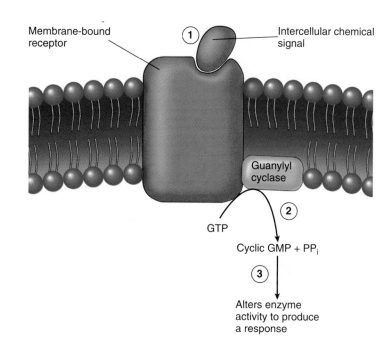

2. The combination activates the enzyme guanylyl cyclase at the inner surface of the cell membrane. Guanylyl cyclase converts GTP to cyclic GMP plus 2 inorganic phosphate groups.

3. Cyclic GMP is an intracellular chemical signal, and it functions to alter the activity of intracellular enzymes to produce a response.

Figure 10.6   Membrane-Bound Receptors That Increase the Synthesis of Intracellular Chemical Signals by Activating Enzymes Directly

- Some intercellular chemical signals bind to their receptor molecules with the effect of directly altering the activity of an enzyme at the inner surface of the cell membrane, which in turn increases or decreases the synthesis of an intracellular chemical signals such as **cyclic guanosine monophosphate (cGMP)** (figure 10.6).
- Some intercellular chemical signals bind to receptors, with the effect of altering the activity of an enzyme at the inner surface of the cell membrane, which in turn adds phosphate groups to certain proteins inside the cells. The proteins with phosphates attached to them produce the response of the cell to the chemical signal (figure 10.7 and table 10.2c).

Comparison of Receptor Responses

Some intercellular chemical signals diffuse across cell membranes and bind to intracellular receptors. Because these intracellular chemical signals are relatively small and are soluble in lipids, they can diffuse through the cell membrane. The chemical signal and the receptor bind to DNA in the nucleus and increase specific messenger RNA synthesis in the nucleus of the cell. The messenger RNA then moves to the ribosomes in the cytoplasm where new proteins are produced (see figure 10.8 and chapter 3). Because of the time required for the synthesis of new proteins, several hours are required between the time the chemical signals bind to their receptors and the response. In contrast, intercellular chemical signals that bind to membrane-bound

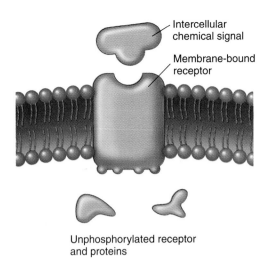

Intercellular
chemical signal

Membrane-bound
receptor

Unphosphorylated receptor
and proteins

(a) The membrane-bound receptor and other proteins
have sites that can be phosphorylated at the inner
surface of the cell membrane. When the receptor
site at the outside of the cell membrane is not
occupied by an intercellular chemical signal these
sites remain unphosphorylated

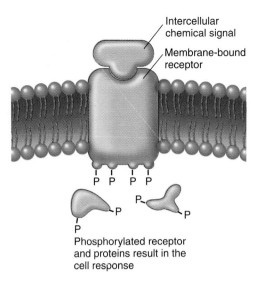

Intercellular
chemical signal

Membrane-bound
receptor

Phosphorylated receptor
and proteins result in the
cell response

(b) The intercellular chemical signal binds to its receptor
site on the outside of the cell membrane, and this
causes an enzyme at the inner surface of the cell
membrane to phosphorylate the sites on the receptor
and associated proteins. These phosphorylated
proteins produce a response inside the cell.

Figure 10.7   Membrane-Bound Receptors That Phosphorylate Intracellular Proteins

1. The intercellular chemical signal
diffuses through the cell membrane
and enters the cytoplasm of the cell.

2. The chemical signal combines with the
receptor in the nucleus (or in the
cytoplasm).

3. The receptor with the chemical signal
bound to it interacts with DNA and
increases the synthesis of specific
messenger RNA molecules.

4. The messenger RNA (mRNA)
molecules pass from the nucleus to
the cytoplasm.

5. In the cytoplasm of the cell, messenger
RNA molecules combine with
ribosomes. New protein molecules,
which produce the response of the cell
to the chemical signal, are
synthesized.

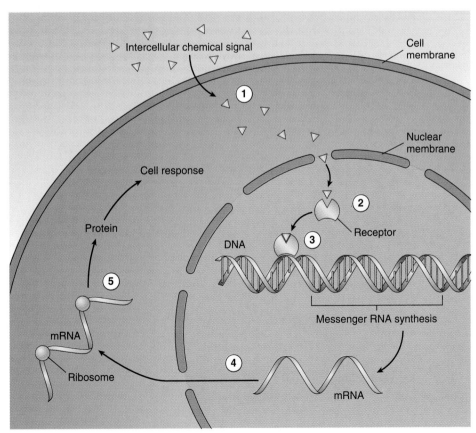

Figure 10.8   Intercellular Receptors That Diffuse into Cells and Bind to Intracellular Receptors

receptors produce rapid responses. For example, a few intercellular chemical signals can bind to their membrane-bound receptors and each activated receptor can produce many intracellular chemical signal molecules. The intracellular chemical signal molecules, in turn, rapidly activate many specific enzymes inside the cell. This pattern of response is called a **cascade effect** because a few intercellular chemical signals can produce many intracellular chemical signals, and the intracellular chemical signals can, in turn, quickly activate many enzymes inside the cell.

---

1 | **P R E D I C T**

A drug binds to a receptor and prevents the response of a target tissue to a chemical signal. It is known that the drug is lipid-soluble and it prevents the synthesis of messenger RNA. Explain how the chemical signal produces a response in its target tissue.

✔ *Answer on page 290*

Hormones

The term **endocrine** (en′dō-krin) is derived from the Greek words *endo* and *krino* meaning "within" and "to separate." The word implies that intercellular chemical signals are produced within and secreted from **endocrine glands**, but the chemical signals have effects at locations that are away from, or separate from, the endocrine glands that secrete them. The

intercellular chemical signals are transported in the blood to tissues some distance from the glands. Examples of endocrine glands are the thyroid and the adrenal glands. In contrast, **exocrine** (ek′sō-krin) **glands** secrete their products into ducts, which exit the glands and carry the secretory products to an external or internal surface, such as the skin or digestive tract. Examples of exocrine glands are the sweat and the salivary glands. The **endocrine system** consists of all the endocrine glands of the body (figure 10.9).

The intercellular chemical signals secreted by endocrine glands are called **hormones** (hōr′mōnz), a term derived from the Greek word *hormon* meaning to "set into motion," because hormones set responses by cells into motion. Traditionally a hormone is defined as an intercellular chemical signal, produced in minute amounts by a collection of cells, that is secreted into the circulatory system to be transported some distance, and that acts on tissues at another site in the body to influence their activity in a specific way. All hormones exhibit most of these characteristics. **Neurohormones** are hormones secreted from cells of the nervous system.

Hormones are distributed in the blood to all parts of the body, but only certain tissues, called **target tissues**, respond to each type of hormone. A target tissue for a hormone is made up of cells that have receptor molecules for the hormone. Each hormone can bind only to its receptor molecules and cannot influence the function of cells that do not have receptor molecules for the hormone (figure 10.10).

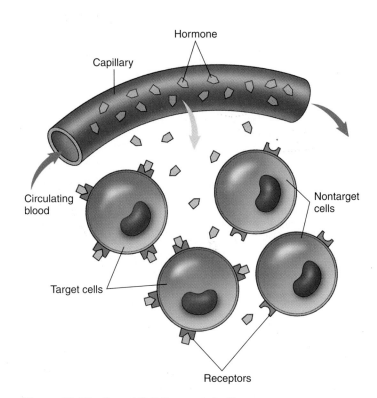

Figure 10.10 Target Cell Response to Hormones

Hormones are secreted into the blood and distributed throughout the body, where they diffuse from the blood into the interstitial fluid (yellow arrow). Only target cells have receptors to which hormones can bind; therefore, even though a hormone is distributed throughout the body, only target cells for that hormone can respond to it.

Figure 10.9 Endocrine Glands and Their Locations in the Human Body

Hypothalamus

Pituitary

Thymus

Adrenals

Ovaries (female)

Pineal body

Thyroid

Parathyroids (posterior part of thyroid)

Pancreas (islets)

Testes (male)

Chemistry

Hormones fall into the following chemical categories:

1. *Proteins, peptides, and amino acid derivatives.*
   Hormones in this category bind to membrane-bound receptors, with the exception of peptide hormones secreted by the thyroid gland, which diffuse through membranes and bind to intracellular receptors.
   a. Some hormones are proteins, consisting of many amino acids bound together by peptide bonds. Carbohydrate molecules are bound to some of the protein hormones. Most hormones of the anterior pituitary gland, including those that control functions such as growth, metabolism, and reproductive functions, are examples of protein hormones.
   b. Peptide hormones consist of short chains of amino acids. The hormones of the posterior pituitary gland that control functions such as milk "let-down" in the breast and urine volume in the kidneys are examples of peptide hormones.
   c. Some hormones consist of single amino acids that have been chemically modified. Hormones secreted by the adrenal medulla, which help a person prepare for physical activity or respond to emergency conditions, are examples.

2. *Lipid hormones.*
   a. Steroid hormones are lipids, all of which are derived from cholesterol. The steroids all have a structure that varies only slightly among the different types. The small differences, however, give each type of steroid unique functional characteristics. Steroid hormones are produced mostly by the adrenal cortex and the gonads (testes and ovaries). Hormones in this category diffuse across the cell membrane and bind to intracellular receptor molecules.
   b. The **eicosanoids** (ī'kō-să-noydz) make up a class of chemicals derived from the fatty acid arachidonic acid. The eicosanoids include the prostaglandins, thromboxanes, prostacyclins, and leukotrienes. A major group of eicosanoids is the **prostaglandins** (pros'tă-glan'dinz) which are produced by many tissues and generally have local effects. They play important roles in regulating smooth muscle contractions and inflammation. They bind to membrane-bound receptors that are associated with G proteins to produce a response.

Regulation of Hormone Secretion

The secretion of hormones is controlled by negative-feedback mechanisms (see chapter 1). Negative-feedback mechanisms keep the body functioning within a narrow range of values consistent with life. For example, insulin is a hormone that regulates the concentration of blood glucose, or blood sugar. When blood glucose levels increase after a meal, insulin is secreted. Insulin acts on several target tissues and causes them to take up glucose, causing blood glucose levels to decline. As the blood glucose levels begin to fall, however, the rate at which insulin is secreted falls also. As insulin levels fall, the rate at which glucose is taken up by the tissues decreases, keeping the blood glucose levels from declining too much. This negative-feedback mechanism counteracts increases and decreases in blood glucose levels to maintain homeostasis.

Hormone secretion is regulated in three ways. The secretion of some hormones is regulated by one of these methods, whereas the secretion other hormones can be regulated by two or even all of these methods:

1. *Blood levels of chemicals.* The secretion of some hormones is directly controlled by the blood levels of certain chemicals. For example, insulin secretion is controlled by blood glucose levels, and secretion of parathyroid hormone is controlled by blood calcium levels.
2. *Hormones.* The secretion of some hormones is controlled by other hormones. For example, hormones from the pituitary gland act on the ovaries and the testes, causing those organs to secrete sex hormones.
3. *Nervous system.* The secretion of some hormones is controlled by the nervous system. An example is epinephrine, which is released from the adrenal medulla as a result of nervous system stimulation.

The Endocrine Glands and Their Hormones

The endocrine system consists of ductless glands, which secrete hormones directly into the circulatory system (table 10.3; see figure 10.9). The endocrine glands are supplied by an extensive network of blood vessels; organs with the richest blood supply include endocrine glands such as the adrenal and thyroid glands.

Did You Know?

Specific hormones are given as treatments for certain illnesses. Hormones that are soluble in lipids, such as steroids, can be taken orally because they can diffuse across the wall of the stomach and intestine into the circulatory system. Examples include the synthetic estrogen and progesterone-like hormones in birth control pills and steroids that reduce the severity of inflammation, such as prednisone (pred'ni-sōn). In contrast to lipid-soluble hormones, protein hormones cannot diffuse across the wall of the intestine because they are not lipid-soluble. Protein hormones are broken down to individual amino acids before they are transported across the wall of the digestive system. The normal structure of a protein hormone is therefore destroyed, and its physiological activity is lost. Consequently, protein hormones must be injected rather than taken orally. The most commonly administered protein hormone is insulin, which is prescribed for the treatment of diabetes mellitus.

Table 10.3 Endocrine Glands, Hormones, and Their Target Tissues

Gland	Hormone	Target Tissue	Response
Pituitary gland			
Anterior	Growth hormone	Most tissues	Increases protein synthesis, breakdown of lipids, and release of fatty acids from cells; increases blood glucose levels
	Thyroid-stimulating hormone (TSH)	Thyroid gland	Increases thyroid hormone secretion (thyroxine and triiodothyronine)
	Adrenocorticotropic hormone (ACTH)	Adrenal cortex	Increases secretion of glucocorticoid hormones such as cortisol; increases skin pigmentation at high concentrations
	Melanocyte-stimulating hormone (MSH)	Melanocytes in skin	Increases melanin production in melanocytes to make the skin darker in color
	Luteinizing hormone (LH) or interstitial cell stimulating hormone (ICSH)	Ovary in females, testis in males	Promotes ovulation and progesterone production in the ovary, testosterone synthesis and support for sperm cell production in testis
	Follicle-stimulating hormone (FSH)	Follicles in ovary in females, seminiferous tubules in males	Promotes follicle maturation and estrogen secretion in ovary; sperm cell production in testis
	Prolactin	Ovary and mammary gland in females, testis in males	Stimulates milk production and prolongs progesterone secretion following ovulation and during pregnancy in women; increases sensitivity to LH in males
Posterior	Antidiuretic hormone (ADH)	Kidney	Increases water reabsorption (less water is lost as urine)
	Oxytocin	Uterus	Increases uterine contractions
		Mammary gland	Increases milk "let-down" from mammary glands
Thyroid gland	Thyroid hormones (thyroxine and triiodothyronine)	Most cells of the body	Increase metabolic rates, essential for normal process of growth and maturation
	Calcitonin	Primarily bone	Decreases rate of bone breakdown; prevents large increase in blood calcium levels
Parathyroid glands	Parathyroid hormone	Bone, kidney	Increases rate of bone breakdown by osteoclasts; increases vitamin D synthesis, essential for maintenance of normal blood calcium levels

continued next page

Some glands of the endocrine system perform functions in addition to hormone secretion. For example, the endocrine part of the pancreas has cells that secrete hormones. The much larger exocrine portion of the pancreas secretes digestive enzymes. Portions of the ovaries and testes secrete hormones. Other parts of the ovaries and testes produce oocytes (female sex cells) or sperm cells (male sex cells), respectively.

The Pituitary and Hypothalamus

The **pituitary** (pi-too'i-tār-rē) gland, or **hypophysis** (hī-pof'i-sis), is a small gland about the size of a pea (figure 10.11). It rests in a depression of the sphenoid bone inferior to the hypothalamus of the brain. The **hypothalamus** (hī'pō-thal'ă-mŭs) is an important autonomic nervous system and endocrine control center of the brain located inferior

Table 10.3	Endocrine Glands, Hormones, and Their Target Tissues *(continued)*		
Gland	**Hormone**	**Target Tissue**	**Response**
Adrenal glands			
Adrenal medulla	Epinephrine mostly, some norepinephrine	Heart, blood vessels, liver, fat cells	Increases cardiac output; increases blood flow to skeletal muscles and heart; increases release of glucose and fatty acids into blood; in general, prepares the body for physical activity
Adrenal cortex	Mineralocorticoids (aldosterone)	Kidneys; to lesser degree, intestine and sweat glands	Increase rate of sodium transport into body; increase rate of potassium excretion; secondarily favor water retention
Adrenal cortex	Glucocorticoids (cortisol)	Most tissues (e.g., liver, fat, skeletal muscle, immune tissues)	Increase fat and protein breakdown; increase glucose synthesis from amino acids; increase blood nutrient levels; inhibit inflammation and immune response
	Adrenal androgens	Most tissues	Insignificant in males; increase female sexual drive, pubic hair and axillary hair growth
Pancreas	Insulin	Especially liver, skeletal muscle, adipose tissue	Increases uptake and use of glucose and amino acids
	Glucagon	Primarily liver	Increases breakdown of glycogen and release of glucose into the circulatory system
Reproductive organs			
Testes	Testosterone	Most tissues	Aids in sperm cell production, maintenance of functional reproductive organs, secondary sexual characteristics, and sexual behavior
Ovaries	Estrogens and progesterone	Most tissues	Aid in uterine and mammary gland development and function, external genitalia structure, secondary sexual characteristics, sexual behavior, and menstrual cycle
Uterus, ovaries, inflamed tissues	Prostaglandins	Most tissues	Mediate inflammatory responses; increase uterine contractions, and ovulation
Thymus gland	Thymosin	Immune tissues	Promotes immune system development and function
Pineal body	Melatonin	At least the hypothalamus	Inhibits secretion of gonadotropin-releasing hormone, thereby inhibiting reproduction

to the thalamus. The pituitary gland is located posterior to the optic chiasma and is connected to the hypothalamus by a stalk called the **infundibulum** (in-fŭn-dib′ū-lŭm). The pituitary gland is divided into two parts: the **anterior pituitary** is made up of epithelial cells derived from the embryonic oral cavity, and the **posterior pituitary** is an extension of the brain and is made up of nerve cells. The hormones secreted from each lobe of the pituitary gland are listed in table 10.3.

Hormones from the pituitary gland control the functions of many other glands in the body, such as the ovaries, testes, thyroid gland, and adrenal cortex (see figure 10.11). The pituitary gland also secretes hormones that influence growth, kidney function, birth, and milk production by the breast. The pituitary gland historically was referred to as the **master gland** of the body because it controls the function of so many other glands. It is now known, however, that the pituitary gland is itself controlled in two ways by the hypothalamus of the brain:

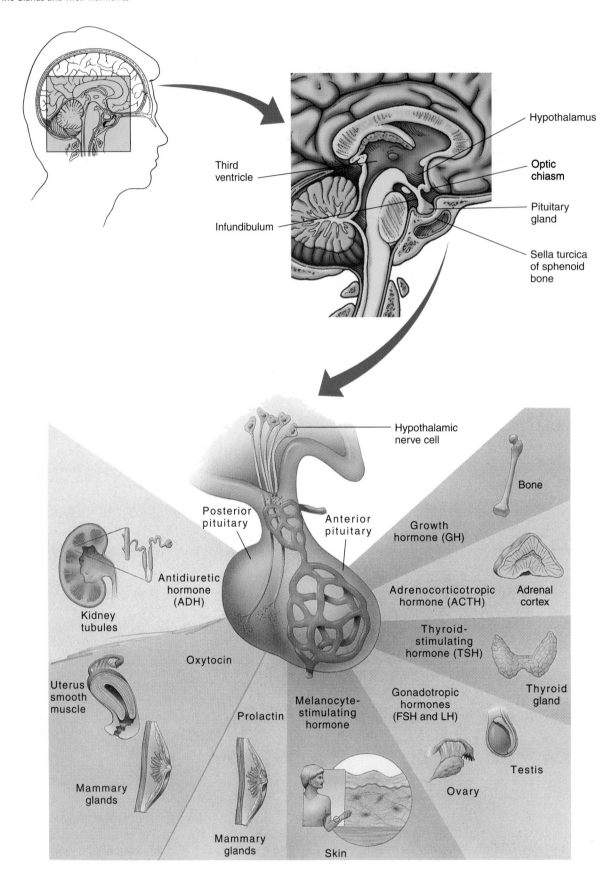

Figure 10.11 The Pituitary Gland Hormones and their Target Tissues

Overview of the pituitary gland, hormones secreted by the pituitary gland, and their target tissues. Hormones secreted by the posterior pituitary are indicated by the blue shading and hormones secreted by the anterior pituitary by lavender shading. The inset shows the location of the pituitary gland and its relationship to the hypothalamus of the brain. The infundibulum connects the hypothalamus and the pituitary gland.

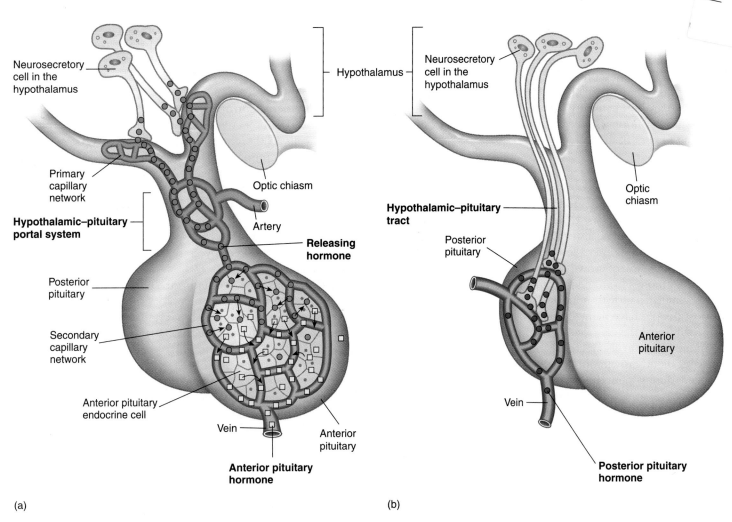

Figure 10.12   The Hypothalamus and Pituitary

(a) Hormones are secreted from the hypothalamic nerve cells as a result of certain stimuli acting on the brain. They pass through the hypothalamic-pituitary portal system to the anterior pituitary, where they influence the secretion of anterior pituitary hormones. Hormones secreted from the anterior pituitary pass through the blood to their target tissues. (b) Some neurosecretory cells of the hypothalamus have axons that extend to the posterior pituitary and make up the secretory part of the posterior pituitary. In response to stimulation, hormones are released from the axon endings of the nerve cells located in the posterior pituitary gland and pass through the blood to target tissues.

1. The secretion of hormones from the anterior pituitary is controlled by **releasing hormones**, which are chemical signals produced by nerve cells of the hypothalamus (figure 10.12*a*). Each releasing hormone either stimulates or inhibits the release of a specific anterior pituitary hormone. The releasing hormones enter a capillary bed in the hypothalamus and are transported through veins to a second capillary bed in the anterior pituitary. There they leave the blood and bind to membrane-bound receptors involved with the regulation of anterior pituitary hormone secretion. The capillary beds and veins that transport the hormones are called the **hypothalamic–pituitary** (hī′pō-thal′ă-mik–pi-too′i-tār-ē) **portal system.**

2. Secretion of hormones from the posterior pituitary is controlled by nervous system stimulation of nerve cells within the hypothalamus (figure 10.12*b*). These nerve cells have their cell bodies in the hypothalamus. Their axons extend through the infundibulum to the posterior pituitary. Hormones are produced in the nerve cell bodies and transported through the axons to the posterior pituitary, where they are stored in the axon endings. When these nerve cells are stimulated, action potentials from the hypothalamus travel along the axons to the posterior pituitary and cause the release of hormones from the axon endings in the posterior pituitary.

   Within the hypothalamus and pituitary, the nervous and endocrine systems are closely interrelated. Emotions such as joy and anger, as well as chronic stress, influence the endocrine system through the hypothalamus. Conversely, hormones of the endocrine system can influence the functions of the hypothalamus and other parts of the brain.

Hormones of the Anterior Pituitary

Growth hormone (GH) stimulates the growth of bones, muscles, and other organs by increasing protein synthesis. It also resists protein breakdown during periods of food deprivation and favors fat breakdown. Too little growth hormone secretion can be the result of abnormal development of the pituitary gland. A young person suffering from a deficiency of growth hormone remains a small, though normally proportioned, person called a **pituitary dwarf** (dwŏrf). This condition can be treated by administering growth hormone. Excess growth hormone secretion can result from hormone-secreting tumors of the pituitary gland. If excess growth hormone is present before bones complete their growth in length, exaggerated bone growth occurs. The result is **gigantism** (jī'an-tizm), and the person becomes abnormally tall. If excess hormone is secreted after growth in bone length is complete, growth in bone diameter, but not in length, continues. As a result, the facial features and hands become abnormally large, a condition called **acromegaly** (ak-rō-meg'ă-lē).

The secretion of growth hormone is controlled by two releasing hormones from the hypothalamus. One releasing hormone stimulates growth hormone secretion; the other inhibits it. Most people have a rhythm of growth hormone secretion, with daily peak levels occurring during deep sleep. Growth hormone secretion also increases during periods of fasting and exercise. Blood growth hormone levels do not become greatly elevated during periods of rapid growth, although children tend to have somewhat higher blood levels of growth hormone than do adults. In addition to growth hormone, genetics, nutrition, and sex hormones influence growth.

Part of the effect of growth hormone is influenced by a group of protein chemical signals called **somatomedins**. Growth hormone increases somatomedin secretion from tissues such as the liver, and the somatomedin molecules bind to receptors on cells of tissues such as bone and cartilage and stimulate growth.

Did You Know?

Because growth hormone is a protein, it is difficult to artificially produce using conventional techniques. There are two possible sources of growth hormone for people who suffer from a low rate of growth hormone secretion. It can be extracted from the pituitary glands of people who have died, and human genes for growth hormone have been successfully introduced into bacteria using genetic engineering techniques. The gene in the bacteria causes growth hormone synthesis, and the growth hormone can be extracted from the medium in which the bacteria are grown. Thus modern genetic engineering has provided a source of human growth hormone. A major concern regarding the use of growth hormones extracted from the pituitaries of cadavers is the possibility of human immunodeficiency virus infection (HIV; the virus that causes acquired immunodeficiency syndrome [AIDS]) and other viral infections. Genetically engineered growth hormone is therefore the only source of human growth hormone that is now administered to people who produce inadequate quantities.

Thyroid-stimulating hormone (TSH) molecules bind to membrane-bound receptors on cells of the thyroid gland and cause the cells to secrete thyroid hormone. When too much TSH is secreted, it causes the thyroid gland to enlarge and secrete too much thyroid hormone. When too little TSH is secreted, the thyroid gland decreases in size, and too little thyroid hormone is secreted. The rate of TSH secretion is increased by a releasing hormone from the hypothalamus.

Adrenocorticotropic (a-drē'nō-kōr'ti-kō-trō'pik) **hormone (ACTH)** molecules bind to membrane-bound receptors on cells in the cortex of the adrenal glands. ACTH increases the secretion of a hormone from the adrenal cortex called **cortisol** (kōr'ti-sol), and ACTH is required to keep the adrenal cortex from degenerating. ACTH molecules also bind to melanocytes in the skin and increase skin pigmentation (see chapter 5). One symptom of too much ACTH secretion is a darkening of the skin. The rate of ACTH secretion is increased by a releasing hormone from the hypothalamus.

Gonadotropins (gō'nad-ō-trō'pinz) are hormones that bind to membrane-bound receptors on the cells of the gonads (ovaries and testes). They regulate the growth, development, and functions of the gonads. In females, **luteinizing** (loo'tē-ĭ-nīz-ing) **hormone (LH)** causes the ovulation of oocytes and the secretion of the sex hormones estrogen and progesterone from the ovaries. In males, LH stimulates the secretion of the sex hormone testosterone from the testes. LH is sometimes referred to as **interstitial cell-stimulating hormone (ICSH)** in males because it stimulates interstitial cells of the testes to secrete testosterone. **Follicle-stimulating hormone (FSH)** stimulates the development of follicles in the ovaries and sperm cells in the testes. Without LH and FSH, the ovaries and testes decrease in size, no longer produce oocytes or sperm cells, and no longer secrete hormones. A single releasing hormone from the hypothalamus increases the secretion of both LH and FSH.

Prolactin (prō-lak'tin) molecules bind to membrane-bound receptors in cells of the breast and help promote development of the breast during pregnancy and stimulates the production of milk in the breast following pregnancy. The regulation of prolactin secretion is complex, and several substances released from the hypothalamus may regulate its secretion. There are two main releasing hormones: one increases prolactin secretion and one decreases it.

Melanocyte-stimulating (mel'ă-nō-sīt) **hormone (MSH)** molecules bind to membrane-bound receptors on melanocytes and causes them to synthesize melanin. Oversecretion of MSH causes the skin to darken. The structure of MSH is similar to that of ACTH, and both hormones cause the skin to darken. Regulation of MSH is not well understood, but there appears to be two releasing hormones from the hypothalamus: one increases MSH secretion and one decreases it.

Hormones of the Posterior Pituitary

Antidiuretic (an'tē-dī-ū-ret'ik) **hormone (ADH)** molecules bind to membrane-bound receptors and increase water reabsorption by kidney tubules. This results in less water lost as urine. ADH can also cause blood vessels to constrict

(a)

(b)

(c)

(d)

Figure 10.13 The Thyroid and Parathyroid Glands

(*a*) Anterior view of the thyroid gland. (*b*) Posterior view of the thyroid gland with the four small parathyroid glands embedded in the posterior surface of the thyroid gland. (*c*) Three-dimensional interpretive drawing of thyroid follicles and parafollicular cells. (*d*) Light micrograph of thyroid tissue.

when released in large amounts. Consequently, it is sometimes called **vasopressin**. Reduced ADH release from the posterior pituitary results in the formation of very large amounts of dilute urine and may lead to dehydration and low blood levels of important ions because they are lost in the urine.

Oxytocin (ok′sĭ-tō′sin) molecules bind to membrane-bound receptors and cause contraction of the muscle of the uterus and milk ejection, or milk "let-down," from the breasts in lactating women. Commercial preparations of oxytocin are given under certain conditions to assist in childbirth and to constrict uterine blood vessels following childbirth.

The Thyroid Gland

The **thyroid** (thī′royd) **gland** is made up of two lobes connected by a narrow band called the **isthmus** (is′mŭs). The lobes are located on either side of the trachea, just inferior to the larynx (figure 10.13*a* and *b*). The thyroid gland is one of the largest endocrine glands. It appears more red than surrounding tissues because it is highly vascular. It is surrounded by a connective tissue capsule. The thyroid gland contains numerous **thyroid follicles**, which are small spheres with walls that consist of simple cuboidal epithelium (figure 10.13*c* and *d*). Each thyroid follicle is filled with proteins to which thyroid hormones are attached. The cells of the

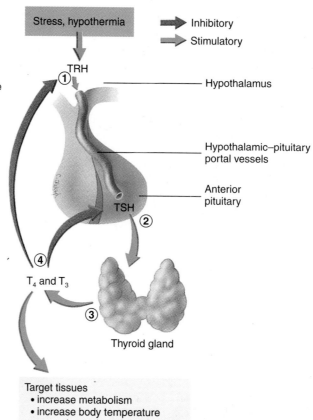

1. Thyroid-releasing hormone (TRH) is released from nerve cells within the hypothalamus and passes through the hypothalamic–pituitary portal blood vessels to the anterior pituitary.

2. TRH causes cells of the anterior pituitary to secrete thyroid-stimulating hormone (TSH), which passes through the general circulation to the thyroid gland.

3. TSH stimulates the thyroid gland to release thyroid hormones (T$_3$ and T$_4$) into the general circulation.

4. T$_3$ and T$_4$ act on target tissues to produce a response and have an inhibitory effect on the secretion of TRH from the hypothalamus and TSH from the anterior pituitary gland.

Figure 10.14   Regulation of Thyroid Hormone Secretion

thyroid follicles synthesize thyroid hormones, which are stored in the follicles. Between the follicles is a network of loose connective tissue that contains capillaries and scattered **parafollicular** (par-ă-fo-lik′ū-lăr) cells (figure 10.13*d*).

The main function of the thyroid gland is to secrete **thyroid hormones**. The thyroid hormone molecules bind to intracellular receptors in cells and regulate the rate of metabolism in the body (see table 10.3). Without a normal rate of thyroid hormone secretion, growth and development cannot proceed normally. A lack of thyroid hormones is called **hypothyroidism** (hī′pō-thī′royd-izm). In infants, hypothyroidism can result in **cretinism** (krē′tin-izm), a condition in which the person is mentally retarded and has a short stature with abnormally formed skeletal structures. In adults, the lack of thyroid hormones results in a reduced rate of metabolism, sluggishness, a reduced ability to perform routine tasks, and **myxedema** (mik-se-dē′mă), which is the accumulation of fluid and other molecules in the subcutaneous tissue. An elevated rate of thyroid hormone secretion is known as **hyperthyroidism** (hī-per-thī′royd-izm). It results in an elevated rate of metabolism, extreme nervousness, and chronic fatigue. **Graves' disease** is a type of hyperthyroidism resulting from the production of abnormal proteins by the immune system that are similar in structure and function to TSH. Graves' disease is often accompanied by bulging of the eyes, a condition called **exophthalmia** (ek-sof-thal′mē-ă).

The thyroid gland requires iodine to synthesize thyroid hormones. Iodine is taken up by the thyroid follicles in which hormone synthesis occurs. One thyroid hormone, called **thyroxine** (thī-rok′sin) or **tetraiodothyronine** (tet′ră-ī′ō-dō-thī′rō-nēn), contains four iodine atoms and is abbreviated T$_4$. The other thyroid hormone, called **triiodothyronine** (trī-ī′ō-dō-thī′rō-nēn), contains three iodine atoms and is abbreviated T$_3$. If the quantity of iodine present is not sufficient, the production and secretion of the thyroid hormones decrease.

Thyroid hormone secretion is regulated by TSH from the anterior pituitary (figure 10.14). Small fluctuations occur in blood TSH levels on a daily basis, with a small increase at night. Increasing blood levels of TSH increase the synthesis and secretion of thyroid hormones, and decreasing blood levels of TSH decrease them. The thyroid hormones, in turn, have a negative-feedback effect on the hypothalamus and pituitary so that increasing levels of thyroid hormones inhibit the secretion of TSH-releasing hormone from the hypothalamus and inhibit TSH secretion from the anterior pituitary gland. Decreasing thyroid hormone levels allow additional releasing hormone and TSH to be secreted. Because of the negative-feedback effect, the thyroid hormones fluctuate within a narrow concentration range in the blood.

When thyroid hormone secretion is reduced, the secretion of TSH-releasing hormone from the hypothalamus and

TSH secretion from the anterior pituitary gland increase. Decreased secretion of thyroid hormones therefore allows the anterior pituitary to secrete TSH in large amounts. Excess TSH causes the thyroid gland to enlarge, a condition called a **goiter** (goy'ter).

---

2 ▌ **P R E D I C T**

In people with Graves' disease, the immune system produces a large amount of a protein that is so much like TSH that it binds to cells of the thyroid gland and acts like TSH. Unlike TSH, however, the secretion of this protein does not respond to negative feedback. Predict the effect of this abnormal antibody on the structure and function of the thyroid gland and the release of hormones from the hypothalamus and anterior pituitary gland.

✔ *Answer on page 290*

In addition to secreting thyroid hormones, the thyroid gland secretes a hormone called **calcitonin** (kal-si-tō'nin) from the parafollicular cells (see figure 10.13c). Calcitonin is secreted if the blood concentration of calcium ions becomes too high, and it causes calcium ion levels to decrease to their normal range (figure 10.15). Calcitonin molecules bind to membrane-bound receptors of cells and reduce the rate of calcium ion resorption from bone by inhibiting osteoclasts. Calcitonin may function to prevent blood calcium ion levels from becoming overly elevated following a meal that contains a high concentration of calcium ions.

Calcitonin helps prevent elevated blood calcium ion levels, but a lack of calcitonin secretion does not result in a prolonged increase in those levels. Other mechanisms controlling blood calcium ion levels are able to compensate for the lack of calcitonin secretion.

The Parathyroid Glands

Four tiny **parathyroid** (par-ă-thī'royd) **glands** are embedded in the posterior wall of the thyroid gland (see figure 10.13b). The parathyroid glands secrete a hormone called **parathyroid hormone (PTH)**, which is essential for the regulation of blood calcium levels (see table 10.3). PTH is more important than calcitonin in regulating blood levels of calcium. PTH molecules bind to membrane-bound receptors of cells and increase the absorption of calcium ions from the intestine by causing an increase in active vitamin D formation. PTH also increases the resorption (breakdown) of bone tissue to release calcium ions into the circulatory system and decreases the rate at which calcium ions are lost in the urine. PTH acts on its target tissues to raise blood calcium levels to normal.

Active vitamin D increases absorption of calcium by the intestine and raises blood calcium levels. Vitamin D is produced from precursors in the skin that are modified by the liver and kidneys. Ultraviolet light acting on the skin is required for the first stage of vitamin D synthesis, and the final stage of synthesis in the kidney is stimulated by PTH. Vitamin D can also be supplied in the diet.

---

3 ▌ **P R E D I C T**

Explain why a lack of vitamin D results in bones that are softer than normal.

✔ *Answer on page 290*

Decreasing blood calcium levels stimulate an increase in PTH secretion (see figure 10.15). For example, if too little calcium is consumed in the diet or if a person suffers from a prolonged lack of vitamin D, blood calcium levels decrease, and PTH secretion increases. The increased PTH increases the rate of bone resorption. Blood calcium levels can be maintained within a normal range, but prolonged resorption of bone results in reduced bone density. The reduced bone density causes soft, flexible bones that are easily deformed in young people and porous, fragile bones in older people.

Increasing blood calcium levels cause a decrease in PTH secretion (see figure 10.15). The decreased PTH secretion results in a reduction in blood calcium levels. In addition, increasing blood calcium levels stimulate calcitonin secretion, which also causes blood calcium levels to decline (see figure 10.15).

An abnormally high rate of PTH secretion is called **hyperparathyroidism**. It can result from a tumor of a parathyroid gland. The elevated blood levels of PTH increase bone resorption and elevate blood calcium levels. As a result, bones can become soft, deformed, and easily fractured. In addition, the elevated blood calcium levels make nerve and muscle less excitable, resulting in fatigue and muscle weakness. The excess calcium can be deposited in soft tissues of the body, and kidney stones can result. The calcium deposits in soft tissues cause inflammation.

An abnormally low rate of PTH secretion is called **hypoparathyroidism**. It can be the result of injury or the surgical removal of the thyroid and parathyroid glands. The low blood levels of PTH result in a reduced rate of bone resorption and reduced vitamin D formation. As a result, blood calcium levels decrease. In response to low blood calcium levels, nerves and muscles become excitable and produce spontaneous action potentials. The result is frequent muscle cramps or tetanus. Severe tetanus can affect the respiratory muscles; breathing stops resulting in death.

The Adrenal Glands

The **adrenal** (ă-drē'năl) **glands**, or **suprarenal glands**, are two small glands that are located superior to each kidney (see figure 10.9 and table 10.3). Each adrenal gland has an inner part, called the **adrenal medulla**, and an outer part, called the **adrenal cortex**. The adrenal medulla and the adrenal cortex function as separate endocrine glands.

The Adrenal Medulla

The principal hormone released from the adrenal medulla is **epinephrine** (ep'i-nef'rin), or **adrenalin** (ă-dren'ă-lin), but

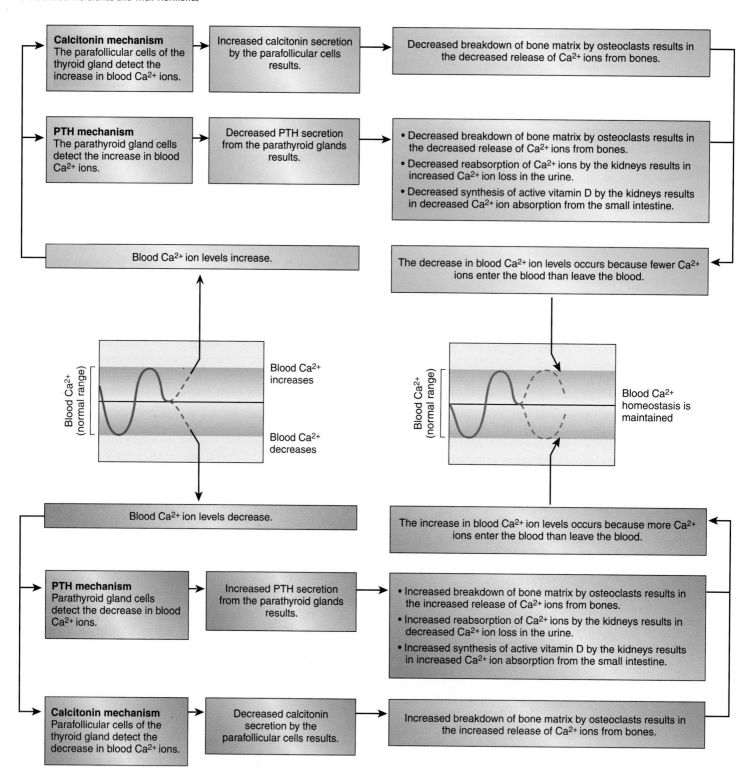

Figure 10.15 Regulation of Blood Calcium Ion Levels

small amounts of **norepinephrine** (nōr′ep-i-nef′rin) are also released. Epinephrine and norepinephrine are released in response to stimulation by the sympathetic nervous system, which becomes most active when a person is excited or physically active (figure 10.16). These hormone molecules bind to membrane-bound receptors in their target tissues.

Stress and low blood glucose levels can also result in increased sympathetic stimulation of the adrenal medulla. Epinephrine and norepinephrine are referred to as the **fight-or-flight** hormones because of their role in preparing the body for vigorous physical activity. Some of the major effects of the hormones released from the adrenal medulla are

Figure 10.16   Regulation of Adrenal Medullary Secretions

Stimulation of the hypothalmus by stress, physical activity, or low blood glucose levels causes action potentials to travel through the sympathetic nervous system to the adrenal medulla. In response, the adrenal medulla releases epinephrine and smaller amounts of norepinephrine into the general circulation. These hormones have several effects on the body to prepare it for physical activity.

1. Increases in the breakdown of glycogen to glucose in the liver, the release of the glucose into the blood, and the release of fatty acids from fat cells. The glucose and fatty acids are used as energy sources to maintain the body's increased rate of metabolism.
2. Increase in the heart rate, which causes the blood pressure to increase.
3. Stimulation of smooth muscle in the walls of arteries supplying the internal organs and the skin, but not those supplying skeletal muscle. The blood flow to internal organs and the skin decreases, and the functions of the internal organs decrease. Blood flow through skeletal muscles increases.
4. Increase in blood pressure because of smooth muscle contraction in the walls of blood vessels in the internal organs and the skin.
5. Increase in the metabolic rate of several tissues, especially skeletal muscle, cardiac muscle, and nervous tissue.

Responses to hormones from the adrenal medulla reinforce the effect of the sympathetic division of the autonomic nervous system. Thus the adrenal medulla and the sympathetic division function together to prepare the body for physical activity, to produce the "fight-or-flight" response, and to produce many of the responses to stress.

The Adrenal Cortex

Three classes of steroid hormones are secreted from the adrenal cortex. The molecules of all three classes of steroid hormones enter their target cells and bind to intracellular receptor molecules. The hormones and the receptors of each class, however, have unique structural and functional characteristics.

The **glucocorticoids** (gloo-kō-kōr′ti-koydz) help regulate blood nutrient levels in the body. The major glucocorticoid hormone is **cortisol** (kōr′ti-sol), which increases the breakdown of protein and fat and increases their conversion to forms that can be used as energy sources by the body. For example, cortisol acts on the liver, causing it to convert amino acids to glucose, and it acts on adipose tissue, causing fat stored in fat cells to be broken down to fatty acids. The glucose and fatty acids are released into the circulatory system and taken up by tissues and used as a source of energy. Cortisol also causes proteins to be broken down to amino acids, which are then released into the circulatory system (figure 10.17*a*).

In times of stress, cortisol is secreted in larger than normal amounts. It aids the body in responding to stressful conditions by providing energy sources for tissues. Cortisol

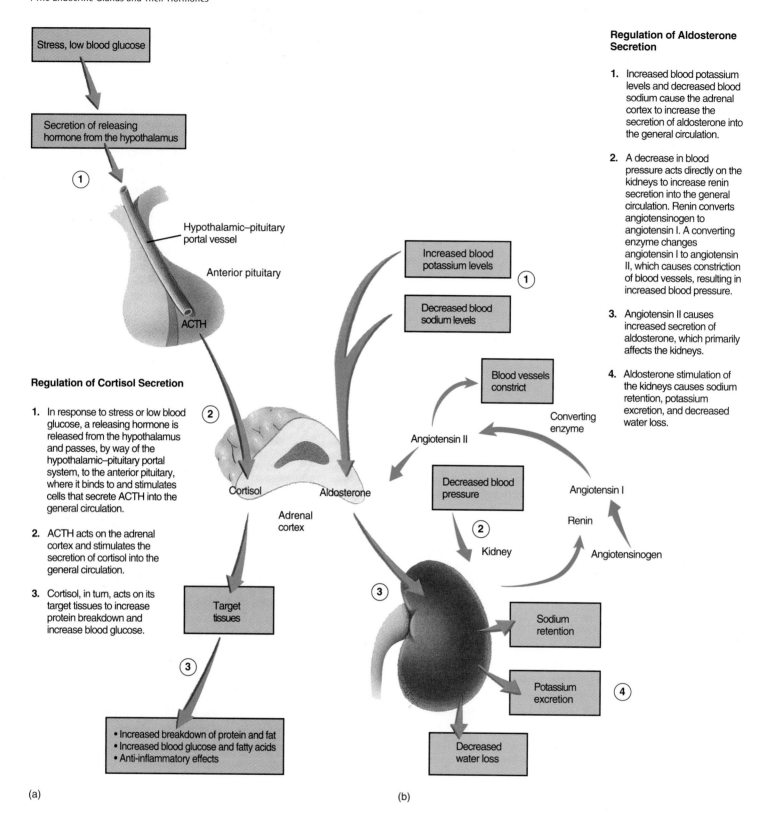

Stress, low blood glucose

Secretion of releasing hormone from the hypothalamus

(1)

Hypothalamic–pituitary portal vessel

Anterior pituitary

ACTH

Regulation of Cortisol Secretion

1. In response to stress or low blood glucose, a releasing hormone is released from the hypothalamus and passes, by way of the hypothalamic–pituitary portal system, to the anterior pituitary, where it binds to and stimulates cells that secrete ACTH into the general circulation.

2. ACTH acts on the adrenal cortex and stimulates the secretion of cortisol into the general circulation.

3. Cortisol, in turn, acts on its target tissues to increase protein breakdown and increase blood glucose.

(2)

Cortisol

Aldosterone

Adrenal cortex

Target tissues

(3)

• Increased breakdown of protein and fat
• Increased blood glucose and fatty acids
• Anti-inflammatory effects

Regulation of Aldosterone Secretion

1. Increased blood potassium levels and decreased blood sodium cause the adrenal cortex to increase the secretion of aldosterone into the general circulation.

2. A decrease in blood pressure acts directly on the kidneys to increase renin secretion into the general circulation. Renin converts angiotensinogen to angiotensin I. A converting enzyme changes angiotensin I to angiotensin II, which causes constriction of blood vessels, resulting in increased blood pressure.

3. Angiotensin II causes increased secretion of aldosterone, which primarily affects the kidneys.

4. Aldosterone stimulation of the kidneys causes sodium retention, potassium excretion, and decreased water loss.

Increased blood potassium levels

Decreased blood sodium levels

(1)

Blood vessels constrict

Converting enzyme

Angiotensin II

Angiotensin I

Decreased blood pressure

Renin

(2)

Kidney

Angiotensinogen

(3)

Sodium retention

Potassium excretion

(4)

Decreased water loss

(a)

(b)

Figure 10.17 Regulation of Cortisol and Aldosterone Secretion
(*a*) Cortisol. (*b*) Aldosterone.

also reduces the inflammatory response. **Cortisone** (kōr′ti-sōn), a steroid closely related to cortisol, is often given as a medication to reduce inflammation such as occurs during certain allergic responses and injuries.

When blood glucose levels decline, cortisol secretion increases. The low blood glucose acts on the hypothalamus to increase the secretion of the releasing hormone, which, in turn, stimulates ACTH secretion from the anterior pituitary. ACTH, in turn, stimulates cortisol secretion.

Adrenocorticotropic hormone (ACTH) molecules from the anterior pituitary bind to membrane-bound receptors and regulate the secretion of cortisol from the adrenal cortex. Without ACTH, the adrenal cortex atrophies and loses its ability to secrete cortisol.

The second class of hormones secreted by the adrenal cortex, the **mineralocorticoids** (min′er-al-ō-kōr′ti-koydz), help regulate blood volume and blood levels of potassium and sodium ions. **Aldosterone** (al-dos′ter-ōn) is the major hormone of this class (see figure 10.17*b*). Aldosterone molecules bind to receptor molecules primarily in the kidney, but it also affects the intestine, sweat glands, and salivary glands. Aldosterone causes sodium ions and water to be retained in the body and increases the rate at which potassium is eliminated.

Blood levels of potassium and sodium ions directly affect the adrenal cortex to influence aldosterone secretion. The adrenal gland is much more sensitive to changes in blood potassium levels than to changes in blood sodium levels. The rate of aldosterone secretion increases when blood potassium levels increase or when blood sodium levels decrease.

Changes in blood pressure indirectly affect the rate of aldosterone secretion. Low blood pressure causes the release of a type of protein molecule called **renin** (rē′nin) from the kidney. Renin, which acts as an enzyme, causes a blood protein called **angiotensinogen** (an′jē-ō-ten-sin′ō-jen) to be converted to **angiotensin I** (an-jē-ō-ten′sin). Then, a protein called **angiotensin-converting enzyme** causes angiotensin I to be converted to **angiotensin II**. Angiotensin II causes smooth muscle in blood vessels to constrict, and angiotensin II acts on the adrenal cortex to increase aldosterone secretion. Aldosterone causes retention of sodium and water, which causes an increase in blood volume (see figure 10.17*b*). Both blood vessel constriction and increased blood volume help raise blood pressure.

The third class of hormones secreted by the adrenal cortex is the **androgens** (Gr. *andros,* male; an′drō-jenz) They are named for their ability to stimulate the development of male sexual characteristics. Small amounts of androgens are secreted from the adrenal cortex in both males and females. In adult males, most androgens are secreted by the testes. In adult females, the adrenal androgens influence the female sex drive. If the secretion of sex hormones from the adrenal cortex is abnormally high, exaggerated male

characteristics develop in both males and females. This condition is most apparent in females and in males before puberty, when the effects are not masked by the secretion of androgens by the testes.

The Pancreas, Insulin, and Diabetes

The endocrine part of the **pancreas** (pan′krē-as) consists of **pancreatic islets** (islets of Langerhans) dispersed among the exocrine portion of the pancreas (figure 10.18). The islets secrete two hormones—insulin and glucagon—which function to help regulate blood nutrient levels, especially blood glucose (table 10.4). **Beta cells** of the pancreatic islets secrete insulin, and **alpha cells** of the pancreatic islets secrete glucagon.

It is very important to maintain blood glucose levels within a normal range of values (figure 10.19). A decline in the blood glucose level below its normal range causes the nervous system to malfunction because glucose is the nervous

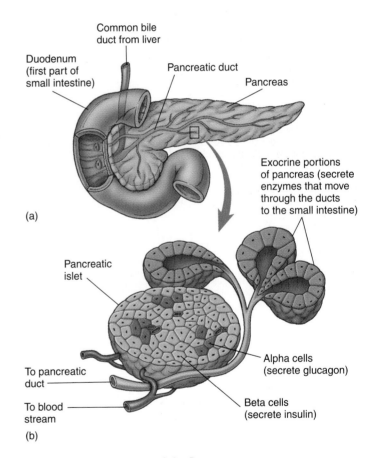

(a)

(b)

Figure 10.18   Structure of the Pancreas

(*a*) Anatomy of the pancreas. (*b*) The endocrine portion of the pancreas is made up of scattered pancreatic islets. Alpha cells secrete glucagon, and beta cells secrete insulin. The exocrine portion of the pancreas produces digestive enzymes that are carried through a system of ducts to the small intestine.

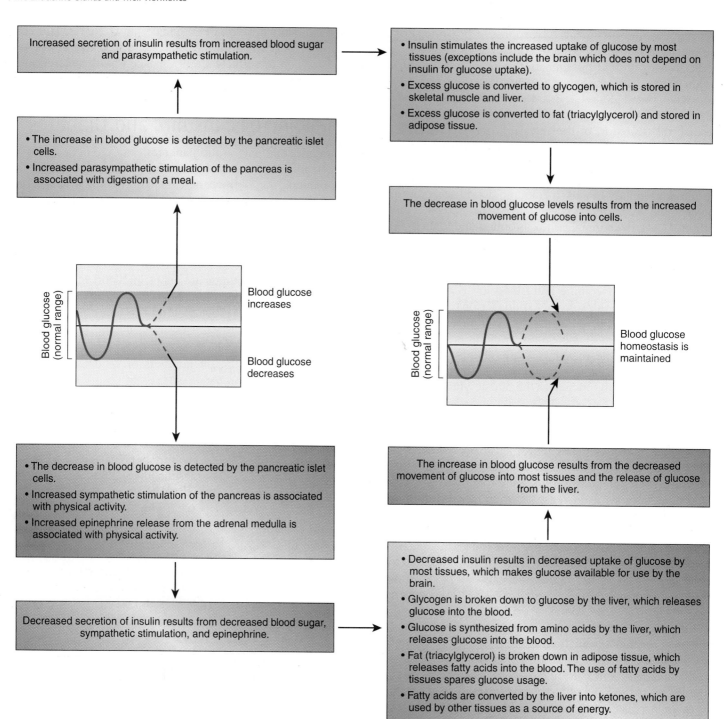

Increased secretion of insulin results from increased blood sugar and parasympathetic stimulation.

- The increase in blood glucose is detected by the pancreatic islet cells.
- Increased parasympathetic stimulation of the pancreas is associated with digestion of a meal.

Blood glucose (normal range)

Blood glucose increases

Blood glucose decreases

- The decrease in blood glucose is detected by the pancreatic islet cells.
- Increased sympathetic stimulation of the pancreas is associated with physical activity.
- Increased epinephrine release from the adrenal medulla is associated with physical activity.

Decreased secretion of insulin results from decreased blood sugar, sympathetic stimulation, and epinephrine.

- Insulin stimulates the increased uptake of glucose by most tissues (exceptions include the brain which does not depend on insulin for glucose uptake).
- Excess glucose is converted to glycogen, which is stored in skeletal muscle and liver.
- Excess glucose is converted to fat (triacylglycerol) and stored in adipose tissue.

The decrease in blood glucose levels results from the increased movement of glucose into cells.

Blood glucose (normal range)

Blood glucose homeostasis is maintained

The increase in blood glucose results from the decreased movement of glucose into most tissues and the release of glucose from the liver.

- Decreased insulin results in decreased uptake of glucose by most tissues, which makes glucose available for use by the brain.
- Glycogen is broken down to glucose by the liver, which releases glucose into the blood.
- Glucose is synthesized from amino acids by the liver, which releases glucose into the blood.
- Fat (triacylglycerol) is broken down in adipose tissue, which releases fatty acids into the blood. The use of fatty acids by tissues spares glucose usage.
- Fatty acids are converted by the liver into ketones, which are used by other tissues as a source of energy.

Figure 10.19 Regulation of Blood Glucose Levels

Table 10.4   Effects of Insulin and Glucagon on Target Tissues

Target Tissue	Insulin Responses	Glucagon Responses
Skeletal muscle, cardiac muscle, cartilage, bone fibroblasts, blood cells, and mammary glands	Increases glucose uptake and glycogen synthesis; increases uptake of amino acids	Has little effect
Liver	Increases glycogen synthesis; increases use of glucose for energy	Causes rapid increase in the breakdown of glycogen to glucose and release of glucose into the blood; increases the formation of glucose from amino acids and, to some degree, from fats; increases metabolism of fatty acids
Adipose cells	Increases glucose uptake, glycogen synthesis, fat synthesis	High concentrations cause breakdown of fats; probably unimportant under most conditions
Nervous system	Has little effect except to increase glucose uptake in the satiety center	Has no effect

system's main source of energy. When blood glucose decreases, fats and proteins are broken down rapidly by other tissues to provide an alternative energy source. As fats are broken down, acidic substances are released into the circulatory system as fatty acids and **ketones** (kē'tōnz). When blood glucose levels are very low, the breakdown of fats can cause the release of enough fatty acids and ketones to cause the pH of the body fluids to decrease below normal, a condition called **acidosis** (as-i-dō'sis). The amino acids of proteins are broken down and used to synthesize glucose by the liver. If blood glucose levels are too high, the kidneys produce large volumes of urine containing substantial amounts of glucose. Because of the rapid loss of water in the form of urine, dehydration can result.

Insulin (in'sŭ-lin) is released from the beta cells primarily in response to the elevated blood glucose levels and increased parasympathetic stimulation that is associated with digestion of a meal. Increased blood levels of certain amino acids also stimulate insulin secretion. Decreased insulin secretion results from decreasing blood glucose levels and from stimulation by the sympathetic division of the nervous system. Sympathetic stimulation of the pancreas occurs during physical activity. The decreased insulin levels allow the blood glucose to be conserved to provide the brain with adequate glucose and to allow other tissues to metabolize fatty acids and glycogen stored in the cells.

The major target tissues for insulin are the liver, adipose tissue, muscles, and the area of the hypothalamus that controls appetite, called the **satiety** (sa'tī-ĕ-tē) **center**. Insulin binds to membrane-bound receptors and, either directly or indirectly, increases the rate of glucose and amino acid uptake in these tissues. Glucose is converted to glycogen or fat, and the amino acids are used to synthesize protein. The effects of insulin on target tissues are summarized in table 10.4.

Diabetes mellitus (dī-ă-bē'tēz' me-lī'tŭs) can result from any of the following: secretion of too little insulin from the pancreas, insufficient numbers of insulin receptors on target cells, or defective receptors that do not respond normally to insulin.

In people who have diabetes mellitus, tissues cannot take up glucose effectively, causing blood glucose levels to become very high, a condition called **hyperglycemia** (hī'per-glī-sē'mē-ă). Because glucose cannot enter cells of the satiety center of the brain without insulin, the satiety center responds as if there were very little blood glucose, resulting in an exaggerated appetite. The excess glucose in the blood is excreted in the urine, causing the urine volume to be much greater than normal. Because of excessive urine production, the person has a tendency to become dehydrated and thirsty. Even though blood glucose levels are high, fats and proteins are broken down to provide an energy source for metabolism, resulting in the wasting away of body tissues, acidosis, and ketosis. People with this condition also exhibit a lack of energy.

Did You Know?

When too much insulin is present, such as occurs when a diabetic is injected with too much insulin or has not eaten after an insulin injection, blood glucose levels become very low. The brain, which depends primarily on glucose for an energy source, malfunctions. This condition, called insulin shock, can include symptoms of disorientation and convulsions, and may result in loss of consciousness.

Glucagon (gloo'kă-gon) is released from the alpha cells when blood glucose levels are low. Glucagon molecules bind to membrane-bound receptors primarily in the liver and cause the conversion of glycogen stored in the liver to glucose. The glucose is then released into the blood to increase blood glucose levels. After a meal, when blood glucose levels are elevated, glucagon secretion is reduced.

4 **PREDICT**

How is the rate of insulin and glucagon secretion affected immediately following a large meal rich in carbohydrates, and after 12 hours without eating.

✔ *Answer on page 290*

Insulin and glucagon function together to regulate blood glucose levels (see figure 10.19). When blood glucose levels increase, insulin secretion increases, and glucagon secretion decreases. When blood glucose levels decrease, the rate of insulin secretion declines, and the rate of glucagon secretion increases. Other hormones, such as epinephrine, cortisol, and growth hormone, also function to maintain blood levels of nutrients. When blood glucose levels decrease, these hormones are secreted at a greater rate. Epinephrine and cortisol cause the breakdown of protein and fat and the synthesis of glucose to help increase blood levels of nutrients. Growth hormone slows protein breakdown and favors fat breakdown.

The Testes and Ovaries

The testes of the male and the ovaries of the female secrete sex hormones, in addition to producing sperm cells or oocytes. The hormones produced by these organs play important roles in the development of sexual characteristics. Structural and functional differences between males and females and the ability to reproduce all depend on the sex hormones (see figure 10.9 and table 10.3).

The main hormone produced in the male is **testosterone** (tes'tos'tĕ-rōn). It is responsible for the growth and development of the male reproductive structures, muscle enlargement, growth of body hair, voice changes, and the male sexual drive.

In the female two main classes of hormones affect sexual characteristics: **estrogen** (es'trō-jen) and **progesterone** (prō-jes'ter-ōn). Together these hormones contribute to the development and function of female reproductive structures and other female sexual characteristics. These characteristics include enlargement of the breasts and distribution of fat, which influences the shape of the hips, breasts, and legs. The female menstrual cycle is controlled by the cyclical release of estrogen and progesterone from the ovaries.

LH and FSH stimulate the secretion of hormones from the ovaries and testes. Releasing hormone from the hypothalamus controls the rate of LH and FSH secretion in males and females. LH and FSH, in turn, control the secretion of hormones from the ovaries and testes. Hormones secreted by the ovaries and testes also have a negative-feedback effect on the hypothalamus and anterior pituitary. The control of hormones that regulate reproductive functions is discussed in greater detail in chapter 19.

The Thymus Gland

The thymus gland lies in the upper part of the thoracic cavity (see figure 10.9 and table 10.3). It is important in the function of the immune system. Part of the function of the thymus gland is to secrete a hormone called **thymosin** (thī'mō-sin), which helps in the development of certain white blood cells, called T cells. T cells help protect the body against infection by foreign organisms. The thymus gland is most important early in life, becoming smaller in the adult. If an infant is born without a thymus gland, the immune system does not develop normally, and the body is less capable of fighting infections (see chapter 14).

The Pineal Body

The **pineal** (pin'ē-ăl) **body** is a small pinecone-shaped structure located superior and posterior to the thalamus of the brain (see chapter 8). The pineal body produces a hormone called **melatonin** (mel-ă-tōn'in), which is thought to decrease the secretion of LH and FSH by decreasing the release of hypothalamic-releasing hormones (see table 10.3). Thus, melatonin acts to inhibit the functions of the reproductive system. Animal studies have demonstrated that the amount of light available controls the rate of melatonin secretion. In many animals, short day length causes an increase in melatonin secretion, whereas longer day length causes a decrease in melatonin secretion. Some evidence suggests that melatonin may play an important role in the onset of puberty in humans. Tumors may develop in the pineal body, which, in some cases, can increase pineal secretions and in others decrease them.

5 **PREDICT**

Predict the effect on a young person's reproductive system of a tumor that destroys the ability of the pineal body to secrete melatonin.

✔ *Answer on page 290*

Other Hormones

Cells in the lining of the stomach and small intestine secrete hormones that stimulate the production of digestive juices from the stomach, pancreas, and liver. These hormones aid the process of digestion by causing secretion of digestive juices when food is present in the digestive system but not at other times. Hormones secreted from the small intestine also help regulate the rate at which food passes from the stomach into the small intestine, so that food enters the small intestine at an optimal rate (see chapter 16).

Prostaglandins are widely distributed in tissues of the body and function as intercellular signals. Unlike most hormones, they are usually not transported long distances in the circulatory system but function mainly as autocrine or paracrine chemical signals (see table 10.1). Thus, their effects occur in the tissues where they are produced. Some prostaglandins cause relaxation of smooth muscle, such as dilation of blood vessels. Others cause contraction of smooth muscle, such as contraction of the uterus during the delivery of a baby. Because of their action on the uterus, prostaglandins have been used medically to initiate abortion. Prostaglandins also play a role in inflammation. They are released by damaged tissues and cause blood vessel dilation, localized swelling, and pain. Prostaglandins produced by platelets appear to be necessary for blood clotting to occur normally. The ability of aspirin and related substances to reduce pain and inflammation, help prevent the painful cramping of uterine smooth muscle, and treat headache is a result of their inhibitory effect on prostaglandin synthesis.

The kidneys secrete a hormone in response to reduced oxygen levels in the kidney. The hormone is called **erythropoietin** (ĕ-rith′rō-poy′ĕ-tin). It acts on bone marrow to increase the production of red blood cells (see chapter 11).

In pregnant women, the placenta is an important source of hormones that function to maintain pregnancy and stimulate breast development. These hormones include estrogen, progesterone, and **human chorionic gonadotropin** (gō′nad-ō-trō′pin), which is similar in structure and function to LH. These hormones are essential to the maintenance of pregnancy (see chapter 20).

Clinical Focus   Hormones and Stress

Stress, in the form of disease, physical injury, or emotional anxiety initiates a specific response from the body that involves the nervous and endocrine systems. The stressful condition influences the hypothalamus, and through the hypothalamus the sympathetic division of the autonomic nervous system is activated. The sympathetic division prepares the body for physical activity. It increases heart rate and blood pressure, shunts blood from the gut and other visceral structures to skeletal muscles, and increases the rate of metabolism in several tissues, especially in skeletal muscle. Part of the response of the sympathetic division is due to the release of epinephrine from the adrenal medulla.

In addition to sympathetic responses, stress causes the release of ACTH from the pituitary. ACTH acts on the adrenal cortex to cause the release of glucocorticoids. These hormones increase blood glucose levels and break down protein and fat, making nutrients more readily available to tissues.

Although the ability to respond to stress is adaptive for short periods of time, responses triggered by stressful conditions are harmful if they occur for long periods. Prolonged stress can lead to hypertension (elevated blood pressure), heart disease, ulcers, inhibited immune system function, and other conditions. Humans are frequently exposed to prolonged mental stress from high-pressure jobs, the inability to meet monetary obligations, or social expectations. Although responses to stress prepare a person for physical activity, often increased physical activity is not an appropriate response to the situation causing the stress. Long-term exposure to stress under conditions in which physical activity and emotions must be constrained may be harmful. Techniques that effectively reduce responses to stressful conditions are of substantial advantage to people who are exposed to chronic stress. Biofeedback, meditation, or other relaxation exercises are useful. Getting adequate rest, relaxation, and regular physical exercise are important in maintaining good health and reducing unhealthy responses to stressful situations.

Systems Pathology
graves' disease

GRAVES' DISEASE (HYPERTHYROIDISM)

Mrs. G. owns a business, has several employees, and works hard to manage her business and make time for her husband and two children. Over several months, she slowly recognized that she felt warm when others did not, she would sweat excessively and her skin was often flushed. She often felt as if her heart was pounding, she was much more nervous than usual, and it was difficult for her to concentrate. She began to feel weak and lose weight even though her appetite was greater than normal. Her family recognized some of these changes and that her eyes seemed larger than usual. They encouraged her to see her physician. After an examination and some blood tests, it was concluded that she had Graves' disease, a type of hyperthyroidism.

Background Information

Graves' disease is an example of altered regulation of hormone secretion. It is characterized by the elevated secretion of thyroid hormones from the thyroid gland. In approximately 95% of Graves' disease cases, an unusual antibody type is produced by the immune system, which binds to receptors on the cells of the thyroid follicle and stimulates them to secrete increased amounts of thyroid hormone. The secretion of the releasing hormone and thyroid-stimulating hormone is inhibited by elevated thyroid hormones. The antibody is produced in large amounts, however, and is not inhibited by thyroid hormones. A very elevated rate of thyroid hormone secretion is therefore maintained. In addition, the size of the thyroid gland increases and connective tissue components are deposited behind the eyes, causing them to bulge (figure A). The thyroid gland can enlarge somewhat or it can become very large. Enlargement of the thyroid gland is called a goiter.

Mrs. G. was treated with radioactive iodine (^{131}I) atoms that were actively transported into thyroid cells where they destroyed a substantial portion of the thyroid gland. Data in-

Figure A Person with Hyperthyroidism

dicate that this treatment has few side effects and is effective in treating most cases of Graves' disease. Other options include drugs that inhibit the synthesis and secretion of thyroid hormones and surgery to remove part of the thyroid gland.

6   P R E D I C T

Explain why removal of part of the thyroid gland is an effective treatment for Graves' disease.

✔ *Answer on page 290*

Systems Interactions	The Effect of Graves' Disease (hyperthyroidism) on other Systems
System	Effects
Integumentary	Excessive sweating, flushing, and warm skin resulted from the elevated body temperature caused by the increase rate of metabolism. Sweating and dilation of blood vessels in the skin are mechanisms by which the skin increases heat loss. Fine, soft, straight hair, along with hair loss, result from the reduced protein synthesis. The elevated rate of metabolism makes amino acids unavailable for protein synthesis.
Skeletal	Some increased bone resorption, which can decrease bone density, and increased blood calcium levels can occur in severe cases.
Muscular	Muscle atrophy and muscle weakness are the result of increased metabolism. Elevated metabolism results in the breakdown of muscle and the increased use of muscle proteins as energy sources.
Nervous	Enlargement of the extrinsic eye muscles, edema in the area of the orbits, and the accumulation of fibrous connective tissue results in protrusion of the eyes in 50% to 70% of individuals with Graves' disease. Damage to the retina and optic nerve and paralysis of the extraocular muscles can occur. The effects on the eyes may be influenced directly by the abnormal antibodies, and they may progress even after the hyperthyroid condition is successfully treated. Restlessness, short attention span, compulsive movement, tremor, insomnia, and increased emotional responses are consistent with hyperactivity of the nervous system.
Cardiovascular	Cardiovascular responses are consistent with an increased rate of metabolism and increased stimulation by the sympathetic division of the autonomic nervous system. There is an increased amount of blood pumped by the heart and increased blood flow through the tissues, including the skin. The heart rate is greater than normal, heart sounds are louder than normal, and the heart beats may be out of rhythm periodically.
Lymphatic, Immune	Antibodies that bind to receptors for thyroid-stimulating hormone on the cells of the thyroid gland have been found in nearly all people who suffer from Graves' disease. The condition, therefore, is classified as an autoimmune disease in which antibodies produced by one's lymphatic system results in abnormal functions.
Respiratory	Breathing may be labored, and the volume of air taken in with each breath may be decreased. Weak contractions of muscles of inspiration contribute.
Digestive	There is weight loss and an associated increase in appetite. Increased peristalsis in the intestines lead to frequent stools or diarrhea. Nausea, vomiting, and abdominal pain also result. There is an increased use of hepatic glycogen stores and of adipose and protein stores for energy, and there is a decrease in serum lipid levels (including triacylglyceroles, phospholipids, and cholesterol) and increased tendency to develop vitamin deficiencies. There is a reduced ability of the body to absorb nutrients from the intestine and increased metabolism. This results in an increased use of body stores of fat for energy and increased catabolism of proteins for energy.
Reproductive	Reduced regularity of menstruation or lack of menstruation may occur in women because of the elevated metabolism. In men the primary effect is a loss of sex drive.

Summary

The nervous and endocrine systems are the two major regulatory systems in the body.

- The nervous system controls structures by sending action potentials along axons, which release chemicals signals at their ends near the cells they control, whereas the endocrine system releases chemicals into the circulatory system, which carries the chemicals to the cells they control.
- The endocrine system has a more general effect, acts more slowly, and has a longer lasting effect than the nervous system.

Functions of the Endocrine System

The main functions of the endocrine system include regulation of

- Water balance; uterine contractions during parturition: milk release from the breasts; metabolism; tissue maturation; sodium, potassium, and calcium ion concentration of blood; heart rate; blood pressure; preparation for physical activity; blood glucose concentration; immune cell production; and reproductive functions in males and females.

Chemical Signals

Chemical signals bind to receptor sites on receptor molecules.

- Intracellular chemical signals are produced in one part of a cell and travel to another part of the same cell and bind to receptors.
- Intercellular chemical signals are released from one cell, are carried in the intercellular fluid, and bind to receptors in other cells.
- Intercellular chemical signals can be classified as autocrine, paracrine, hormone, neurohormone, neuromodulator, neurotransmitter, or pheromone chemical signals.

Receptors

- Chemical signals bind to receptor sites on receptor molecules to produce a response.
- Intracellular receptors are located in the cytoplasm or nuclei and can regulate enzyme activity or regulate the synthesis of specific messenger RNA.
- Membrane-bound receptors can produce a response by directly opening ion channels, activating G proteins, or activating enzymes that synthesize intracellular chemical signals, or by phosphorylating proteins inside the cell.

Hormones

- Endocrine glands produce hormones that are released into the circulatory system and travel some distance, where they act on target tissues to produce a response.
- A target tissue for a given hormone has receptor molecules for that hormone.

Chemistry

- Hormones are basically proteins, peptides, or lipids.
- Protein, and most peptide hormones bind to receptors on the cell membrane and cause permeability changes or the production of a second messenger inside the cell. Eicosanoids

also bind to receptors on the cell membrane. Lipid-soluble hormones, such as the steroids and thyroid hormones, enter the cell and bind to receptors inside the cell.

- The combining of hormones with their receptors results in a response.

Regulation of Hormone Secretion

- The secretion of hormones is controlled by negative-feedback mechanisms.
- Secretion of hormones from a specific gland is controlled by blood levels of some chemical, another hormone, or nervous system.
- The endocrine system consists of ductless glands.
- Some glands of the endocrine system perform more than one function.

The Endocrine Glands and Their Hormones

The Pituitary and Hypothalamus

- The pituitary is connected to the hypothalamus of the brain by the infundibulum. It is divided into the anterior and posterior pituitary.
- Secretions from the anterior pituitary are controlled by hypothalamic-releasing hormones that pass through the hypothalamic-pituitary portal system from the hypothalamus.
- Hormones secreted from the posterior pituitary are controlled by nervous impulses that pass from the hypothalamus through the infundibulum.
- The hormones released from the anterior pituitary are growth hormone (GH), thyroid-stimulating hormone (TSH), adrenocorticotropic hormone (ACTH), luteinizing hormone (LH), follicle-stimulating hormone (FSH), prolactin, and melanocyte-stimulating hormone (MSH).
- Hormones released from the posterior pituitary include antidiuretic hormone (ADH) and oxytocin.

The Thyroid Gland

- The thyroid gland secretes thyroid hormones, which control the metabolic rate of tissues, and calcitonin, which helps regulate blood calcium levels.

The Parathyroid Glands

- The parathyroid glands secrete parathyroid hormone, which helps regulate blood levels of calcium. Active vitamin D also helps regulate blood levels of calcium.

The Adrenal Glands

- The adrenal medulla secretes primarily epinephrine and some norepinephrine. These hormones help prepare the body for physical activity.
- The adrenal cortex secretes three classes of hormones.
- Glucocorticoids (cortisol) reduce inflammation and break down fat and protein, making them available as energy sources to other tissues.
- Mineralocorticoids (aldosterone) help regulate sodium and potassium levels and water volume in the body. Renin, secreted by the kidneys, helps regulate blood pressure by

increasing angiotensin II and aldosterone production. These hormones cause blood vessels to constrict and enhance sodium and water retention by the kidney.
- Adrenal androgens increase female sexual drive; normally adrenal androgens have little effect in males.

The Pancreas, Insulin, and Diabetes

- The pancreas secretes insulin in response to elevated levels of blood glucose and amino acids. Insulin increases the rate at which many tissues, including adipose tissue, liver, and skeletal muscles, take up glucose and amino acids.
- The pancreas secretes glucagon in response to reduced blood glucose and increases the rate at which the liver releases glucose into the blood.

The Testes and Ovaries

- The testes secrete testosterone, and the ovaries secrete estrogen and progesterone. These hormones help control reproductive processes.
- LH and FSH from the pituitary gland control hormone secretion from the ovaries and testes.

The Thymus Gland

- The thymus gland secretes thymosin, which enhances the ability of the immune system to function.

The Pineal Body

- The pineal body secretes melatonin, which may help regulate the onset of puberty by acting on the hypothalamus.

Other Hormones

- Hormones secreted by cells in the stomach and intestine help regulate stomach, pancreatic, and liver secretions.
- The prostaglandins are hormones that have a local effect, produce numerous effects on the body, and play a role in inflammation.
- Erythropoietin from the kidney stimulates erythrocyte production.
- The placenta secretes human chorionic gonadotropin, estrogen, and progesterone, which are essential to the maintenance of pregnancy.

Content Review

1. What are the major functional differences between the endocrine and the nervous systems?
2. Explain the relationship between a chemical signal and its receptor.
3. List the major differences between intracellular and intercellular chemical signals.
4. List the intercellular chemical signals that are classified on the basis of the location of the cells from which they are secreted and the location of their target cells.
5. Describe the mechanism by which membrane-bound receptors produce responses in their target tissues.
6. Define endocrine gland and hormone.
7. What makes one tissue a target tissue and another not a target tissue for a hormone?
8. Into what chemical categories can hormones be classified?
9. Compare the means by which hormones that can and cannot cross the cell membrane produce a response.
10. Name three ways that hormone secretion is regulated.
11. Describe how secretions of the anterior and posterior pituitary hormones are controlled.
12. What are the functions of growth hormone? What happens when too little or too much growth hormone is secreted?
13. Describe the effect of gonadotropins on the ovary and testis.
14. What are the functions of the thyroid hormones, and how is their secretion controlled? What happens when too little or too much of the thyroid hormones is secreted?
15. Explain how calcitonin, parathyroid hormone, and vitamin D are involved in maintaining blood calcium levels. What happens when too little or too much parathyroid hormone is secreted?
16. List the hormones secreted from the adrenal gland, give their functions, and compare the means by which the secretion rate of each is controlled.
17. What are the major functions of insulin and glucagon? How is their secretion regulated? What is the effect if too little insulin is secreted or the target tissues are not responsive to insulin?
18. List the effects of testosterone, progesterone, and estrogen.
19. What hormones are produced by the thymus gland and pineal body? Name the effects of these hormones.
20. List the effects of prostaglandins. How is aspirin able to reduce the severity of the inflammatory response?
21. List the hormones secreted by the placenta.

Develop Your Reasoning Skills

1. Aldosterone and antidiuretic hormone play important roles in the regulation of blood volume and concentration of blood. The response to one of these hormones is evident within minutes and the response to the other requires several hours. Explain the difference in response time for these two hormones.
2. Biceps Benny figured that if a small amount of a vitamin was good, a lot should do more good. He therefore began to take vitamins that included a large amount of vitamin D. Predict the effect of vitamin D on Biceps' blood calcium levels and on the rate of secretion of hormones responsible for the regulation of blood calcium levels.
3. What would be the consequences if the adrenal cortex degenerated and no longer secreted hormones?
4. Predict the consequences of elevated aldosterone secretion from the adrenal cortex and explain how they occur.

5. Explain how the blood levels of glucocorticoids, epinephrine, insulin, and glucagon change after a person has gone without food for 24 hours.
6. Stetha Scope wanted to go to medical school to become a physician. While attending college she knew her grades had to be excellent. Stetha worked very hard and worried constantly. By the end of each school year she had a cold and suffered from stomach pains. Explain why she might be susceptible to these symptoms.

Answers to Predict Questions

1. p. 268 Because the drug binds to a receptor and prevents the response of a target tissue to a chemical signal and because the drug is lipid-soluble, it is likely that the drug diffuses across the cell membrane of the cell and binds to the receptor for the chemical signal, which is inside the cell, and prevents the chemical signal from binding to its receptor site. Thus, the chemical signal functions by diffusing across the cell membrane and binding to an intracellular receptor. The response of the intracellular receptor is to produce new messenger RNA, which leads to the synthesis of new proteins (see chapter 3 for a description of the role of messenger RNA in protein synthesis). The new proteins produce the response of the cell to the chemical signal.

2. p. 277 The protein that is similar to TSH causes oversecretion of the thyroid gland (hyperthyroidism). Because the production of the protein cannot be inhibited by thyroid hormones, oversecretion of the thyroid gland is prolonged. Symptoms associated with hypersecretion of thyroid hormone become obvious. Because the protein acts like TSH, the rate of synthesis and secretion of thyroid hormone is increased, and the thyroid gland enlarges. In addition, the protein does have a negative feedback effect on the hypothalamus and pituitary gland. Releasing hormone secretion from the hypothalamus and TSH secretion from the anterior pituitary gland are therefore inhibited.

3. p. 277 Insufficient vitamin D results in insufficient calcium absorption by the intestine. As a result, blood calcium levels begin to fall. In response to the low blood calcium levels, parathyroid hormone is secreted from the parathyroid glands. Parathyroid hormone acts primarily on bone, causing bone to be broken down and calcium to be released into the blood to maintain blood calcium levels within the normal range. In adults, so much calcium can eventually be removed from bones that they become soft, fragile, and easily broken. In children, the condition is called rickets, and the bones can become bent and deformed.

4. p. 284 After a large meal, glucose enters the blood from the intestine. The increasing blood glucose stimulates insulin secretion and decreases glucagon secretion. Well before 12 hours without eating, blood glucose would have started to decrease. Decreasing blood glucose levels result in a decreased rate of insulin secretion and a stimulation of glucagon secretion.

5. p. 284 The pineal body secretes melatonin, which inhibits the release of reproductive hormones by acting on the hypothalamus of the brain. If the pineal body secretes less melatonin, it no longer should have an inhibitory effect on the hypothalamus. As a result, reproductive hormones could be secreted in greater amounts, which would result in exaggerated development of the reproductive system in young people with this condition. The evidence for this mechanism is not as clear in humans as it is in other animals.

6. p. 286 Removal of part of the thyroid gland reduces the amount of thyroid hormone secreted by the gland. Usually enough thyroid tissue can be removed to cause the amount of thyroid hormone secreted to be reduced to a normal range of values. In addition, the remaining thyroid tissue normally does not hypertrophy enough to cause the thyroid tissue to produce more than enough thyroid hormone, although there are exceptions. The removal of the thyroid tissue does not remove the influence of the abnormal antibodies on the tissues behind the eyes. Thus, in many cases the effect of the condition on the eyes is not improved.

Chapter Eleven

Blood

anticoagulant
(an'tē-kō-ag'ū-lant) Chemical that prevents coagulation, or blood clotting; antithrombin is an example.

clot retraction
Condensation of the clot into a denser, compact structure.

erythropoietin
(ĕ-rith-rō-poy'ĕ-tin) Protein hormone produced by the kidneys that stimulates red blood cell formation in red bone marrow.

fibrin
(fī'brin) [L. *fibra*, fiber] A threadlike protein fiber derived from fibrinogen by the action of thrombin; forms a clot, that is, a network of fibers that traps blood cells, platelets, and fluid, which stops bleeding.

fibrinolysis
(fī'bri-nol'i-sis) [L. *fibra*, fiber; Gr. *lysis*, dissolution] The breakdown of a clot by the blood protein plasmin.

hematocrit
(hē'mă-tō-krit; hem'a-tō-krit) [Gr. *hemato*, blood + *krino*, to separate] The percentage of total blood volume composed of red blood cells.

hemoglobin
(hē-mō-glō'bin) A molecule in red blood cells consisting of four globin proteins, each with an iron-containing red pigment heme; transports oxygen and carbon dioxide.

plasma
(plaz'mă) Fluid part of the blood; blood minus the formed elements.

platelet
(plāt'let) A cell fragment involved in platelet plug and clot formation; also called a thrombocyte.

Red blood cell
Biconcave disk that contains hemoglobin, which transports oxygen and carbon dioxide; a mature red blood cell does not have a nucleus.

White blood cell
Nucleated cell involved in immunity. The five types of white blood cells are neutrophils, eosinophils, basophils, lymphocytes, and monocytes.

Objectives

After reading this chapter, you should be able to:

1. List the functions of blood.
2. Name the components of plasma and give their functions.
3. Describe the origin and production of the formed elements.
4. Describe the structure, function, and life history of red blood cells.
5. Compare the structures and functions of the five different types of white blood cells.
6. Describe the origin and structure of platelets.
7. Explain the formation and function of platelet plugs and clots.
8. Describe the regulation of clot formation and how clots are removed.
9. Explain the basis of ABO and Rh incompatibilities.
10. Describe diagnostic blood tests and the normal values for the tests, and give examples of disorders that produce abnormal test values.

Blood has always fascinated humans, and historically there has been much speculation about its function. For example, blood was considered to be the "essence of life" because loss of blood can result in death; blood was also thought to define our character and emotions. People of a noble bloodline were described as "blue bloods," whereas criminals were considered to have "bad blood." It was said that anger caused the blood "to boil" and fear caused blood "to curdle." The scientific study of blood, however, reveals a story as fascinating as any of these speculations. Blood performs many functions essential to life and often can reveal much about our state of health.

Functions of Blood

Blood is pumped by the heart through blood vessels, which extend throughout the body. Blood helps to maintain homeostasis in several ways:

1. *Transport of gases, nutrients, and waste products.* Oxygen enters blood in the lungs and is carried to cells. Carbon dioxide, produced by cells, is carried in the blood to the lungs, from which it is expelled. Ingested nutrients, ions, and water are transported by the blood from the digestive tract to cells, and the waste products of the cells are transported to the kidneys for elimination.

2. *Transport of processed molecules.* Many substances are produced in one part of the body and transported in the blood to another part, where they are modified. For example, the precursor to vitamin D is produced in the skin (see chapter 5) and transported by the blood to the liver and then to the kidneys for processing into active vitamin D. The active vitamin D is transported to the small intestines, where it promotes the uptake of calcium. Another example is lactic acid produced by skeletal muscles during anaerobic respiration (see chapter 7). The lactic acid is carried to the liver, where it is converted into glucose.

3. *Transport of regulatory molecules.* Many of the hormones and enzymes that regulate body processes are carried from one part of the body to another within the blood.

4. *Regulation of pH and osmosis.* Buffers (see chapter 2), which help keep the blood's pH within its normal limits of 7.35 to 7.45, are found in the blood. The osmotic composition of blood is also critical for maintaining normal fluid and ion balance.

5. *Maintenance of body temperature.* Blood is involved with body temperature regulation because warm blood is transported from the interior to the surface of the body, where heat is released from the blood.

6. *Protection against foreign substances.* Cells and chemicals of the blood constitute an important part of the immune system, protecting against foreign substances such as microorganisms and toxins.

7. *Clot formation.* Blood clotting provides protection against excessive blood loss when blood vessels are damaged. When tissues are damaged, the blood clot that forms is also the first step in tissue repair and the restoration of normal function (see chapter 4).

Composition of Blood

Blood is a type of connective tissue that consists of cells and cell fragments surrounded by a liquid matrix. The cells and cell fragments are the **formed elements**, and the liquid is the **plasma** (plaz′mă) (figure 11.1). The formed elements account for slightly less than half and plasma accounts for slightly more than one-half the total blood volume. The total blood volume in the average adult is about 4 to 5 liters in females and 5 to 6 liters in males. Blood makes up about 8% of total body weight.

Plasma

Plasma is a pale yellow fluid that consists of about 91% water; 7% proteins; and 2% other substances, such as ions, nutrients, gases, and waste products (see figure 11.1 and table 11.1). Plasma proteins include albumin, globulins, and fibrinogen. **Albumin** (al-bū′min) makes up 58% of the plasma proteins. Although the osmotic pressure (see chapter 3) of blood results primarily from sodium chloride, albumin makes an important contribution. The water balance between blood and tissues is determined by the movement of water into and out of the blood by osmosis. **Globulins** (glob′ū-linz) account for 38% of the plasma proteins. Some globulins, such as antibodies and complement, are part of the immune system (see chapter 14). Other globulins function as transport molecules because they bind to molecules such as hormones (see chapter 10) and carry them in the blood throughout the body. **Fibrinogen** (fī-brin′ō-jen) constitutes 4% of plasma proteins and is responsible for the formation of blood clots (see discussion on p. 300).

Plasma volume remains relatively constant. Normally water intake through the digestive tract closely matches water loss through the kidneys, lungs, digestive tract, and skin. Oxygen enters blood in the lungs, and carbon dioxide enters blood from tissues. Other suspended or dissolved substances in the blood come from the liver, kidneys, intestines, endocrine glands, and immune tissues such as the spleen. The concentration of these other substances is also regulated and maintained within narrow limits.

Formed Elements

About 95% of the volume of the formed elements consists of **red blood cells (RBCs)**, or **erythrocytes** (ĕ-rith′rō-sītz). The remaining 5% of the volume of the formed elements consists of **white blood cells (WBCs)**, or **leukocytes** (loo′kō-sītz), and cell fragments called **platelets** (plāt′letz), or **thrombocytes** (throm′bō-sītz). Red blood cells are 700 times more numerous than white blood cells and 17 times more numerous than platelets. The formed elements of the blood are outlined and illustrated in table 11.2.

Production of Formed Elements

The process of blood cell production is called **hematopoiesis** (hē′mă-tō-poy-ē′sis). In the fetus, hematopoiesis occurs in several tissues such as the liver, thymus gland, spleen, lymph

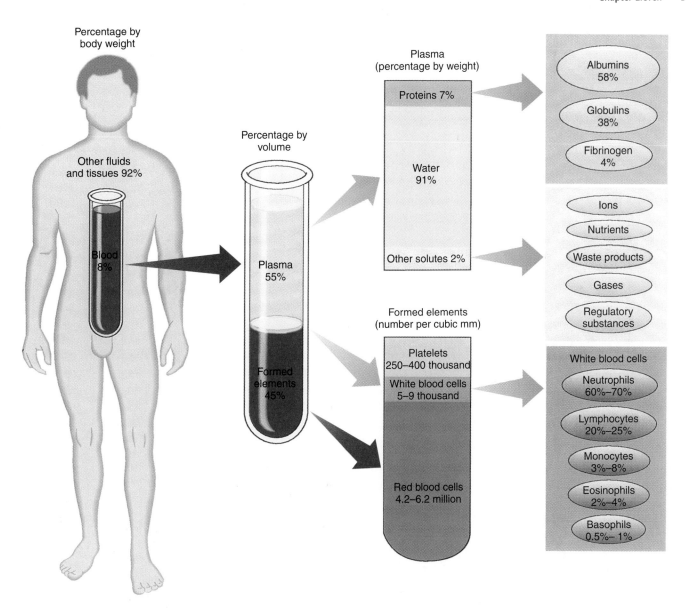

Figure 11.1   Composition of Blood

Approximate values for the components of blood in a normal adult.

Table 11.1	Composition of Plasma
Plasma Components	**Functions and Examples**
Water	Acts as a solvent and suspending medium for blood components
Proteins	Maintain osmotic pressure (albumin), destroy foreign substances (antibodies and complement), transport molecules (globulins), and form clots (fibrinogen)
Ions	Involved in osmotic pressure (sodium and chloride ions), membrane potentials (sodium and potassium ions), and acid–base balance (hydrogen, hydroxide, and bicarbonate ions)
Nutrients	Source of energy and "building blocks" of more complex molecules (glucose, amino acids, triacylglycerides)
Gases	Involved in aerobic respiration (oxygen and carbon dioxide)
Waste products	Breakdown products of protein metabolism (urea and ammonia salts), erythrocytes (bilirubin), and anaerobic respiration (lactic acid)
Regulatory substances	Catalyze chemical reactions (enzymes) and stimulate or inhibit many body functions (hormones)

Table 11.2 Formed Elements of the Blood

Cell Type	Illustration	Description	Function
Red blood cell (erythrocyte)		Biconcave disk; no nucleus; contains hemoglobin, which colors the cell red; 7.5 μm in diameter	Transports oxygen and carbon dioxide
White blood cell (leukocyte)		Spherical cell with a nucleus; white in color because it lacks hemoglobin	Five types of white blood cells, each with specific functions
Granulocytes			
Neutrophil		Nucleus with two to four lobes connected by thin filaments; cytoplasmic granules stain a light pink or reddish purple; 10–12 μm in diameter	Phagocytizes microorganisms and other substances
Basophil		Nucleus with two indistinct lobes; cytoplasmic granules stain blue-purple; 10–12 μm in diameter	Releases histamine, which promotes inflammation, and heparin, which prevents clot formation
Eosinophil		Nucleus often bilobed; cytoplasmic granules stain orange-red or bright red; 11–14 μm in diameter	Releases chemicals that reduce inflammation; attacks certain worm parasites
Agranulocytes			
Lymphocyte		Round nucleus; cytoplasm forms a thin ring around the nucleus; 6–14 μm in diameter	Produces antibodies and other chemicals responsible for destroying microorganisms; contributes to allergic reactions, graft rejection, tumor control, and regulation of the immune system
Monocyte		Nucleus round, kidney, or horseshoe-shaped; contains more cytoplasm than does lymphocyte; 12–20 μm in diameter	Phagocytic cell in the blood; leaves the blood and becomes a macrophage, which phagocytizes bacteria, dead cells, cell fragments, and other debris within tissues
Platelet (thrombocyte)		Cell fragment surrounded by a plasma membrane and containing granules; 2–4 μm in diameter	Forms platelet plugs; releases chemicals necessary for blood clotting

nodes, and red bone marrow. After birth, hematopoiesis is confined primarily to red bone marrow, but some white blood cells are produced in lymphatic tissues (see chapter 14).

All the formed elements of blood are derived from a single population of cells called **stem cells**. These stem cells differentiate to give rise to different cell lines, each of which ends with the formation of a particular type of formed element (figure 11.2). The development of each cell line is regulated by specific growth factors. That is, the type of formed element derived from the stem cells and how many formed elements are produced are determined by the growth factor.

Red Blood Cells

Normal red blood cells are disk-shaped cells with edges that are thicker than the center of the cell (figure 11.3). Compared to

Did You Know?

Many cancer therapies attack dividing cells such as those found in tumors. An undesirable side effect, however, can be the destruction of nontumor cells that divide rapidly, such as the cells in red bone marrow. After treatment for cancer, growth factors are used to stimulate the rapid regeneration of the red bone marrow. Although not a treatment for the cancer itself, the use of growth factors can speed recovery from the side effects of cancer therapy.

Some types of leukemia and genetic immune deficiency diseases can be treated with a bone marrow transplant containing blood stem cells. To avoid problems of tissue rejection, families with a history of these disorders can freeze the umbilical cord blood of their newborn children. The cord blood contains many stem cells and can be used instead of a bone marrow transplant.

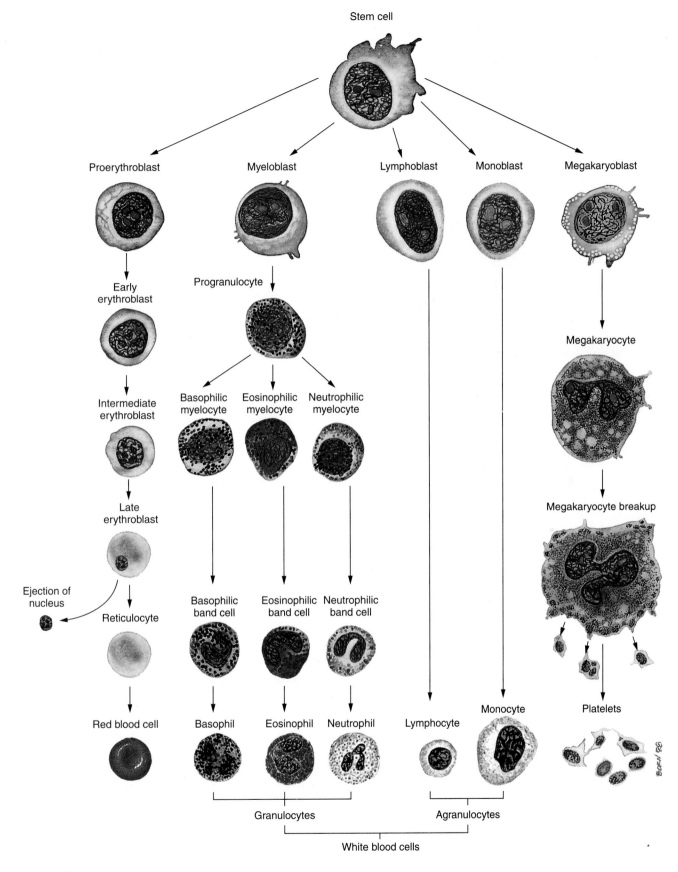

Figure 11.2 Hematopoiesis

Stem cells gives rise to the cell lines that produce the formed elements.

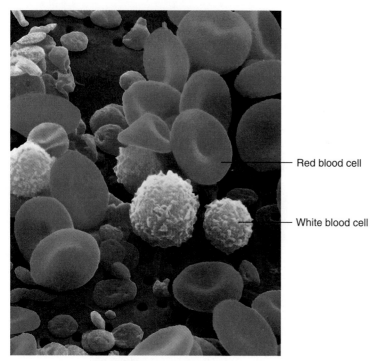

Red blood cell

White blood cell

Figure 11.3   Red and White Blood Cells

The red blood cells are biconcave disks with a thin center. The white blood cells are spherical and have cytoplasmic extensions.

a flat disk of the same size, the biconcave shape increases the surface area of the red blood cell. The greater surface area makes it easier for gases to move into and out of the red blood cell. In addition, the red blood cell can bend or fold around its thin center, decreasing its size and enabling it to pass more easily through small blood vessels.

During their development, red blood cells lose their nuclei and most of their organelles. Consequently, they are unable to divide. Red blood cells live for about 120 days in males and 110 days in females. The main component of an red blood cell is the pigmented protein **hemoglobin** (hē-mō-glō′bin), which accounts for about a third of the cell's volume and is responsible for its red color.

Function

The primary functions of red blood cells are to transport oxygen from the lungs to the various tissues of the body and to assist in the transport of carbon dioxide from the tissues to the lungs. Oxygen transport is accomplished by hemoglobin, which consists of four protein chains and four heme groups. Each protein, called a **globin** (glō′bin), is bound to one **heme** (hēm), a red-pigmented molecule. Each heme contains one iron atom, which is necessary for the normal function of hemoglobin. When hemoglobin is exposed to oxygen, one oxygen molecule binds to the iron atom of each heme. Hemoglobin that is bound to oxygen is bright red in color, whereas hemoglobin without bound oxygen is a darker red color. Hemoglobin is responsible for 98.5% of the oxygen transported in blood. The remaining 1.5% is transported dissolved in plasma.

Because iron is necessary for oxygen transport, it is not surprising that two-thirds of the body's iron is found in hemoglobin. Small amounts of iron are required in the diet to replace the small amounts lost in the urine and feces. Women need more dietary iron than men do because women lose iron as a result of menstruation.

Did You Know?

Carbon monoxide is a gas produced by the incomplete combustion of hydrocarbons such as gasoline. It binds to the iron in hemoglobin about 210 times as readily as does oxygen and does not tend to dissociate. As a result, the hemoglobin bound to carbon monoxide no longer transports oxygen. Nausea, headache, unconsciousness, and death are possible consequences of prolonged exposure to carbon monoxide.

Carbon dioxide transport involves bicarbonate ions, hemoglobin, and plasma. Approximately 70% of the carbon dioxide in blood is transported in the form of bicarbonate ions. The enzyme **carbonic anhydrase** (kar-bon′ik an-hī′drās), found primarily inside red blood cells, catalyzes a reaction that converts carbon dioxide (CO_2) and water (H_2O) into a hydrogen ion (H^+) and a bicarbonate ion (HCO_3^-) (see chapter 15 for more details).

$$CO_2 \; + \; H_2O \; \rightleftarrows \; H^+ \; + \; HCO_3^-$$

Carbon dioxide can bind to the globin part of hemoglobin. About 23% of the carbon dioxide in blood is transported bound to hemoglobin or other blood proteins. The remaining 7% of carbon dioxide is transported dissolved in plasma.

Life History of Red Blood Cells

Under normal conditions, about 2.5 million red blood cells are destroyed every second. Fortunately, new red blood cells are produced as rapidly as old red blood cells are destroyed. Stem cells form **proerythroblasts** (prō-ĕ-rith′rō-blastz), which give rise to the red blood cell line (see figure 11.2). Red blood cells are the final cells produced from a series of cell divisions. After each cell division, the newly formed cells change and become more like a mature red blood cell. For example, following one of these cell divisions, the newly formed cells manufacture large amounts of hemoglobin. After the final cell division, the nucleus is lost from the cell, and a completely mature red blood cell is formed.

The process of cell division requires the vitamins folate and B_{12}, which are necessary for the synthesis of DNA (see chapter 3). Iron is required for the production of hemoglobin. Consequently, lack of folate, vitamin B_{12}, or iron can interfere with normal red blood cell production.

Red blood cell production is stimulated by low blood oxygen levels. Typical causes of low blood oxygen are decreased numbers of red blood cells, decreased or defective hemoglobin, diseases of the lungs, high altitude, inability of the cardiovascular system to deliver blood to tissues, and increased tissue demands for oxygen such as during endurance exercises.

Low blood oxygen levels increase red blood cell production by increasing the formation of the glycoprotein **erythropoietin** (ĕ-rith-rō-poy′ĕ-tin) by the kidneys (figure 11.4). Erythropoietin stimulates red bone marrow to produce more red blood cells. Thus, when oxygen levels in the blood decrease, the production of erythropoietin increases, which increases red blood cell production. The increased number of red blood cells increases the ability of the blood to transport oxygen. This mechanism returns blood oxygen levels to normal and maintains homeostasis by increasing the delivery of oxygen to tissues. Conversely, if blood oxygen levels increase, less erythropoietin is released, and red blood cell production decreases.

---

1   P R E D I C T

Cigarette smoke produces carbon monoxide. If a nonsmoker smoked a pack of cigarettes a day for a few weeks, what would happen to the number of red blood cells in the person's blood? Explain.

✔ *Answer on page 310*

Old, abnormal, or damaged red blood cells are removed from the blood by macrophages located in the spleen and liver (figure 11.5). Within the macrophage the globin part of the molecule is broken down into amino acids that are reused to produce other proteins. The iron released from heme is transported in the blood to the red bone marrow and is used to produce new hemoglobin. Only small amounts of iron are required in the daily diet because the iron is recycled. The heme molecules are converted to **bilirubin** (bil-i-roo′bin), a yellow pigment molecule. Bilirubin normally is taken up by the liver and released into the small intestine as part of the bile (see chapter 16). If the liver is not functioning normally, or if the flow of bile from the liver to the small intestine is hindered, bilirubin builds up in the circulation and produces **jaundice** (jawn′dis), a yellowish color of the skin. After it enters the intestine, bilirubin is converted by bacteria into other pigments. Some of these pigments give feces their brown color, whereas others are absorbed from the intestine into the blood, modified by the kidneys, and excreted in the urine, contributing to the characteristic yellow color of urine.

White Blood Cells

White blood cells or **leukocytes**, are spherical cells that are whitish in color because they lack hemoglobin (see figure 11.3). They are larger than red blood cells, and they have a nucleus (see table 11.2). Although white blood cells are components of the blood, the blood serves primarily as a means to transport these cells to other tissues of the body. White blood cells can leave the blood and move by **ameboid** (ă-mē′boyd) **movement** through the tissues. In this process, the cell projects a cytoplasmic extension that attaches to an object. Then the rest of the cell's cytoplasm flows into the extension. White blood cells have two primary functions: (1) to protect the body against invading microorganisms and (2) to remove dead cells and debris from the tissues by phagocytosis.

White blood cells are named according to their appearance in stained preparations. Those containing large cytoplasmic granules are **granulocytes** (gran′ū-lō-sītz), and those with very small granules that cannot be easily seen with the light microscope are **agranulocytes** (ă-gran′ū-lō-sītz).

There are three kinds of granulocytes. **Neutrophils** (noo′trō-filz) are the most common type of white blood cell (figure 11.6). They usually remain in the blood for a short time

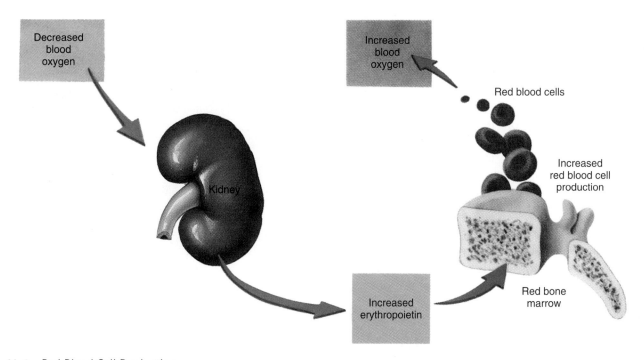

Figure 11.4   Red Blood Cell Production

In response to decreased blood oxygen, the kidneys release erythropoietin. The increased erythropoietin stimulates red blood cell production in the red bone marrow. This process results in increased blood oxygen levels.

1. The globin chains of hemoglobin are broken down to individual amino acids (lavender arrow) and are metabolized or used to build new proteins.

2. Iron is released from the heme of hemoglobin. The heme is converted into bilirubin.

3. Iron is transported in the blood to the red bone marrow and used in the production of new hemoglobin (green arrows).

4. Bilirubin is taken up by the liver.

5. Bilirubin is excreted from the liver as part of the bile.

6. Bilirubin derivatives contribute to the color of feces or are reabsorbed from the intestine into the blood and excreted from the kidneys in the urine.

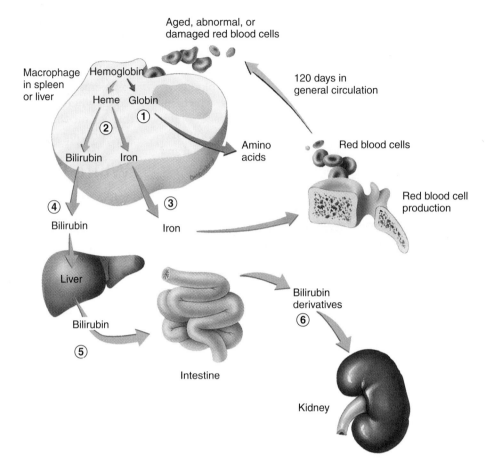

Figure 11.5 Hemoglobin Breakdown

Macrophages in the spleen and liver break down hemoglobin. Globin is converted to amino acids, and heme is converted to iron and bilirubin. Iron is used in the production of new hemoglobin, and the bilirubin is released into the small intestine as part of the bile.

(10 to 12 hours), move into other tissues, and phagocytize microorganisms and other foreign substances. Dead neutrophils, cell debris, and fluid can accumulate as **pus** at sites of infections. **Basophils** (bā′sō-filz) and **eosinophils** (ē-ō-sin′ō-filz) are involved in regulating the inflammatory response (see chapters 4 and 14). Basophils release histamine and other chemicals that promote inflammation. Basophils also release heparin, which prevents the formation of clots. Eosinophils release chemicals that reduce inflammation. In addition, chemicals from eosinophils are involved with the destruction of certain worm parasites.

There are two kinds of agranulocytes. **Lymphocytes** (lim′fō-sītz) are the smallest of the white blood cells (see figure 11.6). There are several types of lymphocytes, and they play an important role in the body's immune response. Their diverse activities involve the production of antibodies and other chemicals that destroy microorganisms, contribute to allergic reactions, reject grafts, control tumors, and regulate the immune system. Chapter 14 considers these cells in more detail. **Monocytes** (mon′ō-sītz) are the largest of the white blood cells. After they leave the blood and enter tissues, monocytes enlarge and become **macrophages** (mak′rō-fā-jez), which phagocytize bacteria, dead cells, cell fragments, and any other debris within the tissues. In addition,

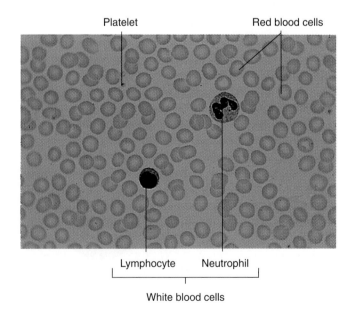

Figure 11.6 Photomicrograph of a Blood Smear

A thin film of blood is spread on a microscope slide, and the blood cells are stained. The red blood cells are pink, the white blood cells have purple-stained nuclei, and the platelets are purple-stained cell fragments.

macrophages can break down phagocytized foreign substances and present the processed substances to lymphocytes, which results in activation of the lymphocytes (see chapter 14).

Platelets

Platelets (plāt′letz), or **thrombocytes** (throm′bō-sītz), are minute fragments of cells, each consisting of a small amount of cytoplasm surrounded by a cell membrane (see figure 11.6). They are produced in the red bone marrow from **megakaryocytes** (meg-ă-kar′ē-ō-sītz), which are large cells (see figure 11.2). Small fragments of these cells break off and enter the blood as platelets, which play an important role in preventing blood loss. This prevention is accomplished in two ways: (1) the formation of platelet plugs, which seal holes in small vessels, and (2) the formation of clots, which help seal off larger wounds in the vessels.

Preventing Blood Loss

When a blood vessel is damaged, blood can leak into other tissues and interfere with normal tissue function, or blood can be lost from the body. Small amounts of blood loss from the body can be tolerated, but new blood must be produced to replace the lost blood. If large amounts of blood are lost, death can occur. Fortunately, when a blood vessel is damaged, blood vessel constriction, platelet plug formation, and blood clotting help prevent the loss of blood.

Blood Vessel Constriction

When a blood vessel is damaged, smooth muscle in the vessel wall contracts. In small vessels, this constriction can close off the vessels completely and stop the flow of blood through the vessels. In larger vessels, the constriction reduces blood loss and allows time for other processes to stop the bleeding. Contraction of blood vessels can occur as a result of nervous system reflexes and chemicals released by platelets. For example, platelets release **thromboxanes** (throm′bok-zānz), which are derived from prostaglandins (see chapter 10).

Platelet Plugs

A **platelet plug** is an accumulation of platelets that can seal up small breaks in blood vessels. Platelet plug formation is very important in maintaining the integrity of the circulatory system because small tears occur in the smaller vessels and capillaries many times each day, and platelet plug formation quickly closes them. People who lack the normal number of platelets tend to develop numerous small hemorrhages in their skin and internal organs.

The formation of a platelet plug can be described as a series of steps, but in actuality many of the events occur at the same time (figure 11.7). **Platelet adhesion** results in platelets sticking to collagen exposed by blood vessel damage. Most platelet adhesion is mediated through **von Willebrand's factor,** which is a protein produced and secreted by blood vessel endothelial cells. von Willebrand's factor forms a bridge between collagen and platelets by binding to platelet surface receptors and collagen. After platelets adhere to collagen, they become activated, change shape, and release chemicals. In the **platelet release reaction,** platelets extrude chemicals, such as ADP and thromboxane, which activate other platelets. These activated platelets also release ADP and thromboxane, which activates more platelets. Thus, a cascade of chemical release activates many platelets. As platelets become activated they also express integrins called **fibrinogen receptors,** which can bind to fibrinogen, a plasma protein. In **platelet aggregation,** fibrinogen

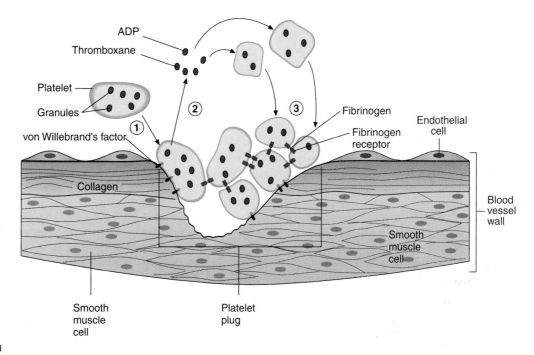

1. Platelet adhesion occurs when von Willebrand's factor connects collagen and platelets.

2. The platelet release reaction is the release of ADP, thromboxanes, and other chemicals that activate other platelets.

3. Platelet aggregation occurs when fibrinogen receptors on activated platelets bind to fibrinogen, connecting the platelets to one another. A platelet plug is formed by the accumulating mass of platelets.

Figure 11.7 Platelet Plug Formation

forms bridges between the fibrinogen receptors of numerous platelets, resulting in the formation of a platelet plug. Activated platelets also produce chemicals, such as phospholipids, that are important for blood clotting.

Blood Clotting

Blood vessel constriction and platelet plugs alone are not sufficient to close large tears or cuts in blood vessels. When a blood vessel is severely damaged, **blood clotting**, or **coagulation** (kō-ag-ū-lā'shŭn), results in the formation of a clot. A **clot** is a network of threadlike protein fibers, called **fibrin** (fī'brin), that traps blood cells, platelets, and fluid.

The formation of a blood clot depends on a number of proteins found within plasma called **clotting factors**. Normally the clotting factors are inactive and do not cause clotting. Following injury, however, the clotting factors are activated to produce a clot. This is a complex process involving many chemical reactions, but it can be summarized in three main stages (figure 11.8).

1. The chemical reactions can be started in two ways: (a) just as with platelets, the contact of inactive clotting factors with exposed connective tissue can result in their activation; (b) chemicals released from injured tissues, such as **thromboplastin**, can also cause activation of clotting factors. After the initial clotting factors are activated, they in turn activate other clotting factors. A series of reactions results in which each clotting factor activates the next in the series until the clotting factor **prothrombinase** (prō-throm'bi-nās) is formed.

2. Prothrombinase acts on an inactive clotting factor called **prothrombin** (prō-throm'bin), to convert it to its active form called **thrombin** (throm'bin).

3. Thrombin converts the inactive clotting factor **fibrinogen** (fī-brin'ō-jen) into its active form, **fibrin** (fī'brin), which is a threadlike protein. The fibrin threads form a network, which traps blood cells and platelets to form the clot.

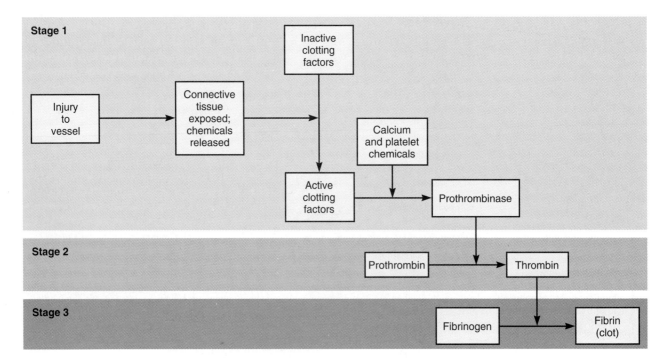

Figure 11.8 Clot Formation

In stage 1, inactive clotting factors are activated by exposure to connective tissue or by chemicals released from tissues. Through a series of reactions, the activated clotting factors form prothrombinase. In stage 2, prothrombin is converted to thrombin by prothrombinase. In stage 3, fibrinogen is converted to fibrin (the clot) by thrombin.

At each step of the clotting process, each clotting factor molecule activates many additional such molecules. Consequently, large quantities of clotting factors are activated, resulting in the formation of the clot.

Most of the clotting factors are manufactured in the liver, and many of them require vitamin K for their synthesis. In addition, many of the chemical reactions of clotting require calcium ions and chemicals released from platelets. Low levels of vitamin K, low levels of calcium, low numbers of platelets, or liver dysfunction can seriously impair the blood-clotting process.

Control of Clot Formation

Without control, clotting would spread from the point of its initiation throughout the entire circulatory system. The blood contains several **anticoagulants** (an'tē-kō-ag'ū-lantz), which prevent clotting factors from forming clots. **Antithrombin** (an-tē-throm'bin) and **heparin** (hep'ă-rin), for example, inactivate thrombin. Without thrombin, fibrinogen is not converted to fibrin, and there is no clot formation. Normally there are enough anticoagulants in the blood to prevent clot formation. At an injury site, however, the stimulation for activating clotting factors is very strong. Enough clotting factors are activated that the anticoagulants no longer can prevent a clot from forming. Away from the injury site, however, there are enough anticoagulants to prevent clot formation from spreading.

Clot Retraction and Fibrinolysis

After a clot has formed, it begins to condense into a more compact structure by a process known as **clot retraction**. Platelets contain contractile proteins, actin and myosin, which operate in a similar fashion to the actin and myosin in muscle (see chapter 7). Platelets form small extensions that attach to fibrin. Contraction of the extensions pulls on the fibrin and is responsible for clot retraction. **Serum** (sēr'ŭm), which is plasma without the clotting factors, is squeezed out of the clot during clot retraction.

Consolidation of the clot pulls the edges of the damaged blood vessel together, helping to stop the flow of blood, reducing the probability of infection, and enhancing healing. The damaged vessel is repaired by the movement of fibroblasts into the damaged area and the formation of new connective tissue. In addition, epithelial cells around the wound divide and fill in the torn area (see chapter 4).

Clots are dissolved by a process called **fibrinolysis** (fī-bri-nol'-i-sis) (figure 11.9). An inactive plasma protein called **plasminogen** (plaz-min'ō-jen) is converted to its active form, **plasmin** (plaz'min). Thrombin, other clotting factors activated during clot formation, and **tissue plasminogen activator (t-PA)**, released from surrounding tissues can stimulate the conversion of plasminogen to plasmin. Over a period of a few days, plasmin slowly breaks down the fibrin.

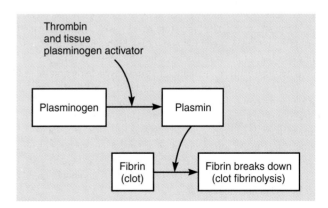

Figure 11.9 Fibrinolysis

Thrombin and tissue plasminogen activator convert plasminogen into plasmin, which breaks down the fibrin in a blood clot, resulting in clot fibrinolysis.

Blood Grouping

If large quantities of blood are lost during surgery or in an accident, shock can develop as a result of inadequate blood flow to essential organs. Blood volume must be increased, or the person could die. A **transfusion** is the transfer of blood, parts of blood, or solutions into a person's blood. In many cases the return of blood volume to normal levels is all that is necessary. This can be accomplished by the transfusion of plasma or prepared solutions that have the proper amounts of solutes. When large quantities of blood are lost, however, red blood cells must also be replaced so that the oxygen-carrying capacity of the blood is restored.

Early attempts to transfuse blood were often unsuccessful because they resulted in **transfusion reactions**, which included clumping of blood cells, rupture of blood cells, and clotting within blood vessels. It is now known that transfusion reactions are caused by interactions between antigens and antibodies (see chapter 14). In brief, the surfaces of red blood cells have molecules called **antigens** (an'ti-jenz), and the plasma includes proteins called **antibodies** (an'te-bod-ēz). Antibodies are very specific, meaning that each antibody can combine only with a certain antigen. When the antibodies in the plasma bind to the antigens on the surface of the red blood cells, they form molecular bridges that connect the red blood cells together. As a result, **agglutination** (ă-gloo-ti-nā'shŭn), or clumping of the cells, occurs. The combination of the antibodies with the antigens also can initiate reactions that cause **hemolysis** (hē-mol'i-sis), or rupture of the red blood cells. The debris formed from the ruptured red blood cells can trigger clotting within small blood vessels. As a result of these changes, tissue damage and death may occur.

The antigens on the surface of red blood cells have been categorized into **blood groups**. Although many blood groups are recognized, the ABO and Rh blood groups are the most important for transfusion reactions.

> ### Did You Know?
>
> Current research is being conducted in an attempt to develop artificial hemoglobin. One chemical that has been used in clinical trials is a perfluorochemical (per-floo'rō-kem'i-kăl) emulsion called Fluosol (flu'ō-sol) DA, a white liquid with a high oxygen affinity. Although the usefulness of hemoglobin substitutes is currently limited because artificial hemoglobin is destroyed fairly quickly in the body, future work may uncover more successful substitutes that can provide long-term relief for patients with blood disorders.
>
> The use of artificial hemoglobin could eliminate some of the disadvantages of using blood for transfusions. With artificial hemoglobin, transfusion reactions would not occur because of mismatched blood, and transferring diseases such as hepatitis or AIDS would be eliminated. In addition, artificial hemoglobin could be used when blood is not available.

ABO Blood Group

In humans, blood is categorized by the **ABO blood group** system. The ABO antigens appear on the surface of the red blood cells. Type A blood has type A antigens, type B blood has type B antigens, type AB blood has both types of antigens, and type O blood has neither A nor B antigens (figure 11.10). In addition, plasma from type A blood contains type B antibodies, which act against type B antigens; whereas plasma from type B blood contains type A antibodies, which act against type A antigens. Type AB blood has neither type of antibody, and type O blood has both A and B antibodies.

The ABO blood types are not found in equal numbers. In Caucasians in the United States the distribution is type O, 47%; type A, 41%; type B, 9%; and type AB, 3%. Among African-Americans the distribution is type O, 46%; type A, 27%; type B, 20%; and type AB, 7%.

The reason for the presence of A and B antibodies in blood is not clearly understood. Antibodies do not normally develop against an antigen unless the body is exposed to that antigen. For example, this means that a person with type A blood should not have type B antibodies unless he or she has received a transfusion of type B blood, which contains type B antigens. People with type A blood do have type B antibodies, however, even though they never have received a transfusion of type B blood. One possible explanation is that type A or B antigens on bacteria or food in the digestive tract stimulate the formation of antibodies against antigens that are different from one's own antigens. In support of this explanation is the observation that A and B antibodies are not found in the blood until about 2 months after birth. For example, a person with type A blood would produce type B antibodies against the B antigens on bacteria or food. A person with type A antigens would not produce antibodies against the A antigen on bacteria because mechanisms exist in the body to prevent the production of antibodies that would react with the body's own antigens (see chapter 14).

A **donor** is a person who gives blood, and a **recipient** is a person who receives blood. Usually a donor can give blood to a recipient if they both have the same blood type. For example, a person with type A blood could donate to another person with type A blood. There would be no ABO transfusion reaction because the recipient has no antibodies against the type A antigen. On the other hand, if type A blood were donated to a person with type B blood, a transfusion reaction would occur because the person with type B blood has antibodies against the type A antigen, and agglutination would result (figure 11.11).

Historically, people with type O blood have been called universal donors because they usually can give blood to the other ABO blood types without causing an ABO transfusion reaction. Their red blood cells have no ABO surface antigens and therefore do not react with the recipient's A or B antibodies. For example, if type O blood is given to a person with type A blood, the type O red blood cells do not react with the type B antibodies in the recipient's blood. In a similar fashion, if type O blood is given to a person with type B blood, there would be no reaction with the recipient's type A antibodies.

It should be noted, however, that the term universal donor is misleading. In two circumstances transfusion of type O blood can produce a transfusion reaction. First, mismatching blood groups other than the ABO blood group can cause a transfusion reaction. To reduce the likelihood of a transfu-

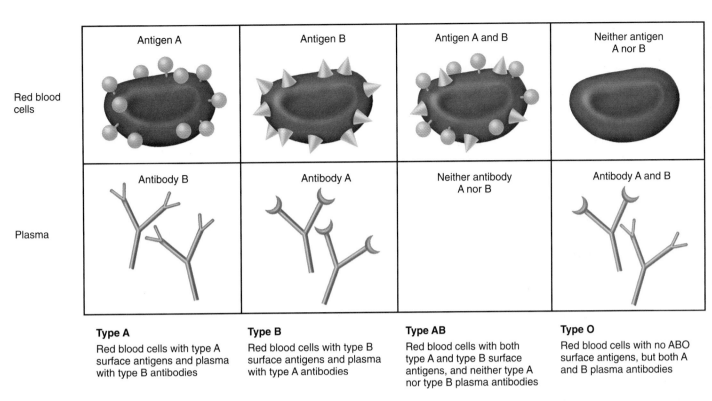

| Antigen A | Antigen B | Antigen A and B | Neither antigen A nor B |

| Antibody B | Antibody A | Neither antibody A nor B | Antibody A and B |

Type A
Red blood cells with type A surface antigens and plasma with type B antibodies

Type B
Red blood cells with type B surface antigens and plasma with type A antibodies

Type AB
Red blood cells with both type A and type B surface antigens, and neither type A nor type B plasma antibodies

Type O
Red blood cells with no ABO surface antigens, but both A and B plasma antibodies

Figure 11.10   ABO Blood Groups
The antigens found on the surface of the red blood cells of each blood type and the antibodies found in the plasma of each blood type are shown.

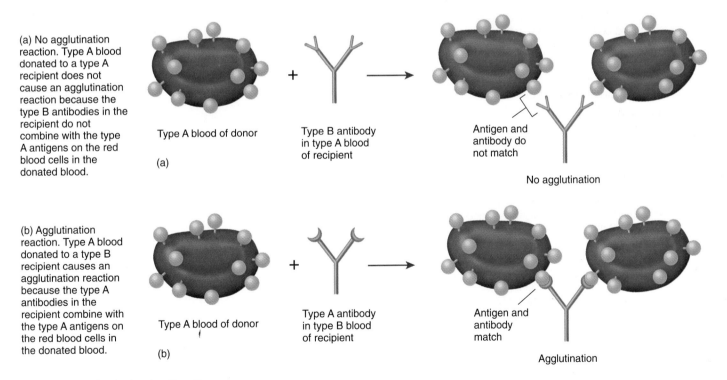

(a) No agglutination reaction. Type A blood donated to a type A recipient does not cause an agglutination reaction because the type B antibodies in the recipient do not combine with the type A antigens on the red blood cells in the donated blood.

Type A blood of donor

Type B antibody in type A blood of recipient

Antigen and antibody do not match

No agglutination

(a)

(b) Agglutination reaction. Type A blood donated to a type B recipient causes an agglutination reaction because the type A antibodies in the recipient combine with the type A antigens on the red blood cells in the donated blood.

Type A blood of donor

Type A antibody in type B blood of recipient

Antigen and antibody match

Agglutination

(b)

Figure 11.11   Agglutination Reaction

sion reaction, all the blood groups must be correctly matched. Second, antibodies in the blood of the donor can react with antigens on the red blood cells in the blood of the recipient. For example, type O blood has type A and B antibodies. If type O blood is transfused into a person with type A blood, the A antibodies (in the type O blood) react against the A antigens (on the red blood cells in the type A blood). Usually such reactions are not serious because the antibodies in the donor's blood are diluted in the blood of the recipient, and few reactions take place. Because type O blood sometimes causes transfusion reactions in these situations, however, it is given to a person with another blood type only in life-or-death conditions.

Rh Blood Group

Another important blood group is the **Rh blood group**, so named because it was first studied in the rhesus monkey. People are Rh-positive if they have certain Rh antigens on the surface of their red blood cells, and they are Rh-negative if they do not have these Rh antigens. About 85% of Caucasians and 95% of African-Americans are Rh-positive. The ABO blood type and the Rh blood type usually are designated together. For example, a person designated as A positive is type A in the ABO blood group and Rh-positive. The rarest combination in the United States is AB negative, which occurs in less than 1% of all Americans.

Antibodies against the Rh antigens do not develop unless an Rh-negative person is exposed to Rh-positive red blood cells. This can occur through a transfusion or by the transfer of blood across the placenta to a mother from her fetus. When an Rh-negative person receives a transfusion of Rh-positive blood, the recipient becomes sensitized to the Rh antigens and produces Rh antibodies. If the Rh-negative person is unfortunate enough to receive a second transfusion of Rh-positive blood after becoming sensitized, a transfusion reaction results.

Rh incompatibility can pose a major problem in some pregnancies, when the mother is Rh-negative and the fetus is Rh-positive (figure 11.12). If fetal blood leaks through the placenta and mixes with the mother's blood, the mother becomes

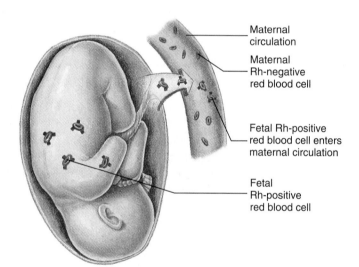

1. Before or during delivery, Rh-positive red blood cells from the fetus enter the blood of an Rh-negative woman through a tear in the placenta.

2. The mother is sensitized to the Rh antigen and produces Rh antibodies. Because this usually happens after delivery, there is no effect on the fetus in the first pregnancy.

3. During a subsequent pregnancy with an Rh-positive fetus, Rh-positive red blood cells cross the placenta, enter the maternal circulation, and stimulate the mother to produce antibodies against the Rh antigen. Antibody production is rapid because the mother has been sensitized to the Rh antigen. The Rh antibodies from the mother cross the placenta, causing agglutination and hemolysis of fetal red blood cells, and hemolytic disease of the newborn develops.

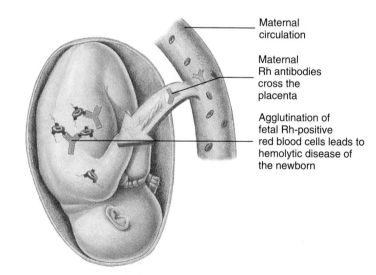

Figure 11.12 Hemolytic Disease of the Newborn

sensitized to the Rh antigen. The mother produces Rh antibodies that cross the placenta and cause agglutination and hemolysis of fetal red blood cells. This disorder is called **hemolytic** (hē-mō-lit′ik)) **disease of the newborn (HDN)**, or **erythroblastosis fetalis** (ĕ-rith′rō-blas-tō′sis fē-ta′lis), and it can be fatal to the fetus. In the first pregnancy, there is often no problem. The leakage of fetal blood is usually the result of a tear in the placenta that takes place either late in the pregnancy or during delivery. Thus there is not enough time for the mother to produce sufficient numbers of Rh antibodies to harm the fetus. In later pregnancies, however, a problem can arise because the mother has been sensitized to the Rh antigen. Consequently, if the fetus is Rh-positive and if any fetal blood leaks into the mother's blood, she rapidly produces large amounts of Rh antibodies, which can cross the placenta to the fetus, and HDN develops.

Prevention of HDN is often possible if the Rh-negative woman is given an injection of a specific type of antibody preparation called anti-Rho(D) immune globulin (RhoGAM). The injection can be given during the pregnancy, before delivery, or immediately after each delivery, miscarriage, or abortion. The injection contains antibodies against Rh antigens. The injected antibodies bind to the Rh antigens of any fetal red blood cells that may have entered the mother's blood. This treatment inactivates the fetal Rh antigens and prevents sensitization of the mother.

If HDN develops, treatment consists of slowly removing the blood of the fetus or newborn and replacing it with Rh-negative blood. The newborn's skin is also exposed to fluorescent light because it helps break down bilirubin in the blood as the blood flows through the skin. The bilirubin is derived from the hemoglobin released from ruptured red blood cells. High levels of bilirubin are toxic to the nervous system and can cause destruction of brain tissue.

Diagnostic Blood Tests

Type and Crossmatch

To prevent transfusion reactions the blood is typed, and a crossmatch is made. **Blood typing** determines the ABO and Rh blood groups of the blood sample. Typically, the cells are separated from the serum. The cells are tested with known antibodies to determine the type of antigen on the cell surface. For example, if a patient's blood cells agglutinate when mixed with type A antibodies but do not agglutinate when mixed with type B antibodies, it is concluded that the cells have type A antigen. In a similar fashion, the serum is mixed with known cell types (antigens) to determine the type of antibodies in the serum.

Normally, donor blood must match the ABO and Rh type of the recipient. Because other blood groups can cause a transfusion reaction, however, a crossmatch is performed. In a **crossmatch**, the donor's blood cells are mixed with the recipient's serum, and the donor's serum is mixed with the recipient's cells. The donor's blood is considered safe for transfusion only if no agglutination occurs in either match.

Complete Blood Count

The **complete blood count (CBC)** is an analysis of the blood that provides much information. It consists of a red blood cell count, hemoglobin and hematocrit measurements, and a white blood cell count.

Red Blood Cell Count

Blood cell counts are usually done electronically with a machine, but they can be done manually with a microscope. A normal **red blood cell count (RBC)** for a male is 4.6 to 6.2 million red blood cells per cubic millimeter of blood, and for a female it is 4.2 to 5.4 million per cubic millimeter of blood. **Polycythemia** (pol′ē-sī-thē′mē-ă) is an overabundance of red blood cells. It can result from a decreased oxygen supply, which stimulates erythropoietin production, or from red bone marrow tumors. Because red blood cells tend to stick to one another, increasing the number of red blood cells makes it more difficult for blood to flow. Consequently, polycythemia increases the workload of the heart and can cause the heart to fail. It also can reduce blood flow through tissues and, if severe, can result in plugging of small blood vessels (capillaries).

Hemoglobin Measurement

The hemoglobin measurement determines the amount of hemoglobin in a given volume of blood, usually expressed as grams of hemoglobin per 100 milliliters of blood. The normal hemoglobin measurement for a male is 14 to 18 grams (g)/100 milliliters (mL) of blood, and for a female it is 12 to 16 g/100 mL of blood. An abnormally low hemoglobin measurement is an indication of **anemia** (ă-nē′mē-ă), which is either a reduced number of red blood cells or a reduced amount of hemoglobin in each red blood cell.

Hematocrit Measurement

The percentage of total blood volume composed of red blood cells is the **hematocrit** (hē′mă-tō-krit, hem′a-tō-krit). One way to determine hematocrit is to place blood in a tube and spin the tube in a centrifuge. The formed elements are heavier than the plasma and are forced to one end of the tube. White blood cells and platelets form a thin, whitish layer, called the **buffy coat**, between the plasma and the red blood cell (figure 11.13). The red blood cells account for 40% to 52% of the total blood volume in males and 38% to 48% in females. Because the hematocrit measurement is based on volume, it is affected by the number and size of red blood cells. For example, a decreased hematocrit can result from a decreased number of normal-sized red blood cells or a normal number of small-sized red blood cells. The average size of an red blood cell is calculated by dividing the hematocrit by the red blood cell count. A number of disorders cause red blood cells to be smaller or larger than normal. For example, inadequate iron in the diet can impair hemoglobin production. Consequently, during their formation, red blood cells do not fill up with hemoglobin, and they remain smaller than normal.

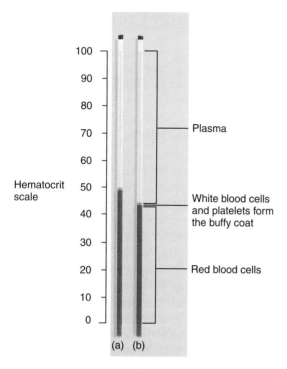

Figure 11.13 Hematocrit

Normal hematocrits of (*a*) male and (*b*) female. Blood is separated into plasma, red blood cells, and a small amount of white blood cells and platelets, which rest on the red blood cells. The hematocrit measurement includes only the red blood cells and does not measure the white blood cells and platelets.

White Blood Cell Count

A **white blood cell count (WBC) count** measures the total number of white blood cells in the blood. There are normally 5000 to 9000 white blood cells per cubic millimeter of blood. **Leukopenia** (loo-kō-pē′nē-ă) is a lower than normal WBC count and often indicates decreased production or destruction of the red marrow. Radiation, drugs, tumors, viral infections, or a deficiency of the vitamins folate or B_{12} can cause leukopenia. **Leukocytosis** (loo′kō-sī-tō′sis) is an abnormally high WBC count. **Leukemia** (loo-kē′mē-ă), a cancerous tumor of the red marrow, and bacterial infections often cause leukocytosis.

White Blood Cell Differential Count

A **white blood cell differential count** determines the percentage of each of the five kinds of white blood cells in the white blood cell count. Normally neutrophils account for 60% to 70%, lymphocytes 20% to 25%, monocytes 3% to 8%, eosinophils 2% to 4%, and basophils 0.5% to 1% of all white blood cells. Much insight about a patient's condition can be obtained from a white blood cell differential count. For example, in bacterial infections, the neutrophil count is often

greatly increased, whereas in allergic reactions the eosinophil and basophil counts are elevated.

Clotting

Two measurements that test the ability of the blood to clot are the platelet count and the prothrombin time.

Platelet Count

A normal **platelet count** is 250,000 to 400,000 platelets per cubic millimeter of blood. **Thrombocytopenia** (throm′bō-sī-tō-pē′nē-ă) is a condition in which the platelet count is greatly reduced, resulting in chronic bleeding through small vessels and capillaries. It can be caused by decreased platelet production as a result of hereditary disorders, lack of vitamin B_{12} (pernicious anemia), drug therapy, or radiation therapy.

Prothrombin Time Measurement

Prothrombin time is a measure of how long it takes for the blood to start clotting, which is normally 9 to 12 seconds. Prothrombin time is determined by adding thromboplastin to whole plasma. Thromboplastin is a chemical released from injured tissues that starts the process of clotting (see figure 11.8). Prothrombin time is officially reported as the International Normalized Ratio (INR), which standardizes the time it takes to clot on the basis of the slightly different thromboplastins used by different labs. Because many clotting factors have to be activated to form prothrombin, a deficiency of any one of them can cause an abnormal prothrombin time. Vitamin K deficiency, certain liver diseases, and drug therapy can cause an increased prothrombin time.

Blood Chemistry

The composition of materials dissolved or suspended in the plasma can be used to assess the functioning of many of the body's systems. For example, high blood glucose levels can indicate that the pancreas is not producing enough insulin, high blood urea nitrogen (BUN) is a sign of reduced kidney function, increased bilirubin can indicate liver dysfunction, and high cholesterol levels can indicate an increased risk of developing cardiovascular disease. A number of blood chemistry tests are routinely done when a blood sample is taken, and additional tests are available.

3   **P R E D I C T**

When a patient complains of acute pain in the abdomen, the physician suspects appendicitis, which is a bacterial infection of the appendix. What blood test could provide supporting evidence for the diagnosis?

✔ *Answer on page 310*

Clinical Focus   Some Disorders of the Blood

Anemia

Anemia (ă-nē′mē-ă) is a deficiency of normal hemoglobin in the blood, resulting from a decreased number of red blood cells, a decreased amount of hemoglobin in each red blood cell, or both. Anemia can also be the result of abnormal hemoglobin production.

Anemia reduces the ability of the blood to transport oxygen. People with anemia suffer from a lack of energy and feel excessively tired and listless. They may appear pale and quickly become short of breath with only slight exertion.

One general cause of anemia is insufficient production of red blood cells. **Aplastic** (ā-plas′tik) **anemia** is caused by an inability of the red bone marrow to produce red blood cells. It is usually acquired as a result of damage to the red marrow by chemicals such as benzene, drugs such as certain antibiotics and sedatives, or radiation.

Red blood cell production also can be lower than normal as a result of nutritional deficiencies. **Iron-deficiency anemia** results from a deficient intake or absorption of iron or from excessive iron loss. Consequently not enough hemoglobin is produced, the number of red blood cells decreases, and the red blood cells that are manufactured are smaller than normal.

Folate deficiency can also cause anemia. Inadequate amounts of folate in the diet is the usual cause of folate deficiency, with the disorder developing most often in the poor, in pregnant women, and in chronic alcoholics. Because folate helps in the synthesis of DNA, a folate deficiency results in fewer cell divisions and, therefore, decreased red blood cell production.

Another type of nutritional anemia is **pernicious** (per-nish′ŭs) **anemia**, which is caused by inadequate vitamin B_{12}. Because vitamin B_{12} is important for folate synthesis, inadequate vitamin B_{12} intake can also result in decreased red blood cell production. Although inadequate levels of vitamin B_{12} in the diet can cause pernicious anemia, the usual cause is insufficient absorption of the vitamin. Normally the stomach produces **intrinsic factor**, a protein that binds to vitamin B_{12}. The combined molecules pass into the lower intestine, where intrinsic factor facilitates the absorption of the vitamin. Without adequate levels of intrinsic factor, insufficient vitamin B_{12} is absorbed, and pernicious anemia develops. Most cases of pernicious anemia probably result from an autoimmune disease in which the body's immune system damages the cells in the stomach that produce intrinsic factor.

Another general cause of anemia is loss or destruction of red blood cells. **Hemorrhagic** (hem-ŏ-raj′ik) **anemia** results from a loss of blood such as can result from trauma, ulcers, or excessive menstrual bleeding. Chronic blood loss, in which small amounts of blood are lost over a period of time, can result in iron-deficiency anemia. **Hemolytic** (hē-mō-lit′ik) **anemia** is a disorder in which red blood cells rupture or are destroyed at an excessive rate. It can be caused by inherited defects in the red blood cells. For example, one kind of inherited hemolytic anemia results from a defect in the cell membrane that causes red blood cells to rupture easily. Many kinds of hemolytic anemia result from unusual damage to the red blood cells by drugs, snake venom, artificial heart valves, autoimmune disease, or hemolytic disease of the newborn.

Anemia can result from a reduced rate of synthesis of the globin chains in hemoglobin. **Thalassemia** (thal-ă-sē′mē-ă) is a hereditary disease found in people of Mediterranean, Asian, and African ancestry. If hemoglobin production is severely depressed, death usually occurs before age 20. In less severe cases, thalassemia produces a mild anemia.

Some anemias are caused by defective hemoglobin production. **Sickle-cell anemia** is a hereditary disease found mostly in African-Americans that results in the formation of an abnormal hemoglobin. The red blood cells assume a rigid, sickle shape and plug up small blood vessels. They are also more fragile than normal. In severe cases, there is so much abnormal hemoglobin production that the disease is usually fatal before age 30. In many cases, however, the production of normal hemoglobin compensates for the abnormal hemoglobin, and the person exhibits no symptoms.

Leukemia

Leukemia (loo-kē′mē-ă) is a cancer in which abnormal production of one or more of the white blood cell types occurs. Because these cells are usually immature or abnormal and lack normal immunological functions, people with leukemia are very susceptible to infections. The excess production of white blood cells in the red marrow can also interfere with red blood cell and platelet formation and thus lead to anemia and bleeding.

Disseminated Intravascular Coagulation

Disseminated intravascular coagulation (DIC) is a complex disorder involving clotting throughout the vascular system followed by bleeding. Normally excessive clotting is prevented by anticoagulants. DIC can develop when these control mechanisms are overwhelmed. Many conditions can cause DIC by overstimulating blood clotting. Examples include massive tissue damage, such as burns, or alteration of the lining of blood vessels caused by infections or snake bites. If DIC occurs slowly, the predominant effect is thrombosis and blockage of blood vessels. If DIC occurs rapidly, massive clot formation occurs, quickly using up available blood clotting factors and platelets. The result is continual bleeding around wounds, intravenous lines, catheters, and deep tissues. The best therapy for DIC is to treat and stop whatever condition is stimulating blood clotting.

von Willebrand's Disease

von Willebrand's disease is the most common inherited bleeding disorder, occurring as frequently as 1 in 1000 individuals. von Willebrand's factor helps platelets adhere to collagen and become activated. In von Willebrand's disease, platelet plug formation and the contribution of activated platelets to blood clotting is impaired. Treatments for von Willebrand's disease include injections of von Willebrand's factor or the administration of drugs that increase von Willebrand's factor levels in the blood.

Hemophilia

Hemophilia (hē-mō-fil′ē-ă) is a genetic disorder in which clotting is abnormal or absent. It is most often found in people from northern Europe and their descendants. Hemophilia is a sex-linked trait, and it occurs almost exclusively in males (see chapter 20). There are several types of hemophilia, each the result of a deficiency or dysfunction of a clotting factor. Treatment of hemophilia involves injection of the missing clotting factor taken from donated blood or produced by genetic engineering.

Infectious Diseases of the Blood

After entering the body, many microorganisms are transported by the blood to the tissues they infect. For example, the poliovirus enters through the small intestine and is carried to nervous tissue. After microorganisms are established at a site of infection, some of them can enter the blood. These microorganisms can be transported to other locations in the body, multiply within the blood, or be eliminated by the body's immune system.

Septicemia (sep-ti-sē′mē-ă), or blood poisoning, is the spread of microorganisms and their toxins by the blood. Often septicemia results from the introduction of microorganisms by a medical procedure such as the insertion of an intravenous tube into a blood vessel. The release of toxins by bacteria can cause **septic shock**, which can produce a decrease in blood pressure that can result in death.

There are a few diseases in which microorganisms actually multiply within blood cells. **Malaria** (mă-lār′ē-ă) is caused by a protozoan that is introduced into the blood by the bite of the *Anopheles* mosquito. Part of the protozoan's development occurs inside red blood cells. The symptoms of chills and fever are pro-

duced by toxins released when the protozoan causes the red blood cells to rupture. **Infectious mononucleosis** (mon′ō-noo-klē-ō′sis) is caused by a virus (Epstein-Barr virus) that infects the salivary glands and lymphocytes. The lymphocytes are altered by the virus, and the immune system attacks and destroys the lymphocytes. The immune system response is believed to produce the symptoms of fever, sore throat, and swollen lymph nodes. The human immunodeficiency virus (HIV) also infects lymphocytes and causes immune system suppression, resulting in **acquired immunodeficiency syndrome (AIDS)** (see chapter 14).

The presence of microorganisms in blood is a concern when transfusions are made, because it is possible to infect the blood recipient. Blood is routinely tested in an effort to eliminate this risk, especially for AIDS and hepatitis. **Hepatitis** (hep-ă-tī′tis) is an infection of the liver caused by several different kinds of viruses. After recovering, hepatitis victims can become carriers. Although they show no signs of the disease, they release the virus into their blood or bile. To prevent infection of others, anyone who has had hepatitis is asked not to donate blood products.

Summary

Functions of Blood

- Blood transports gases, nutrients, waste products, processed molecules, and hormones.
- Blood protects against disease and is involved in temperature, fluid, pH, and ion regulation.
- Blood clotting prevents fluid and cell loss and is part of tissue repair.

Composition of Blood

- Blood is a connective tissue consisting of plasma and formed elements.
- Total blood volume is approximately 5 liters.

Plasma

- Plasma is 91% water and 9% suspended or dissolved substances.
- Plasma maintains osmotic pressure, is involved in immunity, prevents blood loss, and transports molecules.

Formed Elements

- The formed elements are cells (red blood cells and white blood cells) and cell fragments (platelets).

Production of Formed Elements

- Formed elements arise (hematopoiesis) in red bone marrow from stem cells.

Red Blood Cells

- Red blood cells are disk-shaped cells containing hemoglobin, which transports oxygen and carbon dioxide. Red blood cells also contain carbonic anhydrase, which is involved with carbon dioxide transport.
- In response to low blood oxygen levels, the kidneys produce erythropoietin, which stimulates red blood cell production in red bone marrow.
- Worn-out red blood cells are phagocytized by macrophages in the spleen or liver. Hemoglobin is broken down, iron and amino acids are reused, and heme becomes bilirubin that is secreted in bile.

White Blood Cells

- White blood cells protect the body against microorganisms and remove dead cells and debris.
- Granulocytes contain cytoplasmic granules: and there are three types of granulocytes: neutrophils are small phagocytic cells, eosinophils reduce inflammation, and basophils promote inflammation.
- Agranulocytes have two types of very small granules: lymphocytes are involved in antibody production and other immune system responses; monocytes become macrophages that ingest microorganisms and cellular debris.

Platelets

- Platelets are cell fragments involved with preventing blood loss.

Preventing Blood Loss

Blood Vessel Constriction

- Blood vessels constrict in response to injury, resulting in decreased blood flow.

Platelet Plugs

- Minor damage to blood vessels is repaired by platelet plugs.
- Platelets use integrins to adhere to collagen, release chemicals (ADP and thromboxanes) that activate other platelets, and connect to one another with fibrinogen to form platelet plugs.

Blood Clotting

- Blood clotting, or coagulation, is formation of a clot (a network of protein fibers called fibrin).
- There are three steps in the clotting process: Activation of clotting factors by connective tissue and chemicals, resulting in the formation of prothrombinase. Conversion of prothrombin to thrombin by prothrombinase. Conversion of fibrinogen to fibrin by thrombin.

Control of Clot Formation

- Anticoagulants in the blood, such as antithrombin and heparin, prevent clot formation.

Clot Retraction and Fibrinolysis

- Clot retraction condenses the clot, pulling the edges of damaged tissue closer together.
- Serum is plasma without clotting factors.
- Fibrinolysis (clot breakdown) is accomplished by plasmin.

Blood Grouping

- Blood groups are determined by antigens on the surface of red blood cells.
- Antibodies can bind to red blood cell antigens, resulting in agglutination or hemolysis of red blood cells.

ABO Blood Group

- Type A blood has A antigens, type B blood has B antigens, type AB blood has A and B antigens, and type O blood has neither A or B antigens.
- Type A blood has B antibodies, type B blood has A antibodies, type AB blood has neither A or B antibodies, and type O blood has both A and B antibodies.
- Mismatching the ABO blood group can result in transfusion reactions.

Rh Blood Group

- Rh-positive blood has Rh antigens, whereas Rh-negative blood does not.
- Antibodies against the Rh antigen are produced when an Rh-negative person is exposed to Rh-positive blood.
- The Rh blood group is responsible for hemolytic disease of the newborn.

Diagnostic Blood Tests

Type and Crossmatch

- Blood typing determines the ABO and Rh blood groups of a blood sample.
- A crossmatch tests for agglutination reactions between donor and recipient blood.

Complete Blood Count

- The complete blood count consists of the following: red blood cell count, hemoglobin measurement (grams of hemoglobin per 100 milliliters of blood), hematocrit measurement (percent volume of red blood cells), and white blood cell count.

White Blood Cell Differential Count

- The white blood cell differential count determines the percentage of each type of white blood cell.

Clotting

- Platelet count and prothrombin time measure the ability of the blood to clot.

Blood Chemistry

- The composition of materials dissolved or suspended in plasma (e.g., glucose, urea nitrogen, bilirubin, and cholesterol) can be used to assess the functioning and status of the body's systems.

Content Review

1. Describe the functions of blood.
2. Define plasma. List the functions of plasma.
3. Define the formed elements, and name the different types of formed elements. Explain how and where the formed elements arise through hematopoiesis.
4. Describe the two basic parts of a hemoglobin molecule. Which part is associated with iron? What gases are transported by each part?
5. What is the role of carbonic anhydrase in gas transport?
6. Why are the vitamins folate and B_{12} important in red blood cell production?
7. Explain how low blood oxygen levels result in increased red blood cell production.
8. Where are red blood cells broken down? What happens to the breakdown products?
9. Give two functions of white blood cells.
10. Name the five types of white blood cells, and state a function for each type.
11. What are platelets, and how are they formed?
12. Describe the role of blood vessel constriction and platelet plugs in preventing bleeding. Describe the three steps of platelet plug formation.
13. What are clotting factors? Describe the three steps of activation that result in the formation of a clot.
14. Explain the function of anticoagulants in the blood, and give an example of an anticoagulant.
15. What is clot retraction, and what does it accomplish?
16. Define fibrinolysis, and name the chemicals responsible for this process.
17. What are blood groups, and how do they cause transfusion reactions? List the four ABO blood types. Why is type O blood considered a universal donor?
18. What is meant by the term Rh-positive? How can Rh incompatibility affect a pregnancy?
19. For each of the following tests, define the test and give an example of a disorder that would cause an abnormal test result:
    a. Type and crossmatch
    b. Red blood cell count
    c. Hemoglobin measurement
    d. Hematocrit measurement
    e. White blood cell count
    f. White blood cell differential count
    g. Platelet count
    h. Prothrombin time
    i. Blood chemistry tests

Develop Your Reasoning Skills

1. Red Packer, a physical education major, wanted to improve his performance in an upcoming marathon race. About 6 weeks before the race, 1 liter of blood was removed from his body, and the formed elements were separated from the plasma. The formed elements were frozen, and the plasma was reinfused into his body. Just before the race, the formed elements were thawed and injected into his body. Explain why this procedure, called blood doping or blood boosting, would help Red's performance. Can you suggest any possible bad effects?

2. Chemicals such as benzene can destroy red bone marrow, causing aplastic anemia. What symptoms would you expect to develop as a result of the lack of (a) red blood cells, (b) platelets, and (c) white blood cells?

3. E. Z. Goen habitually used barbiturates to depress feelings of anxiety. Because barbiturates suppress the respiratory centers in the brain, they cause hypoventilation (i.e., slower than normal rate of breathing). What happens to the red blood cell count of a habitual user of barbiturates? Explain.

4. What blood problems would you expect to observe in a patient after total gastrectomy (removal of the stomach)?

5. According to the old saying, "Good food makes good blood." Name three substances in the diet that are essential for "good blood." What blood disorders develop if these substances are absent from the diet?

6. Why do anemic patients often have gray-colored feces? (*Hint:* The feces is lacking its normal coloration.)

Answers to Predict Questions

1. p. 297 Carbon monoxide binds to the iron of hemoglobin and prevents the transport of oxygen. The decreased oxygen stimulates the release of erythropoietin, which increases red blood cell production in red bone marrow, causing the number of red blood cells in the blood to increase.

2. p. 304 People with type AB blood were called universal recipients because they could receive type A, B, AB, or O blood with little likelihood of a transfusion reaction. Type AB blood does not have antibodies against type A or B antigens. Transfusion of these antigens in type A, B, or AB blood does not therefore cause a transfusion reaction in a person with type AB blood. The term is misleading, however, for two reasons. First, other blood groups can cause a transfusion reaction. Second, antibodies in the donor's blood can cause a transfusion reaction. For example, type O blood contains A and B antibodies that can react against the A and B antigens in type AB blood.

3. p. 306 An increase in the white blood cell count often indicates a bacterial infection. A white blood cell differential count with an abnormally high neutrophil percentage supports the diagnosis.

Chapter Twelve

The Heart

atrioventricular (AV) node
(ā′trē-ō-ven-trik′ū-lăr) Small collection of specialized cardiac muscle fibers located in the lower part of the right atrium that gives rise to the atrioventricular bundle; conducts action potentials from the right atrium to the atrioventricular bundle.

atrium, pl. atria
(ā′trē-ŭm) [L., entrance chamber] One of two chambers of the heart that collects blood during ventricular contraction; each atrium pumps blood into a ventricle to complete ventricular filling at the end of ventricular relaxation.

baroreceptor
(bar′ō-rē-sep′ter) Sensory nerve endings in the walls of the aorta and internal carotid arteries; sensitive to stretching of the wall caused by increased blood pressure.

bicuspid valve
(bī-kŭs′pid, mitral) Valve consisting of two cusps of tissue; located between the left atrium and left ventricle of the heart.

cardiac output (CO)
(kar′dē-ak) Volume of blood pumped by either ventricle of the heart per minute; also called minute volume.

diastole
(dī-as′tō-lē) [Gr. *diastole*, dilation] Period of relaxation of the heart chambers during which they fill with blood; usually refers to ventricular relaxation.

semilunar valve
(sem-ē-loo′năr) One of two valves in the heart composed of three crescent-shaped cusps that prevent flow of blood back into the ventricles following ejection; semilunar valves are located at the beginning of the aorta and pulmonary trunk.

sinoatrial (SA) node
(sī′nō-ā′trē-ăl) Collection of specialized cardiac muscle fibers located near the entry of the superior vena cava into the right atrium; acts as the "pacemaker" of the cardiac conduction system.

systole
(sis′tō-lē) [Gr. *systole*, a contracting] Contraction of the heart chambers during which blood leaves the chambers; usually refers to ventricular contraction.

tricuspid valve
(trī-kŭs′pid) Valve consisting of three cusps of tissue; located between the right atrium and right ventricle of the heart.

ventricle
(ven′-tri-kl) [L. *venter*, belly] One of two chambers of the heart that pumps blood into arteries.

Objectives

After reading this chapter, you should be able to:

1. Describe the size, shape, and location of the heart.
2. Give the location and function of the coronary arteries.
3. Describe the chambers of the heart.
4. Name the valves of the heart and state their location and function.
5. List the components of the heart wall and describe the structure and function of each.
6. Describe the flow of blood through the heart and name each of the chambers and structures through which the blood passes.
7. Describe the changes that occur in membrane permeability during each phase of an action potential in cardiac muscle. Compare the permeability changes to those in cardiac muscle during an action potential.
8. Explain the structure and function of the conduction system of the heart.
9. Define each wave of the electrocardiogram and relate each of them to contractions of the heart.
10. Describe the cardiac cycle and the relationship between contraction of each of the chambers, the pressure in each of the chambers, the phases of the electrocardiogram, and the heart sounds.
11. Describe intrinsic and extrinsic regulation of the heart.
12. Give the conditions for which the major heart medications and treatments are administered.

The heart is commonly treated as if it were the seat of certain strong emotions. A very determined person may be described as having "a lot of heart," and a person who has been disappointed romantically can be described as having a "broken heart." A popular holiday in February not only dramatically distorts the heart's anatomy, it also attaches romantic emotions to it. The heart is a muscular organ that pumps blood as its main function. Emotions are a product of brain function.

Water and other liquids flow through a pipe only if they are forced to do so. The force is commonly produced by a pump, which increases the pressure of the liquid at the pump above the pressure in the pipe. Thus, the liquid flows from the pump through the pipe from an area of higher pressure to an area of lower pressure. If the pressure produced by the pump increases, flow of liquid through the pipe increases. If the pressure produced by the pump decreases, flow of liquid through the pipe decreases.

Like a pump that forces water to flow through a pipe, the heart contracts forcefully to pump blood through the blood vessels of the body (figure 12.1). The heart of a healthy adult, at rest, pumps approximately 5 liters (L) of blood per minute. For most people, the heart continues to pump at approximately that rate for more than 75 years; and, during short periods of vigorous exercise, the amount of blood pumped per minute increases several fold. If the heart loses its pumping ability for even a few minutes, however, blood flow through the blood vessels stops, and the life of the individual is in danger.

The heart is actually two pumps in one. The right side of the heart forces blood to flow to the lungs and back to the left side of the heart through vessels called the **pulmonary circulation** (figure 12.2). The left side of the heart forces blood to flow to all other tissues of the body and back to the right side of the heart through vessels called the **systemic circulation**.

Functions of the Heart

Functions of the heart include

1. *Generating blood pressure.* Contractions of the heart generate blood pressure, which is responsible for blood movement through the blood vessels.
2. *Routing blood.* The heart separates the pulmonary and systemic circulations and ensures better oxygenation of blood flowing to tissues.
3. *Ensuring one-way blood flow.* The valves of the heart ensure a one-way flow of blood through the heart and blood vessels.
4. *Regulating blood supply.* Changes in the rate and force of contraction match blood delivery to the changing metabolic needs of the tissues, such as during rest, exercise, and changes in body position.

Size, Form, and Location of the Heart

The adult heart has the shape of a blunt cone and is slightly larger than a closed fist. The heart is located in the thoracic cavity between the lungs within the **mediastinum** (me′dē-astī′nŭm) (figure 12.3). The blunt, rounded point of the cone is the **apex** (ā′peks, tip); and the larger, flat portion at the opposite end of the cone is the **base**. The apex is the most inferior part of the heart; it is directed anteriorly and to the left, and it can be found deep to the fifth intercostal (between the ribs) space. The base is directed superiorly and slightly posteriorly. The most superior portion of the base can be found deep to the second intercostal space.

It is important to know the location of the heart. Placing a stethoscope to hear the heart sounds, placing electrodes on the chest to record an electrocardiogram (ECG), and performing cardiopulmonary resuscitation (CPR) depend on a knowledge of the heart's position.

Figure 12.1 The Cardiovascular System

The heart, blood, and blood vessels are the major components of the cardiovascular system.

Carotid artery
Jugular vein
Aorta
Superior vena cava
Pulmonary trunk
Heart
Brachial artery
Inferior vena cava
Femoral artery and vein

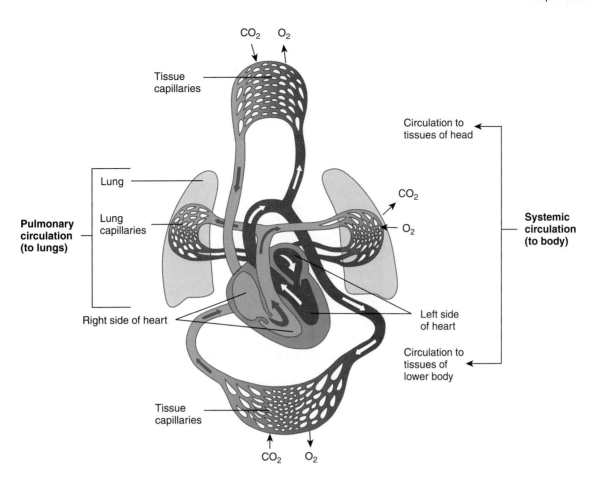

Figure 12.2   Overview of the Circulatory System

The circulatory system consists of the pulmonary and systemic circulations. The right side of the heart forces blood to flow through vessels to the lungs and back to the left side of the heart through the pulmonary circulation. The left side of the heart forces blood to flow through vessels to the tissues of the body and back to the right side of the heart through the systemic circulation.

Anatomy of the Heart

Pericardium

The heart is surrounded by a space called the **pericardial** (per-i-kar′dē-ăl) **cavity** (see chapter 1). The pericardial cavity is formed by the **pericardium** (per-i-kar′dē-ŭm), or **pericardial sac**, which is a double-layered, closed sac that surrounds the heart and anchors it within the mediastinum (see figures 12.3 and 12.4). The pericardium consists of a tough, fibrous connective tissue outer layer called the **fibrous pericardium** and an inner layer of flat epithelial cells and a thin layer of connective tissue called the **serous pericardium**. The portion of the serous pericardium lining the fibrous pericardium is the **parietal pericardium**, whereas the portion covering the heart surface is the **visceral pericardium**, or **epicardium** (ep-i-kar′dē-ŭm). The parietal and visceral pericardia are continuous with each other where the great vessels enter or leave the heart. The pericardial cavity, located between the visceral and parietal pericardia, is filled with a thin layer of **pericardial fluid** produced by the serous pericardium. The pericardial fluid helps reduce friction as the heart moves within the pericardial sac.

> ### Did You Know?
>
> **Pericarditis** (per′i-kar-dī′tis) is an inflammation of the serous pericardium. The cause is frequently unknown, but it can result from infection, diseases of connective tissue, or damage due to radiation treatment for cancer. It can be extremely painful, with sensations of pain referred to the back and to the chest, which can be confused with the pain of a myocardial infarction (heart attack). Pericarditis can result in a small amount of fluid accumulation within the pericardial sac.
>
> **Cardiac tamponade** (tam-pŏ-nād′) is a potentially fatal condition in which fluid or blood accumulates in the pericardial sac. The fluid compresses the heart from the outside. The heart is a powerful muscle, but it relaxes passively. When it is compressed by fluid within the pericardial sac, it cannot dilate when the cardiac muscle relaxes. Consequently, the heart cannot fill with blood during relaxation, which makes it impossible for it to pump. Cardiac tamponade can cause a person to die quickly unless the fluid is removed. Causes of cardiac tamponade include rupture of the heart wall following a myocardial infarction, rupture of blood vessels in the pericardium after a malignant tumor invades the area, damage to the pericardium resulting from radiation therapy, and trauma such as occurs in a traffic accident.

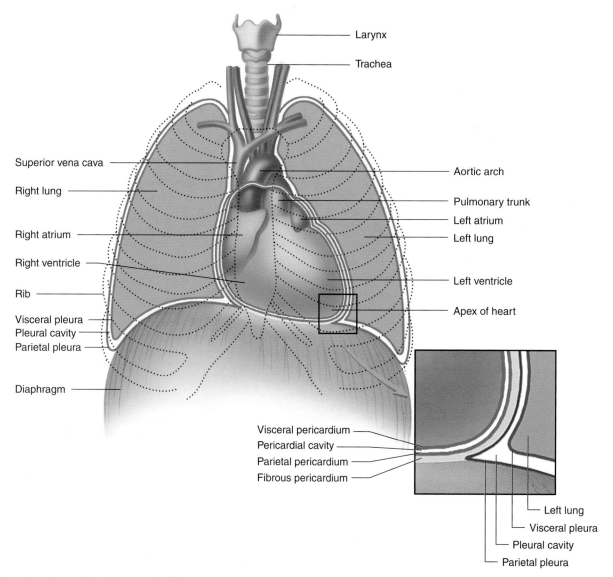

Figure 12.3 Location of the Heart in the Thorax

The heart is deep to the sternum and angled to the left. The apex of the heart is at the level of the fifth intercostal space, approximately 9 cm to the left of the midline. The most superior portion of the base is at the level of the second intercostal space. The insert shows part of the pericardial sac and its relationship to the pleural cavity. The visceral pericardium forms the inner layer and covers the surface of the heart; the pericardial cavity contains a small amount of pericardial fluid; and the parietal pericardium and the fibrous pericardium form the outer layer of the pericardial sac.

External Anatomy

The right and left **atria** (a′trē-ă; entrance chambers; sing. atrium) are located at the base of the heart, and the right and left **ventricles** (ven′tri-klz) extend from the base of the heart toward the apex (figure 12.5). A **coronary** (kōr′o-nār-ē, circling like a crown) **sulcus** (sul′kus, ditch) extends around the heart, separating the atria from the ventricles. In addition, two sulci, which indicate the division between the right and left ventricles, extend inferiorly from the coronary sulcus. One extends inferiorly from the coronary sulcus on the anterior surface of the heart, and the other extends inferiorly from the coronary sulcus on the posterior surface of the heart (not visible in figure 12.5).

Six large veins carry blood to the heart (see figure 12.5): the **superior vena cava** and **inferior vena cava** carry blood from the body to the right atrium, and four **pulmonary veins** carry blood from the lungs to the left atrium. Two arteries, the **pulmonary trunk** and the **aorta**, exit the heart. The pulmonary trunk, arising from the right ventricle, splits into the right and left **pulmonary arteries**, which carry blood to the lungs. The aorta carries blood from the left ventricle to the body.

Blood Supply to the Heart

Coronary Arteries

Cardiac muscle in the wall of the heart is thick and metabolically very active. The coronary arteries supply blood to the wall of the heart (figure 12.6*a*). Two **coronary arteries** originate from the base of the aorta, just above the aortic semilunar valves. The **left coronary artery** originates on the left side of the aorta. Its branches supply much of the anterior wall of

Figure 12.4   Heart in the Pericardium

The heart is located in the pericardium, which consists of an outer fibrous pericardium and an inner serous pericardium. The serous pericardium has two parts: the parietal pericardium lines the fibrous pericardium, and the visceral pericardium (epicardium) covers the surface of the heart. The pericardial cavity, between the parietal and visceral pericardium, is filled with a small amount of pericardial fluid.

(a)

Figure 12.5   Anterior View of the Heart

(a) The two atria (right and left) are located superiorly, and the two ventricles (right and left) are located inferiorly. The superior and inferior venae cavae enter the right atrium. The pulmonary veins enter the left atrium. The pulmonary trunk exits the right ventricle, and the aorta exits the left ventricle.

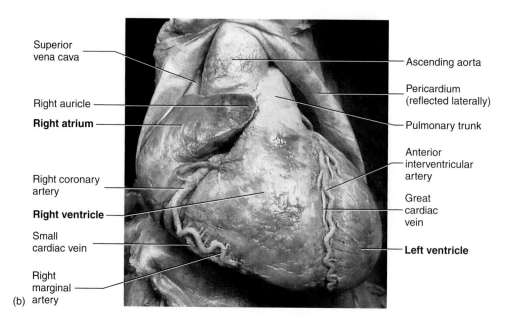

Figure 12.5 Anterior View of the Heart

(*b*) Photograph of the anterior surface of the heart.

(b)

Labels on photograph:
Superior vena cava
Right auricle
Right atrium
Right coronary artery
Right ventricle
Small cardiac vein
Right marginal artery
Ascending aorta
Pericardium (reflected laterally)
Pulmonary trunk
Anterior interventricular artery
Great cardiac vein
Left ventricle

the heart and most of the left ventricle. The **right coronary artery** originates on the right side of the heart and supplies most of the wall of the right ventricle. Both the right and left coronary arteries lie within the coronary sulcus.

In a resting person, blood flowing through the coronary arteries of the heart gives up approximately 70% of its oxygen. In comparison, blood flowing through arteries to skeletal muscle gives up only about 25% of its oxygen. The percentage of oxygen the blood releases to skeletal muscle increases to 70% or more during exercise. The percentage of oxygen the blood releases to cardiac muscle cannot increase substantially dur-

ing exercise. Cardiac muscle is therefore very dependent on an increased rate of blood flow through the coronary arteries above its resting level to provide an adequate oxygen supply during exercise.

1 **PREDICT**

Predict the effect on the heart if blood flow through the anterior interventricular artery is restricted or completely blocked (*Hint:* see figure 12.6*a*).

✔ *Answer on page 339*

(a)

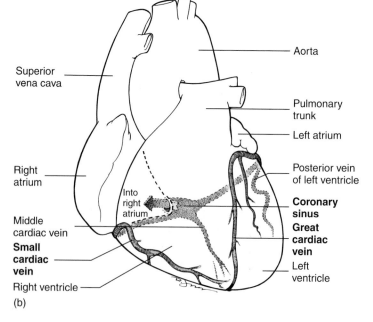

(b)

Figure 12.6 Blood Supply to the Heart

The vessels of the anterior surface of the heart are seen directly and are a darker color, whereas the vessels of the posterior surface are seen through the heart and are a lighter color. (*a*) Coronary arteries supply blood to the wall of the heart. (*b*) Cardiac veins carry blood from the wall of the heart back to the right atrium.

Did You Know?

When a blood clot, or **thrombus** (throm′bŭs), suddenly blocks a coronary blood vessel, a **heart attack,** or **coronary thrombosis** (throm′b¯o-sis), occurs. The area that has been cut off from its blood supply suffers from a lack of·oxygen and nutrients and dies if the blood supply is not quickly reestablished. The region of dead heart tissue is called an **infarct** (in′farkt). If the infarct is large enough, the heart may be unable to pump enough blood to keep the person alive.

In some cases, it is possible to treat heart attacks with enzymes such as **streptokinase** (strep-tō-kī′nās) or **tissue plasminogen** (plaz-min′ō-jen) **activator (t-PA),** which break down blood clots. One of the enzymes is injected into the circulatory system of a heart attack patient, where it reduces or removes the blockage in the coronary artery. If the clot is broken down quickly, the blood supply to cardiac muscle is reestablished, and the heart may suffer little permanent damage.

Coronary arteries can become blocked more gradually by **atherosclerotic** (ath′er-ō-skler-ot′ik) **lesions.** These thickenings in the walls of arteries can contain deposits that are high in cholesterol and other lipids. The lesions protrude into the lumen (opening) of the arteries, thus restricting blood flow. The ability of cardiac muscle to function is reduced when it is deprived of an adequate blood supply. The person suffers from fatigue and often pain in the area of the

chest and usually in the left arm with the slightest exertion. The pain is called **angina pectoris** (an-jī′nă pek′tō-ris).

Angioplasty (an′jē-ō-plas-tē) is surgical procedure in which a small balloon is threaded through the aorta and into a coronary artery. After the balloon has entered a partially blocked coronary artery, it is inflated, flattening the atherosclerotic deposits against the vessel walls and opening the blocked blood vessel. This technique improves the function of cardiac muscle in patients suffering from an inadequate blood flow to the cardiac through the coronary arteries. Some controversy exists about its effectiveness, at least in some patients, because dilation of the coronary arteries can be reversed within a few weeks or months and because blood clots can form in coronary arteries following angioplasty. Small rotating blades and lasers are also used to remove lesions from coronary vessels, or a small coil device, called a **stent,** is placed in the vessels to hold them open following angioplasty.

A **coronary bypass** is a surgical procedure that relieves the effects of obstructions in the coronary arteries. The technique involves taking healthy segments of blood vessels from other parts of the patient's body and using them to bypass, or create an alternative path around, obstructions in the coronary arteries. The technique is common for those who suffer from severe blockage of parts of the coronary arteries.

Cardiac Veins

The **cardiac veins** drain blood from the cardiac muscle. They are nearly parallel to the coronary arteries and most carry blood from cardiac muscle to the **coronary sinus,** a large vein located within the coronary sulcus on the posterior aspect of the heart. Blood flows from the coronary sinus into the right atrium (figure 12.6*b*).

Heart Chambers and Internal Anatomy

The heart is a muscular pump consisting of four chambers: the two atria and two ventricles (figure 12.7).

Right and Left Atria

The atria of the heart receive blood from veins. The atria function primarily as reservoirs, where blood returning from veins collects before it enters the ventricles. Contraction of the atria forces blood into the ventricles to complete ventricular filling. The right atrium has two major openings, where large veins enter the heart from various parts of the body: the superior vena cava and the inferior vena cava (see figure 12.7). In addition, a smaller coronary sinus enters the right atrium from the wall of the heart (see figure 12.6*b*). The left atrium has four openings that receive the four pulmonary veins from the lungs (see figure 12.7). The two atria are separated from each other by a partition consisting of cardiac muscle called the **interatrial septum.**

Right and Left Ventricles

The ventricles of the heart are its major pumping chambers. They eject blood into the arteries and force it to flow through the circulatory system. The atria open into the ventricles, and each ventricle has one large outflow route located superiorly near the midline of the heart. The right ventricle opens into the pulmonary trunk, and the left ventricle opens into the aorta. The two ventricles are separated from each other by the muscular **interventricular septum** (see figure 12.7).

The wall of the left ventricle is thicker than the wall of the right ventricle because it generates a greater pressure than the right ventricle. When the left ventricle contracts, the pressure increases to approximately 120 mm Hg. When the right ventricle contracts, the pressure increases to approximately one-fifth of the pressure in the left ventricle, even though the left and right ventricles pump nearly the same volume of blood.

Heart Valves

Valves called **atrioventricular valves** are located between the right atrium and the right ventricle and between the left atrium and left ventricle. The atrioventricular valve between the right atrium and the right ventricle has three cusps and is called the **tricuspid valve.** The atrioventricular valve between the left atrium and left ventricle has two cusps and is called the **bicuspid,** or **mitral** (resembling a bishop's miter, a two-pointed hat) **valve** (figures 12.8*b* and 12.9). These valves allow blood to flow from the atria into the ventricles but prevent it from

Figure 12.7 Internal Anatomy of the Heart

The heart is cut in a frontal plane to show the internal anatomy.

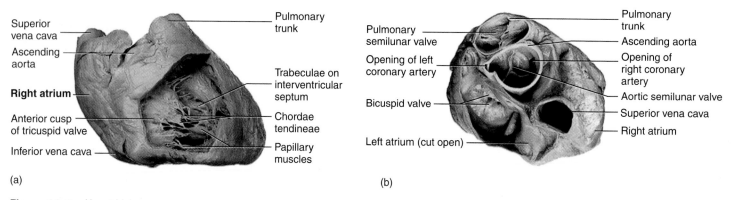

(a)

(b)

Figure 12.8 Heart Valves

(*a*) View of the tricuspid valve, the chordae tendineae, and the papillary muscles. (*b*) A superior view of the heart valves. Note the three cusps of each semilunar valve meeting to prevent the backflow of blood.

flowing back into the atria. When the ventricles relax, blood flows from the atria into the ventricles and the valves are pushed open into the ventricles (figure 12.9*a*). In contrast, when the ventricles contract, blood pushes the valves back toward the atria, and the atrioventricular openings close as the valve cusps meet (figure 12.9*b*).

Each ventricle contains cone-shaped muscular pillars called **papillary** (pap′ĭ-lār-ē, nipple- or pimple-shaped) **muscles**. These muscles are attached by thin, strong connective tissue strings called **chordae tendineae** (kōr′dē ten′di-nē-ē, heart strings) to the free margins of the cusps of the atrioventricular valves. When the ventricles contract, the papillary muscles

contract and prevent the valves from opening into the atria by pulling on the chordae tendineae attached to the valve cusps (see figures 12.8*b* and 12.9).

The aorta and pulmonary trunk possess **aortic** and **pulmonary semilunar** (halfmoon-shaped) **valves**, respectively. Each valve consists of three pocketlike semilunar cusps (figures 12.8*b* and 12.9). When the ventricles contract, blood flowing out of the ventricles pushes against each valve, forcing the cusp to open (see figure 12.9*b*). When the ventricles relax, blood flows back from the aorta or pulmonary trunk toward the ventricle, it enters the pockets of the cusps, causing them to bulge toward and meet in the center of the aorta or

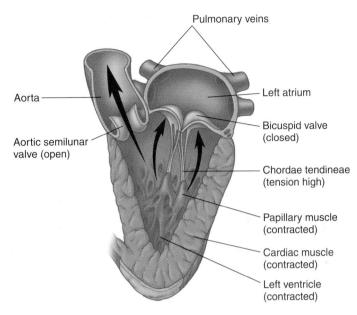

(a) When the bicuspid valve is open, the cusps of the valve are pushed by blood into the ventricle. The tension on the chordae tendineae is low, and the papillary muscles are relaxed. Blood flows from the left atrium into the left ventricle. When the aortic semilunar valve is closed, the cusps of the valve overlap as they are pushed by the blood in the aorta toward the ventricle. There is no blood flow from the aorta into the ventricle.

(b) When the bicuspid valve is closed, the cusps of the valves overlap as they are pushed by the blood toward the left atrium. There is no blood flow from the ventricle into the atrium. The tension on the chordae tendineae is increased, and the papillary muscles are contracted. When the aortic semilunar valve is open, the cusps of the valve are pushed by the blood toward the aorta. Blood then flows from the left ventricle into the aorta.

Figure 12.9   Function of the Heart Valves

(a) Valve positions when blood is flowing into the left ventricle. (b) Valve positions when blood is flowing out of the left ventricle.

Figure 12.10   Skeleton of the Heart

The skeleton of the heart consists of fibrous connective tissue rings that surround the heart valves and separates the atria from the ventricles.

pulmonary trunk, thus closing the vessels and keeping blood from flowing back into the ventricles (see 12.9a).

A plate of fibrous connective tissue, sometimes called the **skeleton of the heart**, consisting mainly of fibrous rings around the atrioventricular and semilunar valves, provides a solid support for the valves (figure 12.10). This connective tissue plate also serves as electrical insulation between the atria and the ventricles and provides a rigid site of attachment for the cardiac muscle.

Route of Blood Flow Through the Heart

Blood flow through the heart is depicted in figure 12.11. Even though blood flow through the heart is described for the right and then the left side of the heart, it is important to understand that both atria contract at the same time, and both ventricles contract at the same time. This concept is most important when the electrical activity, pressure changes, and heart sounds are considered.

Blood enters the right atrium from the systemic circulation through the superior and inferior venae cavae, and from heart muscle through the coronary sinus (see figure 12.11a and b). Most of the blood flowing into the right atrium flows through the tricuspid valve into the right ventricle while the right ventricle relaxes following the previous contraction. The right atrium then contracts, and enough blood is pushed from the right atrium into the right ventricle to complete right ventricular filling.

Following right atrial contraction, the right ventricle begins to contract. Contraction of the right ventricle pushes blood against the tricuspid valve, forcing it closed. After pressure within the right ventricle increases, the pulmonary semilunar valve is forced open, and blood flows into the pulmonary trunk.

The pulmonary trunk branches to form the pulmonary arteries, which carry blood to the lungs, where carbon dioxide is released and oxygen is picked up. Blood returning from the lungs enters the left atrium through the four pulmonary veins (see figure 12.11*a* and *b*). Most of the blood flowing into the left atrium passes through the bicuspid valve into the left ventricle while the left ventricle relaxes following the previous contraction. The left atrium then contracts, and enough blood is pushed from the left atrium into the left ventricle to complete left ventricular filling.

Following left atrial contraction, the left ventricle begins to contract. Contraction of the left ventricle pushes blood against the bicuspid valve, forcing it closed. After pressure within the left ventricle increases, the aortic semilunar valve is forced open, and blood flows into the aorta (see figure 12.11*a* and *b*). Blood flowing through the aorta

is distributed to all parts of the body, except to that part of the lung supplied by the pulmonary blood vessels.

Histology of the Heart

Heart Wall

The heart wall is composed of three layers of tissue: the epicardium, the myocardium, and the endocardium (figure 12.12). The **epicardium** (ep-i-kar′dē-ŭm), also called the **visceral pericardium**, is a thin serous membrane forming the smooth outer surface of the heart. It consists of simple squamous epithelium overlying a layer of loose connective tissue and fat. The thick middle layer of the heart, the **myocardium** (mī-ō-kar′dē-ŭm), is composed of cardiac muscle cells and is

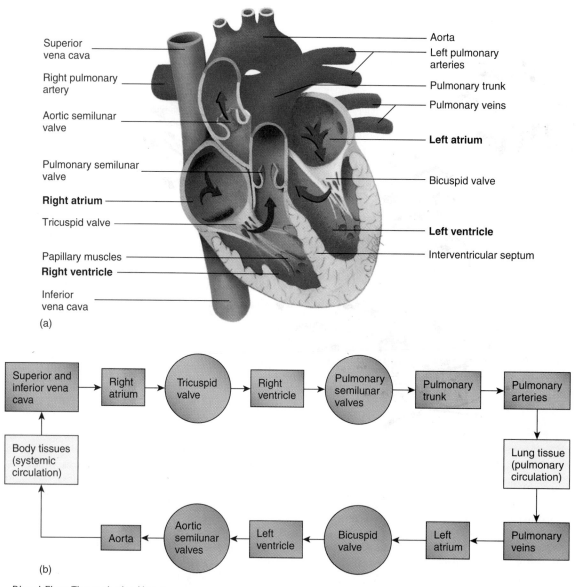

(a)

(b)

Figure 12.11　Blood Flow Through the Heart

(*a*) Frontal section of the heart revealing the four chambers and direction of blood flow through the heart. (*b*) Diagram listing in order the structures through which blood flows in the systemic and pulmonary circulations. The heart valves are indicated by circles, deoxygenated blood (blue); oxygenated blood (red).

Figure 12.12   Heart Wall

Part of the wall of the heart has been removed, enlarged, and rotated so that the inner surface is visible. The enlarged section illustrates the epicardium (visceral pericardium), the myocardium, and the endocardium.

(a)

(b)

Figure 12.13   Cardiac Muscle Cells

(*a*) Cardiac muscle cells are branching cells with centrally located nuclei. As in skeletal muscle, sarcomeres join end-to-end to form myofibrils, and mitochondria provide ATP for contraction. The cells are joined to one another by intercalated disks, which allow action potentials to pass from one cardiac muscle cell to the next. Sarcoplasmic reticulum and T tubules are visible but are not as numerous as they are in skeletal muscle. (*b*) A light micrograph of cardiac muscle tissue. The cardiac muscle fibers appear to be striated because of the arrangement of the individual myofilaments.

responsible for the ability of the heart to contract. The smooth inner surface of the heart chambers is the **endocardium** (en-dō-kar′dē-ŭm), which consists of simple squamous epithelium over a layer of connective tissue. The endocardium allows blood to move easily through the heart. Each heart valve is formed by a fold of endocardium with connective tissue between the two layers.

The surfaces of the interior walls of the ventricles are modified by ridges and columns of cardiac muscle. Smaller muscular ridges are also found in portions of the atria.

Cardiac Muscle

Cardiac muscle cells are elongated, branching cells that contain one, or occasionally two, centrally located nuclei (figure 12.13). The cardiac muscle cells contain actin and myosin myofilaments

(a)

Permeability changes in skeletal muscle:
1. **Depolarization phase**
   - Voltage-gated Na^+ ion channels open.
   - Voltage-gated K^+ ion channels begin to open.

2. **Repolarization phase**
   - Voltage-gated Na^+ ion channels close.
   - Voltage-gated K^+ ion channels continue to open.
   - Voltage-gated K^+ ion channels close at the end of repolarization and return the membrane potential to its resting value.

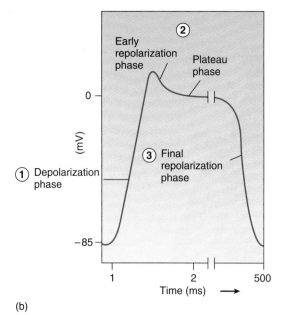

(b)

Permeability changes in cardiac muscle:
1. **Depolarization phase**
   - Voltage-gated Na^+ ion channels open.
   - Voltage-gated K^+ ion channels close.
   - Voltage-gated Ca^{2+} ion channels begin to open.

2. **Early repolarization and plateau phases**
   - Voltage-gated Na^+ ion channels close.
   - Some voltage-gated K^+ ion channels open, causing early repolarization.
   - Voltage-gated Ca^{2+} ion channels are open, producing the plateau by slowing further repolarization.

3. **Final repolarization phase**
   - Voltage-gated Ca^{2+} ion channels close.
   - Many voltage-gated K^+ ion channels open.

Figure 12.14   Comparison of Action Potentials in Skeletal and Cardiac Muscle

(*a*) Action potential in skeletal muscle (red line) consists of depolarization and repolarization phases. (*b*) An action potential in cardiac muscle (blue line) consists of depolarization, early repolarization, plateau, and final repolarization phases. Cardiac muscle does not repolarize as rapidly as skeletal muscle (indicated by the break in the curve) because of the plateau phase.

organized to form sarcomeres, which join end-to-end to form myofibrils (see chapter 7). The actin and myosin myofilaments are responsible for muscle contraction, and their organization gives cardiac muscle a striated (banded) appearance. The striations are less regularly arranged and less numerous than is the case in skeletal muscle.

Adenosine triphosphate (ATP) provides the energy for cardiac muscle contraction, and, as in other tissues, ATP production depends on oxygen availability. Cardiac muscle cells are rich in mitochondria, which produce ATP at a rate rapid enough to sustain the normal energy requirements of cardiac muscle. An extensive capillary network provides an adequate oxygen supply to the cardiac muscle cells. Unlike skeletal muscle, however, cardiac muscle cannot develop a significant oxygen debt. Development of a large oxygen debt could result in muscular fatigue and cessation of cardiac muscle contraction.

Cardiac muscle cells are organized into spiral bundles or sheets. The cells are bound end-to-end and laterally to adjacent cells by specialized cell-to-cell contacts called **intercalated** (in-ter′kă-lā-ted) **disks** (see figure 12.13). The membranes of the disks are highly folded, and the adjacent cells fit together, greatly increasing contact between them. Specialized cell membrane structures in the intercalated disks called **gap junctions** (see chapter 4) reduce electrical resistance between the cells, allowing action potentials to pass easily from one cell to adjacent cells. Cardiac muscle cells therefore behave as a single electrical unit. The highly coordinated contractions of the heart depend on this characteristic.

Electrical Activity of the Heart
Action Potentials in Cardiac Muscle

Like action potentials in skeletal muscle and neurons, those in cardiac muscle exhibit depolarization followed by repolarization of the resting membrane potential. In cardiac muscle, however, the **plateau phase**, which is a period of slow repolarization, greatly prolongs the action potential (figure 12.14) In contrast to action potentials in skeletal muscle, which take less than 2 milliseconds (ms) to complete, action potentials in cardiac muscle take approximately 200 to 500 ms to complete.

Action potentials are conducted from cell to cell in cardiac muscle. Not only does the action potential take longer, but the rate of conduction throughout the heart is slower than the rate of conduction of action potentials in skeletal muscle and neurons.

In cardiac muscle each action potential consists of a rapid **depolarization phase** followed by a rapid, but partial early **repolarization phase**. Then a longer period of slow repolarization, called the **plateau phase**, occurs. At the end of the plateau phase, a more rapid **final repolarization phase** takes place. During the final repolarization phase the membrane potential returns to its resting level (figure 12.14).

Changes in membrane channels are responsible for the changes in the permeability of the cell membrane that produce action potentials. The depolarization phase of the action potential results from three permeability changes. **Voltage-gated sodium ion channels** open, increasing the permeability of the cell membrane to sodium ions. Sodium ions then diffuse into the cell, causing depolarization. Voltage-gated potassium ion channels quickly close, decreasing the permeability of the cell membrane to potassium ions. The decreased diffusion of potassium ions out of the cell also causes depolarization. **Voltage-gated sodium ion channels** slowly open, increasing the permeability of the cell membrane to calcium ions. Calcium ions then diffuse into the cell and cause depolarization. It is not until the plateau phase that most of the voltage-gated calcium ion channels are opened.

Early repolarization occurs when the voltage-gated sodium ion channels close and a small number of **voltage-gated potassium ion channels** open. Diffusion of sodium ions into the cell stops and there is some movement of potassium ions out of the cell. These changes in ion movement result in an early, but small repolarization.

The plateau phase occurs as voltage-gated calcium ion channels continue to open, and the diffusion calcium ions into the cell counteracts the potential change produced by the diffusion of potassium ions out of the cell. The plateau phase ends and final repolarization begins as the voltage-gated calcium ion channels close, and many voltage-gated potassium ion channels open. Diffusion of calcium ions into the cell decreases and diffusion of potassium ions out of the cell increases. These changes cause the membrane potential to return to its resting level.

The **sinoatrial (SA)** (sī'nō-ā'trē'-ăl) **node**, which functions as the pacemaker of the heart, is located in the superior wall of the right atrium and initiates the contraction of the heart. The SA node is the pacemaker because it produces action potentials at a faster rate than other areas of the heart. The SA node has a larger number of voltage-gated calcium ion channels than other areas of the heart. As soon as the resting membrane potential is reestablished after an action potential, some of the voltage-gated calcium ion channels open spontaneously. As they open, calcium ions begin to diffuse into the cell and cause depolarization. The depolarization stimulates additional voltage-gated calcium ion channels to open and voltage-gated sodium ion channels to open. Thus, additional calcium ions and sodium ions diffuse into the cell and cause further depolarization. Quickly, threshold is reached and another action potential is produced.

Action potentials in cardiac muscle exhibit a **refractory period**, like that of action potentials in skeletal muscle and in neurons. The refractory period lasts about the same length of time as the prolonged action potential in cardiac muscle, however. That amount of time allows cardiac muscle to contract and almost complete relaxation before another action potential can

2   P R E D I C T

Why is it important to prevent tetanic contractions in cardiac muscle but not in skeletal muscle?

✔ *Answer on page 339*

be produced. The long refractory period in cardiac muscle prevents tetanic contractions from occurring, thus ensuring a rhythm of contraction and relaxation for cardiac muscle.

Conduction System of the Heart

Contraction of the atria and ventricles is coordinated by specialized cardiac muscle cells in the wall of the heart that form the **conduction system of the heart** (figure 12.15). Action potentials originate in the SA node and spread over the right and left atria, causing them to contract.

A second area of the heart, called the **atrioventricular (AV)** (ā-trē-ō-ven'trik'-ū'lăr) **node**, is located in the lower portion of the right atrium. When action potentials reach the AV node, they spread slowly through it and then into a bundle of specialized cardiac muscle called the **atrioventricular bundle**, or **bundle of His**. The slow rate of action potential conduction in the AV node allows the atria to complete their contraction before action potentials are delivered to the ventricles.

After action potentials pass through the AV node, they are transmitted through the atrioventricular bundle, which projects through the fibrous connective tissue plate that separates the atria from the ventricles (see figure 12.10). The atrioventricular bundle then divides into two branches of conducting tissue called the **left** and **right bundle branches** (see figure 12.15). At the tips of the left and right bundle branches, the conducting tissue forms many small bundles of **Purkinje** (pŭr-kĭn'jē) **fibers**. These Purkinje fibers pass to the apex of the heart and then extend to the cardiac muscle of the ventricle walls. The atrioventricular bundle, the bundle branches, and the Purkinje fibers are composed of specialized cardiac muscle fibers that conduct action potentials more rapidly than do other cardiac

3   P R E D I C T

If blood supply is reduced in a small area of the heart through which the left bundle branch passed, predict the effect on ventricular contractions.

✔ *Answer on page 339*

muscle fibers. Consequently, action potentials are rapidly delivered to all the cardiac muscle of the ventricles. The coordinated contraction of the ventricles depends on the rapid conduction of action potentials by the conduction system.

Following their contraction, the ventricles begin to relax. After the ventricles have completely relaxed, another action potential originates in the SA node to begin the next cycle of contractions.

1. Action potentials originate in the sinoatrial (SA) node and travel across the wall of the atrium (arrows) from the SA node to the atrioventricular (AV) node.

2. Action potentials pass through the atrioventricular AV node and along the AV bundle, which extends from the AV node, through the fibrous skeleton, into the interventricular septum.

3. The AV bundle divides into right and left bundle branches, and action potentials descend to the apex of each ventricle along the bundle branches.

4. Action potentials are carried by the Purkinje fibers from the bundle branches to the ventricular walls.

Figure 12.15   Conduction System of the Heart

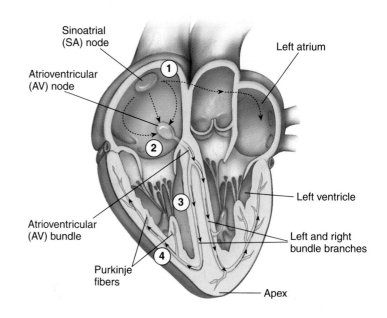

The SA node is the pacemaker of the heart because action potentials originate spontaneously in it faster than in other areas of the heart. Other cardiac muscle cells, however, are capable of producing action potentials spontaneously. For example, if the SA node is unable to function, another area of the heart, such as the AV node, becomes the pacemaker. The resulting heart rate is much slower than normal. When action potentials originate in an area of the heart other than the SA node, the result is called an **ectopic** (ek-top′ik) **beat**.

Did You Know?

Cardiac muscle can also act as if there are thousands of pacemakers, each making a very small portion of the heart contract rapidly and independently of all other areas. This condition is called **fibrillation** (fī-bri-lā′shŭn), and it reduces the output of the heart to only a few milliliters of blood per minute when it occurs in the ventricles. Death of the individual results in a few minutes unless fibrillation of the ventricles is stopped.

To stop the process of fibrillation, defibrillation is used, in which a strong electrical shock is applied to the chest region. The electrical shock causes simultaneous depolarization of all cardiac muscle fibers. During this depolarization, the normal difference in the electrical charge across the cell membrane is reduced. Following depolarization, the SA node can recover and produce action potentials before any other area of the heart. Consequently, the normal pattern of action potential generation and the normal rhythm of contraction can be reestablished.

Fibrillation of the heart is more likely to occur when action potentials originate at ectopic sites in the heart. For example, people who have ectopic beats that originate from one of their ventricles are more likely to develop fibrillation of the heart than people who have normal heart beats.

Electrocardiogram

Action potentials conducted through the heart during the cardiac cycle produce electrical currents that can be measured at the surface of the body. Electrodes placed on the surface of

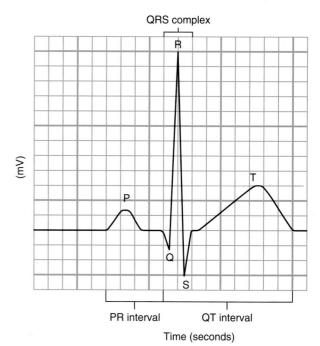

Figure 12.16   Electrocardiogram

Major waves and intervals of the ECG are labeled.

the body and attached to a recording device can detect the small electrical changes resulting from the action potentials in all of the cardiac muscle cells. The record of these electrical events is an **electrocardiogram** (**ECG** or **EKG**) (figure 12.16).

The normal ECG consists of a P wave, a QRS complex, and a T wave. The **P wave** results from depolarization of the atrial myocardium, and the beginning of the P wave precedes the onset of atrial contraction. The **QRS complex** consists of three individual waves: the Q, R, and S waves. The QRS complex results from depolarization of the ventricles, and the beginning of the QRS complex precedes ventricular contraction. The **T wave** represents repolarization of the ventricles, and the beginning of the T wave precedes ventricular relaxation. A wave representing repolarization of the atria cannot be seen because it occurs during the QRS complex.

Table 12.1   Major Cardiac Arrhythmias

Condition	Symptoms	Possible Causes
Abnormal Heart Rhythms		
Tachycardia	Heart rate in excess of 100 bpm	Elevated body temperature, excessive sympathetic stimulation, toxic conditions
Bradycardia	Heart rate less than 60 bpm	Elevated stroke volume in athletes, excessive vagus nerve stimulation, nonfunctional SA node, carotid sinus syndrome
Sinus arrhythmia	Heart rate varies as much as 5% during respiratory cycle and up to 30% during deep respiration	Cause not always known; occasionally caused by ischemia, inflammation, or cardiac failure
Paroxysmal atrial tachycardia	Sudden increase in heart rate to 95–150 bpm for a few seconds or even for several hours; P waves precede every QRS complex; P wave inverted and superimposed on T wave	Excessive sympathetic stimulation, abnormally elevated permeability of cardiac muscle to calcium ions
Atrial flutter	As many as 300 P waves/min and 125 QRS complexes/min; resulting in two or three P waves (atrial contractions) for every QRS complex (ventricular contraction)	Ectopic beats in the atria
Atrial fibrillation	No P waves, normal QRS and T waves, irregular timing, ventricles are constantly stimulated by atria, reduced ventricle filling; increased chance of fibrillation	Ectopic beats in the atria
Ventricular tachycardia	Frequently causes fibrillation	Often associated with damage to AV node or ventricular muscle
Heart Blocks		
SA node block	No P waves, low heart rate resulting from AV node acting as the pacemaker, normal QRS complexes and T waves	Ischemia, tissue damage resulting from infarction; cause sometimes is not known
AV node blocks		
First-degree	P-R interval greater than 0.2 s	Inflammation of AV bundle
Second-degree	P-R interval 0.25–0.45 s; some P waves trigger QRS complexes and others do not; examples of 2:1, 3:1, and 3:2 P wave/QRS complex ratios	Excessive vagus nerve stimulation, AV node damage
Complete heart block	P wave dissociated from QRS complex, atrial rhythm about 100 bpm, ventricular rhythm less than 40 bpm	Ischemia of AV node or compression of AV bundle
Premature Contractions		
Premature atrial contractions	Occasional shortened intervals between one contraction and the succeeding contraction; frequently occurs in healthy people	Excessive smoking, lack of sleep, too much coffee
Premature ventricular contractions (PVCs)	Prolonged QRS complex, exaggerated voltage because only one ventricle may depolarize, possible inverted T wave, increased probability of fibrillation	Ectopic beat in ventricles, lack of sleep, too much coffee, irritability; occasionally occurs with coronary thrombosis

The time between the beginning of the P wave and the beginning of the QRS complex is the **P-Q interval**, commonly called the **P-R interval** because the Q wave is very small. During the P-Q interval the atria contract and begin to relax. At the end of the P-Q interval the ventricles begin to depolarize.

The **Q-T interval** extends from the beginning of the QRS complex to the end of the T wave and represents the length of time required for ventricular depolarization and repolarization. Table 12.1 describes several conditions associated with abnormal heart rhythms.

4   P R E D I C T

Explain how the ECG appears for a person who has many ectopic beats originating from her atria.

✔ *Answer on page 339*

The ECG is not a direct measurement of mechanical events in the heart, and neither the force of contraction nor the blood pressure can be determined from it. Each deflection in the ECG record, however, indicates an electrical event within the heart and correlates with a subsequent mechanical event. Consequently, it is an extremely valuable diagnostic tool in identifying a number of cardiac abnormalities, particularly because it is painless, easy to record, and does not require surgical procedures. Abnormal heart rates or rhythms, abnormal conduction pathways such as blockages in the conduction pathways, hypertrophy or atrophy of portions of the heart, and the approximate location of damaged cardiac muscle can be determined from analysis of an ECG.

Cardiac Cycle

The heart can be viewed as two separate pumps represented by the right and left halves of the heart. Each pump consists of a primer pump—the atrium—and a power pump—the ventricle. The atria act as primer pumps because they complete the filling of the ventricles with blood, and the ventricles act as power pumps because they produce the major force that causes blood to flow through the pulmonary and systemic arteries. The term **cardiac cycle** refers to the repetitive pumping process that begins with the onset of cardiac muscle contraction and ends with the beginning of the next contraction (figure 12.17). Pressure changes produced within the heart chambers as a result of cardiac muscle contraction are responsible for blood movement because blood moves from areas of higher pressure to areas of lower pressure.

Atrial systole (sis′tō-lē, a contracting) refers to contraction of the two atria. **Ventricular systole** refers to contraction of the two ventricles. **Atrial diastole** (dī-as′tō-lē, dilation) refers to relaxation of the two atria, and **ventricular diastole** refers to relaxation of the two ventricles. When the terms **systole** and **diastole** are used alone they refer to ventricular contraction and relaxation, because the ventricles contain more cardiac muscle than the atria and produce a far greater pressure, which forces blood to circulate throughout the vessels of the body.

The major events of the cardiac cycle are

1. At the beginning of ventricular diastole, the pulmonary and aortic semilunar valves close. The tricuspid and bicuspid valves open, and blood flows directly from the atria into the relaxed ventricles. During the previous ventricular systole, the atria were relaxed and blood collected in them. When the ventricles relax and the tricuspid and bicuspid valves open, blood flows into the ventricles (see figure 12.17a) and fills them to approximately 70% of their volume.
2. At the end of ventricular diastole, the atria contract. Atrial systole forces additional blood to flow into the ventricles to complete their filling (see figure 12.17b). The pulmonary and aortic semilunar valves remain closed.
3. After atrial systole is complete, ventricular systole begins. Almost immediately, the tricuspid and bicuspid

valves close, and the pressure in the ventricles increases until it exceeds the pressure in the pulmonary trunk and aorta. When the pressure in the ventricles exceeds the pressure in the pulmonary trunk and aorta, the pulmonary semilunar and the aortic semilunar valves are forced open, and blood is ejected into the pulmonary trunk and aorta (see figure 12.17c).

At the beginning of the next ventricular diastole, the pressure in the ventricles decreases. The pulmonary and aortic semilunar valves close and prevent blood from flowing back into the ventricles. The blood forced into the pulmonary trunk and aorta flows toward the lungs and the systemic vessels. The pressure continues to decline in the ventricles until finally the tricuspid and bicuspid valves open once again, at the beginning of ventricular diastole, and blood enters the ventricles from the atria.

Incompetent valves do not close completely and therefore they leak when they are supposed to be closed. Incompetent valves allow blood to flow in the reverse direction. For example, an incompepent bicuspid valve allows blood to flow from the left ventrical to the left atrium during ventricular systole. This reduces the amount of blood pumped into the aorta. It also dramatically increases the blood pressure in the left atrium and in the pulmonary veins during ventricular systole. During diastole, the excess blood pumped into the atrium once again flows into the ventricle along with the blood that normally flows from the lungs to the left atrium. Therefore, the volume of blood entering the left ventricle is greater than normal. The increased filling of the left ventricle gradually causes it to hypertrophy and can lead to heart failure. The increased pressure in the pulmonary veins can cause edema in the lungs.

5   **P R E D I C T**

Predict the effect of a leaky (incompetent) pulmonary semilunar valve on the volume of blood in the right ventricle just before ventricular contraction. Predict the effect of a severely narrowed opening through the aortic semilunar valves on the amount of work the heart must do to pump the normal volume of blood into the aorta during each beat of the heart.

✔ *Answer on page 339*

Heart Sounds

A **stethoscope** (steth′ō-skōp) is used to listen to heart sounds (figure 12.18). There are two main heart sounds. The **first heart sound** can be represented by the syllable **lubb**, and the **second heart sound** can be represented by **dupp**. The first heart sound has a lower pitch than the second. The first heart sound occurs at the beginning of ventricular systole and results from closure of the tricuspid and bicuspid valves (figure 12.17c). The second heart sound occurs at the beginning of ventricular diastole and results from closure of the semilunar valves (figure 12.17a). The valves usually do not make sounds when they open.

Diastole

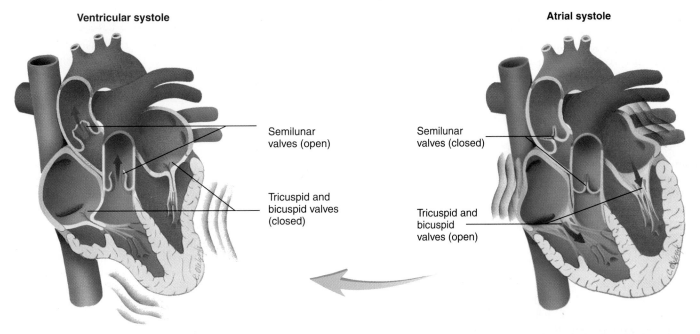

(a) At the beginning of ventricular diastole, the ventricles relax and the aortic and pulmonary semilunar valves close (the second heart sound). The tricuspid and bicuspid valves open and blood flows into the ventricles and the ventricles fill to approximately 70% of their volume.

Aortic semilunar valve (closed)

Pulmonary semilunar valve (closed)

Tricuspid valve (open)

Bicuspid valve (open)

Ventricular systole

Semilunar valves (open)

Tricuspid and bicuspid valves (closed)

Atrial systole

Semilunar valves (closed)

Tricuspid and bicuspid valves (open)

(c) After atrial systole is complete, ventricular systole begins. Almost immediately, the tricuspid and bicuspid valves close (the first heart sound). The pressure in the ventricles increases until it exceeds the pressure in the pulmonary trunk and aorta. As a result, the pulmonary semilunar and the aortic semilunar valves are forced open and blood is ejected into the pulmonary trunk and aorta.

(b) At the end of ventricular diastole, the atria contract. Atrial systole forces additional blood to flow into the ventricles to complete their filling.

Figure 12.17   The Cardiac Cycle

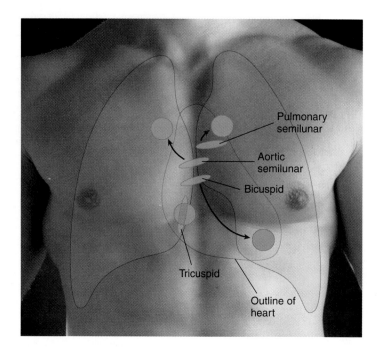

Pulmonary
semilunar

Aortic
semilunar

Bicuspid

Tricuspid

Outline of
heart

Figure 12.18   Location of the Heart Valves in the Thorax

Surface markings of the heart in the male. The positions of the four heart valves are indicated by blue ellipses, and the sites where the sounds of the heart valves are best heard with the stethoscope are indicated by pink circles.

Clinically, ventricular systole occurs between the first and second heart sounds. Ventricular diastole occurs between the second heart sound and the first heart sound of the next beat. Because ventricular diastole lasts longer than ventricular systole, there is less time between the first and second heart sounds than between the second heart sound and the first heart sound of the next beat.

6   PREDICT

Compare the rate of blood flow out of the ventricles between the first and second heart sounds of the same beat with the rate of blood flow out of the ventricles between the second heart sound of one beat and the first heart sound of the next beat.

✔ *Answer on page 339*

Abnormal heart sounds called **murmurs** are usually a result of faulty valves. For example, an **incompetent valve** fails to close tightly and blood leaks through the valve when it is closed. A murmur caused by an incompetent valve makes a swishing sound immediately after closure of the valve. For example, an incompetent bicuspid valve results in a swishing sound immediately after the first heart sound.

When the opening of a valve is narrowed, or **stenosed** (sten′ōzd), a swishing sound precedes closure of the stenosed valve. For example, when the bicuspid valve is stenosed, a swishing sound precedes the first heart sound.

7   PREDICT

If normal heart sounds are represented by lubb-dupp, lubb-dupp, what does a heart sound represented by lubb-duppshhh, lubb-duppshhh represent? What does lubb-shhhdupp, lubb-shhhdupp represent (assume that shhh represents a swishing sound)?

✔ *Answer on page 339*

Regulation of Heart Function

Cardiac output (CO) is the volume of blood pumped by either ventricle of the heart each minute. Cardiac output can be calculated by multiplying the stroke volume times the heart rate. **Stroke volume (SV)** is the volume of blood pumped per ventricle each time the heart contracts, and the **heart rate (HR)** is the number of times the heart contracts each minute.

$$\underset{\text{(mL/min)}}{\text{CO}} = \underset{\text{(mL/beat)}}{\text{SV}} \times \underset{\text{(beats/min)}}{\text{HR}}$$

Under resting conditions, the heart rate is approximately 72 beats/min and the stroke volume is approximately 70 mL/beat. Consequently, the cardiac output is slightly more than 5 L/min:

$$CO = SV \times HR$$

$$= 70 \text{ mL/beat} \times 72 \text{ beats/min}$$

$$= 5040 \text{ mL/min (approximately 5 L/min)}$$

Clinical Focus   Conditions and Diseases Affecting the Heart

Heart Diseases

Inflammation of Heart Tissues

Endocarditis (en'dō-kar-dī'tis) is inflammation of the endocardium. It affects the valves more severely than other areas of the heart and may lead to deposition of scar tissue, causing valves to become stenosed or incompetent.

Myocarditis (mī'ō-kar-dī'tis) is inflammation of the myocardium and can lead to heart failure.

Pericarditis (per'i-kar-dī'tis) is inflammation of the pericardium. Pericarditis can result from bacterial or viral infections and can be extremely painful.

Rheumatic (roo-mat'ik) **heart disease** can result from a **streptococcal** (strep'tō-kok'ăl) **infection** in young people. Toxin produced by the bacteria can cause an immune reaction called rheumatic fever approximately 2 to 4 weeks after the infection. The immune reaction can cause inflammation of the endocardium, called **rheumatic endocarditis** (en'dō-kar-dī'tis). The inflamed valves, especially the bicuspid valve, can become stenosed or incompetent. The effective treatment of streptococcal infections with antibiotics has reduced the frequency of rheumatic heart disease.

Reduced Blood Flow to Cardiac Muscle

Coronary heart disease reduces the amount of blood that the coronary arteries are able to deliver to the myocardium. The reduction in blood flow can damage the myocardium. The degree of damage depends on the size of the arteries involved, whether occlusion (blockage) is partial or complete, and whether occlusion is gradual or sudden. As the walls of the arteries thicken and harden with age, the volume of blood they can supply to the heart muscle declines, and the ability of the heart to pump blood decreases. Inadequate blood flow to the heart muscle can result in **angina pectoris** (an-jī'nă pek'tō-ris), which is a poorly localized sensation of pain in the region of the chest, left arm, and left shoulder.

Degenerative changes in the artery wall can cause the inside surface of the artery to become roughened. The chance of platelet aggregation increases at the rough surface, which increases the change of **coronary thrombosis** (throm-bō'sis), the formation of a blood clot in a coronary vessel. Inadequate blood flow can cause an **infarct** (in'farkt), an area of damaged cardiac tissue. A heart attack is often referred to as a coronary thrombosis or a **myocardial infarction**. The outcome of coronary thrombosis depends on the extent of the damage to heart muscle caused by inadequate blood flow and whether other blood vessels can supply enough blood to maintain the function of the heart. Death can occur swiftly if the infarct is large; if the infarct is small, the heart can continue to function. In some cases, the infarct weakens the wall of the heart, and the wall ruptures; but in most cases scar tissue replaces damaged cardiac muscle in the area of the infarct.

People who survive infarctions often lead fairly normal lives if they take precautions. Most cases call for moderate exercise, adequate rest, a disciplined diet, and reduced stress. Small doses of aspirin and treatments, including drugs, to reduce elevated blood pressure appear to provide protection against the development of myocardial infarcts.

Congenital Conditions Affecting the Heart

Congenital heart disease is heart disease present at birth and is the result of abnormal development of the heart. The following are common congenital defects:

A **septal defect** is a hole in a septum between the left and right sides of the heart. The hole may be in the interatrial or interventricular septum. These defects allow blood to flow from one side of the heart to the other and, as a consequence, greatly reduce the pumping effectiveness of the heart.

Patent ductus arteriosus (dŭk'tŭs artēr'ē-ō-sŭs) results when a blood vessel called the **ductus arteriosus**, which is present in the fetus, fails to close after birth. The ductus arteriosus extends between the pulmonary trunk and the aorta. It allows blood to pass from the pulmonary trunk to the aorta, thus bypassing the lungs. This is normal before birth because the lungs are not functioning. If the ductus arteriosus fails to close after birth, however, blood flows in the opposite direction, from the aorta to the pulmonary trunk. As a consequence, blood flows through the lungs under a higher pressure and damages them. In addition, the amount of work required of the left ventricle to maintain an adequate systemic blood pressure increases.

Stenosis (ste-nō'sis) **of the heart valves** is a narrowed opening through one or more of the heart valves. In aortic or pulmonary semilunar valve stenosis, the workload of the heart is increased because the ventricles must contract with a much greater force to pump blood from the ventricles. Stenosis of the bicuspid valve prevents the flow of blood into the left ventricle, causing blood to back up in the left atrium and the lungs, resulting in edema in the lungs. Stenosis of the tricuspid valve causes blood to back up in the right atrium and systemic veins, causing edema in the periphery.

Cyanosis (sī-ă-nō'sis) is a symptom of inadequate heart function in babies suffering from congenital heart disease. The term "blue baby" is sometimes used to refer to infants with cyanosis. The blueness of the skin is caused by low oxygen levels in the blood in peripheral blood vessels.

Conditions Associated with Aging

Several heart diseases develop as people become elderly, and the diseases gradually become more severe as people grow older. The following conditions are common in elderly people:

Heart failure is the result of progressive weakening of the heart muscle and the failure of the heart to pump blood effectively. High blood pressure, which is called **hypertension** (hī'per-ten'shŭn) increases the afterload on the heart. Hypertension can produce significant heart enlargement and can finally result in heart failure. Advanced age, malnutrition, chronic infections, toxins, severe anemias, or hyperthyroidism can cause degeneration of the heart muscle, resulting in heart failure. Heredity factors can also be responsible for increased susceptibility to heart failure.

Heart function in the elderly gradually becomes less efficient. Although the age at which the heart becomes less efficient varies considerably and depends on many factors, by age 70 cardiac output often decreases by approximately one-third. Because of the decrease in reserve strength of the heart, many elderly people are often limited in their ability to respond to emergencies, infections, blood loss, or stress.

The heart rate and the stroke volume vary considerably among people. Athletes tend to have a larger stroke volume and lower heart rate at rest because exercise has increased the size of their hearts. Nonathletes are more likely to have a higher heart rate and lower stroke volume. During exercise the heart in a nonathlete can increase to 190 beats/min and the stroke volume can increase to 115mL/beat. Therefore, the cardiac output increases to approximately 22 L/min:

$$CO = SV \times HR$$
$$= 115 \text{ mL/beat} \times 190 \text{ beats/min}$$
$$= 21,850 \text{ mL/min (approximately 22 L/min)}$$

This produces a cardiac output that is several times greater than the cardiac output under resting conditions. Athletes can increase their cardiac output to a greater degree than nonathletes.

The control mechanisms that modify the stroke volume and the heart rate are classified as intrinsic and extrinsic mechanisms.

Intrinsic Regulation of the Heart

Intrinsic regulation of the heart refers to mechanisms contained within the heart itself. The force of contraction produced by cardiac muscle is related to the degree of stretch of cardiac muscle fibers. The amount of blood in the ventricles at the end of ventricular diastole determines the degree to which cardiac muscle fibers are stretched. **Venous return** is the amount of blood that returns to the heart, and the degree to which the ventricular walls are stretched at the end of diastole is called **preload**. If venous return increases, the heart fills to a greater volume and stretches the cardiac muscle fibers, producing an increased preload. In response to the increased preload, cardiac muscle fibers contract with a greater force. The greater force of contraction causes an increased volume of blood to be ejected from the heart, resulting in an increased stroke volume. As venous return increases, resulting in an increased preload, cardiac output increases. Conversely, if venous return decreases, resulting in a decreased preload, the cardiac output decreases. The relationship between preload and stroke volume is called **Starling's law of the heart**.

Because venous return is influenced by many conditions, Starling's law of the heart has a major influence on cardiac output. For example, muscular activity during exercise causes increased venous return, resulting in an increased preload, stroke volume, and cardiac output. This is beneficial because an increased cardiac output is needed during exercise to supply oxygen to exercising skeletal muscles.

Afterload refers to the pressure against which the ventricles must pump blood. People suffering from hypertension have an increased afterload because they have an elevated aortic pressure during contraction of the ventricles. The heart must do more work to pump blood from the left ven-

Did You Know?

Although heart failure can occur in young people, it usually results from a progressive weakening of the heart muscle in elderly people. A failing heart gradually enlarges and eventually fails. In heart failure, the heart is not capable of pumping all the blood that is returned to it because further stretching of the cardiac muscle fibers does not increase the stroke volume of the heart. Consequently, blood backs up in the veins. For example, heart failure that affects the right ventricle is called **right heart failure** and causes blood to back up in the veins that return blood from systemic vessels to the heart. Filling of the veins with blood causes edema, especially in the legs and feet. Edema results from the accumulation of fluid in tissues outside of blood vessels. Heart failure that affects the left ventricle is called **left heart failure** and causes blood to back up in the veins that return blood from the lungs to the heart. Filling of these veins causes edema in the lungs, which makes breathing difficult.

tricle into the aorta, which increases the workload on the heart and can eventually lead to heart failure. A reduced afterload decreases the work the heart must do. People who have a lower blood pressure have a reduced afterload and develop heart failure less often than people who have hypertension. The afterload, however, influences cardiac output less than preload influences it. The afterload must increase substantially before it decreases the volume of blood pumped by a healthy heart.

Extrinsic Regulation of the Heart

Extrinsic regulation refers to mechanisms external to the heart, such as either hormonal or nervous regulation (figure 12.19). Nervous influences are carried through the autonomic nervous system. Both sympathetic and parasympathetic nerve fibers innervate the heart, and have a major effect on the SA-node. Stimulation by sympathetic nerve fibers causes the heart rate and the stroke volume to increase, whereas stimulation by parasympathetic nerve fibers causes the heart rate to decrease.

The **baroreceptor** (bar'ō-rē-sep'ter) **reflex** plays an important role in regulating the function of the heart. **Baroreceptors** are stretch receptors that monitor blood pressure in the aorta and in the wall of the internal carotid arteries, which carry blood to the brain (see figure 12.19). Changes in blood pressure result in changes in the stretch of the walls of these blood vessels. Thus, changes in blood pressure cause changes in the frequency of action potentials produced by the baroreceptors. The action potentials are transmitted along nerve fibers from the stretch receptors to the medulla oblongata of the brain.

Within the medulla oblongata of the brain is a **cardioregulatory center**, which receives and integrates action potentials from the baroreceptors. The cardioregulatory center controls the action potential frequency in sympathetic and parasympathetic nerve fibers that extend from the brain and spinal cord to the heart. The cardioregulatory center also influences sympathetic stimulation of the adrenal gland (see

1. Afferent (green) neurons carry action potentials from baroreceptors to the cardioregulatory center. Chemoreceptors in the medulla oblongata influence the cardioregulatory center.

2. The cardioregulatory center controls the frequency of action potentials in the parasympathetic (red) neurons extending to the heart. The parasympathetic neurons decrease the heart rate.

3. The cardioregulatory center controls the frequency of action potential in the sympathetic (blue) neurons extending to the heart. The sympathetic neurons increase the heart rate and the stroke volume.

4. The cardioregulatory center influences the frequency of action potentials in the sympathetic (blue) neurons extending to the adrenal medulla. The sympathetic neurons increase the secretion of epinephrine and some norepinephrine into the general circulation. Epinephrine and norepinephrine increase the heart rate and stroke volume.

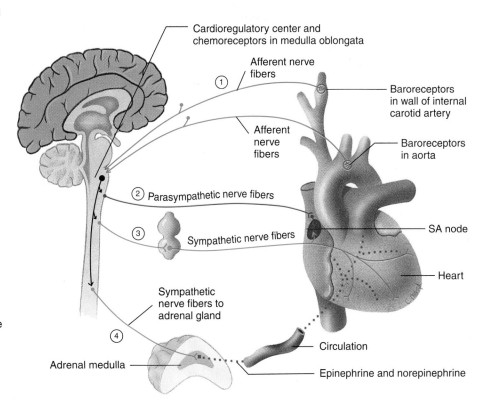

Figure 12.19 Extrinsic Regulation of the Heart

figure 12.19). Epinephrine and norepinephrine, released from the adrenal gland increase the stroke volume and heart rate.

When the blood pressure increases, the baroreceptors are stimulated. There is increased frequency of action potentials, sent along the nerve fibers to the medulla of the brain. This prompts the cardioregulatory center to increase parasympathetic stimulation and to decrease sympathetic stimulation of the heart. As a result, the heart rate and stroke volume decrease, causing blood pressure to decline (figure 12.20).

When the blood pressure decreases, there is less stimulation of the baroreceptors. A lower frequency of action potentials is sent to the medulla of the brain and this triggers a response in the cardioregulatory center. The cardioregulatory center responds by increasing sympathetic stimulation of the heart and decreasing parasympathetic stimulation. Consequently, the heart rate and stroke volume increase. If the decrease in blood pressure is large, sympathetic stimulation of the adrenal medulla also increases. The epinephrine and norepinephrine secreted by the adrenal medulla increase the heart rate and stroke volume, also causing the blood pressure to increase toward its normal value (see figure 12.20).

---

8   P R E D I C T

In response to a severe hemorrhage, blood pressure lowers, the heart rate increases dramatically, and the stroke volume lowers. If low blood pressure activates a reflex that increases sympathetic stimulation of the heart, why is the stroke volume low?

✔ *Answer on page 340*

Emotions integrated in the cerebrum of the brain can influence the heart. Excitement, anxiety, or anger can affect the cardioregulatory center, resulting in increased sympathetic stimulation of the heart and an increased cardiac output. Depression, on the other hand, can increase parasympathetic stimulation of the heart, causing a slight reduction in cardiac output.

Epinephrine and small amounts of norepinephrine released from the adrenal medulla in response to exercise, emotional excitement, or stress also influence the heart's function (see figures 12.19 and 12.20). Epinephrine and norepinephrine bind to receptor molecules on cardiac muscle and cause increased heart rate and stroke volume.

The medulla oblongata of the brain also contains chemoreceptors that are sensitive to changes in pH and carbon dioxide levels (see figure 12.19). A decrease in pH, often caused by an increase in carbon dioxide, results in sympathetic stimulation of the heart (figure 12.21).

Changes in the extracellular concentration of potassium, calcium, and sodium ions, which influence other electrically excitable tissues, also affect cardiac muscle function. Excess extracellular potassium ions cause the heart rate and stroke volume to decrease. If the extracellular potassium ion concentration increases further, normal conduction of action potentials through cardiac muscle is blocked, and death can result. An excess of extracellular calcium ions causes the heart to contract arrhythmically. Reduced extracellular calcium ions cause both the heart rate and stroke volume to decrease.

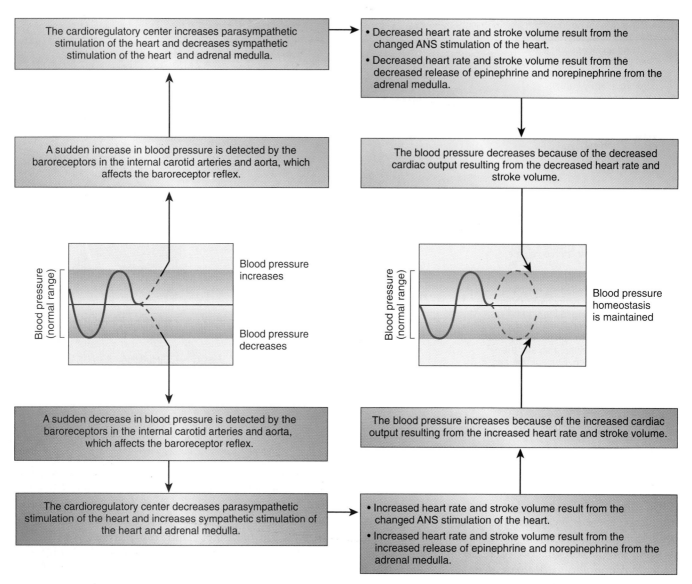

The cardioregulatory center increases parasympathetic stimulation of the heart and decreases sympathetic stimulation of the heart and adrenal medulla.

- Decreased heart rate and stroke volume result from the changed ANS stimulation of the heart.
- Decreased heart rate and stroke volume result from the decreased release of epinephrine and norepinephrine from the adrenal medulla.

A sudden increase in blood pressure is detected by the baroreceptors in the internal carotid arteries and aorta, which affects the baroreceptor reflex.

The blood pressure decreases because of the decreased cardiac output resulting from the decreased heart rate and stroke volume.

Blood pressure (normal range)

Blood pressure increases

Blood pressure decreases

Blood pressure (normal range)

Blood pressure homeostasis is maintained

A sudden decrease in blood pressure is detected by the baroreceptors in the internal carotid arteries and aorta, which affects the baroreceptor reflex.

The blood pressure increases because of the increased cardiac output resulting from the increased heart rate and stroke volume.

The cardioregulatory center decreases parasympathetic stimulation of the heart and increases sympathetic stimulation of the heart and adrenal medulla.

- Increased heart rate and stroke volume result from the changed ANS stimulation of the heart.
- Increased heart rate and stroke volume result from the increased release of epinephrine and norepinephrine from the adrenal medulla.

Figure 12.20 Homeostasis: Baroreceptor Reflex

The baroreceptor reflex helps maintain homeostasis in response to changes in blood pressure.

Did You Know?

During exercise, the cardiac output of the heart increases, resulting in increased delivery of blood to skeletal muscles. Cardiac output increases because of the increased heart rate and stroke volume that result from increased sympathetic stimulation of the heart and from the effects of epinephrine and norepinephrine on cardiac muscle. Starling's law of the heart also contributes to the increase in stroke volume during exercise. Blood vessels in exercising skeletal muscles dilate, which increases blood flow to the muscle tissue. The dilation of the blood vessels also increases venous return to the heart because the rate of blood flow from exercising skeletal muscle through the veins is greatly increased. As venous return increases, preload increases, and cardiac muscle is stretched. Consequently, the muscle contracts more forcefully (Starling's law) and stroke volume increases.

Body temperature affects metabolism in the heart like it affects other tissues. Elevated body temperature increases the heart rate, and reduced body temperature slows the heart rate. For example, during fever the heart rate is usually elevated. During heart surgery the body temperature is sometimes intentionally lowered to slow the heart rate and metabolism.

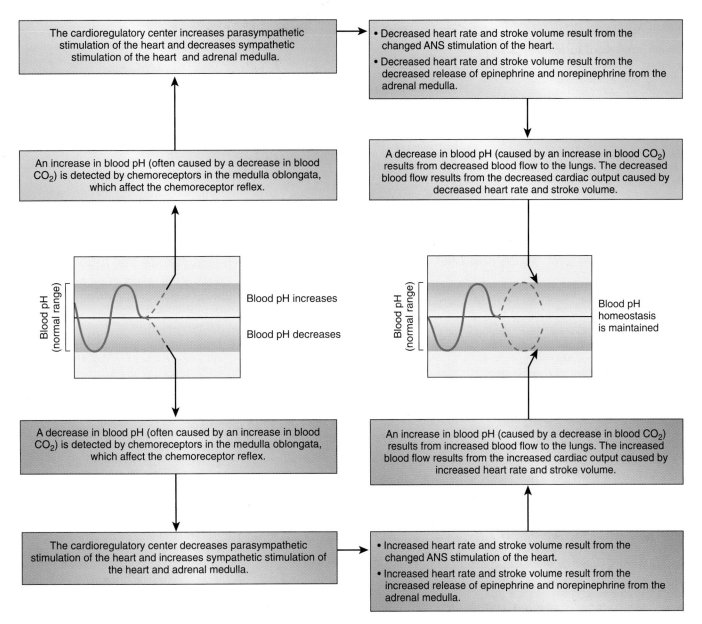

Figure 12.21   Homeostasis: Chemoreceptor Reflex

The chemoreceptor reflex helps maintain homeostasis in response to changes in blood pH and CO_2 levels.

Clinical Focus   Treatment and Prevention of Heart Disease

Heart Medications

Digitalis

Digitalis (dij'i-tal'is) slows and strengthens contractions of the heart muscle. This drug is frequently given to people who suffer from heart failure, although it can also be used to treat atrial tachycardia.

Nitroglycerin

During exercise, when the heart rate and stroke volume are increased, dilation of blood vessels in the exercising skeletal muscles and constriction in most other blood vessels results in an increased venous return to the heart and an increased preload. **Nitroglycerin** (nī-trō-glis'er-in) causes dilation of all of the veins and arteries without an increase in heart rate or stroke volume. When all blood vessels dilate, a greater volume of blood pools in the dilated blood vessels, causing a decrease in the venous return to the heart. The reduced preload causes cardiac output to decrease, re-

sulting in a decreased amount of work performed by the heart. Nitroglycerin is frequently given to people who suffer from coronary artery disease, which restricts coronary blood flow. The decreased work performed by the heart reduces the amount of oxygen required by the cardiac muscle. In addition, dilation of coronary arteries can increase blood flow to cardiac muscle. Consequently, the heart does not suffer from a lack of oxygen, and angina pectoris does not develop.

Beta-Adrenergic Blocking Agents

Beta-adrenergic (bā-tă ad-rĕ-ner'jik) **blocking agents** reduce the rate and strength of cardiac muscle contractions, thus reducing the oxygen demand of the heart. They bind to receptors for norepinephrine and epinephrine and prevent these substances from having their normal effects. Beta-adrenergic blocking agents are often used to treat people who suffer from rapid heart rates, certain types of arrhythmias, and hypertension.

Calcium Channel Blockers

Calcium channel blockers reduce the rate at which calcium ions diffuse into cardiac muscle cells and smooth muscle cells. Because the action potentials that produce cardiac muscle contractions depend in part on the flow of calcium ions into the cardiac muscle cells, the calcium channel blockers can be used to control the force of heart contractions and reduce arrhythmia, tachycardia, and hypertension. Because entry of calcium into smooth muscle cells causes contraction, calcium channel blockers cause dilation of blood vessels. They dilate coronary blood vessels and increase blood flow to cardiac muscle. Consequently, they can be used to treat angina pectoris.

Antihypertensive Agents

Several drugs are used specifically to treat hypertension. These drugs reduce blood pressure and therefore reduce the work required by the heart to pump blood. In addition, the reduction of blood pressure reduces the risk of heart attacks and strokes. Medications used to treat hypertension include drugs that reduce the activity of the sympathetic division, those that dilate arteries and veins, those that increase urine production (diuretics), and those that block the conversion of angiotensin I to angiotensin II (see chapter 13).

Anticoagulants

Anticoagulants (an'tē-kō-ag'ū-lants) prevent clot formation in persons with damage to heart valves or blood vessels or in persons who have had a myocardial infarction. Aspirin functions as a weak anticoagulant by inhibiting the synthesis of prostaglandins in platelets, which in turn reduces clot formation. Some data suggest that taking a small dose of aspirin regularly reduces the chance of a heart attack. One aspirin each day may benefit those who are likely to experience a coronary thrombosis. Most of the research has been done for males, but data indicate that aspirin can also reduce the chance of heart attacks in females.

Instruments

Artificial Pacemaker

An **artificial pacemaker** is an instrument placed beneath the skin that is equipped with an electrode that extends to the heart. An artificial pacemaker provides an electrical stimulus to the heart at a set frequency. Artificial pacemakers are used in patients in whom the natural pacemaker of the heart does not produce a heart rate high enough to sustain normal physical activity. Modern electronics has made it possible to design artificial pacemakers that can increase the heart rate as physical activity increases. In addition, special artificial pacemakers can defibrillate the heart if it becomes arrhythmic. It is likely that rapid development of electronics for artificial pacemakers will further increase the degree to which the pacemakers can regulate the heart.

Heart–Lung Machine

A **heart–lung machine** serves as a temporary substitute for the patient's heart and lungs. It pumps blood throughout the body and oxygenates and removes carbon dioxide from the blood. It has made possible many surgeries on the heart and lungs.

Surgical Procedures

Heart Valve Replacement or Repair

Heart valve replacement or repair is a surgical procedure performed on those who have diseased valves that are so deformed and scarred from conditions such as endocarditis that the valves are severely incompetent or stenosed. Substitute valves made of synthetic materials such as plastic or Dacron are effective; valves transplanted from pigs are also used.

Heart Transplants

Heart transplants are possible when the immune characteristics of a donor and the recipient are closely matched. The heart of a recently deceased donor is transplanted to the recipient, and the diseased heart of the recipient is removed. People who have received heart transplants must remain on drugs that suppress their immune responses for the rest of their lives. Unless they do so, their immune system rejects the transplanted heart.

Artificial Hearts

Artificial hearts have been used on an experimental basis to extend the lives of individuals until an acceptable transplant can be found or to replace the heart permanently. The technology currently available for artificial hearts has not yet reached the point at which a high quality of life can be achieved with a permanent artificial heart.

Prevention of Heart Disease

Proper nutrition is important in reducing the risk of heart disease. A recommended diet is low in fats, especially saturated fats and cholesterol, and low in refined sugar. Diets should be high in fiber, whole grains, fruits, and vegetables. Total food intake should be limited to avoid obesity, and sodium chloride intake should be reduced.

Tobacco and excessive use of alcohol should be avoided. Smoking increases the risk of heart disease by at least 10-fold, and excessive use of alcohol also substantially increases the risk of heart disease.

Chronic stress, frequent emotional upsets, and a lack of physical exercise can increase the risk of cardiovascular disease. Remedies include relaxation techniques and aerobic exercise programs involving gradual increases in duration and difficulty in activities such as swimming, walking, jogging, or aerobic dancing.

Hypertension is an abnormally high systemic blood pressure. Hypertension affects approximately one-fifth of the population. Regular blood pressure measurements are important because hypertension does not produce obvious symptoms. If hypertension cannot be controlled by diet and exercise, it is important to treat the condition with prescribed drugs. The cause of hypertension in the majority of cases is unknown.

Systems Pathology

myocardial infarction

MYOCARDIAL INFARCTION

Mr. P. was an overweight, out-of-shape executive who regularly consumed food with a high fat content and smoked. He viewed his job as frustrating because he was frequently confronted with stressful deadlines. He had not had a physical examination for several years so he was not aware that his blood pressure was high. One evening, Mr. P. was walking to his car after work when he began to feel pain in his chest that also radiated down his left arm. Shortly after the onset of pain he became out of breath, developed marked pallor, became dizzy, and had to lie down on the sidewalk. The pain in his chest and arm was poorly localized, but intense and he became anxious and then disoriented. Mr. P. lost consciousness, although he did not stop breathing. After a short delay, one of his coworkers noticed him and called for help. When paramedics arrived, they determined that Mr. P's blood pressure was low and he exhibited arrhythmia and tachycardia. The paramedics transmitted the electrocardiogram they took to a physician by way of their electronic communication system, and they discussed Mr. P.'s symptoms with the physician who was at the hospital. The paramedics were directed to administer oxygen and medication to control arrythmias and to transport him to the hospital. At the hospital, tissue plasminogen activator (t-PA) was administered, which improved blood flow to the damaged area of the heart by activating plasminogen which dissolves blood clots. Blood levels of enzymes such as creatine phosphokinase increased in Mr. P.'s blood over the next few days, which confirmed that damage to cardiac muscle resulted from an infarction.

In the hospital, Mr. P. began to experience shortness of breath because of pulmonary edema, and after a few days in the hospital he developed pneumonia. He was treated for pneumonia and gradually improved over the next few weeks. An **angiogram** (an′jē-ō-gram) (figure A), which is an imaging technique used to visualize the coronary arteries, was performed several days after Mr. P.'s infarction. The angiogram indicated that Mr. P. suffered damage to a significant part of the lateral wall of his left ventricle and that neither angioplasty nor bypass surgery were necessary, although Mr. P. has some serious restrictions to blood flow in his coronary arteries.

Background Information

Mr. P. experienced a myocardial infarction. A thrombosis in one of the branches of the left coronary artery reduced blood supply to the lateral wall of the left ventricle, resulting in

Occluded coronary artery

Figure A

An angiogram (an′jē-ō-gram) is a picture of a blood vessel. It is usually obtained by placing a catheter into a blood vessel and injecting a dye that can be detected with x-rays. Note the occluded (blocked) coronary blood vessel in this angiogram, which has been computer-enhanced to show colors.

ischemia of the left ventricle wall. That t-PA was an effective treatment is consistent with the conclusion that the infarction was due to a thrombosis. An ischemic area of the heart wall was not able to contract normally and, therefore, the pumping effectiveness of the heart was dramatically reduced. The reduced pumping capacity of the heart was responsible for the low blood pressure, which caused the blood flow to his brain to decrease resulting in confusion, disorientation, and possibly unconsciousness.

Low blood pressure, increasing blood carbon dioxide levels, pain, and anxiousness increased sympathetic stimulation of the heart and adrenal glands. Increased sympathetic stimulation of the adrenal medulla resulted in the release of epinephrine from the adrenal medulla. Increased parasympathetic stimulation of the heart resulted from pain sensations. The heart rate was periodically arrhythmic because of the combined effects of parasympathetic stimulation, epinephrine and norepinephrine from the adrenal gland, and sympathetic stimulation. In addition, ectopic beats were produced by the ischemic areas of the left ventricle.

Pulmonary edema resulted from the increased pressure in the pulmonary veins because of the reduced ability of the left ventricle to pump blood. The edema allowed bacteria to infect the lungs and cause pneumonia.

The heart began to beat rhythmically in response to medication because the infarction did not damage the conducting system of the heart, which is an indication that there were no permanent arrhythmias. Permanent arrhythmias are indications of damage done to cardiac muscle cells specialized to conduct action potentials in the heart.

Analysis of the electrocardiogram, blood pressure measurements, and the angiogram indicated that the infarction, in this case, was located on the left side of Mr P.'s heart.

Mr. P.'s physician made it very clear to him that he was lucky to have survived a myocardial infarction and recommended a weight-loss program and a low-sodium and low-fat diet. Mr. P.'s physician also recommended that Mr. P. regularly take a small amount of aspirin and stop smoking. He explained that Mr. P. would have to take medication for high blood pressure if his blood pressure did not decrease in response to the recommended changes. After a period of recovery, the physician recommended an aerobic exercise program and suggested that Mr. P. seek ways to reduce the stress associated with his job. Mr. P. followed the doctor's recommendations, and after several months he began to feel better than he had in years and his blood pressure was normal.

9 P R E D I C T

Severe ischemia in the wall of a ventricle can result in the death of cardiac muscle cells. Inflammation around the necrotic tissue results and macrophages invade the necrotic tissue and phagocytize dead cells. At the same time, blood vessels and connective tissue grow into the necrotic area and begin to deposit connective tissue to replace the necrotic tissue. A person who entered the hospital at about the same time with a very similar condition to Mr. P.'s was recovering. After about a week, his blood pressure suddenly decreased to very low levels and he died within a very short time. Upon autopsy, a large amount of blood was found in the pericardial sac, and the wall of the left ventricle was ruptured. Explain.

✔ *Answer on page 340*

Systems Interactions	Effects of Myocardial Infarctions on Other Systems
System	**Interactions**
Integumentary	Pallor of the skin resulted from intense vasoconstriction of peripheral blood vessels, including those in the skin.
Muscular	Reduced skeletal muscle activity required for activities such as walking result because of the effect of a lack of blood flow to the brain and because blood is shunted from blood vessels that supply skeletal muscles to those that supply the heart and brain.
Nervous	Decreased blood flow to the brain, decreased blood pressure, and pain because of ischemia of heart muscle result in increased sympathetic and parasympathetic stimulation of the heart. Loss of consciousness occurs when the blood flow to the brain decreases enough to result in too little oxygen to maintain normal brain function, especially in the reticular activating system.
Endocrine	When blood pressure decreases to low values, antidiuretic hormone (ADH) is released from the posterior pituitary gland and renin, released from the kidney, activates the renin–angiotensin–aldosterone mechanism. ADH, secreted in large amounts, and angiotensin II cause vasoconstriction of peripheral blood vessels. ADH and aldosterone act on the kidneys to retain water and ions. An increased blood volume increases venous return, which results in an increased stroke volume of the heart and an increase in blood pressure unless damage to the heart is very severe.
Lymphatic or Immune	White blood cells, including macrophages, move to the area of cardiac muscle damage and phagocytize any dead cardiac muscle cells.
Respiratory	Decreased blood pressure results in a decreased blood flow to the lungs. The decrease in gas exchange results in increased blood CO_2 levels, acidosis, and decreased blood O_2 levels. Initially, respiration becomes deep and labored because of the elevated CO_2 levels, decreased blood pH, and depressed O_2 levels. If the blood O_2 levels decrease too much the person loses consciousness. Pulmonary edema can result when the pumping effectiveness of the left ventricle is substantially reduced.
Digestive	Intense sympathetic stimulation decreases blood flow to the digestive system to very low levels, which often results in increased nausea and vomiting.
Urinary	Blood flow to the kidney decreases dramatically in response to sympathetic stimulation. If the kidney becomes ischemic, damage to the kidney tubules can occur, resulting in the development of acute renal failure. Acute renal failure results in reduced urine production. Increased blood urea nitrogen, increased blood levels of potassium ions, and edema are indications that the kidneys cannot eliminate waste products and excess water. If damage is not too great, the period of reduced urine production may last up to 3 weeks, and then the rate of urine production slowly returns to normal as the kidney tubules heal.

Summary

Functions of the Heart

The heart functions include
- The heart generates blood pressure.
- The heart routes blood through the systemic and pulmonary circulation.
- The pumping action of the heart and the valves of the heart ensure a one-way flow of blood through the heart and blood vessels.
- The heart helps regulate blood supply to tissues.

Size, Form, and Location of the Heart

- The heart is approximately the size of a fist and is located in the pericardial cavity.

Anatomy of the Heart

Pericardium

- The pericardial sac consists of a fibrous and serous pericardium. The fibrous pericardium is lined by the parietal pericardium.
- The outer surface of the heart is lined by the visceral pericardium (epicardium).
- Between the visceral and parietal pericardium is the pericardial cavity, which is filled with pericardial fluid.

External Anatomy

- Atria are separated externally from the ventricles by the coronary sulcus. The right and left ventricles are separated externally by the interventricular sulci.
- The inferior and superior venae cavae enter the right atrium. The four pulmonary veins enter the left atrium.
- The pulmonary trunk exits the right ventricle, and the aorta exits the left ventricle.

Blood Supply to the Heart

- The left and right coronary arteries originate from the base of the aorta and supply the heart. Blood returns from heart tissue to the right atrium through the coronary veins and coronary sinus.

Heart Chambers and Internal Anatomy

- There are four chambers in the heart. The left and right atria receive blood from veins and function mainly as reservoirs. Contraction of the atria completes ventricular filling.
- The atria are separated internally from each other by the interatrial septum.
- The ventricles are the main pumping chambers of the heart. The right ventricle pumps blood into the pulmonary trunk and the left ventricle, which has a thicker wall, and pumps blood into the aorta.
- The ventricles are separated internally by the interventricular septum.

Heart Valves

- The heart valves ensure one-way flow of blood.
- The tricuspid valve (three cusps) separates the right atrium and right ventricle, and the bicuspid valve (two cusps) separates the left atrium and left ventricle.

- The papillary muscles attach by the chordae tendineae to the cusps of the tricuspid and bicuspid valves and adjust tension on the valves.
- The aorta and pulmonary trunk are separated from the ventricles by the semilunar valves.
- The skeleton of the heart is a plate of fibrous connective tissue that separates the atria from the ventricles, acts as an electrical barrier between the atria and ventricles, and supports the valves of the heart.

Route of Blood Flow Through the Heart

- The left and right sides of the heart can be considered separate pumps.
- Blood flows from the systemic vessels to the right atrium and from the right atrium to the right ventricle. From the right ventricle blood flows to the pulmonary trunk and from the pulmonary trunk to the lungs. From the lungs blood flows through the pulmonary veins to the left atrium, and from the left atrium blood flows to the left ventricle. From the left ventricle blood flows into the aorta and then through the systemic vessels.

Histology of the Heart

Heart Wall

- The heart wall consists of the outer epicardium, the middle myocardium, and the inner endocardium.

Cardiac Muscle

- Cardiac muscle is striated and depends on ATP for energy. It depends on aerobic metabolism.
- Cardiac muscle cells are joined by intercalated disks that allow action potentials to be propagated throughout the heart.

Electrical Activity of the Heart

Action Potentials in Cardiac Muscle

- Action potentials in cardiac muscle are prolonged compared with those in skeletal muscle and have a depolarization phase, a plateau phase, and a repolarization phase.
- The depolarization is due mainly to opening of the voltage-gated sodium ion channels, and the plateau phase is due to opened voltage-gated calcium ion channels. Repolarization at the end of the plateau phase is due to the opening of potassium ion channels for a brief period.
- The prolonged action potential in cardiac muscle ensures that contraction and relaxation occurs and prevents tetany in cardiac muscle.
- The SA node located in the upper wall of the right atrium is the normal pacemaker of the heart and cells of the SA node have more voltage-gated calcium ion channels than other areas of the heart.

Conduction System of the Heart

- The conduction system of the heart is made up of specialized cardiac muscle cells.
- The SA node produces action potentials that are propagated over the atria to the AV node.

- The AV node and atrioventricular bundle conduct action potentials to the ventricles.
- The right and left bundle branches conduct action potentials from the atrioventricular bundle through Purkinje fibers to the ventricular muscle.
- An ectopic beat results from an action potential that originates in an area of the heart other than the SA node.

Electrocardiogram

- The ECG is a record of electrical events within the heart.
- The ECG can be used to detect abnormal heart rates or rhythms, conduction pathways, hypertrophy or atrophy of the heart, and the approximate location of damaged cardiac muscle.
- The normal ECG consists of a P wave (atrial depolarization), a QRS complex (ventricular depolarization), and a T wave (ventricular repolarization).
- Atrial contraction occurs during the P-Q interval, and the ventricles contract and relax during the Q-T interval.

Cardiac Cycle

- Atrial systole is contraction of the atria, and ventricular systole is contraction of the ventricles. Atrial diastole is relaxation of the atria, and ventricular diastole is relaxation of the ventricles.
- During atrial systole, filling of the right ventricle is completed.
- During ventricular systole, the tricuspid valve closes, and blood forces open the pulmonary semilunar valve; blood flows into the pulmonary trunk. Also, the bicuspid valve closes, and blood forces open the aortic semilunar valve; blood flows into the aorta.

Heart Sounds

- The first heart sound results from closure of the tricuspid and bicuspid valves. The second heart sound results from closure of the aortic and pulmonary semilunar valves.

- Abnormal heart sounds are called murmurs. They can result from incompetent (leaky) valves or stenosed (narrowed) valves.

Regulation of Heart Function

- Cardiac output (volume of blood pumped per ventricle per minute) is equal to the stroke volume (volume of blood ejected per beat) times the heart rate (beats per minute).

Intrinsic Regulation of the Heart

- Intrinsic regulation refers to regulation that is contained in the heart.
- As venous return to the heart increases, the heart wall is stretched, and the increased stretch of the ventricular walls is called preload.
- An increase in preload causes the stroke volume to increase (Starling's law of the heart) and heart rate to increase.
- Afterload is the pressure against which the ventricles must pump blood.

Extrinsic Regulation of the Heart

- Extrinsic regulation refers to nervous and hormonal mechanisms.
- Sympathetic stimulation increases stroke volume and heart rate; parasympathetic stimulation decreases heart rate.
- The baroreceptor reflex detects changes in blood pressure and causes a decrease in heart rate and stroke volume in response to a sudden increase in blood pressure or an increase in heart rate and stroke volume in response to a sudden decrease in blood pressure.
- Emotions influence heart function by increasing sympathetic stimulation of the heart in response to exercise, excitement, anxiety, or anger and by increasing parasympathetic stimulation in response to depression.
- Alterations in body fluid levels of carbon dioxide, pH, and ion concentrations, as well as changes in body temperature, influence heart function.

Content Review

1. Describe the size and location of the heart, including its base and apex.
2. Describe the structure and function of the pericardium.
3. Describe the vessels that supply blood to the cardiac muscle.
4. Define coronary thrombosis and infarct. How do atherosclerotic lesions affect the heart?
5. What chambers make up the left and right side of the heart? What are their functions?
6. Describe the structure and location of the tricuspid, bicuspid, and semilunar valves. What is the function of these valves?
7. What are the functions of the atria and ventricles?
8. Starting in the right atrium, describe the flow of blood through the heart.
9. Describe the three layers of the heart, and state their functions.
10. Describe the forces that cause blood to flow through the right and left side of the heart during atrial diastole, atrial systole, ventricular diastole, and ventricular systole.
11. Describe the events that result in an action potential in cardiac muscle.

12. Explain how cardiac muscle cells in the SA node produce action potentials spontaneously and why the SA node is the pacemaker of the heart.
13. What is the function of the conduction system of the heart? Starting with the SA node, describe the route taken by an action potential as it goes through the conduction system of the heart.
14. Explain the electrical events that generate each portion of the electrocardiogram. How do they relate to contraction events?
15. What contraction and relaxation events occur during the P-Q interval and the Q-T interval of the electrocardiogram?
16. Define cardiac cycle, systole, and diastole.
17. What events cause the first and second heart sounds?
18. Define murmur. Describe how either an incompetent or a stenosed valve can cause a murmur.
19. Define cardiac output, stroke volume, and heart rate.
20. What is Starling's law of the heart? What effect does an increase or a decrease in venous return have on cardiac output?

21. Describe the effect of parasympathetic and sympathetic stimulation on heart rate and stroke volume.
22. How does the nervous system detect and respond to the following:
    a. A decrease in blood pressure
    b. An increase in blood pressure
23. What is the effect of epinephrine on the heart rate and stroke volume?
24. Explain how emotions affect heart function.
25. What effects do the following have on cardiac output:
    a. Decrease in blood pH
    b. Increase in blood carbon dioxide
26. How do changes in body temperature influence the heart rate?

Develop Your Reasoning Skills

1. A friend tells you that her son had an ECG, and it revealed that he has a slight heart murmur. Should you be convinced that he has a heart murmur? Explain.
2. Predict the effect on Starling's law of the heart if the parasympathetic (vagus) nerves to the heart are cut.
3. An experiment is performed on a dog in which the arterial blood pressure in the aorta is monitored before and after the common carotid arteries are clamped (at time A). Explain the change in arterial blood pressure (*Hint:* Baroreceptors are located in the internal carotid arteries, which are superior to the site of clamping of the common carotid arteries).
4. Predict the consequences on the heart if a person took a large dose of a drug that blocks all calcium ion channels.
5. What happens to cardiac output following the ingestion of a large amount of fluid?
6. The cardiac output of athletes and nonathletes at rest can be equal, but while they are exercising, the total cardiac output is much greater in an athlete than in a nonathlete. Athletes have a lower heart rate than nonathletes at rest and when exercising at the same level of exertion. Explain.
7. Explain why the walls of the ventricles are thicker than those of the atria.

Answers to Predict Questions

1. p. 316 The anterior interventricular artery supplies blood to the anterior wall of the heart and to much of the left ventricle. A blocked anterior interventricular artery reduces the oxygen supply to the portion of the heart that is supplied by that artery, and the cardiac muscle in that area is not able to contract effectively. Thus, the left ventricle on the anterior surface of the heart does not contract normally.
2. p. 323 It is important to prevent tetanic contractions in cardiac muscle because the cycle of contraction and relaxation stops during tetanic contractions causing the pumping action of the heart to stop. In skeletal muscle, the cycle of contraction and relaxation is not important as a pump, but it is important to maintain a static contracted state to maintain posture or to hold a limb in a specific position.
3. p. 323 If the normal blood supply is reduced in a small area of the heart through which the left bundle branch passes, conduction of action potentials through that side of the heart is reduced or blocked. As a consequence, the left side of the heart contracts more slowly. The right side of the heart contracts more normally. The reduced rate of contraction of the left ventricle reduces the pumping effectiveness of the left ventricle.
4. p. 325 If many ectopic action potentials arise in the atria, heart rate increases. Each ectopic action potential initiates a new cardiac cycle. It is possible for some ectopic action potentials arising in the atria to occur while the ventricle is depolarized; but these action potentials do not initiate ventricular contractions. There can, therefore, be more P waves than QRS complexes in the electrocardiogram. If ectopic action potentials do not occur in a regular fashion, they can cause the heart to beat at an irregular rate, or arrhythmically.
5. p. 326 A leaky pulmonary semilunar valve results in an increased right ventricular volume just before ventricular contraction. During ventricular relaxation, the pulmonary semilunar valve closes in a normal person, and blood flows out of the right ventricle through the pulmonary trunk. When the pulmonary semilunar valve is incompetent, some blood leaks back into the right ventricle from the pulmonary trunk during ventricular relaxation. When this blood is added to the blood that normally enters the right ventricle from the right atrium, there is a greater than normal volume of blood in the right ventricle just before ventricular contraction.

   A severely narrowed opening through the aortic semilunar valve increases the amount of work the heart must do to pump the normal volume of blood into the aorta. A greater pressure is required in the ventricle to force the same amount of blood through the narrowed opening during ventricular contraction.
6. p. 328 Most of the ventricular contraction occurs between the first and second heart sounds of the same beat. Between the first and second heart sounds, blood therefore is ejected from the ventricles into the pulmonary trunk and the aorta. Between the second heart sound of one beat and the first heart sound of the next beat, the ventricles are relaxing. Little blood passes from the ventricles into the aorta or pulmonary trunk during that period.
7. p. 328 The shhh sound made after a heart sound is created by the backward flow of blood after closure of a leaky or incompetent valve. A swishing sound immediately after the second heart sound (lubb-duppshhh)

represents a leaky aortic semilunar or pulmonary semilunar valve. The shhh sound before a heart sound is created by blood being forced through a narrowed, or stenosed, valve just before the valve closes. The lubb-shhhdupp suggests that there is a swishing sound immediately before the second heart sound; thus indicating a stenosed aortic or pulmonary semilunar valve.

8. p. 331 In response to severe hemorrhage, blood pressure decreases, which is detected by baroreceptors. A reduced frequency of action potentials is sent from the baroreceptors to the medulla oblongata. This causes the cardioregulatory center to increase sympathetic stimulation of the heart and increase the heart rate. Sympathetic stimulation of the heart also increases stroke volume, as long as the volume of blood returned to the heart is adequate. Following hemorrhage, however, the blood volume in the body is reduced, and the venous return to the heart from the body is reduced. As a consequence, the volume of blood in the heart is lower than normal. Because of Starling's law, the stroke volume is reduced. The heart rate is increased, but the volume of blood returning to the heart is decreased; thus the ventricle does not fill with blood. As a consequence, the stroke volume is low, and the heart rate is high.

9. p. 336 Rupture of the left ventricle can occur several days after a myocardial infarction. As the necrotic tissues are being removed by macrophages, the wall of the ventricle becomes thinner and may bulge during systole. If the wall of the ventricle becomes very thin before new connective tissue is deposited, it can rupture. If the left ventricle ruptures, blood flows from the left ventricle into the pericardial sac, resulting in cardiac tamponade. As blood fills the pericardial sac, it compresses the ventricle from the outside. As a consequence, the ventricle is not able to fill with blood and its pumping ability is rapidly eliminated. In response to a ruptured wall of the left ventricle death occurs quickly.

Chapter Thirteen

Blood Vessels and Circulation

artery
(ar′ter-ē) Blood vessel that carries blood away from the heart.

capillary
(kap′i-lār-ē) Minute blood vessel consisting of only simple squamous epithelium and a basement membrane; major site for the exchange of substances between the blood and tissues.

chemoreceptor reflex
(kem′ō-rē-sep′tŏr, ke′mō-rē-sep′tŏr) Process in which chemoreceptors detect changes in oxygen levels, carbon dioxide levels, and pH in the blood and produce changes in heart rate, force of heart contraction, and blood vessel diameter that return these values toward their normal levels.

hepatic portal system
(he-pat′ik) Blood flow through the veins that begin as capillary beds in the intestine, spleen, and stomach and that carry blood to the liver, where they end as a capillary bed.

mean arterial blood pressure (MAP)
The average arterial blood pressure. It is slightly less than the average of the systolic and diastolic blood pressures because diastole lasts longer than systole.

peripheral circulation
(pĕ-rif′ĕ-răl) Blood flow through all blood vessels that carry blood away from the heart (arteries), the capillaries, and all vessels that carry blood back to the heart (veins); consists of the systemic circulation and the pulmonary circulation; includes all blood flow, except that through the heart tissue itself.

pulmonary vessels
(pŭl′mō-nār-ē) Blood flow through the system of blood vessels that carry blood from the right ventricle of the heart to the lungs and back from the lungs to the left atrium.

systemic vessels
(sis-tem′ik) blood flow through the system of blood vessels that carry blood from the left ventricle of the heart to the tissues of the body and back from the body to the right atrium.

vasoconstriction
(vā′sō-kon-strik′shŭn) Decreased diameter of blood vessels.

vasodilation
(vā′sō-dī-lā′shŭn) Increased diameter of blood vessels.

vein
(vān) Blood vessel that carries blood toward the heart.

venous return
(vē′nŭs) Volume of blood returning to the heart.

Objectives

After reading this chapter, you should be able to:

1. Describe the structure and function of arteries, capillaries, and veins.
2. Describe the changes that occur in arteries as they age.
3. Describe the pulmonary part of the circulatory system.
4. List the major arteries that supply each of the major body areas and describe their functions.
5. List the major veins that carry blood from each of the major body areas and describe their functions.
6. Describe how blood pressure can be measured.
7. Explain how blood pressure and resistance to flow change as blood flows through the blood vessels.
8. Describe the exchange of material across the capillary wall.
9. Explain how local control mechanisms and nervous control regulate blood flow.
10. Describe the short-term and long-term mechanisms that regulate arterial pressure.

The blood vessels of the body are extensive enough to carry blood to within two or three cell diameters of nearly all the trillions of cells that make up the body. Blood flow through all of these blood vessels is regulated so that cells are provided with adequate nutrients. In most cases, when blood vessels are damaged, they repair themselves. The intricate blood vessels and their coordinated functions make the design of complex urban water systems seem rather simple by comparison.

Blood vessels outside of the heart are placed into two classes: (1) the **systemic vessels**, which transport blood through all parts of the body from the left ventricle and back to the right atrium, and (2) the **pulmonary vessels**, which transport blood from the right ventricle through the lungs and back to the left atrium (see chapter 12 and figure 12.2). The pulmonary vessels and the systemic vessels together constitute the **peripheral circulation**.

Functions of the Peripheral Circulation

Although the heart provides the major force that causes blood to circulate, the peripheral circulation functions to

1. *Carry blood.* Blood vessels carry blood to all tissues of the body and back to the heart.
2. *Exchange nutrients, waste products, and gases.* Nutrients and oxygen diffuse from blood vessels to cells in essentially all areas of the body. Waste products and carbon dioxide diffuse from the cells where they are produced to blood vessels.
3. *Transport.* Hormones, components of the immune system, molecules required for coagulation, enzymes, nutrients, gases, waste products, and other substances are transported in the blood to all areas of the body.
4. *Regulate blood pressure.* The peripheral circulatory system and the heart work together to regulate blood pressure within a normal range of values.
5. *Direct blood flow.* The peripheral circulatory system directs blood to tissues when increased blood flow is required to maintain homeostasis.

General Features of Blood Vessel Structure

Arteries (ar′ter-ēz) are blood vessels that carry blood away from the heart. Blood is pumped from the ventricles of the heart into large elastic arteries, which branch repeatedly to form progressively smaller arteries. As they become smaller, the arteries undergo a gradual transition from having walls containing more elastic tissue than smooth muscle to having walls with more smooth muscle than elastic tissue. The arteries are normally classified as (1) elastic arteries, (2) muscular arteries, or (3) arterioles, although they form a continuum from the largest to the smallest branches.

Blood flows from arterioles into **capillaries** (kap′i-lār-ēz), where exchange occurs between the blood and tissue fluid. Capillaries have thinner walls. Blood flows through them more slowly, and there are far more of them than any other blood vessel type.

From the capillaries, blood flows into veins. **Veins** (vānz) are blood vessels that carry blood toward the heart. Compared with arteries, the walls of veins are thinner and contain less elastic tissue and fewer smooth muscle cells. Going from capillaries toward the heart, small-diameter veins come together to form larger diameter veins, which are fewer in number. Veins increase in diameter and decrease in number as they project toward the heart, and their walls increase in thickness. Veins are classified as (1) venules, (2) small veins, (3) medium-sized veins, or (4) large veins.

Blood vessel walls consist of three layers, except in capillaries and venules. The relative thickness and composition of each layer varies with the type and diameter of the blood vessel. From the inner to the outer wall of the blood vessels, the layers, or **tunics** (too′niks), are (1) the tunica intima, (2) the tunica media, and (3) the tunica adventitia, or tunica externa (figures 13.1 and 13.2).

The **tunica intima** (too′ni-kă in′ti-mă) consists of an endothelium composed of simple squamous epithelial cells, a basement membrane, and a small amount of connective tissue. In muscular arteries, the tunica intima also contains a layer of thin elastic connective tissue. The **tunica media**, or middle layer, consists of smooth muscle cells arranged circularly around the blood vessel. It also contains variable amounts of elastic and collagen fibers, depending on the size and type of the vessel. In muscular arteries, there is a layer of elastic connective tissue at the outer margin of the tunica media. The **tunica adventitia** (ad-ven-tish′ă) is composed of connective tissue, which varies from dense connective tissue adjacent to the tunica media to loose connective tissue toward the outer portion of the blood vessel wall.

Arteries

Elastic arteries are the largest diameter arteries and have the thickest walls. A greater proportion of their walls is elastic tissue, and a smaller proportion is smooth muscle compared with other arteries (see figure 13.1a). Elastic arteries are stretched when the ventricles of the heart pump blood into them. The elastic recoil of the elastic arteries prevents blood pressure from falling rapidly and maintains blood flow while the ventricles are relaxed.

The **muscular arteries** include medium-sized and small-diameter arteries. The walls of medium-sized arteries are relatively thick compared with their diameter. Most of the thickness of the wall results from smooth muscle cells of the tunica media (see figure 13.1b). Medium-sized arteries are frequently called **distributing arteries** because the smooth muscle tissue enables these vessels to control blood flow to different regions of the body. Contraction of the smooth muscle in blood vessels, which is called **vasoconstriction** (vā′sō-kon-strik′shŭn),

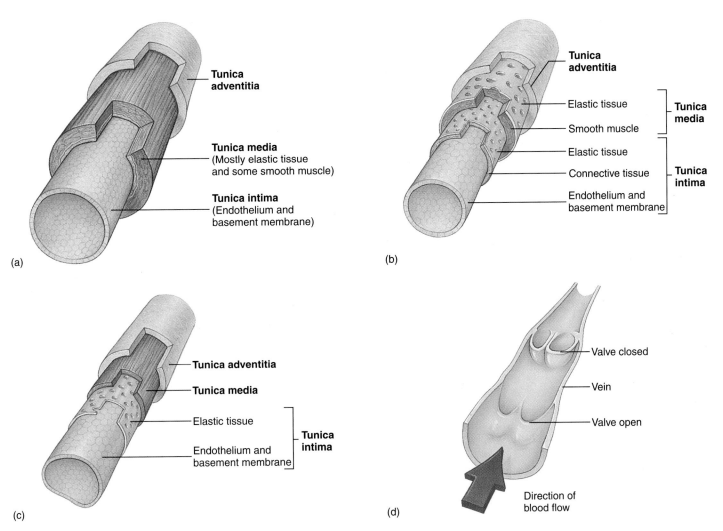

(a)

Tunica
adventitia

Tunica media
(Mostly elastic tissue
and some smooth muscle)

Tunica intima
(Endothelium and
basement membrane)

(b)

Tunica
adventitia

Elastic tissue ⎤
                ⎥ Tunica
Smooth muscle ⎦ media

Elastic tissue ⎤
                ⎥
Connective tissue ⎥ Tunica
                ⎥ intima
Endothelium and ⎥
basement membrane ⎦

(c)

Tunica adventitia

Tunica media

Elastic tissue ⎤
                ⎥ Tunica
Endothelium and ⎥ intima
basement membrane ⎦

(d)

Valve closed

Vein

Valve open

Direction of
blood flow

Figure 13.1   Blood Vessel Structure

The tunica intima of arteries and veins includes the endothelium, its basement membrane, and a thin layer of elastic connective tissue. The tunica media includes a smooth muscle layer and a layer of elastic connective tissue with some collagen fibers, which is variable in thickness. The tunica adventitia consists of the connective tissue layers surrounding the vessel. (*a*) Elastic artery: Large-diameter artery with thick walls that contain a large amount of elastic connective tissue in the tunica media. (*b*) Muscular artery: Muscular arteries have a distinctive layer of smooth muscle cells in the tunica media, and they constrict and dilate. (*c*) Medium vein: Veins have thinner walls. The tunica media is thinner than the tunica media in arteries and contains fewer smooth muscle cells. The dominant layer in the veins is the tunica adventitia. (*d*) Valves in a vein: The valves in veins are folds in the endothelium that allow blood to flow toward the heart but not in the opposite direction.

decreases blood vessel diameter and blood flow. Relaxation of the smooth muscle in blood vessels, which is called **vasodilation** (vā′sō-dī-lā′shŭn), increases blood vessel diameter and blood flow.

Medium-sized arteries supply blood to small arteries. **Small arteries** have about the same structure as the medium-sized arteries, except that small arteries have a smaller diameter and their walls are thinner. The smallest of the small arteries have only three or four layers of smooth muscle in their walls.

Arterioles (ar′ter-ē′ōlz) transport blood from small arteries to capillaries and are the smallest arteries in which the three tunics can be identified. The tunica media consists of only one or two layers of circular smooth muscle cells. Small arteries and arterioles are adapted for vasodilation and vasoconstriction.

Capillaries

Capillary walls consist of **endothelium** (en-dō-thē′lē-ŭm), which is a layer of simple squamous epithelium surrounded by a delicate loose connective tissue. Each capillary is 0.5 to 1 millimeter (mm) long. Capillaries branch without changing their diameter, which is approximately the same as the diameter of a red blood cell (7.5 μm) (figure 13.3).

Blood flows from arterioles into capillaries, which branch to form networks (figure 13.4). Red blood cells flow through most capillaries in single file and are frequently folded as they pass through the smaller-diameter capillaries. Blood flow through capillaries is regulated by smooth muscle cells called **precapillary sphincters** located at the origin of the branches. As blood flows through capillaries, blood gives up

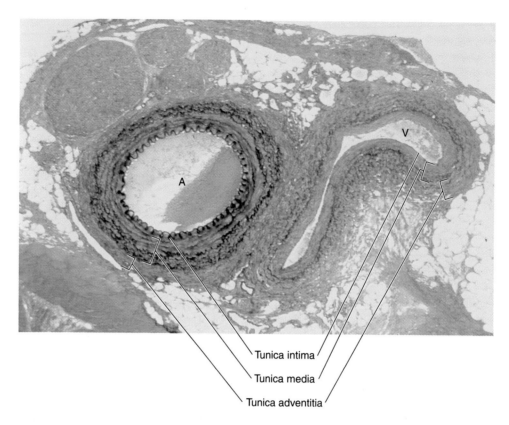

Tunica intima

Tunica media

Tunica adventitia

Figure 13.2 Photomicrograph of an Artery and a Vein

The typical structure of a medium-sized artery (A) and vein (V). The predominant layer in the wall of the artery is the tunica media with its circular layers of smooth muscle. In the vein, the wall is thinner, the tunica media is thinner, and the dominant layer in its wall is the tunica adventitia.

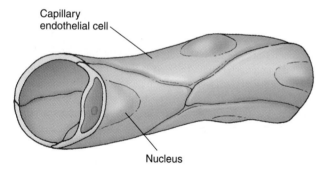

Capillary
endothelial cell

Nucleus

Figure 13.3 Capillary

A section of a capillary showing that it is composed of flattened endothelial cells.

oxygen and nutrients to the tissue spaces and takes up carbon dioxide and other by-products of metabolism. Capillary networks are more numerous and more extensive in the lungs and in highly metabolic tissues, such as the liver, kidneys, skeletal muscle, and cardiac muscle, than in other tissue types.

Veins

Blood flows from capillaries into venules and from venules into small veins. **Venules** (ven′oolz) are tubes with a diameter

Arteriole

Precapillary
sphincters

Capillaries

Venule

Capillary
network

Figure 13.4 Capillary Network

An arteriole giving rise to a capillary network. The network forms numerous branches. Blood flows from capillaries into venules. Smooth muscle cells, called precapillary sphincters, regulate blood flow through the capillaries. Blood flow decreases when the precapillary sphincters constrict and increases when they dilate.

slightly larger than that of capillaries and are composed of endothelium resting on a delicate connective tissue layer. The structure of venules, except for their diameter, is very similar to that of capillaries. **Small veins** are slightly larger in diameter than venules, and their walls contain a continuous layer of smooth muscle cells.

Medium-sized veins collect blood from small veins and deliver it to large veins. Three thin but distinctive layers make up the wall of the medium-sized and large veins. The tunica intima is composed of endothelium, a basement membrane, and a thin layer of elastic connective tissue. The tunica media contains some circular smooth muscle and sparsely scattered elastic fibers. The predominant layer is the outer tunica adventitia, which consists primarily of dense collagen fibers (see figures 13.1c and 13.2).

Veins having diameters greater than 2 mm contain **valves**, which allow blood to flow toward the heart but not in the opposite direction. Each valve consists of folds in the tunica intima that form two flaps, which are shaped like and function like the semilunar valves of the heart. There are many valves in medium-sized veins (see figure 13.1d). There are more valves in veins of the lower limbs than in veins of the upper limbs. This prevents the flow of blood toward the feet in response to the pull of gravity.

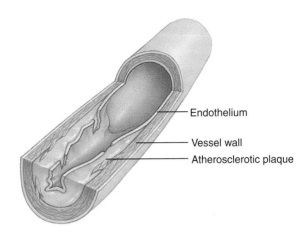

Figure 13.5 Atherosclerotic Plaque in an Artery
Atherosclerotic plaques develop within the tissue of the artery wall.

Did You Know?

Varicose (văr′ĭ-kōs) **veins** result when the veins of the lower limbs become so dilated that the cusps of the valves no longer overlap to prevent the backflow of blood. As a consequence, venous pressure is greater than normal in the veins of the lower limbs and can result in edema. Some people have a genetic tendency for the development of varicose veins. The development of varicose veins is encouraged by conditions that increase the pressure in veins, causing them to stretch. Examples include standing in place for prolonged periods of time and pregnancy. Standing in place allows the pressure of the blood to stretch the veins, and pregnancy allows compression of the veins in the pelvis by the enlarged uterus, resulting in increased venous pressure in the veins that drain the lower limbs. Blood in the veins can become so stagnant that the blood clots. The clots, called **thromboses** (throm-bō′sēz), can result in inflammation of the veins, a condition called **phlebitis** (fle-bī′tis). If the condition becomes severe enough, the blocked veins can prevent blood flow through capillaries that are drained by the veins. The lack of blood flow can lead to tissue death, or **necrosis** (nĕ-krō′sis), and infection of the tissue with anaerobic bacteria, a condition called **gangrene** (gang′grēn). In addition, fragments of the clots can dislodge and travel through the veins to the lungs where they can cause severe damage. Fragments of thromboses, which dislodge and float in the blood, are called **emboli** (em′bō-lī).

Aging of the Arteries

The walls of all arteries undergo changes as they age. Some arteries change more rapidly than others and some individuals are more susceptible to change than others. The most significant effects of aging occur in the large elastic arteries such as the aorta, large arteries carrying blood to the brain, and coronary arteries.

Changes in arteries that make them less elastic are referred to as **arteriosclerosis** (ar-tēr′ē-ō-skler-ō′sis; hardening of the arteries). These changes occur in nearly every individual, and they become more severe with advancing age. A type of arteriosclerosis called **atherosclerosis** (ath′er-ō-skler-ō′sis) results from the deposition of material in the walls of arteries to form plaques (figure 13.5). The material includes a fatlike substance containing cholesterol. The fatty material can eventually be dominated by the deposition of dense connective tissue and calcium salts.

The development of atherosclerosis is influenced by several factors. Lack of exercise, smoking, obesity, and a diet high in cholesterol and fats appear to increase the severity and the rate at which atherosclerosis develops. Severe atherosclerosis is more prevalent in some families than in others, which suggests a genetic influence. Some evidence suggests that a low-fat diet, mild exercise, and relaxation exercises slow the progression of atherosclerosis and may even reverse its progression to some degree.

Atherosclerosis greatly increases resistance to blood flow because the deposits reduce the inside diameter of the arteries. The increased resistance hampers normal circulation to tissues and greatly increases the work performed by the heart. The rough atherosclerotic plaques attract platelets, which adhere to them and increase the chance of thrombus formation.

Blood Vessels of the Pulmonary Circulation

Blood from the right ventricle is pumped into the **pulmonary** (pŭl′mō-nār-ē, relating to the lungs) **trunk** (figures 13.6 and 13.7). This short vessel branches into the **right** and **left pulmonary arteries**, which extend to the right and left lungs, respectively. Poorly oxygenated blood is carried by these arteries to the pulmonary capillaries, where oxygen is taken up by the blood and carbon dioxide is released. Four **pulmonary veins** (two from each lung) exit the lungs and carry the oxygenated blood to the left atrium.

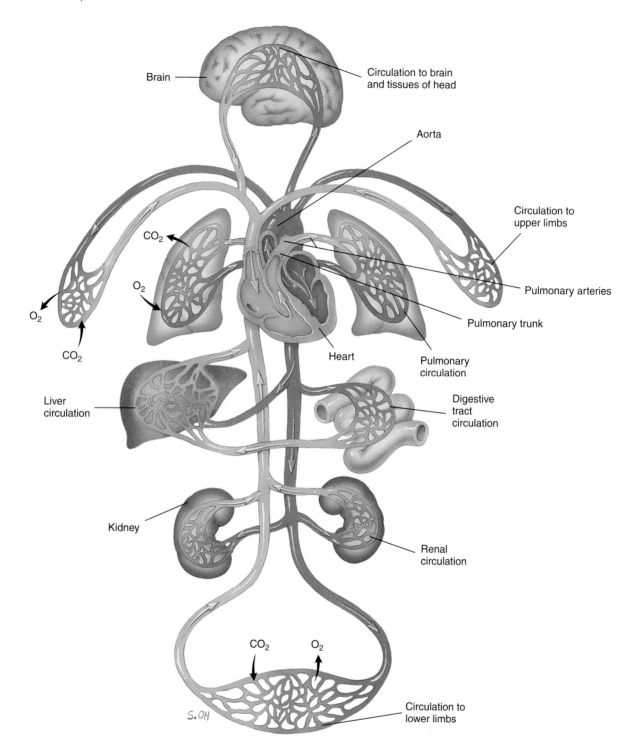

Brain — Circulation to brain and tissues of head

Aorta

Circulation to upper limbs

CO_2

O_2

O_2

CO_2

Pulmonary arteries

Pulmonary trunk

Heart

Pulmonary circulation

Liver circulation

Digestive tract circulation

Kidney

Renal circulation

CO_2 O_2

S. OH

Circulation to lower limbs

Figure 13.6   Blood Flow Through the Circulatory System

Blood is returned from the body to the right atrium. After passing from the right atrium to the right ventricle, blood is pumped into the pulmonary trunk. The pulmonary trunk divides into the right and left pulmonary arteries, which carry oxygen-poor blood to the lungs. In the lung capillaries, carbon dioxide is given off, and oxygen is picked up by the blood. Blood, now rich in oxygen, flows from each lung to the left atrium. Blood then passes from the left atrium to the left ventricle. The left ventricle then pumps the blood into the aorta, which distributes the blood through its branches to all of the body.

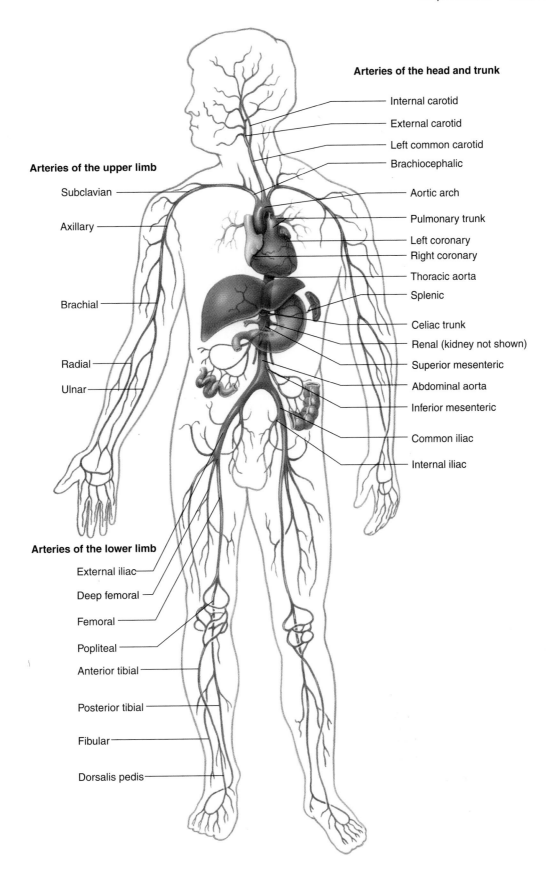

Arteries of the head and trunk

Internal carotid
External carotid
Left common carotid
Brachiocephalic
Aortic arch
Pulmonary trunk
Left coronary
Right coronary
Thoracic aorta
Splenic
Celiac trunk
Renal (kidney not shown)
Superior mesenteric
Abdominal aorta
Inferior mesenteric
Common iliac
Internal iliac

Arteries of the upper limb

Subclavian
Axillary
Brachial
Radial
Ulnar

Arteries of the lower limb

External iliac
Deep femoral
Femoral
Popliteal
Anterior tibial
Posterior tibial
Fibular
Dorsalis pedis

Figure 13.7   The Major Arteries
The major arteries that carry blood from the left ventricle of the heart to the tissues of the body.

Blood Vessels of the Systemic Circulation: Arteries

The **systemic circulation** is the flow of blood through the system of blood vessels that carry blood from the left ventricle of the heart to the tissues of the body and back to the right atrium. Oxygenated blood from the pulmonary veins passes from the left atrium into the left ventricle and from the left ventricle into the aorta. Blood is distributed from the aorta to all portions of the body (see figures 13.6 and 13.7).

Aorta

All arteries of the systemic circulation branch directly or indirectly from the **aorta** (ā-ōr′tă). The aorta is usually considered in three parts: the ascending aorta, the aortic arch, and the descending aorta. The descending aorta is further divided into the thoracic aorta and the abdominal aorta (figure 13.8*a*).

The part of the aorta that passes superiorly from the left ventricle is called the **ascending aorta**. The right and left **coronary arteries** arise from the base of the ascending aorta and supply blood to the cardiac muscle (see chapter 12).

The aorta arches posteriorly and to the left as the **aortic arch**. Three major arteries, which carry blood to the head and upper limbs, originate from the aortic arch. They are the brachiocephalic artery, the left common carotid artery, and the left subclavian artery (figure 13.8*a*).

The **descending aorta** is the longest part of the aorta. It extends through the thorax and abdomen to the upper margin of the pelvis. The part of the descending aorta that extends through the thorax to the diaphragm is called the **thoracic** (thō-ras′ik) **aorta** (see figure 13.8*b*). The part of the descending aorta that extends from the diaphragm to the point at which it divides into the two **common iliac** (il′ē-ak, relating to the flank area) **arteries** is called the **abdominal** (ab-dom′i-năl) **aorta** (figure 13.8*a* and *c*).

Figure 13.8 Branches of the Aorta

(*a*) The aorta is considered in three portions: the ascending aorta, the aortic arch, and the descending aorta. The descending aorta consists of the thoracic and abdominal aorta. (*b*) The thoracic aorta. (*c*) The abdominal aorta.

Superficial temporal artery

Occipital artery

Maxillary artery

Lingual artery

Internal carotid artery

External carotid artery

Carotid sinus

Vertebral artery

Common carotid artery

Facial artery

Superior thyroid artery

Subclavian artery

Brachiocephalic artery

Internal thoracic artery

Figure 13.9   Arteries of the Head and Neck

The brachiocephalic artery, the right common carotid artery, and the right vertebral artery are major arteries that supply the head and neck. The right common carotid artery branches off the brachiocephalic artery, and the vertebral artery branches off the subclavian artery.

Did You Know?

An **arterial aneurysm** (an'ū-rizm) is a localized dilation of an artery that usually develops in response to trauma or a congenital (existing at birth) weakness of the artery wall. Rupture's of aneurysms are serious. Rupture of a large aneurysm of the aorta is almost always fatal, and rupture of an aneurysm of an artery in the brain causes massive damage to brain tissue and even death. If aneurysms are discovered they often can be surgically corrected. For example, large aneurysms of the aorta that leak blood slowly can often be surgically repaired.

Arteries of the Head and Neck

The first vessel to branch from the aortic arch is the **brachiocephalic** (brā'kē-ō-se-fal'ik, vessel to the arm and head) **artery**. It is a short artery, and it branches at the level of the clavicle to form the **right common carotid** (ka-rot'id) **artery**, which transports blood to the right side of the head and neck, and the **right subclavian** (sŭb-klā'vē-an) **artery**, which transports blood to the right upper limb (see figures 13.8a and 13.9).

There is no brachiocephalic artery on the left side of the body. Instead, the left common carotid and left subclavian arteries branch directly off the aortic arch (see figures 13.7 and

13.8a). They are the second and third branches of the aortic arch. The **left common carotid artery** transports blood to the left side of the head and neck, and the **left subclavian artery** transports blood to the left upper limb.

The common carotid arteries extend superiorly along each side of the neck to the angle of the mandible, where they branch into **internal** and **external carotid arteries** (see figure 13.9). The base of each internal carotid artery is slightly dilated to form a **carotid sinus**, which contains structures important in monitoring blood pressure (baroreceptors). The external carotid arteries have several branches that supply the structures of the neck, face, nose, and mouth. The internal carotid arteries pass through the carotid canals and supply most of the blood to the brain.

Some of the blood to the brain is supplied by the **vertebral** (ver'tĕ-brăl) **arteries**, which branch from the subclavian arteries (see figure 13.9) and pass to the head through the transverse foramina of the cervical vertebrae. The vertebral arteries then pass into the cranial vault through the foramen magnum. Branches of the vertebral arteries supply blood to the spinal cord, as well as to the vertebrae, muscles, and ligaments in the neck.

Within the cranial vault, the vertebral arteries unite to form a single **basilar** (bas'i-lăr) **artery** located along the

Table 13.1   Major Branches of the Aorta (see figures 13.7 and 13.8)

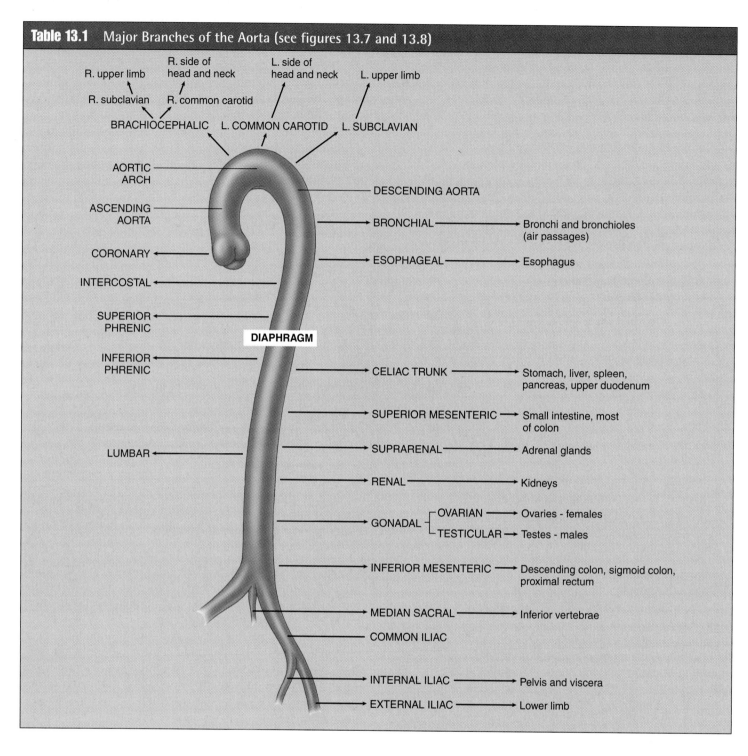

anterior, inferior surface of the brainstem. The basilar artery gives off branches that supply blood to the pons, cerebellum, and midbrain. It also forms right and left branches that connect with the right and left internal carotid arteries. These blood vessels form a system of vessels called the **cerebral arterial circle** or the **circle of Willis** at the base of the brain. The vessels that supply blood to most of the brain branch off of the cerebral arterial circle. Most of the blood supply to the brain is through the internal carotid arteries; however, not enough blood is supplied to the brain to maintain life if either the carotid arteries or the vertebral arteries are blocked.

1   **P R E D I C T**

The term carotid means to put to sleep, implying that, if the carotid arteries are blocked for several seconds, the patient can lose consciousness. Interruption of the blood supply for a few minutes can result in permanent brain damage. What is the physiological significance of atherosclerosis in the carotid arteries?

✔ *Answer on page 372*

Arteries of the Upper Limbs

The arteries of the upper limbs are named differently as they pass into different body regions, even though no major branching occurs. The subclavian artery, located deep to the clavicle, becomes the **axillary** (ak′sil-ār-ē) **artery**, in the axilla (armpit). The **brachial artery**, located in the arm, is a continuation of the axillary artery (see figure 13.7). Blood pressure measurements are normally taken from the brachial artery. The brachial artery branches at the elbow to form the **ulnar** (ul′năr) **artery** and the **radial** (rā′dē-ăl) **artery**, which supply blood to the forearm and hand. The radial artery is the artery most commonly used for taking a pulse. The pulse can be detected conveniently on the thumb (radial) side of the anterior surface of the wrist.

The Thoracic Aorta and Its Branches

The branches of the thoracic aorta can be divided into two groups: the **visceral** (vis′er-ăl) **arteries** supply the thoracic organs, and the **parietal arteries** (pă-rī′ĕ-tăl) supply the thoracic wall (table 13.1). The visceral branches of the thoracic aorta supply the esophagus, trachea, parietal pericardium, and part of the lung. The major parietal arteries are the **posterior intercostal** (in-ter-kos′tăl) **arteries**, which arise from the thoracic aorta and extend between the ribs. They supply intercostal muscles, the vertebrae, the spinal cord, and deep muscles of the back (see figure 13.8a and b). The **superior phrenic** (fren′ik) **arteries** supply the diaphragm.

The **internal thoracic arteries** are branches of the subclavian arteries. They descend along the internal surface of the anterior thoracic wall and give rise to branches called the **anterior intercostal arteries**, which extend between the ribs to supply the anterior chest wall (see figure 13.8a and b).

The Abdominal Aorta and Its Branches

The branches of the abdominal aorta, like those of the thoracic aorta, can be divided into visceral and parietal groups. The visceral arteries are divided into paired and unpaired branches. There are three major unpaired branches: the **celiac** (sē′lē-ak) **trunk, superior mesenteric** (mez-en-ter′ik) **artery**, and the **inferior mesenteric artery**. The celiac trunk supplies blood to the stomach, pancreas, spleen, upper duodenum, and liver. The superior mesenteric artery supplies blood to the small intestine and the upper portion of the colon, and the inferior mesenteric artery supplies blood to the remainder of the colon (see figure 13.8a and c).

There are three paired visceral branches of the abdominal aorta. The **renal** (rē′nal) **arteries** supply the kidneys and the **suprarenal** (sū′pră-rē′năl) **arteries** supply the adrenal glands. The **testicular arteries** supply the testes in males or the **ovarian arteries** supply the ovary in females.

The parietal branches of the abdominal aorta supply the diaphragm and abdominal wall. The **inferior phrenic arteries** supply the diaphragm, the **lumbar arteries** supply the lumbar vertebrae and back muscles, and the **median sacral artery** supplies the inferior vertebrae.

Arteries of the Pelvis

The abdominal aorta divides at the level of the fifth lumbar vertebra into two **common iliac arteries**. Each common iliac artery divides to form an **external iliac artery**, which enters a lower limb, and an **internal iliac artery**, which supplies the pelvic area (see figure 13.7). Visceral branches of the internal iliac artery supply organs such as the urinary bladder, rectum, uterus, and vagina. Parietal branches supply blood to the walls and floor of the pelvis; the lumbar, gluteal, and proximal thigh muscles; and the external genitalia.

Arteries of the Lower Limbs

Like the arteries of the upper limbs, arteries of the lower limbs are named differently as they pass into different body regions, even though there are no major branches. The external iliac artery, in the pelvis, becomes the **femoral** (fem′ŏ-ral, relating to the thigh) **artery** in the thigh, and it becomes the **popliteal** (pop-lit′ē-ăl) **artery** in the popliteal space, which is the posterior region of the knee. The popliteal artery branches slightly inferior to the knee to give off the **anterior tibial artery** and the **posterior tibial artery**. The anterior and posterior tibial arteries give rise to arteries that supply blood to the feet (see figure 13.7). The anterior tibial artery becomes the **dorsalis pedis** (dōr-sāl′lis pē′dis) **artery** at the ankle.

> **Did You Know?**
>
> A pulse can be easily detected in the femoral artery, the popliteal artery, and the dorsalis pedis artery. In the case of hemorrhage in one of the lower limbs, pressure can be applied to the femoral artery to stop the bleeding.

Blood Vessels of the Systemic Circulation: Veins

The **superior vena cava** (vē′nă kā′vă, venous cave) returns blood from the head, neck, thorax, and upper limbs to the right atrium of the heart, and the **inferior vena cava** returns blood from the abdomen, pelvis, and lower limbs to the right atrium (figure 13.10).

Veins of the Head and Neck

The two pairs of major veins that drain blood from the head and neck are the **external** and **internal jugular** (jŭg′ū-lar, neck) **veins** (figure 13.11). The external jugular veins are the more superficial of the two sets, and they drain blood from the posterior head and neck. The external jugular veins empty primarily into the subclavian veins. The internal jugular veins are much larger and deeper. They drain blood from the brain and the anterior head, face, and neck. The internal jugular veins join the **subclavian veins** on each side of the body to form the **brachiocephalic veins**. The brachiocephalic veins join to form the superior vena cava.

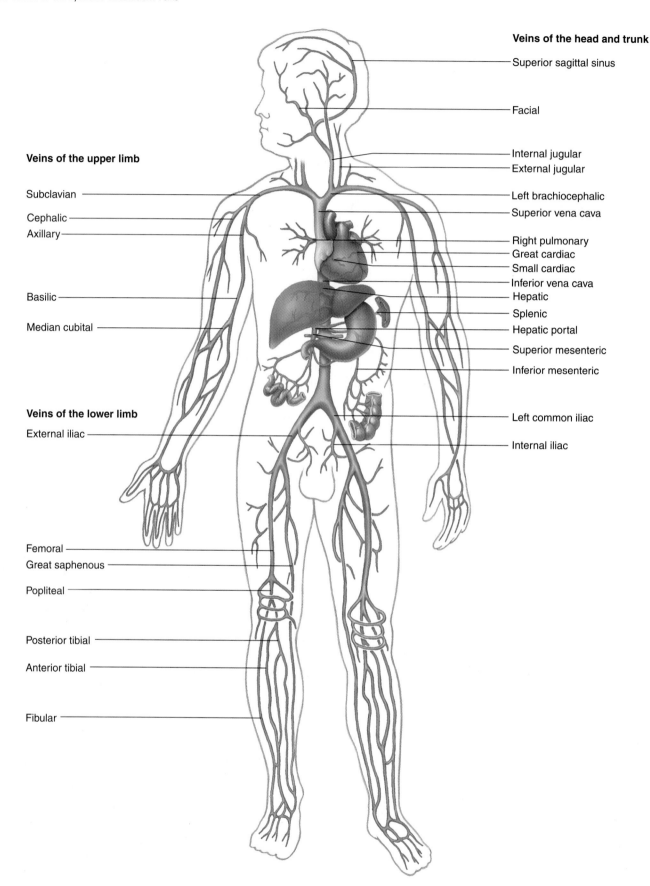

Veins of the head and trunk

Superior sagittal sinus

Facial

Internal jugular

External jugular

Left brachiocephalic

Superior vena cava

Right pulmonary

Great cardiac

Small cardiac

Inferior vena cava

Hepatic

Splenic

Hepatic portal

Superior mesenteric

Inferior mesenteric

Left common iliac

Internal iliac

Veins of the upper limb

Subclavian

Cephalic

Axillary

Basilic

Median cubital

Veins of the lower limb

External iliac

Femoral

Great saphenous

Popliteal

Posterior tibial

Anterior tibial

Fibular

Figure 13.10   The Major Veins

The major veins carry blood from the tissues of the body and return it to the right atrium.

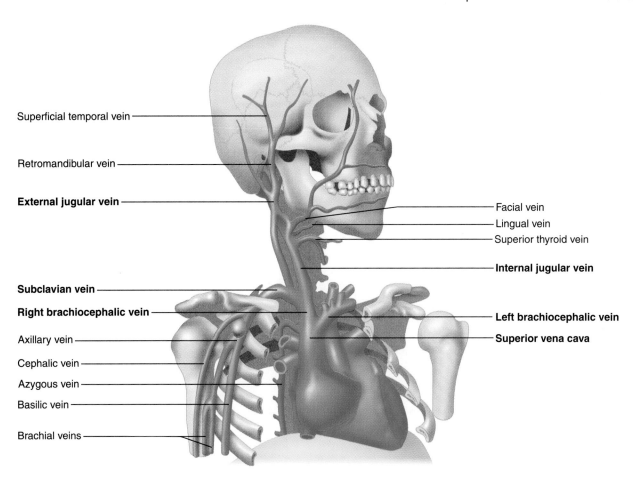

Figure 13.11   The Veins of the Head and Neck

The external and internal jugular veins drain blood from the head and neck. The internal jugular veins join the subclavian veins on each side of the body to form the brachiocephalic veins. The external jugular veins drain into the subclavian veins.

Veins of the Upper Limbs

The veins of the upper limbs can be divided into deep and superficial groups. The deep veins, which drain the deep structures of the upper limbs, follow the same course as the arteries and are named for the arteries they accompany. The only noteworthy deep veins are the **brachial veins**, which accompany the brachial artery and empty into the axillary vein. The superficial veins drain the superficial structures of the upper limbs and then empty into the deep veins. The **cephalic** (sě'fal'ik, toward the head) **vein**, which empties into the **axillary vein** and the **basilic** (ba-sil'ik, toward the base of the arm) **vein**, which becomes the axillary vein, are the major superficial veins (see figure 13.10). Many of their tributaries in the forearm and hand can be seen through the skin. The **median cubital** (kū'bi-tal, elbow) **vein** usually connects the cephalic vein or its tributaries with the basilic vein. Although this vein varies in size among people, it is usually quite prominent on the anterior surface of the upper limb at the level of the elbow, an area called the **cubital fossa**, and is often used as a site for drawing blood.

Veins of the Thorax

Three major veins return blood from the thorax to the superior vena cava: the **right** and **left brachiocephalic veins** and the

azygos (az-ī'gos or az'i-gos, unpaired) **vein** (figure 13.12). Blood drains from the anterior thoracic wall by way of the **anterior intercostal veins**. These veins empty into the **internal thoracic veins**, which empty into the brachiocephalic veins. Blood from the posterior thoracic wall is collected by **posterior intercostal veins**, which drain into the azygos vein on the right and the **hemiazygos vein** or **accessory hemiazygos vein** on the left. The hemiazygos and accessory hemiazygos veins empty into the azygos vein, which drains into the superior vena cava (see figure 13.12).

Veins of the Abdomen and Pelvis

Blood from the posterior abdominal wall drains into the azygos vein. Blood from the rest of the abdomen and from the pelvis and lower limbs returns to the heart through the inferior vena cava. The gonads (testes or ovaries), kidneys, adrenal glands, and liver are the only abdominal organs outside the pelvis from which blood drains directly into the inferior vena cava. The **internal iliac veins** drain the pelvis and join the **external iliac veins** from the lower limbs to form the **common iliac veins**. The common iliac veins combine to form the inferior vena cava (table 13.2; see figure 13.10).

Blood from the capillaries within most of the abdominal viscera, such as the stomach, intestines, pancreas, and spleen, drains through a specialized system of blood vessels to the

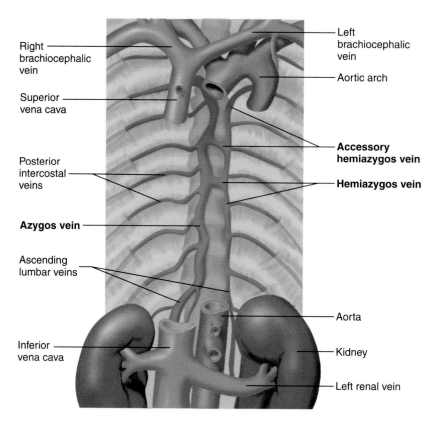

Figure 13.12 Veins of the Thoracic Wall
The azygos and hemiazygos veins and their tributaries.

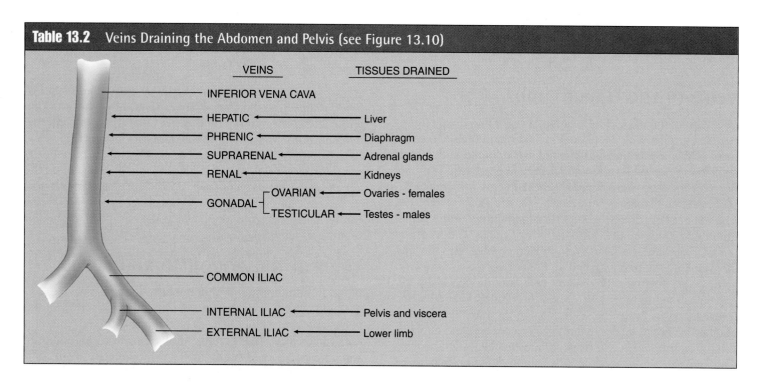

Table 13.2 Veins Draining the Abdomen and Pelvis (see Figure 13.10)

VEINS	TISSUES DRAINED
INFERIOR VENA CAVA	
HEPATIC ←	Liver
PHRENIC ←	Diaphragm
SUPRARENAL ←	Adrenal glands
RENAL ←	Kidneys
GONADAL ⎡ OVARIAN ←	Ovaries - females
⎣ TESTICULAR ←	Testes - males
COMMON ILIAC	
INTERNAL ILIAC ←	Pelvis and viscera
EXTERNAL ILIAC ←	Lower limb

liver. The liver is a major processing center for substances absorbed by the intestinal tract. A **portal** (pōr′tăl) **system** is a vascular system that begins and ends with capillary beds and has no pumping mechanism such as the heart between them. The **hepatic** (he-pa′tik, relating to the liver) **portal system** (figure 13.13 and table 13.3) begins with capillaries in the viscera and ends with capillaries in the liver. The major tributaries of the hepatic portal system are the **splenic** (splen′ik) **vein** and the **superior mesenteric vein**. The **inferior mesenteric vein** empties into the splenic vein. The splenic vein carries blood from the spleen and pancreas. The superior and inferior mesenteric veins carry blood from the intestines.

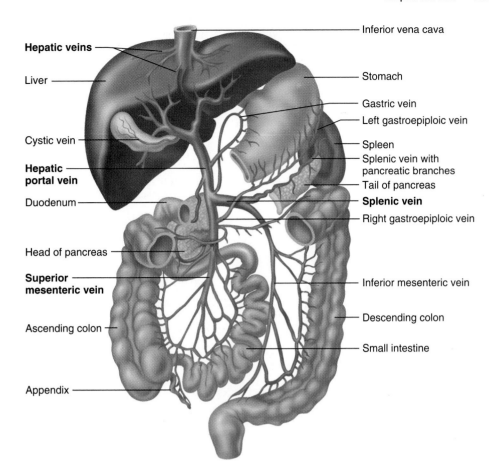

Inferior vena cava

Hepatic veins

Liver

Stomach

Gastric vein

Left gastroepiploic vein

Cystic vein

Spleen

Splenic vein with
pancreatic branches

**Hepatic
portal vein**

Tail of pancreas

Splenic vein

Duodenum

Right gastroepiploic vein

Head of pancreas

**Superior
mesenteric vein**

Inferior mesenteric vein

Descending colon

Ascending colon

Small intestine

Appendix

Figure 13.13   Veins of the Hepatic Portal System

The hepatic portal system begins as capillary beds in the stomach, pancreas, spleen, small intestine, and large intestine. It carries blood to a series of capillaries in the liver. Blood from the liver flows through the hepatic veins, which then enter the inferior vena cava.

Blood from the liver flows into **hepatic veins**, which join the inferior vena cava. Blood entering the liver through the **hepatic portal vein** is rich with nutrients collected from the intestines, but it may also contain a number of toxic substances harmful to the tissues of the body. Within the liver, nutrients are taken up and stored or modified so they can be used by other cells of the body. Toxic substances are converted to nontoxic substances and are removed from the blood or are carried by the blood to the kidneys.

Veins of the Lower Limbs

The veins of the lower limbs, like those of the upper limbs, consist of deep and superficial groups. The deep veins follow the same path as the arteries and are named for the arteries they accompany. The superficial veins consist of the great and small **saphenous** (să-fē′nŭs or sa′fě-nŭs, visible) **veins**. The **great saphenous vein** originates over the dorsal and medial side of the foot and ascends along the medial side of the leg and thigh to empty into the femoral vein (see figure 13.10). The **small saphenous vein** begins over the lateral side of the foot and empties into the **popliteal vein** which, in turn, empties into the femoral vein. The femoral vein empties into the external iliac vein.

Did You Know?

The great saphenous vein often is removed surgically and used in coronary bypass surgery. Portions of the saphenous vein are grafted to create a route of blood flow that bypasses blocked portions of the coronary arteries. The circulation interrupted by the removal of the saphenous vein flows through other veins of the lower limb. The internal thoracic artery is now being used for coronary bypasses. The distal end of the artery is freed and attached to a coronary artery at a point that bypasses the blocked portion of the coronary artery. This technique appears to be better than using the saphenous vein because it does not become blocked as fast.

The Physiology of Circulation

The function of the entire circulatory system is to maintain adequate blood flow to all tissues. An adequate blood flow is required to provide nutrients and oxygen to tissues and to remove waste products of metabolism from the tissues. Blood flows through the arterial system primarily as a result of the pressure produced by contractions of the heart ventricles.

Table 13.3 Hepatic Portal System (see figure 13.13)

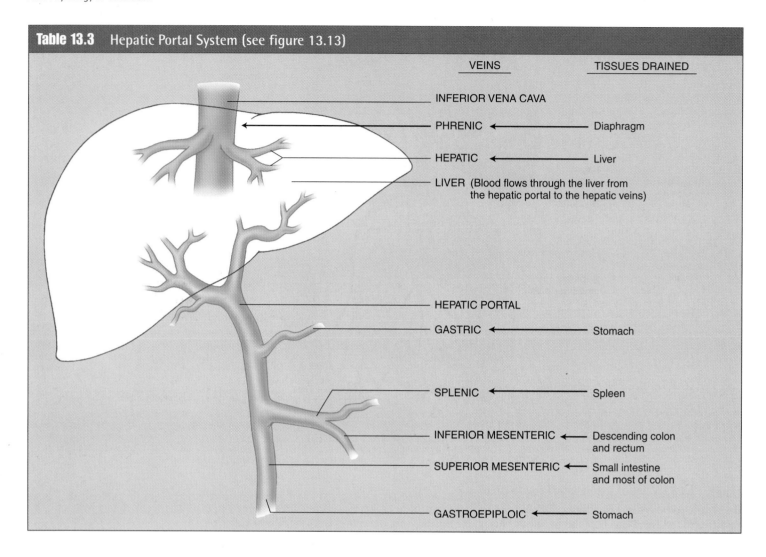

VEINS	TISSUES DRAINED
INFERIOR VENA CAVA	
PHRENIC ←	Diaphragm
HEPATIC ←	Liver
LIVER (Blood flows through the liver from the hepatic portal to the hepatic veins)	
HEPATIC PORTAL	
GASTRIC ←	Stomach
SPLENIC ←	Spleen
INFERIOR MESENTERIC ←	Descending colon and rectum
SUPERIOR MESENTERIC ←	Small intestine and most of colon
GASTROEPIPLOIC ←	Stomach

Blood Pressure

Blood pressure is a measure of the force blood exerts against the blood vessel walls. In arteries, blood pressure values exhibit a cycle dependent on the rhythmic contractions of the heart. During ventricular systole, the heart pushes blood into the arteries, and the pressure reaches a maximum called the **systolic pressure**. When the ventricles relax, blood pressure in the arteries falls to a minimum value called the **diastolic pressure**. The standard unit for measuring blood pressure is millimeters of mercury (mm Hg). If the blood pressure is 100 mm Hg, the pressure is great enough to lift a column of mercury 100 mm.

The **auscultatory** (aws-kŭl′tă-tō-rē) **method** of determining blood pressure is used under most clinical conditions (figure 13.14). A blood pressure cuff connected to a **sphygmomanometer** (sfig′mō-mă-nom′ĕ-ter) is placed around the patient's arm, and a **stethoscope** (steth′ō-skōp) is placed over the brachial artery. The blood pressure cuff is then inflated until the brachial artery is completely blocked. Because no blood flows through the constricted area, no sounds can be heard through the stethoscope at this point. The pressure in the cuff is then gradually lowered. As soon as the pressure in the cuff

declines below the systolic pressure, blood flows through the constricted area each time the left ventricle contracts. The blood flow is turbulent immediately downstream from the constricted area. This turbulence produces vibrations in the blood and surrounding tissues that can be heard through the stethoscope. These sounds are called **Korotkoff** (Kō-rot′kof) **sounds**, and the pressure at which the first Korotkoff sound is heard is the systolic pressure.

As the pressure in the blood pressure cuff is lowered still more, the Korotkoff sounds change tone and loudness. When the pressure has dropped until the brachial artery is no longer constricted and blood flow is no longer turbulent, the sound disappears completely. The pressure at which the Korotkoff sounds disappear is the diastolic pressure. The brachial artery remains open during systole and diastole, and continuous blood flow is reestablished.

The systolic pressure is the maximum pressure produced in the large arteries. It is also a good measure of the maximum pressure within the left ventricle. The diastolic pressure is close to the lowest pressure within the large arteries. During relaxation of the left ventricle, the aortic semilunar valve closes, trapping the blood that was ejected during ventricular contraction in the aorta. The pressure in the ventricles

1. There is no blood flow and no sound is heard when the cuff pressure is high enough to keep the brachial artery closed.

2. **Systolic pressure** is the pressure at which a sound is first heard. When cuff pressure decreases and is no longer able to keep the brachial artery closed, blood is pushed through the partially opened brachial artery during systole producing turbulent blood flow and a sound. The brachial artery remains closed during diastole.

3. As cuff pressure continues to decrease, the brachial artery opens even more during systole. At first, the artery is closed during diastole, but as cuff pressure continues to decrease, the brachial artery partially opens during diastole. Turbulent blood flow during systole produces Korotkoff's sounds, although the pitch of the sounds change as the artery becomes more open.

4. **Diastolic pressure** is the pressure at which the sound disappears. Eventually cuff pressure decreases below the pressure in the brachial artery and it remains open during systole and diastole. Nonturbulent flow is reestablished and no sounds are heard.

Figure 13.14   Blood Pressure Measurement

---

falls to 0 mm Hg during ventricular relaxation. The blood trapped in the elastic arteries is compressed by the recoil of the elastic arteries, however, and the pressure falls more slowly, reaching the diastolic pressure.

Pressure and Resistance

The values for systolic and diastolic pressure vary among healthy people, making the range of normal values quite broad. In addition, the values for blood pressure in a normal person are affected by factors such as physical activity and emotions. A standard blood pressure for a resting young adult male is 120 mm Hg for the systolic pressure and 80 mm Hg for the diastolic pressure, which is reported as 120/80.

Did You Know?

Hypertension, or high blood pressure, affects about 20% of all people at some time in their lives. Generally, a person is considered hypertensive if the systolic blood pressure is greater than 140 mm Hg and the diastolic blood pressure is greater than 90 mm Hg (table 13.4).

Chronic hypertension has an adverse effect on the heart and the blood vessels. A systolic pressure of 130 to 139 mm Hg or a diastolic pressure of 85 to 89 is considered to be high normal. Individuals with high normal pressure should monitor their blood pressure for changes and consider life-style changes that can reduce blood pressure.

Hypertension requires the heart to perform a greater-than-normal amount of work because of the increased afterload on the heart (see chapter 12). The extra work leads to hypertrophy of cardiac muscle, especially in the left ventricle, and can lead to heart failure. Hypertension also increases the rate of arteriosclerosis development. Arteriosclerosis, in turn, increases the chance that blood clots will form and that blood vessels will rupture. Common conditions associated with hypertension are cerebral hemorrhage, coronary infarction, hemorrhage of renal blood vessels, and poor vision resulting from burst blood vessels in the retina.

Treatments that dilate blood vessels, increase the rate of urine production, or decrease cardiac output are normally used for hypertension. Low-salt diets also are normally recommended to reduce the amount of sodium chloride and water absorbed from the intestine into the bloodstream.

Table 13.4 Blood Pressure Classifications

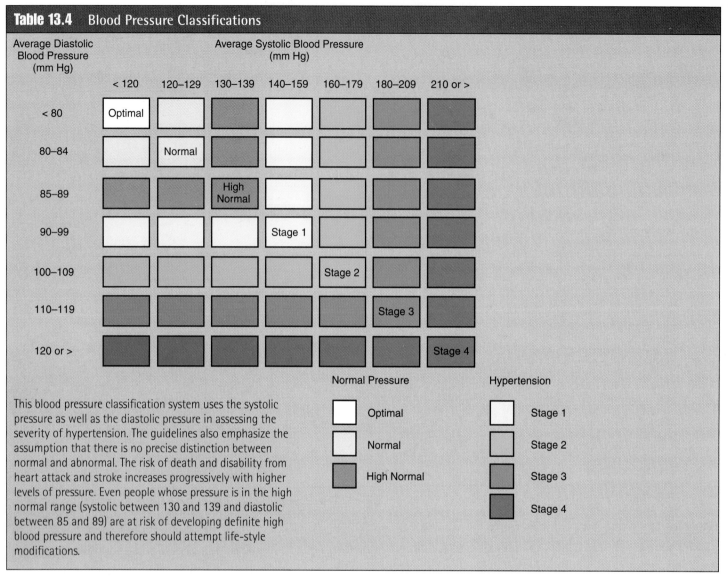

Average Diastolic Blood Pressure (mm Hg)	Average Systolic Blood Pressure (mm Hg)						
	< 120	120–129	130–139	140–159	160–179	180–209	210 or >
< 80	Optimal						
80–84		Normal					
85–89			High Normal				
90–99				Stage 1			
100–109					Stage 2		
110–119						Stage 3	
120 or >							Stage 4

Normal Pressure

☐ Optimal
☐ Normal
☐ High Normal

Hypertension

☐ Stage 1
☐ Stage 2
☐ Stage 3
☐ Stage 4

This blood pressure classification system uses the systolic pressure as well as the diastolic pressure in assessing the severity of hypertension. The guidelines also emphasize the assumption that there is no precise distinction between normal and abnormal. The risk of death and disability from heart attack and stroke increases progressively with higher levels of pressure. Even people whose pressure is in the high normal range (systolic between 130 and 139 and diastolic between 85 and 89) are at risk of developing definite high blood pressure and therefore should attempt life-style modifications.

Source: National High Blood Pressure Education Program, National Institutes of Health, Bethesda, MD.

Blood pressure falls progressively as blood flows from arteries through the capillaries and veins to about 0 mm Hg or even slightly lower by the time blood is returned to the right atrium. In addition, the pressure is damped, in that the difference between the systolic and diastolic pressures is decreased in the small-diameter vessels. By the time blood reaches the capillaries, there is no variation in blood pressure, and only a steady pressure of about 30 mm Hg remains (figure 13.15).

The greater the resistance in a blood vessel, the more rapidly the pressure decreases as blood flows through it. The most rapid decline in blood pressure occurs in the arterioles and capillaries, because their small diameters increase the resistance to blood flow. Blood pressure declines slowly as blood flows from large to medium-sized arteries because their diameters are larger and the resistance to blood flow is not great.

Resistance to blood flow in veins is low because of their larger diameters. Also, the valves that prevent backflow of blood in the veins, as well as skeletal muscle movements that periodically compress veins, force blood to flow toward the heart. Consequently, blood flows through veins, even though the pressure in them is low.

The muscular arteries, arterioles, and precapillary sphincters are capable of constricting (vasoconstriction) and dilating (vasodilation). If constriction occurs, resistance to blood flow increases, and the volume of blood flow through the vessels declines. Because they are able to constrict and dilate, muscular arteries help control the amount of blood flowing to each region of the body. In contrast, arterioles and precapillary sphincters regulate blood flow through local tissues.

Pulse Pressure

The difference between the systolic and diastolic pressure is called the **pulse pressure**. If a person has a systolic pressure of 120 mm Hg and a diastolic pressure of 80 mm Hg, the pulse

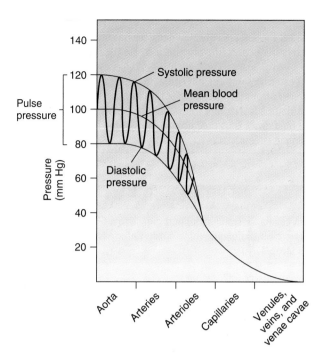

Figure 13.15   Changes of Blood Pressure in Arteries, Capillaries, and Veins

Blood pressure fluctuations between systole and diastole are damped in small arteries and arterioles. There are no large fluctuations in blood pressure in capillaries and veins. The blood pressure continually declines until it reaches zero in the venae cavae.

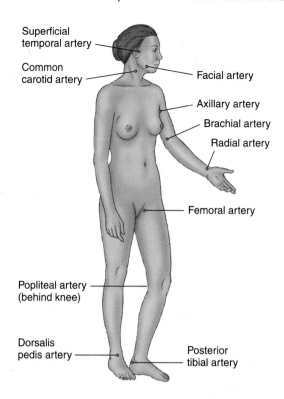

Figure 13.16   Major Points Where the Pulse Can Be Monitored

Each pulse point is named after the artery in which the pulse can be detected.

pressure is 40 mm Hg. When the stroke volume increases, the systolic pressure increases more than the diastolic pressure, causing the pulse pressure to increase. During periods of exercise, the stroke volume and pulse pressure are increased substantially.

In those who suffer from arteriosclerosis, the arteries are less elastic than normal. In these people, arterial pressure increases rapidly and falls rapidly, resulting in a large pulse pressure. The same amount of blood ejected into a less elastic artery results in a higher systolic pressure than that in a more elastic artery. In people who suffer from arteriosclerosis, the pulse pressure is greater than normal, even though the same amount of blood is ejected into the aorta as in a normal person. Arteriosclerosis increases the amount of work performed by the heart because the left ventricle must produce a greater pressure to eject the same amount of blood into a less elastic artery. In severe cases, the increased workload on the heart leads to heart failure.

Ejection of blood from the left ventricle into the aorta produces a pressure wave, or **pulse**, which travels rapidly along the arteries. A pulse can be felt at locations where large arteries are close to the surface of the body. It is helpful to know the major locations where the pulse can be detected because monitoring the pulse is important clinically. The heart rate, heart rhythm, and other characteristics can be determined by feeling the pulse (figure 13.16). For example, a weak pulse usually indicates a decreased stroke volume or increased constriction of the arteries.

2   P R E D I C T

A weak pulse occurs in response to premature beats of the heart and during cardiovascular shock that is due to hemorrhage. Stronger than normal pulses occur in a healthy person during exercise. Explain the causes for the changes in the pulse under these conditions.

✔ *Answer on page 372*

Capillary Exchange

There are about 10 billion capillaries in the body. Nutrients diffuse across the capillary walls into the tissue spaces, and waste products diffuse in the opposite direction. In addition, a small amount of fluid is forced out of the capillaries into the tissue spaces at their arteriolar ends. Most of that fluid, but not all, reenters the capillaries at their venous ends.

Two major forces are responsible for the movement of fluid through the capillary wall (figure 13.17). Blood pressure forces fluid out of the capillary, and osmosis moves fluid into it. Fluid moves by osmosis from the tissue space into the capillary because blood has a greater osmotic pressure than does the interstitial fluid. The greater the concentration of molecules dissolved in a fluid, the greater the osmotic pressure of the fluid (see chapter 3). The greater osmotic pressure of blood is caused by the large concentration of blood proteins (see chapter 11) that are unable to cross the capillary wall. The concentration of proteins in the tissue space is much lower than that in the blood. The capillary wall acts as a selectively permeable membrane, which prevents proteins from moving from the capillary into the interstitial space but allows fluid to move across the wall of the capillary.

At the arteriole end of the capillary, the movement of fluid out of the capillary resulting from blood pressure is greater than the movement of fluid into the capillary as a result of osmosis. Consequently, there is a net movement of fluid out of the capillary into the tissue space (see figure 13.17).

At the venous end of the capillary, blood pressure is lower than at the arteriolar end because of the resistance to blood flow through the capillary (see figure 13.15). Consequently, the movement of fluid out of the capillary resulting from blood pressure is less than the movement of fluid into the capillary resulting from osmosis, and there is a net movement of fluid from the tissue space into the capillary (see figure 13.17).

Approximately nine-tenths of the fluid that leaves the capillary at the arteriolar end reenters the capillary at its venous end. The remaining one-tenth of the fluid enters the lymphatic capillaries and is eventually returned to the general circulation (see chapter 14).

Did You Know?

Edema, or swelling, results from a disruption in the normal inwardly and outwardly directed pressures across the capillary walls. For example, inflammation results in an increase in the permeability of capillaries. Proteins, mainly albumen, leak out of the capillaries into the interstitial spaces. The proteins increase the osmotic pressure in the interstitial spaces. Consequently, fluid passes from the arteriolar end of capillaries into the interstitial spaces at a greater rate, and fluid passes from the interstitial spaces into the venous ends of capillaries at a slower rate. The lymphatic capillaries cannot carry all of the fluid away. Thus fluid accumulates in the interstitial spaces, resulting in edema.

3   P R E D I C T

Explain edema, or swelling, (a) in response to a decrease in plasma protein concentration and (b) as a result of increased blood pressure within a capillary.

✔ *Answer on page 372*

Local Control of Blood Vessels

Local control of blood flow is achieved by periodic contraction and relaxation of the precapillary sphincters. Blood flow through the capillaries is cyclical because of this contraction and relaxation. The precapillary sphincters are controlled by the metabolic needs of the tissues. Blood flow increases when oxygen levels decrease or, to a lesser degree, when glucose, amino acids, fatty acids, and other nutrients decrease. Blood flow also increases when by-products of metabolism build up in tissue spaces. An increase in carbon dioxide or a decrease in

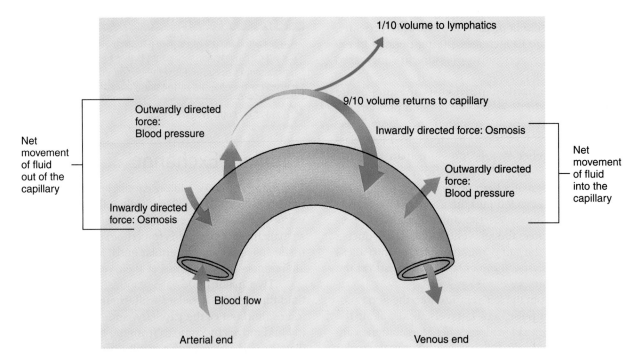

Figure 13.17   Capillary Exchange

At the arteriolar end of the capillary, the force causing fluid to leave the capillary is greater than force attracting fluid into it. Consequently, fluid leaves the capillary at its arteriolar end. At the venous end of the capillary, the blood pressure is decreased, making the force that attracts fluid into the capillary greater than the force that causes fluid to leave the capillary. Approximately nine-tenths of the fluid is returned to the capillary at its venous end. The remaining one-tenth of the fluid volume enters the lymphatic capillaries.

pH causes the precapillary sphincters to relax. For example, during exercise, the metabolic needs of skeletal muscle increase dramatically, and the by-products of metabolism are produced at a more rapid rate. The precapillary sphincters therefore dilate, and blood flow through capillaries in exercising muscle increases dramatically (figure 13.18 and table 13.5).

4   P R E D I C T

When blood flow to a tissue has been blocked for a short time, blood flow through that tissue increases to as much as 5 times its normal value after the removal of the blockage. On the basis of what you know about the local control of blood flow, explain why this happens.

✔ *Answer on page 372*

In addition to the control of blood flow through existing capillaries, if the metabolic activity of a tissue increases often, additional capillaries gradually grow into the area. The additional capillaries allow local blood flow to be increased to a level that matches the metabolic demand of the tissue. For example, the density of capillaries in the well-trained skeletal muscles of athletes is greater than that in poorly trained skeletal muscles (see table 13.5).

Nervous Control of Blood Vessels

Nervous control of blood vessels is carried out primarily through the sympathetic division of the autonomic nervous system. Sympathetic vasoconstrictor fibers innervate most blood vessels of the body, except the capillaries and precapillary sphincters, which have no nerve supply (figure 13.19).

An area of the lower pons and upper medulla oblongata, called the **vasomotor center**, continually transmits a low frequency of action potentials to the sympathetic vasoconstrictor fibers. As a consequence, the peripheral blood vessels are continually in a partially constricted state, a condition called **vasomotor** (vā-sō-mō′ter) **tone**. An increase in vasomotor tone causes blood vessels to constrict further and blood pressure to increase. A decrease in vasomotor tone causes blood vessels to dilate and blood pressure to decrease. Nervous control of blood vessel diameter is an important way blood pressure is regulated.

Nervous control of blood vessels also causes blood to be shunted from one large area of the body to another. For example, nervous control of blood vessels during exercise increases vasomotor tone in the viscera and skin and reduces vasomotor

(a)   Precapillary sphincters relax because of an increase in vasodilator substances such as CO$_2$ and H$^+$ ions (decreased pH).

The need for O$_2$, glucose, amino acids, fatty acids, and other nutrients cause precapillary sphincters to relax.

(b)   Removal of vasodilator substances and a reduced need for O$_2$ and other nutrients cause precapillary sphincters to contract.

Figure 13.18   Control of Local Blood Flow Through Capillary Beds
(*a*) Dilation of precapillary sphincters. (*b*) Constriction of precapillary sphincters.

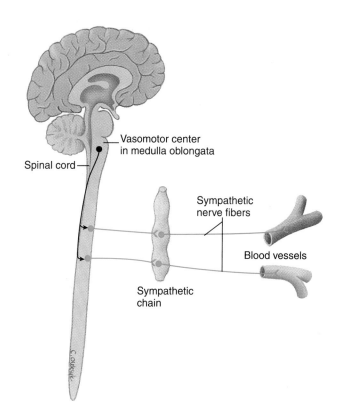

Figure 13.19   Nervous Regulation of Blood Vessels
Most arteries and veins are innervated by sympathetic nerve fibers. The vasomotor center within the medulla oblongata regulates the frequency of action potentials in nerve fibers that innervate blood vessels. Increased action potential frequencies cause vasoconstriction and decreased action potential frequencies cause vasodilation in most blood vessels.

Table 13.5   Homeostasis: Local Control of Blood Flow*

Stimulus	Response
Regulation by Metabolic Need of Tissues	
Increased carbon dioxide and decreased pH or decreased nutrients, such as oxygen, glucose, amino acids and fatty acids, as a result of increased metabolism	Relaxation of precapillary sphincters and subsequent increase in blood flow through capillaries
Decreased carbon dioxide and increased pH or increased nutrients, such as oxygen, glucose, amino acids, and fatty acids	Contraction of precapillary sphincters and subsequent decrease in blood flow through capillaries
Regulation by Nervous Mechanisms	
Increased physical activity or increased sympathetic activity	Constriction of blood vessels in skin and viscera
Increased body temperature detected by neurons of the hypothalamus	Dilation of blood vessels in skin (see chapter 5)
Decreased body temperature detected by neurons of the hypothalamus	Constriction of blood vessels in skin (see chapter 5)
Decrease in skin temperature below a critical value	Dilation of blood vessels in skin (protects skin from extreme cold)
Anger or embarrassment	Dilation of blood vessels in skin of face and upper thorax
Regulation by Hormonal Mechanisms (reinforces increased activity of the sympathetic division)	
Increased physical activity and increased sympathetic activity, causing release of epinephrine and small amounts of norepinephrine from the adrenal medulla	Constriction of blood vessels in skin and viscera; dilation of blood vessels in skeletal and cardiac muscle
Long-Term Local Blood Flow	
Increased metabolic activity of tissues over a long period such as in athletes who train regularly	Increased number of capillaries
Decreased metabolic activity of tissues over a long period such as during periods of reduced physical activity	Decreased number of capillaries

*The mechanisms operate when the systemic blood pressure is maintained within a normal range of values.

tone in exercising skeletal muscles. As a result, blood flow to the viscera and skin decreases, and blood flow to skeletal muscle increases. Nervous control of blood vessels during exercise and dilation of precapillary sphincters as muscle activity increases function together to increase blood flow through exercising skeletal muscle by severalfold (see table 13.5).

5   PREDICT

Raynaud's syndrome is a condition in which blood vessels, primarily in the digits, undergo exaggerated vasoconstriction in response to exposure to cold or emotions. Although treatments are available for Raynaud's syndrome patients, predict the consequences for the digits of a person who suffers from severe Raynaud's syndrome. Explain why the consequences occur.

✔ *Answer on page 372*

Regulation of Arterial Pressure

An adequate blood pressure is required to maintain blood flow through the blood vessels of the body, and several regulatory mechanisms ensure that an adequate blood pressure is maintained. The **mean arterial blood pressure (MAP)** is slightly less than the average of the systolic and diastolic pressures in the aorta because diastole lasts longer than systole. The mean arterial pressure is about 70 mm Hg at birth, is maintained at about 95 mm Hg from adolescence to middle age, and may reach 110 mm Hg in a healthy older person.

The MAP in the body is equal to the **cardiac output (CO)** times the **peripheral resistance (PR)**, which is the resistance to blood flow in all the blood vessels.

$$MAP = CO \times PR$$

Because the cardiac output is equal to the **heart rate (HR)** times the **stroke volume (SV)**, the mean arterial pressure is equal to the heart rate times the stroke volume times the peripheral resistance.

$$MAP = HR \times SV \times PR$$

Thus, the MAP increases in response to increases in HR, SV, or PR and MAP decreases in response to decreases in HR, SV, or PR.

The MAP is controlled on a minute-to-minute basis by changes in the heart rate, stroke volume, and peripheral resistance. For example, when blood pressure suddenly drops because of hemorrhage or some other cause, control systems attempt to reestablish blood pressure by increasing the HR, SV, and PR so that blood pressure is maintained at a value consistent with life. Mechanisms are also activated to increase the blood volume to its normal value.

Baroreceptor Reflexes

Baroreceptor reflexes activate responses that keep the blood pressure within its normal range of values.

Baroreceptors respond to stretch in arteries caused by increased pressure. They are scattered along the walls of most of the large arteries of the neck and thorax, and there are many in the carotid sinus at the base of the internal carotid artery and in the walls of the aortic arch (figure 13.20). Action potentials are transmitted from the baroreceptors to the medulla oblongata along afferent nerve fibers.

A sudden increase in blood pressure stretches the artery walls and increases action potential frequency in the baroreceptors. The increased action potential frequency delivered to the vasomotor and cardioregulatory centers in the medulla oblongata causes responses that lower the blood pressure. One major response is a decrease in vasomotor tone, resulting in vasodilation of blood vessels and a decrease in peripheral resistance. Other responses, controlled by the cardioregulatory center, are an increase in the parasympathetic stimulation of the heart, which decreases the heart rate, and a decrease in sympathetic stimulation of the heart, which reduces the stroke volume. The decreased heart rate, stroke volume, and peripheral resistance lower the blood pressure toward its normal value (figure 13.21).

A sudden decrease in blood pressure results in a decreased action potential frequency in the baroreceptors. The decreased action potential frequency delivered to the vasomotor and cardioregulatory centers in the medulla oblongata produces responses that raise blood pressure. There is an increase in sympathetic stimulation of the heart, which increases the heart rate and stroke volume, and an increase in vasomotor tone, which increases peripheral resistance. The increased heart rate, stroke volume, and peripheral resistance raise the blood pressure toward its normal value (see figure 13.20 and 13.21).

These **baroreceptor reflexes** regulate blood pressure on a moment-to-moment basis. When a person rises rapidly from a sitting or lying position to a standing position, blood pressure in the neck and thoracic regions drops dramatically as a result of the pull of gravity on the blood. This reduction can be so great that blood flow to the brain is reduced enough to cause dizziness or even loss of consciousness. The falling blood pressure activates the baroreceptor reflexes, which reestablish normal blood pressure within a few seconds. In a healthy person, a temporary sensation of dizziness is all that may be experienced.

6   P R E D I C T

Explain how the baroreceptor reflex responds if a person does a headstand.

✔ *Answer on page 372*

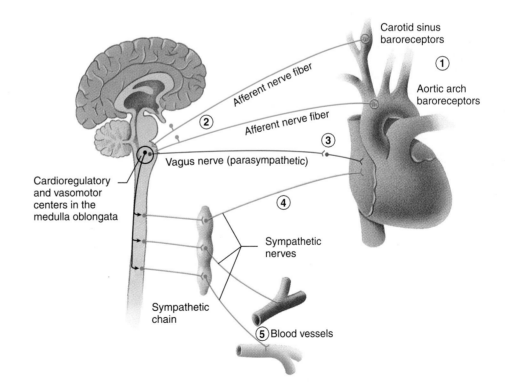

1. Baroreceptors in the carotid sinus and aortic arch monitor blood pressure.

2. Action potentials are conducted to the cardioregulatory and vasomotor centers in the medulla oblongata.

3. Increased parasympathetic stimulation of the heart decreases the heart rate.

4. Increased sympathetic stimulation of the heart increases the heart rate and stroke volume.

5. Increased sympathetic stimulation of blood vessels increases vasoconstriction.

Carotid sinus baroreceptors

Aortic arch baroreceptors

Afferent nerve fiber

Afferent nerve fiber

Vagus nerve (parasympathetic)

Cardioregulatory and vasomotor centers in the medulla oblongata

Sympathetic nerves

Sympathetic chain

Blood vessels

Figure 13.20   The Baroreceptor Reflex Mechanisms

Baroreceptor reflex control of blood pressure.

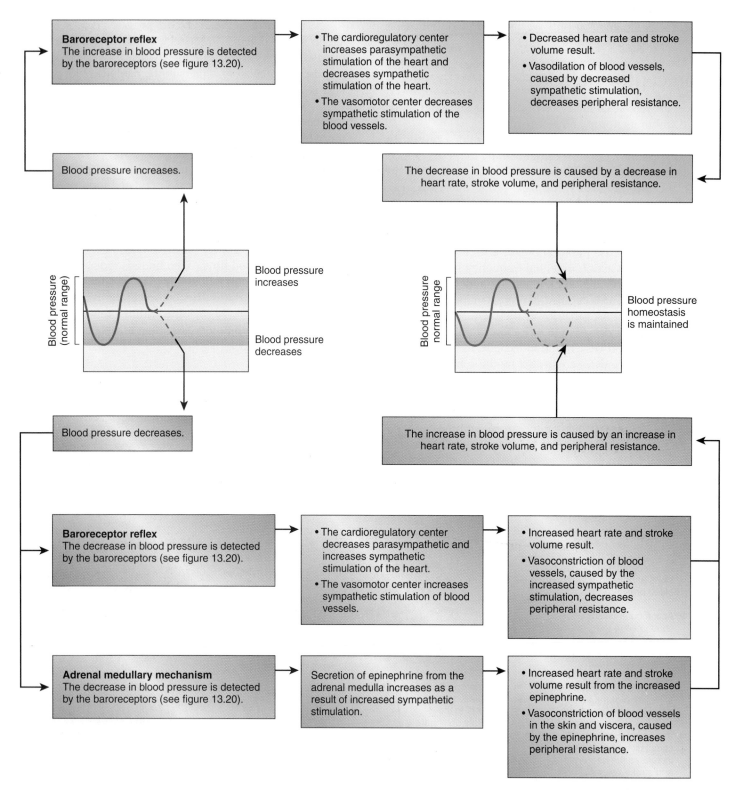

Figure 13.21 Homeostasis: Baroreceptor Reflex Mechanism
The regulation of blood pressure by the baroreceptor mechanism.

Chemoreceptor Reflexes

Carotid bodies are small structures that lie near the carotid sinuses, and **aortic bodies** are structures near the aortic arch. These structures contain sensory receptors that respond to changes in blood oxygen concentration, carbon dioxide concentration, and

pH. Because they are sensitive to chemical changes in the blood, they are called **chemoreceptors**. They send action potentials along afferent nerve fibers to the medulla oblongata (figure 13.22). There are also chemoreceptors in the medulla oblongata.

When oxygen levels decrease, carbon dioxide levels increase, or pH decreases, the chemoreceptors respond with an

1. Chemoreceptors in the carotid and aortic bodies monitor blood O_2, CO_2, and pH.

2. Chemoreceptors in the medulla oblongata monitor blood CO_2 and pH.

3. Decreased blood O_2, increased CO_2, and decreased pH decrease parasympathetic stimulation of the heart, which increases the heart rate.

4. Decreased blood O_2, increased CO_2, and decreased pH increase sympathetic stimulation of the heart, which increases the heart rate and stroke volume.

5. Decreased blood O_2, increased CO_2, and decreased pH increase sympathetic stimulation of blood vessels, which increases vasoconstriction.

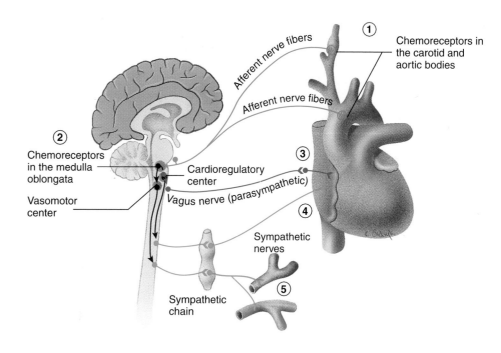

Figure 13.22 Chemoreceptor Reflex Control of Blood Pressure

increased frequency of action potentials and activate the **chemoreceptor reflex**. In response, the vasomotor and cardiovascular centers decrease parasympathetic stimulation of the heart, which increases the heart rate; increases sympathetic stimulation of the heart, which increases the heart rate and stroke volume; and increases the vasomotor tone, resulting in an increased blood pressure. The increased blood pressure causes a greater rate of blood flow to the lungs, which helps increase blood oxygen levels and reduce blood carbon dioxide levels. The chemoreceptor reflex functions under emergency conditions and usually does not play an important role in the regulation of the cardiovascular system. It responds strongly only when the oxygen levels in the blood fall to very low levels or when carbon dioxide levels become substantially elevated.

Hormonal Mechanisms

In addition to the rapidly acting baroreceptor and chemoreceptor reflexes, there are important hormonal mechanisms that help control blood pressure.

Adrenal Medullary Mechanism

Stimuli that result in increased sympathetic stimulation of the heart and blood vessels also cause increased stimulation of the adrenal medulla. The adrenal medulla responds by releasing epinephrine into the blood (figure 13.23). Epinephrine increases heart rate and stroke volume and causes vasoconstriction, especially of blood vessels in the skin and viscera. Epinephrine also causes vasodilation of blood vessels in skeletal muscle and cardiac muscle. Epinephrine therefore increases the supply of blood flowing to skeletal and cardiac muscle, and this prepares one for physical activity.

Renin-Angiotensin-Aldosterone Mechanism

In response to reduced blood pressure, the kidneys release an enzyme called **renin** (rē′nin) into the circulatory system (figure 13.24). Renin acts on the blood protein **angiotensinogen** (an′jē-ō-ten-sin′ō-jen) to produce **angiotensin I** (an-jē-ō-ten′ sin). Another enzyme called **angiotensin-converting enzyme**, found in large amounts in organs such as the lungs, acts on angiotensin I to convert it to its most active form called **angiotensin II**. Angiotensin II is a potent vasoconstrictor substance. Thus, in response to a reduced blood pressure, the release of renin by the kidney acts to increase the blood pressure toward its normal value.

Angiotensin II also acts on the adrenal cortex to increase the secretion of **aldosterone** (al-dos′ter-ōn). Aldosterone acts on the kidneys causing them to conserve sodium ions and water. As a result, the volume of water lost from the blood into the urine is reduced. The decrease in urine volume results in less fluid loss from the body, which functions to maintain blood volume (see figure 13.24). An adequate blood volume is essential for the maintenance of normal venous return to the heart and therefore for the maintenance of blood pressure (see chapter 12).

Vasopressin Mechanism

When blood pressure drops or the concentration of solutes in the plasma increases, neurons in the hypothalamus respond by causing the release of **antidiuretic** (an′tē-dī-ū-ret′ik)

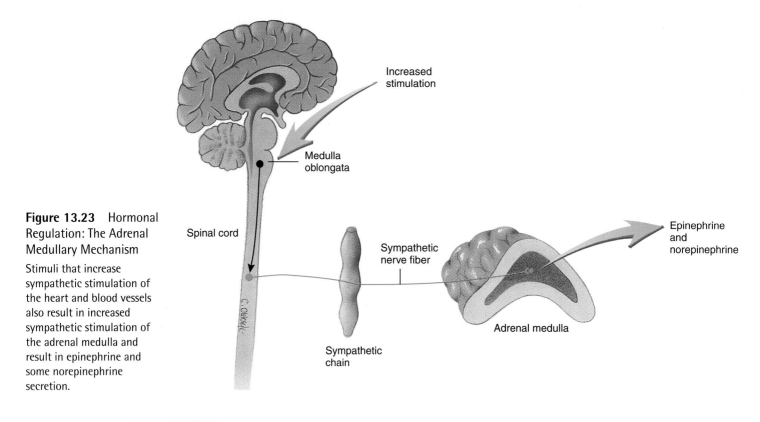

Figure 13.23 Hormonal Regulation: The Adrenal Medullary Mechanism

Stimuli that increase sympathetic stimulation of the heart and blood vessels also result in increased sympathetic stimulation of the adrenal medulla and result in epinephrine and some norepinephrine secretion.

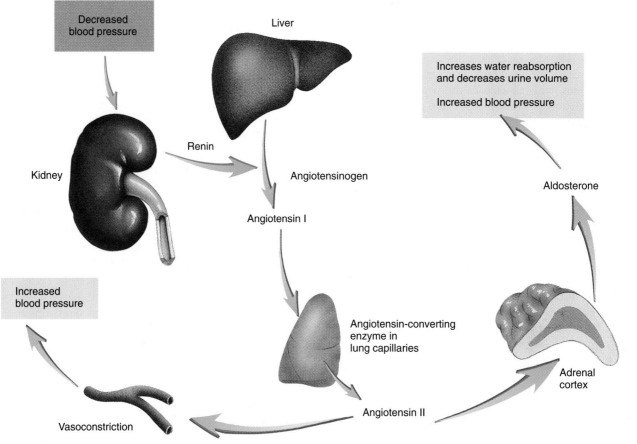

Figure 13.24 Hormonal Regulation: The Renin-Angiotensin-Aldosterone Mechanism

Decreased blood pressure is detected by the kidney, resulting in increased renin secretion. The result is vasoconstriction, increased water reabsorption, and decreased urine volume. These changes function to maintain blood pressure.

hormone (ADH), also called **vasopressin** (vă-sō-pres'in), from the posterior pituitary gland (figure 13.25). ADH acts on the kidneys and causes a greater reabsorption of water by the kidneys, thereby decreasing urine volume. This response helps maintain blood volume and blood pressure. The release of large amounts of ADH causes vasoconstriction of blood vessels, which causes blood pressure to increase.

Atrial Natriuretic Mechanism

A peptide hormone called **atrial natriuretic** (ā'trē-ăl nă'trē-ū-ret'ik) **hormone** is released primarily from specialized cells of the right atrium in response to elevated blood pressure. Atrial natriuretic hormone acts on the kidneys and causes them to promote the loss of sodium ions in the urine and to increase urine volume. Loss of water in the urine causes blood volume to decrease, thus decreasing the blood pressure (figure 13.26).

Short-Term and Long-Term Regulation

Baroreceptor mechanisms are most important in controlling blood pressure on a short-term basis (see figures 13.20 and 13.21). They are sensitive to sudden changes in blood pressure, and they respond quickly. The renin-angiotensin-aldosterone system and atrial natriuretic hormone, are more important in the maintenance of blood pressure on a long-term basis. They are influenced by small changes in blood pressure and respond by gradually bringing the blood pressure back to its normal range (see figure 13.26).

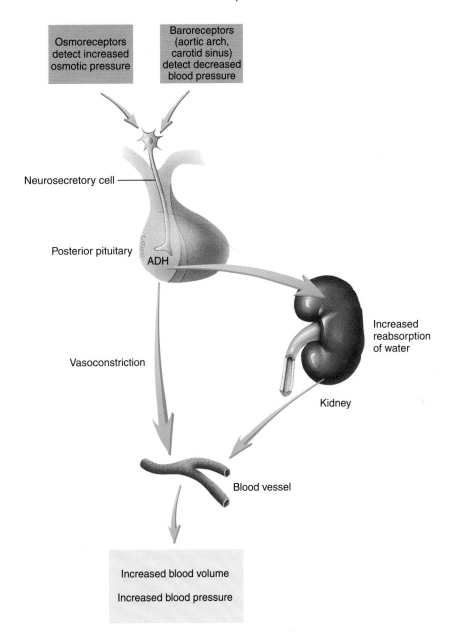

Figure 13.25 Hormonal Regulation: The Vasopressin (ADH) Mechanism

Increases in osmolality of blood or decreases in blood pressure result in ADH secretion. ADH increases water reabsorption by the kidney, and large amounts of ADH result in vasoconstriction. These changes function to maintain blood pressure.

Atrial natriuretic mechanism
Increased atrial blood pressure is detected by cardiac muscle cells.

→

Secretion of atrial natriuretic hormone by cardiac muscle cells increases.

→

Increased atrial natriuretic hormone decreases sodium reabsorption in the kidneys; more sodium and water are lost in the urine.

Renin–angiotensin–aldosterone mechanism
Increased blood pressure is detected by the kidneys.

→

Decreased secretion of renin from the juxtaglomerular apparati results in decreased conversion of angiotensinogen to angiotensin I. Less angiotensin I results in less formation of angiotensin II.

→

- Decreased angiotensin II results in vasodilation.
- Decreased angiotensin II reduces aldosterone secretion from the adrenal cortex.
- Decreased aldosterone decreases sodium reabsorption in the kidneys; more sodium and water are lost in the urine.

- A decrease in blood pressure results from a decrease in peripheral resistance caused by vasodilation.
- A decrease in blood pressure results from decreased blood volume as water is lost in the urine.

Blood pressure increases.

Blood pressure (normal range)

Blood pressure increases

Blood pressure decreases

Blood pressure (normal range)

Blood pressure homeostasis is maintained

Blood pressure decreases.

- An increase in blood pressure results from an increase in peripheral resistance caused by vasoconstriction.
- An increase in blood pressure results from increased blood volume as less water is lost in the urine.

Renin–angiotensin–aldosterone mechanism
Decreased blood pressure is detected by the kidneys.

→

Increased secretion of renin from the juxtaglomerular apparati results in increased conversion of angiotensinogen to angiotensin I. More angiotensin I results in more formation of angiotensin II.

→

- Increased angiotensin II results in vasoconstriction.
- Increased angiotensin II increases aldosterone secretion from the adrenal cortex.
- Increased aldosterone increases sodium reabsorption in the kidneys; less sodium and water are lost in the urine.

Vasopressin (ADH) mechanism
Decreased blood pressure is detected by baroreceptors, resulting in decreased stimulation of the hypothalamus.

→

Increased ADH secretion from the posterior pituitary.

→

- Increased ADH results in vasoconstriction.
- Increased ADH decreases urine volume and more water returns to the blood.

Figure 13.26   Homeostasis: Long-Term Regulation of Blood Pressure

Clinical Focus   Circulatory Shock

Circulatory shock is defined as inadequate blood flow throughout the body. As a consequence, tissues suffer damage resulting from a lack of oxygen. Severe shock may damage vital body tissues and lead to death.

There are several causes of circulatory shock, but hemorrhagic shock resulting from excessive blood loss can be used to illustrate the general characteristics of shock. If hemorrhagic shock is not severe, blood pressure decreases only a moderate amount. Under these conditions, the mechanisms that normally regulate blood pressure function to reestablish normal pressure and blood flow. The baroreceptor reflexes produce strong sympathetic responses, resulting in intense vasoconstriction and increased heart rate.

As a result of the reduced blood flow through the kidneys, increased amounts of renin are released. The elevated renin level results in a greater rate of angiotensin formation, causing vasoconstriction and increased aldosterone release from the adrenal cortex. Aldosterone, in turn, promotes water and salt retention by the kidneys. In response to reduced blood pressure, antidiuretic hormone (ADH) is released from the posterior pituitary gland, and ADH also enhances the retention of water by the kidneys. An intense sensation of thirst leads to increased water intake, which helps restore the normal blood volume.

In mild cases of shock, the baroreceptor reflexes can be adequate to compensate for blood loss until the blood volume is restored, but in more severe cases, all mechanisms are required to sustain life.

In even more severe cases of shock, the regulatory mechanisms are not adequate to compensate for the effects of shock. As a consequence, a positive-feedback cycle begins to develop in which the blood pressure regulatory mechanisms lose their ability to control the blood pressure, and shock worsens. As shock becomes worse, the effectiveness of the regulatory mechanisms deteriorates even further. The positive-feedback cycle proceeds until death occurs or until treatment, such as a transfusion, terminates the cycle. Several types of shock are classified by the cause of the condition:

1. **Hypovolemic shock** is the result of reduced blood volume. **Hemorrhagic shock** is caused by internal or external bleeding. **Plasma loss shock** results from a loss of plasma. An example is the loss of plasma from severely burned areas. **Interstitial fluid loss shock** is reduced blood volume resulting from a loss of interstitial fluid. Examples include diarrhea, vomiting, or dehydration.

2. **Neurogenic shock** is caused by vasodilation in response to emotional upset or anesthesia.

3. **Anaphylactic shock** is caused by an allergic response, resulting in the release of inflammatory substances that cause vasodilation and an increase in capillary permeability. Large amounts of fluid then move from capillaries into the interstitial spaces.

4. **Septic shock,** or **"blood poisoning,"** is caused by infections that result in the release of toxic substances into the circulatory system, depressing the activity of the heart and leading to vasodilation and increased capillary permeability.

5. **Cardiogenic shock** results from a decrease in cardiac output caused by events that decrease the ability of the heart to function. Heart attack (myocardial infarction) is a common cause of cardiogenic shock. Fibrillation of the heart, which can be initiated by stimuli such as cardiac arrhythmias or exposure to electrical shocks, also results in cardiogenic shock.

Summary

The peripheral circulatory system can be divided into the systemic and the pulmonary vessels. The peripheral circulatory system and the heart are regulated to maintain sufficient blood flow to tissues.

Functions of the Peripheral Circulation

The peripheral circulation functions to carry blood, exchange nutrients and gases, transport hormones, regulate blood pressure, and direct blood flow.

General Features of Blood Vessel Structure

- Blood is pumped from the heart through elastic arteries, muscular arteries, and arterioles to the capillaries.
- Blood returns to the heart from the capillaries through venules, small veins, and large veins.
- Except for capillaries and venules, blood vessels have three layers:
  - The tunica intima consists of endothelium, basement membrane, and connective tissue.
  - The tunica media, the middle layer, contains circular smooth muscle and elastic fibers.
  - The outer tunica adventitia is connective tissue.

Arteries

- Large elastic arteries have many elastic fibers but little smooth muscle in their walls and carry blood from the heart to smaller arteries with little decrease in pressure.
- Muscular arteries have much smooth muscle and some elastic fibers and undergo vasodilation and vasoconstriction to control blood flow to different regions of the body.
- Arterioles are the smallest arteries and have smooth muscle cells and a few elastic fibers and undergo vasodilation and vasoconstriction to control blood flow to local areas.

Capillaries

- Capillaries consist of only endothelium and are surrounded by a basement membrane and loose connective tissue.
- Nutrient and waste product exchange is the principal function of capillaries.
- Blood is supplied to capillaries by arterioles. Precapillary sphincters regulate blood flow through capillary networks.

Veins

- Venules are endothelium surrounded by a basement membrane.

- Small veins are venules covered with a layer of smooth muscle.
- Medium-sized and large veins contain less smooth muscle and elastic fibers than arteries of the same size.
- Valves prevent the backflow of blood in the veins.

Aging of the Arteries

- Arteriosclerosis results from a loss of elasticity primarily in the aorta, large arteries, and coronary arteries.
- Atherosclerosis results from the deposition of plaques rich in cholesterol in the wall of blood vessels, reducing the diameter of the vessels.

Blood Vessels of the Pulmonary Circulation

- The pulmonary circulation moves blood to and from the lungs. The pulmonary trunk carries oxygen-poor blood from the heart to the lungs, and pulmonary veins carry oxygen-rich blood from the lungs to the left atrium of the heart.

Blood Vessels of the Systemic Circulation: Arteries

Aorta

- The aorta leaves the left ventricle to form the ascending aorta, aortic arch, and descending aorta, which consists of the thoracic and abdominal aorta.

Arteries of the Head and Neck

- The brachiocephalic, left common carotid, and left subclavian arteries branch from the aortic arch to supply the head and the upper limbs.
- The common carotid arteries and the vertebral arteries supply the head. The common carotid arteries divide to form the external carotids (which supply the face and mouth) and the internal carotids (which supply the brain).

Arteries of the Upper Limbs

- The subclavian artery continues as the axillary artery and then as the brachial artery, which branches to form the radial and ulnar arteries.

The Thoracic Aorta and Its Branches

- The thoracic aorta has visceral branches, which supply the thoracic organs, and parietal branches, which supply the thoracic wall.

The Abdominal Aorta and Its Branches

- The abdominal aorta has visceral branches, which supply the abdominal organs, and parietal branches, which supply the abdominal wall.

Arteries of the Pelvis

- Branches of the internal iliac arteries supply the pelvis.

Arteries of the Lower Limbs

- The common iliac arteries give rise to the external iliac arteries, and the external iliac artery continues as the femoral artery and then as the popliteal artery in the leg. The popliteal artery divides to form the anterior and posterior tibial arteries.

Blood Vessels of the Systemic Circulation: Veins

- The superior vena cava drains the head, neck, thorax, and upper limbs. The inferior vena cava drains the abdomen, pelvis, and lower limbs.

Veins of the Head and Neck

- The internal jugular veins drain the brain, anterior head, and anterior neck.
- The external jugular veins drain the posterior head and posterior neck.

Veins of the Upper Limbs

- The deep veins are the brachial, axillary, and subclavian; the superficial veins are the basilic, cephalic, and median cubital.

Veins of the Thorax

- The left and right brachiocephalic veins and the azygos veins return blood to the superior vena cava.

Veins of the Abdomen and Pelvis

- Posterior abdominal wall veins join the azygos veins.
- Veins from the kidneys, adrenal glands, and gonads directly enter the inferior vena cava.
- Veins from the stomach, intestines, spleen, and pancreas connect with the hepatic portal vein, which transports blood to the liver for processing. The hepatic veins from the liver join the inferior vena cava.

Veins of the Lower Limbs

- The deep veins course with the deep arteries and have similar names.
- The superficial veins are the small and great saphenous veins.

The Physiology of Circulation

Blood Pressure

- Blood pressure is a measure of the force exerted by blood against the blood vessel wall. Blood pressure moves blood through vessels.
- Blood pressure can be measured by listening for Korotkoff sounds produced as blood flows through arteries partially constricted by a blood pressure cuff.

Pressure and Resistance

- Blood pressure fluctuates between 120 mm Hg (systolic) and 80 mm Hg (diastolic) in the aorta. If constriction of blood vessels occurs, resistance to blood flow increases, and blood flow decreases.

Pulse Pressure

- Pulse pressure is the difference between systolic and diastolic pressure. Pulse pressure increases when stroke volume increases.
- A pulse can be detected when large arteries are near the surface of the body.

Capillary Exchange

- Most exchange across the wall of the capillary is by diffusion.
- Blood pressure, capillary permeability, and osmosis affect movement of fluid across the wall of the capillaries. There is a net movement of fluid from the blood into the tissues. The fluid gained by the tissues is removed by the lymphatic system.

Local Control of Blood Vessels

- Blood flow through a tissue is usually proportional to the metabolic needs of the tissue and is controlled by the precapillary sphincters.

Nervous Control of Blood Vessels

- The vasomotor center (sympathetic division) controls blood vessel diameter. Other brain areas can excite or inhibit the vasomotor center.
- Vasomotor tone is a state of partial contraction of blood vessels.
- The nervous system is responsible for routing the flow of blood, except in the capillaries and precapillary sphincters, and is responsible for maintaining blood pressure.

Regulation of Arterial Pressure

- Mean arterial pressure (MAP) is proportional to cardiac output times the peripheral resistance.

Baroreceptor Reflexes

- Baroreceptors are sensory receptors that are sensitive to stretch.
  - Baroreceptors are located in the carotid sinuses and the aortic arch.
  - The baroreceptor reflex changes peripheral resistance, heart rate, and stroke volume in response to changes in blood pressure.

Chemoreceptor Reflexes

- Chemoreceptors are sensitive to changes in blood oxygen, carbon dioxide, and pH.
  - Chemoreceptors are located in the carotid bodies and the aortic bodies.
- The chemoreceptor reflex increases peripheral resistance in response to low oxygen levels.

Hormonal Mechanisms

- Epinephrine released from the adrenal medulla as a result of sympathetic stimulation increases heart rate, stroke volume, and vasoconstriction.
- Renin is released by the kidneys in response to low blood pressure. Renin promotes the production of angiotensin, which, when activated, causes vasoconstriction and an increase in aldosterone secretion. Aldosterone reduces urine output. Angiotensin can also cause vasoconstriction.
- ADH released from the posterior pituitary causes vasoconstriction and reduces urine output.
- Atrial natriuretic hormone is released from the heart when atrial blood pressure increases. It stimulates an increase in urine production, causing a decrease in blood volume and blood pressure.

Short-Term and Long-Term Regulation

- The baroreceptor mechanisms are most important in short-term regulation of blood pressure.
- Hormonal mechanisms, such as the renin-angiotensin-aldosterone system and atrial natriuretic hormone, are more important in long-term regulation of blood pressure.

Content Review

1. Name, in order, all the types of blood vessels, starting at the heart, going to the tissues, and returning to the heart.
2. Name the three layers of a blood vessel. What kinds of tissue are in each layer?
3. Relate the structure of the different types of arteries to their functions.
4. Describe the structure of capillaries, and explain their major function.
5. Describe the structure of a capillary network. Name the structure that regulates blood flow through the capillary network.
6. Describe the structure of veins.
7. What is the function of valves in blood vessels and in which blood vessels are valves found?
8. Describe the changes that occur in arteries as they age.
9. List the different parts of the aorta. Name the major arteries that branch from the aorta and deliver blood to the vessels that supply the heart, the head and upper limbs, and the lower limbs.
10. Name the arteries that supply the major areas of the head, upper limbs, thorax, abdomen, and lower limbs. Describe the area each artery supplies.
11. Name the major vessels that return blood to the heart. What area of the body does each drain?
12. List the veins that drain blood from the thorax, abdomen, and pelvis. What specific area of the body does each drain? Describe the hepatic portal system.
13. List the major veins that drain the upper and lower limbs.
14. Define blood pressure, and describe how it is normally measured.
15. Describe the changes in blood pressure starting in the aorta, moving through the vascular system, and returning to the right atrium.
16. Define pulse pressure, and explain what information can be determined from monitoring the pulse.
17. Explain how blood pressure and osmosis affect the movement of fluid between capillaries and tissues. What happens to excess fluid that enters the tissues?
18. Explain what is meant by the local control of blood flow through tissues, and describe what carries out local control.
19. Describe nervous control of blood vessels. Define vasomotor tone.
20. Define mean arterial pressure. How is it related to heart rate, stroke volume, and peripheral resistance?
21. Where are baroreceptors located? Describe the baroreceptor reflex when blood pressure increases and when it decreases.
22. Where are the chemoreceptors for carbon dioxide and pH located? Describe what happens when oxygen levels in the blood decrease.
23. For each of the following hormones—epinephrine, renin, angiotensin, aldosterone, ADH, and atrial natriuretic hormone—state where each is produced, what stimulus causes an increased hormone production, and what effect the hormone has on the circulatory system.

Develop Your Reasoning Skills

1. For each of the following destinations, name all the arteries that a red blood cell encounters if it starts its journey in the left ventricle:
   a. The brain
   b. External part of the skull
   c. The left hand
   d. Anterior portion of the right leg
2. For each of the following starting places, name all the veins that a red blood cell encounters on its way back to the right atrium:
   a. The left side of the brain
   b. External part of the right side of the skull
   c. The left hand
   d. Medial portion of right leg
   e. Kidney
   f. Small intestine
3. High blood pressure can be caused by advanced atherosclerosis of the renal arteries, even though there appears to be enough blood flow to allow a normal volume of urine to be produced. Explain how atherosclerosis of the renal arteries can result in high blood pressure.
4. Hugo Faster ran a race. During the race his stroke volume and heart rate increased. Vasoconstriction occurred in his viscera, and his blood pressure increased, but not dramatically. Explain these changes in his circulatory system.
5. Nitroglycerin is a drug often given to people who suffer from angina pains. This drug causes vasodilation of arteries and veins, which results in a reduced amount of work performed by the heart. Explain why dilation of arteries and veins reduces the amount of work performed by the heart.

Answers to Predict Questions

1. p. 350 Atherosclerosis slowly increases the resistance to blood flow. Blood flow through atherosclerotic carotid arteries to the brain therefore decreases. In advanced stages of arteriosclerosis, the resistance to blood flow increases so much that the blood flow to the brain is reduced significantly. Results include confusion, loss of memory, and a reduced ability to perform other normal brain functions.

2. p. 359 Premature beats of the heart result in contraction of the heart muscle before the heart has time to fill to its normal capacity. The volume of blood ejected by the left ventricle of the heart is therefore reduced (reduced stroke volume) (see chapter 12). The reduced stoke volume is responsible for the weak pulse. In response to cardiovascular shock that is due to hemorrhage, the stroke volume is also reduced because less blood flows into the heart between beats. The reduced stroke volume is responsible for the weak pulses. In a person who is exercising, both the heart rate and the stroke volume increase. The increased stroke volume results in a stronger than normal pulse.

3. p. 360 Decreased plasma protein concentration reduces the osmotic pressure of the blood. Edema results primarily because the osmotic pressure that causes fluid to move from the interstitial space into the capillary at its venous end is reduced. Consequently, less fluid returns to the capillary at its venous end, and fluid accumulates in the interstitial space, resulting in edema. Fluid normally leaves the arterial end of the capillary because the capillary blood pressure is greater than the osmotic pressure.

   Increased blood pressure within the capillary forces more fluid to leave the capillary at its arteriolar end. There is no increased tendency for fluid to reenter the capillary at its venous end. The extra fluid that leaves the capillary can accumulate in the tissue space and result in edema.

4. p. 361 When a blood vessel is blocked, oxygen and nutrients are depleted, and waste products accumulate in tissue supplied by the blocked blood vessel. The reduced supply of oxygen and nutrients and the accumulated waste products all cause relaxation of the precapillary sphincters and greatly increase blood flow through the area when the block is removed.

5. p. 362 Severe vasoconstriction that results from Raynaud's syndrome causes the digits to appear white because of the lack of blood flow through the capillary beds in the digits. The intensity of the vasoconstriction is more severe when the digits are exposed to cold temperatures. If the vasoconstriction is severe enough, there is not enough blood flow to the digits to supply nutrients to the tissues in the digits. A result may be the development of necrotic tissue and gangrene.

6. p. 363 During a headstand, gravity acting on the blood causes the blood pressure to increase in the areas of the aortic arch and carotid sinus baroreceptors. The increased pressure activates the baroreceptor reflexes, resulting in an increased parasympathetic stimulation and a decreased sympathetic stimulation of the heart. The heart responds with a decreased heart rate. Because standing on one's head also causes blood from the periphery to run downhill to the heart, the venous return increases, causing the stroke volume to increase as a result of Starling's law of the heart. Some peripheral vasodilation also might occur. The increased pressure detected by the baroreceptors reduces sympathetic stimulation of blood vessels (reduces vasomotor tone), allowing them to dilate in an attempt to reduce the blood pressure.

Chapter Fourteen

The Lymphatic System and Immunity

adaptive immunity
(i-mū′ni-tē) Immune response in which there is an ability to recognize, remember, and destroy a specific antigen.

antibody
(an′tē-bod-ē) Protein found in the plasma that is responsible for antibody-mediated (humoral) immunity; binds specifically to antigen.

antibody-mediated immunity
(an′tē-bod-ē) Immunity resulting from B cells and the production of antibodies.

antigen
(an′ti-jen) Any substance that induces a state of sensitivity or resistance to microorganisms or toxic substances after a latent period; substance that stimulates adaptive immunity.

cell-mediated immunity
Immunity resulting from the actions of T cells.

complement
(kom′plĕ-ment) Group of serum proteins that stimulates phagocytosis, inflammation, and lysis of cells.

cytokine
(sī′tō-kīn) Protein or peptide secreted by one cell as a regulator of neighboring cells; activates B cells, helper T cells, macrophages, and other immune cells; promotes cell division, phagocytosis, and inflammation.

innate immunity
(i′nāt, i-nāt′) Immune response that is the same upon each exposure to an antigen; there is no ability to remember a previous exposure to a specific antigen.

interferon
(in-ter-fēr′on) A protein that inhibits viral replication; there are several different types of interferons.

lymph node
(limf) Encapsulated mass of lymphatic tissue found along lymphatic vessels; functions to filter lymph and produce lymphocytes.

memory cell
Lymphocytes derived from B or T cells that have been exposed to an antigen; when exposed to the same antigen a second time, memory cells rapidly respond to provide immunity.

vaccine
(vak′sēn, vak-sen′) Preparation of killed microorganisms, altered microorganisms, or derivatives of microorganisms intended to produce immunity. Vaccines are usually administered by injection, but sometimes they are taken orally.

Objectives

After reading this chapter, you should be able to:

1. Describe the functions of the lymphatic system.

2. Explain how lymph is formed and transported.

3. Describe the structure and function of tonsils, lymph nodes, the spleen, and the thymus.

4. Define innate immunity and describe the cells and chemical mediators involved.

5. List the events that occur during an inflammatory response and explain their significance.

6. Define the term antigen.

7. Describe the origin, development, activation, and proliferation of lymphocytes.

8. Define antibody-mediated immunity and cell-mediated immunity and name the cells responsible for each.

9. Diagram the structure of an antibody and describe the effects produced by antibodies.

10. Discuss the primary and secondary responses to an antigen. Explain the basis for long-lasting immunity.

11. Describe the functions of T cells.

12. Explain how innate, antibody-mediated, and cell-mediated immunity can function together to eliminate an antigen.

13. Define and give examples of immunotherapy.

14. Explain the four ways that adaptive immunity can be acquired.

One of the basic tenets of life is that many organisms consume or use other organisms in order to survive. Some microorganisms, such as certain bacteria or viruses, use humans as a source of nutrients and as an environment where they can survive and reproduce. As a result, some microorganisms can damage the body, causing disease or even death. Not surprisingly, the body has ways to resist or destroy harmful microorganisms. This chapter considers how the lymphatic system and the components of other systems, such as white blood cells and phagocytes, continually provide protection against invading microorganisms.

Lymphatic System

The **lymphatic** (lim-fat′ik) **system** includes lymph, lymphocytes, lymphatic vessels, lymph nodes, tonsils, the spleen, and the thymus gland (figure 14.1).

Functions of the Lymphatic System

The lymphatic system is part of the body's defense system against microorganisms and other harmful substances. In addition, it helps to maintain fluid balance in tissues and to absorb fats from the digestive tract.

1. *Fluid balance.* About 30 liters (L) of fluid pass from the blood capillaries into the interstitial spaces each day, whereas only 27 L pass from the interstitial spaces back into the blood capillaries (see chapter 13). If the extra 3 L of interstitial fluid remained in the interstitial spaces, edema would result, causing tissue damage and eventually death. The 3 L of fluid enters the lymphatic capillaries, where the fluid is called **lymph** (limf, meaning clear spring water), and it passes through the lymphatic vessels to return to the blood. In addition to water, lymph contains solutes derived from two sources: (a) substances in plasma, such as ions, nutrients, gases, and some proteins, pass from blood capillaries into the interstitial spaces and become part of the lymph; and (b) substances, such as hormones, enzymes, and waste products, derived from cells within the tissues are also part of the lymph.
2. *Fat absorption.* The lymphatic system absorbs fats and other substances from the digestive tract (see chapter 16). Special lymphatic vessels called **lacteals** (lak′tē-ălz) are located in the lining of the small intestine. Fats enter the lacteals and pass through the lymphatic vessels to the venous circulation. The lymph passing through these lymphatic vessels has a milky appearance because of its fat content, and it is called **chyle** (kīl).
3. *Defense.* Microorganisms and other foreign substances are filtered from lymph by lymph nodes and from blood by the spleen. In addition, lymphocytes and other cells are capable of destroying microorganisms and foreign substances.

Lymphatic Capillaries and Vessels

The lymphatic system, unlike the circulatory system, does not circulate fluid to and from tissues. Instead, the lymphatic system carries fluid in one direction, from tissues to the circulatory system. The removal of fluid begins in **lymphatic capillaries**, which are tiny, closed-ended vessels consisting of simple squamous epithelium. Fluid moves from blood vessels into tissue spaces, and some of the fluid moves from the tissue spaces into lymphatic capillaries to become lymph (figure 14.2a). The lymphatic capillaries are more permeable than blood capillaries because they lack a basement membrane, and fluid moves easily into the lymphatic capillaries. The overlapping squamous cells, however, act as valves that prevent the back-flow of fluid (figure 14.2b).

Lymphatic capillaries are in almost all tissues of the body except the central nervous system, bone marrow, and tissues without blood vessels such as the epidermis and cartilage. A superficial group of lymphatic capillaries drains the dermis and hypodermis, and a deep group drains muscle, viscera, and other deep structures.

The lymphatic capillaries join to form larger **lymphatic vessels**, which resemble small veins (see figure 14.2b). Small lymphatic vessels have a beaded appearance because of one-way valves that are similar to the valves of veins. When a lymphatic vessel is compressed, backward movement of lymph is prevented by the valves. Consequently, lymph moves from the tissues toward the larger lymphatic vessels. Three factors assist in the transport of lymph through the lymphatic vessels: (1) contraction of surrounding skeletal muscle during activity, (2) contraction of smooth muscle in the lymphatic vessel wall, and (3) pressure changes in the thorax during respiration.

The lymphatic vessels converge and eventually empty into the blood at two locations in the body. Lymphatic vessels from the upper right limb and the right half of the head, neck, and chest form the **right lymphatic duct**, which empties into the right subclavian vein. Lymphatic vessels from the rest of the body enter the **thoracic duct**, which empties into the left subclavian vein (see figure 14.1 and figure 14.3).

Lymphatic Organs

Lymphatic organs include the tonsils, lymph nodes, the spleen, and the thymus gland. **Lymphatic tissue**, which consists of many lymphocytes and other cells, is found within lymphatic organs. The lymphocytes originate from red bone marrow (see chapter 11) and are carried by the blood to lymphatic organs. When the body is exposed to microorganisms or foreign substances, the lymphocytes divide and increase in number. The increased number of lymphocytes is part of the immune response that causes the destruction of microorganisms and foreign substances. In addition to cells, lymphatic tissue has very fine reticular fibers (see chapter 4). These fibers form an interlaced network that holds the lymphocytes and other cells in place. When lymph or blood filters through lymphatic organs, the fiber network also traps microorganisms and other items in the fluid.

Tonsils

There are three groups of tonsils (figure 14.4). The **palatine** (pal′ă-tīn) **tonsils** usually are referred to as "the tonsils," and

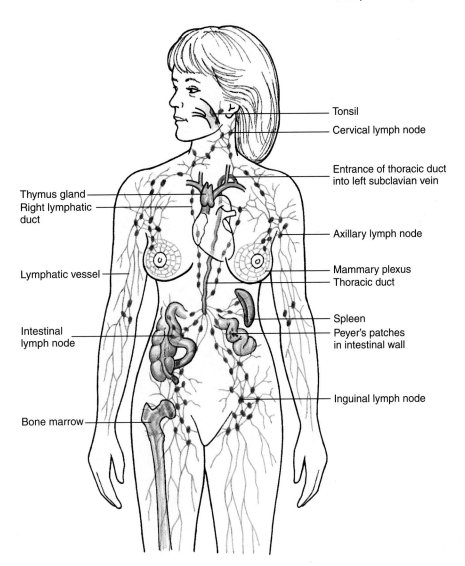

Tonsil

Cervical lymph node

Entrance of thoracic duct
into left subclavian vein

Thymus gland

Right lymphatic
duct

Axillary lymph node

Mammary plexus
Thoracic duct

Lymphatic vessel

Spleen
Peyer's patches
in intestinal wall

Intestinal
lymph node

Inguinal lymph node

Bone marrow

Figure 14.1   The Lymphatic System

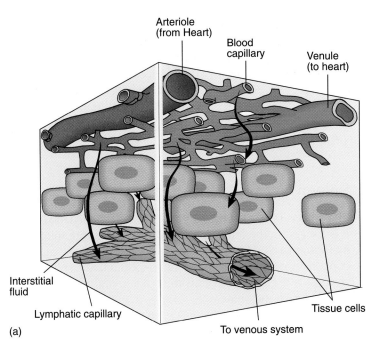

Arteriole
(from Heart)

Blood
capillary

Venule
(to heart)

Interstitial
fluid

Lymphatic capillary

Tissue cells

To venous system

(a)

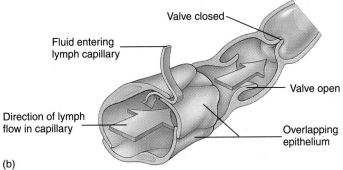

Valve closed

Fluid entering
lymph capillary

Direction of lymph
flow in capillary

Valve open

Overlapping
epithelium

(b)

Figure 14.2   Lymph Formation and Movement

(*a*) Movement of fluid from blood capillaries into tissues and from tissues
into lymphatic capillaries to form lymph. (*b*) The overlap of epithelial
cells of the lymphatic capillary allows easy entry of fluid but prevents
movement back into the tissue. Valves, located farther along in lymphatic
vessels, also ensure one-way flow of lymph.

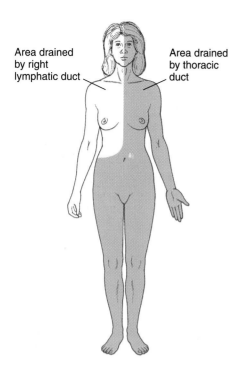

Figure 14.3 Lymph Drainage

Lymph from the blue area drains through the thoracic duct. Lymph from the white area drains through the right lymphatic duct.

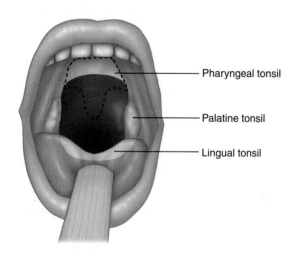

Figure 14.4 Location of the Tonsils

Anterior view of the oral cavity showing the tonsils. Part of the palate is removed (dashed line) to show the pharyngeal tonsils.

they are located on each side of the posterior opening of the oral cavity. The **pharyngeal** (fă-rin′jē-ăl) **tonsil**, or **adenoid** (ad′ĕ-noyd), is located near the internal opening of the nasal cavity. If enlarged, a pharyngeal tonsil can interfere with normal breathing. The **lingual** (ling′gwăl) **tonsil** is on the posterior surface of the tongue.

The tonsils form a protective ring of lymphatic tissue around the openings between the nasal and oral cavities and the pharynx. They provide protection against pathogens and other potentially harmful material entering from the nose

and mouth. Sometimes the tonsils become chronically infected and must be removed. In adults the tonsils decrease in size and may eventually disappear.

Lymph Nodes

Lymph nodes are rounded structures, varying in size from that of small seeds to that of shelled almonds. Lymph nodes are distributed along the various lymphatic vessels (see figure 14.1), and most lymph passes through at least one lymph node before entering the blood. Although lymph nodes are found throughout the body, there are three superficial aggregations of lymph nodes on each side of the body: inguinal nodes in the groin, axillary nodes in the axilla (armpit), and cervical nodes in the neck.

Lymph nodes are surrounded by a dense connective tissue capsule and are divided into compartments that contain lymphatic tissue and lymph sinuses (figure 14.5). The lymphatic tissue consists of lymphocytes and other cells that can form dense aggregations of tissue called **lymph nodules**. **Lymph sinuses** are spaces between lymphatic tissue which contain macrophages on a network of fibers. Lymph enters the lymph node through afferent vessels, passes through the lymphatic tissue and sinuses, and exits through efferent vessels.

As lymph moves through the lymph nodes, two functions are performed. One function is activation of the immune system. Microorganisms or other foreign substances in the lymph can stimulate lymphocytes in the lymphatic tissue to start dividing. The lymph nodules containing the rapidly dividing lymphocytes are called **germinal centers**. The newly produced lymphocytes are released into the lymph and eventually reach the blood, where they circulate and enter other lymphatic tissues. Another function of the lymph nodes is the removal of microorganisms and foreign substances from the lymph by macrophages.

1	**P R E D I C T**

Cancer cells can spread from a tumor site to other areas of the body through the lymphatic system. At first, however, as the cancer cells pass through the lymphatic system they are trapped in the lymph nodes, which filter the lymph. During radical cancer surgery, malignant (cancerous) lymph nodes are removed, and their vessels are cut and tied off to prevent the spread of the cancer. Predict the consequences of tying off the lymphatic vessels.

✔ *Answer on page 398*

Spleen

The **spleen** (splēn) is roughly the size of a clenched fist, and it is located in the left, superior corner of the abdominal cavity (figure 14.6). The spleen filters blood instead of lymph and contains two specialized types of lymphoid tissue. **White pulp** surrounds the arteries within the spleen, and **red pulp** is associated with the veins.

Cells within the spleen detect and respond to foreign substances in the blood and destroy worn-out red blood cells.

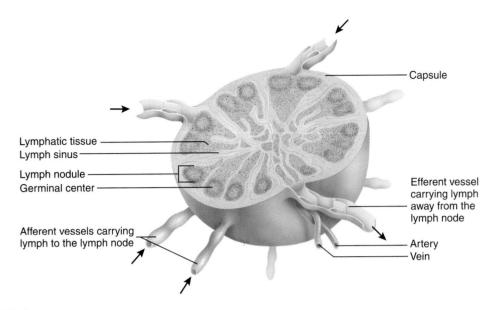

Figure 14.5 Lymph Node

Arrows indicate the direction of lymph flow. The germinal centers are sites of lymphocyte production. As lymph moves through the lymph sinuses, macrophages remove foreign substances.

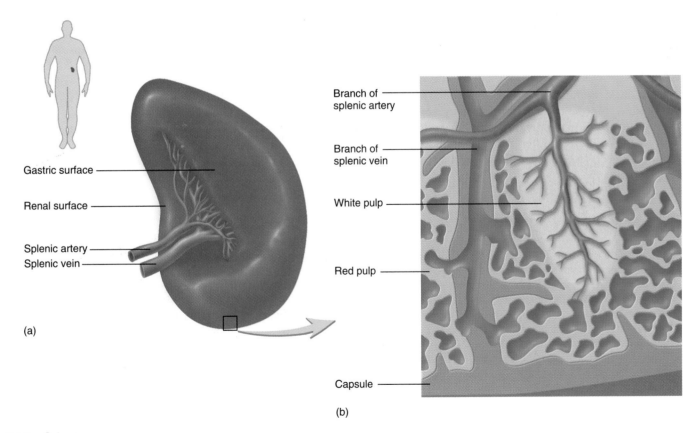

Figure 14.6 Spleen

(a) Inferior view of the spleen. (b) Section showing the arrangement of arteries, veins, white pulp, and red pulp.

Lymphocytes in the white pulp can be stimulated in the same manner as in lymph nodes. Before blood leaves the spleen through veins, it passes through the red pulp. Macrophages in the red pulp remove foreign substances and worn-out red blood cells through phagocytosis (see chapter 11).

The spleen also functions as a blood reservoir, holding a small volume of blood. In emergency situations such as hemorrhage, smooth muscle in splenic blood vessels and in the splenic capsule can contract. The result is the movement of a small amount of blood out of the spleen into the general circulation.

Thymus

The **thymus** (thī'mŭs) is a bilobed gland roughly triangular in shape (see figure 14.1). It is located in the superior mediastinum, the partition dividing the thoracic cavity into left and right parts. It was once thought that the thymus increases in size until puberty after which it dramatically decreases in size. It is now believed that the thymus increases in size until the first year of life, after which it remains approximately the same size, even though the size of the individual increases. After 60 years of age, it decreases in size, and in older adults, the thymus may be so small that it is difficult to find during dissection. Although the size of the thymus is fairly constant throughout much of life, by 40 years of age much of the thymus has been replaced with adipose tissue.

The thymus functions as a site for the production and maturation of lymphocytes. Large numbers of lymphocytes are produced in the thymus, but for unknown reasons, most degenerate. While in the thymus, lymphocytes do not respond to foreign substances. After thymic lymphocytes have matured, however, they enter the blood and travel to other lymphatic tissues, where they help to protect against microorganisms and other foreign substances.

Immunity

Immunity (i-mū'ni-tē) is the ability to resist damage from foreign substances, such as microorganisms, and harmful chemicals, such as toxins released by microorganisms. Immunity is categorized as innate immunity or adaptive immunity. In **innate** (i'nāt, i-nāt') **immunity**, the body is born with the ability to recognize and rapidly destroy certain foreign substances, but the ability to destroy them does not improve each time the body is exposed to them. In **adaptive immunity**, the ability of the body to recognize and destroy foreign substances improves each time the body encounters the foreign substance. The distinction between innate and adaptive immunity involves the concepts of specificity and memory. **Specificity** is the immune system's ability to recognize a particular substance. For example, innate immunity can act against bacteria in general, whereas adaptive immunity can distinguish among different kinds of bacteria. **Memory** is the immune system's ability to "remember" previous encounters with a particular substance and, as a result, respond to it more rapidly than in the first encounter.

In innate immunity, each time the body is exposed to a substance, the response is the same because there is no memory of previous encounters. For example, each time a bacterial cell is introduced into the body, it is phagocytized with the same speed and efficiency. In adaptive immunity, the response during the second exposure is faster and stronger than the response to the first exposure because the immune system exhibits memory for the bacteria from the first exposure. For example, following initial exposure to the bacteria, the body

Clinical Focus Disorders of the Lymphatic Systems

It is not surprising that many infectious diseases produce symptoms associated with the lymphatic system, because the lymphatic system is involved with the production of lymphocytes that fight infectious diseases, as well as filtering blood and lymph to remove microorganisms. **Lymphadenitis** (lim-fad'ĕ-nī'tis) is an inflammation of the lymph nodes, causing them to become enlarged and tender. It is an indication that microorganisms are being trapped and destroyed within the lymph nodes. **Lymphangitis** (lim-fan-jī'tis) is an inflammation of the lymphatic vessels. This often results in visible red streaks in the skin that extend away from the site of infection. If microorganisms pass through the lymphatic vessels and nodes to reach the blood, **septicemia** (sep-ti-sē'mē-ă), or blood poisoning, can result (see chapter 11).

A **lymphoma** (lim-fō'mă) is a neoplasm (tumor) of lymphatic tissue that is almost always malignant. Lymphomas are usually divided into two groups: **Hodgkin's disease** and all other lymphomas, which are called **non-Hodgkin's lymphomas**. The different types of lymphomas are diagnosed based on their histological appearance and cell of origin.

Typically, a lymphoma begins as an enlarged, painless mass of lymph nodes. Enlargement of the lymph nodes can compress surrounding structures and produce complications. The immune system is depressed, and the patient has an increased susceptibility to infections. Fortunately, treatment with drugs and radiation is effective for many people who suffer from lymphomas.

Bubonic plague and elephantiasis are diseases of the lymphatic system. **Bubonic** (bū-bon'ik) **plague** is caused by bacteria that are transferred to humans from rats by the bite of the rat flea. The bacteria localize in the lymph nodes, causing them to enlarge. The term bubonic is derived from a Greek word referring to the groin, because the disease often causes the inguinal lymph nodes of the groin to swell. Without treatment, septicemia followed rapidly by death occurs in 70% to 90% of those infected. In the sixth, fourteenth, and nineteenth centuries the bubonic plague killed large numbers of people in Europe. Fortunately, there are relatively few cases today.

Elephantiasis (el-ĕ-fan-tī'ă-sis) is caused by long, slender roundworms. The adult worms lodge in the lymphatic vessels and can cause blockage of lymph flow. Consequently, edema develops and a limb can become permanently swollen and enlarged. The resemblance of an affected limb to that of an elephant's leg is the basis for the name of the disease. The offspring of the adult worms pass through the lymphatic system into the blood. They can be transferred from an infected person to other humans by mosquitoes.

can take many days to destroy the bacteria. During this time the bacteria damage tissues, producing the symptoms of disease. After the second exposure to the same bacteria, however, the response is very rapid and effective. The bacteria are destroyed before any symptoms develop, and the person is said to be **immune**. Adaptive immunity is possible because of specificity and memory.

Innate Immunity

Innate immunity is accomplished by mechanical mechanisms, chemical mediators, cells, and the inflammatory response.

Mechanical Mechanisms

Mechanical mechanisms prevent the entry of microorganisms and chemicals into the body in two ways: (1) the skin and mucous membranes form barriers that prevent their entry, and (2) tears, saliva, and urine act to wash them from the surfaces of the body. Microorganisms cannot cause a disease if they cannot get into the body.

Chemical Mediators

Chemical mediators are substances that bring about innate immune responses. Some chemicals that are found on the surface of cells kill microorganisms or prevent their entry into the cells. Lysozyme in tears and saliva kills certain bacteria, and mucus on the mucous membranes prevents the entry of some microorganisms. Other chemical mediators, such as histamine (his′tă-mēn), complement, prostaglandins (pros-tă-glan′dinz), and leukotrienes (loo-kō-trī′ēnz), promote inflammation by causing vasodilation, increasing vascular permeability, and stimulating phagocytosis. In addition, interferons protect cells against viral infections.

Complement

Complement (kom′plĕ-ment) is a group of approximately 20 proteins found in plasma. The operation of complement proteins is very similar to that of clotting proteins (see chapter 11). Normally, complement proteins circulate in the blood in an inactive form. Certain complement proteins can be activated by combining with foreign substances, such as parts of a bacterial cell, or by combining with antibodies (see the discussion, Adaptive Immunity, on p. 381). Once activation begins, a series of reactions results, in which each complement protein activates the next. Certain activated complement proteins promote inflammation and phagocytosis and can directly lyse (rupture) bacterial cells.

Interferons

Interferons (in-ter-fēr′onz) are proteins that protect the body against viral infections. When a virus infects a cell, the cell produces viral nucleic acids and proteins, which are assembled into new viruses. The new viruses are released from the infected cell to infect other cells. Because infected cells usually stop their normal functions or die during viral replication, viral infections are clearly harmful to the body. Fortunately, viruses often stimulate infected cells to produce interferons. Interferons do not protect the cell that produces them. Instead, interferons bind to the surface of neighboring cells where they stimulate the cells to produce antiviral proteins. These antiviral proteins inhibit viral reproduction in the neighboring cells by preventing the production of new viral nucleic acids and proteins.

Some inferons play a role in the activation of immune cells such as macrophages and natural killer cells (see the Cells section, below).

Cells

White blood cells and the cells derived from white blood cells (see chapter 11) are the most important cellular components of immunity. White blood cells are produced in red bone marrow and lymphatic tissue and are released into the blood. Chemicals released from microorganisms or damaged tissues attract the white blood cells, and they leave the blood and enter affected tissues. Important chemicals known to attract white blood cells include complement, leukotrienes, kinins (kī′ninz), and histamine. The movement of white blood cells toward these chemicals is called **chemotaxis** (kem-ō-tak′sis, kē-mō-tak′sis).

Phagocytic Cells

Phagocytosis (fag′ō-sī-tō′sis) is the ingestion and destruction of particles by cells called **phagocytes** (fag′ō-sītz) (see chapter 3). The particles can be microorganisms or their parts, foreign substances, or dead cells from the individual's body. The most important phagocytes are neutrophils and macrophages, although other white blood cells also have limited phagocytic ability.

Neutrophils (noo′trō-filz) are small phagocytic cells that are usually the first cells to enter infected tissues from the blood; however, neutrophils often die after phagocytizing a single microorganism. **Pus** is an accumulation of fluid, dead neutrophils, and other cells at a site of infection.

Macrophages (mak′rō-fā′jes) are monocytes that leave the blood, enter tissues, and enlarge about fivefold. Monocytes and macrophages form the **mononuclear phagocytic system** because they are phagocytes with a single (mono), unlobed nucleus. Sometimes macrophages are given specific names such as dust cells in the lungs, Kupffer cells in the liver, and microglia in the central nervous system. Macrophages can ingest more and larger items than can neutrophils. Macrophages usually appear in infected tissues after neutrophils and are responsible for most of the phagocytic activity in the late stages of an infection, including the cleanup of dead neutrophils and other cellular debris.

In addition to leaving the blood in response to an infection, macrophages are also found in uninfected tissues. If microorganisms enter uninfected tissue, the macrophages may phagocytize the microorganisms before they can replicate or cause damage. For example, macrophages are found beneath body surfaces, such as the skin and mucous membranes, and around blood and lymphatic vessels. They also protect lymph in lymph nodes and blood in the spleen and liver.

Cells of Inflammation

Basophils, which are derived from red bone marrow, are motile white blood cells that can leave the blood and enter infected tissues. **Mast cells**, which are also derived from red bone marrow, are nonmotile cells in connective tissue, especially near capillaries. Like macrophages, mast cells are located at potential points of entry for microorganisms into the body such as the skin, lungs, gastrointestinal tract, and urogenital tract.

Basophils and mast cells can be activated through innate immunity (e.g., by complement) or through adaptive immunity (see the section, Antibodies, on p. 384). When activated, they release chemicals such as histamine and leukotrienes that produce an inflammatory response or activate other mechanisms such as smooth muscle contraction in the lungs.

Eosinophils are produced in red bone marrow, enter the blood, and within a few minutes enter tissues. Enzymes released by eosinophils break down chemicals released by basophils and mast cells. Thus at the same time that inflammation is initiated, mechanisms are activated that contain and reduce the inflammatory response.

Inflammation is beneficial in the fight against microorganisms, but too much inflammation can be harmful, resulting in the unnecessary destruction of healthy tissues as well as the destruction of the microorganisms.

Natural Killer Cells

Natural killer (NK) cells are a type of lymphocyte produced in red bone marrow, and they account for up to 15% of lymphocytes. NK cells recognize classes of cells, such as tumor cells or virus-infected cells in general, rather than specific tumor cells or cells infected by a specific virus. For this reason, and because NK cells do not exhibit a memory response, NK cells are classified as part of innate immunity. NK cells use a variety of methods to kill their target cells, including the release of chemicals that damage cell membranes, causing the cells to lyse.

Inflammatory Response

The **inflammatory response** to injury involves many of the chemicals and cells previously discussed. Most inflammatory responses are very similar, although some details can vary depending on the intensity of the response and the type of injury. A bacterial infection is used here to illustrate an inflammatory response (figure 14.7). The bacteria, or damage to tissues, cause the release or activation of chemical mediators, such as histamine, prostaglandins, leukotrienes, complement, and kinins. The chemicals produce several effects: (1) vasodilation, which increases blood flow and brings phagocytes and other white blood cells to the area; (2) chemotactic attraction

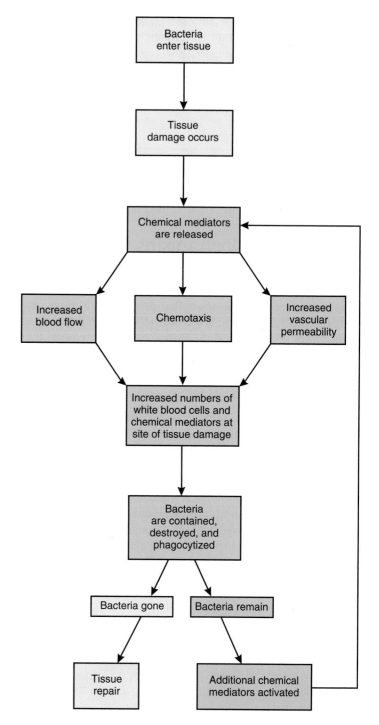

Figure 14.7 Inflammatory Response

Bacteria cause tissue damage and the release of chemical mediators that initiate inflammation and phagocytosis, resulting in the destruction of the bacteria. If any bacteria remain, additional chemical mediators are activated. After all the bacteria are destroyed, the tissue is repaired.

of phagocytes, which leave the blood and enter the tissue; and (3) increased vascular permeability, allowing fibrinogen and complement to enter the tissue from the blood. Fibrinogen is converted to fibrin (see chapter 11), which contains the infection by walling off the infected area. Complement further enhances the inflammatory response and attracts additional phagocytes. This process of releasing chemical mediators and attracting phagocytes and other white blood cells continues until the bacteria are destroyed. Phagocytes (mainly macrophages) remove microorganisms and dead tissue, and the damaged tissues are repaired.

Inflammation can be localized or systemic. **Local inflammation** is an inflammatory response confined to a specific area of the body. Symptoms of local inflammation include redness, heat, swelling, pain, and loss of function. Redness, heat, and swelling result from increased blood flow and increased vascular permeability. Pain is caused by swelling and by chemicals acting on pain receptors. Loss of function results from tissue destruction, swelling, and pain. See section, Inflammation, for more details on the symptoms of inflammation

Systemic inflammation is an inflammatory response that occurs in many parts of the body. In addition to the local symptoms at the sites of inflammation, three additional features can be present:

1. Red bone marrow produces and releases large numbers of neutrophils, which promote phagocytosis.
2. **Pyrogens** (pī′rō-jenz), chemicals released by microorganisms, neutrophils, and other cells, stimulate fever production. Pyrogens affect the body temperature-regulating mechanism in the hypothalamus of the brain. As a consequence, heat production and conservation increase, and body temperature increases. Fever promotes the activities of the immune system, such as phagocytosis, and inhibits the growth of some microorganisms.
3. In severe cases of systemic inflammation, vascular permeability can increase so much that large amounts of fluid are lost from the blood into the tissues. The decreased blood volume can cause shock and death.

Adaptive Immunity

Adaptive immunity involves specificity, the ability to recognize a particular substance, and memory, the ability to respond with increasing effectiveness to successive exposures to the antigen. Substances that stimulate adaptive immunity responses are called **antigens** (an′ti-jenz). Antigens can be divided into two groups: foreign antigens and self-antigens. **Foreign antigens** are introduced from outside the body. Microorganisms, such as bacteria and viruses, cause diseases, and components of microorganism and chemicals released by microorganisms are examples of foreign antigens. Pollen, animal hairs, foods, and drugs can cause an **allergic reaction** because they are foreign antigens that produce an overreaction of the immune system. Transplanted tissues and organs contain foreign antigens, and the response to these antigens can result in the rejection of the transplant.

Self-antigens are molecules produced by the person's body that stimulate an immune system response. The response to self-antigens can be beneficial. For example, the recognition of tumor antigens can result in destruction of the tumor. The response to self-antigens can also be harmful.

Autoimmune disease results when self-antigens stimulate unwanted destruction of normal tissue. An example is rheumatoid arthritis, which results in the destruction of tissue within joints.

The adaptive immune system response to antigens was historically divided into two parts: **humoral immunity** and **cell-mediated immunity**. Early investigators of the immune system found that when plasma from an immune animal was injected into the blood of a nonimmune animal, the nonimmune animal became immune. Because this process involved body fluids (humors), it was called humoral immunity. It was also discovered that blood cells alone could be responsible for immunity, and this process was called cell-mediated immunity.

It is now known that both types of immunity result from the activities of lymphocytes. There are two types of lymphocytes: B cells and T cells. **B cells** give rise to cells that produce proteins called **antibodies** (an′tĕ-bod-ēz), which are found in the plasma. The antibodies are responsible for humoral immunity, which is now called **antibody-mediated immunity**. **T cells** are responsible for cell-mediated immunity. In addition, some T cells are involved with regulating both antibody-mediated and cell-mediated immunity.

Table 14.1 summarizes and contrasts the main features of innate immunity, antibody-mediated immunity, and cell-mediated immunity.

Origin and Development of Lymphocytes

To understand how lymphocytes are responsible for antibody-mediated and cell-mediated immunity, it is important to know how lymphocytes originate and become specialized immune cells. **Stem cells** in red bone marrow are cells that are capable of giving rise to all the blood cells (see figures 11.2 and 14.8). Some stem cells give rise to pre-T cells, which migrate through the blood to the thymus gland, where they divide and are processed into T cells. Other stem cells produce pre-B cells, which are processed in the red bone marrow into B cells.

B cells are released from red bone marrow, and T cells are released from the thymus. Both types of cells move through the blood to lymphatic tissues. These lymphocytes live for a few months to many years and continually circulate between the blood and the lymphatic tissues. Normally there are about five T cells for every B cell in the blood. When stimulated by an antigen, B cells and T cells divide, producing cells that are responsible for the destruction of antigens.

Evidence suggests that small groups of identical B or T cells, called **clones**, are formed during embryonic development. Each clone is derived from a single, unique B or T cell. Although each clone can respond only to a particular antigen, there is such a large variety of clones that the immune system can react to most molecules. Among the molecules to which the clones can respond, however, are self-antigens. Because this response could destroy self-cells, clones acting against self-antigens are normally eliminated or suppressed. Most of this process occurs during prenatal development, but it also continues after birth and throughout a person's lifetime.

Table 14.1 Comparison of Innate Immunity, Antibody-Mediated Immunity, and Cell-Mediated Immunity		
Primary Cells	**Origin of Cells**	**Site of Maturation**
Innate Immunity Neutrophils, eosinophils, basophils, mast cells, monocytes, and macrophages	Red bone marrow	Red bone marrow (neutrophils, eosinophils, basophils, and monocytes) and tissues (mast cells and macrophages)
Antibody–Mediated Immunity B cells	Red bone marrow	Red bone marrow
Cell-Mediated Immunity T cells	Red bone marrow	Thymus gland

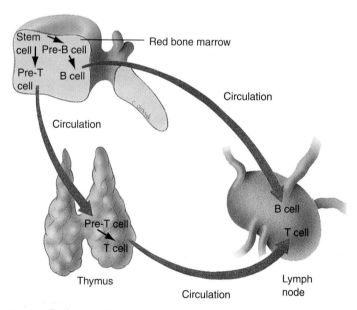

Figure 14.8 Origin and Processing of B Cells and T Cells

Both B cells and T cells originate from a stem cell in red bone marrow. B cells are processed from pre-B cells in the red marrow, whereas T cells are processed from pre-T cells in the thymus. Both B and T cells circulate to other lymphatic tissues, such as lymph nodes.

Activation and Multiplication of Lymphocytes

The specialized B or T cell clones can respond to antigens and produce an adaptive immune response. For the adaptive immune response to be effective, two events must occur: (1) antigen recognition by lymphocytes and (2) proliferation of the lymphocytes recognizing the antigen.

Antigen Recognition

Lymphocytes have proteins, called **antigen-binding receptors**, on their surfaces. Each receptor binds with only a specific antigen. Each clone consists of lymphocytes that have identical antigen-binding receptors on their surfaces. When antigens combine with the antigen-binding receptors, the lymphocytes in a clone can be activated and the adaptive immune response begins.

B and T cells typically recognize antigens after they have been processed or broken down into smaller fragments. Just as a mother cuts food into small pieces and gives them to her child, antigen-presenting cells, such as macrophages, process and present antigens to B and T cells. The antigens are taken into macrophages by endocytosis and broken down into smaller antigen fragments. The processed antigen fragments are bound to major histocompatibility complex molecules, transported to the surface of the macrophages, and displayed (figure 14.9, step 1).

Major histocompatibility complex (MHC) molecules are glycoproteins, and they have binding sites for antigens. Different MHC molecules have different binding sites, that is, they are specific for certain antigens. The MHC molecules function as "serving trays" that hold and present a processed antigen on the outer surface of the cell membrane. The combined MHC molecule and processed antigen can bind to the antigen-binding receptor on a B or T cell and stimulate them. For example, a special type of T cell, called a **helper T cell**, can be stimulated (see figure 14.9, step 2)

The MHC molecule/antigen combination is usually only the first signal necessary to produce a response from a B or T cell. In many cases, **costimulation** by a second signal is also required. Costimulation can be achieved by **cytokines** (sī′tō-kīnz), which are proteins or peptides secreted by one cell as a regulator of neighboring cells. For example, **interleukin-1**

Table 14.1 (continued)

Location of Mature Cells	Primary Secretory Product	Primary Actions	Allergic Reactions
Blood, connective tissue, and lymphatic tissue	Histamine, complement, prostaglandins, leukotrienes, kinins, and interferons	Inflammatory response and phagocytosis	None
Blood and lymphatic tissue	Antibodies	Protection against extracellular antigens (bacteria, toxins, and viruses outside of cells)	Immediate hypersensitivity
Blood and lymphatic tissue	Cytokines	Protection against intracellular antigens (viruses and intracellular bacteria) and tumors; responsible for graft rejection	Delayed hypersensitivity

(in-ter-loo'kin) is a cytokine released by macrophages, which can stimulate helper T cells (see figure 14.9, step 3).

Lymphocytes have other surface molecules besides MHC molecules that help to bind cells together and stimulate a response. For example, **CD4** is a glycoprotein on helper T cells that can bind to the MHC molecule on macrophages (see figure 14.9, step 3). Helper T cells are sometimes referred to as **CD4 cells** for this reason, The CD designation stands for "cluster of differentiation," which is a system used to classify many surface molecules.

Lymphocyte Proliferation

Before exposure to a particular antigen, the number of helper T cells that can respond to that antigen is too small to produce an effective response against it. After the antigen is processed and presented to a helper T cell by a macrophage, the helper T cell responds by producing **interleukin-2 receptors** and **interleukin-2** (see figure 14.9, step 4). Interleukin-2 binds to the receptors and stimulates the helper T cell to divide (see figure 14.9, step 5). The helper T cells produced by this division can again be presented with antigen by macrophages and again be stimulated to divide. Thus, the number of helper T cells is greatly increased (see figure 14.9, step 6)

Did You Know?

Current research is using genetically engineered interleukin-2 as a means of stimulating the immune system. Interleukin-2 may promote the destruction of cancer cells or boost the effectiveness of vaccinations. Conversely, decreasing the production or activity of interleukin-2 can suppress the immune system. For example, cyclosporine, a drug used to prevent the rejection of transplanted organs, inhibits the production of interleukin-2.

It is important for the number of helper T cells to increase because helper T cells are necessary for the activation of most B or T cells (see figure 14.9, step 7). For example, B cells have receptors that can recognize antigens. Most B cells, however, do not respond to antigens without stimulation from helper T cells. This process begins when a B cell takes in the same kind of antigen that stimulated the helper T cell (figure 14.10, step 1). The antigen is processed by the B cell and presented to the helper T cell using a MHC molecule (see figure 14.10, step 2). There is also costimulation involving interleukins (see figure 14.10, step 3). The result is the division of the B cell into two cells (see figure 14.10, step 4). The division process continues, eventually producing many cells that are capable of producing antibodies. Thus, many cells producing antibodies results in sufficient antibodies to destroy all of the antigen.

2 ▮ **P R E D I C T**

How does elimination of the antigen stop the production of antibodies?

✔ *Answer on page 398*

Antibody-Mediated Immunity

Exposure of the body to an antigen can result in the activation of B cells and the production of antibodies. The antibodies bind to the antigens, and through several different mechanisms, the antigens can be destroyed. Because antibodies are in body fluids, antibody-mediated immunity is effective against extracellular antigens, such as bacteria, viruses (when they are outside cells), and toxins. Antibody-mediated immunity is also involved with certain allergic reactions.

1. Antigen-presenting cells such as macrophages take in, process, and display antigens on the cell's surface.

2. The antigens are bound to major histocompatibility complex (MHC) molecules, which function to present the processed antigen to the T-cell antigen-binding receptor of the helper T cell for recognition.

3. Costimulation results from the cytokine interleukin-1, secreted by the macrophage, and the CD4 glycoprotein of the helper T cell.

4. Interleukin-1 stimulates the helper T cell to secrete the cytokine interleukin-2 and to produce interleukin-2 receptors.

5. The helper T cell stimulates itself to divide when interleukin-2 binds to interleukin-2 receptors.

6. The "daughter" helper T cells resulting from this division can be stimulated to divide again if they are exposed to the same antigen that stimulated the "parent" helper T cell. This greatly increases the number of helper T cells.

7. The increased number of helper T cells can facilitate the activation of B cells or T cells.

Figure 14.9 Proliferation of Helper T Cells

An antigen-presenting cell (macrophage) stimulates a helper T cell to divide.

Antibodies

Antibodies are proteins produced in response to an antigen. They are Y-shaped molecules consisting of four polypeptide chains: two identical heavy chains and two identical light chains (figure 14.11). The end of each "arm" of the antibody is the **variable region**, which is the part of the antibody that combines with the antigen. The variable region of a particular antibody can only join with a particular antigen. This is similar to the lock-and-key model of enzymes (see chapter 2). The rest of the antibody is the **constant region**, which has several functions. For example, the constant region can activate complement, or it can attach the antibody to cells such as macrophages, basophils, and mast cells.

Antibodies make up a large portion of the proteins in plasma. Most plasma proteins can be separated into albumin and alpha, beta, and gamma globulin portions. Antibodies are called **gamma globulins** because they are found mostly in the gamma globulin part of plasma. Antibodies are also called **immunoglobulins (Ig)** because they are globulin proteins involved in immunity. The five general classes of immunoglobulins are denoted IgG, IgM, IgA, IgE, and IgD (table 14.2).

Effects of Antibodies

Antibodies can affect antigens either directly or indirectly. Direct effects occur when a single antibody binds to an antigen and inactivates the antigen, or when many antigens are bound together and are inactivated by many antibodies (figure 14.12 *a* and *b*). The ability of antibodies to join antigens together is the basis for many clinical tests, such as blood typing, because when enough antigens are bound together, they form visible clumps.

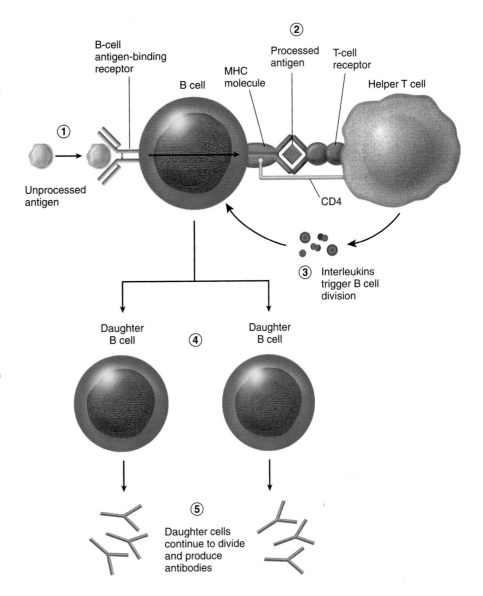

1. Before a B cell can be activated by a helper T cell, the B cell must process the same antigen that activated the helper T cell. The antigen binds to a B-cell antigen-binding receptor, and the receptor and antigen are both taken into the cell by endocytosis.

2. The B cell uses a MHC molecule to present the processed antigen to the helper T cell.

3. The helper T cell responds by releasing various interleukins that stimulate the B cell to divide.

4. The B cell divides, and the resulting daughter cells divide, and so on, eventually producing many cells (only two are shown here).

5. The increased number of cells produce antibodies, which are part of the antibody-mediated immune system response that eliminates the antigen.

Figure 14.10   Proliferation of B Cells
A helper T cell stimulates a B cell to divide.

Did You Know?

Each type of **monoclonal antibody** is a pure antibody preparation that is specific for only one antigen. When the antigen is injected into a laboratory animal, it activates a B-cell clone against the antigen. These B cells are removed from the animal and fused with tumor cells. The resulting cells have two ideal characteristics: (1) they produce only one (mono) specific antibody because they are derived from one B-cell clone, and (2) they divide rapidly because they are derived from tumor cells. The result is many cells producing a specific antibody.

Monoclonal antibodies are used for determining pregnancy and for diagnosing diseases such as gonorrhea, syphilis, hepatitis, rabies, and cancer. These tests are specific and rapid because the monoclonal antibodies bind only to the antigen being tested. Monoclonal antibodies may some day be used to effectively treat cancer by delivering drugs to cancer cells (see the section, Immunotherapy, on p. 388).

Most of the effectiveness of antibodies results from indirect effects (figure 14.12 *c* to *e*). After an antibody has attached by its variable region to an antigen, the constant region of the antibody can activate other mechanisms that destroy the antigen. For example, the constant region of antibodies can activate complement, which stimulates inflammation, attracts white blood cells through chemotaxis, and lyses bacteria. When an antigen combines with the antibody, the constant region triggers a release of inflammatory chemicals from mast cells and basophils. Finally, macrophages can attach to the constant region of the antibody and phagocytize both the antibody and antigen.

Antibody Production

The production of antibodies after the first exposure to an antigen is different from that following a second or subsequent exposure. The **primary response** results from the first

Table 14.2   Classes of Antibodies and Their Functions

Antibody	Total Serum Antibody (%)	Structure	Description
IgG	80–85		Activates complement and functions to increase phagocytosis; can cross the placenta and provide immune protection to the fetus and newborn; responsible for Rh reactions such as hemolytic disease of the newborn
IgM	5–10		Activates complement and acts as an antigen-binding receptor on the surface of B cells; responsible for transfusion reactions in the ABO blood system; often the first antibody produced in response to an antigen
IgA	15		Secreted into saliva, tears, and onto mucous membranes to provide protection on body surfaces; found in colostrum and milk to provide immune protection to the newborn
IgE	0.002		Binds to mast cells and basophis and stimulates the inflammatory response
IgD	0.2		Functions as antigen-binding receptors on B cells

Structure labels: IgG, IgM, IgA, IgE, IgD. Heavy chain. Light chain.

Antigen-binding sites
Heavy chain
Light chain
Variable regions of light and heavy chains
Complement binding site
Constant regions of light and heavy chains
Site of binding to macrophages, basophils, and mast cells

Figure 14.11   Structure of an Antibody

The Y-shaped antibody has two "arms." Each arm has a variable region that functions as an antigen-binding site. The constant region can activate complement or bind to other immune system cells, such as macrophages, basophils, or mast cells.

exposure of a B cell to an antigen (figure 14.13*a*). When the antigen binds to the antigen-binding receptor on the B cell, the B cell undergoes several divisions to form plasma cells and memory B cells. **Plasma cells** produce antibodies. The primary response normally takes 3 to 14 days to produce enough antibodies to be effective against the antigen. In the meantime, the individual usually develops disease symptoms because the antigen has had time to cause tissue damage.

Memory B cells are responsible for the **secondary**, or **memory**, **response**, which occurs when the immune system is exposed to an antigen against which it has already produced a primary response (figure 14.13*b*). When exposed to the antigen, the B memory cells quickly divide to form plasma cells, which rapidly produce antibodies. The secondary response provides better protection than the primary response for two reasons: (1) the time required to start producing antibodies is less (hours to a few days), and (2) more plasma cells and antibodies are produced. As a consequence, the antigen is quickly destroyed, no disease symptoms develop, and the person is immune.

The memory response also includes the formation of new memory cells, which provide protection against additional exposures to a specific antigen. Memory cells are the basis of adaptive immunity. After destruction of the antigen, plasma cells die, the antibodies they released are degraded, and antibody levels decline to the point where they can no longer provide adequate protection. Memory cells persist for many years, however; probably for life in some cases. If memory cell production is not stimulated, or if the memory cells produced are short-lived, it is possible to have repeated infections of the same disease. For example, the same cold virus can cause the common cold more than once in the same person.

3   P R E D I C T

One theory for long-lasting immunity assumes that humans are continually exposed to disease-causing agents. Explain how this exposure could produce lifelong immunity.

✔ *Answer on page 398*

(a) **Inactivates the antigen.** An antibody binds to an antigen and inactivates it.

(b) **Binds antigens together.** Antibodies bind several antigens together.

(c) **Activates the complement cascade.** An antigen binds to an antibody. As a result, the antibody can activate complement proteins, which can produce inflammation, chemotaxis, and lysis.

(d) **Initiates the release of inflammatory chemicals.** An antibody binds to a mast cell or basophil. When an antigen binds to the antibody, it triggers a release of chemicals that cause inflammation.

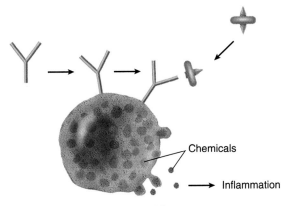

(e) **Facilitates phagocytosis.** An antibody binds to an antigen and then to a macrophage, which phagocytizes the antibody and antigen.

Figure 14.12   Effects of Antibodies

Antibodies directly affect antigens by inactivating the antigens or binding the antigens together. Antibodies indirectly affect antigens by activating other mechanisms through the constant region of the antibody. Indirect mechanisms include increased phagocytosis resulting from antibody attachment to macrophages, increased inflammation resulting from the release of inflammatory chemicals from mast cells or basophils, and activation of complement.

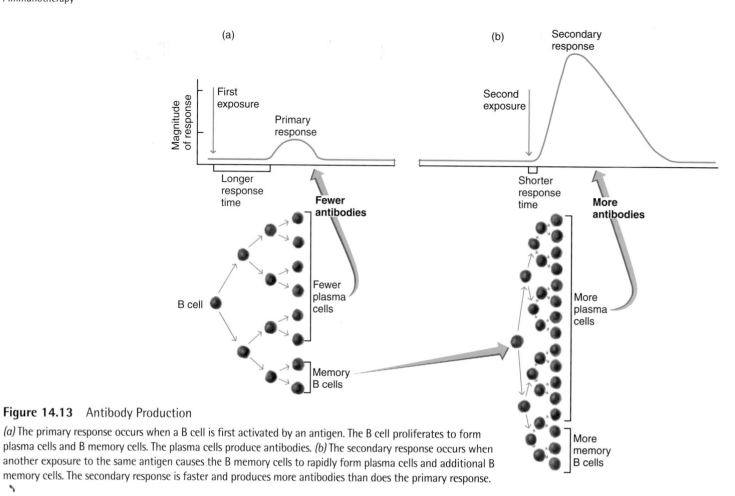

Figure 14.13 Antibody Production

(a) The primary response occurs when a B cell is first activated by an antigen. The B cell proliferates to form plasma cells and B memory cells. The plasma cells produce antibodies. *(b)* The secondary response occurs when another exposure to the same antigen causes the B memory cells to rapidly form plasma cells and additional B memory cells. The secondary response is faster and produces more antibodies than does the primary response.

Cell-Mediated Immunity

Cell-mediated immunity is a function of T cells and is most effective against microorganisms that live inside the cells of the body. Viruses and some bacteria are examples of intracellular microorganisms. Cell-mediated immunity is also involved with some allergic reactions, control of tumors, and graft rejections. T cells have antigen-binding receptors on their surfaces that are especially adept at recognizing antigens on the surfaces of other cells.

After an antigen activates a T cell, the T cell undergoes a series of divisions to produce cytotoxic T cells and memory T cells (figure 14.14). **Cytotoxic** (sī-tō-tok′sik) **T cells** are sometime called **CD8 cells** because they have CD8 glycoproteins on their surfaces. Like the CD4 glycoprotein of helper T cells, the CD8 molecule helps attach the cytotoxic T cell to MHC molecules. The cytotoxic T cells are responsible for the cell-mediated immune response, and the **memory T cells** provide a secondary response and long-lasting immunity in the same fashion as B memory cells.

Cytotoxic T cells have two main effects:

1. They release cytokines that activate additional components of the immune system. For example, some cytokines attract innate immune cells, especially macrophages. These cells are then responsible for phagocytosis of the antigen and the production of an inflammatory response. Cytokines also activate additional T cells, converting them into cytotoxic T cells, which increases the effectiveness of the cell-mediated response.

2. Cytotoxic T cells can come into contact with other cells and kill them. Virus-infected cells have viral antigens, tumor cells have tumor antigens, and tissue transplants have foreign antigens that can stimulate cytotoxic T-cell activity. The cytotoxic T cells bind to the antigens on the surfaces of these cells and cause the cells to lyse.

Immune Interactions

Although the immune system can be described in terms of innate, antibody-mediated, and cell-mediated immunity, there is really only one immune system. These categories are an artificial division that is used to emphasize particular aspects of immunity. Actually, immune system responses often involve components of more than one type of immunity (figure 14.15). For example, although adaptive immunity can recognize and remember specific antigens, once recognition has occurred, many of the events that lead to the destruction of the antigen are innate immunity activities such as inflammation and phagocytosis (see table 14.1).

Immunotherapy

Knowledge of the basic ways that the immune system operates has produced two fundamental benefits: (1) an understanding of the cause and progression of many diseases and (2) the development or proposed development of effective methods to prevent, stop, or even reverse diseases.

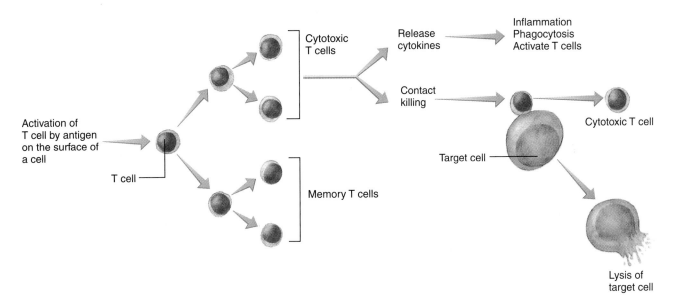

Figure 14.14 Stimulation of and Effects of T Cells

When activated, T cells form cytotoxic T cells and memory T cells. The cytotoxic T cells release cytokines that promote the destruction of the antigen or cause the lysis of target cells, such as virus-infected cells, tumor cells, or transplanted cells. The memory T cells are responsible for the secondary response.

Immunotherapy treats disease by altering immune system function or by directly attacking harmful cells. Some approaches attempt to boost immune system function in general. For example, administering cytokines or other agents can promote inflammation and the activation of immune cells, which can help in the destruction of tumor cells. On the other hand, sometimes inhibiting the immune system is helpful. For example, multiple sclerosis is an autoimmune disease in which the immune system treats self-antigens as foreign antigens, destroying the myelin that covers axons. Interferon beta, which is a cytokine, blocks the expression of MHC molecules that display self-antigens and is now being used to treat multiple sclerosis.

Some immunotherapy takes a more specific approach. For example, vaccination can prevent many diseases (see section, Acquired Immunity, on p. 389). The ability to produce monoclonal antibodies may result in therapies that are effective for treating tumors. If an antigen unique to tumor cells can be found, then monoclonal antibodies could be used to deliver radioactive isotopes, drugs, toxins, enzymes, or cytokines that kill the tumor cell or activate the immune system to kill the cell. Unfortunately, no antigen on tumor cells has been found that is not also found on normal cells. Nonetheless, this approach may be useful if damage to normal cells is minimal.

The use of monoclonal antibodies to treat tumors is mostly in the research stage of development, but a few clinical trials are now yielding promising results. For example, monoclonal antibodies with radioactive iodine (^{131}I) have been found to cause the regression of B-cell lymphomas, while producing few side effects. Herceptin® is a monoclonal antibody that binds to a growth factor receptor that is overexpressed in 25% to 30% of primary breast cancers. The antibody serves to "tag" cancer cells, which are then lysed by natural killer cells. Herceptin® slows disease progression and increases survival time, but is not a cure for breast cancer.

Many other approaches for immunotherapy are being studied, and the development of treatments that use the immune system are certain to increase in the future. Your knowledge of the immune system will enable you to understand and appreciate these therapies.

> **Did You Know?**
>
> An intriguing possibility for reducing the severity of diseases or even curing them is to use neuroendocrine regulation of the immune system. The nervous system regulates the secretion of hormones such as cortisol, epinephrine, endorphins, and enkephalins, for which lymphocytes have receptors. For example, cortisol released during times of stress inhibits the immune system. In addition, most lymphatic tissues, including some individual lymphocytes, receive sympathetic innervation. That there is a neuroendocrine connection to the immune system is clear. The question we need to answer is: Can we use this connection to control our own immunotherapy?

Acquired Immunity

There are four ways to acquire adaptive immunity: active natural, active artificial, passive natural, and passive artificial (figure 14.16). "Natural" and "artificial" refer to the method of exposure. Natural exposure implies that contact with the antigen occurs as part of everyday living and is not deliberate. Artificial exposure is a deliberate introduction of an antigen or antibody into the body.

Active immunity results when an individual is exposed to an antigen (either naturally or artificially) and the response of the individual's own immune system is the cause of the immunity. Passive immunity occurs when another person or an animal develops immunity and the immunity is transferred to a nonimmune individual.

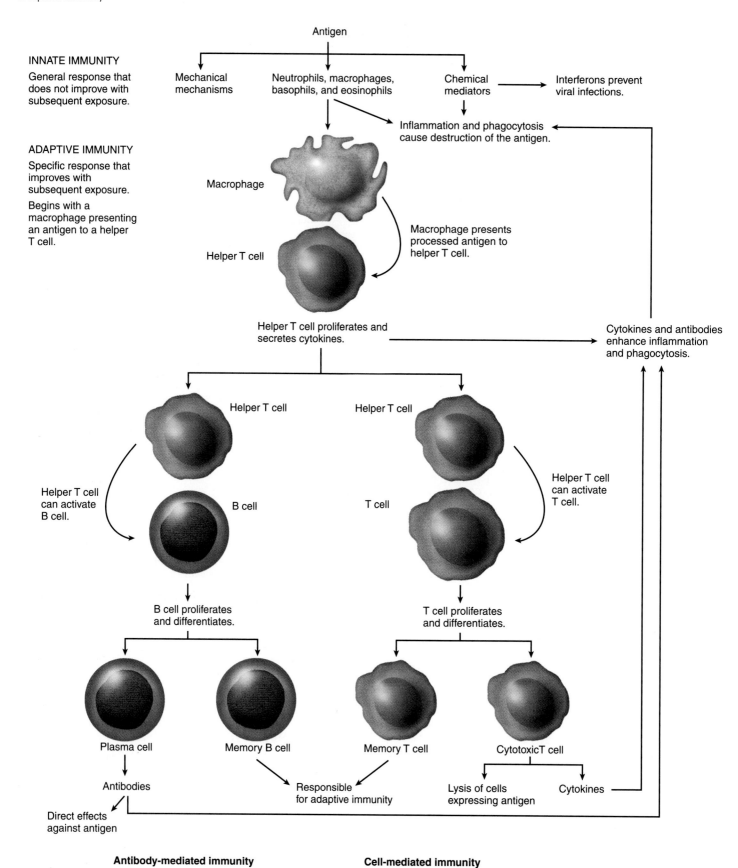

INNATE IMMUNITY
General response that does not improve with subsequent exposure.

ADAPTIVE IMMUNITY
Specific response that improves with subsequent exposure.

Begins with a macrophage presenting an antigen to a helper T cell.

Antigen

Mechanical mechanisms

Neutrophils, macrophages, basophils, and eosinophils

Chemical mediators

Interferons prevent viral infections.

Inflammation and phagocytosis cause destruction of the antigen.

Macrophage

Helper T cell

Macrophage presents processed antigen to helper T cell.

Helper T cell proliferates and secretes cytokines.

Cytokines and antibodies enhance inflammation and phagocytosis.

Helper T cell

Helper T cell

Helper T cell can activate B cell.

B cell

T cell

Helper T cell can activate T cell.

B cell proliferates and differentiates.

T cell proliferates and differentiates.

Plasma cell

Memory B cell

Memory T cell

CytotoxicT cell

Antibodies

Responsible for adaptive immunity

Lysis of cells expressing antigen

Cytokines

Direct effects against antigen

Antibody-mediated immunity
Antibodies act against antigens in solution or on the surfaces of extracellular microorganisms.

Cell-mediated immunity
Cytotoxic T cells act against antigens bound to MHC molecules on the surface of cells; effective against intracellular microorganisms, tumors, and transplanted cells.

Figure 14.15 Immune Interactions

The major interactions and responses of innate and adaptive immunity to an antigen.

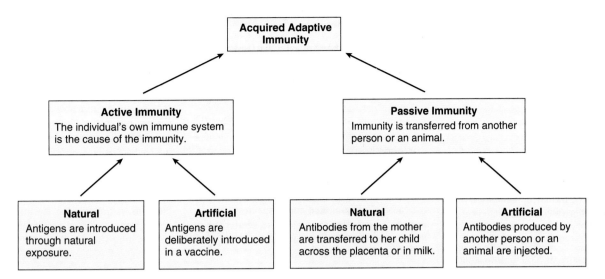

Figure 14.16 Ways to Acquire Adaptive Immunity

Active Natural Immunity

Active natural immunity results from natural exposure to an antigen such as a disease-causing microorganism that stimulates an individual's immune system to respond against the antigen. Because the individual is not immune during the first exposure, he usually develops the symptoms of the disease.

Active Artificial Immunity

In **active artificial immunity**, an antigen is deliberately introduced into an individual to stimulate her immune system. This process is called **vaccination** (vak′si-nā-shŭn), and the introduced antigen is a **vaccine** (vak′sēn, vak-sēn′). Injection of the vaccine is the usual mode of administration. Examples of injected vaccinations are the DTP injection against diphtheria, tetanus, and pertussis (whooping cough); and the MMR injection against mumps, measles, and rubella (German measles). Sometimes the vaccine is ingested, as in the oral poliomyelitis vaccine (OPV).

The vaccine usually consists of some part of a microorganism, a dead microorganism, or a live, altered microorganism. The antigen has been changed so that it will stimulate an immune response but will not cause the symptoms of disease. Because active artificial immunity produces long-lasting immunity without disease symptoms, it is the preferred method of acquiring adaptive immunity.

Passive Natural Immunity

Passive natural immunity results from the transfer of antibodies from a mother to her child across the placenta before birth. During her life, the mother has been exposed to many antigens, either naturally or artificially, and she has antibodies against many of these antigens. These antibodies protect the mother and the developing fetus against disease. Some of the antibodies (IgG) can cross the placenta and enter the fetal blood.

4   P R E D I C T

In some cases, a "booster" shot is used as part of a vaccination procedure. A booster shot is another dose of the original vaccine given some time after the original dose was administered. Why are booster shots given?

✔ *Answer on page 398*

Following birth, the antibodies provide protection for the first few months of the baby's life. Eventually the antibodies are broken down, and the baby must rely on his own immune system. If the mother nurses her baby, antibodies (IgA) in the mother's milk may also provide some protection for the baby.

Passive Artificial Immunity

Achieving **passive artificial immunity** begins with vaccinating an animal such as a horse. After the animal's immune system responds to the antigen, antibodies are removed from the animal and are injected into the individual requiring immunity. Alternatively, a human who has developed immunity through natural exposure or vaccination can be used as a source of antibodies. Passive artificial immunity provides immediate protection because the antibodies either directly or indirectly destroy the antigen. Passive artificial immunity is therefore the preferred treatment when not enough time is available for the individual to develop her own active immunity. The technique provides only temporary immunity, however, because the antibodies are used or eliminated by the recipient.

Antiserum is the general term used for antibodies that provide passive artificial immunity because the antibodies are found in serum, which is plasma minus the clotting factors. Antisera are available against microorganisms that cause disease such as rabies, hepatitis, and measles; bacterial toxins such as tetanus, diphtheria, and botulism; and venoms from poisonous snakes and spiders.

Clinical Focus   Immune System Problems of Clinical Significance

Allergy

An **allergy**, or **hypersensitivity reaction**, is a harmful response to an antigen that does not stimulate an adaptive immune response in most people. Immune and allergic reactions involve the same mechanisms, and the differences between them are unclear. Both require exposure to an antigen and stimulation of antibody-mediated or cell-mediated immunity. If immunity to the antigen is established, later exposure to the antigen results in an immune response that eliminates the antigen, and no symptoms appear. In allergic reactions, the antigen is called the **allergen** (al'er-jen), and later exposure to the allergen stimulates much the same processes that occur during a normal immune response. The processes that eliminate the allergen, however, also produce undesirable side effects such as a strong inflammatory reaction, which can be more harmful than beneficial.

Immediate hypersensitivities produce symptoms within a few minutes of exposure to the allergen and are caused by antibodies. The reaction takes place rapidly because the antibodies are already present because of prior exposure to the allergen. For example, in people with **hay fever**, the allergens, usually plant pollens, are inhaled and absorbed through the respiratory mucous membrane. The resulting localized inflammatory response produces swelling and excess mucus production. In **asthma** (az'mă), resulting from an allergic reaction, the allergen combines with antibodies on mast cells or basophils in the lungs. As a result, these cells release inflammatory chemicals such as leukotrienes and histamine. The chemicals cause constriction of smooth muscle in the walls of the tubes that transport air throughout the lungs. Consequently, less air flows into and out of the lungs, and the patient has difficulty breathing. **Urticaria** (er'ti-kar'i-ă), or **hives**, is a skin rash or localized swelling that can be caused by an ingested allergen. **Anaphylaxis** (an'ă-fī-lak'sis, an'ă-fī-lak'sis) is a systemic allergic reaction, often resulting from insect stings or drugs such as penicillin. The chemicals released from mast cells and basophils cause systemic vasodilation, increased vascular permeability, a drop in blood pressure, and possibly death. Transfusion reactions and hemolytic disease of the newborn (see chapter 11) are also examples of immediate hypersensitivity reactions.

Delayed hypersensitivities take hours to days to develop and are caused by T cells. It takes some time for this reaction to develop because it takes time for the T cells to move by chemotaxis to the allergen. It also takes time for the T cells to release cytokines that

attract other immune system cells involved with producing inflammation. The most common type of delayed hypersensitivity reactions result from contact of an allergen with the skin or mucous membranes. For example, poison ivy, poison oak, soaps, cosmetics, and drugs can cause a delayed hypersensitivity reaction. The allergen is absorbed by epithelial cells, which are then destroyed by T cells, causing inflammation and tissue destruction. Although itching can be intense, scratching is harmful because it damages tissues and causes additional inflammation.

Autoimmune Disease

In **autoimmune disease**, the immune system incorrectly treats self-antigens as foreign antigens. Autoimmune disease operates through the same mechanisms as hypersensitivity reactions except that the reaction is stimulated by self-antigens. Examples of autoimmune diseases include thrombocytopenia, lupus erythematosus, rheumatoid arthritis, rheumatic fever, diabetes mellitus (type 1), and myasthenia gravis.

Immunodeficiency

Immunodeficiency is a failure of some part of the immune system to function properly. It can be congenital (present at birth) or acquired. Congenital immunodeficiencies usually involve failure of the fetus to form adequate numbers of B cells, T cells, or both. **Severe combined immunodeficiency (SCID)**, in which both B cells and T cells fail to form, is probably the best known. Unless the person suffering from SCID is kept in a sterile environment or is provided with a compatible bone marrow transplant, death from infection results.

Acquired immunodeficiency can result from many different causes. For example, inadequate protein in the diet inhibits protein synthesis and, therefore, antibody levels decrease. Immunity can be depressed as a result of stress, illness, or drugs such as those used to prevent graft rejection. Diseases such as leukemia cause an overproduction of lymphocytes that do not function properly.

Acquired immunodeficiency syndrome (AIDS) is a life-threatening disease caused by the **human immunodeficiency virus (HIV)**. Two strains of HIV have been recognized: HIV-1 is responsible for most cases of AIDS, whereas HIV-2 is increasingly being found in West Africa. AIDS was first reported in 1981 in the United States. Since then over 650,000 cases have been reported to the Center for Disease Control (CDC). Evidence suggests that almost everyone

infected will develop symptoms within 10 years, and they will eventually develop the disease if they do not die of some other cause. The few cases of HIV-infected individuals who have not developed AIDS even after many years of being infected are being investigated.

HIV is transmitted from an infected to a noninfected person in body fluids such as blood, semen, or vaginal secretions. The major methods of transmission are intimate sexual contact, contaminated needles used by intravenous drug users, and tainted blood products. Present evidence indicates household, school, or work contacts do not result in transmission.

In the United States, most cases of AIDS have appeared in homosexual or bisexual men and in intravenous drug users. A small percentage of cases have resulted from transfusions or contaminated clotting factors used by hemophiliacs. Sadly, children can be infected before birth, during delivery, or after birth from breast-feeding. A few cases of AIDS have occurred in health care workers accidentally exposed to HIV-infected blood or body fluids, and an even smaller number of cases of health care workers infecting patients has been documented. The most rapidly increasing group of AIDS patients in the United States is heterosexual women or men who have had sexual contact with an infected person. Women in the 15- to 25-year-old age group appear to be especially likely to contract AIDS, possibly because the vaginal mucous membranes of women in this age group are thin and are a less effective barrier to the virus.

In other countries, the pattern of AIDS cases can be different from that in the United States. For example, in Haiti and central Africa, heterosexual transmission is the major route of spread of HIV. Worldwide, about 40% of AIDS cases are women. The World Health Organization estimates that 20 million people have been infected by HIV.

Preventing transmission of HIV is presently the only way to prevent AIDS. The risk of transmission can be reduced by educating the public about safe sexual practices such as reducing the number of one's sexual partners, avoiding anal intercourse, and using a condom. Public education also includes warnings to intravenous drug users of the dangers of using contaminated needles. Ensuring the safety of the blood supply is another important preventive measure. In April, 1985, a test for HIV antibodies in blood became available. Heat treatment of clotting factors taken from blood has also been effective in preventing transmission of HIV to hemophiliacs.

HIV infection begins when the virus binds to a CD4 surface molecule. The CD4 molecule is found primarily on helper T cells but also on certain monocytes, macrophages, neurons, and neuroglial cells. Once attached to a CD4 molecule, the virus injects its genetic material (RNA) and enzymes into the cell. The viral RNA and enzymes produce DNA that can direct the formation of new HIV ribonucleic acid and proteins, that is, additional viruses that can infect other cells. Most of the manifestations of AIDS can be explained by the loss of helper T cell functions or the infection of other cells with CD4 molecules. Without helper T cells, cytotoxic T cell and B cell activation is impaired, and specific resistance is suppressed.

Following infection by the HIV, within 3 weeks to 3 months, some patients develop an acute (sudden) mononucleosislike syndrome that can last up to 14 days. Symptoms include fever, sweats, fatigue, muscle and joint aches, headache, sore throat, diarrhea, rash, and lymphadenopathy (lim-fad-ě-nop′ă-thē; swollen lymph nodes). More commonly there is a persistent version of the syndrome that lasts for several months and includes lymphadenopathy, fever, and fatigue. During this time the patient becomes positive for HIV antibodies, and within a year many patients develop AIDS.

The most common clinical manifestations of AIDS include testing positive for HIV antibodies, a decrease in helper T cell numbers to fewer than 200/mm^3 of blood, and the presence of opportunistic infections or Kaposi's sarcoma. Normally there are about 1200 helper T cells/mm^3 blood, but between the time of infection and the development of AIDS the number of helper T cells decreases. Apparently most HIV replication takes place in the lymph nodes where helper T cells and other immune cells aggregate. As cells in the lymph nodes are destroyed, the number of circulating helper T cells decreases.

Opportunistic infections involve organisms that normally do not cause disease but can do so when the immune system is depressed. Examples include *Pneumocystis carinii* (noo-mō-sis′tis kă-rī′nē-ī) pneumonia (caused by an intracellular fungus); tuberculosis (caused by an intracellular bacterium, *Mycobacterium tuberculosis*); syphilis (caused by a sexually transmitted bacterium, *Treponema pallidum*); candidiasis (kan-di-dī′ă-sis; a yeast infection of the mouth or vagina caused by *Candida albicans*); and protozoans that cause severe, persistent diarrhea. Kaposi's sarcoma is a type of cancer that produces lesions in the skin, lymph nodes, and visceral organs. Also associated with AIDS are symptoms resulting from the effects of HIV on the nervous system, including motor retardation, behavioral changes, progressive dementia, and possibly psychosis.

There currently is no cure for AIDS. Management of AIDS can be divided into two categories: (1) management of secondary infections or malignancies associated with AIDS and (2) treatment of HIV infection itself. The first effective treatment of AIDS was the drug azidothymidine (AZT) (az′i-dō-thī′mi-dēn), also called zidovudine (zī-dō′vū-dēn). AZT inhibits the replication of HIV by preventing HIV ribonucleic acid from producing deoxyribonucleic acid inside cells. AZT can delay the onset of AIDS but does not appear to increase the survival time of AIDS patients. The number of babies who contract AIDS from their HIV-infected mothers can be dramatically reduced, however, by giving AZT to the mothers during pregnancy and to the babies following birth. AZT can produce serious side effects such as anemia or even total bone marrow failure.

Often after 6 to 18 months of treatment with AZT, viral mutations result in HIV that are resistant to AZT. Other drugs that inhibit viral nucleic acid replication, such as dideoxyinosine (DDI) (dī′dē-oks-ē-ī′nō-sēn), have been developed. These drugs have been used for patients who are resistant to or who do not respond to AZT.

A newer group of drugs called **protease** (prō′tē-ās) **inhibitors** are now being tested. Protease inhibitors interfere with viral protease, which is an enzyme necessary for the virus to prepare its own proteins. Examples of protease inhibitors are ritonavir and indinavir. Initial results indicate that the protease inhibitors are much more effective than the drugs that inhibit nucleic acid synthesis. It is also clear that a combination therapy of nucleic acid and protease inhibitors can effectively reduce the number of HIV particles in the blood and prolong life expectancy.

Another advance in AIDS treatment is a test for measuring viral load, which is the quantity of HIV in a milliliter of blood. It has been learned that viral load is a good predictor of how soon a person will develop AIDS. If viral load is high, the onset of AIDS is much sooner than if viral load is low.

It is hoped that the new drug therapies and the ability to monitor viral load can be combined to produce an effective treatment of AIDS by matching drug types and doses with viral load. If viral load can be kept low, then HIV infections may not develop into full-blown AIDS.

An effective treatment for AIDS is not a cure. Even if viral load decreases to the point that the virus is not detected in the blood, the virus may still be hidden in cells throughout the body. In addition, the long-term effects of these drug therapies is unknown. Although research is underway to develop a vaccine, an effective vaccine is not expected in the immediate future.

Tumor Control

According to the concept of **immune surveillance,** the immune system detects tumor cells and destroys them before a tumor can form. T cells, NK cells, and macrophages are involved in the destruction of tumor cells. Immune surveillance may exist for some forms of cancer caused by viruses. The immune response appears to be directed more against the viruses, however, than against tumors in general. Only a few cancers are known to be caused by viruses in humans. For most tumors the response of the immune system may be ineffective and too late.

Transplantation

The genes that code for the production of the MHC molecules are generally called the **major histocompatibility complex genes.** Histocompatibility refers to the ability of tissues (Gr. *histo*) to get along (compatibility) when tissues are transplanted from one individual to another. In humans, the MHC genes are often referred to as **human leukocyte antigen (HLA) genes** because they were first identified in leukocytes. There are millions of possible combinations of the HLA genes, and it is very rare for two individuals (except identical twins) to have the same set of HLA genes. Because they are genetically determined, however, the closer the relationship between two individuals, the greater the likelihood of sharing the same HLA genes.

The immune system can distinguish between self and foreign cells because self-cells have self-HLAs, whereas foreign cells have foreign HLAs. Rejection of a graft is caused by a normal immune response to foreign HLAs.

Graft rejection can occur in two different directions. In **host-versus-graft rejection,** the recipient's immune system recognizes the donor tissue as foreign and rejects the transplant. In a **graft-versus-host rejection,** the donor tissue (e.g., bone marrow) recognizes the recipient's tissue as foreign, and the transplant rejects the recipient, causing destruction of the recipient's tissue and possibly death.

To reduce graft rejection, a tissue match is performed. Only tissue with HLAs similar to the recipient's have a chance of being accepted. An exact match is possible only for a graft from one part to another part of the same person, or between identical twins. For all other graft situations, drugs such as cyclosporine (sī-klō-spōr′in) that suppress the immune system must be administered throughout the patient's life to prevent graft rejection. Unfortunately, the person then has a drug-produced immunodeficiency and is more susceptible to infections.

Systems Pathology

systemic lupus erythematosus

SYSTEMIC LUPUS ERYTHEMATOSUS

Mrs. L. was a 30-year-old divorced woman with two children. Despite the fact that she had to work to support herself and the children, she entered college, determined to become a nurse and provide a better life for her family. Mrs. L. was an excellent student, but her class attendance and her performance on tests was somewhat erratic. Sometimes she seemed very energetic and earned high grades, but other times she seemed depressed and did not do as well. Toward the end of the course, she developed a rash on her face (figure A), a large red lesion on her arm, and was obviously not feeling well.

Mrs. L. went to the instructor to ask if she could take an incomplete grade and take the last exam at a later time. She explained that she has had lupus since she was 25 years old. Normally, medication helps to control her symptoms, but the stress of being a single parent combined with the challenges of school seemed to be making her condition worse. She further explained that the symptoms of lupus come and go, and bedrest was often helpful. Mrs. L. finished the course requirements later that summer. She went on to complete her education and now has a full-time job as a nurse at a local hospital.

Figure A   Systemic Lupus Erythematosus
The butterfly rash resulting from inflammation in the skin caused by systemic lupus erythematosus.

Background Information

Systemic lupus erythematosus (SLE) (lū′pŭs er-i-thē′mă-tō-sŭs) is a disease of unknown cause in which tissues and cells are damaged by the immune system. The name describes some of the characteristics of the disease. The term lupus literally means wolf and was originally used to refer to eroded (as if gnawed by a wolf) lesions of the skin. Erythematosus refers to a redness of the skin resulting from inflammation. Unfortunately, as the term systemic implies, the disorder is not confined to the skin but can affect tissues and cells throughout the body. Another systemic effect is the presence of low-grade fever in most cases of active SLE.

SLE is an autoimmune disorder in which a large variety of antibodies are produced that recognize self-antigens, such as nucleic acids, phospholipids, coagulation factors, red blood cells, and platelets. The combination of the antibodies with self-antigens forms immune complexes that circulate throughout the body to be deposited in various tissues, in which they stimulate inflammation and tissue destruction. Thus, SLE is a disease that can affect many systems of the body. For example, the most common antibodies act against DNA that is released from damaged cells. Normally the liver removes the DNA, but when DNA and antibodies form immune complexes, they tend to be deposited in the kidneys and other tissues.

Approximately 40% to 50% of individuals with SLE develop renal disease. In some cases, the antibodies can bind to antigens on cells, resulting in lysis of the cells. For example, antibodies binding to red blood cells cause hemolysis and the development of anemia.

The cause of SLE is unknown. The most popular hypothesis is that a viral infection disrupts the function of T cells that normally prevent an immune response to self-antigens. Genetic factors probably contribute to the development of the disease. The likelihood of developing SLE is much higher if a family member also has it.

Approximately 1 out of 2000 individuals in the United States have SLE. The first symptoms of SLE usually appear between 15 and 25 years of age, affecting women approximately 9 times as often as men. The progress of the disease is unpredictable, with flare-ups of symptoms followed by periods of remission. The survival after diagnosis is greater than 90% after 10 years. The most frequent causes of death involve kidney failure, CNS dysfunction, infections, and cardiovascular disease.

There is no cure for SLE, nor is there one standard of treatment because the course of the disease is highly variable and there are many differences between patients with SLE. Treatment usually begins with mild medications and proceeds to more and more potent therapies as conditions warrant. Aspirin and nonsteroidal antiinflammatory drugs are used to suppress inflammation. Antimalarial drugs are used to treat skin rash and arthritis in SLE, but the mechanism of action is unknown. Patients who do not respond to these drugs or those with severe SLE are helped by steroids. Although steroids effectively suppress inflammation, they can produce undesirable side effects including suppression of normal adrenal gland functions. In patients with life-threatening SLE, very high doses of steroids are used.

5 **PREDICT**

The red lesion Mrs. L. developed on her arm is called purpura (pŭr'pū-ră), which is caused by bleeding into the skin. The lesions gradually change color and disappear in 2 or 3 weeks. Explain how SLE produces purpura.

✔ *Answer on page 398*

System Interactions

System	Interactions
Integumentary	Skin lesions frequently occur and are made worse by exposure to the sun. There are three forms: (1) an inflammatory redness that can take the form of the butterfly-shaped rash, which extends from the bridge of the nose to the cheeks; (2) small, localized pimplelike eruptions accompanied by scaling of the skin; (3) areas of atrophied, depigmented skin with borders of increased pigmentation. Hair loss results in diffuse thinning of the hair.
Skeletal	Arthritis, tendonitis, and death of bone tissue can develop.
Muscular	Destruction of muscle tissue and muscular weakness.
Nervous	Memory loss, intellectual deterioration, disorientation, psychosis, reactive depression, headache, seizures, nausea, and loss of appetite can occur. Stroke is a major cause of dysfunction and death. Cranial nerve involvement results in facial muscle weakness, drooping of the eyelid, and double vision. Central nervous system lesions can cause paralysis.
Endocrine	Sex hormones may play a role in SLE because 90% of the cases occur in females, and females with SLE have reduced levels of androgens.
Cardiovascular	Inflammation of the pericardium (pericarditis) with chest pain can develop. Damage to heart valves, inflammation of cardiac tissue, tachycardia, arrhythmias, angina, and myocardial infarction also occurs. Hemolytic anemia and leukopenia can be present (see chapter 11). Antiphospholipid antibody syndrome, through an unknown mechanism, increases coagulation and thrombus formation, which increases the risk of stroke and heart attack.
Respiratory	Chest pain caused by inflammation of the pleural membranes; fever, shortness of breath, and hypoxemia caused by inflammation of the lungs; and alveolar hemorrhage can develop.
Digestive	Ulcers develop in the oral cavity and pharynx. Abdominal pain and vomiting are common, but no cause can be found. Inflammation of the pancreas and occasionally enlargement of the liver and minor abnormalities in liver function tests occur.
Urinary	Renal lesions and glomerulonephritis can result in progressive failure of kidney functions. Excess proteins are lost in the urine, resulting in lower than normal blood proteins, which can produce edema.

Summary

Lymphatic System

- The lymphatic system consists of lymph, lymphocytes, lymphatic vessels, lymph nodes, tonsils, the spleen, and the thymus gland.

Functions of the Lymphatic System

- The lymphatic system maintains fluid balance in tissues, absorbs fats from the small intestine, and defends against microorganisms and foreign substances.

Lymphatic Capillaries and Vessels

- Lymphatic vessels carry lymph away from tissues. Valves in the vessels ensure the one-way flow of lymph.
- Skeletal muscle contraction, contraction of lymphatic vessel smooth muscle, and thoracic pressure changes move the lymph through the vessels.

- The thoracic duct and right lymphatic duct empty lymph into the blood.

Lymphatic Organs

- Lymphatic tissue produces lymphocytes, when exposed to foreign substances, and it filters lymph and blood.
- The tonsils protect the openings between the nasal and oral cavities and the pharynx.
- Lymph nodes, located along lymphatic vessels, filter lymph.
- The white pulp of the spleen responds to foreign substances in the blood, whereas the red pulp phagocytizes foreign substances and worn out red blood cells. The spleen also functions as a reservoir for blood.
- The thymus processes lymphocytes that move to other lymphatic tissue to respond to foreign substances.

Immunity

- Immunity is the ability to resist the harmful effects of microorganisms and other foreign substances.

Innate Immunity

Mechanical Mechanisms

- The skin and mucous membranes are barriers that prevent the entry of microorganisms into the body.
- Tears, saliva, and urine act to wash away microorganisms.

Chemical Mediators

- Chemical mediators kill microorganisms, promote phagocytosis, and increase inflammation.
- Lysozyme in tears and complement in plasma are examples of chemicals involved in innate immunity.
- Interferons prevent the replication of viruses.

Cells

- Chemotaxis is the ability of cells to move toward microorganisms or sites of tissue damage.
- Neutrophils are the first phagocytic cells to respond to microorganisms.
- Macrophages are large phagocytic cells that are active in the latter part of an infection. Macrophages are also positioned at sites of potential entry of microorganisms into tissues.
- Basophils and mast cells promote inflammation, whereas eosinophils inhibit inflammation.
- Natural killer cells lyse tumor cells and virus-infected cells.

Inflammatory Response

- Chemical mediators cause vasodilation and increase vascular permeability, allowing the entry of chemicals into damaged tissues. Chemicals also attract phagocytes.
- The amount of chemical mediators and phagocytes increases until the cause of the inflammation is destroyed. Then the tissues undergo repair.
- Local inflammation produces the symptoms of redness, heat, swelling, pain, and loss of function. Symptoms of systemic inflammation include an increase in neutrophil numbers, fever, and shock.

Adaptive Immunity

- Antigens are molecules that stimulate adaptive immunity.
- B cells are responsible for humoral, or antibody-mediated, immunity. T cells are involved with cell-mediated immunity.

Origin and Development of Lymphocytes

- B and T cells originate in red bone marrow. T cells are processed in the thymus and B cells are processed in red bone marrow.
- B and T cells move to lymphatic tissue from their processing sites. They continually circulate from one lymphatic tissue to another.

Activation and Multiplication of Lymphocytes

- B cells and T cells have antigen-binding receptors on their surfaces. Clones are lymphocytes with the same antigen-binding receptor.
- Major histocompatibility complex (MHC) molecules present processed antigens to B or T cells.
- Costimulation by cytokines, such as interleukins, and surface molecules, such as CD4, are required in addition to MHC molecules.
- Macrophages present processed antigens to helper T cells, which divide and increase in number.
- Helper T cells stimulate B cells to divide and differentiate into cells that produce antibodies.

Antibody-Mediated Immunity

- Antibodies are proteins. The variable region combines with antigens and is responsible for antibody specificity. The constant region activates complement or attaches the antibody to cells. The five classes of antibodies are IgG, IgM, IgA, IgE, and IgD.
- Antibodies directly inactivate antigens or cause them to clump together. Antibodies indirectly destroy antigens by promoting phagocytosis and inflammation.
- The primary response results from the first exposure to an antigen. B cells form plasma cells, which produce antibodies, and memory B cells.
- The secondary (memory) response results from exposure to an antigen after a primary response. Memory B cells quickly form plasma cells and new memory B cells.

Cell-Mediated Immunity

- Exposure to an antigen activates cytotoxic T cells and produces memory T cells.
- Cytotoxic T cells lyse virus-infected cells, tumor cells, and tissue transplants. Cytotoxic T cells produce cytokines, which promote inflammation and phagocytosis.

Immune Interactions

Innate immunity, antibody-mediated immunity, and cell-mediated immunity can function together to eliminate an antigen.

Immunotherapy

Immunotherapy stimulates or inhibits the immune system to treat diseases.

Acquired Immunity

- Active natural immunity results from everyday exposure to an antigen against which the person's own immune system mounts a response.
- Active artificial immunity results from deliberate exposure to an antigen (vaccine) to which the person's own immune system responds.
- Passive natural immunity is the transfer of antibodies from a mother to her fetus during gestation or baby during breastfeeding.
- Passive artificial immunity is the transfer of antibodies from an animal or another person to a person requiring immunity.

Content Review

1. List the parts of the lymphatic system, and describe the three main functions of the lymphatic system.
2. What is the function of the valves in lymphatic vessels? What causes lymph to move through lymphatic vessels?
3. Which parts of the body are drained by the right lymphatic duct and which by the thoracic duct?
4. Describe the cells and fibers of lymphatic tissue, and explain the functions of lymphatic tissue.
5. Name the three groups of tonsils. What is their function?
6. Where are lymph nodes found? What is the function of the germinal centers within lymph nodes?
7. Where is the spleen located? What is the function of white pulp and red pulp within the spleen? What other function does the spleen perform?
8. Where is the thymus gland located, and what function does it perform?
9. What is the difference between innate immunity and adaptive immunity?
10. How do mechanical mechanisms and chemical mediators provide protection against microorganisms? Describe the effects of complement and interferons.
11. Describe the functions of the two major phagocytic cell types of the body. What is the mononuclear phagocytic system?
12. Name the cells involved in promoting and inhibiting inflammation.
13. What protective function is performed by natural killer cells?
14. Describe the effects that take place during an inflammatory response. What are the symptoms of local and systemic inflammation?
15. Define antigen. What is the difference between a self-antigen and a foreign antigen?
16. Which cells are responsible for antibody-mediated and for cell-mediated immunity?
17. Describe the origin and development of B and T cells.
18. What is the function of antigen-binding receptors and major histocompatibility proteins?
19. What is costimulation? Give an example.
20. Describe the process by which an antigen can cause an increase in helper T-cell numbers.
21. Describe the process by which helper T cells can stimulate B cells to divide, differentiate, and produce antibodies.
22. What are the functions of the variable and constant regions of an antibody?
23. Describe the direct and indirect ways that antibodies function to destroy antigens.
24. What are the functions of plasma cells and B memory cells?
25. Define the primary and memory (secondary) response. How do they differ from each other in regard to speed of response and amount of antibody produced?
26. What are the functions of cytotoxic T cells and T memory cells?
27. Define active natural, active artificial, passive natural, and passive artificial immunity. Give an example of each.

Develop Your Reasoning Skills

1. A patient is suffering from edema in the lower right limb. Explain why elevation and massage of the limb helps to remove the excess fluid.
2. If the thymus of an experimental animal is removed immediately following birth, the animal exhibits the following characteristics:
   a. It is more susceptible to infections.
   b. It has decreased numbers of lymphocytes.
   c. Its ability to reject grafts is greatly decreased.
   Explain these observations.
3. Adjuvants are substances that slow, but do not stop, the release of an antigen from an injection site into the blood. Suppose injection A of a given amount of antigen is given without an adjuvant and injection B of the same amount of antigen is given with an adjuvant that caused the release of antigen over a period of 2 to 3 weeks. Does injection A or B result in the greater amount of antibody production? Explain.
4. Compare how long active immunity and passive immunity last. Explain the difference between the two types of immunity. In what situations is one type preferred over the other?
5. Tetanus is caused by bacteria (*Clostridium tetani*) that enter the body through wounds in the skin. The bacteria produce a toxin that causes spastic muscle contractions. Death often results from failure of the respiratory muscles. A patient comes to the emergency room after stepping on a nail. If the patient has been vaccinated against tetanus, he is given a tetanus booster shot, which consists of the toxin altered so that it is harmless. If the patient has never been vaccinated against tetanus, he is given an antiserum shot against tetanus. Explain the rationale for this treatment strategy. Sometimes both a booster and an antiserum shot are given, but at different locations of the body. Explain why this is done, and why the shots are given in different locations.
6. A patient had many allergic reactions (see Clinical Focus: Immune System Problems of Clinical Significance on p. 392). As part of the treatment scheme, it was decided to try to identify the allergens that stimulated the allergic reaction. A series of solutions, each containing an allergen that commonly causes a reaction, was composed. Each solution was then injected into the skin at different locations on the patient's back. The following results were obtained:
   a. At one location, within a few minutes the injection site became red and swollen.
   b. At another injection site, swelling and redness did not appear until 2 days later.
   c. No redness or swelling developed at the other sites.
   Explain what happened for each observation and what caused the redness and swelling.

Answers to Predict Questions

1. p. 376 Cutting and tying off the lymphatic vessels prevents the movement of fluid from the affected tissue. The result is edema.

2. p. 383 When the antigen is eliminated, it is no longer available for processing and combining with MHC molecules. Consequently there is no signal to cause lymphocytes to proliferate and produce antibodies.

3. p. 386 The first exposure to the disease-causing agent (antigen) evokes a primary immune system response. Gradually, however, the antibodies degrade, and memory cells die. If, before all the memory cells are eliminated, a second exposure to the antigen occurs, a secondary response results. The memory cells produced could provide immunity until the next exposure to the antigen.

4. p. 391 The booster shot stimulates a memory (secondary) response, resulting in the formation of large amounts of antibodies and memory cells. Consequently there is better, longer lasting immunity.

5. p. 395 SLE is an autoimmune disorder in which self-antigens activate immune responses. Often, this results in the formation of immune complexes and inflammation. Sometimes antibodies bind to antigens on cell membranes, resulting in the rupture of the cell membranes. Purpura results from bleeding into the skin, which means that platelet plug formation, the normal mechanism for repairing small breaks in blood vessels, is not working. In this case of SLE, antibodies are causing the destruction of platelets, and the decreased number of platelets results in decreased platelet plug formation and coagulation (see chapter 11). The condition is called thrombocytopenia.

Chapter Fifteen

Respiratory System

alveolus, pl. alveoli
(al-vē′ō-lŭs) [L., cavity] The saclike endings of the respiratory system, in which gas exchange occurs.

bronchiole
(brong′kē-ōl) One of the finer subdivisions of the bronchial tubes, less than 1 mm in diameter, which has no cartilage in its wall, but relatively more smooth muscle and elastic fibers than larger bronchial tubes have.

bronchus
(brong′kŭs) [Gr. *bronchos*, windpipe] Any one of the air ducts conducting air from the trachea to the bronchioles. A bronchus has cartilage rings or plates in its wall, and it varies in diameter from about 1 cm in the primary bronchi to about 1 mm in the smallest (tertiary) bronchi.

larynx
(lar′ingks) Organ of voice production located between the pharynx and the trachea; it consists of a framework of cartilages and elastic membranes housing the vocal folds (true vocal cords) and the muscles that control the position and tension of these elements.

nasal cavity
(nā′zăl) Cavity divided by the nasal septum; extends from the external nares anteriorly to the nasopharynx posteriorly and is bounded inferiorly by the hard palate.

pharynx
(far′ingks) [Gr. *pharynx*, throat] Upper expanded part of the digestive tract between the esophagus below and the oral and nasal cavities above and in front.

pleural cavity
(ploor′ăl) Space between the parietal and visceral layers of the pleura, normally filled with pleural fluid.

respiratory membrane
(res′pi-ră-tōr-ē, rĕ-spīr′ă-tōr-ē) Membrane in the lungs across which gas exchange occurs with blood; consists of a thin layer of fluid, the alveolar epithelium, the basement membrane of the alveolar epithelium, interstitial space, the basement membrane of the capillary endothelium, and the capillary endothelium.

trachea
(trā′kē-ă) [Gr. *tracheia arteria*, rough artery] Air tube extending from the larynx into the thorax, where it divides to form the two primary bronchi; has 16 to 20 C-shaped pieces of cartilage in its walls.

Objectives

After reading this chapter, you should be able to:

1. Describe the anatomy of the respiratory passages, beginning at the nose and ending with the alveoli.

2. Describe the lungs, the membranes that cover the lungs, and the cavities in which they lie.

3. Explain how contraction of the muscles of respiration causes changes in thoracic volume during quiet breathing and during labored breathing.

4. Describe the changes in alveolar pressure that are responsible for the movement of air into and out of the lungs.

5. Explain how surfactant and pleural pressure prevent the collapse of the lungs and how changes in pleural pressure cause changes in alveolar volume.

6. List the pulmonary volumes and capacities and define each of them.

7. Name the components of the respiratory membrane and explain the factors that affect gas movement through it.

8. Describe the partial pressure gradients for oxygen and carbon dioxide.

9. Explain how oxygen and carbon dioxide are transported in the blood.

10. Describe the respiratory areas of the brainstem and how they produce a rhythmic pattern of ventilation.

11. Name the neural mechanisms that can modify the normal rhythmic pattern of ventilation.

12. Explain how alterations in blood pH, carbon dioxide, and oxygen levels affect ventilation.

13. Describe the regulation of ventilation during exercise and describe the changes in the respiratory system that result from exercise training.

Studying, sleeping, talking, eating, and exercising all involve breathing. From our first breath at birth, the rate and depth of our respiration is unconsciously matched to our activities. Although we can voluntarily stop breathing, within a few minutes we must breathe again. Breathing is so characteristic of life that, along with the pulse, it is one of the first things we check for to determine if an unconscious person is alive.

Respiration includes the following processes: (1) ventilation, or breathing, which is the movement of air into and out of the lungs; (2) gas exchange between the air in the lungs and the blood; (3) transport of oxygen and carbon dioxide in the blood; and (4) gas exchange between the blood and the tissues. The term respiration is also used in reference to cell metabolism. In aerobic respiration, for example, cells use oxygen and produce carbon dioxide. Cellular respiration is considered in chapter 17.

Functions of the Respiratory System

Respiration is necessary because all living cells of the body require oxygen and produce carbon dioxide. The respiratory system assists in gas exchange and performs other functions as well.

1. *Gas exchange.* The respiratory system allows oxygen from the air to enter the blood and carbon dioxide to leave the blood and enter the air. The cardiovascular system transports oxygen from the lungs to the cells of the body and carbon dioxide from the cells of the body to the lungs. Thus the respiratory and cardiovascular systems work together to supply oxygen to all cells and to remove carbon dioxide. Without healthy respiratory and cardiovascular systems, the capacity to carry out normal activity is reduced, and without adequate respiratory and cardiovascular system functions, life itself is impossible.
2. *Regulation of blood pH.* The respiratory system can alter blood pH by changing blood carbon dioxide levels.
3. *Voice production.* Air movement past the vocal cords makes sound and speech possible.
4. *Olfaction.* The sensation of smell occurs when airborne molecules are drawn into the nasal cavity.
5. *Innate immunity* (see chapter 14). The respiratory system provides protection against some microorganisms by preventing their entry into the body and by removing them from respiratory surfaces.

Anatomy of the Respiratory System

The **respiratory system** consists of the nose, the nasal cavity, the pharynx, the larynx, the trachea, the bronchi, and the lungs (figure 15.1). The **upper respiratory tract** refers to the nose, nasal cavity, pharynx, and associated structures; and the **lower**

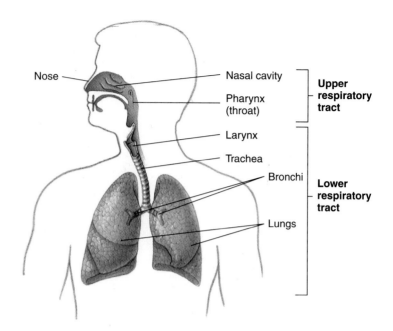

Figure 15.1 The Respiratory System

The major parts of the respiratory system are the nose, nasal cavity, pharynx, larynx, trachea, bronchi, and lungs. Air can also enter the respiratory system through the oral cavity.

respiratory tract includes the larynx, trachea, bronchi, and lungs. Although air frequently passes through the oral cavity, it is considered to be part of the digestive system instead of the respiratory system.

Nose and Nasal Cavity

The term nose refers to the visible structure that forms a prominent feature of the face. Most of the nose is composed of cartilage, although the bridge of the nose consists of bone. The bone and cartilage are covered by connective tissue and skin (figure 15.2).

The **nasal** (nā'zăl) **cavity** extends from the nares to the choane. The **nares** (nā'rēs; sing. nā'ris) are the external openings of the nose and the **choane** (kō'an-ē) are the openings into the pharynx. The **nasal septum** is a partition dividing the nasal cavity into right and left sides. The **hard palate** (pal'ăt) forms the floor of the nasal cavity, separating the nasal cavity from the oral cavity (see chapter 6). Air can flow through the nasal cavity even when the oral cavity is full of food.

Three prominent bony ridges called **conchae** (kon'kē, resembling a conch shell) are present on the lateral walls on each side of the nasal cavity. The conchae increase the surface area of the nasal cavity.

Paranasal (par-ă-nā'săl) **sinuses** are air-filled spaces within bone. The maxillary, frontal, ethmoidal, and sphenoidal sinuses are named after the bones in which they are located. The paranasal sinuses open into the nasal cavity and are lined with a mucous membrane. They reduce the weight of the skull, produce mucus, and influence the quality of the voice by acting as resonating chambers.

Figure 15.2 Nasal Cavity and Pharynx

(*a*) Sagittal section through the nasal cavity and pharynx.
(*b*) Photograph of a sagittal section of the head.

Mucus, produced by the epithelium of the paranasal sinuses, drains through small passageways into the nasal cavity. When the mucous membranes become swollen because of nasal infections, sinus infections, or allergies, these passages can become blocked. The mucus then accumulates within the sinuses, and the increasing pressure can produce a painful sinus headache.

The **nasolacrimal** (nā-zō-lak′ri-măl) **ducts**, which carry tears from the eyes, also open into the nasal cavity. Sensory receptors for the sense of smell are found in the superior part of the nasal cavity (see chapter 9).

Air enters the nasal cavity through the external nares. Just inside the external nares the epithelial lining is composed of stratified squamous epithelium containing coarse hairs. The hairs trap some of the large particles of dust suspended in the air. The rest of the nasal cavity is lined with pseudostratified columnar epithelial cells containing cilia and many mucus-producing goblet cells (see chapter 4). Mucus produced by the goblet cells also traps debris in the air. The cilia sweep the mucus posteriorly to the pharynx, where it is swallowed. As air flows through the nasal cavities, it is humidified by moisture from the mucous epithelium and is warmed by blood flowing through the superficial capillary networks underlying the mucous epithelium.

1	P R E D I C T

Explain what happens to your throat when you sleep with your mouth open, especially when your nasal passages are plugged as a result of having a cold. Explain what may happen to your lungs when you run a long way in very cold weather while breathing rapidly through your mouth.

✔ *Answer on page 429*

Pharynx

The **pharynx** (far'ingks, throat) is the common passageway of both the respiratory and digestive systems. It receives air from the nasal cavity and air, food, and water from the mouth. Inferiorly, the pharynx leads to the rest of the respiratory system through the opening into the larynx and to the digestive system through the esophagus. The pharynx can be divided into three regions: the nasopharynx, the oropharynx, and the laryngopharynx (see figure 15.2*a*).

The **nasopharynx** (nā'zō-far'ingks) is the superior part of the pharynx and extends from the internal nares of the nasal cavity to the level of the **uvula** (ū'vū-lă, a little grape), a soft process that extends from the posterior edge of the soft palate. The **soft palate** forms the floor of the nasopharynx. The nasopharynx is lined with pseudostratified ciliated columnar epithelium that is continuous with the nasal cavity. The auditory tubes open into the nasopharynx, and the posterior part of the nasopharynx contains the **pharyngeal** (fă-rin'jē-ăl) **tonsil**, which aids in defending the body against infection (see chapter 14). The soft palate and uvula are elevated during swallowing; this movement results in the clo-

sure of the nasopharynx, which prevents food from passing from the oral cavity into the nasopharynx.

The **oropharynx** (ōr'ō-far'ingks) extends from the uvula to the epiglottis, and the oral cavity opens into the oropharynx. Thus food, drink, and air all pass through the oropharynx. The oropharynx is lined with stratified squamous epithelium, which protects against abrasion. Two sets of tonsils, the palatine tonsil and the lingual tonsils, are located near the opening between the mouth and the oropharynx. The **palatine** (pal'ă-tīn) **tonsils** are located in the lateral walls near the border of the oral cavity and the oropharynx The **lingual tonsils** are located on the surface of the posterior part of the tongue.

The **laryngopharynx** (lă-ring'gō-far-ingks) passes posterior to the larynx and extends from the tip of the epiglottis to the esophagus. The laryngopharynx is lined with stratified squamous epithelium and ciliated columnar epithelium.

Larynx

The **larynx** (lar'ingks) consists of an outer casing of nine cartilages that are connected to each other by muscles and ligaments (figure 15.3). Three of the nine cartilages are unpaired, and six of them form three pairs. The largest cartilage is the unpaired **thyroid** (thī'royd) **cartilage**, or **Adam's apple**. Thyroid means shield and refers to the shape of the cartilage. The most inferior cartilage of the larynx is the unpaired **cricoid** (krī'koyd, ring-shaped) **cartilage**, which forms the base of the larynx on which the other cartilages rest. The thyroid and cricoid cartilages maintain an open passageway for air movement.

The third unpaired cartilage is the **epiglottis** (ep-i-glot'is, on the glottis). It differs from the other cartilages in that it consists of elastic cartilage rather than hyaline cartilage. Its inferior margin is attached to the thyroid cartilage anteriorly, and the superior part of the epiglottis projects as a free flap toward

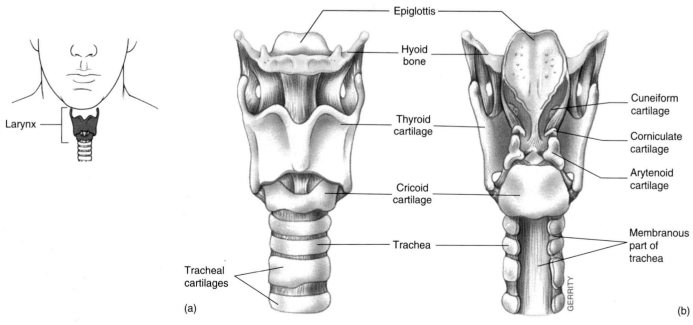

Figure 15.3 Anatomy of the Larynx

(*a*) Anterior view. (*b*) Posterior view.

the tongue. The epiglottis helps prevent swallowed materials from entering the larynx. As the larynx elevates during swallowing, the epiglottis tips posteriorly to cover the opening of the larynx.

The six paired cartilages consist of three cartilages on either side of the posterior part of the larynx (see figure 15.3*b*). The top cartilage on each side is the **cuneiform** (kū′nē-i-fōrm, wedge-shaped) **cartilage**, the middle cartilage is the **corniculate** (kōr-nik′ū-lāt, horn-shaped) **cartilage**, and the bottom cartilage is the **arytenoid** (ar-i-tē′noyd, ladle-shaped) **cartilage**. The arytenoid cartilages articulate with the cricoid cartilage inferiorly. The paired cartilages form an attachment site for the vocal folds.

Two pairs of ligaments extend from the posterior surface of the thyroid cartilage to the paired cartilages. The superior pair forms the **vestibular** (ves-tib′ū-lăr) **folds**, or **false vocal cords**, and the inferior pair composes the **vocal folds**, or **true vocal cords** (figure 15.4). When the vestibular folds come together, they prevent air from leaving the lungs, such as when a person holds his breath. Along with the epiglottis, the vestibular folds also prevent food and liquids from entering the larynx.

The true vocal cords are the primary source of voice production. Air moving past the true vocal cords causes them to vibrate, producing sound. Muscles control the length and tension of the true vocal cords. The force of air moving past the true vocal cords controls the loudness, and the tension of the true vocal cords controls the pitch of the voice. An inflammation of the mucous epithelium of the true vocal cords is called **laryngitis** (lar-in-jī′tis). Swelling of the true vocal cords during laryngitis inhibits voice production.

Did You Know?

The function of the **cough reflex** is to dislodge foreign substances from the trachea. Sensory receptors detect the foreign substances, and action potentials are conducted along the vagus nerves to the medulla oblongata in which the cough reflex is triggered. As a result, air is inspired and the vestibular folds and vocal folds close tightly to trap the inspired air in the lung. Muscle contractions increase pressure in the lungs, which is suddenly released when the vestibular folds and vocal folds open. Air rushes from the lungs at a high velocity, carrying foreign substances with it.

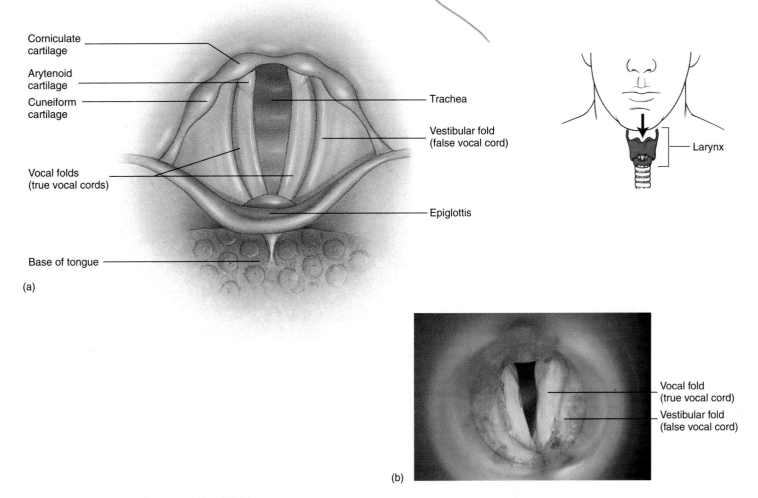

Figure 15.4   The Vestibular and Vocal Folds

(*a*) The vestibular and vocal folds viewed from above, showing their relationship to the paired cartilages of the larynx. (*b*) Photograph of the vestibular and vocal folds.

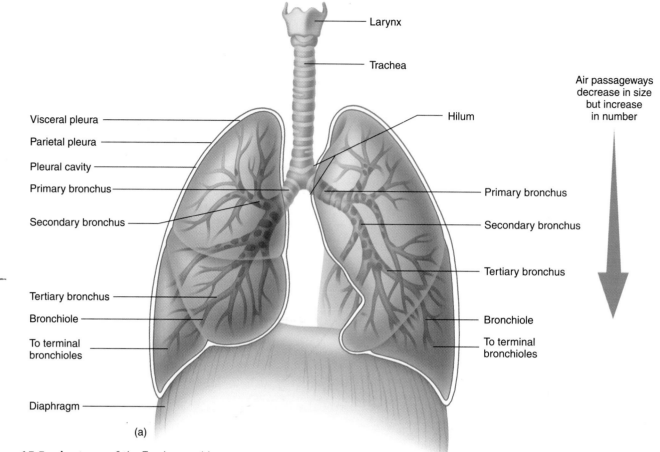

Figure 15.5 Anatomy of the Trachea and Lungs

(*a*) Drawing of the trachea and lungs, showing the branching of the bronchi. Each lung is surrounded by a pleural cavity, formed by the visceral and parietal pleurae.

Trachea

The **trachea** (trā′kē-ă), or windpipe, is a membranous tube that consists of connective tissue and smooth muscle, reinforced with 16 to 20 **C**-shaped pieces of cartilage (see figure 15.3). The adult trachea is about 1.4 to 1.6 centimeters (cm) in diameter. It begins immediately inferior to the cricoid cartilage, which is the most inferior cartilage of the larynx. The trachea projects through the mediastinum, and divides into the right and left primary bronchi at the level of the fifth thoracic vertebra (figure 15.5*a*). The esophagus lies immediately posterior to the trachea (see figure 15.2*a*).

C-shaped cartilages form the anterior and lateral sides of the trachea. The cartilages protect the trachea and maintain an open passageway for air. The posterior wall of the trachea has no cartilage and consists of a ligamentous membrane and smooth muscle (see figure 15.3*b*). The smooth muscle can alter the diameter of the trachea. During coughing, this action causes air to move more rapidly through the trachea, which helps to expel mucus and foreign substances.

The trachea is lined with pseudostratified columnar epithelium, which contains numerous cilia and goblet cells. The cilia propel mucus produced by the goblet cells, as well as foreign particles, toward the larynx, where they enter the esophagus and are swallowed.

2 **P R E D I C T**

Explain what happens to the shape of the trachea when a person swallows a large mouthful of food. Why is this advantageous?

✔ *Answer on page 429*

Did You Know?

Constant irritation to the trachea, such as occurs in people who smoke cigarettes, can cause the tracheal epithelium to change to a more resistant stratified squamous epithelium. The stratified squamous epithelium has no cilia and therefore lacks the ability to clear the airway of mucus and debris. The accumulations of mucus provide a place for microorganisms to grow, resulting in respiratory infections. Constant irritation and inflammation of the respiratory passages stimulate the cough reflex, resulting in "smoker's cough."

In cases of extreme emergency, when the upper air passageway is blocked by a foreign object to the extent that the victim cannot breathe, quick reaction is required to save the person's life. The

(continued)

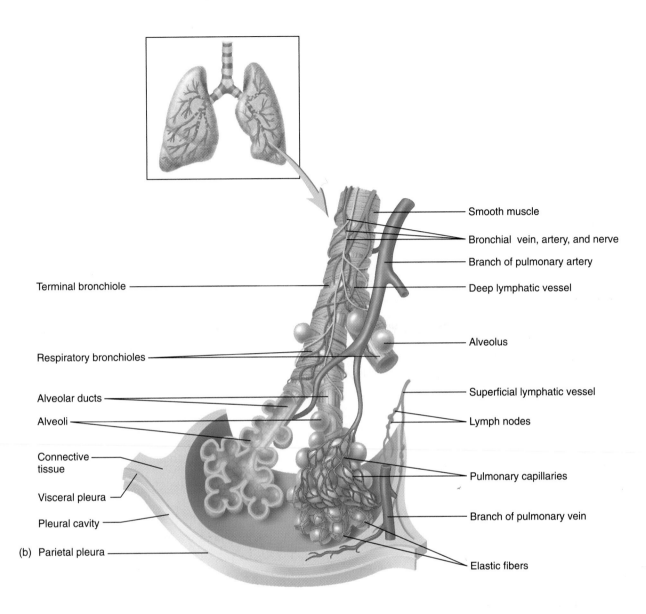

Smooth muscle

Bronchial vein, artery, and nerve

Branch of pulmonary artery

Deep lymphatic vessel

Terminal bronchiole

Alveolus

Respiratory bronchioles

Superficial lymphatic vessel

Alveolar ducts

Lymph nodes

Alveoli

Connective tissue

Pulmonary capillaries

Visceral pleura

Pleural cavity

Branch of pulmonary vein

(b) Parietal pleura

Elastic fibers

Figure 15.5   Anatomy of the Trachea and Lungs

(b) A terminal bronchiole branches to form respiratory bronchioles, which give rise to alveolar ducts. Alveoli connect to the alveolar ducts and respiratory bronchioles.

Heimlich maneuver is designed to force such an object out of the air passage by the sudden application of pressure to the abdomen, forcing air up the trachea to dislodge the obstruction. The person who performs the maneuver stands behind the victim with her arms under the victim's arms and her hands over the victim's abdomen between the navel and the rib cage. With one hand formed into a fist, the other hand suddenly pulls the fist toward the abdomen with an accompanying upward motion. The pressure pushes up on the diaphragm and therefore increases air pressure in the lungs. If this maneuver is done properly, it causes air to flow from the lungs with sufficient force to dislodge most foreign objects.

In rare cases, when the obstruction cannot be removed using the Heimlich maneuver, it may be necessary to form an artificial opening in the victim's air passageway to save his life. The preferred point of entry in an emergency is through the membrane between the cricoid and thyroid cartilages (see figure 15.3a). This procedure is referred to as a **cricothyrotomy** (krī′kō-thī-rot′ō-mē). A tube is inserted into the opening to facilitate the passage of air. A **tracheostomy** (trā′kē-os′tō-mē) is an incision into the trachea, usually between the second and third tracheal cartilage. Because the trachea has several structures overlying its anterior surface, such as arteries, nerves, and part of the thyroid gland, it is not advisable to enter the trachea in emergency cases.

Bronchi

The trachea divides into the left and right **primary bronchi**, singular **bronchus** (brong′kī, brong′kŭs, windpipe). The left primary bronchus is more horizontal than the right primary bronchus because it is displaced by the heart (see figure 15.5*a*). Foreign objects that enter the trachea usually lodge in the right primary bronchus, because the right primary bronchus is more vertical than the left primary bronchus and therefore more in direct line with the trachea. The primary bronchi extend from the trachea to the lungs. Like the trachea, the primary bronchi are lined with pseudostratified ciliated columnar epithelium and are supported by C-shaped pieces of cartilage.

Lungs

The **lungs** are the principal organs of respiration. Each lung is cone-shaped, with its base resting on the diaphragm and its apex extending superiorly to a point about 2.5 cm above the clavicle (see figure 15.5*a*). The right lung has three **lobes** called the superior, middle, and inferior lobes. The left lung has two lobes called the superior and inferior lobes (figure 15.6). The lobes of the lungs are separated by deep, prominent fissures on the surface of the lung. Each lobe is divided into **bronchopulmonary segments** separated from one another by connective tissue septa, but these separations are not visible as surface fissures. Individual diseased bronchopulmonary segments can be surgically removed, leaving the rest of the lung relatively intact, because major blood vessels and bronchi do not cross the septa. There are 9 bronchopulmonary segments in the left lung and 10 in the right lung.

The point of entry for the primary bronchus, blood vessels, and nerves to each lung is called the **hilum** (hī′lŭm), or **root, of the lung**. After entering the lung, the primary bronchus branches many times to form the **tracheobronchial tree** (see figure 15.5*a*). Each primary bronchus divides into secondary bronchi as they enter their respective lungs. The **secondary bronchi**, two in the left lung and three in the right lung, conduct air to each lobe. The secondary bronchi in turn give rise to **tertiary bronchi**, which extend to the bronchopulmonary segments of the lungs. The bronchi continue to branch many times, finally giving rise to **bronchioles** (brong′kē-ōlz). The bronchioles also subdivide numerous times to give rise to **terminal bronchioles**, which then subdivide into **respiratory bronchioles** (figure 15.5*b*). Each respiratory bronchiole subdivides to form **alveolar** (al-vē′ō-lăr) **ducts**, which are like long, branching hallways with many open doorways. The doorways open into **alveoli** (al-vē′ō-lī, hollow sacs), which are small air sacs. The alveoli become so numerous that the alveolar duct wall is little more than a succession of alveoli.

As the air passageways of the lungs become smaller, the structure of their walls changes. The amount of cartilage decreases and the amount of smooth muscle increases, until at the terminal bronchioles, the walls have a prominent smooth muscle layer, but no cartilage. Relaxation and contraction of the smooth muscle within the bronchi and bronchioles can change the diameter of the air passageways. For example, during exercise the diameter can increase, thus increasing the volume of air moved. During an **asthma attack**, however, contraction of the smooth muscle in the terminal bronchioles can result in greatly reduced air flow. In severe cases, air movement can be so restricted that death results.

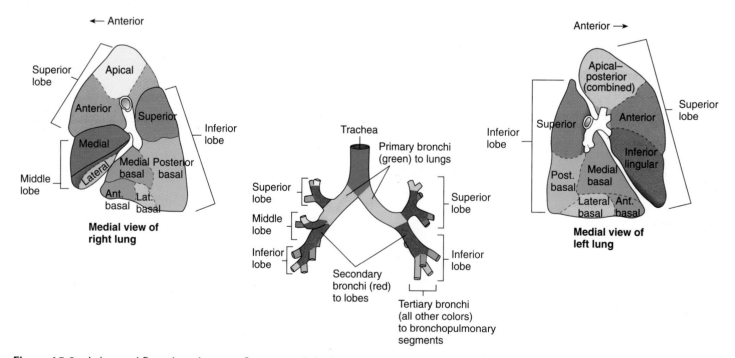

Figure 15.6 Lobes and Bronchopulmonary Segments of the Lungs

The trachea (dark blue), primary bronchi (light green), secondary bronchi (red), and tertiary bronchi (all other colors) are in the center of the figure. A medial view of each lung, shows the lobes and bronchopulmonary segments. In general, each bronchopulmonary segment is supplied by a tertiary bronchus (color-coded to match the bronchopulmonary segment it supplies).

As the air passageways of the lungs become smaller, the lining of their walls also changes. The trachea and bronchi have pseudostratified ciliated columnar epithelium, the bronchioles have ciliated simple columnar epithelium, and the terminal bronchioles have ciliated simple cuboidal epithelium. The ciliated epithelium of the air passageways functions as a mucus–cilia escalator, which traps debris in the air and removes it from the respiratory system.

The walls of the respiratory bronchioles, alveolar ducts, and the alveoli consist of thin, simple squamous epithelium. Gas exchange with blood occurs mainly across the epithelial lining of the alveoli, although some exchange also occurs across the walls of the respiratory bronchioles and alveolar ducts. Rapid diffusion of oxygen and carbon dioxide is possible because of the thin epithelial layer that separates the air from the blood in the pulmonary capillaries. Specialized secretory cells (see the section, Lung Recoil, on page 408) are within the alveolar walls.

Pleural Cavities

The lungs are contained within the thoracic cavity. In addition, each lung is surrounded by a separate **pleural** (ploor′ăl, relating to the ribs) **cavity**. Each pleural cavity is lined with a serous membrane called the **pleura**. The pleura consists of a parietal and visceral part. At the hilum, the **parietal pleura**, which lines the walls of the thorax, diaphragm, and mediastinum, is continuous with the **visceral pleura**, which covers the surface of the lung (see figure 15.5).

The pleural cavity, between the parietal and visceral pleurae, is filled with a small volume of pleural fluid produced by the pleural membranes. The pleural fluid performs two functions: (1) it acts as a lubricant, allowing the visceral and parietal pleurae to slide past each other as the lungs and thorax change shape during respiration, and (2) it helps hold the pleural membranes together. The pleural fluid acts like a thin film of water between two sheets of glass (the visceral and parietal pleurae); the glass sheets can slide over each other easily, but it is difficult to separate them.

3	P R E D I C T

Pleurisy is an inflammation of the pleural membranes. Explain why this condition is so painful, especially when a person takes deep breaths.

✔ *Answer on page 429*

Lymphatic Supply

The lungs have two lymphatic supplies (see figure 15.5*b*). The **superficial lymphatic vessels** are deep to the visceral pleura and function to drain lymph from the superficial lung tissue and the visceral pleura. The **deep lymphatic vessels** follow the bronchi and function to drain lymph from the bronchi and associated connective tissues. No lymphatic vessels are located in the walls of the alveoli. Both the superficial and deep lymphatic vessels exit the lung at the hilum.

Phagocytic cells within the lungs pick up carbon particles and other debris from inspired air and move to the lymphatic vessels. In older people, the surface of the lungs can appear gray to black because of the accumulation of these particles, especially if the person smoked or lived most of his life in a city with air pollution. Cancer cells from the lungs can also spread to other parts of the body through the lymphatic vessels.

Ventilation and Lung Volumes

Ventilation, or **breathing**, is the process of moving air into and out of the lungs. There are two phases of ventilation: (1) **inspiration**, or **inhalation**, is the movement of air into the lungs; (2) **expiration**, or **exhalation**, is the movement of air out of the lungs. Changes in thoracic volume, which produce changes in air pressure within the lungs, are responsible for ventilation.

Changing Thoracic Volume

Muscles associated with the ribs are responsible for ventilation (figure 15.7). The **muscles of inspiration** include the diaphragm and muscles that elevate the ribs and sternum, such as the external intercostals. The **diaphragm** (dī′a-fram, partition) is a large dome of skeletal muscle that separates the thoracic cavity from the abdominal cavity (see figure 7.18). The **muscles of expiration**, such as the internal intercostals, depress the ribs and sternum.

At the end of a normal, quiet expiration, the respiratory muscles are relaxed (see figure 15.7*a*). During quiet inspiration, contraction of the diaphragm causes the dome shape to flatten, which increases the volume of the thoracic cavity. The largest change in thoracic volume results from movement of the diaphragm. Contraction of the external intercostals also increases thoracic volume by lifting the anterior ends of the ribs and sternum (see figure 15.7*b*).

4	P R E D I C T

During inspiration, the abdominal muscles relax. How is this advantageous?

✔ *Answer on page 429*

Expiration during quiet breathing occurs when the diaphragm and external intercostals relax and the elastic properties of the thorax and lungs cause a passive decrease in thoracic volume.

There are several differences between normal, quiet breathing and labored breathing. During labored breathing, all of the inspiratory muscles are active and they contract more forcefully than during quiet breathing, causing a greater increase in thoracic volume (see figure 15.7*b*). During labored breathing, forceful contraction of the internal intercostals and the abdominal muscles produces a more rapid and greater decrease in thoracic volume than would be produced by the passive recoil of the thorax and lungs.

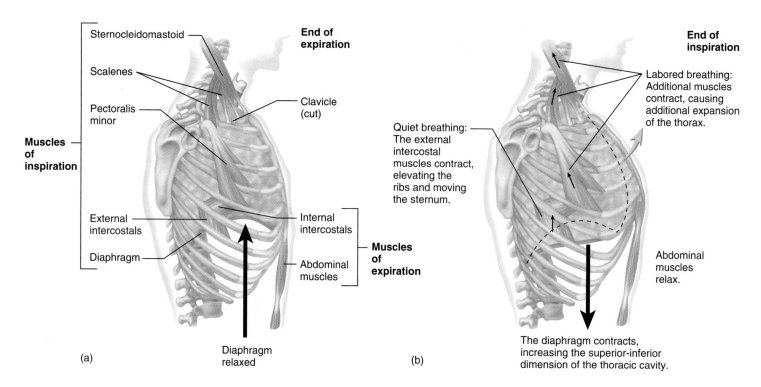

Figure 15.7   Effect of the Muscles of Respiration on Thoracic Volume

(*a*) Muscles of respiration at the end of expiration. (*b*) Muscles of respiration at the end of inspiration.

Pressure Changes and Airflow

The flow of air into and out of the lungs is governed by two physical principles:

1. *Changes in volume result in changes in pressure.* As the volume of a container increases, the pressure within the container decreases. As the volume of a container decreases, the pressure within the container increases. The muscles of respiration change thoracic volume and therefore pressure within the thoracic cavity.

2. *Air flows from areas of higher to lower pressure.* If the pressure is higher at one end of a tube than at the other, air flows from the area of higher pressure toward the area of lower pressure. The greater the pressure difference, the greater the rate of airflow. Air flows through the respiratory passages because of pressure differences between the outside of the body and the alveoli inside the body. These pressure differences are produced by changes in thoracic volume.

   The volume and pressure changes responsible for one cycle of inspiration and expiration can be described as follows:

1. At the end of expiration, **alveolar pressure**, which is the air pressure within the alveoli, is equal to **atmospheric pressure**, which is the air pressure outside the body. There is no movement of air into or out of the lungs because alveolar pressure and atmospheric pressure are equal (figure 15.8*a*).

2. During inspiration, contraction of the muscles of inspiration increases the volume of the thoracic cavity.

The increased thoracic volume causes the lungs to expand, resulting in an increase in alveolar volume (see the section, Changing Alveolar Volume, on p. 410). As the alveolar volume increases, alveolar pressure becomes less than atmospheric pressure, and air flows from outside the body through the respiratory passages to the alveoli (figure 15.8*b*).

3. At the end of inspiration, the thorax and alveoli stop expanding. Alveolar pressure and atmospheric pressure become equal, and airflow stops (figure 15.8*c*).

4. During expiration, the thoracic volume decreases, producing a decrease in alveolar volume. Consequently, alveolar pressure increases above the air pressure outside the body, and air flows from the alveoli through the respiratory passages to the outside (figure 15.8*d*).

   As expiration ends, the decrease in thoracic volume stops and the process repeats beginning at step 1.

Lung Recoil

During quiet expiration, thoracic volume and lung volume decrease because of passive recoil of the thoracic wall and lungs. The recoil of the thoracic wall results from the elastic properties of the thoracic wall tissues. The recoil of the lungs occurs for two reasons: (1) the elastic fibers in the connective tissue of the lungs and (2) surface tension of the film of fluid that lines the alveoli. **Surface tension** exists because the oppositely charged ends of water molecules attract each other (see chapter 2). As the water molecules pull together, they also pull on the alveolar walls, causing the alveoli to recoil and become smaller.

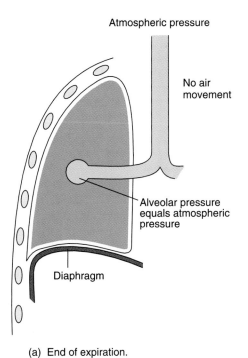

Atmospheric pressure

No air
movement

Alveolar pressure
equals atmospheric
pressure

Diaphragm

(a) End of expiration.

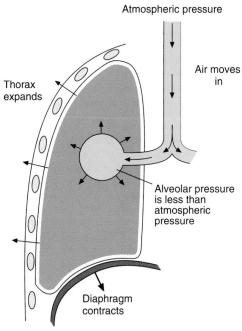

Atmospheric pressure

Air moves
in

Thorax
expands

Alveolar pressure
is less than
atmospheric
pressure

Diaphragm
contracts

(b) During inspiration, increased
thoracic volume results in
decreased pressure inside the
alveoli. Therefore, air moves into
the lungs.

Atmospheric pressure

No air
movement

Alveolar pressure
equals atmosphere
pressure

(c) End of inspiration.

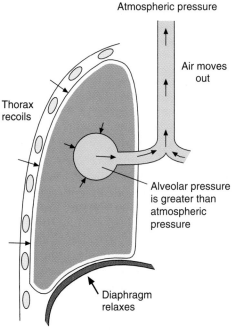

Atmospheric pressure

Air moves
out

Thorax
recoils

Alveolar pressure
is greater than
atmospheric
pressure

Diaphragm
relaxes

(d) During expiration, decreased
thoracic volume results in
increased pressure inside the
alveoli. Therefore, air moves out of
the lungs.

Figure 15.8   Alveolar Pressure Changes During Inspiration and Expiration

The combined space of all the alveoli is represented by a large "bubble." The alveoli are actually microscopic in size and cannot be seen in the illustration.

Two factors keep the lungs from collapsing: (1) surfactant, and (2) pressure in the pleural cavity.

Surfactant

Surfactant (ser-fak′tănt) is a mixture of lipoprotein molecules produced by secretory cells of the alveolar epithelium. The surfactant molecules form a single layer on the surface of the thin fluid layer lining the alveoli, reducing surface tension. Without surfactant, the surface tension causing the alveoli to recoil can be 10 times greater than when surfactant is present. Thus, surfactant greatly reduces the tendency of the lungs to collapse.

Did You Know?

Surfactant is not produced in adequate quantities until about the seventh month of gestation. Thereafter the amount produced increases as the fetus matures. In premature infants, **respiratory distress syndrome (RDS)**, or **hyaline** (hī′ă-lin) **membrane disease,** is caused by too little surfactant. It is common, especially for infants delivered before the seventh month of pregnancy. Because cortisol is needed to make surfactant, cortisol can be given to pregnant women who are likely to deliver prematurely.

If too little surfactant has been produced by the time of birth, the lungs tend to collapse, and a great deal of energy must be exerted by the muscles of respiration to keep the lungs inflated; even then, inadequate ventilation occurs. Without specialized treatment, most babies with this condition die soon after birth as a result of inadequate ventilation of the lungs and fatigue of the respiratory muscles. Treatment strategies include forcing enough oxygen-rich air into the lungs to inflate them and administering human surfactant produced through genetic engineering.

Pleural Pressure

When **pleural pressure**, which is the pressure in the pleural cavity, is less than alveolar pressure, the alveoli tend to expand. This principle can be understood by considering a balloon. The balloon expands when the pressure outside it is less than the pressure inside. This pressure difference is normally achieved by increasing the pressure inside the balloon when a person forcefully blows into it. This pressure difference, however, can also be achieved by decreasing the pressure outside the balloon. For example, if the balloon is placed in a chamber from which air is removed, the pressure around the balloon becomes lower than atmospheric pressure, and the balloon expands. The lower the pressure outside the balloon, the greater the tendency for the higher pressure inside the balloon to cause it to expand. In a similar fashion, decreasing pleural pressure can result in expansion of the alveoli.

Normally, the alveoli are expanded because pleural pressure is lower than alveolar pressure. Pleural pressure is lower than alveolar pressure because of a "suction effect" caused by lung recoil. As the lungs recoil, the visceral and parietal pleurae tend to be pulled apart. Normally the lungs do not pull away from the thoracic wall because pleural fluid holds the visceral and parietal pleurae together. Nonetheless,

this pull decreases pressure in the pleural cavity, an effect that can be appreciated by putting water on the palms of the hands and putting them together. A sensation of negative pressure is felt as the hands are gently pulled apart.

When pleural pressure is lower than alveolar pressure, the alveoli tend to expand. This expansion is opposed by the tendency of the lungs to recoil. If the pleural pressure is sufficiently low, lung recoil is overcome and the alveoli expand. If the pleural pressure is not low enough to overcome lung recoil, then the alveoli collapse.

Did You Know?

A **pneumothorax** (noo-mō-thōr′aks) is the introduction of air into the pleural cavity. Air can enter by an external route when a sharp object, such as a bullet or broken rib, penetrates the thoracic wall; or air can enter the pleural cavity by an internal route if alveoli at the lung surface rupture, such as can occur in a patient with emphysema. When the pleural cavity is connected to the outside by such openings, the pressure in the pleural cavity becomes equal to the air pressure outside the body. Thus, pleural pressure is also equal to alveolar pressure because pressure in the alveoli at the end of expiration is equal to air pressure outside the body. When pleural pressure and alveolar pressure are equal, there is no tendency for the alveoli to expand, lung recoil is unopposed, and the lungs collapse. A pneumothorax can occur in one lung while the lung on the opposite side remains inflated because the two pleural cavities are separated by the mediastinum.

5   P R E D I C T

Treatment of a pneumothorax involves closing the opening into the pleural cavity that caused the pneumothorax. Then a tube is placed into the pleural cavity. In order to inflate the lung, should this tube pump in air under pressure (as in blowing up a balloon) or should the tube apply suction? Explain.

✔ *Answer on page 429*

Changing Alveolar Volume

Changes in alveolar volume result in the changes in alveolar pressure that are responsible for the movement of air into and out of the lungs (see figure 15.8). Alveolar volume changes result from changes in pleural pressure. For example, during inspiration, pleural pressure becomes less than alveolar pressure, and the alveoli expand. The decrease in pleural pressure occurs for two reasons:

1. Increasing the volume of the thoracic cavity results in a decrease in pleural pressure because of the effect of changing volume on pressure.
2. As the lungs expand, lung recoil increases, resulting in an increased suction effect and a lowering of pleural pressure. The increased lung recoil of the stretched lung is similar to the increased force generated in a stretched rubber band.

The events of inspiration and expiration can be summarized as follows. During inspiration, thoracic volume increases, resulting in a decrease in pleural pressure. As pleural pressure decreases, alveolar volume increases, alveolar pressure decreases, and air flows into the lungs. During expiration, pleural pressure increases because of decreased thoracic volume and decreased lung recoil. As pleural pressure increases, alveolar volume decreases, alveolar pressure increases, and air flows out of the lungs.

Pulmonary Volumes and Capacities

Spirometry (spī-rom′ĕ-trē) is the process of measuring volumes of air that move into and out of the respiratory system, and the **spirometer** (spī-rom′ĕ-ter) is the device that is used to measure these pulmonary volumes (figure 15.9*a*). Measurements of the respiratory volumes can provide information about the health of the lungs. The four **pulmonary volumes** and their normal values (figure 15.9*b*) for a young adult male are as follows:

1. **Tidal volume** is the volume of air inspired or expired during quiet breathing (about 500 milliliters; mL).
2. **Inspiratory reserve volume** is the amount of air that can be inspired forcefully after inspiration of the normal tidal volume (≈ 3000 mL).
3. **Expiratory reserve volume** is the amount of air that can be expired forcefully after expiration of the normal tidal volume (≈ 1100 mL).

Figure 15.9   Lung Volumes and Capacities

(*a*) Photograph of a spirometer used to measure lung volumes and capacities. (*b*) Values for the lung volumes and capacities. The values shown in the diagram are values during quiet breathing of a healthy, young, adult male.

4. **Residual volume** is the volume of air still remaining in the respiratory passages and lungs after a maximum expiration ($\approx$ 1200 mL).

The tidal volume increases when a person is more active. Because the maximum volume of the respiratory system does not change from moment to moment, the increase in the tidal volume causes a decrease in the inspiratory and expiratory reserve volumes.

---

6 PREDICT

The **minute ventilation** is the total amount of air moved into and out of the respiratory system each minute, and it is equal to the tidal volume times the respiratory rate. The **respiratory rate** is the number of breaths taken per minute. Calculate the minute ventilation of a resting person, who has a tidal volume of 500 mL and a respiratory rate of 12 respirations/min, and an exercising person, who has a tidal volume of 4000 mL and a respiratory rate of 24 respirations/min.

✔ *Answer on page 429*

A **pulmonary capacity** is the sum of two or more pulmonary volumes (see figure 15.9*b*). For example:

1. **Functional residual capacity** is the expiratory reserve volume plus the residual volume, which is the amount of air remaining in the lungs at the end of a normal expiration ($\approx$ 2300 mL).
2. **Inspiratory capacity** is the tidal volume plus the inspiratory reserve volume, which is the amount of air that a person can inspire maximally after a normal expiration ($\approx$ 3500 mL).
3. **Vital capacity** is the sum of the inspiratory reserve volume, the tidal volume, and the expiratory reserve volume; it is the maximum volume of air that a person can expel from his respiratory tract after a maximum inspiration ($\approx$ 4600 mL).
4. **Total lung capacity** is the sum of the inspiratory and expiratory reserves and the tidal and residual volumes ($\approx$ 5800 mL). The total lung capacity is also equal to the vital capacity plus the residual volume.

Factors such as sex, age, and body size influence the respiratory volumes and capacities. For example, the vital capacity of adult females is usually 20% to 25% less than that of adult males. The vital capacity reaches its maximum amount in the young adult and gradually decreases in the elderly. Tall people usually have a greater vital capacity than short people, and thin people have a greater vital capacity than obese people. Well-trained athletes can have a vital capacity 30% to 40% above that of untrained people. In patients whose respiratory muscles are paralyzed by spinal cord injury or diseases such as poliomyelitis or muscular dystrophy, the vital capacity can be reduced to values not consistent with survival (less than 500–1000 mL).

The **forced expiratory vital capacity** is the rate at which lung volume changes during direct measurement of the vital capacity. It is a simple and clinically important pulmonary test. The individual inspires maximally and then exhales maximally and as rapidly as possible into a spirometer. The spirometer records the volume of air expired per second. This test can be used to help identify conditions in which the vital capacity might not be affected, but in which the expiratory flow rate is reduced. Abnormalities that increase the resistance to airflow slow the rate at which air can be forced out of the lungs. For example, in people who suffer from asthma, contraction of the smooth muscle in the bronchioles increases the resistance to airflow. In people who suffer from emphysema, there are changes in the lung tissue that result in the destruction of the alveolar walls, collapse of the bronchioles, and decreased elasticity of the lung tissue. The collapsed bronchioles increase the resistance to airflow. In people who suffer from chronic bronchitis, the air passages are inflamed. The swelling, increased mucus secretion, and gradual loss of cilia result in narrowed bronchioles and an increased resistance to airflow.

Gas Exchange

Ventilation supplies atmospheric air to the alveoli. The next step in the process of respiration is the diffusion of gases between the alveoli and the blood in the pulmonary capillaries. The **respiratory membrane** is all of the areas in which gas exchange between air and blood occurs. The major area of gas exchange is in the alveoli, although some occurs in the respiratory bronchioles and alveolar ducts. Gas exchange between blood and air does not occur in such other areas of the respiratory passageways as the bronchioles, bronchi, and trachea. The volume of these passageways is therefore called **dead space**.

There are about 300 million alveoli in the lungs. Surrounding each alveolus is a network of capillaries arranged so air in the alveolus is separated by a thin respiratory membrane from the blood contained within the capillaries. The total surface area of the respiratory membrane is about 70 square meters (m^2) in the normal adult, which is approximately the floor area of a 25- $\times$ 30-ft room.

The respiratory membrane (figure 15.10) consists of

1. A thin layer of fluid containing surfactant, which lines the alveolus
2. The alveolar epithelium composed of simple squamous epithelium
3. The basement membrane of the alveolar epithelium
4. A thin interstitial space
5. The basement membrane of the capillary endothelium
6. The capillary endothelium, composed of simple squamous epithelium.

The exchange of gases across the respiratory membrane is influenced by the thickness of the membrane, the total surface area of the membrane, and the partial pressure of gases across the membrane.

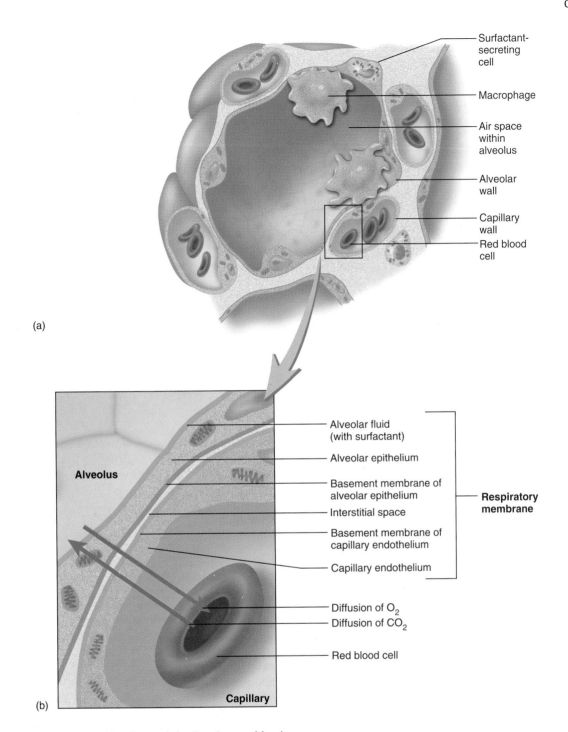

(a)

Surfactant-secreting cell

Macrophage

Air space within alveolus

Alveolar wall

Capillary wall

Red blood cell

Alveolus

Alveolar fluid (with surfactant)

Alveolar epithelium

Basement membrane of alveolar epithelium

Interstitial space

Basement membrane of capillary endothelium

Capillary endothelium

Respiratory membrane

Diffusion of O_2

Diffusion of CO_2

Red blood cell

Capillary

(b)

Figure 15.10   Alveolus and the Respiratory Membrane

(*a*) Section of an alveolus showing the air-filled interior and thin walls composed of simple squamous epithelium. The alveolus is surrounded by elastic connective tissue and blood capillaries containing erythrocytes. (*b*) Diffusion of oxygen and carbon dioxide across the six thin layers of the respiratory membrane

Respiratory Membrane Thickness

Increasing the thickness of the respiratory membrane decreases the rate of diffusion across it. The thickness of the respiratory membrane increases during certain respiratory diseases. For example, in patients with pulmonary edema, fluid accumulates in the alveoli, and gases must diffuse through a thicker than normal layer of fluid. If the thickness of the respiratory membrane is doubled or tripled, the rate of gas exchange is markedly decreased. Oxygen exchange is affected before carbon dioxide exchange because oxygen diffuses through the respiratory membrane about 20 times less easily than does carbon dioxide.

Surface Area

Under resting conditions, a decrease in the surface area of the respiratory membrane to one-third or one-fourth of normal can significantly restrict gas exchange. During strenuous exercise, even small decreases in the surface area of the respiratory membrane can adversely affect gas exchange. A decreased surface area for gas exchange results from the surgical removal of lung tissue, the destruction of lung tissue by cancer, or the degeneration of the alveolar walls by emphysema. Collapse of the lung, for example in pneumothorax, dramatically reduces the volume of the alveoli and reduces the surface area for gas exchange.

Partial Pressure

The pressure exerted by a specific gas in a mixture of gases, such as air, is usually reported as the **partial pressure** of that gas. For example, if the total pressure of all gases in a mixture of gases is 760 mm Hg, which is the atmospheric pressure at sea level, and 21% of the mixture is made up of oxygen, then the partial pressure for oxygen is 160 millimeters of mercury (mm Hg) (0.21 × 760 mm Hg = 160 mm Hg). If the composition of air is 0.04% carbon dioxide at sea level, the partial pressure for carbon dioxide is 0.3 mm Hg (0.0004 × 760 = 0.3 mm Hg) (table 15.1). It is traditional to designate the partial pressure of individual gases in a mixture with a capital P followed by the symbol for the gas. Thus the partial pressure of oxygen is Po_2, and carbon dioxide is Pco_2.

When air is in contact with a liquid such as water, gases such as carbon dioxide and oxygen in the air dissolve in the liquid. The gases dissolve in the liquid until the partial pressure of each gas in the liquid is equal to the partial pressure of that gas in the air. Gases in a liquid, like gases in air, diffuse from areas of higher partial pressure toward areas of lower partial pressure, until the partial pressures of the gases are equal throughout the liquid.

Diffusion of Gases in the Lungs

The cells of the body use oxygen and produce carbon dioxide. Thus, blood returning from tissues and entering the lungs has a decreased Po_2 and increased Pco_2 compared with alveolar air (figure 15.11). Oxygen diffuses from the alveoli into the pulmonary capillaries because the Po_2 in the alveoli is greater than that in the pulmonary capillaries. In contrast, carbon dioxide diffuses from the pulmonary capillaries into the alveoli because the Pco_2 is greater in the pulmonary capillaries than in the alveoli.

When blood enters a pulmonary capillary, the Po_2 and Pco_2 in the capillary are different from the Po_2 and Pco_2 in the alveolus. By the time blood flows through the first third of the pulmonary capillary, an equilibrium is achieved, and the Po_2 and Pco_2 in the capillary are the same as in the alveolus. Thus, the blood gains oxygen and loses carbon dioxide in the lungs.

During breathing, atmospheric air is mixed with alveolar air. The air entering and leaving the alveoli keeps the Po_2 higher in the alveoli than in the pulmonary capillaries. Increasing the rate of ventilation makes the Po_2 even higher in the alveoli than during slow breathing. During heavy breathing, the rate of oxygen diffusion into the pulmonary capillaries increases because the difference in partial pressure between the alveoli and the pulmonary capillaries is increased.

Increasing the rate of ventilation also makes the Pco_2 lower in the alveoli than during slow breathing. Because the alveolar Pco_2 decreases, the difference in partial pressure between the alveoli and the pulmonary capillaries increases, which increases the rate of carbon dioxide diffusion from the pulmonary capillaries into the alveoli.

On the other hand, inadequate ventilation causes a smaller difference in the Po_2 and Pco_2 across the respiratory membrane. The rate of oxygen and carbon dioxide diffusion across the membrane therefore decreases, causing oxygen levels in the blood to decrease and carbon dioxide levels to increase.

Diffusion of Gases in the Tissues

Blood flows from the lungs through the left side of the heart to the tissue capillaries. Figure 15.11 illustrates the partial pressure differences for oxygen and carbon dioxide across the wall of a tissue capillary. Oxygen diffuses from the capillary into the interstitial fluid because the Po_2 in the interstitial fluid is lower than in the capillary. Oxygen diffuses from the interstitial fluid into cells, in which the Po_2 is less than in the interstitial fluid. Within the cells, oxygen is used in aerobic metabolism. There is a constant difference in Po_2 from the tissue capillaries to the cells because oxygen is continuously used by cells. There is also a constant diffusion

Table 15.1	Partial Pressures of Gases at Sea Level							
	Dry Air		Humidified Air		Alveolar Air		Expired Air	
Gases	mm HG	%	mm HG	%	mm HG	%	mm HG	%
Nitrogen	600.2	78.98	563.4	74.09	569.0	74.9	566.0	74.5
Oxygen	159.5	20.98	149.3	19.67	104.0	13.6	120.0	15.7
Carbon dioxide	0.3	0.04	0.3	0.04	40.0	5.3	27.0	3.6
Water vapor	0.0	0.0	47.0	6.20	47.0	6.2	47.0	6.2

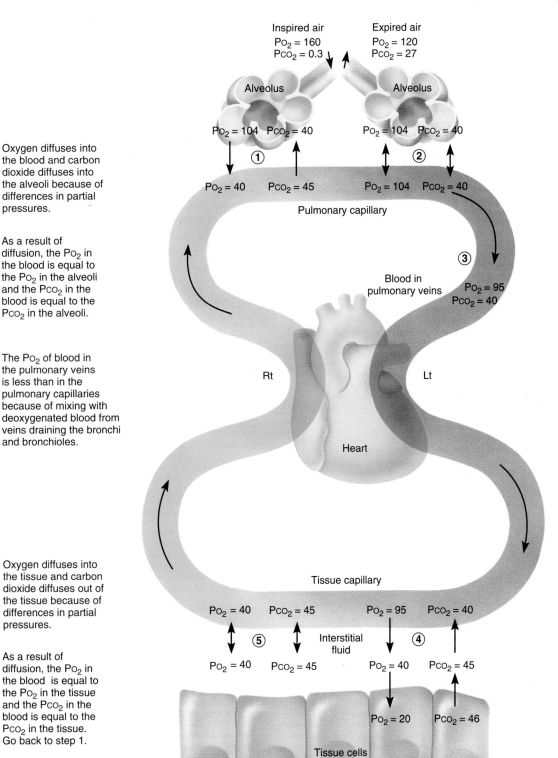

1. Oxygen diffuses into the blood and carbon dioxide diffuses into the alveoli because of differences in partial pressures.

2. As a result of diffusion, the Po_2 in the blood is equal to the Po_2 in the alveoli and the Pco_2 in the blood is equal to the Pco_2 in the alveoli.

3. The Po_2 of blood in the pulmonary veins is less than in the pulmonary capillaries because of mixing with deoxygenated blood from veins draining the bronchi and bronchioles.

4. Oxygen diffuses into the tissue and carbon dioxide diffuses out of the tissue because of differences in partial pressures.

5. As a result of diffusion, the Po_2 in the blood is equal to the Po_2 in the tissue and the Pco_2 in the blood is equal to the Pco_2 in the tissue. Go back to step 1.

Inspired air
$Po_2 = 160$
$Pco_2 = 0.3$

Expired air
$Po_2 = 120$
$Pco_2 = 27$

Alveolus

Alveolus

$Po_2 = 104$ $Pco_2 = 40$

$Po_2 = 104$ $Pco_2 = 40$

①

②

$Po_2 = 40$ $Pco_2 = 45$

$Po_2 = 104$ $Pco_2 = 40$

Pulmonary capillary

③

Blood in pulmonary veins

$Po_2 = 95$
$Pco_2 = 40$

Rt

Lt

Heart

Tissue capillary

$Po_2 = 40$ $Pco_2 = 45$

$Po_2 = 95$ $Pco_2 = 40$

⑤

Interstitial fluid

④

$Po_2 = 40$ $Pco_2 = 45$

$Po_2 = 40$ $Pco_2 = 45$

$Po_2 = 20$ $Pco_2 = 46$

Tissue cells

Figure 15.11   Gas Exchange

Oxygen and carbon dioxide partial pressure diffusion gradients between the alveoli and the pulmonary capillaries and between the tissues and the tissue capillaries.

gradient for carbon dioxide from the cells to the tissue capillaries because carbon dioxide is continuously produced by cells. Carbon dioxide therefore diffuses from cells into the interstitial fluid and from the interstitial fluid into the tissue capillaries.

---

7 P R E D I C T

During exercise, the movement of oxygen into skeletal muscle cells and the movement of carbon dioxide out of skeletal muscle cells increases. Explain how this happens.

✔ *Answer on page 429*

Gas Transport in the Blood

Oxygen Transport

After oxygen diffuses across the respiratory membrane into the blood, about 98.5% of the oxygen combines reversibly with the iron-containing heme groups of hemoglobin (see chapter 11). About 1.5% of the oxygen remains dissolved in the plasma. Hemoglobin with oxygen bound to its heme groups is called **oxyhemoglobin** (ok′sē-hē-mō-glō′bin).

The ability of hemoglobin to bind to oxygen depends on the P_{O_2}. At high P_{O_2}, hemoglobin binds to oxygen and at low P_{O_2} hemoglobin releases oxygen. In the lungs, P_{O_2} normally is sufficiently high that hemoglobin holds as much oxygen as it can. In the tissues, P_{O_2} is lower because the tissues are using oxygen. Consequently, hemoglobin releases oxygen in the tissues. Oxygen then diffuses into cells and is used by the cells in aerobic metabolism. At rest, approximately 23% of the oxygen picked up by hemoglobin in the lungs is released to the tissues.

The amount of oxygen released from oxyhemoglobin is influenced by several factors. More oxygen is released from hemoglobin if (1) the partial pressure of oxygen is low, (2) the partial pressure of carbon dioxide is high, (3) the pH is low, and (4) the temperature is high. Increased muscular activity results in a decreased partial pressure of oxygen, an increased partial pressure of carbon dioxide, a reduced pH, and an increased temperature. Consequently, as much as 73% of the oxygen picked up by hemoglobin in the lungs is released in skeletal muscles during periods of physical exercise.

Carbon Dioxide Transport and Blood pH

Carbon dioxide diffuses from cells, where it is produced, into the tissue capillaries. After it enters the blood, carbon dioxide is transported in three principal ways: (1) About 7% is transported as carbon dioxide dissolved in the plasma, (2) 23% is transported in combination with blood proteins, primarily hemoglobin, and (3) 70% is transported in the form of bicarbonate ions.

Carbon dioxide reacts with water to form carbonic acid, which then dissociates to form hydrogen ions and bicarbonate ions.

$$\underset{\substack{\text{carbon}\\\text{dioxide}}}{CO_2} + \underset{\text{water}}{H_2O} \;\overset{\substack{\text{Carbonic}\\\text{anhydrase}}}{\rightleftarrows}\; \underset{\substack{\text{carbonic}\\\text{acid}}}{H_2CO_3} \;\rightleftarrows\; \underset{\substack{\text{hydrogen}\\\text{ion}}}{H^+} + \underset{\substack{\text{bicarbonate}\\\text{ion}}}{HCO_3^-}$$

An enzyme called **carbonic anhydrase** (kar-bon′ik an-hī′drās) is found inside erythrocytes and on the surface of capillary epithelial cells. Carbonic anhydrase increases the rate at which carbon dioxide reacts with water to form hydrogen ions and bicarbonate ions in the tissue capillaries (figure 15.12). Thus, carbonic anhydrase promotes the uptake of carbon dioxide by erythrocytes.

In the capillaries of the lungs, the process is reversed so that the bicarbonate and hydrogen ions combine to produce carbonic acid, which then forms carbon dioxide and water. The carbon dioxide diffuses into the alveoli and is expired.

Carbon dioxide has an important effect on the pH of blood. As carbon dioxide levels increase, the blood pH decreases (becomes more acidic) because carbon dioxide reacts with water to form carbonic acid. The hydrogen ions that result from the dissociation of carbonic acid are responsible for the decrease in pH. Conversely, as blood levels of carbon dioxide decline, the blood pH increases (becomes less acidic or more basic).

---

8 P R E D I C T

What effect does a rapid rate of respiration have on blood pH? What effect does holding one's breath have on blood pH? Explain.

✔ *Answer on page 429*

Rhythmic Ventilation

The normal rate of respiration in adults is between 12 and 20 respirations per minute. In children, the rates are higher and may vary from 20 to 40 per minute. The generation of the basic rhythm of ventilation is controlled by neurons within the medulla oblongata that stimulate the muscles of respiration. An increased depth of respiration results from stronger contractions of the respiratory muscles caused by recruitment of muscle fibers and increased frequency of stimulation of muscle fibers. The rate of respiration is determined by the number of times respiratory muscles are stimulated.

Respiratory Areas in the Brainstem

In the classic view of respiratory areas, distinct inspiratory and expiratory centers were thought to be located in the brainstem. This view is now known to be too simplistic. Although neurons involved with respiration are aggregated in certain parts of the brainstem, neurons that are active during inspiration are intermingled with neurons active during expiration.

(a) In the tissue capillaries, carbon dioxide released from tissue cells diffuses into red blood cells and combines with water to form carbonic acid, a reaction catalyzed by the enzyme carbonic anhydrase. Carbonic acid then dissociates to form hydrogen ions and bicarbonate ions. This process promotes the uptake and transport of carbon dioxide by red blood cells.

(b) In the pulmonary capillaries, carbon dioxide diffuses out of red blood cells into the alveoli. The loss of carbon dioxide promotes the formation of additional carbon dioxide from carbonic acid, a reaction catalyzed by carbonic anhydrase. Hydrogen ions and bicarbonate ions then combine to replace the carbonic acid. This process promotes the formation and release of carbon dioxide by red blood cells.

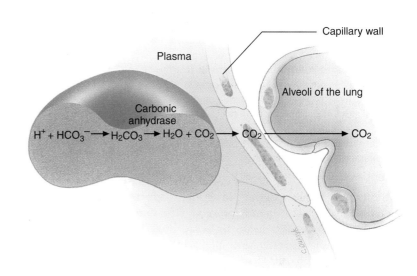

Figure 15.12   Carbon Dioxide Transport and Blood pH

The **medullary respiratory center** consists of **two dorsal respiratory groups**, each forming a longitudinal column of cells located bilaterally in the dorsal part of the medulla oblongata, and two **ventral respiratory groups**, each forming a longitudinal column of cells located bilaterally in the ventral part of the medulla oblongata (figure 15.13). The dorsal respiratory groups are primarily responsible for stimulating contraction of the diaphragm. The ventral respiratory groups are primarily responsible for stimulating the external intercostal, internal intercostal, and abdominal muscles.

The **pontine respiratory group** is a collection of neurons in the pons (see figure 15.13). The precise function of the pontine respiratory group is unknown, but it has connections with the medullary respiratory center and appears to play a role in the switching between inspiration and expiration.

Generation of Rhythmic Ventilation

How the respiratory center generates the basic pattern of spontaneous, rhythmic ventilation is not well understood.

One explanation involves integration of stimuli that start and stop inspiration.

1. *Starting inspiration.* Neurons in the medullary respiratory center constantly receive stimulation from many sources, such as receptors that monitor blood gas levels and the movements of muscles and joints. In addition, stimulation from parts of the brain concerned with voluntary respiratory movements and emotions can occur. When the inputs from all these sources reach a threshold level, neurons that stimulate respiratory muscles produce action potentials and inspiration starts.
2. *Increasing inspiration.* Once inspiration begins, more and more neurons are activated. The result is progressively stronger stimulation of the respiratory muscles that lasts for approximately 2 seconds (s).
3. *Stopping inspiration.* The neurons stimulating the muscles of respiration also stimulate other neurons in the medullary respiratory center that are responsible for stopping inspiration. The neurons responsible for stopping inspiration also receive input from the pontine

Clinical Focus   Respiratory Disorders

Bronchi and Lungs

Bronchitis (brong-kī′tis) is an inflammation of the bronchi caused by irritants, such as cigarette smoke, air pollution, or infections. The inflammation results in swelling of the mucous membrane lining the bronchi, increased mucus production, and decreased movement of mucus by cilia. Consequently, the diameter of the bronchi is decreased, and ventilation is impaired. Bronchitis can progress to emphysema.

Emphysema (em-fi-sē′mă) is the destruction of the alveolar walls. Many individuals have both bronchitis and emphysema, which are often referred to as **chronic obstructive pulmonary disease (COPD)**. Chronic inflammation of the bronchioles, usually caused by cigarette smoke or air pollution, probably initiates emphysema. Narrowing of the bronchioles restricts air movement, and air tends to be retained in the lungs. Coughing to remove accumulated mucus increases pressure in the alveoli, resulting in rupture and destruction of alveolar walls. Loss of alveolar walls has two important consequences: (1) the respiratory membrane has a decreased surface area, which decreases gas exchange, and (2) loss of elastic fibers decreases the ability of the lungs to recoil and expel air. Symptoms of emphysema include shortness of breath and enlargement of the thoracic cavity. Treatment involves removing sources of irritants (e.g., stopping smoking), promoting the removal of bronchial secretions, using bronchiodilators, retraining people to breathe so that expiration of air is maximized, and using antibiotics to prevent infections. The progress of emphysema can be slowed, but there is no cure.

Cystic fibrosis (fī-brō′sis) is an inherited disease that affects the secretory cells lining the lungs, pancreas, sweat glands, and salivary glands. An abnormal transport protein is produced that does not reach the cell surface or does not function normally if it does reach the cell surface. The result is decreased chloride ion secretion out of cells. In the lungs, water normally forms a thin fluid layer over which mucus is moved by ciliated cells. In cystic fibrosis, the decreased chloride ion diffusion results in dehydrated respiratory secretions. The mucus is more viscous, resisting movement by cilia, and it accumulates in the lungs, thereby increasing the likelihood of infections. Chronic airflow obstruction causes difficulty in breathing, and severe coughing in an attempt to remove the mucus can result in pneumothorax and bleeding within the lungs. Once fatal during early childhood, many victims of cystic fibrosis are now surviving into young adulthood. Future treatments could include the development of drugs that correct or assist the normal ion transport mechanism. Alternatively, cystic fibrosis may some day be cured through genetic engineering by inserting functional copies of the defective gene into the cells of a person with the disease. Research on this exciting possibility is currently underway.

Pulmonary fibrosis is the replacement of lung tissue with fibrous connective tissue, making the lungs less elastic and breathing more difficult. Exposure to asbestos, silica, or coal dust is the most common cause.

Lung cancer arises from the epithelium of the respiratory tract. Lung cancer is the most common cause of cancer death in males and females in the United States, and almost all cases occur in smokers. Because of the rich lymph and blood supply in the lungs, cancer in the lung can readily spread to other parts of the lung or body. In addition, the disease is often advanced before symptoms become severe enough for the victim to seek medical aid. Typical symptoms include coughing, sputum production, and blockage of the airways. Treatments include removal of part or all of the lung, chemotherapy, and radiation.

Circulatory System

Disorders of the circulatory system can affect respiratory function. Even when ventilation is adequate, blood flow through the pulmonary capillaries may be inadequate. Disorders that reduce blood flow through lung tissue include **thrombosis of the pulmonary arteries** and reduced cardiac output resulting from **heart attack** or **shock**. **Anemia**, which results in a reduction of the total amount of hemoglobin, reduces the capacity of blood to transport oxygen. **Carbon monoxide** binds more strongly to the hemoglobin molecule than oxygen does. It occupies binding sites, making them unavailable for oxygen transport. Thus carbon monoxide poisoning decreases the ability of hemoglobin to transport oxygen, even though it does not affect the total hemoglobin concentration in the blood.

Nervous System

Sudden infant death syndrome (SIDS), or crib death, is the most frequent cause of death of infants between 2 weeks and 1 year of age. Death results when the infant stops breathing during sleep. Although the cause of SIDS remains controversial, there is evidence that damage to the respiratory center during development is a factor. There is no treatment, but at-risk babies can be placed on monitors that sound an alarm if the baby stops breathing.

Paralysis of the respiratory muscles can result from damage of the spinal cord in the cervical or thoracic regions. The damage interrupts nerve tracts that transmit action potentials to the muscles of respiration. Transection of the spinal cord can result from trauma such as automobile accidents or diving into water that is too shallow. Another cause of paralysis is poliomyelitis (pō′lē-ō-mī′ĕ-lī′tis), a viral infection that damages neurons of the respiratory center or motor neurons that stimulate the muscles of respiration. Finally, anesthetics or central nervous system depressants can depress the function of the respiratory center if they are taken or administered in large enough doses.

Thoracic Wall

Decreased elasticity of the thoracic wall can be caused by severe arthritis or by conditions resulting in severe curvature of the spine, such as **scoliosis** (skō-lē-ō′sis) and **kyphosis** (kī-fō′sis). These conditions reduce the ability of the thoracic cavity to increase its volume when the muscles of inspiration contract, thereby increasing the muscular effort required for inspiration.

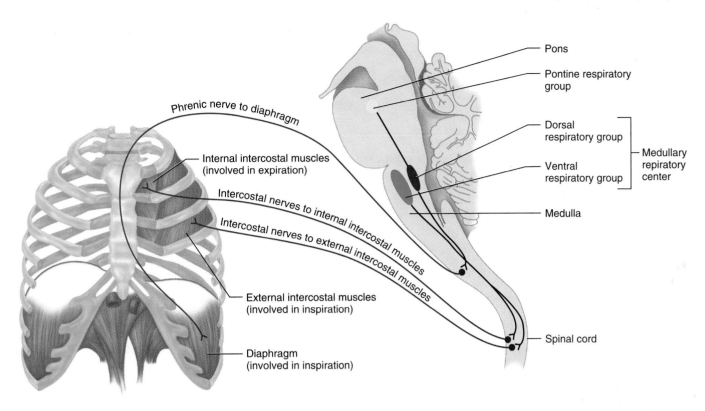

Figure 15.13   Respiratory Structures in the Brainstem

The relationship of respiratory structures to one another and to the nerves innervating the muscles of respiration. The dorsal and ventral respiratory groups are shown only on one side of the medulla oblongata.

respiratory neurons, stretch receptors in the lungs, and probably other sources. When the inputs to these neurons exceeds a threshold level, they cause the neurons stimulating respiratory muscles to be inhibited. Relaxation of respiratory muscles results in expiration, which lasts approximately 3 s. For the next inspiration, go back to step 1.

Modification of Ventilation

Although the medullary neurons establish the basic rate and depth of breathing, their activities can be influenced by input from other parts of the brain and by input from peripherally located receptors.

Nervous Control of Ventilation

Higher brain centers can modify the activity of the respiratory center (figure 15.14). For example, controlling air movements out of the lungs makes speech possible, and emotions can make us sob or gasp. There is conscious control over respiration. It is possible to breathe voluntarily or to stop respiratory movements voluntarily. Some people can hold their breath until they lose consciousness as a result of the lack of oxygen in the brain. Some children have used this strategy to encourage parents to give them what they want. As soon as conscious control of respiration is lost, however, the automatic control of respiration resumes, and the person starts to breathe again.

Several reflexes, such as sneeze and cough reflexes, can modify ventilation. The **Hering-Breuer** (her′ing broy′er) **reflex** functions to support rhythmic respiratory movements by limiting the extent of inspiration (see figure 15.14). As muscles of inspiration contract, the lungs fill with air. Sensory receptors that respond to stretch are located in the lungs, and, as the lungs fill with air, the stretch receptors are stimulated. Action potentials from the lung stretch receptors are then sent to the medulla oblongata, where they inhibit the respiratory center neurons and cause expiration. In infants, the Hering-Breuer reflex plays an important role in regulating the basic rhythm of breathing and in preventing overinflation of the lungs. In adults, however, the reflex is important only when the tidal volume is large, such as during heavy exercise.

Touch, thermal, and pain receptors in the skin also stimulate the respiratory center, which explains the gasp in response to being splashed with cold water or being pinched (see figure 15.14).

Chemical Control of Ventilation

During aerobic respiration, oxygen is consumed and carbon dioxide is produced (see chapter 17). The respiratory system adds oxygen and removes carbon dioxide from the blood. For the respiratory system to maintain these gases at homeostatic levels, there must be some way to monitor gas levels and respond appropriately.

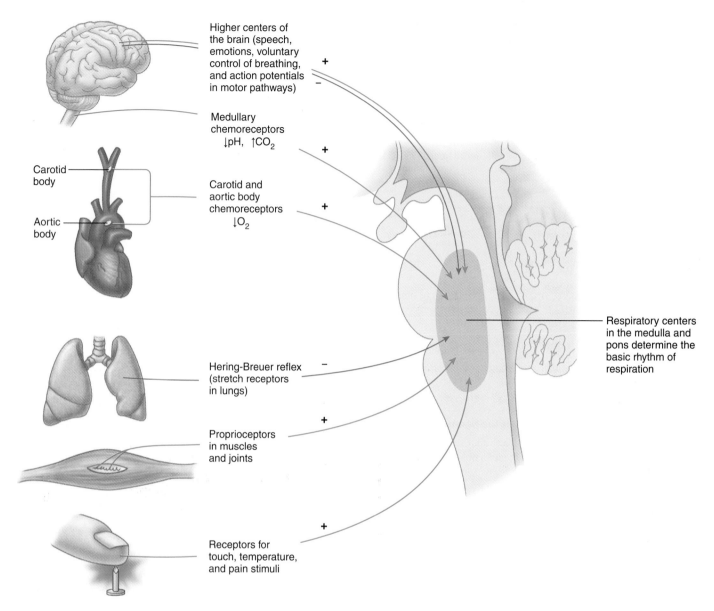

Figure 15.14 Major Regulatory Mechanisms of Ventilation

The major regulatory mechanisms that affect the rate and depth of ventilation are shown. A plus sign indicates an increase in ventilation, and a minus sign indicates a decrease in ventilation.

Carbon dioxide levels in the blood are the major driving force for regulating respiration. Under most circumstances, carbon dioxide levels are much more important than oxygen. A small increase in carbon dioxide levels can cause an increase in ventilation. A large increase, as can occur while holding one's breath, can result in a powerful urge to take a breath. A greater-than-normal amount of carbon dioxide in the blood is called **hypercapnia** (hī-per-kap'nē-ă).

Oxygen is not normally as important as carbon dioxide in regulating ventilation, because hemoglobin is very effective at picking up oxygen in the lungs. Normally there is little variation in the oxygen content of blood leaving the lungs, despite changes in oxygen demand by the body. As long as blood carbon dioxide levels are normal, blood oxygen levels are usually normal as well.

Changes in blood carbon dioxide levels are not directly detected, however. Instead, changes in blood pH are monitored. This can occur because changes in carbon dioxide cause changes in pH (see the section, Carbon Dioxide Transport and Blood pH, on p. 416). Thus, two things are accomplished through the chemical regulation of ventilation: (1) homeostatic levels of carbon dioxide and oxygen are maintained, and (2) pH homeostasis is maintained.

9 P R E D I C T

Explain why a person who breathes rapidly and deeply (hyperventilates) for several seconds experiences a short period of time in which respiration does not occur (apnea) before normal breathing resumes.

✔ *Answer on page 429*

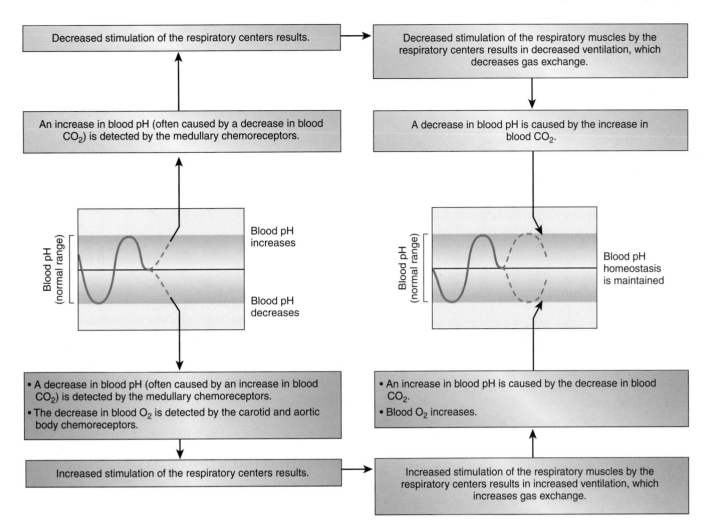

Figure 15.15   Regulation of Blood pH and Gases

Chemoreceptors in the medulla oblongata are sensitive to small changes in blood pH (see figure 15.14). An increase in blood pH, typically caused by a decrease in blood carbon dioxide, can be detected by the chemoreceptors. As a result, the respiratory center decreases ventilation, which decreases the removal of carbon dioxide from the blood. Because carbon dioxide is continually produced, carbon dioxide levels now increase, causing pH to decrease, and homeostasis is maintained (figure 15.15).

The medullary chemoreceptors also respond to a decrease in blood pH, typically caused by an increase in blood carbon dioxide levels. As a result, the respiratory center increases ventilation, which increases the removal of carbon dioxide from the blood. As blood carbon dioxide levels decrease, blood pH increases, and homeostasis is maintained (see figure 15.15).

Chemoreceptors in the carotid and aortic bodies also provide input to the respiratory center (see figure 15.14). These chemoreceptors primarily respond to changes in blood oxygen. Changes in blood oxygen levels can become important when they decline to low levels, a condition called **hypoxia** (hī-pok′sē-ă). Examples include exposure to high altitudes, emphysema, shock, and asphyxiation caused by exposure to reduced oxygen levels but normal carbon dioxide levels. In these situations, the chemoreceptors of the carotid and aortic bodies are strongly stimulated. They send action potentials to the respiratory center and produce an increase in the rate and depth of respiration (see figure 15.15). The increased ventilation increases oxygen diffusion from the alveoli into the blood, resulting in increased blood oxygen.

Did You Know?

Air is composed of 21% oxygen at low and high altitudes. At sea level the atmospheric pressure is 760 mm Hg and PO_2 is about 160 mm Hg (760 mm Hg $\times$ 0.21 = 160 mm Hg). At higher altitudes, the atmospheric pressure is lower, and PO_2 is decreased. For example, at 10,000 ft above sea level, the atmospheric pressure is 523 mm Hg. Consequently, PO_2 is 110 mm Hg (523 mm Hg $\times$ 0.21 = 110 mm Hg). Because PO_2 is lower at high altitudes, the blood levels of oxygen can decline enough to stimulate the carotid and aortic bodies. Oxygen then becomes an important stimulus for an elevated rate and depth of respiration. At high altitudes, the ability of the respiratory system

(continued)

to eliminate carbon dioxide is not adversely affected by the low atmospheric pressure. Thus the blood carbon dioxide levels become lower than normal because of the increased rate and depth of respiration stimulated by the low oxygen blood levels. The decreased blood carbon dioxide levels cause the blood pH to rise to abnormally high levels.

A similar situation can exist in people who have emphysema. Carbon dioxide diffuses across the respiratory membrane more readily than oxygen. Thus the decrease in surface area of the respiratory membrane caused by the disease results in low blood levels of oxygen without elevated blood levels of carbon dioxide. An elevated rate and depth of respiration is the result of the stimulatory effect of low blood levels of oxygen on the carotid and aortic bodies. More severe emphysema, in which the surface area of the respiratory membrane is reduced to a minimum, can also result in elevated blood levels of carbon dioxide.

Effect of Exercise on Ventilation

The mechanisms by which ventilation is regulated during exercise is controversial, and no one factor can account for all the observed responses. Ventilation during exercise can be divided into two phases:

1. *Ventilation increases abruptly.* At the onset of exercise, ventilation immediately increases. This initial increase can be as much as 50% of the total increase that occurs during exercise. The immediate increase in ventilation occurs too quickly to be explained by changes in metabolism or blood gases. As axons pass from the motor cortex of the cerebrum through the motor pathways, numerous collateral fibers project to the respiratory center. During exercise, action potentials in the motor pathways stimulate skeletal muscle contractions and action potentials in the collateral fibers stimulate the respiratory center (see figure 15.14).

Furthermore, during exercise, body movements stimulate proprioceptors in the joints of the limbs. Nerve fibers from these proprioceptors extend to the spinal cord to connect with sensory nerve tracts ascending to the brain. Collateral fibers from these nerve tracts connect to the respiratory center, and movement of the limbs has a strong stimulatory influence on the respiratory center (see figure 15.14).

There may also be a learned component to the ventilation response during exercise. After a period of training the brain "learns" to match ventilation with the intensity of the exercise. Well-trained athletes match their respiratory movements more efficiently with their level of physical activity than do untrained individuals. Thus centers of the brain involved in learning have an indirect influence on the respiratory center, but the exact mechanism for this kind of regulation is unclear.

2. *Ventilation increases gradually.* After the immediate increase in ventilation, ventilation gradually increases and then levels off within 4 to 6 minutes (min) after the onset of exercise. Factors responsible for the immediate increase in ventilation may play a role in the gradual increase as well.

Despite large changes in oxygen consumption and carbon dioxide production during exercise, the *average* arterial oxygen, carbon dioxide, and pH levels remain constant and close to resting levels as long as the exercise is aerobic (see chapter 7). This suggests that changes in blood gases and pH do not play an important role in regulating ventilation during aerobic exercise. During exercise, however, the values of arterial oxygen, carbon dioxide, and pH levels rise and fall more than at rest. Thus, even though their average values do not change, their oscillations may be a signal for helping to control ventilation.

The highest level of exercise that can be performed without causing a significant change in blood pH is called the **anaerobic threshold**. If the exercise intensity is high enough to exceed the anaerobic threshold, then skeletal muscles produce and release lactic acid into the blood. The resulting change in blood pH stimulates the carotid bodies, resulting in increased ventilation. In fact, ventilation can increase so much that arterial carbon dioxide levels decrease below resting levels and arterial oxygen levels increase above resting levels.

Respiratory Adaptations to Exercise

In response to training, athletic performance increases because the cardiovascular and respiratory systems become more efficient at delivering oxygen and picking up carbon dioxide. Ventilation in most individuals does not limit performance because ventilation can increase to a greater extent than does cardiovascular function.

After training, vital capacity increases slightly and residual volume decreases slightly. Tidal volume at rest and during standardized submaximal exercise does not change. At maximal exercise, however, tidal volume increases. After training, respiratory rate at rest or during standardized submaximal exercise is slightly lower, but at maximal exercise, respiratory rate is generally increased.

Minute ventilation is affected by the changes in tidal volume and respiratory rate. After training, minute ventilation is essentially unchanged or slightly reduced at rest, is slightly reduced during standardized submaximal exercise, and is greatly increased at maximal exercise. For example, an untrained person with a minute ventilation of 120 liters per minute (L/min) can increase to 150 L/min after training. Increases to 180 L/min are typical of highly trained athletes.

Clinical Focus   Infectious Diseases of the Respiratory System

Respiratory system infections are the most common types of infections. Most are relatively mild, but some are among the most damaging types of infection. The major respiratory diseases are bacterial and viral, although some are fungal or protozoan infections.

Many respiratory infections are spread by the release of microorganisms from the respiratory tract. For example, a person who sneezes or coughs releases droplets containing microorganisms that can be inhaled by another person. Or, microorganisms released from the respiratory tract of a person can contaminate surfaces such as tabletops. If a person touches the contaminated surface, the microorganisms can then be transferred by the fingers from the contaminated surface to the mouth or nasal passages.

Infections of the Upper Respiratory Tract

Strep throat is caused by streptococcal bacteria (*Streptococcus pyogenes*) and is characterized by inflammation of the pharynx and by fever. Frequently, inflammation of the tonsils and middle ear are involved. Without a throat analysis, the infection cannot be distinguished from viral causes of pharyngeal inflammation. Current techniques allow rapid diagnosis within minutes to hours, and antibiotics are effective in treating strep throat. Scarlet fever occurs in response to certain strains of *S. pyogenes*. This infection is characterized by fever and a pinkish red skin rash produced by a circulating toxin released by the bacteria.

Diphtheria (dif-thēr'ē-ă) was once a major cause of death among children. It is caused by a bacterium (*Corynebacterium diphteriae*). A grayish membrane forms in the throat and can block the respiratory passages totally. A vaccine against diphtheria is part of the normal immunization (DPT) program for children in the United States.

The common cold is the result of a viral infection. Symptoms include sneezing, excessive nasal secretions, and congestion. The infection easily can spread to sinus cavities, lower respiratory passages, and the middle ear. The common cold usually runs its course to recovery in about 1 week.

Infections of the Lower Respiratory Tract

Many of the same infections that mainly affect the upper respiratory tract also can cause laryngitis (inflammation of the larynx) and bronchitis (inflammation of the bronchi).

Whooping cough, or pertussis (per-tŭs'is), is a bacterial infection (caused by *Bordetella pertussis*) that causes a loss of cilia of the respiratory epithelium. Mucus accumulates, and the infected person attempts to cough up the mucous accumulations. The coughing can be severe. A vaccine for whooping cough is part of the normal vaccination procedure (DPT) for children in the United States.

Tuberculosis is caused by the bacterium *Clostridium tuberculosis*. In the lungs, the tuberculosis bacteria form small lumplike lesions called tubercles. The lesions contain degenerating macrophages and tuberculosis bacteria. An immune reaction is directed against the bacteria, which causes the formation of larger lesions and inflammation. The tubercles can rupture, releasing additional bacteria, which infect other parts of the lung or body. A strain of tuberculosis that is resistant to treatment with antibiotics is increasing in frequency in the United States.

Pneumonia refers to many infections of the lungs. Symptoms include fever, difficulty in breathing, and chest pain. Inflammation of the lungs results in pulmonary edema and poor inflation of the lungs with air. Most pneumonias are bacterial, but some are viral. Compared with viral pneumonia, bacterial pneumonia is more severe, produces more edema in the lungs, and is more likely to cause death. A protozoan infection (caused by *Pneumocystis carinii*) that results in pneumocystis (noo-mō-sis'tis) pneumonia is rare, except in persons who have a compromised immune system. This type of pneumonia has become one of the infections commonly suffered by persons who have AIDS.

Flu, or influenza (in-flū-en'ză), is a viral infection of the respiratory system and does not affect the digestive system as is commonly assumed. Flu is characterized by chills, fever, headache, and muscular aches in addition to respiratory symptoms. There are several strains of flu viruses. Flu vaccines are of limited use because it usually takes too long to develop an effective vaccine to be effective during an epidemic. The mortality rate during a flu epidemic is about 1%, and most of those deaths are among the very old and very young. During a flu epidemic, the infection rate is so rapid and the disease is so widespread that the total number of deaths is substantial, even though the percentage of deaths is relatively low.

A number of fungal diseases also affect the respiratory system. The fungal spores usually enter the respiratory system attached to dust particles. Spores in soil and feces of certain animals make the rate of infection high in farm workers and gardeners in certain areas of the country. The infections usually result in minor respiratory infections, but in some cases they can spread to other parts of the body.

Systems Pathology
Asthma

ASTHMA

Mr. W. was an 18-year-old track athlete in seemingly good health. One day he came down with a common cold, resulting in the typical symptoms of nasal congestion and discomfort. After several days he began to cough and wheeze and he thought that his cold had progressed to his lungs. Determined not to get "out of shape" because of his cold, Mr. W. took a few aspirins to relieve his discomfort and went to the track to do some jogging. After a few minutes of exercise he began to wheeze very forcefully and rapidly, and he felt that he could hardly get enough air. Even though he stopped jogging his condition did not improve (figure A). Fortunately, a concerned friend who was also at the track, took him to the emergency room.

Although Mr. W. had no previous history of asthma, careful evaluation by the emergency doctor convinced her that he was probably having an asthma attack. Mr. W. inhaled a bronchiodilator drug, which resulted in rapid improvement of his condition. He was released from the emergency room and referred to his personal physician for further treatment and education about asthma.

Background Information

Asthma (az′mă) is a disease characterized by increased constriction of the trachea and bronchi in response to various stimuli, resulting in a narrowing of the air passageways and decreased ventilation efficiency. Symptoms include wheezing, coughing, and shortness of breath. In contrast to many other respiratory disorders, however, the symptoms of asthma typically reverse either spontaneously or with therapy.

It is estimated that the prevalence of asthma in the United States is from 3% to 6% of the general population. Approximately half the cases first appear before age 10, and twice as many boys as girls develop asthma. Anywhere from 25% to 50% of childhood asthmatics are symptom-free from adolescence onward.

The exact cause or causes of asthma is unknown, but asthma and allergies run strongly in some families. There is no definitive pathological feature or diagnostic test for asthma, but three important features of the disease are chronic airway inflammation, airway hyperreactivity, and airflow obstruction. The inflammatory response results in tissue damage, edema, and mucous buildup, which can block airflow through the bronchi. Airway hyperreactivity is greatly increased contraction of the smooth muscle in the trachea and bronchi in response to a stimulus. As a result of

Figure A   A jogger with asthma.

airway hyperreactivity, the diameter of the airway decreases, and resistance to airflow increases. The effects of inflammation and airway hyperreactivity combine to cause airflow obstruction.

Many cases of asthma appear to be associated with a chronic inflammatory response by the immune system. The number of immune cells in the bronchi increases, including mast cells, eosinophils, neutrophils, macrophages, and lymphocytes. These cells release chemical mediators, such as interleukins, leukotrienes, prostaglandins, platelet-activating factor, thromboxanes, and chemotactic factors. These chemical mediators promote inflammation, increase mucous secretion, and attract additional immune cells to the bronchi, resulting in chronic airway inflammation. Airway hyperreactivity and inflammation appear to be linked by some of the chemical mediators, which increase the sensitivity of the airway to stimulation and cause smooth muscle contraction.

The stimuli that prompt airflow obstruction varies from one individual to another. Some asthmatics have reactions to particular allergens, which are foreign substances that evoke an inappropriate immune system response (see chapter 14). Examples include inhaled pollen, animal dander, and dust mites. Many cases of asthma may be caused by an allergic reaction to substances in the droppings and carcasses of cockroaches, which may explain the higher rate of asthma in poor, urban areas.

On the other hand, inhaled substances, such as chemicals in the workplace or cigarette smoke, can provoke an asthma attack without stimulating an allergic reaction. Over 200 substances have been associated with occupational asthma. An asthma attack can also be stimulated by ingested substances such as aspirin, nonsteroidal antiinflammatory compounds such as ibuprofen (ī-bū′prō-fen), sulfites in food preservative, and tartrazine (tar′tră-zēn) in food colorings. Asthmatics can substitute acetaminophen (as-et-ă-mē′nō-fen, a-set-ă-min′ō-fen; Tylenol) for aspirin.

Other stimuli, such as strenuous exercise, especially in cold weather, can precipitate an asthma attack. Such episodes can often be avoided by using a bronchiodilator drug prior to exercise. Viral infections, emotional upset, stress, and even reflux of stomach acid into the esophagus are known to elicit an asthma attack.

Treatment of asthma involves avoiding the causative stimulus and drug therapy. Steroids and mast cell-stabilizing agents, which prevent the release of chemical mediators from mast cells, are used to reduce airway inflammation. Theophylline (thē-of′i-lēn) and other drugs are commonly used to cause bronchiolar dilation. Although treatment is generally effective in controlling asthma, death by asphyxiation rarely can occur. Most of these deaths probably could have been prevented by earlier and more intensive therapy.

10 PREDICT

It is not usually necessary to assess arterial blood gases in the diagnosis and treatment of asthma. This information, however, can sometimes be useful in cases of severe asthma attacks. Suppose that Mr. W. had a PO_2 of 60 mm Hg and a PCO_2 of 30 mm Hg when he first came to the emergency room. Explain how that could happen.

✔ *Answer on page 429*

System Interactions

System	Interactions
Integumentary	Cyanosis, a bluish skin color, results from a decreased blood oxygen content.
Muscular	Skeletal muscles are necessary for respiratory movements and the cough reflex. Increased muscular work during a severe asthma attack can cause metabolic acidosis because of anaerobic respiration and excessive lactic acid production.
Skeletal	Red bone marrow is the site of production of many of the immune cells responsible for the inflammatory response of asthma. The thoracic cage is necessary for respiration.
Nervous	Emotional upset or stress can evoke an asthma attack. Peripheral and central chemoreceptor reflexes affect ventilation. The cough reflex helps to remove mucus from respiratory passages. Pain, anxiety, and death from asphyxiation can result from the altered gas exchange caused by asthma. One theory of the cause of asthma is an imbalance of the autonomic nervous system (ANS) control of bronchiolar smooth muscle, and drugs that enhance sympathetic effects or block parasympathetic effects are used in asthma treatment.
Endocrine	Steroids from the adrenal gland play a role in regulating inflammation and they are used in asthma therapy.
Cardiovascular	Increased vascular permeability of lung blood vessels results in edema. Blood carries ingested substances that provoke an asthma attack to the lungs. Blood carries immune cells from red bone marrow to the lungs. Tachycardia commonly occurs and the normal effects of respiration on venous return are exaggerated, resulting in large fluctuations of blood pressure.
Lymphatic and Immune	Immune cells release chemical mediators that promote inflammation, increase mucous production, and cause bronchiolar constriction; believed to be a major factor in asthma. Ingested allergens, such as aspirin or sulfites in food, can evoke an asthma attack.
Digestive	Ingested substances, such as aspirin, sulfiting agents (preservatives), tartrazine (tar′tră-zēn, a yellow dye), and certain foods, and reflux of stomach acid into the esophagus can evoke an asthma attack.
Urinary	Modifying hydrogen ion secretion into the urine helps to compensate for acid–base imbalances caused by asthma.

Summary

- Respiration includes the movement of air into and out of the lungs, the exchange of gases between the air and the blood, the transport of gases in the blood, and the exchange of gases between the blood and tissues.

Functions of the Respiratory System

- The respiratory system exchanges oxygen and carbon dioxide between the air and blood, regulates blood pH, produces sounds, moves air over the sensory receptors that detect smell, and protects against some microorganisms.

Anatomy of the Respiratory System

Nose and Nasal Cavity

- The bridge of the nose is bone, and most of the external nose is cartilage.
- The nasal cavity warms, humidifies, and cleans the air.
  The external nares open to the outside, and the internal nares lead to the pharynx.
  The nasal cavity is divided by the nasal septum into right and left parts.
  The paranasal sinuses and the nasolacrimal duct open into the nasal cavity.
  Hairs just inside the external nares trap debris.
  The nasal cavity is lined with pseudostratified epithelium with cilia that traps debris and moves it to the pharynx.

Pharynx

- The nasopharynx joins the nasal cavity through the internal nares and contains the opening to the auditory tube and the pharyngeal tonsils.
- The oropharynx joins the oral cavity and contains the palatine and lingual tonsils.
- The laryngopharynx opens into the larynx and the esophagus.

Larynx

- The larynx consists of three unpaired cartilages and six paired ones. The thyroid cartilage and cricoid cartilage form most of the larynx. The epiglottis covers the opening of the larynx during swallowing.
- The vestibular folds can prevent air, food, and liquids from passing into the larynx.
- The vocal folds (cords) vibrate and produce sounds when air passes through the larynx. The force of air movement controls loudness, and changes in the length and tension of the vocal folds determines pitch.

Trachea

- The trachea connects the larynx to the primary bronchi.

Bronchi

- The primary bronchi extend from the trachea to each lung.

Lungs

- There are two lungs.
- The airway passages of the lungs branch and decrease in size.
  The primary bronchi form the secondary bronchi, which go to each lobe of the lungs.

The secondary bronchi form the tertiary bronchi, which go to each bronchopulmonary segment of the lungs.
The tertiary bronchi branch many times to form the bronchioles.
The bronchioles branch to form the terminal bronchioles, which give rise to the respiratory bronchioles, from which alveolar ducts branch.
Alveoli are air sacs connected to the alveolar ducts and respiratory bronchioles.

- Important features of the tube system.
  The epithelium from the trachea to the terminal bronchioles is ciliated to facilitate removal of debris.
  Cartilage helps to hold the tube system open (from the trachea to the bronchioles).
  Smooth muscle controls the diameter of the tubes (especially the bronchioles).
  The alveoli are formed by simple squamous epithelium, and they facilitate diffusion of gases.

Pleural Cavities

- The pleural membranes surround the lungs and provide protection against friction.

Lymphatic Supply

- The lungs have superficial and deep lymphatic vessels.

Ventilation and Lung Volumes

Changing Thoracic Volume

- Inspiration occurs when the diaphragm contracts and the external intercostal muscles lift the rib cage, thus increasing the volume of the thoracic cavity. During labored breathing additional muscles of inspiration increase rib movement.
- Expiration can be passive or active. Passive expiration during quiet breathing occurs when the muscles of inspiration relax. Active expiration during labored breathing occurs when the diaphragm relaxes and the internal intercostal and abdominal muscles depress the rib cage to forcefully decrease the volume of the thoracic cavity.

Pressure Changes and Airflow

- Respiratory muscles cause changes in thoracic volume, which cause changes in alveolar volume and pressure.
- During inspiration, air flows into the alveoli because atmospheric pressure is greater than alveolar pressure.
- During expiration, air flows out of the alveoli because alveolar pressure is greater than atmospheric pressure.

Lung Recoil

- The lungs tend to collapse because of the elastic recoil of the connective tissue and surface tension of the fluid lining the alveoli.
- The lungs normally do not collapse because surfactant reduces the surface tension of the fluid lining the alveoli and pleural pressure is less than alveolar pressure.

Changing Alveolar Volume

- Increasing thoracic volume results in decreased pleural pressure, increased alveolar volume, decreased alveolar pressure, and air movement into the lungs.

- Decreasing thoracic volume results in increased pleural pressure, decreased alveolar volume, increased alveolar pressure, and air movement out of the lungs.

Pulmonary Volumes and Capacities

- There are four pulmonary volumes: tidal volume, inspiratory reserve, expiratory reserve, and residual volume.
- Pulmonary capacities are the sum of two or more pulmonary volumes and include vital capacity and total lung capacity.
- The forced expiratory vital capacity measures the rate at which air can be expelled from the lungs.

Gas Exchange

- The respiratory membranes are thin and have a large surface area that facilitates gas exchange.
- The components of the respiratory membrane include a film of water, the walls of the alveolus and the capillary, and an interstitial space.

Respiratory Membrane Thickness

- Increases in the thickness of the respiratory membrane results in decreased gas exchange.

Surface Area

- Small decreases in surface area adversely affect gas exchange during strenuous exercise; and, when the surface area is decreased to one-third to one-fourth of normal, gas exchange is inadequate under resting conditions.

Partial Pressure

- The pressure exerted by a specific gas in a mixture of gases is reported as the partial pressure of that gas.
- Oxygen diffuses from a higher partial pressure in the alveoli to a lower partial pressure in the pulmonary capillaries. Oxygen diffuses from a higher partial pressure in the tissue capillaries to a lower partial pressure in the tissue spaces.
- Carbon dioxide diffuses from a higher partial pressure in the tissues to a lower partial pressure in the tissue capillaries. Carbon dioxide diffuses from a higher partial pressure in the pulmonary capillaries to a lower partial pressure in the alveoli.

Gas Transport in the Blood

Oxygen Transport

- Most (98.5%) oxygen is transported bound to hemoglobin. Some (1.5%) oxygen is transported dissolved in plasma.
- Oxygen is released from hemoglobin in tissues when the partial pressure for oxygen is low, the partial pressure for carbon dioxide is high, pH is low, and temperature is high.

Carbon Dioxide Transport and Blood pH

- Carbon dioxide is transported as bicarbonate ions (70%), in combination with blood proteins (23%), and in solution in plasma (7%).
- In tissue capillaries, carbon dioxide combines with water inside the red blood cells to form carbonic acid that dissociates to form bicarbonate ions and hydrogen ions. This reaction promotes the transport of carbon dioxide.
- In lung capillaries, bicarbonate ions combine with hydrogen ions to form carbonic acid. The carbonic acid dissociates to form carbon dioxide that diffuses out of the red blood cells.
- As blood carbon dioxide levels increase, blood pH decreases; as blood carbon dioxide levels decrease, blood pH increases. Changes in ventilation change blood carbon dioxide levels and pH.

Rhythmic Ventilation

Respiratory Areas in the Brainstem

- The medullary respiratory center (dorsal respiratory and ventral respiratory groups) establishes rhythmic ventilation.
- The pontine respiratory group is involved with the switch between inspiration and expiration.

Generation of Rhythmic Ventilation

- Inspiration begins when stimuli from many sources, such as receptors that monitor blood gases, reach a threshold.
- Expiration begins when the neurons causing inspiration are inhibited.

Modification of Ventilation

Nervous Control of Ventilation

- Higher brain centers allow voluntary control of ventilation. Emotions and speech production affect ventilation.
- The Hering-Breuer reflex inhibits the respiratory center when the lungs are stretched during inspiration.
- Touch, thermal, and pain receptors can stimulate ventilation.

Chemical Control of Ventilation

- Chemoreceptors in the medulla oblongata respond to changes in blood pH. Usually changes in blood pH are produced by changes in blood carbon dioxide.
- Carbon dioxide is the major chemical regulator of respiration. An increase in blood carbon dioxide causes a decrease in blood pH, resulting in increased ventilation.
- Low blood levels of oxygen can stimulate chemoreceptors in the carotid and aortic bodies, resulting in increased ventilation.

Effect of Exercise on Ventilation

- Input from higher brain centers and from proprioceptors stimulates the respiratory center during exercise.

Respiratory Adaptations to Exercise

- Training results in increased minute volume at maximal exercise because of increased tidal volume and respiratory rate.

Content Review

1. Define respiration.
2. What are the functions of the respiratory system?
3. Describe the structures of the nasal cavity and their functions.
4. Name the three parts of the pharynx. With what structures does each part communicate?
5. Name and give the functions of the three unpaired cartilages of the larynx.
6. What is the function of the vestibular and vocal folds (cords). How are sounds of different loudness and pitch produced?
7. Starting at the larynx, name in order all the tubes air passes through to reach an alveolus.
8. What is the function of the C-shaped cartilages in the trachea? What happens to the amount of cartilage in the tube system of the respiratory system as the tubes become smaller? Explain why breathing becomes more difficult during an asthma attack.
9. What is the function of the ciliated epithelium in the tracheobronchial tree?
10. Distinguish between the lungs, a lobe of the lung, and a bronchopulmonary segment.
11. Describe the pleurae of the lungs. What is their function?
12. Describe the lymphatic supply of the lungs. What is its function?
13. Explain how the muscles of respiration change thoracic volume.
14. Describe the pressure changes that cause air to move into and out of the lungs. What causes these pressure changes?
15. Give two reasons why the lungs tend to recoil or collapse. What two factors keep the lungs from collapsing?
16. Explain how changes in thoracic volume result in changes in pleural pressure, alveolar volume, alveolar pressure, and airflow during inspiration and expiration.
17. Define tidal volume, inspiratory reserve, expiratory reserve, and residual volume. Define vital capacity, total lung capacity, and forced expiratory vital capacity.
18. List the components of the respiratory membrane. Describe the factors that affect the diffusion of gases across the respiratory membrane. Give some examples of diseases that decrease diffusion by altering these factors.
19. What is the partial pressure of a gas? Describe the diffusion of oxygen and carbon dioxide between the alveoli and pulmonary capillaries and between the tissue capillaries and tissues in terms of partial pressures.
20. List the ways in which oxygen is transported in the blood. What factors promote the release of oxygen in tissues?
21. List the ways in which carbon dioxide is transported in the blood.
22. How does carbon dioxide affect blood pH? How can changes in ventilation affect blood pH?
23. Name the respiratory areas of the brainstem, and explain how rhythmic ventilation is generated.
24. Describe how higher brain centers and the Hering-Breuer reflex can modify ventilation.
25. Explain the role of blood pH, carbon dioxide, and oxygen in modifying ventilation.
26. How is ventilation regulated during exercise?
27. What effect does exercise training have on the respiratory system?

Develop Your Reasoning Skills

1. Cardiopulmonary resuscitation (CPR) has replaced older, less efficient methods of sustaining respiration. The back pressure/arm lift method is one such technique that is no longer used. This procedure is performed with the victim lying face down. The rescuer presses firmly on the base of the scapulae for several seconds, then grasps the arms and lifts them. The sequence is then repeated. Explain why this procedure results in ventilation of the lungs.
2. Another technique for artificial respiration is mouth-to-mouth resuscitation. The rescuer takes a deep breath, blows air into the victim's mouth, and then lets air flow out of the victim. The process is repeated. Explain the following:
   a. Why do the victim's lungs expand?
   b. Why does air move out of the victim's lungs?
3. A person's vital capacity was measured while she was standing and while she was lying down. What difference, if any, in the measurement would you predict and why?
4. If water vapor forms 10% of the gases in air at sea level, what is the partial pressure of water?
5. A patient has pneumonia, and fluids accumulate within the alveoli. Explain why this results in an increased rate of respiration that can be returned to normal with oxygen therapy.
6. A patient has severe emphysema that has extensively damaged the alveoli and reduced the surface area of the respiratory membrane. Although the patient is receiving oxygen therapy, he still has a tremendous urge to take a breath (i.e., he does not feel as if he is getting enough air). Why does this occur?
7. Patients with diabetes mellitus who are not being treated with insulin therapy rapidly metabolize lipids, and acidic by-products of lipid metabolism accumulate in the circulatory system. What effect does this have on ventilation? Why is the change in ventilation beneficial?
8. Ima Anxious was hysterical and was hyperventilating. The doctor made her breathe into a paper bag. Because you are an especially astute student, you say to the doctor, "When Ima was hyperventilating, she was reducing blood carbon dioxide levels; and, when she breathed into the paper bag, carbon dioxide was trapped in the bag, and she was rebreathing it, thus causing blood carbon dioxide levels to increase. As blood carbon dioxide levels increase, the urge to breathe should have increased. Instead, she began to breath more slowly. Please explain." How do you think the doctor would respond? (Hint: Recall that the effect of decreased blood carbon dioxide on the vasomotor center results in vasodilation and a sudden decrease in blood pressure.)
9. Hyperventilating before swimming underwater can increase the time spent underwater. Explain how that could happen. Sometimes, a person who has hyperventilated before swimming underwater, passes out while still under water and drowns. Explain.
10. The blood pH of a runner was monitored during a race. It was noticed that, shortly after the beginning of the race, her blood pH increased for a short time. Propose an explanation that would account for the increased pH values following the start of the race.

Answers to Predict Questions

1. p. 401 When you sleep with your mouth open, less air passes through the nasal passages. This is especially true when nasal passages are plugged because you have a cold. As a consequence, air is not humidified and warmed. The dry air dries the throat and the trachea, thus irritating them.

2. p. 404 When a large mouthful of food is swallowed, the esophagus is enlarged in the area through which the food passes. The bulge in the esophagus applies pressure on the trachea, which is immediately anterior to the esophagus. Because the C-shaped cartilages of the trachea have their open portion facing the esophagus, the posterior wall of the trachea collapses momentarily as the food passes. Thus the passage of food through the esophagus is not hampered by the trachea.

3. p. 407 During respiratory movements, the parietal and visceral pleurae slide over each other. Normally the pleural fluid in the pleural cavities lubricates the surfaces of these membranes. When the pleural membranes are inflamed, their surfaces become roughened. The rough surfaces rub against each other and create an intense pain. The pain is increased when a person takes a deep breath because the movement of the membranes is greater than during normal breaths.

4. p. 407 Relaxation of the abdominal muscles allows the abdominal organs to move inferiorly. Thus, it is easier for the diaphragm to move inferiorly and increase the volume of the thoracic cavity.

5. p. 410 The tube should apply suction. In order for the lung to expand, pressure in the alveoli must be greater than the pressure in the pleural cavity. This can be accomplished by lowering the pressure in the pleural cavity through suction. Applying air under pressure would make the pressure in the pleural cavity greater than the pressure in the alveoli, which would keep the alveoli collapsed.

6. p. 412 The resting person with a tidal volume of 500 mL and a respiratory rate of 12 respirations/min, has a minute ventilation of 6000 mL (500 mL × 12 respirations/min). The exercising person with a tidal volume of 4000 mL and a respiratory rate of 24 respirations/min, has a minute ventilation of 96,000 mL (4000 mL × 24 respirations/min). The difference between the two is 90,000 mL, which means that the exercising person respired 90,000 mL more air per minute than the person at rest.

7. p. 416 During exercise, skeletal muscle cells increase oxygen use in order to produce the ATP molecules required for muscle contraction. The P_{O_2} inside the cells therefore decreases, which increases the diffusion gradient for oxygen, resulting in increased movement of oxygen into the cells. The aerobic production of ATP also produces carbon dioxide (see chapter 7). The partial pressure of carbon dioxide inside the cell therefore increases, which increases the diffusion gradient for carbon dioxide, resulting in increased movement of carbon dioxide out of cells.

8. p. 416 A rapid rate of respiration increases the blood pH because carbon dioxide is eliminated from the blood more rapidly during rapid respiration. As carbon dioxide is lost, hydrogen ions and bicarbonate ions combine to form carbonic acid, which in turn dissociates to form carbon dioxide and water. The decrease in hydrogen ions causes an increase in blood pH. Holding one's breath results in a decrease in pH, because carbon dioxide accumulates in the blood. The carbon dioxide combines with water to form carbonic acid, which dissociates to form hydrogen ions and bicarbonate ions. The increase in hydrogen ions causes a decrease in blood pH.

9. p. 420 When a person breathes rapidly and deeply for several seconds, the carbon dioxide levels decrease, and blood pH increases. Carbon dioxide is an important regulator of respiratory movements. A decrease in blood carbon dioxide and an increase in blood pH result in a reduced stimulus to the respiratory center. As a consequence, respiratory movements stop until blood carbon dioxide levels build up again in the body fluid. This normally takes only a short time.

10. p. 425 A P_{O_2} of 60 mm Hg and a P_{CO_2} of 30 mm Hg are both below normal. The movement of air into and out the lungs is restricted because of the asthma, and there is a mismatch between ventilation of the alveoli and blood flow to the alveoli. Consequently, because of the ineffective ventilation, blood oxygen levels decrease. Mr. W. hyperventilates, which helps to maintain blood oxygen levels but also results in lower than normal blood carbon dioxide levels. (If there was no hyperventilation, one would expect decreased blood oxygen but increased blood carbon dioxide.)

Chapter Sixteen

The Digestive System

bile

(bīl) Fluid secreted from the liver, stored in the gallbladder, and released into the duodenum; emulsifies fats.

chyme

(kīm) [Gr. *chymos*, juice] Semifluid mass of partly digested food passed from the stomach into the duodenum.

colon

(kō′lon) Division of the large intestine that extends from the cecum to the rectum.

defecation

(def-ĕ-kā′shŭn) [L. *defaeco*, to purify] Discharge of feces from the rectum.

deglutition

(dē-gloo-tish′ŭn) [L. *deglutio*, to swallow] The act of swallowing.

duodenum

(doo-ō-dē′nŭm or doo-od′e-nŭm) [L. *duodeni*, twelve] First division of the small intestine; connects the stomach to the jejunum.

esophagus

(ē-sof′ă-gŭs) [Gr. *oisophagos*, gullet] The part of the digestive tract between the pharynx and stomach.

intramural plexus

(in′tră-mū′răl) [L., within the wall] A nerve plexus within the wall of the gastrointestinal tract; involved in local and autonomic control of digestion.

lacteal

(lak′-tē-ăl) Lymphatic vessel in the wall of the small intestine that carries lymph from the intestine and absorbs fat.

mastication

(mas-ti-kā′shŭn) [L. *mastico*, to chew] The process of chewing.

mucosa

(mū-kō′să) Mucous membranes consisting of epithelium, connective tissue, and smooth muscle.

parietal peritoneum

(pă-rī′-ĕ-tăl pě′rĭtō-nē′ŭm) [L., wall] The part of the serous membranes of the abdominal cavity that lines the inner surface of the body wall.

peristaltic waves

(per′i-stal′tik) Waves of contraction and relaxation moving along a tube; propel food along the digestive tube.

pharynx

(far′ingks) [Gr., throat] The part of the digestive and respiratory tubes superior to the larynx and esophagus and inferior and posterior to the oral and nasal cavities.

visceral peritoneum

(vis′er-ăl per′i-tō-nē′ŭm) [L., organ] That part of the serous membrane in the abdominal cavity covering the surface of some abdominal organs.

Objectives

After reading this chapter, you should be able to:

1. List the organs that make up the digestive tract and describe the structure of each.

2. Name the teeth and describe the structure of an individual tooth.

3. Describe the major salivary glands. Compare their structures and functions.

4. Outline the anatomical and physiological characteristics of the stomach that are most important to its function.

5. List the anatomical and histological characteristics of the small intestine that account for its large surface area.

6. Describe the liver and pancreas.

7. List the parts of the large intestine and describe its major features.

8. Explain the functions of the structures in the oral cavity. Describe mastication (chewing) and deglutition (swallowing).

9. List the stomach secretions, describe their functions, and explain how they are regulated.

10. Describe gastric movements and stomach emptying and discuss their regulation.

11. Describe the secretions and movements that occur in the small and large intestines.

12. List the major functions of the pancreas and liver and explain how they are regulated.

13. Define digestion, absorption, and transport.

14. Describe the digestion of and list the breakdown products of carbohydrates, lipids, and proteins.

The old saying, "You are what you eat," is literally true. The molecules used to build the tissues of the body are derived from the food we eat. Every cell of the body needs nourishment, yet most cells cannot leave their position in the body and travel to a food source, so the food must be delivered. The **digestive system** (figure 16.1), with the help of the circulatory system, is like a gigantic "meals on wheels" system, serving over 100 trillion customers the nutrients they need. It also has its own quality control and waste disposal system. In this chapter, the structure and function of the digestive organs and their accessory glands are described.

Functions of the Digestive System

The functions of the digestive system are to

1. *Take in food.* Food and water are taken into the body through the mouth.
2. *Break down the food.* The food that is taken into the body is broken down during the process of digestion from complex molecules to smaller molecules that can be absorbed.

3. *Absorb digested molecules.* The small molecules that result from digestion are absorbed through the walls of the intestine for use in the body.
4. *Provide nutrients.* The process of digestion and absorption provides the body with water, electrolytes, and other nutrients such as vitamins and minerals.
5. *Eliminate wastes.* Undigested material, such as fiber from food, plus waste products excreted into the digestive tract are eliminated in the feces.

Anatomy and Histology of the Digestive System

The digestive system consists of the **digestive tract**, a tube extending from the mouth to the anus, plus the associated organs, which secrete fluids into the digestive tract. The term **gastrointestinal** (**GI**; gas'trō-in-tes'tin-ăl) tract technically only refers to the stomach and intestines but is often used as a synonym for the digestive tract. The inside of the digestive tract is continuous with the outside environment, where it opens at the mouth and anus. Nutrients cross the wall of the digestive tract to enter the circulation.

The digestive tract consists of the oral cavity, pharynx, esophagus, stomach, small intestine, large intestine, and anus. Various parts of the digestive tract are specialized for different functions, but nearly all parts consist of four layers, or tunics: the mucosa, submucosa, muscularis, and serosa or adventitia (figure 16.2). These will be described in order from the inside of the tube.

1. The innermost tunic, the **mucosa** (mū-kō'să), consists of **mucous epithelium**, a loose, irregular connective tissue called the **lamina propria**, and a thin smooth muscle layer, the **muscularis mucosa**. The epithelium is thickened in the mouth, esophagus, and anus to resist abrasion and is thin in the intestine for absorption and secretion.
2. The **submucosa** lies just outside the mucosa. It is a thick layer of loose connective tissue containing nerves, blood vessels, and small glands. An extensive network of nerve cell processes forms a **plexus** (network). The plexus is innervated by parasympathetic nerves.
3. The next tunic is the **muscularis**, which in most parts of the digestive tube consists of an inner layer of **circular smooth muscle** and an outer layer of **longitudinal smooth muscle**. Another nerve plexus, also innervated by parasympathetic nerves, lies between the two muscle layers. Together the nerve plexuses of the submucosa and muscularis compose the **enteric** (en-tĕr'ik, relating to the intestine) **plexus**. This plexus is extremely important in the control of movement and secretion within the tract.
4. The fourth, or outermost, layer of the digestive tract is either a serosa or an adventitia. Some regions of the digestive tract are covered by peritoneum, and other regions are not. The peritoneum, which is a smooth epithelial layer, and its underlying connective tissue are referred to histologically as the **serosa**. In regions of the

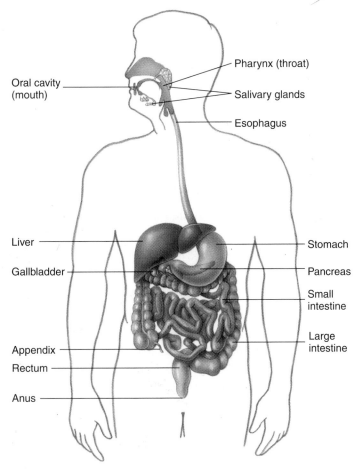

Oral cavity (mouth)

Pharynx (throat)

Salivary glands

Esophagus

Liver

Gallbladder

Appendix

Rectum

Anus

Stomach

Pancreas

Small intestine

Large intestine

Figure 16.1 The Digestive System

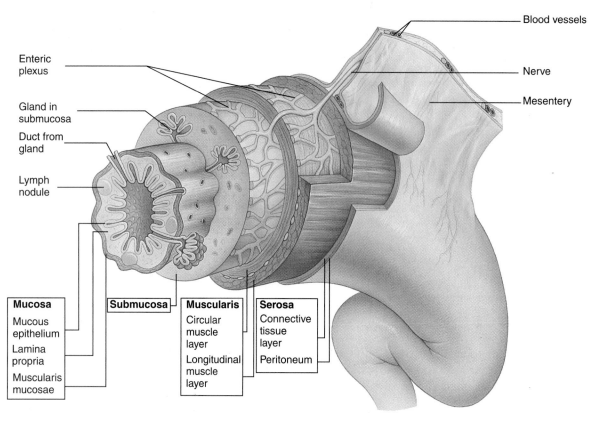

Blood vessels

Nerve

Mesentery

Enteric plexus

Gland in submucosa

Duct from gland

Lymph nodule

Mucosa	**Submucosa**	**Muscularis**	**Serosa**
Mucous epithelium		Circular muscle layer	Connective tissue layer
Lamina propria		Longitudinal muscle layer	Peritoneum
Muscularis mucosae			

Figure 16.2 Digestive Tract Histology

The four tunics are the mucosa, submucosa, muscularis, and serosa or adventitia.

digestive tract not covered by peritoneum, the digestive tract is covered by a connective tissue layer called the **adventitia** (ad'ven-tish'ă; foreign; coming from outside), which is continuous with the surrounding connective tissue.

The liver and pancreas are accessory glands associated with the small intestine (see figure 16.1). Those glands will be described with the small intestine.

Oral Cavity

The **oral cavity** (figure 16.3), or mouth, is the first part of the digestive tract. It is bounded by the lips and cheeks and contains the teeth and tongue. The **lips** are muscular structures, formed mostly by the **orbicularis oris** (ōr-bik'ū-lā'ris ōr'is) **muscle** (see figure 7.15). The outer surfaces of the lips are covered by skin. The keratinized stratified epithelium of the skin is thin at the margin of the lips. The color from the underlying blood vessels can be seen through the transparent epithelium, giving the lips a reddish-pink appearance. At the internal margin of the lips, the epithelium is continuous with the moist stratified squamous epithelium of the mucosa in the oral cavity. The cheeks form the lateral walls of the oral cavity. The **buccinator** (bŭk'si-nā-tōr) **muscle** (see figure 7.15) is located within the cheeks and flattens the cheek against the teeth. The lips and cheeks are important in the process of **mastication** (mas-ti-kā'shŭn), or chewing food. They help manipulate the food within the mouth and hold the food in place while the

teeth crush or tear it. Mastication begins the process of mechanical digestion, in which large food particles are broken down into smaller ones. They also help form words during the speech process.

The **tongue** is a large, muscular organ that occupies most of the oral cavity. The major attachment of the tongue is in the posterior part of the oral cavity. The anterior part of the tongue is relatively free. There is an anterior attachment to the floor of the mouth by a thin fold of tissue called the **frenulum** (fren'ū-lŭm) (see figure 16.3*b*). The muscles associated with the tongue are described in chapter 7.

The tongue moves food in the mouth and, in cooperation with the lips and cheeks, holds the food in place during mastication. It also plays a major role in the process of swallowing. The tongue is a major sensory organ for taste, as well as being one of the major organs of speech.

Teeth

There are 32 **teeth** in the normal adult mouth, located in the mandible and maxillae. The teeth can be divided into quadrants: right upper, left upper, right lower, and left lower. In adults, each quadrant contains one central and one lateral **incisor** (in-sī'zŏr); one **canine** (kā'nīn); first and second **premolars** (prē-mō'lărz); and first, second, and third **molars** (mō'lărz). The third molars are called **wisdom teeth** because they usually appear in a person's late teens or early twenties, when the person is old enough to have acquired some degree of wisdom.

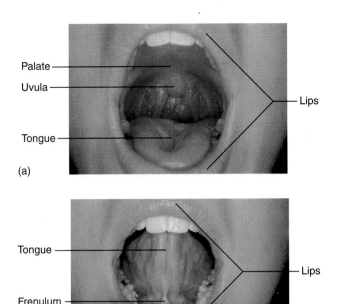

Figure 16.3 The Oral Cavity

(*a*) With the tongue depressed. (*b*) With the tongue elevated.

The teeth of the adult mouth are **permanent**, or **secondary**, teeth (figure 16.4*a*). Most of them are replacements of the 20 **primary**, or **deciduous**, **teeth** (dē-sid′ū-ŭs; those that fall out; also called milk teeth) which are lost during childhood (figure 16.4*b*).

Each tooth (figure 16.4*c*) consists of a **crown** with one or more **cusps** (points), a **neck**, and a **root**. The center of the tooth is a **pulp cavity**, which is filled with blood vessels, nerves, and connective tissue, called **pulp**. The pulp cavity is surrounded by a living, cellular, bonelike tissue called **dentin** (den′tin). The dentin of the tooth crown is covered by an extremely hard, acellular substance called **enamel** (ē-nam′ĕl), which protects the tooth against abrasion and acids produced by bacteria in the mouth. The surface of the dentin in the root is covered with **cementum** (se-men′tŭm), which helps anchor the tooth in the jaw.

The teeth are rooted within **alveoli** (al-vē′ō-lī, sockets) along the alveolar ridges of the mandible and maxillae. The alveolar ridges are covered by dense fibrous connective tissue and moist stratified squamous epithelium, referred to as the **gingiva** (jin′ji-vă), or gums. The teeth are held in place by **periodontal** (per′ē-ō-don′tăl, around the teeth) **ligaments**, which are connective tissue fibers that extend from the alveolar walls and are embedded into the cementum.

Did You Know?

Formation of **dental caries** (kār′ēz), or tooth decay, is the result of the breakdown of enamel by acids produced by bacteria on the tooth surface. Enamel is nonliving and cannot repair itself. Consequently, a dental filling is necessary to prevent further damage. **Periodontal disease** is inflammation and degeneration of the periodontal ligaments, gingiva, and alveolar bone. This disease is the most common cause of tooth loss in adults.

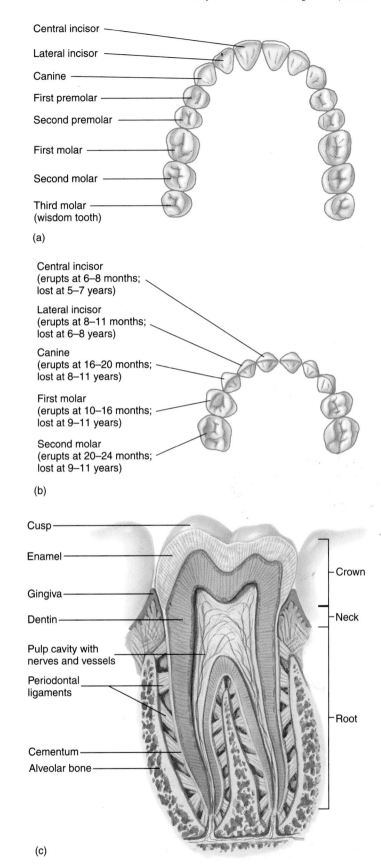

Figure 16.4 The Teeth

(*a*) Permanent teeth. (*b*) Deciduous teeth. (*c*) Molar tooth in place in the alveolar bone, cut in section to show the pulp. The tooth consists of a crown and a root. The tooth is held in the socket by periodontal ligaments.

Palate and Tonsils

The **palate** (pal′ăt), or roof of the oral cavity, consists of two parts. The anterior part contains bone and is called the **hard palate**, whereas the posterior portion consists of skeletal muscle and connective tissue and is called the **soft palate**. The **uvula** (ū′vū-lă, a grape) projects from the posterior edge of the soft palate. The palate separates the oral cavity from the nasal cavity and prevents food from passing into the nasal cavity during chewing and swallowing.

The **tonsils** (ton′silz) are located in the lateral posterior walls of the oral cavity, in the nasopharynx, and in the posterior surface of the tongue. The tonsils are described in chapter 14.

Salivary Glands

There are three pairs of **salivary** (sal′i-vār-ē) **glands**: the parotid, submandibular, and sublingual glands (figure 16.5). They produce **saliva** (să-lī′vă), which is a mixture of **serous** (watery) and **mucous** fluids, containing digestive enzymes. Saliva helps keep the oral cavity moist and begins the process of chemical digestion. All of these salivary glands are compound alveolar glands. They have branching ducts with clusters of alveoli, resembling grapes, at the ends of the ducts (see chapter 4).

The largest of the salivary glands, the **parotid** (pă-rot′id, beside the ear) **glands**, are serous glands located just anterior to each ear. Parotid ducts enter the oral cavity adjacent to the second upper molars.

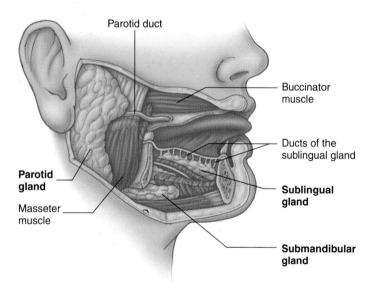

Figure 16.5 Salivary Glands

The large salivary glands are the parotid glands, the submandibular glands, and the sublingual glands.

The **submandibular** (sŭb-man-dib′ū-lăr, below the mandible) **glands** produce more serous than mucous secretions. Each gland can be felt as a soft lump along the inferior border of the mandible. The submandibular ducts open into the oral cavity on each side of the frenulum of the tongue. In certain people, if the mouth is opened and the tip of the tongue is elevated, saliva can squirt out of the mouth from the ducts of these glands.

The **sublingual** (sŭb-ling′gwăl, below the tongue) **glands**, the smallest of the three paired salivary glands, produce primarily mucous secretions. They lie immediately below the mucous membrane in the floor of the oral cavity. Each sublingual gland has 10 to 12 small ducts opening onto the floor of the oral cavity.

Pharynx

The **pharynx** (far′ingks), or throat, which connects the mouth with the esophagus, consists of three parts: the nasopharynx, oropharynx, and laryngopharynx (see chapter 15). Normally, only the oropharynx and laryngopharynx transmit food. The posterior walls of the oropharynx and laryngopharynx are formed by **pharyngeal constrictor muscles**.

Esophagus

The **esophagus** (ē-sof′ă-gŭs) is a muscular tube, lined with moist stratified squamous epithelium, that extends from the pharynx to the stomach. It is about 25 centimeters (cm) long and lies anterior to the vertebrae and posterior to the trachea within the mediastinum. It passes through the diaphragm and ends at the stomach. The esophagus transports food from the pharynx to the stomach. Upper and lower **esophageal sphincters** regulate the movement of food into and out of the esophagus. The lower esophageal sphincter is sometimes called the **cardiac sphincter**. Numerous mucous glands produce a thick, lubricating mucus that coats the inner surface of the esophagus.

Stomach

The **stomach** (figure 16.6) is an enlarged segment of the digestive tract in the left superior part of the abdomen. The opening from the esophagus into the stomach is called the **cardiac opening** because it is near the heart. The region of the stomach around the cardiac opening is called the **cardiac**

(a)

(b)

Figure 16.6   Anatomy and Histology of the Stomach

(a) Cutaway section reveals muscular layers and internal anatomy. (b) A section of the stomach wall that illustrates its histology, including several gastric pits and glands.

region. The most superior part of the stomach is the **fundus** (fŭn′dŭs, the bottom of a round-bottomed leather bottle). The largest part of the stomach is the **body**, which turns to the right, forming a **greater curvature** on the left, and a **lesser curvature** on the right. The opening from the stomach into the small intestine is the **pyloric** (pī-lōr′ik, gatekeeper) **opening**, which is surrounded by a relatively thick ring of smooth muscle called the **pyloric sphincter**. The region of the stomach near the pyloric opening is the **pyloric region**.

> ### Did You Know?
>
> **Hypertrophic pyloric stenosis** is a common defect of the stomach in infants, in which the pylorus is greatly thickened, resulting in interference with normal stomach emptying. Infants with this defect exhibit projectile vomiting. Because the pylorus is blocked, little food enters the intestine, and the infant fails to gain weight. Constipation is also a frequent complication.

The muscular layer of the stomach is different from other regions of the digestive tract in that it consists of three layers: an outer longitudinal layer, a middle circular layer, and an inner oblique layer. These muscular layers produce a churning action in the stomach, important in the digestive process. The submucosa and mucosa of the stomach are thrown into large folds called **rugae** (roo′gē, wrinkles) (see figure 16.6a) when the stomach is empty. These folds allow the mucosa and submucosa to stretch, and the folds disappear as the stomach is filled.

The stomach is lined with simple columnar epithelium. The mucosal surface forms numerous tubelike **gastric pits** (see figure 16.6*b*), which are the openings for the **gastric glands**. The epithelial cells of the stomach can be divided into five groups. The first group consists of **surface mucous cells** on the inner surface of the stomach and lining the gastric pits. Those cells produce mucus, which coats and protects the stomach lining. The remaining four cell types are in the gastric glands. They are **mucous neck cells**, which produce mucus; **parietal cells**, which produce hydrochloric acid and intrinsic factor; **endocrine cells**, which produce regulatory hormones; and **chief cells**, which produce **pepsinogen** (pep-sin′ō-jen), a precursor of the protein-digesting enzyme **pepsin** (pep′sin).

Small Intestine

The **small intestine** is about 6 meters (m) long and consists of three parts: the duodenum, jejunum, and ileum (figure 16.7). The **duodenum** (doo-od′ĕ-nŭm, or doo-ō-dē′nŭm) is about 25 cm long (the term duodenum means 12, suggesting that it is 12 in. long). The **jejunum** (jĕ-joo′nŭm) is about 2.5 m long and makes up two-fifths of the total length of the small intestine. The **ileum** (il′ē-ŭm) is about 3.5 m long and makes up three-fifths of the small intestine.

The duodenum nearly completes a 180-degree arc as it curves within the abdominal cavity. The head of the pancreas lies within this arc. The **common bile duct** from the liver and the **pancreatic duct** from the pancreas join each other and empty into the duodenum (see figure 16.10).

The surface of the duodenum has three modifications that increase surface area about 600-fold: circular folds, villi,

and microvilli. The increased surface area allows more efficient digestion and absorption of food. The mucosa and submucosa form a series of **circular folds** that run perpendicular to the long axis of the digestive tract (figure 16.8*a*). Tiny fingerlike projections of the mucosa form numerous **villi** (vil′ī, sing. villus, shaggy hair), which are 0.5 to 1.5 mm long (figure 16.8*b*). Most of the cells composing the surface of the villi have numerous cytoplasmic extensions, called **microvilli** (mī′krō-vil′ī) (figure 16.8*c* and *d*). Each villus is covered by simple columnar epithelium and contains a blood capillary network and a lymphatic capillary called a **lacteal** (lak′tē-ăl) (figure 16.8*c*). The blood capillary network and the lacteal are very important in transporting absorbed nutrients.

The mucosa of the duodenum is simple columnar epithelium with four major cell types: (1) **absorptive cells**, which have microvilli, produce digestive enzymes, and absorb digested food; (2) **goblet cells**, which produce a protective mucus; (3) granular cells (Paneth's cells), which may help protect the intestinal epithelium from bacteria; and (4) **endocrine cells**, which produce regulatory hormones.

The epithelial cells are produced within tubular glands of the mucosa, called **intestinal glands** (crypts of Lieberkühn), at the base of the villi. Granular and endocrine cells are located in the bottom of the glands. The submucosa of the duodenum contains mucous glands, called **duodenal glands** (Brunner's glands), which open into the base of the intestinal glands.

The jejunum and ileum are similar in structure to the duodenum, except that there is a gradual decrease in the diameter of the small intestine, in the thickness of the intestinal wall, in the number of circular folds, and in the number

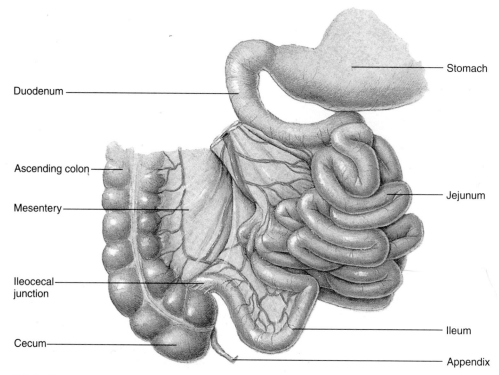

Figure 16.7 The Small Intestine

The duodenum is attached to the stomach and is continuous with the jejunum. The jejunum is continuous with the ileum, which empties into the cecum.

Figure 16.8   Interior View and Histology of the Duodenum

(*a*) The wall of the duodenum has been opened to reveal the circular folds. (*b*) The villi. (*c*) A single villus showing the lacteal and capillary. (*d*) Electron micrograph of the microvilli. The extensive surface area allows more efficient absorption of nutrients.

of villi as one progresses through the small intestine. Lymph nodules are common along the entire length of the digestive tract. Clusters of lymph nodules, called **Peyer's patches**, are numerous in the ileum. These lymphatic tissues in the intestine help protect the intestinal tract from harmful microorganisms.

The junction between the ileum and the large intestine is the **ileocecal** (il'ē-ō-sē'kăl) **junction**. It has a ring of smooth muscle, the **ileocecal sphincter**, and an **ileocecal valve** (this can be seen in figure 16.13*a*), which allows material contained in the intestine to move from the ileum to the large intestine, but not in the opposite direction.

Liver

The **liver** (figure 16.9; see figure 16.1) weighs about 1.36 kilograms (kg) (3 lbs) and is located in the right upper quadrant of the abdomen, tucked against the inferior surface of the diaphragm. It is divided into two major lobes, the **right** and **left lobes**, separated by a connective tissue septum, the **falciform** (fal'si-fōrm) **ligament**. Two smaller lobes, the **caudate** (kaw'dāt) and **quadrate** (kwah'drāt), can be seen from an inferior view. Also seen from the inferior view is the **porta** (gate), which is the "gate" through which blood vessels, ducts, and nerves enter or exit the liver.

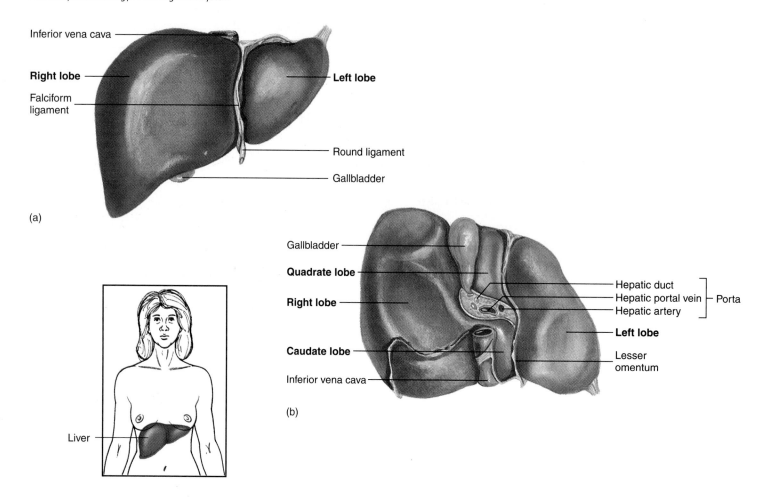

Figure 16.9 The Liver

(*a*) Anterior view. (*b*) Inferior view.

The liver has two sources of blood (see chapter 13). The **hepatic** (he-pa′tik, associated with the liver) **artery** brings oxygen-rich blood to the liver, which supplies liver cells with oxygen. The **hepatic portal vein** carries blood that is oxygen-poor but rich in absorbed materials from the digestive tract to the liver. Liver cells process nutrients and detoxify harmful substances from the blood. Blood exits the liver through **hepatic veins**, which empty into the inferior vena cava.

Right and left **hepatic ducts** transport **bile** out of the liver. The hepatic ducts unite to form a single **common hepatic duct**. The common hepatic duct is joined by the **cystic** (sis′tik) **duct** from the gallbladder to form the **common bile duct**, which joins the pancreatic duct and opens into the duodenum at the **duodenal papilla** (pă-pil′ă) (figure 16.10). The opening into the duodenum is regulated by a sphincter. The **gallbladder** is a small sac on the inferior surface of the liver that stores bile (see figure 16.9).

Many delicate connective tissue septa divide the liver into **lobules** with portal triads at the corners of the lobules. The **portal triads** (three) contain three structures: the hepatic artery, hepatic portal vein, and hepatic duct (figure 16.11). **Hepatic** (he-pa′tik) **cords**, formed by platelike groups of cells called **hepatocytes** (hep′ă-tō-sīts), are located between the center and the margins of each lobule. A cleftlike lumen, the **bile canaliculus** (kan′ă-lik′ū-lŭs, little canal), is between the cells of each cord. Bile, produced by the hepatocytes, flows through the bile canaliculi toward the triad and exits the liver through the hepatic ducts. The hepatic ducts empty into the common hepatic duct. The hepatic cords are separated from one another by blood channels called **hepatic sinusoids** (si′nŭ-soydz or sī′nū-soydz). The sinusoid epithelium contains phagocytic cells that help remove foreign particles from the blood. Blood from the hepatic portal vein and the hepatic artery flows into the sinusoids and becomes mixed. The mixed blood flows toward the center of each lobule into a **central vein**. The central veins from all the lobes unite to form the hepatic veins, which carry blood out of the liver.

Pancreas

The **pancreas** (figure 16.12, and see figure 16.10) is a complex organ composed of both endocrine and exocrine tissues that perform several functions. The endocrine part of the pancreas consists of **pancreatic islets** (islets of Langerhans). The islet cells produce insulin and glucagon, which are very important in controlling blood levels of nutrients such as glucose and amino acids (see chapter 10).

1. The hepatic ducts from the liver lobes combine to form the common hepatic duct.

2. The common hepatic duct combines with the cystic duct from the gallbladder to form the common bile duct.

3. The pancreatic duct carries secretions from the pancreas.

4. The common bile duct and the pancreatic duct combine and empty into the duodenum at the duodenal papilla.

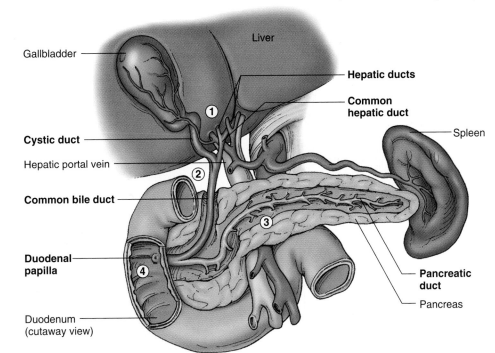

Figure 16.10 The Liver, Gallbladder, Pancreas, and Duct System (shown in green)

The hepatic ducts join to form the common hepatic duct, which joins the cystic duct to form the common bile duct. The common bile duct joins the pancreatic duct and enters the duodenum.

Figure 16.11 Liver Histology

Lobules of the liver with triads at each corner and central veins in the middle.

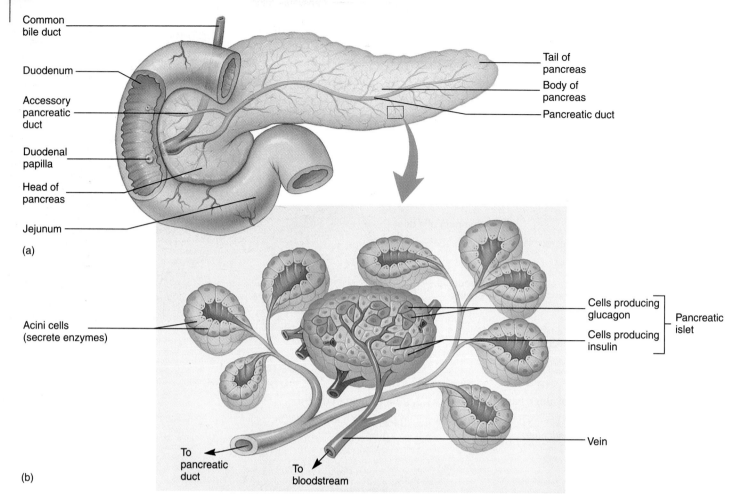

Figure 16.12 Anatomy and Histology of the Pancreas

(*a*) The head of the pancreas lies within the duodenal curvature, with the pancreatic duct emptying into the duodenum. (*b*) Histology of the pancreas showing both the acini and the pancreatic duct system.

The exocrine part of the pancreas is a compound acinar gland (see discussion of glands in chapter four). The **acini** (as′i-nī, grapes) produce digestive enzymes. Clusters of acini are connected by small ducts, which join to form larger ducts, and the larger ducts join to form the **pancreatic duct**. The pancreatic duct joins the common bile duct and empties into the duodenum.

Large Intestine

The **large intestine** (figure 16.13; see figure 16.1) consists of the cecum, colon, rectum, and anal canal.

Cecum

The **cecum** (sē′kŭm, blind) (see figure 16.13) is the proximal end of the large intestine and is where the large and small intestines meet, the ileocecal junction. The cecum is a sac that extends inferiorly about 6 cm past the ileocecal junction. Attached to the cecum is a tube about 9 cm long called the **appendix**.

> **Did You Know?**
>
> **Appendicitis** is an inflammation of the appendix and usually occurs because of obstruction. Secretions from the appendix cannot pass the obstruction and accumulate, causing enlargement and pain. Bacteria in the area can cause infection. Symptoms include sudden abdominal pain, particularly in the right lower portion of the abdomen, along with a slight fever, loss of appetite, constipation or diarrhea, nausea, and vomiting. If the appendix bursts, the infection can spread throughout the peritoneal cavity, causing peritonitis, with life-threatening results. Each year, 500,000 people in the United States suffer an appendicitis. An appendectomy is removal of the appendix.

Colon

The **colon** (kō′lon) (see figure 16.13) is about 1.5 to 1.8 m long and consists of four parts: the ascending colon, the transverse colon, the descending colon, and the sigmoid colon. The **ascending colon** extends superiorly from the cecum to the right colic flexure, near the liver, where it turns to the left. The **transverse colon** extends from the right colic flexure to the left colic flexure near the spleen, where the colon turns inferiorly; and the **descending colon** extends from the left colic flexure to the pelvis, where it becomes the **sigmoid colon**. The sigmoid colon forms an **S**-shaped tube that extends into the pelvic cavity and ends at the rectum.

The mucosal lining of the colon contains numerous straight tubular glands called **crypts**, which contain many mucus-producing goblet cells. The longitudinal muscle layer

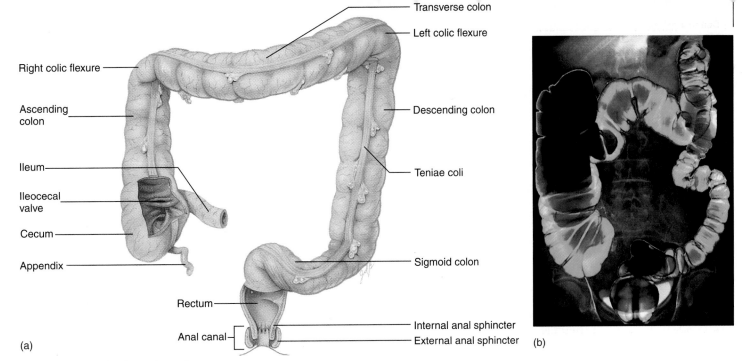

Figure 16.13 The Large Intestine

(a) The cecum, colon, rectum, and anal canal. (b) The photograph shows the large intestine in place in the body.

of the colon does not completely envelope the intestinal wall but forms three bands called **teniae coli** (tē′nē-ē kō′lī).

Rectum

The **rectum** is a straight, muscular tube that begins at the termination of the sigmoid colon and ends at the anal canal (see figure 16.13). The muscular tunic is relatively thick in the rectum compared with the rest of the digestive tract.

Anal Canal

The last 2 to 3 cm of the digestive tract is the **anal canal**. It begins at the inferior end of the rectum and ends at the **anus** (external GI tract opening). The involuntary, smooth muscle layer of the anal canal is even thicker than that of the rectum and forms the **internal anal sphincter** at the superior end of the anal canal. The **external anal sphincter** at the inferior end of the anal canal is formed by voluntary, skeletal muscle.

> **Did You Know?**
>
> **Hemorrhoids** are the enlargement or inflammation of the hemorrhoidal veins, which supply the anal canal. This condition is also called varicose hemorrhoidal veins. Hemorrhoids cause pain, itching, and bleeding around the anus. Treatments include increasing the bulk in the diet, taking sitz baths, and using hydrocortizone suppositories. Surgery may be necessary if the condition is extreme and does not respond to other treatments.

Peritoneum

The body walls and organs of the abdominal cavity are covered with **serous membranes** (figure 16.14). The serous membrane that covers the organs is the **visceral peritoneum**

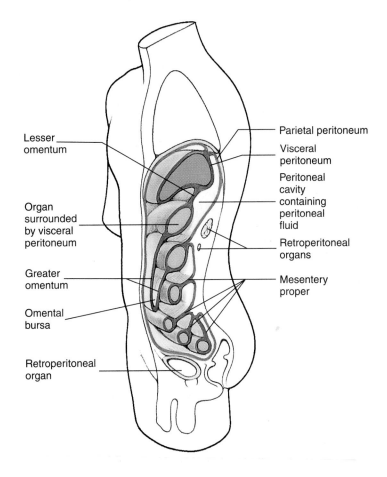

Figure 16.14 Peritoneum and Mesenteries

The parietal peritoneum lines the abdominal cavity (blue), and the visceral peritoneum covers abdominal organs (red). Retroperitoneal organs are behind the parietal peritoneum. The mesenteries are membranes that connect abdominal organs to each other and to the body wall.

(per'i-tō-nē'ŭm, to stretch over). The visceral peritoneum is also called the serosa. The serous membrane that lines the interior of the body wall is the **parietal peritoneum**.

Many of the organs of the abdominal cavity are held in place by connective tissue sheets called **mesenteries** (mes'en-ter-ēz, middle intestine). The mesenteries consist of two layers of serous membranes with a thin layer of loose connective tissue between them. Specific mesenteries are given names. The mesentery connecting the lesser curvature of the stomach to the liver and diaphragm is the **lesser omentum** (ō-men'tŭm, membrane of the bowels), and the mesentery connecting the greater curvature of the stomach to the transverse colon and posterior body wall is the **greater omentum**. The greater omentum is unusual in that it is a long, double fold of mesentery that extends inferiorly from the stomach to create a cavity, or pocket, called the **omental bursa** (ber'să, pocket). Fat accumulates in the greater omentum, giving it the appearance of a fat-filled apron that covers the anterior surface of the abdominal viscera. Although mesentery is a general term referring to the serous membranes attached to the abdominal organs, the term is also used specifically to refer to the mesentery associated with the small intestine, sometimes called the **mesentery proper**.

1   P R E D I C T

If you placed a pin completely through both folds of the greater omentum, through how many layers of simple squamous epithelium would the pin pass?

✔ *Answer on page 463*

Other abdominal organs lie against the abdominal wall, have no mesenteries, and are described as **retroperitoneal** (re'trō-per'i-tō-nē'ăl, behind the peritoneum). The retroperitoneal organs include the duodenum, pancreas, ascending colon, descending colon, rectum, kidneys, adrenal glands, and urinary bladder.

Movements and Secretions in the Digestive System

As food moves through the digestive tract, secretions are added to liquefy and digest the food and to provide lubrication. Each segment of the digestive tract is specialized to assist in moving its contents from the oral end to the anal end. Parts of the digestive system are also specialized to absorb molecules from the digestive tract into the circulation. The processes of secretion, movement, and absorption are regulated by neural and hormonal mechanisms. Enteric plexuses are responsible for controlling **local reflexes**, and do not depend on control from the central nervous system.

Oral Cavity, Pharynx, and Esophagus
Secretions of the Oral Cavity

Saliva is secreted at the rate of approximately 1 liter (L) per day. The serous part of saliva, produced mainly by the parotid and submandibular glands, contains a digestive enzyme called **salivary amylase** (am'il-ās, starch-splitting enzyme) (table 16.1), which breaks the covalent bonds between glucose molecules in starch and other polysaccharides to produce the disaccharides maltose and isomaltose. Maltose and isomaltose have a sweet taste; thus the digestion of polysaccharides by salivary amylase enhances the sweet taste of food.

Food spends very little time in the mouth, however. Therefore, only about 5% of the total carbohydrates are digested in the mouth. Most starches are contained in plant cells, which are surrounded by cell walls composed primarily of the polysaccharide **cellulose** (sel'ū-lōs). Humans lack the necessary enzymes to digest cellulose. Cooking and thorough chewing of food disrupt the cellulose covering and increase the efficiency of the digestive process.

Saliva prevents bacterial infection in the mouth by washing the oral cavity, and it contains **lysozyme** (lī'sō-zīm), which has a weak antibacterial action. A lack of salivary gland secretion (which can result from radiation therapy) increases the chance of ulceration and infection of the oral mucosa and caries formation in the teeth.

The serous part of saliva dissolves molecules, which can only stimulate taste receptors when in solution. It also helps lubricate the food. The mucous secretions of the submandibular and sublingual glands contain a large amount of **mucin** (mū'sin), a proteoglycan that gives a lubricating quality to the secretions of the salivary glands.

Salivary gland secretion is regulated primarily by the autonomic nervous system, with parasympathetic stimulation being the most important. Salivary secretions increase in re-

Table 16.1   Functions of Digestive Secretions

Fluid or Enzyme	Source	Function
Mouth		
Saliva	Salivary glands	Moistens and lubricates food
Salivary amylase	Salivary glands	Digests starch
Stomach		
Hydrochloric acid	Gastric glands	Kills bacteria, activates pepsin
Pepsinogen	Gastric glands	Active form, pepsin, digests protein
Mucus	Mucous cells	Protects stomach lining
Intrinsic factor	Gastric glands	Binds to vitamin B_{12}, aiding in its absorption
Gastrin	Gastric glands	Increases stomach secretions
Small Intestine and Associated Glands		
Bile salts	Liver	Emulsify fats
Bicarbonate ions	Pancreas	Neutralize stomach acid
Trypsin, chymotrypsin	Pancreas	Digest protein
Pancreatic amylase	Pancreas	Digests starch
Pancreatic lipase	Pancreas	Digests lipid
Nucleases	Pancreas	Digest nucleic acid
Mucus	Duodenal glands and goblet cells	Protects duodenum from stomach acid and digestive enzymes
Secretin	Duodenum	Inhibits gastric secretions
		Stimulates sodium bicarbonate secretion from the pancreas and bile secretion from the liver
Cholecystokinin	Duodenum	Inhibits gastric secretion, stimulates gallbladder contraction and pancreas secretion (enzymes)
Gastric inhibitory polypeptide	Duodenum	Inhibits gastric motility and secretion, stimulates gallbladder contraction
Peptidases	Small intestine	Digest polypeptide
Amylase	Small intestine	Digests starch
Lipase	Small intestine	Digests lipid
Sucrase	Small intestine	Digests sucrose
Lactase	Small intestine	Digests lactose
Maltase	Small intestine	Digests maltose

sponse to a variety of stimuli, such as tactile stimulation in the oral cavity and certain tastes, especially sour. Higher brain centers can stimulate parasympathetic activity and thus increase the activity of the salivary glands in response to the thought of food, to odors, or to the sensation of hunger. Sympathetic stimulation increases the mucus content of saliva. When a person becomes frightened and the sympathetic division of the autonomic nervous system is stimulated, the person may have a dry mouth with thick mucus.

Mastication

Food taken into the mouth is chewed, or **masticated** (mas-ti-kā'ted), by the teeth. The incisors and canines primarily cut

and tear food, whereas the premolars and molars primarily crush and grind it. Mastication breaks large food particles into many small ones, which have a much larger total surface area than a few large particles would have. Because digestive enzymes act on molecules only at the surface of the food particles, mastication increases the efficiency of digestion.

Deglutition

Deglutition (dē-gloo-tish'ŭn), or swallowing, can be divided into three separate phases: the voluntary phase, the pharyngeal phase, and the esophageal phase (figure 16.15). During the **voluntary phase**, a bolus, or mass of food, is formed in the mouth. The bolus is pushed by the tongue against the hard

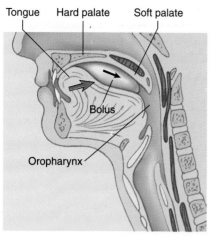

Tongue   Hard palate   Soft palate

Bolus

Oropharynx

(a) During the voluntary phase, a bolus of food (yellow) is pushed by the tongue against the hard palate and posteriorly toward the oropharynx (red arrow indicates tongue movement; black arrow indicates movement of the bolus). Tan: bone, blue: cartilage, red: muscle.

Nasopharynx

①

②

Soft palate

Superior pharyngeal constrictor

Middle pharyngeal constrictor

Epiglottis

Inferior pharyngeal constrictor

Upper esophageal sphincter

Esophagus

Larynx

(b) During the pharyngeal phase, ① the soft palate is elevated, closing off the nasopharynx. ② The pharynx is elevated (red arrows indicate muscle movement).

③

③

Epiglottis

Opening of larynx

(c) Successive constriction of the pharyngeal constrictors ③ from superior to inferior (red arrows) forces the bolus through the pharynx and into the esophagus. As this occurs, the epiglottis is bent down over the opening of the larynx largely by the force of the bolus pressing against it.

(d) As the inferior pharyngeal constrictor contracts ③, the upper esophageal sphincter relaxes ④ (outwardly directed red arrows), allowing the bolus to enter the esophagus.

(e) During the esophageal phase, the bolus is moved by peristaltic contractions of the esophagus toward the stomach (inwardly directed red arrows).

Figure 16.15   Three Phases of Swallowing (Deglutition)

palate, forcing the bolus toward the posterior part of the mouth and into the oropharynx.

The **pharyngeal phase** of swallowing is a reflex that is initiated when a bolus of food stimulates receptors in the oropharynx. This phase of swallowing begins with the elevation of the soft palate, which closes the passage between the nasopharynx and oropharynx. The pharynx elevates to receive the bolus of food from the mouth. The three **pharyngeal constrictor muscles** then contract in succession, forcing the food through the pharynx. At the same time, the upper esophageal sphincter relaxes, and food is pushed into the esophagus. As food passes through the pharynx, the **epiglottis** (ep-i-glot′is, upon the glottis) is tipped posteriorly so that the opening into the larynx is covered, preventing food from passing into the larynx.

---

2   P R E D I C T

What would happen if a person had a cleft of the soft palate, so that the nasopharynx was not closed off during swallowing? What may happen if a person has an explosive burst of laughter while trying to swallow a liquid? What happens if a person tries to swallow and speak at the same time?

✔ *Answer on page 463*

The **esophageal phase** of swallowing is responsible for moving food from the pharynx to the stomach. Muscular contractions of the esophagus occur in **peristaltic** (per-i-stal′tik) **waves**. A wave of relaxation of the circular esophageal muscles precedes the bolus of food down the esophagus, and a wave of strong contraction of the circular muscles follows and propels the bolus through the esophagus. The peristaltic contractions associated with swallowing cause relaxation of the lower esophageal sphincter in the esophagus as the peristaltic waves approach the stomach.

Did You Know?

Gravity assists the movement of material through the esophagus, especially when liquids are swallowed. The peristaltic contractions that move material through the esophagus are sufficiently forceful, however, to allow a person to swallow even while doing a headstand or floating in the zero-gravity environment of space.

Stomach

Secretions of the Stomach

The stomach functions primarily as a storage and mixing chamber for ingested food. As food enters the stomach, it is mixed with stomach secretions to become a semifluid mixture called **chyme** (kīm, juice). Although some digestion and a small amount of absorption occur in the stomach, they are not its principal functions.

Stomach secretions from the gastric glands include mucus, hydrochloric acid, pepsinogen, intrinsic factor, and gastrin (see table 16.1). A thick layer of **mucus** lubricates and protects the epithelial cells of the stomach wall from the damaging effect of the acidic chyme and pepsin. Irritation of

the stomach mucosa stimulates the secretion of a greater volume of mucus. **Hydrochloric acid** produces a pH of about 3.0 in the stomach. **Pepsinogen** is converted by hydrochloric acid to the active enzyme pepsin. **Pepsin** breaks proteins into smaller peptide chains. Pepsin exhibits optimum enzymatic activity at a pH of 3.0 or below. The low pH also kills microorganisms. **Intrinsic** (in-trin′sik) **factor** binds with vitamin B_{12} and makes it more readily absorbed in the ileum. Vitamin B_{12} is important in deoxyribonucleic acid (DNA) synthesis and is important to erythrocyte production. **Gastrin** (gas′trin) is a hormone that helps regulate stomach secretions.

Regulation of Stomach Secretions

Approximately 2 L of gastric secretions (gastric juice) is produced each day. Both nervous and hormonal mechanisms regulate gastric secretions. The neural mechanisms involve central nervous system (CNS) reflexes integrated within the medulla oblongata. Higher brain centers can influence these reflexes. Local reflexes are integrated within the intramural plexus in the wall of the digestive tract and do not involve the CNS. Hormones produced by the stomach and intestine help regulate stomach secretions. Regulation of stomach secretions can be divided into three phases: the cephalic, gastric, and intestinal phases.

The **cephalic** (se-fal′ik) **phase** of stomach secretion (figure 16.16*a*) is anticipatory and prepares the stomach to receive food. In the cephalic phase, sensations of taste, the smell of food, stimulation of tactile receptors during the process of chewing and swallowing, and pleasant thoughts of food stimulate centers within the medulla oblongata that influence gastric secretions. Action potentials are sent from the medulla oblongata along parasympathetic neurons within the vagus nerves to the stomach. Within the stomach wall, the preganglionic neurons stimulate postganglionic neurons in the enteric plexus. The postganglionic neurons stimulate secretory activity in the cells of the stomach mucosa, causing the release of mucus, hydrochloric acid, pepsinogen, and intrinsic factor. Gastrin is also secreted by the stomach as a result of the parasympathetic stimulation. The gastrin enters the circulation and is carried back to the stomach, where it stimulates additional secretory activity.

During the **gastric phase** (figure 16.16*b*), food is present in the stomach and is being mixed with gastric secretions. The gastric phase is responsible for the greatest volume of gastric secretion, and it is activated by the presence of food in the stomach. Distention of the stomach results in the stimulation of stretch receptors. Action potentials generated by these receptors activate CNS reflexes and local reflexes, resulting in secretion of hydrochloric acid and pepsinogen by the gastric glands. Peptides, produced by the action of pepsin on proteins, stimulate the secretion of gastrin, which in turn stimulates additional hydrochloric acid secretion.

The **intestinal phase** of gastric secretion (figure 16.16*c*), is controlled by the entrance of acidic chyme into the duodenum. The presence of chyme in the duodenum initiates both neural and hormonal mechanisms. When the pH of the chyme entering the duodenum drops to 2.0 or below, the inhibitory influence of the intestinal phase is greatest (see figure 16.16*c*). The hormone **secretin** (se-krē′tin), which inhibits gastric secretions, is released from the duodenum. Fatty acids and certain other

Cephalic Phase

1. The taste or smell of food, tactile sensations of food in the mouth, or even thoughts of food stimulate the medulla oblongata (blue arrow).
2. Parasympathetic action potentials are carried by the vagus nerves to the stomach (red arrow).
3. Preganglionic parasympathetic vagus nerve fibers stimulate postganglionic neurons in the enteric plexus of the stomach.
4. Postganglionic neurons stimulate secretion by parietal and chief cells and stimulate gastrin secretion by endocrine cells.
5. Gastrin is carried through the circulation back to the stomach (pink arrow), where it stimulates secretion by parietal and chief cells.

(a)

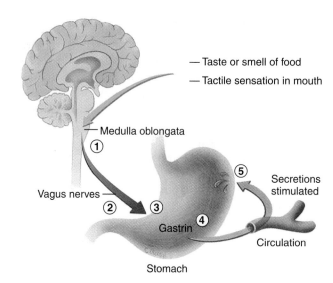

Gastric Phase

1. Distention of the stomach activates a parasympathetic reflex. Action potentials are carried by the vagus nerves to the medulla oblongata (green arrow).

2. The medulla oblongata stimulates stomach secretions (red arrow).

3. Distention of the stomach also activates local reflexes that increase stomach secretions (pink arrow).

(b)

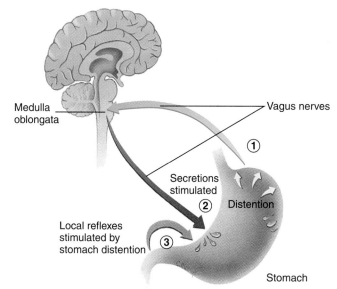

Intestinal Phase

1. Chyme in the duodenum with a pH less than 2 or containing fat digestion products inhibits gastric secretions by three mechanisms (2–4).
2. Afferent vagal action potentials (green arrow) inhibit efferent action potentials from the medulla oblongata (red arrow).
3. Secretin inhibits gastrin secretion in the duodenum (orange arrow).
4. Secretin, gastric inhibitory polypeptide, and cholecystokinin produced by the duodenum (brown arrows) inhibit gastric secretions in the stomach.

(c)

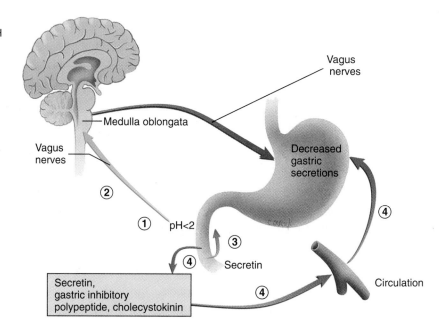

Figure 16.16   The Three Phases of Gastric Secretion

(*a*) Cephalic phase. (*b*) Gastric phase. (*c*) Intestinal phase (increase). (*d*) Intestinal phase (decrease).

lipids in the duodenum initiate the release of two hormones: cholecystokinin (kō′lē-sis-tō-kī′nin) and **gastric inhibitory polypeptide**, which also inhibit gastric secretions. Acidic chyme (pH < 2.0) in the duodenum also inhibits CNS stimulation and initiates local reflexes that inhibit gastric secretion.

Movement in the Stomach

Two types of stomach movement occur: mixing waves and peristaltic waves (figure 16.17). Both types of movements result from smooth muscle contractions in the stomach wall. The contractions occur about every 20 seconds and proceed from the body of the stomach toward the pyloric sphincter. Relatively weak contractions result in **mixing waves**, which thoroughly mix ingested food with stomach secretions to form chyme. Stronger contractions result in **peristaltic waves**, which force the chyme toward and through the pyloric sphincter. The pyloric sphincter usually remains partially closed because of mild tonic contraction. Each peristaltic contraction is sufficiently strong to pump a small amount of chyme through the pyloric opening and into the duodenum.

If the stomach empties too fast, the efficiency of digestion and absorption is reduced. If the rate of emptying is too

Did You Know?

Hunger contractions are peristaltic contractions that approach tetanic contractions for periods of about 2 to 3 minutes. The contractions are increased by low blood glucose levels and are sufficiently strong to create an uncomfortable sensation called a "hunger pang." Hunger pangs usually begin 12 to 24 hours after the previous meal or in less time for some people. If nothing is ingested, they reach their maximum intensity within 3 or 4 days and then become progressively weaker.

slow, the highly acidic contents of the stomach may damage the stomach wall. Stomach emptying is regulated to prevent these two extremes. The hormonal and neural mechanisms that increase stomach secretions also increase stomach motility so that the increased secretions are effectively mixed with the stomach contents.

Did You Know?

Heartburn is a painful or burning sensation in the chest usually associated with backflush of acidic chyme into the esophagus. Overeating, eating fatty foods, lying down immediately after a meal, consuming too much alcohol or caffeine, smoking, or wearing extremely tight clothing can all cause heartburn. Cimetidine (si-met′i-dēn, Tagamet) and ranitidine (ră-nī′ti-dēn; Zantac) are inhibitors of gastric acid secretion by the parietal cells of the stomach. Antacids neutralize acids already secreted into the stomach.

Small Intestine

Secretions of the Small Intestine

Secretions from the mucosa of the small intestine mainly contain mucus, ions, and water. Intestinal secretions lubricate and protect the intestinal wall from the acidic chyme and the action of digestive enzymes. They also keep the chyme in the small intestine in a liquid form to facilitate the digestive process. Most of the secretions entering the small intestine are produced by the intestinal mucosa, but the secretions of the liver and the pancreas also enter the small intestine and play important roles in the process of digestion.

The epithelial cells in the walls of the small intestine have enzymes bound to them that play a significant role

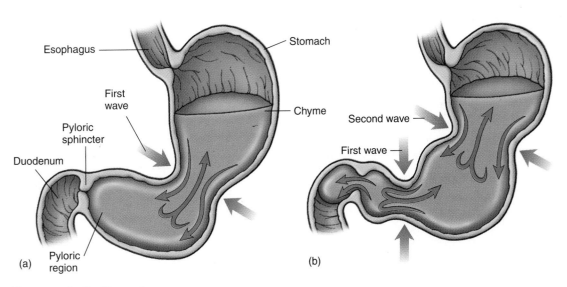

Figure 16.17   Movement in the Stomach

(*a*) Mixing waves that are initiated in the body of the stomach progress toward the pyloric region (red arrows directed inward). The more fluid part of the chyme is pushed toward the pyloric region (blue arrows), whereas the more solid center of the chyme squeezes past the peristaltic constriction back toward the body (orange arrow). (*b*) Additional mixing waves (purple arrows) move in the same direction and in the same way as described in part (*a*) for earlier waves that reach the pyloric region. Some of the most fluid chyme is pushed through the pyloric opening by peristaltic waves into the duodenum (small blue arrows), whereas most of the chyme is forced back toward the body for further mixing (orange arrow).

in the final steps of digestion. **Peptidases** (pep'ti-dās-ez) break peptide bonds to form amino acids. **Disaccharidases** (dī-sak'ă-rid-ās-ez) break down disaccharides, such as maltose and isomaltose, into monosaccharides. The amino acids and monosaccharides can be absorbed by the intestinal epithelium (see table 16.1).

Mucus is produced by duodenal glands and by goblet cells, which are dispersed throughout the epithelial lining of

the entire small intestine and within intestinal glands. Hormones released from the intestinal mucosa stimulate liver and pancreatic secretions. Secretion by duodenal glands is stimulated by the vagus nerve, secretin release, and chemical or tactile irritation of the duodenal mucosa.

Movement in the Small Intestine

Mixing and propulsion of chyme are the primary mechanical events that occur in the small intestine. **Peristaltic contractions** proceed along the length of the intestine for variable distances and cause the chyme to move along the small intestine (figure 16.18a). **Segmental contractions** are propagated for only short distances and function to mix intestinal contents (figure 16.18b).

The ileocecal sphincter at the juncture of the ileum and the large intestine remains mildly contracted most of the time, but peristaltic contractions reaching the ileocecal sphincter from the small intestine cause the sphincter to relax and allow movement of chyme from the small intestine into the cecum. The ileocecal valve is a one-way valve that allows chyme to move from the ileum into the large intestine, but does not allow movement from the large intestine back into the ileum.

Absorption in the Small Intestine

A major function of the small intestine is the absorption of nutrients. Most **absorption** occurs in the duodenum and jejunum, although some absorption also occurs in the ileum (this topic is discussed more fully on p. 451).

Liver

The liver performs important digestive and excretory functions, stores and processes nutrients, synthesizes new molecules, and detoxifies harmful chemicals (table 16.2).

The liver secretes about 700 milliliters (mL) of bile each day. Bile contains no digestive enzymes, but it plays a role in digestion by diluting and neutralizing stomach acid and by increasing the efficiency of fat digestion and absorption. Digestive enzymes cannot act efficiently on large fat globules. **Bile** (bīl) **salts** emulsify fats, breaking the fat globules into smaller droplets, much like the action of detergents in dishwater (see tables 16.1 and 16.2). The small droplets are more easily digested by digestive enzymes. Bile also contains excretory products such as bile pigments, cholesterol, and fats. **Bilirubin** (bil-i-roo'bin) is a bile pigment that results from the breakdown of hemoglobin.

Bile secretion by the liver is stimulated by **secretin**, which is released from the duodenum (figure 16.19).

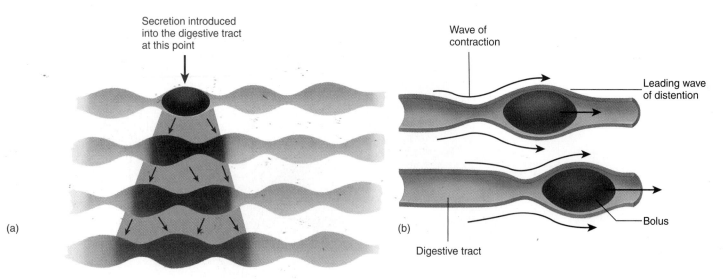

Figure 16.18 Movement in the Small Intestine.

(a) Segmental contractions. Each section of the digestive tract involved in segmental contractions alternates between contraction and relaxation. The series of figures from top to bottom depict a temporal sequence for one part of the small intestine. The arrows indicate the direction material in a given part of the intestine will move with each contraction. Material (brown) introduced at the beginning of the sequence (top figure) is spread out and becomes more diffuse (tan) through time. (b) Peristalsis. A wave of relaxation of the circular muscles is followed by a wave of strong contraction of the circular muscles, which propels the bolus of food through the digestive tract.

Table 16.2   Functions of the Liver

Function	Explanation
Digestion	Bile neutralizes stomach acid and emulsifies fats, which facilitates fat digestion
Excretion	Bile contains excretory products such as cholesterol, fats, and bile pigments such as bilirubin that result from hemoglobin breakdown
Nutrient storage	Liver cells remove sugar from the blood and store it in the form of glycogen; also store fat, vitamins (A, B_{12}, D, E, and K), copper, and iron
Nutrient conversion	Liver cells convert some nutrients into others, for example, amino acids can be converted to lipids or glucose; fats can be converted to phospholipids; vitamin D is converted to its active form
Detoxification of harmful chemicals	Liver cells remove ammonia from the circulation and convert it to urea, which is eliminated in the urine; other substances are detoxified and secreted in the bile or excreted in the urine
Synthesis of new molecules	Synthesizes blood proteins such as albumin, fibrinogen, globulins, and clotting factors

1. Secretin, produced by the duodenum (purple arrows) and carried through the circulation to the liver, stimulates bile secretion by the liver (green arrows inside the liver).
2. Cholecystokinin, produced by the duodenum (pink arrows) and carried through the circulation to the gallbladder, stimulates the gallbladder to contract, releasing bile into the duodenum (green arrow outside the liver).
3. Vagal nerve stimulation of the liver (red arrows) causes the liver to secrete bile and the gallbladder to contract, releasing bile into the duodenum.

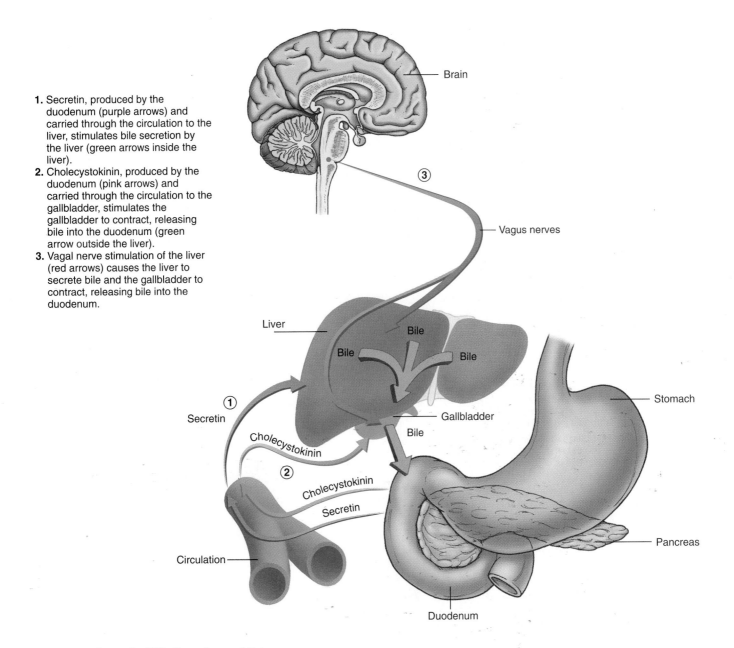

Figure 16.19   Control of Bile Secretion and Release

Cholecystokinin (kō′lē-sis-tō-kī′nin) stimulates the gallbladder to contract and release bile into the duodenum. Parasympathetic stimulation through the vagus nerve also stimulates bile secretion and release.

Most bile salts are reabsorbed in the ileum, and the blood carries them back to the liver, where they are once again secreted into the bile. The loss of bile salts in the feces is reduced by this recycling process.

The liver can remove sugar from the blood and store it in the form of glycogen (see table 16.2). It can also store fat, vitamins, copper, and iron. This storage function is usually short term.

Foods are not always ingested in the proportion needed by the tissues. If this is the case, the liver can convert some nutrients into others (see table 16.2). For example, if a person is on a fad diet that is very high in protein, an oversupply of amino acids and an undersupply of lipids and carbohydrates are delivered to the liver. The liver breaks down the amino acids and cycles many of them through metabolic pathways that use them to produce ATP and to synthesize lipids and glucose.

The liver also transforms some nutrients into more readily usable substances. Ingested fats, for example, are combined with choline and phosphorus in the liver to produce phospholipids, which are essential components of cell membranes.

Many ingested substances are harmful to the cells of the body. In addition, the body itself produces many by-products of metabolism that, if accumulated, are toxic. The liver is one line of defense against many of those harmful substances. It detoxifies them by altering their structure, making their excretion easier (see table 16.2). For example, the liver removes ammonia, which is a toxic by-product of amino acid metabolism, from the circulation and converts it to urea, which is then secreted into the circulation and eliminated by the kidneys in the urine. Other substances are removed from the circulation and excreted by the liver into the bile.

The liver can also produce its own unique new compounds (see table 16.2). Many of the blood proteins, such as albumins, fibrinogen, globulins, and clotting factors, are synthesized in the liver and released into the circulation.

Pancreas

The exocrine secretions of the pancreas include bicarbonate ions, which neutralize the acidic chyme that enters the small intestine from the stomach. The increased pH resulting from the secretion of bicarbonate ions stops pepsin digestion but provides the proper environment for the function of pancreatic enzymes. Pancreatic enzymes are also present in the exocrine secretions and are important for the digestion of all major classes of food (see table 16.1). Without the enzymes produced by the pancreas, lipids, proteins, and carbohydrates are not adequately digested.

The major proteolytic enzymes are **trypsin** (trip′sin) and **chymotrypsin**, (kī-mō-trip′sin) which continue the protein digestion that started in the stomach. **Pancreatic amylase** (am′il-ās′) continues the polysaccharide digestion that was initiated in the oral cavity. The pancreatic enzymes also include a group of lipid-digesting enzymes called pancreatic **lipases** (lip′ās-ez). **Nucleases** (noo′klē-ās-ez) are pancreatic enzymes that reduce DNA and ribonucleic acid to their component nucleotides.

The exocrine secretory activity of the pancreas is controlled by both hormonal and neural mechanisms (figure 16.20). **Secretin** initiates the release of a watery pancreatic solution that

1. Secretin (purple arrows) stimulates the pancreas to release a watery secretion, rich in bicarbonate ions.
2. Cholecystokinin (pink arrows) causes the pancreas to release a secretion rich in digestive enzymes.
3. Parasympathetic stimulation from the vagus nerve (red arrow) causes the pancreas to release a secretion rich in digestive enzymes.

Figure 16.20   Control of Pancreatic Secretions

contains a large amount of bicarbonate ions. The primary stimulus for secretin release is the presence of acidic chyme in the duodenum. **Cholecystokinin** stimulates the pancreas to release an enzyme-rich solution. The primary stimulus for cholecystokinin release is the presence of fatty acids and amino acids in the duodenum, and the enzymes secreted by the pancreas digest fatty acids and amino acids. Parasympathetic stimulation through the vagus nerves also stimulates the secretion of pancreatic juices rich in pancreatic enzymes. Sympathetic action potentials inhibit pancreatic secretion.

---

3   P R E D I C T

Explain how secretin production in response to acidic chyme and bicarbonate ion secretion in response to secretin constitute a negative-feedback mechanism.

✔ *Answer on page 463*

Large Intestine

Normally 18 to 24 hours are required for material to pass through the large intestine in contrast to the 3 to 5 hours required for movement of chyme through the small intestine. While in the colon, chyme is converted to **feces** (fē′sēz). Absorption of water and salts, the secretion of mucus, and extensive action of microorganisms are involved in the formation of feces. The colon stores the feces until they are eliminated by the process of **defecation** (def-ĕ-kā′shŭn).

Numerous microorganisms inhabit the colon. They reproduce rapidly and ultimately constitute about 30% of the dry weight of the feces. Some bacteria in the intestine synthesize vitamin K, which is passively absorbed in the colon.

Every 8 to 12 hours, large parts of the colon undergo several strong contractions called **mass movements**, which propel the colon contents a considerable distance toward the anus. Each mass movement contraction extends over 20 or more centimeters of the large intestine, which is a much longer part of the digestive tract than that covered by a peristaltic contraction. These mass movements are very common following some meals, especially breakfast.

Distention of the rectal wall by feces acts as a stimulus that initiates the **defecation reflex**, which involves local and parasympathetic reflexes. Local reflexes cause weak contractions, whereas parasympathetic reflexes cause strong contractions and are normally responsible for most of the defecation reflex. Action potentials produced in response to the distention travel along afferent nerve fibers to the sacral region of the spinal cord, where efferent action potentials are initiated that reinforce peristaltic contractions in the lower colon and rectum. Efferent action potentials also cause the internal anal sphincter to relax. The external anal sphincter, which is composed of skeletal muscle and is under conscious cerebral control, prevents the movement of feces out of the rectum and through the anal opening. If this sphincter is relaxed voluntarily, feces are expelled. The defecation reflex persists for only a few minutes and quickly dies. Generally the reflex is reinitiated after a period that may be as

long as several hours. Mass movements in the colon are usually the reason for the reinitiation of the defecation reflex.

Defecation is usually accompanied by voluntary movements that support the expulsion of feces. These voluntary movements include a large inspiration of air, followed by closure of the larynx and forceful contraction of the abdominal muscles. As a consequence, the pressure in the abdominal cavity increases and helps force the contents of the colon through the anal canal and out of the anus.

---

4   P R E D I C T

Explain how an enema stimulates defecation.

✔ *Answer on page 463*

Did You Know?

The importance of regularity of defecation has been greatly overestimated. Many people have the misleading notion that a daily bowel movement is critical for good health. As with many other bodily functions, what is "normal" differs from person to person. Some people defecate one or more times per day, but other healthy adults defecate on the average only every other day. A defecation rate of only twice per week is usually described as constipation. Fiber in the diet increases the likelihood of regular bowel movements. Habitually postponing defecation when the defecation reflex occurs can lead to constipation and may eventually result in desensitization of the rectum so that the defecation reflex is greatly diminished.

Digestion, Absorption, and Transport

Digestion is the breakdown of food to molecules that are small enough to be absorbed into the circulation. **Mechanical digestion** breaks large food particles down into smaller ones. **Chemical digestion** involves the breaking of covalent chemical bonds in organic molecules by digestive enzymes (figure 16.21). Carbohydrates are broken down into monosaccharides, proteins are broken down into amino acids, and fats are broken down into fatty acids and glycerol.

Absorption begins in the stomach, where some small, lipid-soluble molecules, such as alcohol and aspirin, can pass through the stomach epithelium into the circulation. Most absorption occurs in the duodenum and jejunum, although some occurs in the ileum. Some molecules can diffuse through the intestinal wall. Others must be transported across the intestinal wall. **Transport** requires a carrier molecule. If the transport is active, energy is required to move the transported molecule across the intestinal wall.

Carbohydrates

Ingested **carbohydrates** (kar-bō-hī′drātz) consist primarily of starches, cellulose, sucrose (table sugar), and small amounts of lactose (milk sugar) and fructose (fruit sugar).

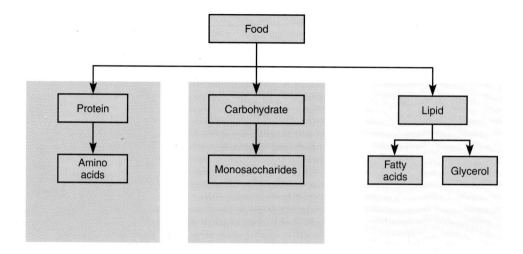

Figure 16.21 Digestion of Food Molecules

Food consists primarily of protein, carbohydrate, and fat. Proteins are broken into amino acids, carbohydrates into monosaccharides, and lipid into fatty acids and glycerol.

Starches, cellulose, sucrose, and fructose are derived from plants. Glycogen and lactose are derived mostly from animals. **Polysaccharides** (pol-ē-sak′ă-rīdz) are large carbohydrates, such as starches, cellulose, and glycogen, which consist of many sugars linked by chemical bonds. Starch and glycogen are broken down by enzymes. Cellulose is a polysaccharide that is not digested but is important for providing fiber in the diet.

Salivary amylase begins the digestion of carbohydrates in the mouth (figure 16.22). The carbohydrates then pass to the stomach, where almost no carbohydrate digestion occurs. In the duodenum, **pancreatic amylase** continues the digestion of carbohydrates, and absorption begins. The amylases break down polysaccharides to **disaccharides** (dī-sak′ă-rīdz, two sugars chemically linked; see chapter 2). A group of enzymes called **disaccharidases** (dī-sak′ă-rid-ās-ez) that are bound to the microvilli of the intestinal epithelium break down the disaccharides to monosaccharides.

The **monosaccharides** (mon-ō-sak′ă-rīdz, single sugars) are taken up by secondary active transport through the intestinal epithelial cells (figure 16.23a, and see chapter 3), and they are carried by the hepatic portal system to the liver. Different types of monosaccharides are converted to **glucose** by liver cells. Glucose is carried from the liver by the circulation throughout the body. Glucose enters the cells by facilitated diffusion. The rate of glucose transport into most types of cells is greatly influenced by **insulin** and can increase 10-fold in the presence of insulin. Without insulin, glucose enters most cells very slowly.

Did You Know?

Insulin normally binds to receptors on target cells and increases the ability of the target cell to take up glucose. In people with **diabetes mellitus,** insulin either is lacking or does not have the normal effect on target cells. As a result, not enough glucose is transported into many cells of the body. Thus, in untreated diabetes, the cells do not have enough energy for normal function, blood glucose levels become elevated, and large amounts of glucose are released into the urine.

Lipids

Lipid molecules are insoluble or only slightly soluble in water (see chapter 2). They include triacylglycerol, phospholipids, steroids, and fat-soluble vitamins. **Triacylglycerol** (trī-as′il-glis′er-ol, also referred to as triglyceride), the most common type of lipid, consists of three fatty acids bound to glycerol. Triacylglycerol is often referred to as fat. Fats are **saturated** if their fatty acids have only single bonds between carbons and **unsaturated** if they have one (monounsaturated) or more (polyunsaturated) double bonds between carbons (see chapter 2). Saturated fats are solid at room temperature, whereas polyunsaturated fats are liquid at room temperature. Saturated fats are found in meat, dairy products, eggs, nuts, coconut oil, and palm oil. Unsaturated fats are found in fish and most plant oils.

The first step in lipid digestion is **emulsification** (ē-mŭl′si-fi-kā′shŭn), which is the transformation of large lipid droplets into much smaller droplets. Emulsification is accomplished by **bile salts** secreted by the liver. The enzymes that digest lipids are soluble in water and can digest the lipids only by acting at the surface of the droplets. The emulsification process increases the surface area of the lipid droplets exposed to the digestive enzymes by increasing the number of lipid droplets and by decreasing the size of each droplet.

Did You Know?

Cystic fibrosis is a hereditary disorder that affects both the respiratory and digestive systems. It results from defective chloride channels which cause cells to produce thick, viscous mucous secretions. Blockage of the pancreatic ducts often occurs so that the pancreatic digestive enzymes are prevented from reaching the duodenum. As a result, fat digestion, which depends on pancreatic enzymes, is slowed or even stopped. Consequently, fats and fat-soluble vitamins are not absorbed, and the patient suffers from vitamin A, D, E, and K deficiencies. These deficiencies result in conditions such as night blindness, skin disorders, rickets, and excessive bleeding. Therapy consists of administering the missing vitamins to the patient and reducing dietary fat intake.

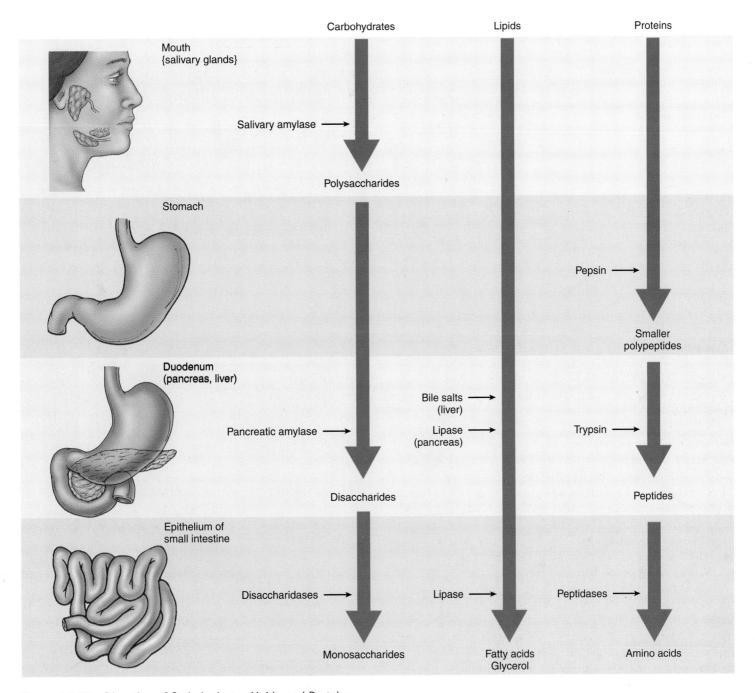

Figure 16.22   Digestion of Carbohydrates, Lipids, and Proteins
The enzymes involved in digesting carbohydrates, lipids, and proteins are depicted as well as the region of the digestive tract where each functions.

Lipase (lip′ās), secreted by the pancreas and intestinal absorptive cells, digests lipid molecules (see figure 16.22). The primary products of this digestive process are fatty acids and glycerol.

In the intestine, bile salts aggregate around small droplets of digested lipids to form **micelles** (mi-selz′, mī-selz′, a small morsel) (figure 16.23*b*). The hydrophobic (water-fearing) ends of the bile salts are directed toward the lipid particles, and the hydrophilic (water-loving) ends are directed outward toward the water environment. When a micelle comes into contact with the epithelial cells of the small intestine, the lipids, fatty acids, and glycerol molecules pass, by means of simple diffusion, from the micelles through the lipid cell membrane of the epithelial cells.

Once inside the intestinal epithelial cells, the fatty acids and glycerols are recombined to form triacylglycerols. These, and other lipids, are packaged inside a protein coat within the epithelial cells of the intestinal villi. The packaged lipids leave the epithelial cells and enter the lacteals. Lacteals are lymphatic capillaries located within the intestinal villi. Lymph containing large amounts of absorbed lipid is called **chyle** (kīl, milky lymph). The lymphatic system carries the chyle to the bloodstream. Packaged lipids are transported to the liver, where they are stored, converted into other molecules, or used as energy. They are also transported to adipose tissue, where they are stored until an energy source is needed elsewhere in the body.

Monosaccharide Transport

1. Monosaccharides are absorbed by secondary active transport into intestinal epithelial cells.

2. Monosaccharides move out of intestinal epithelial cells by facilitated diffusion.

3. They enter the capillaries of the intestinal villi and are carried through the hepatic portal vein to the liver.

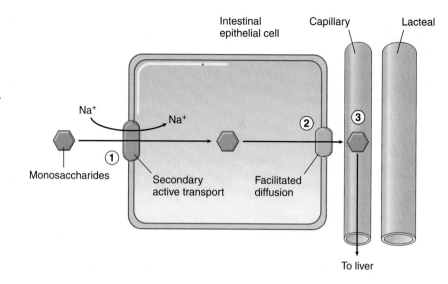

(a)

Lipid Transport

1. Bile salts surround fatty acids and glycerol to form micelles.

2. Micelles attach to the cell membranes of intestinal epithelial cells, and the fatty acids and glycerol pass by simple diffusion into the intestinal epithelial cells.

3. Within the intestinal epithelial cell, the fatty acids and glycerol are converted to triacylglycerol; proteins coat the triacylglycerol to form chylomicrons, which move out of the intestinal epithelial cells by exocytosis.

4. The chylomicrons enter the lacteals of the intestinal villi and are carried through the lymphatic system to the general circulation.

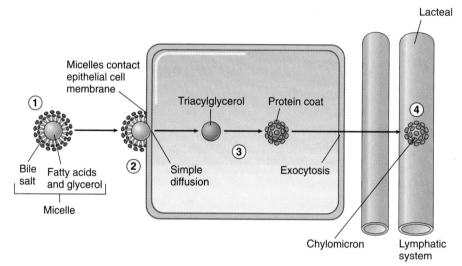

(b)

Amino Acid Transport

1. Amino acids are absorbed by secondary active transport into intestinal epithelial cells.

2. Amino acids move out of intestinal epithelial cells by active transport.

3. They enter the capillaries of the intestinal villi, and are carried through the hepatic portal vein to the liver.

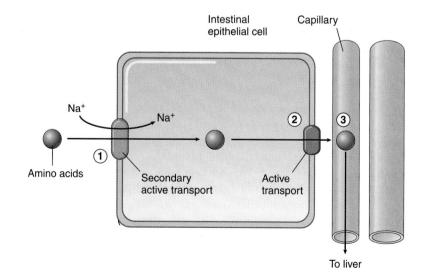

(c)

Figure 16.23 Absorption of Nutrients by the Intestinal Epithelium

In each part of the figure, the blue box represents the intestinal epithelial cell; (*a*) monosaccharide transport, (*b*) lipid transport, (*c*) amino acid transport.

Cholesterol levels in the blood are of great concern to many adults. Cholesterol levels of less than 180 milligrams (mg)/100 mL are considered low, which is usually good, although extremely low cholesterol levels can be harmful. Cholesterol levels above 200 mg/100 mL are considered to be too high. People with high blood cholesterol levels run a much greater risk of heart disease and stroke than people with low cholesterol levels. People with high levels should seek advice from their physician, reduce their intake of foods rich in cholesterol and other fats, and increase their level of exercise. Some people with very high cholesterol levels may have to take medication to reduce their cholesterol levels.

Fats are not soluble in water; thus they are transported in the blood as lipid–protein complexes, or **lipoproteins** (figure 16.24). **Low–density lipoproteins (LDLs)** carry cholesterol to the tissues for use by the cells. When LDLs are in excess, cholesterol is deposited on arterial walls. **High-density lipoproteins (HDLs),** on the other hand, transport cholesterol from the tissues to the liver, where cholesterol is removed from the bloodstream and broken down or excreted in bile. A high HDL/LDL ratio in the bloodstream is related to a lower risk of heart disease. Aerobic exercise is one way to elevate blood levels of HDL.

(a)

- Phospholipid (20%)
- Triacylglycerol (10%)
- Cholesterol (45%)
- Protein (25%)

(b)

- Phospholipid (30%)
- Triacylglycerol (5%)
- Cholesterol (20%)
- Protein (45%)

Figure 16.24   Lipoproteins

(*a*) Low-density lipoprotein (LDL). (*b*) High-density lipoprotein (HDL).

Proteins

Proteins are chains of amino acids. They are found in most of the plant and animal products we eat. **Pepsin** is an enzyme secreted by the stomach, which breaks down **proteins,** producing smaller polypeptide chains (see figure 16.22). Only about 10% to 20% of the total ingested protein is digested by pepsin. After the remaining proteins and polypeptide chains leave the stomach and enter the small intestine, the enzyme **trypsin,** produced by the pancreas, continues the digestive process. Trypsin produces short amino acid chains called **peptides** that are broken down further into **amino acids** by **peptidases.** Peptidases are di-

gestive enzymes bound to the microvilli of the small intestine, which act on smaller peptides to release amino acids.

Absorption of individual amino acids occurs through the intestinal epithelial cells by secondary active transport (see figure 16.23*c*). The amino acids then enter blood capillaries in the villi and are carried by the hepatic portal system to the liver. The amino acids may be modified in the liver, or they may be released into the bloodstream and distributed throughout the body.

Amino acids are actively transported into the various cells of the body. This transport is stimulated by growth hormone and insulin. Most amino acids are used as building blocks to form new proteins, but some may be metabolized, with some of the released energy used to produce adenosine triphosphate. The body cannot store amino acids; thus they are partially broken down and used to synthesize glycogen or fat, which can be stored. The body can store only small amounts of glycogen, so most of the energy is stored as fat.

Water and Minerals

Approximately 9 L of water enters the digestive tract each day (figure 16.25). We ingest about 2 L in food and drink, and the remaining 7 L is from digestive secretions. Approximately 92% of

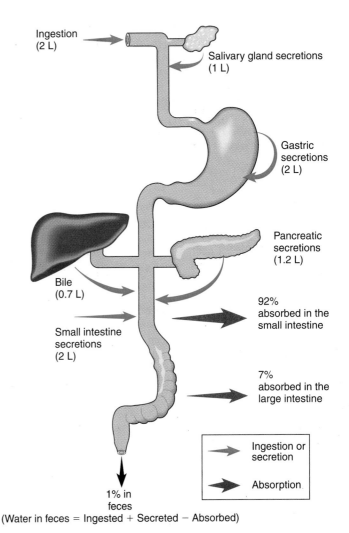

Ingestion (2 L)

Salivary gland secretions (1 L)

Gastric secretions (2 L)

Pancreatic secretions (1.2 L)

Bile (0.7 L)

92% absorbed in the small intestine

Small intestine secretions (2 L)

7% absorbed in the large intestine

| | Ingestion or secretion |
| | Absorption |

1% in feces

(Water in feces = Ingested + Secreted − Absorbed)

Figure 16.25   Water Ingestion, Secretion, and Absorption in the Digestive Tract that water is absorbed in the small intestine, about 7% is absorbed in the large intestine, and about 1% leaves the body in the feces. Water can move in either direction across the wall of the small intestine. The direction of its movement is determined by osmotic gradients across the epithelium. When the chyme is diluted, water moves out of the intestine into the blood. If the chyme is concentrated and contains little water, water moves into the lumen of the small intestine.

Sodium, potassium, calcium, magnesium, and phosphate ions are actively transported from the small intestine. Vitamin D is required for the transport of calcium. Negatively charged chloride ions move passively through the wall of the duodenum and jejunum with the positively charged sodium ions, but chloride ions are actively transported from the ileum.

Clinical Focus   Disorders of the Digestive Tract

Stomach

Vomiting results primarily from irritation of the stomach and small intestine. Action potentials travel through visceral afferent nerves to the vomiting center in the medulla oblongata. After the vomiting center is stimulated and the reflex is initiated, the following events occur:

1. A deep breath is taken.
2. The hyoid bone and larynx are elevated, opening the upper esophageal sphincter.
3. The opening of the larynx is closed.
4. The soft palate is elevated, closing the posterior opening into the nasal cavity.
5. The diaphragm and abdominal muscles are forcefully contracted, strongly compressing the stomach and increasing the intragastric pressure.
6. The lower esophageal sphincter is relaxed, and the gastric contents are forcefully expelled.

Ulcers

Approximately 5% to 12% of the population is affected by **peptic ulcers,** which are lesions in the lining of the stomach or duodenum. Most cases of peptic ulcer apparently result from the infection of a specific bacterium *Helicobacter pylori.* It is also thought that the bacterium is involved in many cases of gastritis and gastric cancer. Conventional wisdom has focused for years on the notion that stress, diet, smoking, or alcohol cause excess acid secretion in the stomach, resulting in ulcers. Even today, antacids are used to treat 90% of all ulcers, with several billion dollars spent on antacids in the United States each year. Antacid therapy does cause the ulcer to heal in most cases. With antacid treatment, however, there is a 50% incidence of relapse within 6 months and a 95% incidence of relapse after 2 years. On the other hand, studies using antibiotic therapy together with bismuth and ranitidine (ră-nǐ′ti-dēn) have

demonstrated an eradication of 95% of gastric ulcers and 74% of duodenal ulcers within 2 months. Dramatically reduced relapse rates have also been obtained. One such study reported a recurrence rate of 8% following antibiotic therapy, compared with a recurrence rate of 86% in controls. One reason that bacterial involvement in ulcers was dismissed for such a long time is that it was assumed that the extreme acid environment would not allow bacteria to survive. Apparently *H. pylori* not only survives in such an environment, but may even thrive there.

The infection rate from *H. pylori* in the United States population is about 1% per year of age: 30% of people that are 30 years old have the bacterium, and 80% of those age 80 are infected. Very little is known concerning how people become infected. Also, with such high rates of infection it is not known why only a small fraction of those infected actually develop ulcers. It may be that the several factors that increase gastric acid secretion predispose a person who is infected by the bacterium to actually develop an ulcer.

Peptic ulcer is classically viewed as a condition in which the stomach acids digest the mucosal lining of the GI tract itself. The most common site of a peptic ulcer is near the pylorus, usually on the duodenal side. This is sometimes called a **duodenal ulcer.** Approximately 80% of all peptic ulcers are actually duodenal. Ulcers that occur in the stomach are often called **gastric ulcers.** Gastric ulcers usually occur along the lesser curvature of the stomach or at the point at which the esophagus enters the stomach. The most common contributing factor to developing peptic ulcers is the oversecretion of gastric juices relative to the degree of mucous and alkaline protection of the small intestine.

People who experience severe anxiety over a long period are the most prone to develop duodenal ulcers. They often have a rate of gastric secretion between meals that is as

much as 15 times the normal amount. This secretion results in highly acidic chyme entering the duodenum. The duodenum is usually protected by sodium bicarbonate, secreted mainly by the pancreas, which neutralizes the chyme. When large amounts of acid enter the duodenum, however, the sodium bicarbonate is not adequate to neutralize it. The acid tends to reduce the mucous protection of the duodenum, perhaps leaving that part of the digestive tract open to action of *H. pylori,* which may further destroy the mucous lining.

In some patients with gastric ulcers, normal or even low levels of gastric hydrochloric acid secretion often occur. The stomachs of these patients, however, have reduced resistance to their own acid. Such inhibited resistance can result from excessive ingestion of alcohol or aspirin.

Reflux of duodenal contents into the pylorus can also cause gastric ulcers. In this case, bile, which is present in the reflux, has a detergent effect that reduces gastric mucosal resistance to acid, and to bacteria.

Liver

Cirrhosis (sir-ō′sis) is a major disease of the liver. It is characterized by damage and death of hepatic cells and replacement by connective tissue. These characteristics are accompanied by loss of normal liver function and interference with blood flow through the liver. Cirrhosis is a common complication of alcoholism.

Hepatitis (hep-ă-tī′tis) is an inflammation of the liver that can result from alcohol consumption or viral infection. If not corrected, liver cells can die and be replaced by scar tissue, resulting in loss of liver function. Death can result from liver failure.

Viral hepatitis is the second most frequently reported infectious disease in the United States. **Hepatitis A** (infectious hepatitis) is usually transmitted by poor sanitation practices or from mollusks, such as oysters, living in contaminated waters. **Hepatitis B** (serum hepatitis) is usually transmitted through blood or other body fluids, such as when blood is transferred through a contaminated hypodermic needle. Symptoms include nausea, diarrhea, loss of appetite, abdominal pain, fever, chills, and malaise. **Jaundice** is seen in about two-thirds of the cases, with yellowing of the skin and sclera of the eyes resulting from the accumulation of bile pigments in those tissues.

Cholesterol, secreted by the liver into the bile, can precipitate in the gallbladder to produce **gallstones.** Occasionally a gallstone may pass out of the gallbladder and enter the cystic duct, blocking release of the bile. Such a condition interferes with normal digestion, and often the gallbladder must be removed surgically.

Intestine

Inflammatory bowel disease (IBD) is the general name given to either Crohn's disease or ulcerative colitis. IBD occurs at a rate in Europe and North America of approximately 4 to 8 new cases per 100,000 people per year, which is much higher than in Asia and Africa. Males and females are affected about equally. IBD is of unknown cause, but infectious, autoimmune, and hereditary factors have been implicated. **Crohn's disease** involves localized inflammatory degeneration that may occur anywhere along the digestive tract but most commonly involves the distal ileum and proximal colon. The degeneration involves the entire thickness of the digestive tract wall. The intestinal wall often becomes thickened, constricting the lumen, with ulcerations and fissures in the damaged areas. The disease causes diarrhea, abdominal pain, fever, and weight loss. Treatment centers around anti-inflammatory drugs, but other treatments, including avoiding foods that increase symptoms and even surgery are employed. **Ulcerative colitis** is limited to the mucosa of the large intestine. The involved mucosa exhibits inflammation, including edema, vascular congestion, hemorrhage, and the accumulation of plasma cells, lymphocytes, neutrophils, and eosinophils. Patients may experience abdominal pain, fever, malaise, fatigue, and weight loss, as well as diarrhea and hemorrhage. In rare cases, severe diarrhea and hemorrhage may require transfusions. Treatment includes the use of anti-inflammatory drugs and, in some cases, avoiding foods that increase symptoms.

Irritable bowel syndrome (IBS) is a disorder of unknown cause in which intestinal mobility is abnormal. The disorder accounts for over half of all referrals to gastroenterologists. Male and female children are affected equally, but adult females are affected twice as often as males. IBS patients experience abdominal pain mainly in the left lower quadrant, especially after eating. They also have alternating bouts of constipation and diarrhea. There is no specific histopathology in the digestive tracts of IBS patients. There are no anatomic abnormalities, no indication of infection, and no sign of metabolic causes. Patients with IBS appear to exhibit greater than normal levels of psychological stress or depression, and show increased contractions of the esophagus and small intestine during times of stress. There is a high familial incidence. Some patients might present with a history of traumatic events such as physical or sexual abuse. Treatments include psychiatric counseling and stress management, diets with increased fiber and limited gas-producing foods, loose clothing, and in some patients, drugs that reduce parasympathetic stimulation of the digestive system may be useful.

Malabsorption syndrome (sprue) is a spectrum of disorders of the small intestine that results in abnormal nutrient absorption. In some people, one type of malabsorption results from the effects of gluten, an insoluble protein present in certain types of grains. The reaction to gluten can destroy newly formed epithelial cells, causing the villi to become blunted and the intestinal surface area to decrease. As a result, the intestinal epithelium is less capable of absorbing nutrients. Tropical malabsorption is apparently caused by bacteria, although no specific bacterium has been identified.

Appendicitis is an inflammation of the appendix and usually occurs because of obstruction of the appendix. Secretions from the appendix cannot pass the obstruction; thus they accumulate, causing enlargement, inflammation, and pain. Bacteria in the area cause the appendix to become infected. If the appendix bursts, the infection can spread throughout the peritoneal cavity with life-threatening results. The right inferior quadrant of the abdomen becomes very tender in people with acute appendicitis as a result of pain referred from the inflamed appendix to the body surface.

Infections of the Digestive Tract

Staphylococcal (staf′i-lō-kok′ăl) **food poisoning** occurs when toxin from the bacteria *Staphylococcus aureus* is ingested. The bacteria usually come from the hands of a person preparing the food. If food is cooked in large volumes at low temperatures (below 60°C) or is allowed to sit for an extended time, the bacteria can reproduce and form toxins. Reheating can eliminate the bacteria but not the toxins. Staphylococcal food poisoning is characterized by nausea, vomiting, and diarrhea from 1 to 6 hours after the contaminated food is ingested.

Salmonellosis (sal′mō-nel-ō′sis) is a disease caused by *Salmonella* bacteria. They are ingested with contaminated food (usually meat, poultry, or milk) and grow in the digestive tract. The disease symptoms are usually seen 18 to 36 hours after the contaminated food has been consumed. Symptoms include nausea, fever, abdominal pain, and diarrhea. The bacteria are generally destroyed by cooking food to temperatures greater than 68°C.

Typhoid (tī′foyd) **fever** is caused by a particularly virulent strain of salmonella bacteria, *Salmonella typhi.* The bacteria can cross the intestinal wall and invade other tissues. The incubation period is normally about 2 weeks. Symptoms include severe fever and headaches, as well as diarrhea. Poor sanitation practices are the main source of contamination, and typhoid fever is still a leading cause of death in many underdeveloped countries.

Cholera (kol′er-ă) is caused by a bacterium (*Vibrio cholerae*) obtained from contaminated water that infects the small intestine. The bacteria produce a toxin that stimulates the secretion of chlorides, bicarbonates, and water from the intestinal tract. The loss of as much as 12 to 20 L of fluid and ions per day causes shock, circulatory collapse, and even death. Cholera was common in the United States and Europe in the 1800s but is not very common in western countries today. Cholera is still a major problem in Asia, particularly in India.

Giardiasis (jē-ar-dī′ă-sis) is a disease caused by a protozoan (*Giardia lamblia*) that invades the intestine. Symptoms include nausea, abdominal cramps, weakness, weight loss, and malaise and can last for several weeks. The disease is transmitted in the form of spores in the feces of humans and wild animals, especially beaver. People who drink unfiltered water from wilderness streams containing spores are often infected.

Intestinal parasites are not uncommon in humans, especially under conditions of poor sanitation. **Tapeworms** (several genera) can infect the digestive tract by way of undercooked beef, pork, or fish. The tapeworms attach to the intestinal wall and may live in the intestine for 25 years, reaching lengths of 6 m. There are few symptoms beyond a vague abdominal discomfort.

Pinworms (*Enterobius vermicularis*) are common in humans. The tiny worm lives in the digestive tract but migrates out of the anus to lay its eggs. This causes a local itching, and the eggs can be spread by contaminated fingers to numerous surfaces. Eggs resist dehydration and can be picked up from contaminated surfaces by other people. It is common for entire households to be contaminated if one child contracts the disease.

Hookworms (*Ancylostoma*) attach to the intestinal wall and feed on the blood and tissue of the host, rather than on partially digested food as other parasites do. Infection can cause anemia and lethargy. Because hookworms are spread through fecal contamination of the soil and bare skin contact with contaminated soil, improved sanitation and the practice of wearing shoes has greatly decreased the incidence of hookworm infection.

Ascariasis (as'kă-rī'ă-sis) is caused by a roundworm (*Ascaris lumbricoides*) and is fairly common in the United States. Ingested eggs hatch in the upper intestine into wormlike larvae that pass into the bloodstream and then into the lungs, where they can cause pulmonary symptoms. Extremely large numbers can cause pneumonia. The larvae enter the throat and are swallowed, thereby returning to the intestinal tract. Adults in the intestinal tract cause few symptoms. The adult worms, however, measuring up to 30 cm, migrate. In some cases, they may emerge from the anus, or they may cut their way through the intestinal wall and infect the abdominal cavity.

Constipation (kon-sti-pā'shŭn) is the slow movement of feces through the large intestine. The feces often become dry and hard because of the increased fluid absorption during the extended time they are retained in the large intestine. Constipation often results from irregular defecation patterns that develop after a prolonged time of inhibiting normal defecation reflexes. Spasms of the sigmoid colon resulting from irritation also can result in slow feces movement and constipation. A diet high in fiber can help prevent constipation.

Diarrhea (dī-ă-rē'ă) is a condition in which the intestinal mucosa secretes large amounts of water and ions in addition to mucus. This condition occurs when the large intestine is irritated and inflamed, such as in patients with **enteritis** (en-ter-ī'tis) bacterial infection of the bowel. Although diarrhea increases fluid and ion loss, it also moves the infected feces out of the intestine more rapidly and speeds recovery from the disease.

Dysentery (dis'en-tār-ē) is a severe form of diarrhea in which blood or mucus is present in the feces. Dysentery can be caused by bacteria, protozoa, or amoebae.

Systems Pathology

diarrhea

DIARRHEA

While on vacation in a foreign country, Mr. T. was shopping with his wife, when he started to experience sharp pains in his abdominal region (figure A). He also began to feel hot and sweaty and felt an extreme urge to defecate. Mr. T. anxiously inquired about the nearest facility. Once his immediate crisis was taken care of, Mr. and Mrs. T. went back to their hotel room, where they remained while Mr. T. recovered. During the next 2 days his stools were frequent and watery. He also vomited a couple of times. Because they were in a foreign country, Mr. T. did not consult a physician. Instead, he rested, took plenty of fluids, and was feeling much better, although a little weak, in a couple of days.

Background

Diarrhea is one of the most common complaints in clinical medicine, and diarrhea affects more than half of the tourists in developing countries. Diarrhea is defined as any change in bowel habits in which stool frequency or volume is increased or in which stool fluidity is increased. Diarrhea is not itself a disease, but is a symptom of a wide variety of disorders. Normally, about 600 mL of fluid enters the colon each day and all but 150 mL is reabsorbed. The loss of more than 200 mL of stool per day is considered abnormal.

Mucus secretion by the colon increases dramatically in response to diarrhea. This mucus contains large quantities of bicarbonate ions, which come from the dissociation of carbonic acid into bicarbonate ions and hydrogen ions within the blood supply to the colon. The bicarbonate ions enter the mucus secreted by the colon, whereas the hydrogen ions remain in the circulation and, as a result, the blood pH decreases. Thus, a condition called metabolic acidosis can develop (see chapter 18).

Diarrhea in tourists usually results from the ingestion of food or water contaminated with bacteria or bacterial toxins. Acute diarrhea is defined as lasting less than 2 to 3 weeks, and diarrhea lasting longer than that is considered chronic. Acute diarrhea is usually self-limiting, but some forms of diarrhea can be fatal if not treated. Diarrhea results from either a decrease in fluid absorption in the gut or an increase in fluid secretion. Some bacterial toxins and other chemicals can also cause an increase in bowel motor activity. As a result, chyme is moved more rapidly through the digestive tract, less nutrients and water are absorbed out of the small intestine, and more water enters the colon. Symptoms can occur in as little

Figure A   Many tourists develop diarrhea.

as 1 to 2 hours after bacterial toxins are ingested to as long as 24 hours or more for some strains of bacteria.

In cases of short-term acute diarrhea, the infectious agent is seldom identified. Nearly any bacterial species is capable of causing diarrhea. Some types of bacterial diarrhea include severe vomiting, whereas others do not. Some bacterial toxins also induce fever. Some viruses and amebic parasites can also cause diarrhea. In most cases, laboratory analysis of food or stool is necessary to identify the causal organism. In cases of mild diarrhea away from home, laboratory evaluation is not practical and therapy consists of treating the symptoms. Fluids and ions must be replaced, and consumption of fluids with ions is important. The diet should be limited to clear fluids during at least the first day or so. Bismuth subsalicylate (sŭb-să-lis'i-lāt) or loperamide (lō-per'ă-mīd) (except in cases of fever) may also be used to help combat secretory diarrhea. Milk and milk products should be avoided. Breads, toast, rice, and baked fish or chicken can be added to the diet with improvement. A normal diet can be resumed after 2 to 3 days.

5	P R E D I C T

Predict the effects of prolonged diarrhea on the circulatory system.

✔ *Answer on page 463*

System Interactions

System	Interactions
Integumentary	Pallor due to vasoconstriction of blood vessels in the skin, resulting from a decrease in blood volume. Pallor and sweating increase in response to abdominal pain and anxiety.
Muscular	Muscular weakness may result due to ion loss, metabolic acidosis, fever, and general malaise. The involuntary stimulus to defecate may become so strong that it overcomes the voluntary control mechanisms.
Nervous	Local reflexes in the colon respond to increased colon fluid volume by stimulating mass movements and the defecation reflex. Abdominal pain, much of which is felt as referred pain, can occur as the result of inflammation and distention of the colon. Decreased function due to ion loss. Reduced blood volume stimulates a sensation of thirst in the CNS.
Endocrine	A decrease in extracellular fluid volume, due to the loss of fluid in the feces, stimulates the release of hormones (antidiuretic hormone from the posterior pituitary and aldosterone from the adrenal cortex) that increase water retention and sodium reabsorption in the kidney. In addition, decreased extracellular fluid volume and anxiety result in increased release of epinephrine and norepinephrine from the adrenal medulla.
Cardiovascular	Movement of extracellular fluid into the colon results in a decreased blood volume. The reduced blood volume activates the baroreceptor reflex and the fluid shift mechanism, which all function to increase blood volume or increase blood pressure.
Lymphatic and Immune	White blood cells migrate to the colon in response to infection and inflammation. In the case of bacterial diarrhea, the immune response is initiated to begin production of antibodies against bacteria and bacterial toxins.
Respiratory	As the result of reduced blood pH, the rate of respiration increases to eliminate carbon dioxide, which helps eliminate excess hydrogen ions.
Urinary	A decrease in urine volume and an increase in urine concentration results from activation of the baroreceptor reflex, which decreases blood flow to the kidney; antidiuretic hormone secretion, which increases water reabsorption in the kidney; and aldosterone secretion, which increases sodium and water reabsorption in the kidney. After a period of approximately 24 hours, the kidney is activated to compensate for metabolic acidosis by increasing hydrogen ion secretion and bicarbonate ion reabsorption.

Summary

Functions of the Digestive System

- The functions of the digestive system are to take in food, break down the food, absorb the digested molecules, and, thus, provide nutrients to the body.

Anatomy and Histology of the Digestive System

- The GI tract is composed of four tunics: mucosa, submucosa, muscularis, and serosa or adventitia.

Oral Cavity

- The lips and cheeks are involved in mastication and speech.
- The tongue is involved in speech, taste, mastication, and swallowing.
- There are 32 permanent teeth, including incisors, canines, premolars, and molars. Each tooth consists of a crown, neck, and root.
- The roof of the oral cavity is divided into the hard and soft palates.
- Salivary glands produce serous and mucous secretions. The three pairs of large salivary glands are the parotid, submandibular, and sublingual glands.

Pharynx

- The pharynx consists of the nasopharynx, oropharynx, and laryngopharynx.

Esophagus

- The esophagus connects the pharynx to the stomach. The upper and lower esophageal sphincters regulate movement.

Stomach

- The stomach has a cardiac opening from the esophagus and a pyloric opening into the duodenum.
- The wall of the stomach consists of three muscle layers: longitudinal, circular, and oblique.
- Gastric glands produce mucus, hydrochloric acid, pepsin, gastrin, and intrinsic factor.

Small Intestine

- The small intestine is divided into the duodenum, jejunum, and ileum.
- Circular folds, villi, and microvilli greatly increase the surface area of the intestinal lining.
- Goblet cells and duodenal glands produce mucus.

Liver

- The liver receives blood from the hepatic artery and the hepatic portal vein.
- Bile leaves the liver through the hepatic duct system. The right and left hepatic ducts join to form the common hepatic duct. The cystic duct joins the common hepatic duct to form the common bile duct. The common bile duct joins the pancreatic duct and empties into the duodenum.
- The liver is divided into lobules with portal triads at the corners. Portal triads contain branches of the hepatic portal vein, hepatic artery, and hepatic duct.
- Hepatic cords, formed by hepatocytes, form the substance of each lobule. A bile canaliculus, between the cells of each cord, joins the hepatic duct system.
- Branches of the hepatic artery and hepatic portal vein empty into hepatic sinusoids, which empty into a central vein in the center of each lobe. The central veins empty into hepatic veins, which exit the liver.

Pancreas

- The pancreas is an endocrine and an exocrine gland. Its endocrine function is to control blood nutrient levels. Its exocrine function is to produce bicarbonate ions and digestive enzymes.

Large Intestine

- The cecum forms a blind sac at the junction of the small and large intestines. The appendix is a blind sac off the cecum.
- The colon consists of ascending, transverse, descending, and sigmoid portions.
- The large intestine contains mucus-producing crypts.
- The rectum is a straight tube that ends at the anal canal.

Anal Canal

- The anal canal is surrounded by an internal anal sphincter (smooth muscle) and an external anal sphincter (skeletal muscle).

Peritoneum

- The peritoneum is a serous membrane that lines the abdominal cavity and covers the organs.
- Mesenteries are double layers of peritoneum that extend from the body wall to many of the abdominal organs.
- Retroperitoneal organs are located behind the parietal peritoneum.

Movements and Secretions in the Digestive System

- The digestive system is regulated by neural and hormonal mechanisms. Intramural plexuses are responsible for local reflexes.

Oral Cavity, Pharynx, and Esophagus

- Amylase in saliva starts starch digestion. Mucin provides lubrication.
- Mastication is accomplished by the teeth, which cut, tear, and crush the food.
- During the voluntary phase of deglutition, a bolus of food is moved by the tongue from the oral cavity to the pharynx.
- During the pharyngeal phase of deglutition, the soft palate closes the nasopharynx, and the epiglottis closes the opening into the larynx. Pharyngeal muscles move the bolus to the esophagus.
- During the esophageal phase of deglutition, a wave of constriction (peristalsis) moves the food down the esophagus to the stomach.

Stomach

- Secretions of the stomach.
  Mucus protects the stomach lining.
  Hydrochloric acid kills microorganisms and activates pepsin.
  Pepsin starts protein digestion.
  Intrinsic factor aids in vitamin B_{12} absorption.
  Gastrin helps regulate stomach secretions and movements.
- Regulation of stomach secretions.
  During the cephalic phase, the stomach secretions are initiated by the sight, smell, taste, or thought of food. Gastrin stimulates stomach secretions.
  During the gastric phase, partially digested proteins or distention of the stomach also promotes secretion.
  During the intestinal phase, acidic chyme in the duodenum stimulates neuronal reflexes and the secretion of hormones that induce and then inhibit gastric secretions. Gastrin stimulates stomach secretion. Secretin, gastric inhibitory polypeptide, and cholecystokinin inhibit gastric secretion.
- Movement in the stomach.
  Mixing waves mix the stomach contents with the stomach secretions to form chyme.
  Peristaltic waves move the chyme into the duodenum.

Small Intestine

- Secretions of the small intestine.
  Mucus protects against digestive enzymes and stomach acids.
  Chemical or tactile irritation, vagal stimulation, and secretion stimulate intestinal secretion.
- Movement in the small intestine.
  Segmental contractions occur over short distances and mix the intestinal contents.
  Peristaltic contractions occur the length of the intestine and propel chyme through the intestine.
- Most absorption occurs in the duodenum and jejunum.

Liver

- The liver produces bile, which contains bile salts that emulsify fats.
- The liver stores and processes nutrients, produces new molecules, and detoxifies molecules.
- The liver produces blood proteins.

Pancreas

- The pancreas produces bicarbonate ions and digestive enzymes.
- Acidic chyme stimulates the release of a watery bicarbonate solution that neutralizes acidic chyme. Fatty acids and amino acids in the duodenum stimulate the release of pancreatic enzymes.

Large Intestine

- The function of the large intestine is feces production and water absorption.
- It takes much longer for material to move through the large intestine than the small intestine.
- In the colon, chyme is converted to feces.
- Mass movements occur three to four times a day.

- Defecation is the elimination of feces. Reflex activity moves feces through the internal anal sphincter. Voluntary activity regulates movement through the external anal sphincter.

Digestion, Absorption, and Transport

- Digestion is the chemical breakdown of organic molecules into their component parts. After the molecules are digested, some diffuse through the intestinal wall; others must be transported across the intestinal wall.

Carbohydrates

- Polysaccharides are split into disaccharides by salivary and pancreatic amylases.
- Disaccharides are broken down to monosaccharides by disaccharidases on the surface of the intestinal epithelium.
- Monosaccharides are absorbed by active transport into the blood and carried by the hepatic portal vein to the liver.
- Glucose is carried in the blood and enters most cells by facilitated diffusion. Insulin increases the rate of glucose transport into most cells.

Lipids

- Bile salts emulsify lipids.
- Pancreatic lipase breaks down lipids. The breakdown products aggregate with bile salts to form micelles.

- Micelles come into contact with the intestinal epithelium, and their contents diffuse into the cells, where they are packaged and released into the lacteals.
- Lipids are stored in adipose tissue and in the liver, which release the lipids into the blood when energy sources are needed elsewhere in the body.

Proteins

- Proteins are split into small polypeptides by enzymes secreted by the stomach and pancreas, and on the surface of intestinal cells.
- Peptidases on the surface of intestinal epithelial cells complete the digestive process.
- Amino acids are absorbed into intestinal epithelial cells.
- Amino acids are actively transported into cells under the influence of growth hormone and insulin.
- Amino acids are used to build new proteins or as a source of energy.

Water and Minerals

- Water can move either direction across the intestinal wall, depending on osmotic conditions. Approximately 99% of the water entering the intestine is absorbed. Most minerals are actively transported across the intestinal wall.

Content Review

1. What are the functions of the digestive system?
2. What are the major layers, or tunics, of the digestive tract?
3. List the functions of the lips, cheeks, and tongue.
4. What are the deciduous and permanent teeth? Name the different kinds of teeth.
5. Describe the parts of a tooth. What are dentin, enamel, and pulp?
6. What are the hard and soft palates? What is the function of the palate?
7. Name and give the location of the three pairs of salivary glands.
8. Where is the esophagus located?
9. Describe the parts of the stomach. How are the stomach muscles different from those in the esophagus?
10. What are gastric pits and gastric glands? Name the secretions they produce.
11. Name and describe the three parts of the small intestine.
12. What are circular folds, villi, and microvilli in the small intestine? What are their functions?
13. Describe the anatomy and location of the liver and pancreas. Describe their duct systems.
14. Describe the parts of the large intestine.

15. What are the peritoneum, mesenteries, and retroperitoneal organs?
16. What are the functions of saliva?
17. Describe the three phases of swallowing.
18. List the stomach secretions, and give their functions.
19. Describe the three phases of stomach secretion.
20. What are the two kinds of stomach movements? What do they accomplish?
21. List the secretions of the small intestine, and give their functions.
22. Describe the kinds of movements in the small intestine, and explain what they accomplish.
23. Describe the functions of the liver.
24. Name the exocrine secretions of the pancreas. What are their functions?
25. How is chyme converted to feces?
26. Describe the defecation reflex.
27. Describe carbohydrate digestion, absorption, and transport.
28. Describe the role of bile salts in lipid digestion and absorption.
29. Describe protein digestion and amino acid absorption. What enzymes are responsible for the digestion?

Develop Your Reasoning Skills

1. While anesthetized, patients sometimes vomit. Given that the anesthetic eliminates the swallowing reflex, explain why it is dangerous for an anesthetized patient to vomit.
2. Achlorhydria (ā-klōr-hī′drē-ă) is a condition in which the stomach stops producing hydrochloric acid and other secretions. What effect does achlorhydria have on the digestive process?
3. Victor Worrystudent developed a duodenal ulcer during final examination week. Describe the possible reasons. Explain what habits could have contributed to the ulcer, and recommend a reasonable remedy.
4. Gallstones sometimes obstruct the common bile duct. What would be the consequences of such a blockage?
5. Many people have a bowel movement shortly after a meal, especially breakfast. Why does this occur?

Answers to Predict Questions

1. p. 442 Four. Each portion of the mesentery has two layers, with a layer of connective tissue in-between. The mesentery is folded back on itself to form the greater omentum.
2. p. 445 It is important to close off the nasopharynx during swallowing so that food, and especially liquid, doesn't pass into the nasal cavity. If a person has a cleft of the soft palate, there is an opening between the oral and nasal cavities, and the nasopharynx is not closed off during swallowing. If a person has an explosive burst of laughter while trying to swallow a liquid, the liquid may be explosively expelled from the mouth and even from the nose. Speaking requires that the epiglottis be elevated so that air can pass out of the larynx. If the epiglottis is elevated while one is swallowing, the food, and especially liquid, may pass into the larynx, causing a person to choke.

3. p. 451 Secretin production in response to acidic chyme in the small intestine stimulates bicarbonate ion secretion from the pancreas, which neutralizes the acidic chyme. Thus secretin prevents the acid levels in the chyme from becoming too great. Because this mechanism keeps the pH of the intestinal contents within a normal range, this is an example of a negative-feedback system.
4. p. 451 Introducing fluid into the rectum by way of an enema causes distention of the rectum. Distention stimulates the defecation reflex.
5. p. 459 The effects of prolonged diarrhea result from a continued loss of fluid and ions. The major effect is on the cardiovascular system, and the effects are much like massive blood loss. Hypovolemia would continue to increase. Blood pressure would decline in a positive-feedback cycle, and, without intervention, could lead to heart failure.

Chapter Seventeen

Nutrition, Metabolism, and Body Temperature Regulation

aerobic respiration
(ār-ō'bik) Breakdown of glucose in the presence of oxygen to produce carbon dioxide, water, and 38 ATP molecules.

anaerobic respiration
(an-ār-ō'bik) Breakdown of glucose in the absence of oxygen to produce lactic acid and two ATP molecules.

carbohydrate
(kar-bō-hī'drāt) Organic molecule made up of one or more monosaccharides; sugars and starches.

citric acid cycle
(sit'rik) Series of chemical reactions wherein citric acid (six-carbon molecule) is converted into a four-carbon molecule, carbon dioxide is formed, and energy is released as ATP. The aerobic phase of catabolism. Also called the tricarboxylic acid (TCA) cycle, or Krebs' cycle.

electron-transport chain
(ē-lek'tron) Series of energy transfer molecules in the inner mitochondrial membrane; they receive energy and use it in the formation of ATP and water.

glycolysis
(glī-kol'i-sis) [Gr. *glykys*, sweet + *lysis*, a loosening] Anaerobic process during which one glucose molecule is converted to two pyruvic acid molecules; a net of two ATP molecules is produced during glycolysis.

lipid
(lip'ĭd) [Gr. *lipos*, fat] Substance composed principally of carbon, oxygen, and hydrogen; generally soluble in nonpolar solvents; fats and cholesterol.

metabolism
(mě-tab'ō-lizm) [Gr. *metabole*, change] Sum of the chemical changes that occur in tissues, consisting of the breakdown of food molecules to produce energy (catabolism) and the buildup of molecules (anabolism, which requires energy).

mineral
(min'er-ăl) Inorganic nutrient necessary for normal metabolic functions.

nutrition
(noo-trish'ŭn) Process by which nutrients are obtained and used in the body.

protein
(prō'tēn) [Gr. *proteios*, primary] Large molecule consisting of amino acids linked by peptide bonds.

vitamin
(vīt'ă-min) [L. *vita*, life; amine, from ammonia] One of a group of organic substances, present in minute amounts in natural foods, that is essential to normal metabolism.

Objectives

After reading this chapter, you should be able to:

1. Define nutrition, essential nutrient, and kilocalorie.

2. For carbohydrates, lipids, and proteins describe their dietary sources, their uses in the body, and the daily recommended amounts of each in the diet.

3. List the common vitamins and minerals and give a function for each.

4. Define metabolism, anabolism, and catabolism.

5. List three ways in which enzyme activity is controlled.

6. Describe glycolysis and name its products.

7. Describe the citric acid cycle and its products.

8. Describe the electron-transport chain and how ATP is produced in the process.

9. Explain how the breakdown of glucose yields two ATP molecules in anaerobic respiration and 38 ATP molecules in aerobic respiration.

10. Describe the basic steps involved in using lipids and amino acids as an energy source.

11. Differentiate between the absorptive and postabsorptive metabolic states.

12. Define metabolic rate.

13. Describe heat production and regulation in the body.

When selecting food to prepare, or when choosing from a menu, we are usually more concerned with the taste of the food than with the nutritional value of the meal. But the food we love to eat provides us with energy and the building blocks necessary to synthesize new molecules. Because we literally are what we eat, we should have a good understanding of nutrition. What happens if we don't obtain enough vitamins, or if we eat too much sugar and fats? Health claims about foods and food supplements bombard us every day. Which ones are ridiculous, and which ones have merit? A basic understanding of nutrition can help us to answer these and other questions so that we can develop a healthy diet.

Nutrition

Nutrition (noo-trish'ŭn) is the process by which food is taken into and used by the body, and it includes digestion, absorption, transport, and metabolism. Nutrition is also the study of food and drink requirements for normal body function.

Nutrients

Nutrients are the chemicals taken into the body that provide energy and building blocks for new molecules. Some substances in food are not nutrients but provide bulk (fiber) in the diet. Nutrients can be divided into six major classes: carbohydrates, lipids, proteins, vitamins, minerals, and water. Carbohydrates, proteins, and lipids are the major organic nutrients and are broken down by enzymes into their individual subunits during digestion. Subsequently, many of these subunits are broken down further to supply energy, whereas other subunits are used as building blocks for making new carbohydrates, proteins, and lipids. Vitamins, minerals, and water are taken into the body without being broken down. They are essential participants in the chemical reactions necessary to maintain life. Some nutrients are required in fairly substantial quantities, and others, called **trace elements**, are required in only minute amounts.

Essential nutrients are nutrients that must be ingested because the body cannot manufacture them or is unable to manufacture adequate amounts of them. The essential nutrients include certain amino acids, certain fatty acids, most vitamins, minerals, water, and some carbohydrates. The term essential does not mean that only the essential nutrients are required by the body. Other nutrients are necessary, but if they are not ingested, they can be synthesized from the essential nutrients. Most of this synthesis takes place in the liver, which has a remarkable ability to transform and manufacture molecules. A balanced diet consists of enough nutrients in the correct proportions to support normal body functions.

The U.S. Department of Agriculture provides directions for obtaining the proper amounts of carbohydrates, lipids, proteins, vitamins, minerals, and fiber in the form of a "food guide pyramid" (figure 17.1). The five major food groups shown in the pyramid are (1) bread, cereal, rice, and pasta; (2) vegetables; (3) fruits; (4) milk, yogurt, and cheese; and

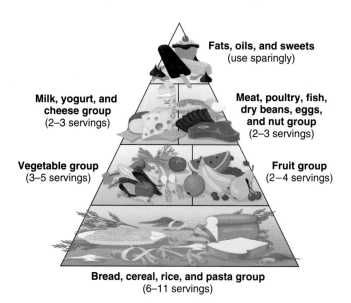

Figure 17.1 Food Pyramid

The pyramid suggests three approaches to a healthy diet: eat different amounts of foods from each basic food group, use fats and sugars sparingly, and choose variety by eating different foods from each major food group each day.

(5) meat, poultry, fish, dry beans, eggs, and nuts. The shape of the pyramid suggests that bread, cereal, rice, pasta, vegetables, and fruits should be the main part of the diet. Fats, oils, and sweets can be used in moderation to improve the flavor of foods. A balanced diet includes a variety of foods from each of the major food groups. Variety is necessary because no one food contains all the nutrients necessary for good health.

Did You Know?

Two studies completed in 2000 compared the eating habits of 67,272 women and 51,529 men to the government's Healthy Eating index, a measure of how well a diet conforms to dietary guidelines and the food pyramid. Those who ate the best, according to the index, were compared to those who ate the worst. This comparison for women showed a 3% decrease in all chronic diseases, a 14% decrease in heart disease, and no reduction in cancer. For men there was an 11% decrease in all chronic diseases, a 28% decrease in heart disease, and no reduction in cancer.

Kilocalories

The energy stored within the chemical bonds of certain nutrients can be used by the body. A **calorie** (kal'ō-rē) (**cal**) is the amount of energy (heat) necessary to raise the temperature of 1 gram (g) of water 1°C. A **kilocalorie** (kil'ō-kal-ō-rē) (**kcal**) is 1000 cal and is used to express the larger amounts of energy supplied by foods and released through metabolism. For example, one slice of white bread contains about 75 kcal, one cup of whole milk contains 150 kcal, a banana contains 100 kcal, a hot dog contains 170 kcal (not counting the bun and dressings), a McDonald's Big Mac has 563 kcal, and a soft drink

Table 17.1 Food Composition

Food	Quantity	Food Energy (kcal)	Carbohydrate (g)	Fat (g)	Protein (g)
Dairy Products					
Whole milk (3.3% fat)	1 cup	150	11	8	8
Low fat milk (2% fat)	1 cup	120	12	5	8
Butter	1 T	100	—	12	—
Grain					
Bread, white enriched	1 slice	75	24	1	2
Bread, whole wheat	1 slice	65	14	1	3
Fruit					
Apple	1	80	20	1	—
Banana	1	100	25	—	1
Orange	1	65	16	—	1
Vegetables					
Corn, canned	1 cup	140	33	1	4
Peas, canned	1 cup	150	29	1	8
Lettuce	1 cup	5	2	—	—
Celery	1 cup	20	5	—	1
Potato, baked	1 large	145	33	—	4
Meat, Fish, and Poultry					
Lean ground beef (10% fat)	3 oz	185	—	10	23
Shrimp, french fried	3 oz	190	9	9	17
Tuna, canned	3 oz	170	—	7	24
Chicken breast, fried	3 oz	160	1	5	26
Bacon	2 slices	85	—	8	4
Hot dog	1	170	1	15	7
Fast Foods					
McDonald's Egg McMuffin	1	327	31	15	19
McDonald's Big Mac	1	563	41	33	26
Taco Bell's beef burrito	1	466	37	21	30
Arby's roast beef	1	350	32	15	22
Pizza Hut Super Supreme	1 slice	260	23	13	15
Long John Silver's fish	2 pieces	366	21	22	22
McDonald's fish fillet	1	432	37	25	14
Dairy Queen malt, large	1	840	125	28	22
Desserts					
Cupcake with icing	1	130	21	5	2
Chocolate chip cookie	1	50	7	2	1
Apple pie	1 piece	135	49	14	3
Soft ice cream	1 cup	377	38	23	7
Beverage					
Cola soft drink	12 oz	145	37		
Beer	12 oz	144	13	—	—
Wine	3 ½ oz	73	2	—	—
Hard liquor (86 proof)	1 ½ oz	105	—	—	—
Miscellaneous					
Egg	1	80	1	6	6
Mayonnaise	1 T	100	—	11	—
Sugar	1 T	45	12	—	—

adds another 145 kcal. For each gram of carbohydrate or protein metabolized by the body, about 4 kcal of energy is released. Fats contain more energy per unit of weight than carbohydrates and proteins, and yield about 9 kcal/g. Table 17.1 lists the kilocalories supplied by some typical foods. A typical diet in the United States consists of 50% to 60% carbohydrates, 35% to 45% fats, and 10% to 15% protein. Table 17.1 also lists the carbohydrate, fat, and protein composition of some foods.

Carbohydrates

Sources in the Diet

Carbohydrates (kar-bō-hī′drātz) include monosaccharides, disaccharides, and polysaccharides (see chapter 2). Although most of the carbohydrates we ingest are derived from plants, lactose and some glycogen are derived from animals. The most common monosaccharides in the diet are glucose and fructose. Plants capture energy from sunlight and use the energy to produce glucose, which can be found in vegetables, fruits, molasses, honey, and syrup. Fructose is most often derived from fruits and berries.

The disaccharide sucrose (table sugar) is what most people think of when they use the term sugar. Sucrose consists of one glucose and one fructose molecule joined together, and its principal sources are sugarcane and sugar beets. Maltose (malt sugar), derived from germinating cereals, is a combination of two glucose molecules, and lactose (milk sugar) consists of one glucose molecule and one galactose molecule.

Complex carbohydrates are large polysaccharides, which are composed of long chains of glucose (see figure 2.11). Examples are starch, glycogen, and cellulose, which differ from one another in the arrangement of the glucose molecules and the structure of the chemical bonds holding them together.

Starch is an energy-storage molecule in plants and is found primarily in vegetables, fruits, and grains. Glycogen is primarily an energy-storage molecule in animals and is located in muscle and in the liver. By the time meats are processed and cooked, they contain little, if any, glycogen. Cellulose forms the cell walls surrounding plant cells.

Uses in the Body

During digestion, polysaccharides and disaccharides are split into monosaccharides, which are absorbed into the blood (see chapter 16). Humans have enzymes that can break the bonds between the glucose molecules of starch and glycogen but do not have enzymes necessary to digest cellulose. It is important to thoroughly cook or chew plant matter. Cooking and chew-ing break down the plant cell walls and expose the starches that are contained inside the cells to digestive enzymes. The undigested cellulose provides fiber, or "roughage," which increases the bulk of feces and promotes defecation.

Fructose and other monosaccharides absorbed into the blood are converted into glucose by the liver. **Glucose**, whether absorbed directly from the digestive tract or produced by the liver, is a primary energy source for most cells, which use the energy derived from the breakdown of glucose to produce ATP. Because the brain relies almost entirely on glucose for its energy, blood glucose levels are carefully regulated.

If an excess amount of glucose is present in the diet, it is used to make glycogen, which is stored in muscle and in the liver. Glycogen can be rapidly converted back to glucose when energy is needed. Because cells can store only a limited amount of glycogen, additional glucose that is ingested is converted into fat for long-term storage in adipose tissue.

In addition to being used as an energy source, sugars also form part of deoxyribonucleic acid (DNA), ribonucleic acid (RNA), and ATP molecules. Sugars also combine with proteins to form glycoproteins, some of which function as receptor molecules on the outer surface of the plasma membrane.

Recommended Consumption

It is recommended that 60% of the daily kilocaloric intake be carbohydrates. Although a minimum level of carbohydrates is not known, it is assumed that amounts of 100 g or less per day result in overuse of the body's proteins and fats for energy sources. Because muscles are primarily protein, the use of proteins for energy can result in the breakdown of muscle tissue. The extensive use of fats as an energy source can result in acidosis (see chapter 18).

Complex carbohydrates are recommended in the diet because starchy foods often contain other valuable nutrients, such as vitamins and minerals, and because the slower rate of digestion and absorption of complex carbohydrates does not result in large increases and decreases in blood glucose levels as the consumption of large amounts of simple sugars does. Although foods containing large amounts of simple sugars, such as soft drinks and candy, are rich in carbohydrates, they have limited nutrient value. For example, a typical soft drink is mostly sucrose, containing 9 teaspoons of sugar per 12-oz container. In excess, the consumption of these kinds of foods can result in obesity and tooth decay.

Lipids

Sources in the Diet

Lipids (lip′idz) include triacylglycerol, steroids, phospholipids, and fat-soluble vitamins. **Triacylglycerols** (trī-as′il-glis′er-olz), also called **triglycerides** (trī-glis′er-īdz), are the most common type of lipid in the diet, accounting for about 95% of the total lipid intake. Triacylglycerol molecules consist of three fatty acids bound to one glycerol molecule (see figure 2.12). Triacylglycerol is often referred to as fat. Fats are **saturated** if their fatty acids have only single covalent bonds carbons and unsaturated if they have one (monounsaturated) or more (polyunsaturated) double covalent bonds between carbons (see figure 2.13). Saturated fats are solid at room temperature, whereas polyunsaturated fats are liquid at room temperature. Saturated fats are found in meat, dairy products, eggs, nuts, coconut oil, and palm oil (see table 17.1). Monounsaturated fats include olive and peanut oils; and polyunsaturated fats are found in fish, safflower, sunflower, and corn oils.

> ### Did You Know?
>
> Solid fats, such as shortening and margarine, work better than liquid oils in preparing some foods such as pastries. Polyunsaturated vegetable oils can be changed from a liquid to a solid by making them more saturated, that is, by decreasing the number of double covalent bonds in their polyunsaturated fatty acids. To saturate an unsaturated oil, hydrogen gas is bubbled through it. As hydrogen binds to the fatty acids, double covalent bonds are converted to single covalent bonds, producing a change in molecular shape that solidifies the oil. The more saturated the product, the harder it becomes at room temperature.

The remaining 5% of ingested lipids include steroids and phospholipids. Cholesterol (kō-les′ter-ol) is a steroid (see chapter 2) found in high concentrations in the brain, the liver, and egg yolks; but it is also present in whole milk, cheese, butter, and meats. Cholesterol is not found in plants. Phospholipids, such as lecithin (les′i-thin), are major components of cell membranes, and they are found in a variety of foods. A good source of lecithin is egg yolks.

Uses in the Body

Triacylglycerol is an important source of energy that can be used to produce ATP. A gram of triacylglycerol delivers over twice as many calories as does a gram of carbohydrate or protein. Some cells, such as skeletal muscle cells, derive most of their energy from triacylglycerol.

Ingested triacylglycerol molecules not immediately used are stored in adipose tissue or in the liver. When energy is required, the stored triacylglycerol is broken down, and the fatty acids are released into the blood. The fatty acids can be taken up and used by various tissues. In addition to storing energy, adipose tissue surrounds, pads, and protects organs. Adipose tissue located under the skin is an insulator, which prevents heat loss.

Cholesterol is an important molecule with many functions in the body. It is obtained in food or it can be manufactured by the liver and most other tissues. Cholesterol is a component of the cell membrane, and it can be modified to form other useful molecules such as bile salts and steroid hormones. Bile salts emulsify fats, which is important for fat digestion and absorption (see chapter 16). Steroid hormones include the sex hormones estrogen, progesterone, and testosterone, which regulate the reproductive system. Prostaglandins, which are derived from fatty acids, are involved in inflammation, tissue repair, smooth muscle contraction, and other functions.

Phospholipids are part of the cell membrane and are used to construct myelin sheaths around the axons of nerve cells. Lecithin is found in bile and helps emulsify fats.

Recommended Consumption

The American Heart Association recommends that fats account for no more than 30% of the total kilocaloric intake, with 8% to 10% coming from saturated fats, up to 10% from polyunsaturated fats, and up to 15% from monounsaturated fats. Cholesterol should be limited to 300 mg (the amount in one egg yolk) or less per day. These guidelines reflect the belief that excess amounts of fats, especially saturated fats and cholesterol, contribute to cardiovascular disease. The typical American diet derives 35% to 45% of its kilocalories from fats, indicating that most Americans need to reduce fat consumption. See table 17.1 for a sampling of fat composition in foods.

If insufficient amounts of fats are consumed, the body can synthesize fats from carbohydrates and proteins. Linoleic (lin-ō-lē′ik) acid, alpha linolenic (lin-ō-len′ik) acid, and eicosapentaenoic (ī-kō′să-pen-tă-nō′ik) acid (EPA), however, are fatty acids that cannot be manufactured by the body and therefore are essential fatty acids.

> ### Did You Know?
>
> The essential fatty acids can be used to synthesize prostaglandins that affect blood clotting. Linoleic acid can be converted to arachidonic (ă-rak-i-don′ik) acid, which is used to produce prostaglandins that *increase* blood clotting. Alpha-linolenic acid can be converted to EPA, which is used to produce prostaglandins that *decrease* blood clotting. Normally, most prostaglandins are synthesized from linoleic acid because it is more plentiful in the body. Individuals, however, who consume foods rich in EPA, such as herring, salmon, tuna, and sardines, increase the synthesis of prostaglandins from EPA. Individuals who eat these fish two or more times per week have a lower risk of heart attack than those who don't, probably because of reduced blood clotting. Although EPA can be obtained using fish oil supplements, this is not currently recommended because fish oil supplements contain high amounts of cholesterol, vitamins A and D, and uncommon fatty acids, all of which can cause health problems when taken in large amounts.

Proteins

Sources in the Diet

Proteins (prō′tēnz) are chains of amino acids (see figure 2.14). They are found in most of the plant and animal products we eat (see table 17.1). Our bodies can manufacture 12 of the 20 amino acids, but the other 8, called essential amino acids, must be obtained in the food we eat. If adequate amounts of the essential amino acids are ingested, they can be used to manufacture the 12 nonessential amino acids. A complete protein food contains all eight essential amino acids in the needed proportions, whereas an incomplete protein food does not. Animal proteins tend to be complete proteins, whereas plant proteins tend to be incomplete. Examples of complete proteins are red meat, fish, poultry, milk, cheese, and eggs. Examples of incomplete proteins are leafy green vegetables, grains, and legumes (peas and beans). If two incomplete proteins such as rice and beans are ingested, each can provide amino acids lacking in the other. Thus a vegetarian diet, if balanced correctly, can provide all of the essential amino acids.

Uses in the Body

Proteins perform numerous functions in the human body, as the following examples illustrate. Collagen provides structural strength in connective tissue, as does keratin in the skin. The combination of actin and myosin makes muscle contraction possible. Enzymes are responsible for regulating the rate of chemical reactions in the body, and protein hormones regulate many physiological processes (see chapter 10). Proteins in the blood act as clotting factors, transport molecules, and buffers (which prevent changes in pH). Proteins also function as ion channels, carrier molecules, and receptor molecules in the cell membrane. Antibodies, lymphokines, and complement are all proteins that function in the immune system.

Proteins can also be used as a source of energy, yielding approximately the same amount of energy as that derived from carbohydrates. If excess proteins are ingested, the energy from the proteins can be used for the production of glycogen and fat molecules, which can be stored. When protein intake is adequate in a healthy adult, the synthesis and breakdown of proteins occur at the same rate.

Recommended Consumption

The recommended daily consumption of protein for an adult is 0.8 g/kilogram (kg) of body weight per day, or about 10% of the total kilocalories. See table 17.1 for a sampling of protein composition in foods.

Vitamins

Vitamins (vīt′ă-minz, life-giving chemicals) are organic molecules that exist in minute quantities in food and are essential to normal metabolism (table 17.2). **Essential vitamins** cannot be produced by the body and must be obtained through the diet. Because no single food item or nutrient class provides all the essential vitamins, it is necessary to maintain a balanced diet by eating a variety of foods. The absence of an essential vitamin in the diet can result in a specific deficiency disease. A few vitamins, such as vitamin K, are produced by intestinal bacteria, and a few can be formed by the body from substances called provitamins. A **provitamin** is a part of a vitamin that can be assembled or modified by the body into a functional vitamin. Beta carotene is an example of a provitamin that can be modified by the body to form vitamin A. The other provitamins are **7-dehydrocholesterol** (dē-hī′drō-kō-les′ter-ol), which can be converted to vitamin D, and **tryptophan** (trip′tō-fan), which can be converted to niacin.

Vitamins are not broken down by catabolism but are used by the body in their original or slightly modified forms. After the chemical structure of a vitamin is destroyed, its function is usually lost. The chemical structure of many vitamins is destroyed by heat, such as when food is overcooked.

Most vitamins function as **coenzymes**, which combine with enzymes to make the enzymes functional (see chapter 2). Vitamins B_2 and B_3, biotin (bī′ō-tin), and pantothenic (pan-tō-then′ik) acid are critical to the production of energy. Folate (fō′lāt) and vitamin B_{12} are involved in nucleic acid synthesis. Vitamins A, B_1, B_6, B_{12}, C, and D are necessary for growth. Vitamin K is necessary for the synthesis of proteins involved in blood clotting (see table 17.2).

1	P R E D I C T

Predict what would happen if vitamins were broken down during the process of digestion rather than being absorbed intact into the circulation.

✔ *Answer on page 486*

Vitamins are either fat-soluble or water-soluble. **Fat-soluble vitamins**, such as vitamins A, D, E, and K, are absorbed from the intestine along with lipids. Some of them can be stored in the body for a long time. Because they can be stored, it is possible to accumulate these vitamins in the body to the point of toxicity. **Water-soluble vitamins**, such as the B vitamins and vitamin C, are absorbed with water from the intestinal tract and remain in the body only a short time before being excreted.

Vitamins were first identified at the beginning of the twentieth century. They were found to be associated with certain foods that were known to protect people from diseases like rickets and beriberi. In 1941, the first Food and Nutrition Board established the **recommended dietary allowances (RDAs)**, which are the nutrient intakes that are sufficient to meet the needs of nearly all people in certain age and gender groups. RDAs have been established for different-aged males and females, starting with infants and continuing on to adults. RDAs are also set for pregnant and lactating women. The RDAs have been reevaluated every 4 to 5 years and updated, when necessary, on the basis of new information.

The RDAs establish a minimum intake of vitamins and minerals that should protect almost everyone (97%) in a given group from diseases caused by vitamin or mineral deficiencies. Although personal requirements can vary, the RDAs are a good benchmark. The further dietary intake is below the RDAs, the more likely a nutritional deficiency can occur. On the other hand, the consumption of too large a quantity of some nutrients can have harmful effects. For example, the long-term ingestion of 3 to 10 times the RDA for vitamin A can cause bone and muscle pain, skin disorders, hair loss, and increased liver size. The long-term consumption of 5 to 10 times the RDA of vitamin D can result in the deposition of calcium in the kidneys, heart, and blood vessels, and the regular consumption of more than 2 g of vitamin C daily can cause stomach inflammation and diarrhea.

Table 17.2 The Principal Vitamins

Vitamin	Fat (F)- or Water (W)- Soluble	Source	Function	Symptoms of Deficiency	Reference Daily Intake (RDI)s[a]
A (retinol)	F	From provitamin carotene found in yellow and green vegetables: preformed in liver, egg yolk, butter, and milk	Necessary for rhodopsin synthesis, normal health of epithelial cells, and bone and tooth growth	Rhodopsin deficiency, night blindness, retarded growth, skin disorders and increase in infection risk	1000 RE[b]
B_1 (thiamine)	W	Yeast grains, and milk	Involved in carbohydrate and amino acid metabolism, necessary for growth	Beriberi—muscle weakness (including cardiac muscle), neuritis, and paralysis	1.5 mg
B_2 (riboflavin)	W	Green vegetables, liver, wheat germ, milk, and eggs	Component of flavin adenine dinucleotide; involved in citric acid cycle	Eye disorders and skin cracking, especially at corners of the mouth	1.7 mg
B_3 (niacin)	W	Fish, liver, red meat, yeast, grains, peas, beans, and nuts	Component of nicotinamide adenine dinucleotide; involved in glycolysis and citric acid cycle	Pellagra—diarrhea, dermatitis, and nervous system disorder	20 mg
Pantothenic acid	W	Liver, yeast, green vegetables, grains, and intestinal bacteria	Constituent of coenzyme-A, glucose production from lipids and amino acids, and steroid hormone synthesis	Neuromuscular dysfunction and fatigue	10 mg
Biotin	W	Liver, yeast, eggs, and intestinal bacteria	Fatty acid and nucleic acid synthesis; movement of pyruvic acid into citric acid cycle	Mental and muscle dysfunction, fatigue, and nausea	0.3 mg
B_6 (pyridoxine)	W	Fish, liver, yeast, tomatoes, and intestinal bacteria	Involved in amino acid metabolism	Dermatitis, retarded growth, and nausea	2.0 mg
Folate	W	Liver, green leafy vegetables, and intestinal bacteria	Nucleic acid synthesis, hematopoiesis; prevents birth defects	Macrocytic anemia (enlarged red blood cells) and spina bifida	0.4 mg
B_{12} (cobalamins)	W	Liver, red meat, milk, and eggs	Necessary for red blood cell production, some nucleic acid and amino acid metabolism	Pernicious anemia and nervous system disorders	6 μg
C (ascorbic acid)	W	Citrus fruit, tomatoes, and green vegetables	Collagen synthesis; general protein metabolism	Scurvy—defective bone formation and poor wound healing	60 mg
D (cholecalciferol, ergosterol)	F	Fish liver oil, enriched milk, and eggs; provitamin D converted by sunlight to cholecalciferol in the skin	Promotes calcium and phosphorus use; normal growth and bone and teeth formation	Rickets—poorly developed, weak bones, osteomalacia; bone reabsorption	400 IU[c]

continued next page

[a]RDIs for people over 4 years of age; IU = international units.
[b]Retinol equivalents (RE). 1 retinol equivalent = 1 μg retinol or 6 μg β-carotene.
[c]As cholecalciferol. 1 μg cholecalciferol = 40 IU (international units) vitamin D.

Table 17.2   The Principal Vitamins *(continued)*

Vitamin	Fat (F)- or Water (W)- Soluble	Source	Function	Symptoms of Deficiency	Reference Daily Intake (RDI)s[a]
E (tocopherol, tocotrienols)	F	Wheat germ, cotton seed, palm, and rice oils; grain, liver, and lettuce	Prevents the oxidation of cell membranes and DNA	Hemolysis of red blood cells	30 IU
K (phylloquinone)	F	Alfalfa, liver, spinach, vegetable oils, cabbage, and intestinal bacteria	Required for synthesis of a number of clotting factors	Excessive bleeding due to retarded blood clotting	80 μg

[a]RDIs for people over 4 years of age; IU = international units.

Did You Know?

Damage from free radicals may contribute to aging and certain diseases, such as atherosclerosis and cancer. **Free radicals** are molecules, produced as part of normal metabolism, which are missing an electron. Free radicals can replace the missing electron by taking an electron from cell molecules, such as fats, proteins, or DNA, resulting in damage to the cell. The loss of an electron from a molecule is called oxidation. **Antioxidants** are substances that prevent oxidation of cell components by donating an electron to free radicals. Examples of antioxidants include beta carotene (provitamin A), vitamin C, and vitamin E.

Many studies have been done to determine whether or not taking large doses of antioxidants are beneficial. Although future research may suggest otherwise, the consensus among scientists establishing the RDAs is the best evidence presently available does not support the claims that taking large doses of antioxidants prevents chronic disease or otherwise improves health. On the other hand, the amount of antioxidants normally found in a balanced diet that includes fruits and vegetables rich in antioxidants, combined with the complex mix of other chemicals found in food, can be beneficial.

Minerals

Minerals (min′er-ălz) are inorganic nutrients that are essential for normal metabolic functions. Minerals are taken into the body by themselves or in combination with organic molecules. They constitute about 4% to 5% of the total body weight and are involved in a number of important functions, such as establishing resting membrane potentials and generating action potentials; adding mechanical strength to bones and teeth; combining with organic molecules; or acting as coenzymes, buffers, or regulators of osmotic pressure. A balanced diet can provide all the necessary minerals, with a few possible exceptions. For example, women who suffer from excessive menstrual bleeding may need an iron supplement. Table 17.3 lists some minerals and their functions.

Daily Values

Daily Values are dietary reference values now appearing on food labels to help consumers plan a healthy diet. Daily Values are based on two other sets of reference values: Reference Daily Intakes and Daily Reference Values. The **Reference Daily Intakes (RDIs)** are based on the 1968 RDAs for certain vitamins and minerals. RDIs have been set for four categories of people: infants, toddlers, people over 4 years of age, and pregnant or lactating women. Generally, the RDIs are set to the highest 1968 RDA value of an age category. For example, the highest RDA for iron in males over 4 years of age is 10 mg/day and for females over 4 years of age is 18 mg/day. Thus, the RDI for iron is set at 18 mg/day.

The **Daily Reference Values (DRVs)** are set for total fat, saturated fat, cholesterol, total carbohydrate, dietary fiber, sodium, potassium, and protein. To make food labels less confusing, only Daily Values appear on the labels. In addition, not all possible Daily Values are required to be listed.

The Daily Values appearing on food labels are based on a 2000 kcal reference diet, which approximates the weight maintenance requirements of postmenopausal women, women who exercise moderately, teenage girls, and sedentary men (figure 17.2). On large food labels, additional

Nutrition Facts
Serving Size 1 oz. (28g/About 32 chips)
Servings Per Container 2.5

Amount Per Serving	
Calories 160	Calories from Fat 90

	% Daily Value*
Total Fat 10g	16%
Saturated Fat 1.5g	7%
Cholesterol 0mg	0%
Sodium 170mg	7%
Total Carbohydrate 15g	5%
Dietary Fiber 1g	4%
Sugars less than 1g	
Protein 2g	

Vitamin A 0%	•	Vitamin C 0%
Calcium 2%	•	Iron 0%

* Percent Daily Values are based on a 2,000 calorie diet. Your daily values may be higher or lower depending on your calorie needs:

		Calories:	2,000	2,500
Total Fat	Less than		65g	80g
Sat Fat	Less than		20g	25g
Cholesterol	Less than		300mg	300mg
Sodium	Less than		2,400mg	2,400mg
Total Carbohydrate			300g	375g
Dietary Fiber			25g	30g

Calories per gram:
Fat 9 • Carbohydrate 4 • Protein 4

Figure 17.2 Food Label
Courtesy of FDA.

Table 17.3 Important Minerals

Mineral	Function	Symptoms of Deficiency	Reference Daily Intake (RDIs)[a]
Calcium	Bone and teeth formation, blood clotting, muscle activity, and nerve function	Spontaneous action potential generation in neurons and tetany	1 g
Chlorine	Blood acid–base balance; hydrochloric acid production in stomach	Acid–base imbalance	3.4 g
Chromium	Associated with enzymes in glucose metabolism	Unknown	120 μg
Cobalt	Component of vitamin B_{12}; red blood cell production	Anemia	Unknown
Copper	Hemoglobin and melanin production, electron-transport system	Anemia and loss of energy	2.0 mg
Fluorine	Provides extra strength in teeth; prevents dental caries	No real pathology	2.5 mg
Iodine	Thyroid hormone production, maintenance of normal metabolic rate	Goiter and decrease in normal metabolism	150 μg
Iron	Component of hemoglobin; ATP production in electron-transport system	Anemia, decreased oxygen transport, and energy loss	18 mg
Magnesium	Coenzyme constituent; bone formation; muscle and nerve function	Increased nervous system irritability, vasodilation, and arrhythmias	400 mg
Manganese	Hemoglobin synthesis; growth; activation of several enzymes	Tremors and convulsions	3.5 mg
Molybdenum	Enzyme component	Unknown	75 μg
Phosphorus	Bone and teeth formation; important in energy transfer (ATP); component of nucleic acids	Loss of energy and cellular function	1 g
Potassium	Muscle and nerve function	Muscle weakness, abnormal electrocardiogram, and alkaline urine	2 g
Selenium	Component of many enzymes	Unknown	55 μg
Sodium	Osmotic pressure regulation; nerve and muscle function	Nausea, vomiting, exhaustion, and dizziness	500 mg[b]
Sulfur	Component of hormones; several vitamins, and proteins	Unknown	Unknown
Zinc	Component of several enzymes; carbon dioxide transport and metabolism; necessary for protein metabolism	Deficient carbon dioxide transport and deficient protein metabolism	15 mg

[a]RDIs for people over 4 years of age, except for sodium.
[b]The estimated minimum for people over 10 years of age. The maximum Daily Value for sodium is 2400 mg.

information is listed based on a daily intake of 2500 kcal, which is adequate for young men.

The Daily Values for energy-producing nutrients are determined as a percentage of daily kilocaloric intake: 60% for carbohydrates, 30% for total fats, 10% for saturated fats, and 10% for proteins. The Daily Value for fiber is 11.5 g for each 1000 kcal of intake. The Daily Values for a nutrient in a 2000 kcal/day diet can be calculated on the basis of the recommended daily percentage of the nutrient and the kilocalories in a gram of the nutrient. For example, carbohydrates should be 60% of a 2000 kcal/day diet, or 1200 kcal/day (0.60 × 2000). Because there are 4 kilocalories in a gram of carbohydrate, the Daily Value for carbohydrate is 300 g/day (1200/4).

The Daily Values for some nutrients is the uppermost limit considered desirable because of the link between these nutrients and certain diseases. Thus, the Daily Values for total fats is less than 65 g, saturated fats is less than 20 g, and cholesterol is less than 300 mg because of their association with increased risk of heart disease. The Daily Value for sodium is less than 2400 mg because of its association with high blood pressure in some people.

For a particular food, the Daily Values are used to calculate the **Percent Daily Value (% Daily Value)** for some of the nutrients in one serving of the food (see figure 17.2). For example, if a serving of food has 10 g of fat and the Daily Value for total fat is 65 g, then the % Daily Value is 16% (10/65 =

0.16 or 16%). The Food and Drug Administration (FDA) requires % Daily Values to be on food labels so that the public has useful and accurate dietary information.

2   P R E D I C T

One serving of a food has 30 g of carbohydrate. What % Daily Value for carbohydrate is on the food label for this food?

✔ *Answer on page 486*

The % Daily Values for nutrients related to energy consumption are based on a 2000 kcal/day diet. For people who maintain their weight on a 2000 kcal/day diet, the total of the % Daily Values for each of these nutrients should add up to no more than 100%. For individuals consuming more or fewer kilocalories per day than 2000 kcal, however, the total of the % Daily Values can be more than 100%. For example, for a person consuming 2200 kcal/day, the total of the % Daily Values for each of these nutrients should add up to no more than 110% because 2200/2000 = 1.10 or 110%.

3   P R E D I C T

Suppose a person consumes 1800 kcal/day. What total % Daily Values for energy-producing nutrients is recommended?

✔ *Answer on page 486*

When using the % Daily Values of a food to determine how the amounts of certain nutrients in the food fit into the overall diet, the number of servings in a container or package needs to be considered. For example, suppose a small (2.25 oz) bag of corn chips has a % Daily Value of 16% for total fat. One might suppose that eating the bag of chips accounts for 16% of total fat for the day. The bag, however, contains 2.5 servings. Therefore, if all the chips in the bag are consumed, they account for 40% (16% × 2.5) of the maximum recommended total fat.

Metabolism

Metabolism (mě-tab′ō-lizm, change) is the total of all the chemical changes that occur in the body. It consists of **anabolism** (ă-nab′ō-lizm), the energy-requiring process by which small molecules are joined to form larger ones, and **catabolism** (kă-tab′ō-lizm), the energy-releasing process by which large molecules are broken down into smaller ones. Anabolism occurs in all cells of the body as they divide to form new cells, maintain their own intracellular structure, and produce molecules such as hormones, neurotransmitters, or extracellular matrix molecules for export. Catabolism begins during the process of digestion and is concluded within individual cells. The energy derived from catabolism is used to drive anabolic reactions.

Metabolism can be divided into the chemical changes that occur during digestion and the chemical processes that occur after the products of digestion are taken up by cells. The chemical processes that occur within cells are often referred to as **cellular metabolism**. The digestive products of carbohydrates, proteins, and lipids can be further broken down inside cells. The energy released during this breakdown can be used to combine ADP and an inorganic phosphate group (P_i) to form **ATP** (figure 17.3).

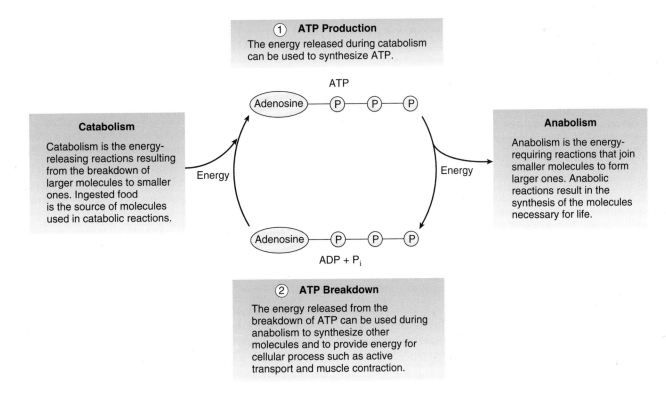

Figure 17.3   The Interconversion of ADP and ATP

Energy from metabolism is required to form ATP from ADP and phosphate (P). Energy and a phosphate are given off when ATP is converted back to ADP.

Figure 17.4 Biochemical Pathway

Each step in the pathway is regulated by a specific enzyme. Substance D can inhibit enzyme 1, thus regulating its own production. Some of the energy released by reactions in the pathway can be used to synthesize ATP.

ATP is often called the energy currency of the cell. When ATP is broken down to ADP, the released energy can be used to drive chemical reactions such as those involved in active transport, muscle contraction, and synthesis of molecules. Because the body has high energy demands, it uses ATP rapidly.

Regulation of Metabolism

The products of digestion, such as glucose, fatty acids, and amino acids, are molecules containing energy within their chemical bonds. The release of all this energy in one chemical reaction would damage cells. Instead, a series of chemical reactions, called a **biochemical pathway**, controls the energy release. At some of the steps, small amounts of energy are released, part of which is used to synthesize ATP (figure 17.4). About 40% of the energy in foods is incorporated into ATP; the rest is lost as heat.

There are many different biochemical pathways inside cells. Which pathways function and how much each pathway is used is determined by enzymes, because each step in the pathway requires a specific enzyme (see chapter 2). In turn, enzymes are regulated in several ways:

1. *Enzyme synthesis.* Enzymes are proteins and their synthesis depends upon DNA (see chapter 3). Thus, the type of enzymes present in cells is under genetic control.
2. *Receptor-mediated enzyme activity.* The combination of a chemical signal, such as a neurotransmitter or hormone, with a membrane-bound or intracellular receptor can activate or inhibit enzyme activity (see chapter 10).
3. *Product control of enzyme activity.* The end product of a biochemical pathway can inhibit the enzyme responsible for the first reaction in the pathway. This negative-feedback mechanism prevents accumulation of the intermediate products and the end product of the pathway (see figure 17.4).

Carbohydrate Metabolism

Monosaccharides are the breakdown products of carbohydrate digestion. Of these, glucose is the most important as far as cellular metabolism is concerned. Glucose is transported in the circulation to all tissues of the body, where it is used to produce energy. Any excess glucose in the blood following a meal can be used to form **glycogen** (glī'kō-jen), or it can be partially broken down, and the components used to form fat. Glycogen is a short-term energy storage molecule, which can only be stored by the body in limited amounts, whereas fat is a long-term energy storage molecule, which can be stored in the body in large amounts. Most of the body's glycogen is in skeletal muscle and in the liver.

Glycolysis

Glycolysis (glī-kol'i-sis) is a series of chemical reactions that occurs in the cytoplasm of most cells and results in the breakdown of glucose to two **pyruvic** (pī-roo'vik) **acid molecules** (figure 17.5). When glucose is converted to pyruvic acid, two ATP molecules are used and four ATP molecules are produced, for a net gain of two ATP molecules.

Glucose consists of many hydrogen atoms covalently bonded to the carbon atoms of the molecule. During the

Figure 17.5   Glycolysis and Anaerobic Respiration

Through the process of glycolysis, one glucose molecule is converted to two molecules of pyruvic acid, and two molecules of ATP and NADH are formed (the many reactions of this pathway are not shown). In anaerobic respiration, the pyruvic acid produced in glycolysis is converted to lactic acid. This conversion requires energy, which can be obtained from the NADH generated in glycolysis.

breakdown of glucose, a hydrogen ion (H^+) and two electrons (e^-) are released and can attach to a **carrier molecule**, which functions to move the hydrogen ion and electrons to other parts of the cell. A very common carrier molecule in cells is **nicotinamide adenine dinucleotide** (nik-ō-tin′a-mīd ad′ĕ-nēn dī-noo′klē-ō-tīd) (**NADH**).

$$NAD^+ + 2\,e^- + H^+ \rightarrow NADH$$

The hydrogen ion and high-energy electrons in the NADH molecules can be used in other chemical reactions or in the production of ATP molecules in the electron-transport chain (described on p. 476).

The pyruvic acid and NADH produced in glycolysis can be used in two different biochemical pathways, depending on the availability of oxygen. If the cell has adequate amounts of oxygen, the pyruvic acid and NADH produced in glycolysis are used in aerobic respiration to produce many more ATP. If the amounts of oxygen are inadequate, then in addition to aerobic respiration, anaerobic respiration can take place. Anaerobic respiration does not require oxygen and functions to quickly produce a few ATP molecules when oxygen availability limits aerobic respiration.

Anaerobic Respiration

Anaerobic (an-ār-ō′bik) **respiration** is the breakdown of glucose in the absence of oxygen to produce two molecules of **lactic** (lak′tik) **acid** and two molecules of ATP (see figure 17.5). The ATP thus produced is a source of energy during activities such as intense exercise when insufficient oxygen is delivered to tissues. Anaerobic respiration can be divided into two phases:

1. *Glycolysis.* The first phase of anaerobic respiration is glycolysis, in which glucose undergoes several reactions to produce two pyruvic acid molecules, two ATP, and two NADH.

2. *Lactic acid formation.* The second phase is the conversion of pyruvic acid to lactic acid, a reaction that requires the input of energy from the NADH produced in phase 1 of anaerobic respiration.

Lactic acid is released from the cells that produce it and is transported by the blood to the liver. When oxygen becomes available, the lactic acid in the liver can be converted through a series of chemical reactions into glucose. The glucose then can be released from the liver and transported in the blood to cells that use glucose as an energy source. Some of the reactions that convert lactic acid into glucose require the input of ATP (energy) produced by aerobic respiration. The oxygen necessary to make enough ATP for the synthesis of glucose from lactic acid contributes to the **oxygen debt** (see chapter 7).

Aerobic Respiration

Aerobic (ār-ō′bik) **respiration** (figure 17.6) is the breakdown of glucose in the presence of oxygen to produce carbon dioxide, water, and 38 molecules of ATP. Aerobic respiration can be divided into four phases:

1. *Glycolysis.* The first phase of aerobic respiration, as in anaerobic respiration, is glycolysis. The six-carbon glucose molecule is broken down to form two molecules of pyruvic acid, each of which consists of three carbon atoms. Two ATP and two NADH molecules are also produced.

2. *Acetyl-coenzyme A formation.* In the second phase, each pyruvic acid moves from the cytoplasm into a mitochondrion, where enzymes remove a carbon atom from the three-carbon pyruvic acid molecule to form carbon dioxide and a two-carbon acetyl (as′e-til, a-set′il) group. Hydrogen ions and electrons are released in the reaction, which can be used to produce NADH. Each acetyl group combines with coenzyme A (CoA), derived from vitamin B_2, to form **acetyl-CoA**. Because two pyruvic molecules are produced in phase 1, phase 2 results in two acetyl-CoA's, two carbon dioxide, and two NADH molecules for each glucose molecule.

3. *Citric acid cycle.* In the third phase, each acetyl-CoA combines with a four-carbon molecule to form a six-carbon citric acid molecule, which enters the citric acid cycle. The **citric** (sit′rik) **acid cycle** is also called the **tricarboxylic** (trī-kar-bok′sil-ik) **acid (TCA) cycle** (citric acid has three carboxylic acid groups) or the **Krebs' cycle**, after its discoverer, the British biochemist Sir Hans Krebs. The citric acid cycle is a series of reactions wherein the six-carbon citric acid molecule is converted, in a number of steps, into a four-carbon molecule (see figure 17.6). The four-carbon molecule can then combine with another acetyl-CoA molecule to form another citric acid molecule, and reinitiate the cycle. During the cycle, two carbon atoms are used to form carbon dioxide; and energy, hydrogen ions, and electrons are released. Some of the energy can be used to produce ATP. Most of the energy, hydrogen ions, and

Figure 17.6 Aerobic Respiration

Aerobic respiration involves four steps (indicated by the circled numbers): (1) glycolysis, (2) acetyl-CoA formation, (3) citric acid cycle, and (4) electron-transport chain. The number of carbon atoms in a molecule is indicated after the molecule's name. As glucose is broken down, the carbon atoms from glucose are incorporated into carbon dioxide.

electrons are used to form NADH molecules and another carrier molecule called **flavin** (flā′vin) **adenine dinucleotide (FADH$_2$)**. These molecules are used in the electron-transport chain to generate additional ATP. Carbon dioxide diffuses out of the cell and into the blood. It is transported by the circulatory system to the lungs, where it is expired. Thus the carbon atoms that constitute food molecules such as glucose are eventually eliminated from the body as carbon dioxide. We literally breathe out part of the food we eat!

4. *Electron-transport chain.* The **electron-transport chain** is a series of electron-transport molecules attached to the inner mitochondrial membrane (figure 17.7). This membrane divides the interior of the mitochondrion into an inner and outer compartment. Electrons are transferred from NADH and FADH$_2$ to the electron-transport carriers, and hydrogen ions are released into the inner mitochondrial compartment. Some of the electron-transport carriers are also hydrogen ion pumps, which use some of the energy from the transported electrons to pump hydrogen ions from the inner to the outer mitochondrial compartment. Because of an increased hydrogen ion concentration in the outer compartment, the hydrogen ions pass by diffusion back into the inner compartment. The hydrogen ions pass through special channels in the inner mitochondrial membrane that couple the movement of the hydrogen ions to ATP production. In the last step of the electron-transport chain, two hydrogen ions and two electrons combine with an oxygen atom to form water.

$$2\,H^+ + 2\,e^- + 1/2\,O_2 \rightarrow H_2O$$

Without oxygen to accept the hydrogen ions and electrons, the citric acid cycle and the electron-transport chain cannot function. Note that the oxygen we breath in is eventually bound to two hydrogen atoms to become water, which has many uses in the body (see chapter 2).

---

4   **P R E D I C T**

Many poisons function by blocking certain steps in the metabolic pathways. For example, cyanide blocks the last step in the electron-transport chain. Explain why this blockage causes death.

✔ *Answer on page 486*

1. NADH and FADH$_2$ transfer their electrons to the electron-transport chain.

2. As the electrons move through the electron-transport chain, some of their energy is used to pump hydrogen ions into the outer compartment, resulting in a higher concentration of hydrogen ions in the outer than in the inner compartment.

3. The hydrogen ions diffuse back into the inner compartment through special channels that couple the hydrogen ion movement with the production of ATP. The electrons, hydrogen ions, and oxygen combine to form water.

4. ATP is transported out of the inner compartment by a carrier molecule that exchanges ATP for ADP. A different carrier molecule moves phosphate into the inner compartment.

Figure 17.7   The Electron-Transport Chain

The electron-transport chain in the inner membrane consists of four protein complexes (purple; numbered I to IV) with carrier molecules. As electrons are transferred from one carrier molecule to another, they lose energy that is used to move hydrogen ions out of the inner compartment. Hydrogen ions move back into the inner compartment through special channels (ATP synthase; green), which produce ATP. Carrier molecules (brown) move ATP out of and ADP and P$_i$ into the inner compartment.

Summary of Anaerobic and Aerobic Respiration

In anaerobic respiration, each glucose molecule ($C_6H_{12}O_6$) yields two ATP and two lactic acid molecules ($C_3H_6O_3$) through glycolysis:

$$C_6H_{12}O_6 + 2\ ADP + P_i \rightarrow 2\ C_3H_6O_3 + 2\ ATP$$

In contrast, in aerobic respiration, each glucose molecule yields 38 ATP:

$$C_6H_{12}O_6 + 6\ O_2 + 38\ ADP + 38\ P_i \rightarrow$$
$$6\ CO_2 + 6\ H_2O + 38\ ATP$$

Of the 38 ATP molecules, 2 are produced in glycolysis, 2 are produced in the citric acid cycle, and 34 are formed through the electron-transport chain. Thus, aerobic respiration is much more efficient at producing ATP than is anaerobic respiration. In addition, many of the chemical reactions of aerobic respiration can be used to produce energy from other food molecules, such as lipids and proteins (see sections on Lipid and Protein Metabolism on pp. 477–479).

The number of ATP molecules produced during aerobic respiration can also be reported as 36 ATP molecules. The two NADH molecules produced by glycolysis cannot cross the inner mitochondrial membrane; thus their electrons are donated to a shuttle molecule that carries the electrons to the electron-transport chain. Depending on the shuttle molecule, each glycolytic NADH molecule can produce two or three ATP molecules. In skeletal muscle and in the brain, only 2 ATP molecules are produced for each NADH molecule formed during glycolysis, resulting in a total number of 36 ATP molecules; but in the liver, kidneys, and heart, 3 ATP molecules are produced for each NADH molecule, and the total number of ATP molecules formed is 38.

Lipid Metabolism

Triacylglycerol, or fat, is the body's main energy storage molecule. In a normal person, fat is responsible for about 99% of the body's energy storage, and glycogen accounts for the remaining 1%.

Between meals, triacylglycerol in adipose tissue is broken down into fatty acids and glycerol. Some of the fatty acids produced are released into the blood. Other tissues, especially skeletal muscle and the liver, use the fatty acids as a source of energy.

The metabolism of fatty acids takes place in the mitochondria. It occurs by a series of reactions wherein two carbon atoms are removed from the end of a fatty acid chain to form acetyl-CoA (figure 17.8). As the process continues, carbon atoms are removed two at a time until the entire fatty acid chain is converted into acetyl-CoA. Acetyl-CoA can enter the citric acid cycle and be used to generate ATP. In the liver, two acetyl-CoA molecules can also combine to form **ketones** (kē′tōnz). The ketones are released into the blood and travel to other tissues, especially skeletal muscle. In these tissues, the ketones are converted back to acetyl-CoA, which can enter the citric acid cycle to produce ATP.

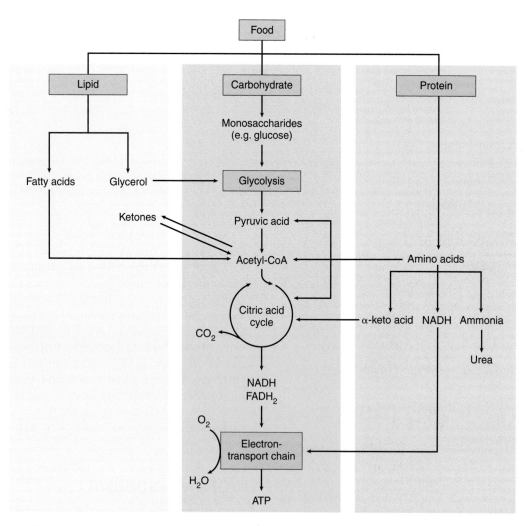

Figure 17.8 The Overall Pathways for the Metabolism of Food

Carbohydrates, fats, and proteins enter biochemical pathways to produce energy in the cell.

Protein Metabolism

Amino acids are the products of protein digestion. Once amino acids are absorbed into the body, they are quickly taken up by cells, especially in the liver. Amino acids are used primarily to synthesize needed proteins and only secondarily as a source of energy. If amino acids are used as a source of energy, they can be used in two ways (see figure 17.8): (1) The amino acids can be converted into the molecules of carbohydrate metabolism, such as pyruvic acid and acetyl-coenzyme A. These molecules can be metabolized to yield ATP. (2) The amine group ($-NH_2$) can be removed from the amino acid, leaving ammonia and an α-keto acid. In this process, NADH is produced, which can enter the electron-transport chain to produce ATP. Ammonia is toxic to cells, so it is converted by the liver into urea, which is carried by the blood to the kidneys, where it is eliminated. The keto acid can enter the citric acid cycle or can be converted into pyruvic acid, acetyl-CoA, or glucose. Although proteins can be used as an energy source, they are not considered to be major storage molecules.

Metabolic States

There are two major metabolic states in the body. The first is the **absorptive state**, the period immediately after a meal when nutrients are being absorbed through the intestinal wall into the circulatory and lymphatic systems (figure 17.9). The absorptive state usually lasts about 4 hours after each meal, and most of the glucose that enters the circulation is used by cells to provide the energy they require. The remainder of the glucose is converted into glycogen or fats. Most of the absorbed fats are deposited in adipose tissue. Many of the absorbed amino acids are used by cells in protein synthesis, some are used for energy, and others enter the liver and are converted to fats or carbohydrates.

The second state, the **postabsorptive state**, occurs late in the morning, late in the afternoon, or during the night after each absorptive state is concluded (figure 17.10). Normal blood glucose levels range between 70 and 110 mg/100 mL, and it is vital to the body's homeostasis that this range be maintained. During the postabsorptive state, blood glucose levels are maintained by the conversion of other molecules to glucose. The first source of blood glucose during the postabsorptive state is the glycogen stored in the liver. This glycogen supply can provide glucose for only about 4 hours, however. The glycogen stored in skeletal muscles can also be used during times of vigorous exercise. As the glycogen stores are depleted, fats are used as an energy source. The glycerol from triacylglycerols can be converted to glucose. The fatty acids from fat can be converted to acetyl-CoA, moved into the citric acid cycle, and used as a source of energy to produce ATP. In the liver, acetyl-CoA can be used to produce ketone bodies that

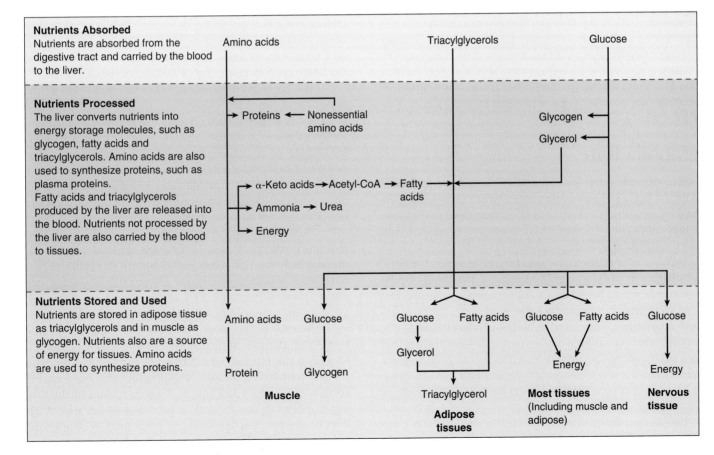

Figure 17.9   Events of the Absorptive State

In the absorptive state, nutrients are used as energy or stored.

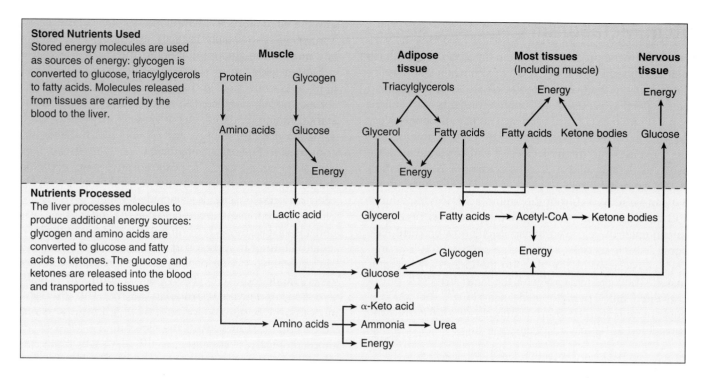

Figure 17.10 Events of the Postabsorptive State

In the postabsorptive state, stored nutrients are used for energy.

other tissues can use for energy. The use of fatty acids as an energy source can partly eliminate the need to use glucose for energy, resulting in reduced glucose removal from the blood and maintaining blood glucose levels at homeostatic levels. The amino acids of proteins can be converted into glucose or can be used for energy production, again sparing blood glucose.

Metabolic Rate

The **metabolic rate** is the total amount of energy produced and used by the body per unit of time. Metabolic rate is usually estimated by measuring the amount of oxygen used per minute. One liter of oxygen consumed by the body is estimated to produce 4.825 kcal of energy.

Metabolic energy can be used in three ways: for basal metabolism, for muscle contraction, and for the assimilation of food, which involves such processes as the production of digestive enzymes and the active transport of digested molecules. The **basal metabolic rate (BMR)** is the metabolic rate calculated in expended kilocalories per square meter of body surface area per hour. BMR is measured when a person is awake but restful and has not eaten for 12 hours. A typical BMR for a 70-kg (154-lb) male is 38 kcal/m²/hour.

BMR is the energy needed to keep the resting body functional. Active transport mechanisms, muscle tone, maintenance of body temperature, beating of the heart, and other activities are supported by basal metabolism. A number of

factors can affect the BMR. Males have a higher BMR than females, younger people have a higher BMR than older people, and fever can increase BMR. Greatly reduced kilocaloric input, such as during dieting or fasting, depresses BMR.

The daily input of energy should equal the energy demand of metabolism; otherwise, a person will gain or lose weight. For a 23-year-old, 70-kg (154-lb) male to maintain his weight, the input should be 2700 kcal/day; for a 58-kg (128-lb) female of the same age, 2000 kcal/day is necessary. A pound of body fat contains about 3500 kcal. Reducing kilocaloric intake by 500 kcal/day can result in the loss of 1 lb of fat per week. Clearly, adjusting kilocaloric input is an important way to control body weight.

The other way to control weight is through energy expenditure. Physical activity through skeletal muscle movement greatly increases metabolic rate. In the average person, basal metabolism accounts for about 60% of energy expenditure, muscular activity 30%, and assimilation of food about 10%. Of these amounts, energy loss through muscular activity is the only component that a person reasonably can control. A comparison of the number of kilocalories gained from food and the number of kilocalories burned during exercise reveals why losing weight is a difficult task. For example, if brisk walking uses 225 kcal/h, it takes 20 min of brisk walking to burn off the 75 kcal in one slice of bread (75/225 = 0.33 h). Research suggests that a combination of appropriate physical activity and appropriate kilocaloric intake is the best approach to maintaining a healthy body composition and weight.

5 **P R E D I C T**

If watching TV uses 95 kcal/h, how long does it take to burn off the kilocalories in one cola or beer (see table 17.1). If jogging at a pace of 6 mph uses 580 kcal/h, how long does it take to use the kilocalories in one cola or beer?

✔ *Answer on page 486*

Did You Know?

Studies in mice, rats, and other animals indicate that life span can be increased by approximately one-third by decreasing normal kilocaloric intake 30% to 50%, provided that the diet includes enough protein, fat, vitamins, and minerals. Why life span increases is not understood, but one proposed explanation for this phenomenon is that reduced kilocaloric intake in some way reduces free radical damage to mitochondria. It has been suggested that humans might derive a similar benefit by reducing kilocaloric input, starting at age 20. Unlike laboratory animals, however, humans would have to voluntarily restrict their kilocaloric intake by 30% to 50%, which is an unlikely behavioral change for most humans. Restriction of kilocaloric intake to increase longevity is an interesting idea, but much more needs to be learned before it will be known if this approach is beneficial to humans.

Body Temperature Regulation

Humans are **homeotherms** (hō′mē-ō-thermz, meaning uniform warming), or **warm-blooded animals**; that is, we can maintain a constant body temperature, even though the environmental temperature varies. Maintenance of a constant body temperature is very important to homeostasis. Most enzymes are very temperature-sensitive and function only within narrow temperature ranges. Environmental temperatures are too low for normal enzyme function. The heat produced by metabolism and muscle contraction helps maintain the body temperature at a steady, elevated level that is high enough for normal enzyme function. Excessively high temperatures can alter enzyme structure, resulting in the loss of the enzyme's function.

Free energy is the total amount of energy that can be liberated by the complete catabolism of food. About 40% of the total energy released by catabolism is used to accomplish biological work such as anabolism, muscular contraction, and other cellular activities. The remaining energy is lost as **heat**.

6 **P R E D I C T**

Explain why we become warm during exercise, and explain the usefulness of shivering when it is cold.

✔ *Answer on page 486*

Normal body temperature is regulated like other homeostatic conditions in the body. The average normal temperature is usually considered to be 37°C (98.6°F) when it is measured orally, and 37.6°C (99.7°F) when it is measured rectally. Rectal temperature comes closer to the true core body temperature, but an oral temperature is more easily obtained in older children and adults and therefore is the preferred measure. The normal oral temperature may vary from person to person, with a range of approximately 36.1°C to 37.2°C (97°F to 99°F).

Body temperature is maintained by balancing heat input with heat loss. Heat exchanged between the body and the environment occurs in a number of ways (figure 17.11). **Radiation** is the gain or loss of heat as infrared energy between two objects that are not in physical contact with each other. For example, heat can be gained by radiation from the sun, a hot coal, or the hot sand of a beach. On the other hand, heat can be lost as radiation to cool vegetation, water in the ocean, and snow on the ground. **Conduction** is the exchange of heat between objects that are in direct contact with each other, such as the bottom of the feet and the ground. **Convection** is a transfer of heat between the body and the air. A cool breeze results in movement of air over the body and loss of heat from the body. **Evaporation** is the conversion of water from a liquid to a gaseous form. As water evaporates from body surfaces, heat is lost.

The amount of heat exchanged between the environment and the body is determined by the difference in temperature between the body and the environment. The greater the temperature difference, the greater the rate of heat exchange. Control of the temperature difference can be used to regulate body temperature. If environmental temperature is very cold, such as on a winter day, there is a large temperature difference between the body and the environment, and there is a large loss of heat. The loss of heat can be decreased by behaviorally selecting a warmer environment, such as going inside a heated house, or by insulating the exchange surface by putting on extra clothes. Physiologically, temperature difference can be

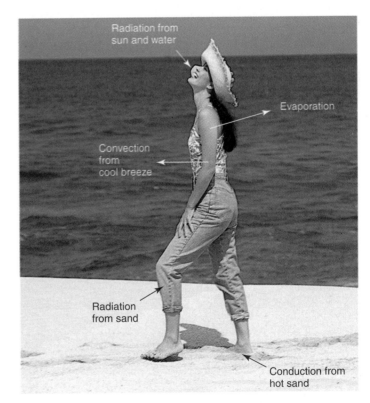

Figure 17.11   Heat Exchange

Heat exchange between a person and the environment occurs by convection, radiation, evaporation, and conduction.

controlled through dilation and constriction of blood vessels in the skin. When these blood vessels dilate, they bring warm blood to the surface of the body, raising skin temperature, whereas blood vessel constriction decreases blood flow and lowers skin temperature (see figure 5.8).

7   P R E D I C T

Explain why constriction of skin blood vessels on a cold winter day is beneficial.

✔ *Answer on page 486*

When environmental temperature is greater than body temperature, dilation of blood vessels to the skin brings blood to the skin, causing an increase in skin temperature that decreases the gain of heat from the environment. At the same time, evaporation carries away excess heat to prevent heat gain and overheating.

Body temperature regulation is an example of a negative-feedback system (figure 17.12). Maintenance of a specific body temperature is accomplished by neurons in the hypothalamus, which regulate body temperature around a set point. A small area in the anterior part of the hypothalamus can detect slight increases in body temperature through changes in blood temperature. As a result, mechanisms that cause heat loss, such as dilation of blood vessels to the skin and sweating, are activated, and body temperature decreases. A small area in the posterior hypothalamus can detect slight decreases in body temperature and can initiate heat gain by increasing muscular activity (shivering) and by initiating constriction of blood vessels in the skin.

Under some conditions, the hypothalamus set point is actually changed. For example, during a fever, the set point is raised. Heat-conserving and heat-producing mechanisms are stimulated, and body temperature increases. In recovery from a fever, the set point is reduced to normal. Heat loss mechanisms are initiated, and body temperature decreases.

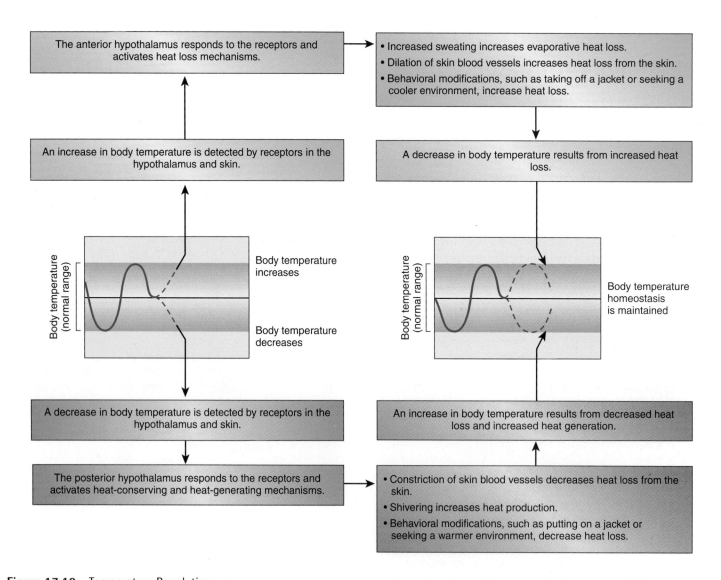

Figure 17.12 Temperature Regulation

Hyperthermia is a condition in which heat gain exceeds heat loss in the body. Hyperthermia can result from exposure to a hot environment, exercise, or fever. Prolonged exposure to a hot environment can lead to **heat exhaustion,** a condition in which normal temperature reduction mechanisms are working, but they cannot keep pace with the excessive environmental heat, and the body temperature rises. Heat exhaustion is characterized by cool, wet skin caused by heavy sweating. Weakness, dizziness, and nausea usually occur as well. The heavy sweating can lead to dehydration, decreased blood volume, decreased blood pressure, and increased heart rate. Treatment involves increasing heat loss by moving the person to a cooler environment, decreasing heat production by decreasing muscular activity, and replacing lost body fluids. **Heat stroke** results from an increase in the level of the hypothalamic set point and is characterized by a dry, flushed skin because sweating is inhibited. The person becomes confused and irritable, and can even become comatose. Treatment is the same as for heat exhaustion, but also involves increasing evaporation from the skin by applying water to the skin or by placing the person into cool water.

Hypothermia is a condition in which heat loss exceeds heat gain. The normal temperature increase mechanisms are working in the body, but they cannot keep pace with heat loss, and the body temperature decreases. Hypothermia usually results from a prolonged exposure to a cold environment or even to a cool, damp environment, because the moisture draws heat away from the body. Treatment for hypothermia is to rewarm the body at a rate of a few degrees per hour. **Frostbite** is local damage to the skin or deeper tissues resulting from prolonged exposure to a cold environment. The best treatment for frostbite is immersion in a warm water bath. Rubbing the affected area and local, dry heat should be avoided.

Clinical Focus   Starvation and Obesity

Starvation is the inadequate intake of nutrients or the inability to metabolize or absorb nutrients. Starvation can be caused by a number of factors, such as prolonged fasting, anorexia, deprivation, or disease. No matter what the cause, starvation takes approximately the same course and consists of three phases. The events of the first two phases occur even during relatively short periods of fasting or dieting. The third phase occurs in prolonged starvation and ends in death.

During the first phase of starvation, blood glucose levels are maintained through the production of glucose from glycogen, proteins, and fats. At first, glycogen is broken down into glucose. Enough glycogen is stored in the liver to last only a few hours, however. Thereafter, blood glucose levels are maintained by the breakdown of proteins and fats. Fats are decomposed into fatty acids and glycerol. Fatty acids can be used as a source of energy, especially by skeletal muscle, thus decreasing the use of glucose by tissues other than the brain. The brain cannot use fatty acids as an energy source, so the conservation of glucose is critical to normal brain function. Glycerol can be used to make a small amount of glucose, but most of the glucose is formed from the amino acids of proteins. In addition, some amino acids can be used directly for energy.

In the second stage, which can last for several weeks, fats are the primary energy source. The liver metabolizes fatty acids into ketone bodies that can be used as a source of energy. After about a week of fasting, the brain begins to use ketone bodies, as well as glucose, for energy. This usage decreases the demand for glucose, and the rate of protein breakdown diminishes but does not stop. In addition, there is a selective use of proteins; proteins not essential for survival are used first.

The third stage of starvation begins when the fat reserves are nearly depleted and the body switches to proteins as the major energy source. Muscles, the largest source of protein in the body, are rapidly depleted. At the end of this stage, proteins essential for cellular functions are broken down, and cell function degenerates. Death can occur very rapidly.

Symptoms of starvation, in addition to weight loss, include apathy, listlessness, withdrawal, and increased susceptibility to infectious diseases. Few people die directly from starvation because they usually die of some infectious disease first. Other signs of starvation may include changes in hair color, flaky skin, and massive edema in the abdomen and lower limbs, causing the abdomen to appear bloated.

During the process of starvation, the body's ability to consume normal volumes of food also decreases. Foods high in bulk but low in protein content often cannot reverse the process of starvation. Intervention involves feeding the starving person low-bulk foods containing ample protein, calories, vitamins, and minerals. The process of starvation also results in dehydration, and rehydration is an important part of intervention. Even with intervention, a victim may be so affected by disease or weakness that he or she cannot recover.

Obesity

Obesity is the storage of excess fat, and it results from the ingestion of more food than is necessary for the body's energy needs. Obesity can be defined on the basis of body weight, body mass index, or body fat. "Desirable body weight" is listed in a table produced by the Metropolitan Life Insurance Company and indicates, for any height, the weight associated with a maximum life span. Overweight is defined as weighing 10% more than the "desirable weight," and obesity is weighing 20% more than the "desirable weight." **Body mass index (BMI)** can be calculated by dividing a person's weight (Wt) in kilograms by the square of his or her height (Ht) in meters: $BMI = Wt/Ht^2$. A BMI greater than 25 to 27 is overweight, and a value greater than 30 is defined as obese. About 10% of Americans have a BMI of 30 or greater. In terms of the percent of the total body weight contributed by fat, 15% body fat in men and 25% body fat in women is associated with reduced health risks. Obesity is defined to be more than 25% body fat in men and 30% to 35% in women.

The distribution of fat in obese individuals can vary. Fat can be found mainly in the upper body, such as in the abdominal region, or it can be associated with the hips and buttocks. These distribution differences can be clinically significant because upper body obesity is associated with an increased likelihood of diabetes mellitus, cardiovascular disease, stroke, and death.

In some cases, a specific cause of obesity can be identified. For example, a tumor in the hypothalamus can stimulate overeating. In most cases, however, no specific cause can be recognized. In fact, obesity can occur for many reasons, and obesity in an individual can have more than one cause. There seems to be a genetic component for obesity, and, if one or both parents are obese, their children are more likely to also be obese. Environmental factors such as eating habits, however, can also play an important role. For example, adopted children can exhibit similarities in obesity to their adoptive parents. In addition, psychological factors such as overeating as a means for dealing with stress can contribute to obesity.

In **hypertrophic** (hī-per-trof′ik) **obesity,** the number of adipose cells is usually normal, but the amount of fat contained in each adipose cell is increased. This type of obesity is characteristic of adult-onset obesity. People who were thin or of average weight and quite active when young become less active as they age. Although they no longer use as many kilocalories, they still consume the same amount of food as when they were younger. The excess kilocalories (see discussion, Metabolic Rate, on p. 480) are used to synthesize fat. In this type of obesity, the amount of fat in each adipose cell increases, and, if the amount of stored fat continues to increase, the total number of adipose cells may also increase. It is estimated that the average U.S. resident gains 1.25 to 1.5 lb of fat per year after age 25 and, at the same time, loses 0.25 to 0.5 lb of lean body weight (muscle mass) per year.

In **hyperplastic** (hī-per-plas′tik) **obesity,** which is characteristic of juvenile-onset obesity, the number of adipose cells is increased. This condition may also be accompanied by an increase in cell size (hypertrophic obesity). Hyperplastic obesity has a very strong hereditary component, but family eating habits can also have a great influence. People with hyperplastic obesity are obese as children and become more obese with age. This type of obesity is a major health problem in school-aged children.

Summary

Nutrition

Nutrients

- Nutrition is the taking in and the use of food.
- Nutrients are the chemicals used by the body and consist of carbohydrates, lipids, proteins, vitamins, minerals, and water.
- Essential nutrients cannot be produced by the body or cannot be produced in adequate amounts.

Kilocalories

- A kilocalorie is the energy required to raise the temperature of 1000 g of water from 14°C to 15°C. A kilocalorie is the unit of measurement used to express the energy content of food.

Carbohydrates

- Carbohydrates include monosaccharides, disaccharides, and polysaccharides.
- Most carbohydrates we ingest are from plants.
- Carbohydrates are used as an energy source and for making DNA, RNA, and ATP.
- The recommended amount of carbohydrate is 60% of the kilocaloric intake.

Lipids

- Lipids include triacylglycerol, phospholipids, steroids, and fat-soluble vitamins. Triacylglycerol is a major source of energy. Prostaglandins are involved in inflammation, tissue repair, and smooth muscle contraction. Cholesterol and phospholipids are part of the cell membrane. Some steroid hormones regulate the reproductive system.
- It is recommended that fats account for no more than 30% of the total kilocaloric intake.

Proteins

- Proteins are chains of amino acids.
- Animal proteins tend to be complete proteins, whereas plant proteins tend to be incomplete.
- Proteins are involved in structural strength, muscle contraction, regulation, buffering, clotting, transport, ion channels, receptors, and the immune system.
- The recommended daily consumption of protein is 0.8 g/kg of body weight per day.

Vitamins

- Most vitamins are not produced by the body and must be obtained in the diet. Some vitamins can be formed from provitamins.
- Vitamins are important in energy production, nucleic acid synthesis, growth, and blood clotting.
- Vitamins are classified as either fat-soluble or water-soluble.
- Recommended dietary allowances (RDAs) are a guide for estimating the nutritional needs of groups of people on the basis of their age, sex, and other factors.

Minerals

- Minerals are necessary for normal metabolism and they add mechanical strength to bones.

Daily Values

- Daily Values are dietary references that can be used to help plan a healthy diet.
- Daily Values for vitamins and minerals are based on Reference Daily Intakes (RDIs), which are generally the highest 1968 RDA value of an age category.
- Daily Values are based on Daily Reference Values. The Daily Reference Values for energy-producing nutrients (carbohydrates, total fat, saturated fat, and proteins) and dietary fiber are recommended percentages of the total kilocalories ingested daily for each nutrient. The Daily

Reference Values for total fats, saturated fats, cholesterol, and sodium are the uppermost limit considered desirable because of their link to diseases.

- The % Daily Value is the percent of the recommended Daily Value of a nutrient found in one serving of a particular food.

Metabolism

- Metabolism consists of anabolism and catabolism. Anabolism is the synthesis of molecules and requires energy. Catabolism is the breaking down of molecules and gives off energy.
- The energy in carbohydrates, lipids, and proteins is used to produce ATP.

Regulation of Metabolism

- Biochemical pathways are a series of chemical reactions, some of which release energy that can be used to synthesize ATP.
- Each step in a biochemical pathway requires enzymes.
- Enzyme synthesis is determined by DNA. Enzyme activity is modified by receptor-mediated and end-product processes.

Carbohydrate Metabolism

- Glycolysis is the breakdown of glucose to two pyruvic acid molecules. Two ATP molecules are also produced.
- Anaerobic respiration is the breakdown of glucose in the absence of oxygen to two lactic acid molecules and two ATP molecules.
- Lactic acid can be converted to glucose using aerobically produced ATP; the necessary oxygen is the oxygen debt.
- Aerobic respiration is the breakdown of glucose in the presence of oxygen to produce carbon dioxide, water, and 38 molecules of ATP.
    The first phase of aerobic metabolism is glycolysis.
    The second phase of aerobic metabolism is the conversion of pyruvic acid to acetyl-CoA.
    The third phase of aerobic metabolism is the citric acid cycle.

The fourth phase is the electron-transport chain, which uses carrier molecules such as NADH to synthesize ATP.

Lipid Metabolism

- Lipids are broken down in adipose tissue, and fatty acids are released into the blood.
- Fatty acids are taken up by cells and broken down into acetyl-CoA, which can enter the citric acid cycle. Acetyl-CoA can also be converted into ketones by the liver. Ketones released from the liver into the blood are used as energy sources by other cells.

Protein Metabolism

- Amino acids are used to synthesize proteins.
- Amino acids can be used for energy, and ammonia is produced as a by-product.
    Ammonia is converted to urea and excreted by the kidneys.

Metabolic States

- In the absorptive state, nutrients are used as energy or stored.
- In the postabsorptive state, stored nutrients are used for energy.

Metabolic Rate

- Metabolic rate is the total energy expenditure per unit of time.
- Metabolic energy is used for basal metabolism, muscular activity, and the assimilation of food.

Body Temperature Regulation

- Body temperature is a balance between heat gain and heat loss.
- Heat is produced through metabolism.
- Heat is exchanged through radiation, conduction, convection, and evaporation.
- The greater the temperature difference, the greater the rate of heat exchange.
- Body temperature is regulated at a "set point" by neural circuits in the hypothalamus.

Content Review

1. Define a nutrient, and list the six major classes of nutrients. What is an essential nutrient?
2. What is a kilocalorie?
3. List some sources of carbohydrates, fats, and proteins in the diet.
4. List the recommended consumption amounts of carbohydrates, fats, and proteins.
5. What are vitamins and provitamins? Name the water-soluble vitamins and the fat-soluble vitamins. List some of the functions of vitamins.
6. What are the Recommended Dietary Allowances (RDAs)?
7. List some of the minerals, and give their functions.
8. What are the Daily Values? How are the Daily Values related to total daily kilocaloric intake? Why are some Daily Values considered to be the uppermost amount that should be consumed?
9. Define a % Daily Value.
10. Define a biochemical pathway. How are the steps in a biochemical pathway controlled? What are three ways in which enzymes are regulated?

11. Describe glycolysis. What molecule is the end product of glycolysis? How many ATP and NADH molecules are produced?
12. What determines whether the pyruvic acid produced in glycolysis becomes lactic acid or acetyl-CoA?
13. Describe the two phases of anaerobic respiration. How many ATP molecules are produced? What happens to the lactic acid produced when oxygen becomes available?
14. Define aerobic respiration, and state how many ATP molecules are produced.
15. Why is the citric acid cycle a cycle?
16. What is the function of the electron-transport chain?
17. What happens to the carbon atoms in ingested food during metabolism? What happens to the oxygen we breathe in during metabolism?
18. Describe the events occurring during the absorptive and postabsorptive metabolic states.
19. What is meant by metabolic rate? Name three ways that the body uses metabolic energy.
20. Describe how heat is produced by and lost from the body. How is body temperature regulated?

Develop Your Reasoning Skills

1. One serving of a food has 2 g of saturated fat. What % Daily Value for saturated fat would appear on a food label for this food? (See bottom of figure 17.2 for information needed to answer this question.)
2. An active teenage boy has a daily intake of 3000 kcal/day. What is the maximum amount (weight) of total fats he should consume according to the Daily Values?
3. If the teenager in question 2 eats a food that has a total fat content of 10 g/serving, what is his total fat % Daily Value?
4. Suppose the food in question 3 is in a package that lists a serving size of 1/2 cup with 4 servings in the package. If the teenager eats half the contents of the package (1 cup), how much of his % Daily Value does he consume?
5. Why can some people lose weight on a 1200 cal/k day diet and other people cannot?
6. Lotta Bulk, a bodybuilder, wanted to increase her muscle mass. Knowing that proteins are the main components of muscle, she consumed large amounts of protein daily (high-protein diet), along with small amounts of lipid and carbohydrate. Explain why this strategy will or will not work.

7. After consuming a high-protein diet for several days, does Lotta Bulk's urine contain less, the same, or more urea than before she consumed the proteins? Explain.
8. Thyroid hormone is known to increase the activity of the sodium–potassium exchange pump, which is an active-transport mechanism, therefore increasing the breakdown of ATP. If a person produced excess amounts of thyroid hormone, what effect would this have on basal metabolic rate, body weight, and body temperature? How might the body attempt to compensate for the changes in body weight and temperature?
9. On learning that sweat evaporation results in the loss of calories, an anatomy and physiology student decides that sweating is an easier way to lose weight than dieting. He knows that a liter (about a quart) of water weighs 1000 g, which is equivalent to 580,000 cal (or 580 kcal) of heat when lost as sweat. Instead of reducing his caloric intake by 580 kcal/day, if he loses a liter of sweat every day in the sauna he believes he will lose about a pound of fat a week. Will this approach work? Explain.

Answers to Predict Questions

1. p. 469 If vitamins are broken down during the process of digestion, their structures are destroyed, and, as a result, their ability to function as vitamins is lost. Because vitamins cannot be synthesized in adequate amounts, vitamin deficiency diseases would occur.
2. p. 473 The Daily Value for carbohydrate is 300 g/day. One serving of food with 30 g of carbohydrate has a % Daily Value of 10% (30/300 = 0.10 or 10%).
3. p. 473 On a 1800 kcal/day diet, the total percentage of Daily Values for energy-producing nutrients should add up to no more than 90%, because 1800/2000 = 0.9 or 90%.
4. p. 476 If electrons in the electron-transport chain cannot be donated to oxygen atoms in the last step of the electron-transport chain, the entire chain and the citric acid cycle stop, no

ATP is produced aerobically, and death results because too little energy is available for the body to maintain vital functions. Anaerobic metabolism can provide energy for only very short periods of time and cannot sustain life very long.

5. p. 481 The kilocalories in a beer or cola is about 145 kcal. It takes about 1.5 h to burn off these kilocalories while watching TV (145/95 = 1.5 h) and about 15 min while jogging (145/580 = 0.25 h). Although it may be difficult to burn off kilocalories through exercise, it is clear that exercise can significantly increase kilocalorie use.
6. p. 481 When muscles contract, they must use ATP as the energy source for the contractions. As more ATP is produced, heat is also produced. During exercise, the large amounts of

heat can raise body temperature, and we feel warm. Shivering consists of small, rapid muscle contractions that produce heat in an effort to prevent a decrease in body temperature in the cold. When the body temperature declines below normal, shivering is initiated involuntarily.

7. p. 482 Constriction of blood vessels to the skin reduces blood flow to the skin, which cools as a result. The benefit is that less heat is lost through the skin to the environment and the internal body temperature is maintained. As the difference in temperature between the skin and the environment decreases, less heat is lost. If the skin temperature decreases too much, however, dilation of blood vessels to the skin occurs, which functions to prevent the skin from becoming so cold that it is damaged.

Chapter Eighteen

Urinary System and Fluid Balance

acidosis

(as-i-dō'sis) Condition characterized by a lower than normal blood pH (pH of 7.35 or lower).

aldosterone

(al-dos'ter-ōn) Steroid hormone produced by the adrenal cortex that facilitates exchange of potassium for sodium in the distal tubule and collecting duct, causing sodium reabsorption and potassium and hydrogen ion secretion.

alkalosis

(al-kă-lō'sis) Condition characterized by a higher than normal blood pH (pH of 7.45 or above).

antidiuretic hormone (ADH)

(an'tē-dī-ū-ret'ik) Hormone secreted from the posterior pituitary that acts on the kidneys to reduce the output of urine; also called vasopressin.

atrial natriuretic hormone (ANH)

(ā'trē-ăl nā'trē-ū-ret'ik) Hormone released from cardiac muscle cells in the atrial wall of the heart in response to increased blood pressure; lowers blood pressure by increasing the rate of urine production.

filtration

(fil-trā'shŭn) Movement of a liquid under pressure through a filter, which prevents some or all of the substances in the liquid from passing through the filter.

filtration membrane

Membrane formed by the glomerular capillary endothelium, the basement membrane, and the podocytes of Bowman's capsule.

micturition reflex

(mik-choo-rish'ŭn) Contraction of the urinary bladder stimulated by stretching of the urinary bladder wall; results in emptying of the urinary bladder.

nephron

(nef'ron) [Gr. *nephros*, kidney] Functional unit of the kidney, consisting of the glomerulus, Bowman's capsule, proximal tubule, loop of Henle, and distal tubule.

renin

(rē'nin, ren'in) Enzyme secreted by the kidney that converts angiotensinogen to angiotensin I.

tubular reabsorption

Movement of materials from the filtrate of a nephron into the blood by means of diffusion or active transport.

tubular secretion

Movement of materials from the blood into the filtrate of a nephron by means of active and passive transport.

Objectives

After reading this chapter, you should be able to:

1. List the structures that make up the urinary system and describe the overall functions it performs.

2. Describe the location and anatomy of the kidneys.

3. Describe the structure of the nephron and the location of the parts of the nephron in the kidney.

4. List the components of the filtration barrier and describe the composition of the filtrate.

5. Describe the ureters, urinary bladder, and urethra.

6. Identify the principal factors that influence filtration pressure and explain how they affect the rate of filtrate formation.

7. Give the function of the proximal tubule, descending and ascending limbs of Henle's loop, distal tubule, and collecting duct. Discuss how the movement of substances across the walls of these structures influences the composition of the filtrate.

8. Explain how antidiuretic hormone, aldosterone, and atrial natriuretic hormone influence the volume and concentration of urine.

9. Describe the micturition reflex.

10. Describe the mechanisms by which sodium ions, potassium ions, and calcium ions are regulated in the extracellular fluid.

11. Illustrate how the mechanisms that regulate the body fluid pH function by explaining how they respond to decreasing and increasing pH in the body fluids.

Most people know that each person has two kidneys, their general location, and that they are essential to the maintenance of life, but fewer people are aware of the many functions the kidneys perform. Most people have a much better understanding of the function of the urinary bladder, and a great appreciation for the attention that is required when it is filled with the urine produced by the kidneys.

The **urinary** (ūr′i-nār-ē) **system** consists of two kidneys, two ureters, the urinary bladder, and the urethra (figure 18.1). A large volume of blood flows through the kidneys, which removes substances from the blood to form urine. The urine contains excess water and ions, metabolic wastes such as urea, and toxic substances consumed with food. The urine produced by the kidneys flows through the ureters to the urinary bladder, where it is stored until it is eliminated through the urethra.

The kidneys can suffer extensive damage and still maintain their extremely important role in the maintenance of homeostasis. As long as about one-third of one kidney remains functional, survival is possible. If the functional ability of the kidneys fails completely, however, death will result without special medical treatment.

Functions of the Urinary System

The major functions of the urinary system are performed by the kidneys, and the kidneys play the following essential roles in controlling the composition and volume of body fluids:

1. *Excretion.* The kidneys are the major excretory organs of the body. They remove waste products, many of which are toxic, from the blood. Most waste products are metabolic by-products of cells and substances absorbed from the intestine. The skin, liver, lungs, and intestines eliminate some of these waste products, but they cannot compensate if the kidneys fail to function.
2. *Blood volume control.* The kidneys play an essential role in controlling blood volume by regulating the volume of urine produced.
3. *Ion concentration regulation.* The kidneys help regulate the concentration of the major ions in the body fluids.
4. *pH regulation.* The kidneys help regulate the pH of the body fluids. Buffers in the blood and the respiratory system also play important roles in the regulation of pH.
5. *Red blood cell concentration.* The kidneys participate in the regulation of *red blood cell* production and, therefore, in controlling the concentration of *red blood cells* in the blood.
6. *Vitamin D synthesis.* The kidneys, along with the skin and the liver, participate in the synthesis of vitamin D.

Urinary System

Kidneys

The **kidneys** are bean-shaped organs, each about the size of a tightly clenched fist. They lie on the posterior abdominal wall behind the peritoneum to either side of the vertebral column

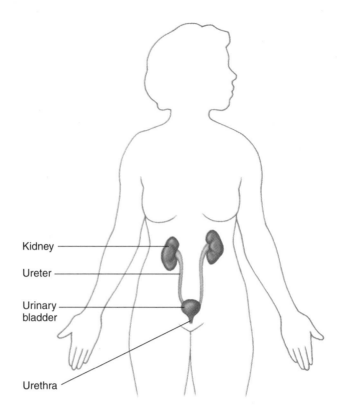

Kidney

Ureter

Urinary bladder

Urethra

Figure 18.1 The Urinary System
The urinary system consists of two kidneys, two ureters, a urinary bladder, and a urethra.

(figure 18.2). Structures that are behind the peritoneum are said to be **retroperitoneal** (re′trō-per′i-tō-ne′ăl). A connective tissue **renal capsule** surrounds each kidney. Around the renal capsule is a thick layer of fat called the **renal fat pad**, which protects the kidney from mechanical shock. On the medial side of each kidney is the **hilum** (hī′lŭm, a small amount), where the renal artery and nerves enter and where the renal vein and ureter exit the kidney. The hilum opens into a cavity called the **renal sinus**, which is filled with fat and other connective tissues (figure 18.3).

The kidney is divided into an outer **cortex** and an inner **medulla**, which surrounds the renal sinus. The bases of several cone-shaped **renal pyramids** are located at the boundary between the cortex and the medulla, and the tips of the renal pyramids project toward the center of the kidney. A funnel-shaped structure called a **calyx** (kā′liks, cup of a flower) surrounds the tip of each renal pyramid. The calyces from all the renal pyramids join together to form a larger funnel called the **renal pelvis**, which is located in the renal sinus. The renal pelvis then narrows to form a small tube, the **ureter** (ū-rē′ter or ū′re-ter), which exits the kidney and connects to the urinary bladder. Urine passes from the tips of the renal pyramids into the calyces. From the calyces, urine collects in the renal pelvis and exits the kidney through the ureter (see figure 18.3).

The functional unit of the kidney is the **nephron** (nef′ron), and there are approximately 1.3 million of them in each kidney. Each nephron consists of an enlarged ending called a renal corpuscle, a proximal tubule, a loop of Henle, or nephronic loop,

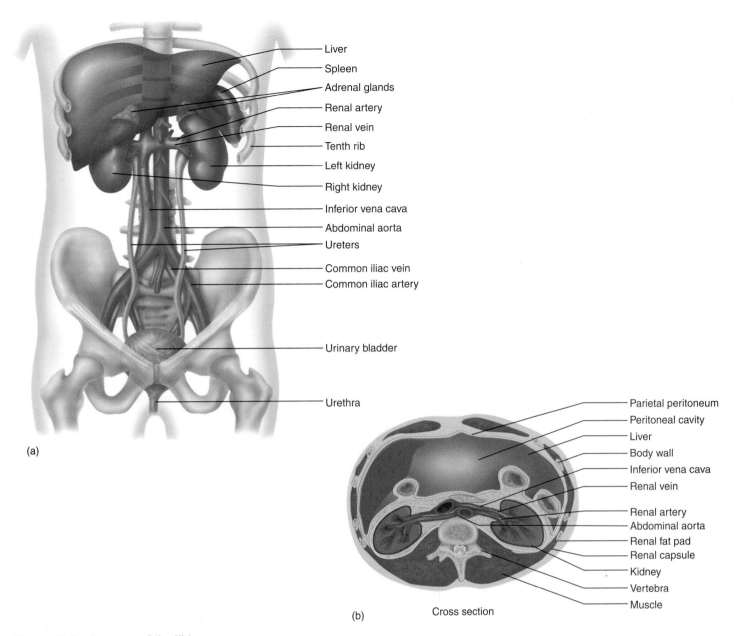

Figure 18.2 Anatomy of the Kidney

(*a*) The kidneys are located in the abdominal cavity, with the right kidney just inferior to liver and the left kidney inferior to the spleen. The ureters extend from the kidneys to the urinary bladder within the pelvic cavity. An adrenal gland is located at the superior pole of each kidney. (*b*) In this cross section of the abdominal area, the retroperitoneal location (behind the peritoneum) of the kidneys can be seen. A renal fat pad surrounds each of the kidneys. The renal arteries extend from the abdominal aorta to each kidney, and the renal veins extend from the kidneys to the inferior vena cava.

and a distal tubule (figure 18.4). Fluid enters the renal corpuscle and then flows into the proximal tubule. From there, it flows into the loop of Henle. Each loop of Henle has a **descending limb**, which extends toward the renal sinus, and an **ascending limb**, which extends back toward the cortex. The fluid flows through the ascending limb of the loop of Henle to the distal tubule. The distal tubule empties into a **collecting duct**, which carries the fluid from the cortex, through the medulla, and empties its contents into a calyx. Many distal tubules empty into each collecting duct.

The renal corpuscle and both convoluted tubules are in the renal cortex (see figure 18.4). The collecting duct and loop of Henle enter the medulla. Approximately 15% of the

nephrons have loops of Henle that extend deeply into the medulla of the kidney. The other nephrons (85%) have loops of Henle that do not extend deeply into the medulla.

The **renal corpuscle** of the nephron consists of Bowman's capsule and the glomerulus (see figure 18.4; figure 18.5). The wall of Bowman's capsule is indented to form a double-walled chamber. The indentation is occupied by a tuft of capillaries called the **glomerulus** (glō-mār′ū-lŭs), which resembles a ball of yarn. The cavity of Bowman's capsule opens into the proximal tubule, which carries fluid away from the capsule. The inner wall of Bowman's capsule surrounds the glomerulus and consists of specialized cells called **podocytes** (pod′ō-sīts).

Renal capsule
Cortex
Medulla

Arteries and veins in the renal sinus

Hilum (indentation)

Renal sinus (space)

Renal artery

Calyx

Renal vein

Renal pyramid

Renal pelvis

Ureter

(a)

Figure 18.3 Longitudinal Section of the Kidney

(*a*) The cortex forms the outer part of the kidney, and the medulla forms the inner part. A central cavity, called the renal sinus, contains the renal pelvis, blood vessels, fat, and other connective tissues. The renal pyramids extend from the renal sinus to the cortex of the kidney. The tip of each renal pyramid is surrounded by a calyx. The calyx extends from the tip of the renal pyramid to the renal pelvis. Urine flows from the tip of the renal pyramid through the calyx and renal pelvis into the ureter. (*b*) Photograph of a longitudinal section through a kidney.

Cortex
Medulla

Renal artery
Renal vein

Renal sinus
Renal pelvis
Major calyx
Minor calyx

Renal papilla
Renal pyramid
Ureter

Renal column
Hilum (indentation)

Renal capsule

The glomerular capillaries have pores in their walls, and the podocytes have cell processes with gaps between them. The endothelium of the glomerular capillaries, the podocytes, and the basement membrane between them form a **filtration membrane**. In the first step of urine formation, fluid called **filtrate** is filtered from the glomerular capillaries into Bowman's capsule through the filtration membrane.

A large part of the descending limb has very thin walls made up of simple squamous epithelium. The remainder of the nephron and collecting duct are made up of simple cuboidal epithelium. The cells of the proximal tubules, ascending limb of Henle's loops, distal tubules, and collecting ducts have microvilli and many mitochondria. The proximal tubule, ascending limb of Henle's loop, and the collecting

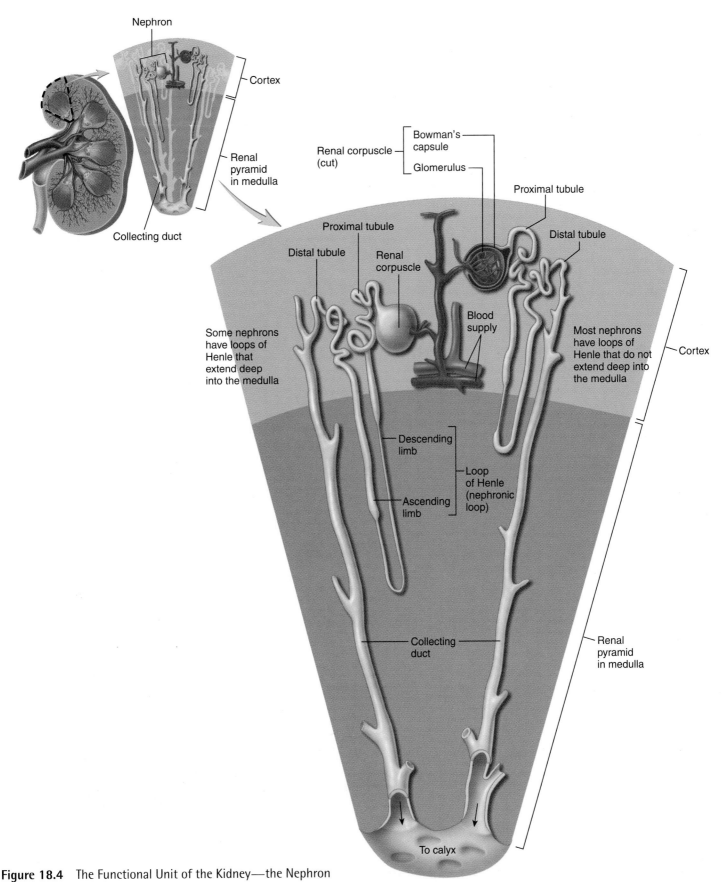

Figure 18.4 The Functional Unit of the Kidney—the Nephron

Each nephron consists of a renal corpuscle, a proximal tubule, a loop of Henle, and a distal tubule. The distal tubule joins the collecting duct, which extends to the tip of the renal pyramid. The renal corpuscle, the proximal tubule, and the distal tubule are in the cortex of the kidney. The loops of Henle and the collecting ducts extend into the medulla of the kidney. Most nephrons have loops of Henle that do not extend deep into the medulla, but some nephrons have loops of Henle that do extend deep into the medulla.

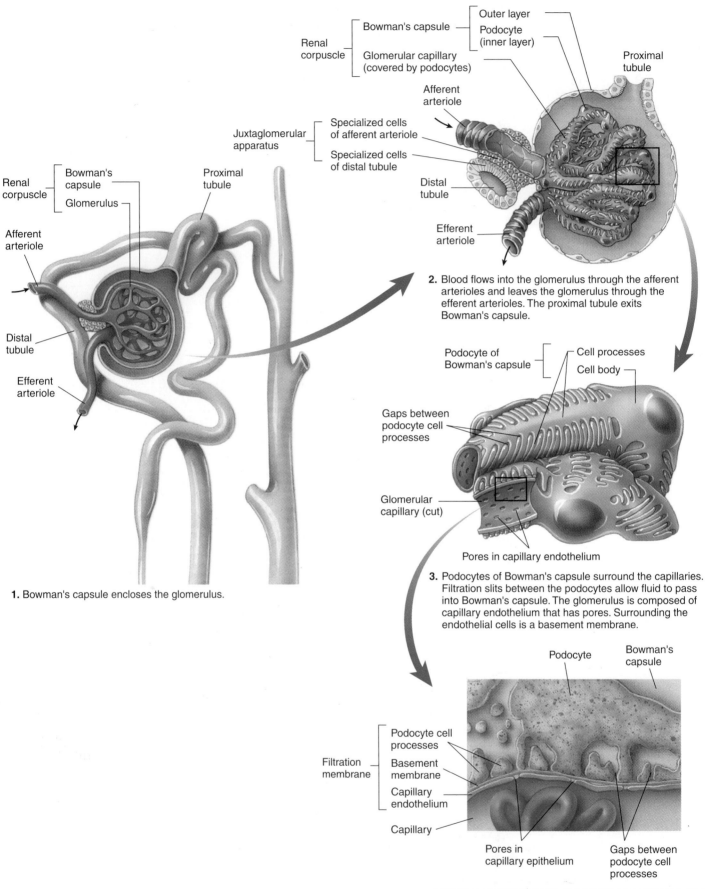

Renal corpuscle
— Bowman's capsule
— Glomerular capillary (covered by podocytes)

Bowman's capsule
— Outer layer
— Podocyte (inner layer)

Proximal tubule

Afferent arteriole

Juxtaglomerular apparatus
— Specialized cells of afferent arteriole
— Specialized cells of distal tubule

Distal tubule

Efferent arteriole

Renal corpuscle
— Bowman's capsule
— Glomerulus

Proximal tubule

Afferent arteriole

Distal tubule

Efferent arteriole

1. Bowman's capsule encloses the glomerulus.

2. Blood flows into the glomerulus through the afferent arterioles and leaves the glomerulus through the efferent arterioles. The proximal tubule exits Bowman's capsule.

Podocyte of Bowman's capsule
— Cell processes
— Cell body

Gaps between podocyte cell processes

Glomerular capillary (cut)

Pores in capillary endothelium

3. Podocytes of Bowman's capsule surround the capillaries. Filtration slits between the podocytes allow fluid to pass into Bowman's capsule. The glomerulus is composed of capillary endothelium that has pores. Surrounding the endothelial cells is a basement membrane.

Podocyte

Bowman's capsule

Filtration membrane
— Podocyte cell processes
— Basement membrane
— Capillary endothelium
— Capillary

Pores in capillary epithelium

Gaps between podocyte cell processes

4. Capillary endothelial cells, the basement membrane, and podocytes make up the filtration membrane of the kidney.

Figure 18.5   The Renal Corpuscle and the Filtration Membrane duct actively transport molecules and ions across the wall of the nephron, where as the descending limb of Henle's loop is very permeable to water and solutes.

Arteries and Veins

The **renal arteries** branch off the abdominal aorta and enter the kidneys (figure 18.6). They give rise to several **interlobar arteries**, which pass between the renal pyramids. The interlobar arteries give rise to the **arcuate arteries**, which arch between the cortex and medulla. **Interlobular arteries** branch off the arcuate arteries to project into the cortex. The **afferent arterioles** arise from branches of the interlobular arteries and extend to the glomerular capillaries. **Efferent arterioles** extend from the

glomerular capillaries to the **peritubular capillaries**, which surround the proximal and distal tubules and the loops of Henle (see figure 18.6). The **vasa recta** (vā′să rek′tă) are specialized portions of the peritubular capillaries which extend deep into the medulla of the kidney. Blood from the peritubular capillaries, including the vasa recta, enters the interlobular veins. The veins of the kidney run parallel to the arteries and have similar names (see figure 18.6).

A specialized structure called the **juxtaglomerular** (jŭks′-tă-glŏ-mer′ū-lăr) **apparatus** is formed where the distal tubule projects between the afferent arteriole and the efferent arteriole next to Bowman's capsule. The specialized walls of the distal tubule and afferent arteriole form the juxtaglomerular apparatus (see figure 18.5).

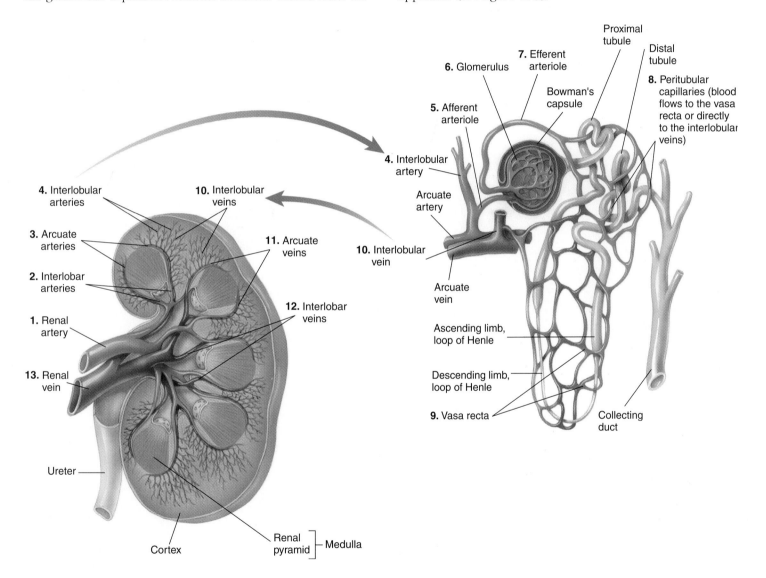

Figure 18.6   Blood Flow Through the Kidney

(a) Renal arteries (1) project to the renal sinus, and interlobar arteries (2) extend from the renal sinus through the renal columns to the arcuate arteries (3) and from the arcuate arteries to the interlobular arteries (4). Veins are also illustrated. Interlobular veins (10) carry blood to arcuate veins (11). Arcuate veins carry blood to the interlobar veins (12), and the interlobar veins carry blood to the renal vein (13). (b) The circulation through the kidney from arcuate arteries and back to the arcuate veins is illustrated. Blood flows from the arcuate arteries (3) to the interlobular arteries (4). Blood flows from the interlobular arteries through the afferent arterioles (5) to the glomerular capillaries (6), and from the glomerular capillaries to the efferent arterioles (7). Blood then flows through the peritubular capillaries (8) and through the vasa recta (9) to the interlobular vein (10) and then to the arcuate vein (11).

Ureters, Urinary Bladder, and Urethra

The **ureters** are small tubes that carry urine from the renal pelvis of the kidney to the posterior inferior portion of the urinary bladder (figure 18.7). The **urinary bladder** is a hollow muscular container that lies in the pelvic cavity just posterior to the pubic symphysis. It functions to store urine, and its size depends on the quantity of urine present. The urinary bladder can hold from a few milliliters to a maximum of about 1000 milliliters (mL) of urine. When the urinary bladder reaches a volume of a few hundred milliliters, a reflex is activated, which causes the smooth muscle of the urinary bladder to contract, and most of the urine flows out of the urinary bladder through the urethra.

The **urethra** is a tube that exits the urinary bladder inferiorly and anteriorly. The triangle-shaped portion of the urinary bladder located between the opening of the ureters and the opening of the urethra is called the **trigone** (trī′gōn). The urethra carries urine from the urinary bladder to the outside of the body.

The ureters and the urinary bladder are lined with transitional epithelium, which is specialized to stretch (see chapter 4). As the volume of the urinary bladder increases, the epithelial cells change from columnar to flat epithelial cells, and the number of epithelial cell layers decreases. As the volume of the urinary bladder decreases, transitional epithelial cells assume their columnar shape and form a greater number of cell layers.

The walls of the ureter and urinary bladder are composed of layers of smooth muscle. Regular waves of smooth muscle contractions produce the force that causes urine to flow from the kidneys through the ureters to the urinary bladder. Contractions of smooth muscle in the urinary bladder force urine to flow from the bladder through the urethra.

At the junction of the urinary bladder and urethra, the smooth muscle of the bladder wall forms the **internal urinary sphincter**. No well-defined internal urinary sphincter is found

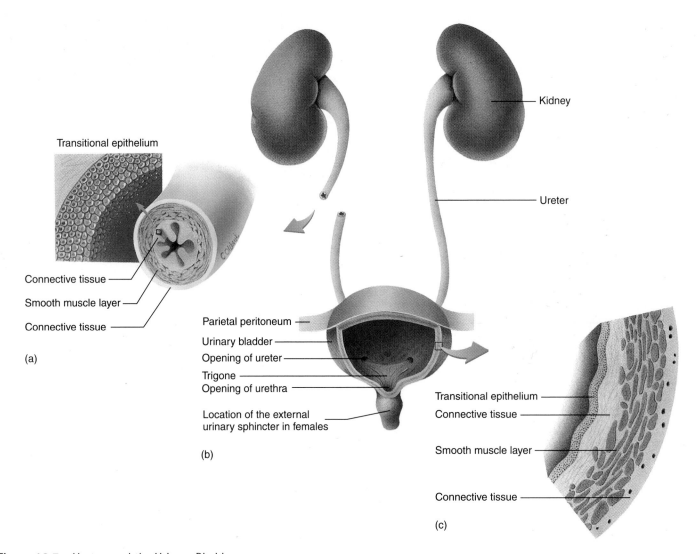

Figure 18.7   Ureters and the Urinary Bladder

(*a*) Ureters extend from the renal pelvis of each kidney to the urinary bladder. (*b*) The walls of the ureters are lined with transitional epithelium, which is surrounded by connective tissue, smooth muscle layers, and a connective tissue layer. (*c*) The wall of the urinary bladder is lined with transitional epithelium, which is surrounded by connective tissue, smooth muscle layers, and a connective tissue layer.

in females. Elastic fibers at the junction of the urinary bladder and urethra keep urine from passing through the urethra until the urinary bladder pressure increases. The internal urinary sphincter of males is under involuntary control. Contraction of the internal urinary sphincter during ejaculation prevents semen from entering the urinary bladder and keeps urine from flowing through the urethra. The **external urinary sphincter** is formed of skeletal muscle that surrounds the urethra as the urethra extends through the pelvic floor. The external urinary sphincter is under involuntary and voluntary control. It controls the flow of urine through the urethra.

In the male, the urethra extends to the end of the penis, where it opens to the outside. The female urethra is much shorter (approximately 4 cm) than the male urethra (approximately 20 cm) and opens into the vestibule anterior to the vaginal opening.

> **1   P R E D I C T**
>
> Cystitis (sis-tī′tis), which is an inflammation of the urinary bladder, is often caused by bacterial infections. Typically bacteria from outside the body enter the bladder. Are males or females more prone to cystitis caused by urinary bladder infections? Explain.

✔ *Answer on page 518*

Urine Production   *introduction*

Urine is mostly water and contains organic waste products such as urea, uric acid, and creatinine (krē′ă-tēn), as well as excess ions, such as sodium, potassium, chloride, bicarbonate, and hydrogen (table 18.1). The three processes critical to the formation of urine are filtration, reabsorption, and secretion (figure 18.8).

Filtration is the movement of water, ions, and small molecules through the filtration membrane of the renal corpuscle. The portion of the plasma entering the nephron is called the **filtrate**. **Tubular reabsorption** is the movement of substances from the filtrate back into the blood of the peritubular capillaries. Certain molecules and ions are reabsorbed by processes such as active transport. Water is reabsorbed by osmosis. In general, the useful substances that enter the filtrate are reabsorbed, and metabolic waste products remain in the filtrate and are eliminated. For example, when proteins are metabolized,

ammonia is a by-product. Ammonia, which is toxic to humans, is converted into urea by the liver. Urea forms part of the filtrate and, although some of it is reabsorbed, much of it is eliminated in the urine. **Tubular secretion** is the transport of substances, usually waste products, into the filtrate. Urine produced by the nephrons therefore consists of the substances that are filtered and secreted from the peritubular capillaries into the nephron, minus those substances that are reabsorbed.

Filtration

An average of 21% of the blood pumped by the heart each minute flows through the kidneys. Of the total volume of blood plasma that flows through the glomerular capillaries, about 19% passes through the filtration membrane into Bowman's capsule to become filtrate. In all of the nephrons of both kidneys, about 180 liters (L) of filtrate is produced each day, but only about 1% or less of the filtrate becomes urine because most of the filtrate is reabsorbed.

Table 18.1   Concentrations of Major Substances in Urine (Average Values)

Substance	Plasma	Urine
Water (L/day)		1.4
Organic molecules (mg/100 mL)		
Protein	3900–5000	0*
Glucose	100	0
Urea	26	1820
Uric acid	3	42
Creatinine	1	196
Ions (mEq/L)		
Sodium	142	128
Potassium	5	60
Chloride	103	134
Bicarbonate	28	14
Specific gravity (g/ml)†		1.005–1.030
pH		4.5–8.0

*Trace amounts of protein can be found in the urine.
†The specific gravity increases as the concentration of solutes in urine increase.

Urine formation results from the following three processes:

1. Filtration   Filtration (blue arrow) is the movement of materials across the filtration membrane into the lumen of Bowman's capsule to form filtrate.

2. Reabsorption   Solutes are reabsorbed (purple arrow) across the wall of the nephron by transport processes, such as active transport and cotransport.

Water is reabsorbed (green arrow) across the wall of the nephron by osmosis.

3. Secretion   Solutes are secreted (orange arrow) across the wall of the nephron into the filtrate.

Figure 18.8   Urine Formation

The filtration membrane allows some substances, but not others, to pass from the blood into Bowman's capsule. Water and solutes of small size readily pass through the openings of the filtration membrane, but blood cells and proteins, which are too large to pass through the filtration membrane, do not enter Bowman's capsule. Albumin, a blood protein with a diameter slightly less than the openings in the filtration membrane, enters the filtrate in very small amounts. Negative charges on the albumin proteins are repelled by the negative charges of the filtration membrane. Consequently, the filtrate contains no cells and only a small amount of protein.

The formation of filtrate depends on the pressure difference between the glomerular capillaries and Bowman's capsule, called the **filtration pressure**. It forces fluid from the glomerular capillaries through the filtration membrane into Bowman's capsule (figure 18.9). Under most conditions, the filtration pressure remains within a narrow range of values. However, when the filtration pressure increases, both the filtrate and urine volumes increase. When the filtration pressure decreases, the filtrate volume and the urine volume decrease.

The filtration pressure is influenced by the blood pressure in the glomerular capillary, the blood protein concentration, and the pressure in Bowman's capsule. The blood pressure is normally higher in the glomerular capillaries than it is in most capillaries. The filtration pressure increases if the blood pressure in the glomerular capillaries increases further. The filtration pressure decreases if the blood pressure in the glomerular capillary decreases.

The concentration of proteins in the blood opposes the effect of blood pressure on the filtration pressure because of osmosis (see chapter 3). An increase in blood protein concentration reduces the filtration pressure, and a decrease in blood protein concentration increases the filtration pressure. The pressure in Bowman's capsule also opposes the effect of blood pressure on the filtration pressure. For example, an increase in the pressure in Bowman's capsule reduces the filtration pressure.

The blood pressure within the glomerular capillaries is fairly constant because the afferent arterioles either dilate or constrict to regulate the blood pressure in the glomerular capillaries. Also, the concentration of blood proteins and the pressure inside Bowman's capsule are fairly constant. As a consequence, the filtration pressure and the rate of filtrate formation are maintained within a narrow range of values most of the time.

The filtration pressure does change dramatically under some conditions. Strong sympathetic stimulation in response to periods of excitement, rigorous physical activity, or emergency conditions cause renal blood vessels to undergo vasoconstriction. The blood pressure in the glomerular capillaries decreases, causing the filtration pressure to decrease. The rate of filtrate and urine formation can be reduced to nearly zero.

Decreases in the concentration of plasma proteins, caused by conditions such as inflammation of the liver, increase the filtration pressure. The increased filtration pressure causes the filtrate and urine volume to increase.

> **Did You Know?**
>
> During **cardiovascular shock,** renal blood vessels constrict, and blood flow to the kidneys is decreased to a very low rate. One of the dangers of cardiovascular shock is that the renal blood flow can be so low that the kidneys suffer from a lack of oxygen. If the oxygen level remains too low for a long enough time, permanent kidney damage or complete failure of the kidneys results. One important reason for treating cardiovascular shock quickly is to avoid damage to the kidneys.

Reabsorption

As the filtrate flows from Bowman's capsule through the proximal tubule, loop of Henle, distal tubule, and collecting duct, many of the solutes in the filtrate are reabsorbed. About 99% of the original filtrate volume is reabsorbed and enters the

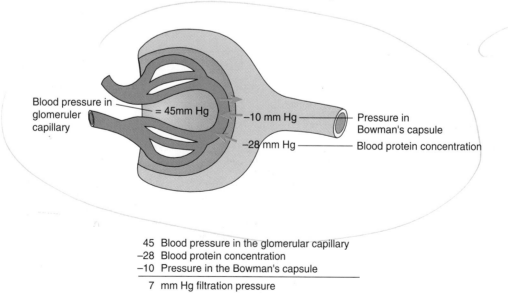

```
  45  Blood pressure in the glomerular capillary
 -28  Blood protein concentration
 -10  Pressure in the Bowman's capsule
───────────────────────────────────────────
   7  mm Hg filtration pressure
```

Figure 18.9 Filtration Pressure

Filtration pressure across the filtration membrane is equal to the blood pressure in the glomerular capillary minus the osmotic pressure because of the plasma proteins in the glomerular capillary and the pressure in Bowman's capsule.

peritubular capillaries. The reabsorbed filtrate flows through the renal veins to enter the general circulation. Only 1% of the original filtrate volume becomes urine (figure 18.10). Because excess ions and metabolic waste products are not readily reabsorbed, the small volume of urine produced contains a high concentration of metabolic waste products.

The proximal tubule is the primary site for the reabsorption of solutes and water. The cuboidal cells of the proximal tubule have numerous microvilli and mitochrondria, and they are well adapted to transport molecules and ions across the wall of the nephron by active transport and secondary active transport. Substances transported from the proximal tubule

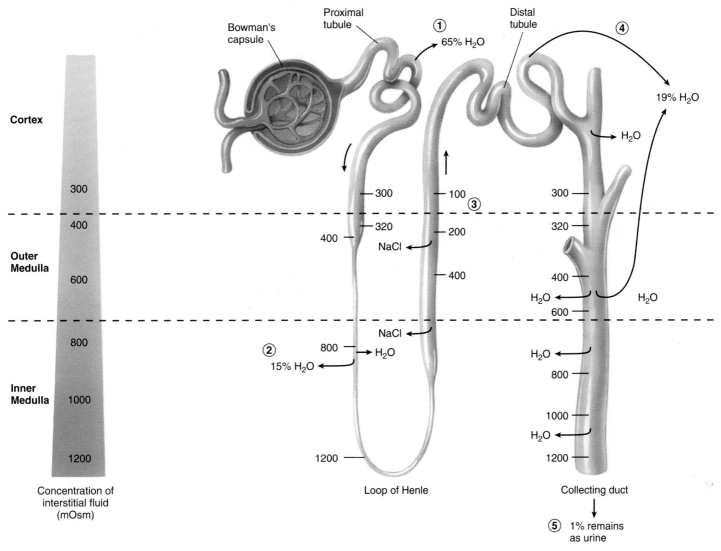

Figure 18.10   Water Reabsorption from the Filtrate

1. Approximately 180 L of filtrate enters the nephrons each day. Of that volume 65% is reabsorbed and passes into the peritubular capillaries. In the proximal tubules, solutes are actively reabsorbed, and water follows the reabsorbed solutes because the cells of the tubule wall are permeable to water.

2. An additional 15% of the filtrate volume is reabsorbed in the descending limb of Henle's loop. The descending limb of Henle's loop passes through the concentrated interstial fluid of the medulla. Because the wall of the descending limb of Henle's loop is permeable to water, water diffuses from the tubule into the more concentrated fluid of the medulla. The water enters the vasa recta which removes the excess fluid.

3. The ascending limb of Henle's loop is not permeable to water. Sodium and chloride ions are actively transported from the filtrate into the medulla. Consequently, the volume of the filtrate does not change as it passes through the ascending limb of Henle's loop, but the concentration is greatly reduced and it becomes less concentrated than the interstitial fluid.

4. The distal tubule and collecting duct actively transport sodium and chloride ions from the tubule and they are permeable to water if ADH is present. If ADH is present, water diffuses from the less concentrated filtrate into the peritubular capillaries and vasa recta. By the time the filtrate has reached the tips of the renal pyramids of the medulla an additional 19% of the filtrate has been reabsorbed.

5. Approximately 1% (1–2 L/day) of the filtrate remains as urine.

- Solutes are transported by active transport and secondary active transport out of the proximal tubules.
- Water moves by osmosis out of the proximal tubule.
- 65% of the filtrate volume is reabsorbed from the proximal tubule and enters the peritubular capillary.

Blood flow

Solutes   H₂O

Peritubular capillary

Interstitial fluid

Filtrate flow

Proximal tubule

Figure 18.11   Reabsorption in the Proximal Tubule

Solutes such as sodium ions, potassium ions, chloride ions, glucose, and amino acids are reabsorbed by active transport and secondary active transport by epithelial cells of the proximal tubule. Water follows the solutes because of osmosis. As a result, solutes plus 65% of the volume of the filtrate are reabsorbed from the proximal tubule and enters the peritubular capillaries.

include proteins; amino acids; glucose; and fructose molecules; as well as sodium, potassium, calcium, bicarbonate, and chloride ions. The proximal tubule is permeable to water. As solute molecules are transported out of the proximal tubule to the peritubular capillaries, water moves by osmosis in the same direction. Consequently, 65% of the filtrate volume is reabsorbed from the proximal tubule (see figures 18.10 and 18.11).

The descending limb of the loop of Henle functions to further concentrate the filtrate. The renal medulla contains very concentrated interstitial fluid that has large amounts of sodium chloride and urea. The wall of the descending limb is permeable to water and moderately permeable to solutes. As the filtrate passes through the descending limb of the loop of Henle into the medulla of the kidney, water moves out of the nephron by osmosis, and some solutes move into the nephron by diffusion. By the time the filtrate has passed through the descending limb, another 15% of the filtrate volume has been reabsorbed, and the filtrate is as concentrated as the interstitial fluid of the medulla. The reabsorbed filtrate enters the vasa recta (see figures 18.10 and 18.12).

The ascending limb of the loop of Henle functions to dilute the filtrate by removing solutes. The cuboidal epithelial cells of the ascending limb actively transport sodium ions out of the nephron, and the negatively charged chloride ions are transported by secondary active transport. The ascending limb is not permeable to water, however. As a result, sodium and chloride ions, but little water, are removed from the filtrate. Because of the efficient removal of sodium and chloride ions, the highly concentrated filtrate that enters the ascending limb of Henle's loop is converted to a dilute solution by the time it reaches the distal tubule (see figures 18.10 and 18.13). As the filtrate enters the distal tubule, it is more dilute than the interstitial fluid of the renal cortex. Also, because of the volume of

filtrate reabsorbed in the proximal tubule and the descending limb of Henle's loop, only about 20% of the original filtrate volume remains. The solutes transported from the ascending limb of the loop of Henle enter the interstitial fluid of the medulla and help keep the concentration of solutes in the medulla high. Excess solutes enter the vasa recta.

The cuboidal cells of the distal tubule and collecting duct function to remove water and additional solutes. Solutes such as sodium and chloride ions are actively reabsorbed, and 19% of the original filtrate volume is reabsorbed by osmosis, leaving about 1% of the original filtrate as urine (see figures 18.10 and 18.14). The reabsorbed water and solutes from the distal tubule enter the peritubular capillaries and enter the vasa recta from the collecting ducts. The reabsorption of water and solutes from the distal tubule and collecting duct is controlled by hormones, which have a great influence on urine concentration and volume (see under Regulation of Urine Concentration and Volume, which follows).

2   P R E D I C T

People who suffer from untreated diabetes mellitus can experience very high levels of glucose in the blood. The glucose can easily cross the filtration membrane into Bowman's capsule. Normally all the glucose is reabsorbed from the nephron. If the concentration of glucose in the nephron becomes too high, however, not all the glucose can be reabsorbed because the number of transport molecules in the cells of the proximal tubule is limited. How does the volume of urine produced by a person with untreated diabetes mellitus differ from that of a normal person, and how does the concentration of the urine differ from that of a normal person?

✔ *Answer on page 518*

- Solutes are transported by active transport and secondary active transport out of the ascending limb of the loop of Henle.
- Water does not leave the ascending limb of the loop of Henle because it is not permeable to water.
- The filtrate becomes more dilute than the interstitial fluid.

- Solutes diffuse slowly into the descending limb of the loop of Henle.
- Water moves quickly by osmosis out of the descending limb of the loop of Henle.
- 15% of the filtrate volume is reabsorbed from the descending limb of the loop of Henle.

Figure 18.13 Reabsorption in the Ascending Limb of the Loop of Henle

Sodium, potassium, and chloride ions are transported by active transport and secondary active transport out of the ascending limb of the loop of Henle. The wall of the ascending limb of the loop of Henle is not permeable to water. The filtrate is more dilute than the interstitial fluid by the time it exits the ascending limb and enters the distal tubule.

Figure 18.12 Reabsorption in the Descending Limb of the Loop of Henle

The wall of the descending limb of the loop of Henle is permeable to water, and to a lesser extent to solutes. The interstitial fluid and the vasa recta in the medulla of the kidney have a high solute concentration. Solutes diffuse slowly into the descending limb of the loop of Henle, and water moves quickly by osmosis out of the descending limb of the loop of Henle into the interstitial fluid. An additional 15% of the filtrate volume is reabsorbed from the descending limb of the loop of Henle. The vasa recta carry the excess water away from the medulla.

Filtrate flow

- Solutes are transported by active transport and secondary active transport out of the distal tubule and collecting duct.
- Water moves by osmosis from the distal tubule and collecting duct.
- Approximately 19% of the filtrate is reabsorbed from the distal tubule and collecting duct.

H_2O

Solutes

Peritubular capillary or vasa recta | Interstitial fluid | Distal tubule or collecting duct

Figure 18.14   Reabsorption in the Distal Tubule and Collecting Duct

Solutes are transported by active transport and secondary active transport out of the distal tubule and collecting duct. When ADH is present, the distal tubules and collecting ducts are permeable to water. Water moves by osmosis out of the distal tubule and collecting duct into the more concentrated interstitial fluid of cortex and medulla. The reabsorbed water and solutes from the distal tubule enter the peritubular capillaries and enter the vasa recta from the collecting ducts.

In summary, most of the useful solutes that pass through the filtration membrane into Bowman's capsule are reabsorbed in the proximal tubule. Filtrate volume is reduced by 65% in the proximal tubule and by 15% in the descending limb of the loop of Henle. In the ascending limb of the loop of Henle, sodium chloride, but little water, is removed from the filtrate. Consequently, the filtrate becomes dilute. In the distal tubule and the collecting duct, additional sodium chloride is removed, water moves out by osmosis, and the filtrate volume is reduced by another 19%, leaving 1% of the original filtrate volume as urine.

Secretion

Some substances, including by-products of metabolism that become toxic in high concentrations and drugs or molecules not normally produced by the body, are secreted into the nephron from the peritubular capillaries. As with tubular reabsorption, tubular secretion can be either active or passive. For example, ammonia diffuses into the lumen of the nephron, whereas hydrogen ions, potassium ions, creatinine, histamine, and penicillin are actively transported into the nephron.

Hydrogen ions are actively transported into the proximal tubule. The epithelial cells actively transport large quantities of hydrogen ions across the wall of the nephron into the filtrate. The secretion of hydrogen ions plays an important role in the regulation of the body fluid pH.

In the proximal tubule, potassium ions are reabsorbed. In the distal tubule and collecting duct, potassium ions are secreted.

Regulation of Urine Concentration and Volume

Given a solution in a container, such as a pan on a stove, it is possible to decrease the concentration of the solution by adding water to it. It is also possible to increase the concentration of the solution by boiling the water in the pan, thus removing water from the solution by evaporation. Similarly, the kidneys function to maintain the concentration of the body fluids by increasing water reabsorption from the filtrate when the body fluid concentration increases and by reducing water reabsorption from the filtrate when the body fluid concentration decreases. The volume and composition of urine therefore changes, depending on conditions in the body. If body fluid concentration increases above normal levels, the kidneys produce a smaller than normal amount of concentrated urine. This eliminates solutes and conserves water, both of which help to lower the body fluid concentration back to normal. On the other hand, if the body fluid concentration decreases, the kidneys produce a large volume of dilute urine. As a result, water is lost, solutes are conserved, and the body fluid concentration increases.

Urine production also maintains blood volume and therefore blood pressure. An increase in blood volume can increase blood pressure, and a decrease in blood volume can decrease blood pressure. When blood volume increases above normal, the kidneys produce a large amount of dilute urine. The loss of water in the urine lowers blood volume.

Conversely, if blood volume decreases below normal, the kidneys produce smaller than normal amounts of concentrated urine to conserve water and maintain blood volume.

Hormonal Mechanisms

Antidiuretic Hormone

Antidiuretic (an'tē-dī-ū-ret'ik) **hormone (ADH)**, secreted by the posterior pituitary gland, passes through the circulatory system to the kidneys. ADH regulates the amount of water re-

absorbed by the distal tubules and collecting ducts. When ADH levels increase, the permeability to water of the distal tubules and collecting ducts increases, and more water is reabsorbed from the filtrate. Consequently, an increase in ADH results in the production of a small volume of concentrated urine. On the other hand, when ADH levels decrease, the distal tubules and collecting ducts become less permeable to water. As a result, less water is reabsorbed, and a large volume of dilute urine is produced (figures 18.15 and 18.16).

The release of ADH from the posterior pituitary is regulated by the hypothalamus. Certain cells of the hypothalamus

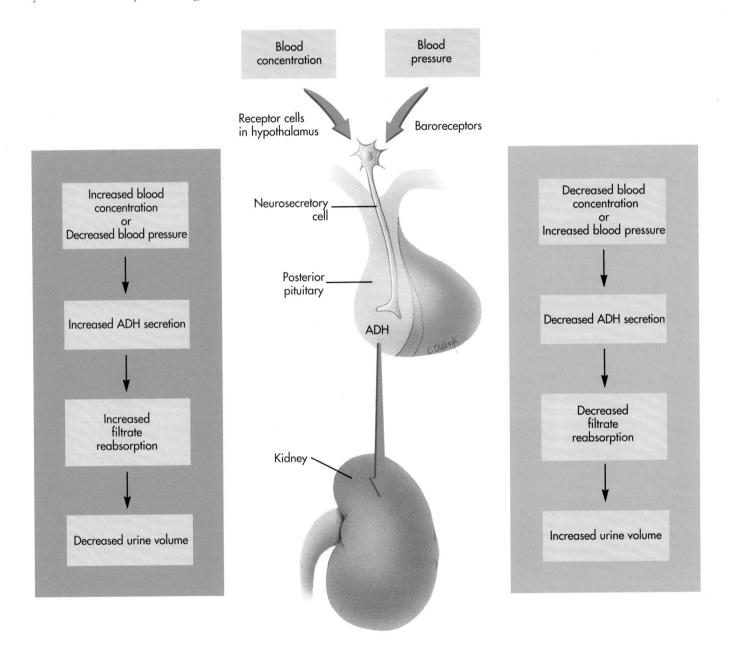

Figure 18.15   Control of ADH Secretion and Its Effect on the Nephron

Increased blood concentration or decreased blood pressure results in increased ADH secretion from the posterior pituitary. The increased ADH acts on the distal tubules and collecting ducts, causing an increased reabsorption of water from the nephrons and the production of a decreased volume of concentrated urine. Decreased blood concentration or increased blood pressure results in decreased ADH secretion from the posterior pituitary. The decreased ADH causes a decreased reabsorption of water from the nephron and the production of a large volume of dilute urine.

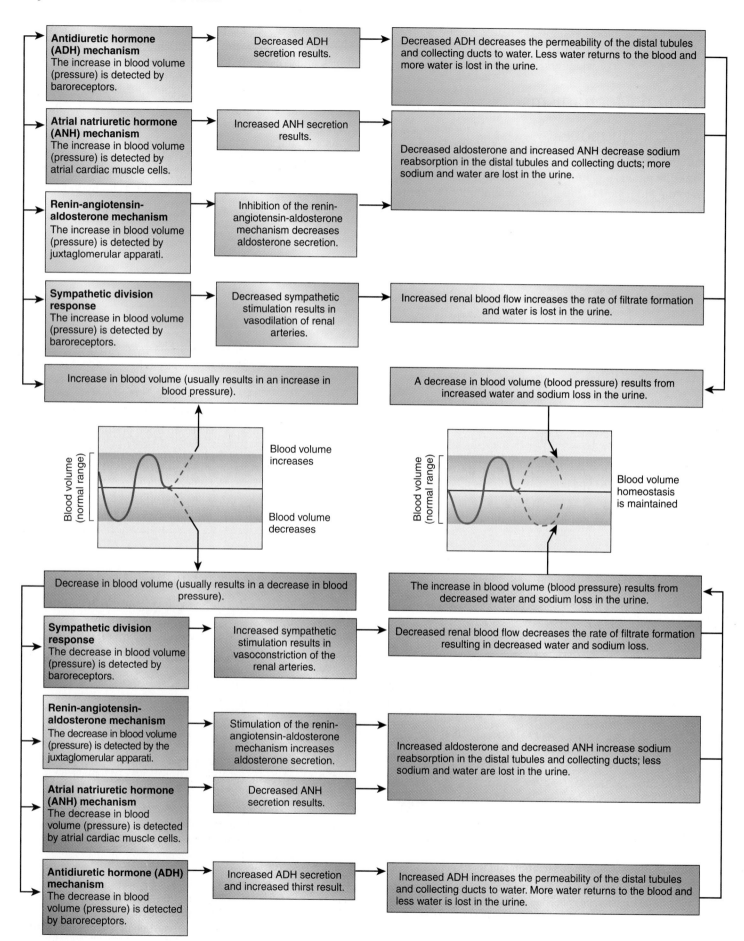

Figure 18.16 Homeostasis: Hormonal Regulation of Blood Volume and Its Effect on Urine Volume and Concentration

are sensitive to changes in the solute concentration of the interstitial fluid within the hypothalamus. An increased solute concentration of the blood and interstitial fluid results in action potentials being sent along the axons of the ADH-secreting neurons of the hypothalamus to the posterior pituitary, causing ADH to be released from the ends of the axons (see chapter 10). A reduced solute concentration in the blood and interstitial fluid within the hypothalamus causes inhibition of ADH release.

Baroreceptors that monitor blood pressure also influence ADH secretion. Increased blood pressure causes a decrease in ADH secretion, and decreased blood pressure increases ADH secretion (see figures 18.15 and 18.16).

renin is released from the kidney. The resultant increase in aldosterone causes an increase in sodium reabsorption from the nephron. Water follows the sodium ions. Thus the volume of water lost in the form of urine declines. This method of conserving water helps prevent a further decline in blood pressure (see figure 18.16).

3   P R E D I C T

Drugs that increase the urine volume are called **diuretics** (dī-ū-ret'iks). Some diuretics inhibit the active transport of sodium ions in the nephron. Explain how these diuretic drugs could cause an increase in urine volume.

✔ *Answer on page 518*

Did You Know?

Diabetes insipidus is a pathological condition in which the posterior pituitary fails to secrete ADH or the kidney tubules do not respond to the presence of ADH. In people suffering from diabetes insipidus, much of the filtrate entering the proximal and distal tubules becomes urine. People with this condition can produce as much as 20 to 30 L of urine each day. Because they lose so much water, they are continually in danger of severe dehydration. Even though they produce dilute urine, producing such a large volume of urine also results in the loss of large amounts of sodium, calcium, and other ions. The resulting ionic imbalances cause the nervous system and cardiac muscle to function abnormally. People suffering from diabetes insipidus can be successfully treated by taking ADH in the form of either a nasal spray or an injection.

Did You Know?

Alcohol and caffeine are examples of diuretics. Alcohol inhibits the secretion of ADH from the posterior pituitary. Consequently, the consumption of alcoholic beverages results in the production of a large volume of dilute urine. The volume of urine lost easily can exceed the volume of water consumed with the alcohol. Consequently, several hours after drinking alcoholic beverages, such as the morning after an intense celebration, dehydration and intense thirst can occur. Caffeine also is a diuretic. Caffeine and related substances act on the kidneys by increasing blood flow to the kidney and by increasing the loss of sodium and chloride in the urine. Both the increased blood flow to the kidney and the increased loss of sodium and chloride in the urine increase urine volume.

Renin-Angiotensin-Aldosterone

Renin (rē'nin or ren'in) and **angiotensin** (an'jē-ō-ten'sin) help regulate **aldosterone** (al-dos'ter-ōn) secretion. Renin is secreted by cells of the juxtaglomerular apparati in the kidneys. Renin is an enzyme that acts on a protein produced by the liver called **angiotensinogen** (an'jē-ō-ten-sin'ō-jen). Amino acids are removed from angiotensinogen, leaving **angiotensin I**. Angiotensin I is rapidly converted to a smaller peptide called **angiotensin II** by **angiotensin-converting enzyme**. Angiotensin II acts on the adrenal cortex, causing it to secrete aldosterone (see chapter 13).

Aldosterone increases the rate of active transport of sodium ions in the distal tubule and collecting duct. In the absence of aldosterone, large amounts of sodium ions remain in the nephron and become part of the urine. A high sodium ion concentration in the filtrate causes water to remain in the nephron and increases urine volume. When the rate of active transport of sodium ions is slow, urine volume therefore, increases, and the urine contains a high concentrations of sodium. Because chloride ions are attracted by the positive charge on the sodium ions, chloride ions follow the sodium ions.

When blood pressure suddenly decreases or when the concentration of sodium ions in the blood becomes too low,

Atrial Natriuretic Hormone

Atrial natriuretic (nā'trē-ū-ret'ik) **hormone (ANH)** is secreted from cardiac muscle cells in the right atrium of the heart when blood pressure in the right atrium increases. Atrial natriuretic hormone acts on the kidney to decrease sodium ion reabsorption. Sodium ions and water therefore remain in the nephron to become urine. The increased loss of sodium ions and water as urine reduces the blood volume and the blood pressure (see figure 18.16).

4   P R E D I C T

Ivy Salina worked as a nurse in a hospital. Because she was very observant, she recognized that one of her patients received a much larger volume of an intravenous (IV) saline solution than she was supposed to receive. A saline solution consists of sodium chloride, but it sometimes contains other solutes such as small amounts of potassium chloride. Saline solutions have the same concentration as body fluids. Predict the effect of the large volume of IV saline solution on the rate of urine production, and describe the role of ADH and atrial natriuretic hormone in the control of the change in urine production.

✔ *Answer on page 518*

Effect of Sympathetic Innervation on Kidney Function

Sympathetic neurons with norepinephrine as their neurotransmitter substance innervate the blood vessels of the kidney. Sympathetic stimulation constricts the arteries, causing a decrease in renal blood flow and filtrate formation. Intense sympathetic stimulation causes the rate of filtrate formation to decrease to only a few milliliters per minute. Consequently only a small volume of urine is produced (see figure 18.16). Decreases in blood pressure, such as during shock, are detected by baroreceptors and the result is to increase sympathetic stimulation of renal blood arteries. Other conditions such as intense physical activity or trauma increase sympathetic stimulation of renal blood arteries and decrease urine production to very low levels. Increased blood pressure is detected by barorectors and decreases sympathetic stimulation of renal blood arteries. Urine volume increases in response to a decrease in sympathetic stimulation of renal arteries (see figure 18.16).

Urine Movement

The **micturition** (mik-choo-rish′ŭn) **reflex** is activated by stretch of the urinary bladder wall. As the bladder fills with urine, pressure increases, and stretch receptors in the wall of the bladder are stimulated. Action potentials are conducted from the bladder to the spinal cord through the pelvic nerves. Integration of the reflex occurs in the spinal cord, and action potentials are conducted along parasympathetic nerve fibers to the urinary bladder. Parasympathetic action potentials cause the urinary bladder to contract and the internal urinary sphincters in males to relax (figure 18.17). The external urinary sphincter is normally contracted as a result of stimulation from the somatic motor nervous system. Because of the micturition reflex, action potentials conducted along somatic motor nerve fibers to the external urinary sphincter also decrease, which causes the sphincter to relax. The micturition reflex is an automatic reflex, but it can be inhibited or stimulated by higher centers in the brain. The higher brain centers prevent micturition by sending action potentials through the spinal cord to decrease the intensity of the autonomic reflex that stimulates urinary bladder contractions and to stimulate nerve fibers that keep the external urinary sphincter contracted. The ability to voluntarily inhibit micturition develops at the age of 2 to 3 years.

When the desire to urinate exists, the higher brain centers send action potentials to the spinal cord to facilitate the micturition reflex and inhibit the external urinary sphincter. Awareness of the need to urinate occurs because stretch of the urinary bladder stimulates afferent nerve fibers that increase action potentials carried to the brain by ascending fibers in the spinal cord. Irritation of the urinary bladder or the urethra by bacterial infections or by other conditions can also initiate the urge to urinate, even though the bladder is nearly empty.

Body Fluid Compartments

For a 70-kilogram (kg) adult male, approximately 40 L, or 60% of the total body weight, consists of water. A smaller percentage of the body weight of the adult female consists of water because females generally have a greater percentage of body fat than males. Water and ions dissolved in it are distributed in two major compartments (table 18.2). Water and ions move between these compartments, but their movement is regulated.

The **intracellular fluid compartment** includes the fluid inside all the cells of the body. The cell membranes of the individual cells enclose the intracellular compartment, which actually consists of trillions of small compartments. The composition of the fluid in these compartments and the regulation of fluid movement across cell membranes are similar. Approximately two-thirds of all the water in the body is in the intracellular fluid compartment.

The **extracellular fluid compartment** includes all the fluid outside the cells. It constitutes approximately one-third of the total body water. The extracellular fluid compartment includes the interstitial fluid, the plasma within blood vessels, and fluid in the lymphatic vessels. A small portion of the extracellular fluid volume is separated by membranes into subcompartments. These special subcompartments contain fluid with a different composition from the remainder of the extracellular fluid. Included among the subcompartments are the aqueous and vitreous humor of the eye, cerebrospinal fluid, synovial fluid in joint cavities, serous fluid in the body cavities, and fluid secreted by glands.

Composition of the Fluid in the Body Fluid Compartments

Intracellular fluid has a similar composition from cell to cell. The intracellular fluid contains a relatively high concentration of ions, such as potassium, calcium, magnesium, phosphate, and sulfate ions, compared with the extracellular fluid. It has a lower concentration of sodium, chloride, and bicarbonate ions than that of the extracellular fluid. The concentration of protein in the intracellular fluid is also greater than that in the extracellular fluid. Like intracellular fluid, the extracellular fluid also has a fairly consistent composition from one area of the body to another.

Exchange Between Body Fluid Compartments

The cell membranes that separate the body fluid compartments are selectively permeable. Water continually passes through them, but they are much less permeable to ions dissolved in the water. Water movement is regulated mainly by hydrostatic pressure differences and osmotic differences between the compartments. For example, water moves across the wall of the capillary at the arteriolar end of the capillary because the blood pressure is great enough to force fluid through the wall of the capillary into the interstitial space. At

Control of the micturition reflex by higher brain centers

A. Ascending pathways carry an increased frequency of action potentials up the spinal cord to the brain when the urinary bladder becomes stretched. This increases the conscious desire to urinate.

B. Descending pathways carry action potentials to the sacral region of the spinal cord to tonically inhibit the micturition reflex, preventing automatic urination when the bladder is full. Descending pathways carry action potentials to the sacral region of the spinal cord to stimulate the reflex when stretch of the urinary bladder produces the conscious urge to urinate and when one voluntarily chooses to urinate. This reinforces the micturition reflex.

Micturition reflex

1. Urine in the urinary bladder stretches the bladder wall.

2. Action potentials produced by the stretch receptors are carried along pelvic nerves (green line) to the sacral region of the spinal cord.

3. Action potentials are carried by the parasympathetic nerves (red line) to contract the smooth muscles of the urinary bladder. Decreased action potentials carried by the somatic motor nerves (purple line) cause the external urinary sphincter to relax.

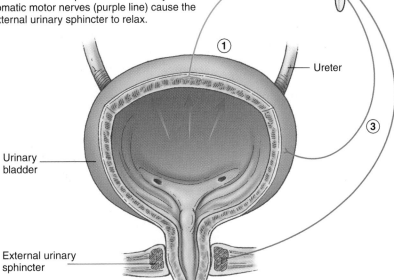

Brainstem

Ureter

Urinary bladder

External urinary sphincter

Figure 18.17   The Micturition Reflex

Table 18.2	Approximate Volumes of Body Fluid Compartments*			Extracellular Fluid	
Age of Person	Total Body Water	Intracellular Fluid	Plasma	Interstitial	Total
Infants	75	45	4	26	30
Adult males	60	40	5	15	20
Adult females	50	35	5	10	15

*Expressed as percentage of body weight.

the venous end of the capillary, the blood pressure is much lower, and fluid returns to the capillary because the osmotic pressure is higher inside the capillary than outside it (see chapter 13).

The major influence controlling the movement of water between the intracellular and extracellular spaces is osmosis. For example, if the extracellular concentration of ions increases, water moves by osmosis from cells into the extracellular fluid.

The intracellular fluid can help maintain the extracellular fluid volume if it is depleted. When a person becomes dehydrated, the concentration of ions in the extracellular fluid increases. As a consequence, water moves from the intracellular fluid to the extracellular fluid, thus maintaining the extracellular fluid volume. Because blood is an important component of the extracellular fluid volume, this process helps to maintain blood volume. Movement of water from the intracellular fluid compartment to the extracellular fluid compartment can help prolong the time a person can survive conditions such as dehydration or cardiovascular shock.

If the concentration of ions in the extracellular fluid decreases, water moves, by osmosis, from the extracellular fluid into the cells. The water movement can cause the cells to swell. Under most conditions, the movement of water between the intracellular and extracellular fluid compartments is maintained within limits that are consistent with survival of the individual.

Regulation of Extracellular Fluid Composition

Homeostasis requires that the intake of substances such as water and ions equals their elimination. Ingestion of water and ions adds these substances to the body; they are excreted from the body by organs such as the kidneys and, to a lesser degree, by the skin, liver, and gastrointestinal tract. Greater quantities of water and ions are lost from the body in the form of perspiration on warm days than on cool days, and varying amounts of water and ions can be lost in the form of feces. Over a long period, the total amount of water and ions in the body does not change unless the individual is growing, gaining weight, or losing weight. The regulation of water and ions involves the coordinated participation of several organ systems, but the most important organ in regulating the loss of water and ions from the body is the kidney.

Thirst

Water intake is controlled by neurons in the hypothalamus, collectively called the **thirst center**. When the concentration of blood increases, the thirst center responds by initiating the sensation of thirst. When water or some other dilute solution is consumed, the concentration of the blood decreases, and the sensation of thirst also decreases. When blood pressure decreases, such as during shock, the thirst center is activated, and the sensation of thirst is triggered. Consumption of water increases the blood volume and allows the blood pressure to increase toward its normal value. Other stimuli in addition to changes in solute concentration and blood pressure can trigger the sensation of thirst. For example, if the mucosa of the mouth becomes dry, the thirst center is activated. Thirst is one of the important means of regulating extracellular fluid volume and concentration.

Ions

The kidneys and other organ systems function to regulate the composition of the extracellular fluid. If the water content or concentration of ions in the extracellular fluid deviates from their normal range, cells cannot control the movement of substances across their cell membranes or the composition of their intracellular fluid. The consequence is abnormal cell function or even cell death. Keeping the extracellular fluid composition within a normal range of values is therefore required to sustain life.

Regulating the concentrations of positively charged ions such as sodium, potassium, and calcium in the body fluids is particularly important. Action potentials, contraction of muscles, and maintenance of normal cell membrane permeability depend on the maintenance of a narrow range of concentrations for these ions. Important mechanisms control the concentrations of these ions in the body. Negatively charged ions such as chloride are secondarily regulated by the mechanisms that control the positively charged ions. The negatively charged ions are attracted to positively charged ions; when the positively charged ions are transported, the negatively charged ions move with them.

Sodium Ions   Salt intake

Sodium ions are major ions in the extracellular fluid. About 90% to 95% of the osmotic pressure of the extracellular fluid results from sodium ions and from the negative ions associated with them.

The recommended intake of sodium is 2.4 to 3 grams per day (g/day), which is more than the body actually requires each day. Most people in the United States consume two to three times the recommended amount of sodium. The kidneys provide the major route by which the excess sodium ions are excreted.

Stimuli that control aldosterone secretion influence the reabsorption of sodium from nephrons of the kidneys and the total amount of sodium in the body fluids. Reabsorption of sodium ions from the distal tubules and collecting duct is very efficient, and little sodium is lost in the urine when aldosterone is present. When aldosterone is absent, reabsorption of sodium in the nephron is greatly reduced, and the amount of sodium lost in the urine increases.

Sodium ions are also excreted from the body in **sweat**. Normally only a small quantity of sodium is lost each day in the form of sweat, but the amount increases during conditions of heavy exercise in a warm environment.

Because sodium ions have such a large effect on the osmotic pressure of the extracellular fluid, mechanisms that influence sodium ion concentrations in the extracellular fluid also influence the extracellular fluid volume. The mechanisms that play important roles in controlling the sodium ion concentration in the extracellular fluid and the extracellular fluid volume are the renin-angiotensin-aldosterone mechanism, the atrial natri-

uretic mechanism, and antidiuretic hormone. These mechanisms are illustrated in figure 18.18. For example, low blood pressure increases renin and ADH secretion. The result is an increase in sodium ion and water reabsorption in the kidney to bring blood pressure and the sodium ion concentration back to their normal ranges. Increased blood pressure inhibits renin and ADH secretion, and it stimulates atrial natriuretic hormone secretion. The

Low blood pressure stimulates renin secretion from the kidney. Renin stimulates the production of angiotensin I, which is converted to angiotensin II, which in turn stimulates aldosterone secretion from the adrenal cortex. Aldosterone stimulates Na$^+$ ion and water reabsorption in the kidney.

(a)

(b) Increased blood pressure (BP) in the right atrium of the heart causes increased secretion of atrial natriuretic hormone, which increases sodium ion excretion and water loss in the form of urine.

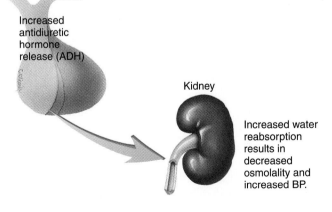

Increased blood osmolality affects hypothalamic neurons, and decreased blood pressure affects baroreceptors in the aortic arch, carotid sinuses, and atrium. As a result of these stimuli, an increased rate of ADH secretion from the posterior pituitary results, which increases water reabsorption.

(c)

Increased blood osmolality affects hypothalamic neurons, and large decreases in blood pressure affects baroreceptors in the aortic arch, carotid sinuses, and atrium. As a result of these stimuli, an increase in thirst results, which increases water intake.

(d)

Figure 18.18   Homeostasis: Regulation of Sodium Ion Levels in the Blood and Other Extracellular Fluid result is a decrease in sodium ion reabsorption and an increase in urine production to bring blood pressure and the sodium ion concentration in the blood to their normal ranges.

Potassium Ions

Electrically excitable tissues such as muscle and nerve are highly sensitive to slight changes in the extracellular potassium concentration. The extracellular concentration of **potassium ions** must be maintained within a narrow range for these tissues to function normally.

Aldosterone plays a major role in regulating the concentration of potassium ions in the extracellular fluid. Dehydration, circulatory system shock resulting from plasma loss, and tissue damage due to injuries such as severe burns, all cause extracellular potassium ions to become more concentrated than normal. In response, aldosterone secretion from the adrenal cortex increases and causes potassium secretion to increase (figure 18.19).

If the potassium concentration in the extracellular fluid becomes reduced, aldosterone secretion from the adrenal cortex decreases. In response, the rate of potassium secretion by the kidney is reduced (see figure 18.19).

Calcium Ions

The extracellular concentration of **calcium ions**, like that of other ions, is maintained within a narrow range. Increases and decreases in the extracellular concentration of calcium ions have dramatic effects on the electrical properties of excitable tissues. Decreased extracellular calcium ion concentrations make cell membranes more permeable to sodium ions, thus making them more electrically excitable. Decreased extracellular concentrations of calcium ions cause spontaneous action potentials in nerve and muscle cells, resulting in hyperexcitability and tetany of muscles. Increased extracellular calcium ion concentrations make cell membranes less permeable to sodium ions, thus making them less electrically excitable. Increased extracellular concentrations of calcium ions inhibit action potentials in nerve and muscle cells, resulting in reduced excitability and either muscle weakness or paralysis.

Parathyroid hormone (PTH), secreted by the parathyroid glands, increases extracellular calcium ion concentration. The rate of PTH secretion is regulated by the extracellular calcium ion concentration (figure 18.20). An elevated calcium ion concentration inhibits, and a reduced concentration stimulates, the secretion of PTH. PTH causes osteoclasts to degrade bone and

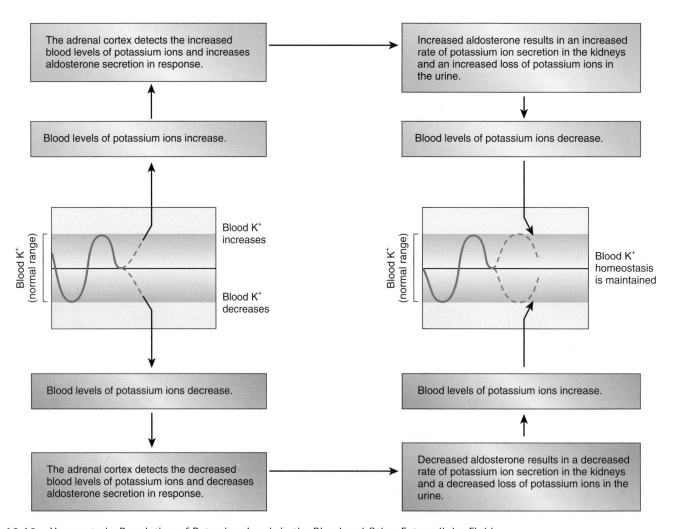

Figure 18.19 Homeostasis: Regulation of Potassium Levels in the Blood and Other Extracellular Fluid

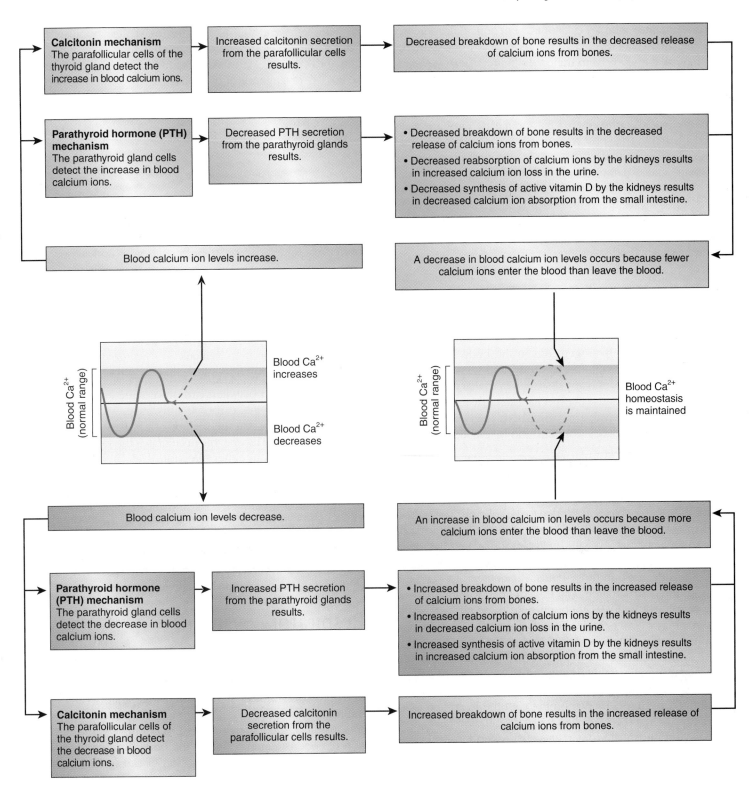

Figure 18.20   Homeostasis: Regulation of Calcium Levels in the Blood and Other Extracellular Fluid

release calcium ions into the body fluids. PTH also increases the rate of calcium ion reabsorption from kidney nephrons and the rate of calcium absorption from the intestine.

Vitamin D increases calcium ion concentration in the blood by increasing the rate of calcium absorption by the intestine and calcium reabsorption by the kidneys. Some vitamin D is consumed in food and the rest is produced by the

body (see chapter 5). PTH affects the intestinal uptake of calcium ions because PTH increases the rate of vitamin D production in the body.

Calcitonin (kal-si-tō′nin) is secreted by the thyroid gland. Calcitonin reduces the blood calcium ion concentration when it is too high. An elevated blood calcium ion concentration causes the thyroid gland to secrete calcitonin, and a low blood calcium ion concentration inhibits calcitonin secretion. Calcitonin reduces the rate at which bone is broken down and decreases the release of calcium ions from bone (see figure 18.20).

Phosphate and Sulfate Ions

Some ions, such as **phosphate ions** and **sulfate ions**, are reabsorbed by active transport in the kidneys. The rate of reabsorption is slow so that, if the concentration of these ions in the filtrate exceeds the ability of the nephron to reabsorb them, the excess is excreted into the urine. As long as the concentration of these ions is low, nearly all of them are reabsorbed by active transport. This mechanism plays a major role in regulating the concentration of phosphate ions and sulfate ions in the body fluid.

Regulation of Acid–Base Balance

The concentration of hydrogen ions in the body fluids is reported as the pH of body fluids. The body fluid pH is maintained between 7.35 and 7.45, and any deviation from that range is life-threatening. Consequently, the mechanisms that regulate body pH are critical for survival. The pH of body fluids is controlled by buffers, by the respiratory system, and by the kidneys.

Buffers

Buffers are chemicals that resist a change in the pH of a solution when either acids or bases are added to the solution. The buffers found in the body fluids contain salts of either weak acids or weak bases that combine with hydrogen ions when hydrogen ions increase in those fluids or release hydrogen ions when hydrogen ions decrease in those fluids. Buffers tend to keep the hydrogen ion concentration, and thus the pH, within a narrow range of values (figure 18.21) because of these characteristics. The three major buffers in the body fluids are the proteins, the phosphate buffer system, and the bicarbonate buffer system.

Proteins and phosphate ions in the body fluids combine with a large number of hydrogen ions. When the hydrogen ion concentration increases, proteins and phosphate ions prevent a decrease in pH by combining with the hydrogen ions. Conversely, when the hydrogen ion concentration decreases, proteins and phosphate ions release hydrogen ions, preventing an increase in pH.

The following reaction illustrates how phosphate buffers work:

$$HPO_4^{2-} \quad + \quad H^+ \quad \rightleftarrows \quad H_2PO_4^-$$

| monohydrogen phosphate ion | | hydrogen ion | | dihydrogen phosphate ion |

Monohydrogen phosphate (HPO_4^{2-}) combines with hydrogen ions to form dihydrogen phosphate ($H_2PO_4^-$) when excess hydrogen ions are present. When hydrogen ion concentration declines, some of the hydrogen ions separate from the dihydrogen phosphate ions.

Proteins are able to function as buffers because amino acids in the proteins have side chains that function as weak acids and weak bases. Many side chains contain carboxyl groups ($-COOH$) or amine groups ($-NH_2$). Both of these groups are able to function as buffers because of the following reactions:

$$-COO^- \quad + \quad H^+ \quad \rightleftarrows \quad -COOH$$

| carboxyl group (ionized) | | hydrogen ion | | carboxyl group |

$$-NH_2 \quad + \quad H^+ \quad \rightleftarrows \quad -NH_3^+$$

| amine group | | hydrogen ion | | ammonium group |

The bicarbonate buffer system is unable to combine with as many hydrogen ions as can proteins and phosphate buffers, but the bicarbonate buffer system is critical because it can be regulated by the respiratory and urinary systems. Carbon dioxide (CO_2) combines with water (H_2O) to form carbonic acid (H_2CO_3), which in turn forms hydrogen ions (H^+) and bicarbonate ions (HCO_3^-) as follows:

$$H_2O \quad + \quad CO_2 \quad \rightleftarrows \quad H_2CO_3 \quad \rightleftarrows \quad H^+ \quad + \quad HCO_3^-$$

| water | | carbon dioxide | | carbonic acid | | hydrogen ion | | bicarbonate ion |

The reaction between carbon dioxide and water is catalyzed by an enzyme, carbonic anhydrase, which is found in red blood cells and on the surface of capillary epithelial cells (see chapter 15). The enzyme accelerates the rate at which the reaction proceeds in either direction.

The higher the concentration of carbon dioxide, the greater the amount of carbonic acid formed, and the greater the number of hydrogen ions and bicarbonate ions formed. This results in a decreased pH. The reaction is reversible, however. If carbon dioxide levels decline, the equilibrium shifts in the opposite direction. That is, hydrogen and bicarbonate ions combine to form carbonic acid, which then dissociates to form carbon dioxide and water, and the pH increases.

Respiratory System

The **respiratory system** responds rapidly to a change in pH and functions to bring the pH of body fluids back toward its normal range. Increasing carbon dioxide levels and decreasing body fluid pH stimulate neurons in the respiratory center of the brain and cause the rate and depth of ventilation to increase. As a result of the increased rate and depth of ventilation, carbon dioxide is eliminated from the body through the lungs at a greater rate, and the concentration of carbon dioxide in the body fluids decreases. As carbon dioxide levels decline, the concentration of hydrogen ions also declines. The pH therefore increases back to its normal range (see figure 18.21).

| 5 | P R E D I C T |

Under stressful conditions some people hyperventilate. Predict the effect of the rapid rate of ventilation on the pH of body fluids. In addition, explain why a person who is hyperventilating may benefit from breathing into a paper bag.

✔ *Answer on page 518*

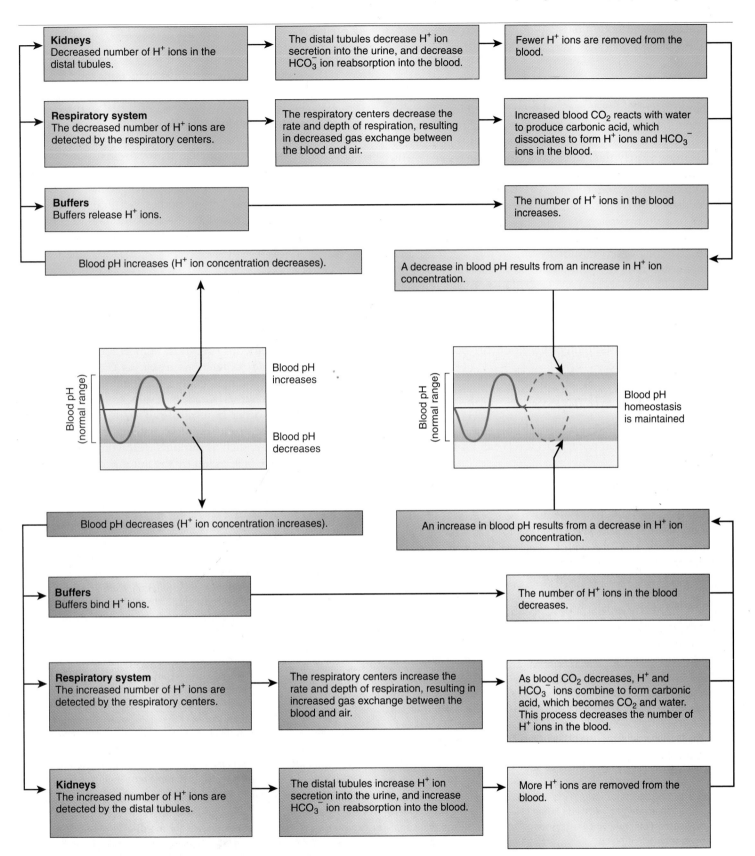

Figure 18.21   Homeostasis: Control of Blood pH and Other Extracellular Fluid

If carbon dioxide levels become too low or the pH of the body fluids is elevated, the rate and depth of respiration decline. As a consequence, the rate at which carbon dioxide is eliminated from the body is reduced. Carbon dioxide then accumulates in the body fluids because it is continually produced as a by-product of metabolism. As carbon dioxide accumulates in the body fluids, so do hydrogen ions, resulting in a decreased pH.

Kidneys

The nephrons of the kidneys secrete hydrogen ions into the urine and therefore can directly regulate pH of the body fluids. The kidney is a powerful regulator of pH, but it responds more slowly than does the respiratory system. Cells in the walls of the distal tubule are primarily responsible for the secretion of hydrogen ions. As the pH of the body fluids decreases below normal, the rate at which the distal tubules secrete hydrogen ions increases (see figure 18.21). At the same time, reabsorption of bicarbonate ions increases. The increased rate of hydrogen ion secretion and the increased rate of bicarbonate ion reabsorption both cause the blood pH to increase toward its normal value. On the other hand, as the body fluid pH increases above normal, the rate of hydrogen ion secretion by the distal tubules declines, and the amount of bicarbonate ions lost in the urine increases. Consequently, the blood pH decreases toward its normal value.

Acidosis and Alkalosis

Failure of the buffer systems, the respiratory system, or the urinary system to maintain normal pH levels can result in acidosis or alkalosis.

Acidosis

Acidosis (as-i-dō'sis) occurs when the blood pH falls below 7.35. The central nervous system malfunctions, and the individual becomes disoriented and, as the condition worsens, can become comatose. Acidosis is separated into two categories. **Respiratory acidosis** results when the respiratory system is unable to eliminate adequate amounts of carbon dioxide. Carbon dioxide accumulates in the circulatory system, causing the pH of the body fluids to decline. **Metabolic acidosis** results from excess production of acidic substances, such as lactic acid and ketone bodies, because of increased metabolism, or a decreased ability of the kidneys to eliminate hydrogen ions in the urine.

Alkalosis

Alkalosis (al-kă-lō'sis) occurs when the blood pH increases above 7.45. A major effect of alkalosis is hyperexcitability of the nervous system. Peripheral nerves are affected first, resulting in spontaneous nervous stimulation of muscles. Spasms and tetanic contractions result, as can extreme nervousness or convulsions. Tetany of respiratory muscles can cause death. **Respiratory alkalosis** results from hyperventilation, such as can occur in response to stress. **Metabolic alkalosis** usually results from the rapid elimination of hydrogen ions from the body, such as during severe vomiting, or when excess aldosterone is secreted by the adrenal cortex.

Clinical Focus   Disorders of the Urinary System

Inflammation of the Kidneys

Glomerulonephritis (glō-măr'ū-lō-nef'rī-tis) is an inflammation of the filtration membrane within the renal corpuscle. The permeability of the filtration membrane increases, and plasma proteins and white blood cells enter the filtrate. The plasma proteins cause the urine volume to increase because they increase the osmotic concentration of the filtrate.

Acute glomerulonephritis often occurs 1 to 3 weeks after a severe bacterial infection such as streptococcal sore throat or scarlet fever. Antigen–antibody complexes associated with the infection become deposited in the filtration membrane and cause inflammation. Acute glomerular nephritis normally subsides after several days.

Chronic glomerulonephritis is long term and usually progressive. The filtration membrane thickens and eventually is replaced by connective tissue. In its early stages, chronic glomerulonephritis resembles the acute form. In the advanced stages, many of the renal corpuscles are replaced by connective tissue, and the kidneys eventually become nonfunctional.

Renal Failure

Renal failure can result from any condition that interferes with kidney function. **Acute renal failure** occurs when damage to the kidney is rapid and extensive. It leads to the accumulation of urea and other metabolites in the blood and to acidosis. If renal failure is complete, death can occur in 1 to 2 weeks. Acute renal failure can result from acute glomerulonephritis, or it can be caused by damage to or blockage of the renal tubules. Lack of blood supply or exposure to certain toxic substances can cause damage to the epithelial cells of the nephron and lead to acute renal failure.

Chronic renal failure is the result of permanent damage to so many nephrons that the remaining nephrons are inadequate for normal kidney function. Chronic renal failure can result from chronic glomerulonephritis, trauma to the kidneys, tumors, urinary tract obstruction by kidney stones, or severe lack of blood supply resulting from arteriosclerosis. Chronic renal failure leads to the inability to eliminate toxic metabolic by-products. Water retention and edema result from the accumulation of solutes in the body fluids. Potassium levels become elevated, and acidosis develops. The toxic effects of accumulated metabolic waste products are mental confusion, coma, and finally death, when chronic renal failure is severe.

Treatments for Renal Failure

Hemodialysis (hē'mō-dī-al'i-sis) is used when a person is suffering from severe acute or chronic kidney failure. The procedure substitutes for the excretory functions of the kidney. Hemodialysis is based on blood flow through tubes composed of a selectively permeable membrane. Blood is usually taken from an artery, passed through the tubes of the dialysis machine, and then returned to a vein (figure A). On the outside of the dialysis tubes is a fluid, called dialysis fluid, which contains the same concentration of solutes as normal plasma except for the metabolic waste products. As a consequence, the metabolic wastes diffuse from the blood to the dialysis fluid. The dialysis membrane has pores that are too small to allow plasma proteins to pass through them, and, because the dialysis fluid contains the same beneficial solutes as the plasma, the net movement of these substances is zero.

Peritoneal (per′i-tō-nē′ăl) dialysis is sometimes used to treat people suffering from kidney failure. The mechanisms by which peritoneal dialysis works are the same as those for hemodialysis. The dialysis fluid flows through a tube inserted into the peritoneal cavity, however. The visceral and parietal peritoneum act as the dialysis membrane. Waste products diffuse from the blood vessels beneath the peritoneum, across the peritoneum, and into the dialysis fluid.

Kidney transplants are sometimes performed on people who suffer from severe renal failure. Usually the donor has suffered an accidental death and had granted permission to have his or her kidneys used for transplantation. An attempt is made to match the immune characteristics of the donor and recipient to reduce the tendency for the recipient's immune system to reject the transplanted kidney. Even with careful matching, recipients have to take medication for the rest of their lives to suppress their immune systems so that rejection is less likely. The major cause of kidney transplant failure is rejection by the recipient's immune system. In most cases, the transplanted kidney functions well, and the tendency for the recipient's immune system to reject the transplanted kidney can be controlled.

Blockage and Inflammation of the Renal Pelvis and Ureters

Kidney stones, or renal calculi (cal′cū-lī), are the precipitates of substances such as uric acid that usually form in the renal pelvis. They can cause irritation and increase the chance of kidney infection, and small parts can break off and pass through the ureter. Passage of a kidney stone through the ureter is usually very painful. An ultrasound technique called lithotripsy (lith′ō-trip-sē) has been developed to pulverize kidney stones and does not require surgery. The ultrasound waves are focused on the kidney stones, and the stones are normally crushed by this process and eliminated in

Figure A   Hemodialysis

During hemodialysis, blood flows through a system of tubes composed of a selectively permeable membrane. Dialysis fluid, the composition of which is similar to that of normal blood, except that the concentration of waste products is very low, flows in the opposite direction on the outside of the dialysis tubes. Waste products, such as urea, diffuse from the blood into the dialysis fluid. Other substances, such as sodium, potassium, and glucose, can diffuse from the blood into the dialysis fluid if they are present in higher than normal concentrations, because these substances are present in the dialysis fluid at the same concentrations found in normal blood.

the urine. Surgical techniques can also be used to remove kidney stones.

Inflammation of the Urinary Bladder

Cystitis is inflammation of the urinary bladder, usually resulting from bacterial infection. The inflammation causes diffuse pain in the lower back and a burning sensation during urination. The irritation of the urinary bladder results in a frequent urge to urinate. Diagnosis of urinary bladder infections is usually confirmed by examining cells found in a urine sample. Normal urine contains very few cells. Urine from a person with cystitis can have a large number of transitional epithelial cells from the urinary bladder and blood cells. White blood cells and occasionally red blood cells are present because of the inflammatory response created by the bacterial infection. Cystitis is normally treated with antibiotics. It is important to recognize cystitis early and treat it, because the infection can ascend along the ureters and result in kidney infection.

Systems Pathology

acute renal failure

ACUTE RENAL FAILURE

A large piece of machinery overturned at the construction site where Mr. H. worked, trapping him beneath it. His legs were severely crushed, although they healed after several months. Mr. H. nearly lost his life, however, because of the acute renal failure that developed because of his injury. Mr. H. was trapped in a very difficult place to reach for several hours. During that time his blood pressure decreased to very low levels because of the blood loss, the edema in the inflamed tissues, and emotional shock. After he was removed, fluid replacement in the form of both intravenous saline solutions and blood transfusions were given and his blood pressure was successfully returned to its normal range. Twenty-four hours after the accident, however, his urine volume began to decrease. His urinary sodium ion concentration increased, his urine osmolality decreased, his urine concentration decreased, and casts and cellular debris were evident in his urine.

For approximately 7 days Mr. H. exhibited reduced urine production. During this period, renal dialysis was required to maintain his blood volume and ion concentrations within normal ranges. After approximately 7 days, his kidneys gradually began to produce large quantities of urine. Careful observation was required to keep his blood pressure and ion concentrations within normal ranges. Substantial quantities of water, sodium ions, and potassium ions had to be administered to him. After about 3 weeks, the functions of his kidneys slowly began to improve, although many months passed before his kidney functions had returned to normal.

Background Information

The events after 24 hours are consistent with acute renal failure caused by prolonged low blood pressure and lack of blood flow to the kidneys. The reduced blood flow to the kidneys was severe enough to result in damage to the epithelial lining of the kidney tubules. The period of reduced urine volume resulted from tubular damage. Dead and damaged tubular cells sloughed off into the tubules and blocked them so that filtrate could not flow through the tubules. In addition, the filtrate leaked from the blocked or partially blocked tubules back into the interstitial spaces and, therefore, back into the circulatory system. As a result, the amount of filtrate that became urine was markedly reduced.

Blood levels of urea and of creatine increased because of the reduction in filtrate formation and reduced function of the tubular epithelium. The kidney's ability to eliminate metabolic waste products was therefore reduced. The small amount of urine produced had a high sodium ion concentration but an osmolality which was close to the concentration of the body fluids because the kidney was not able to reabsorb sodium ions and because the urine-concentrating ability of the kidney was severely damaged.

After 7 days, the nephrons were partially healed and could produce urine, but the ability of the nephrons to concentrate urine was not yet normal. Large volumes of urine that contained significant amounts of sodium and potassium ions were therefore produced. The kidneys were able to produce urine that was more concentrated than the body fluids, but the concentrating ability of the kidneys was still below normal. As time passed, the concentrating ability of the kidneys improved and eventually became normal once again.

6 PREDICT

Nine days after the accident, Mr. H. began to appear pale, he became dizzy on standing and lethargic. His hematocrit was elevated and his heart was arrythmic. He was very weak. Explain these manifestations.

✔ *Answer on page 518*

System Interactions: Effect of Renal Failure on Other Systems

System	Interactions
Integumentary	Pallor results from anemia, and bruising results from reduced clotting proteins in the blood because they are lost in the urine. When the urea concentration in the blood is very high it can give a yellow caste to light-skinned people, and white crystals of urea, called uremic frost, may appear on areas of the skin where there is heavy perspiration.
Skeletal	Changes in the skeletal system is not significant unless kidney damage results in chronic kidney failure. Bone reabsorption can result because of excessive and chronic loss of calcium ions in the urine when the kidneys produce large volumes of urine. Also, vitamin D levels may be reduced.
Muscular	Neuromuscular irritability results from the toxic effect of metabolic wastes on the central nervous system and ionic imbalances such as elevated blood potassium ion levels. Involuntary jerking and twitching can occur as neuromuscular irritability develops. Tremor of the hands is an indication of the toxic effects of metabolic wastes on the cerebrum.
Nervous	Elevated blood potassium ion levels and the toxic effects of metabolic wastes result in depolarization of neurons. Slowing of nerve conduction, burning sensations, pain, numbness, or tingling result. Also, decreased mental acuity, reduced ability to concentrate, apathy, and lethargy result. Periods of lethargy can alternate with restlessness and insomnia. In severe cases, the patient can become confused and comatose.
Endocrine	Major predictable hormone deficiencies include vitamin D deficiency. In addition, the secretion of reproductive hormones decreases due to the effects of metabolic wastes and ionic imbalances on the hypothalamus.
Cardiovascular	Water and sodium ion retention can result in edema in peripheral tissues and in the lung. Also, increased blood pressure and congestive heart failure may result. Elevated blood potassium ion levels result in dysrhythmias and can cause cardiac arrest. Anemia due to decreased erythropoietin production by the damaged kidney and decreased half-life of red blood cells can result. Anemia is more likely because of the blood lost as a result of the crushing injury. Nosebleeds and bruising occur due to reduced concentration of clotting factors because they are lost in the urine.
Lymphatic	There are no major direct effects on the lymphatic system with the exception that increased lymph flow occurs as a result of edema.
Respiratory	Early during acute renal failure the depth of breathing increases and becomes labored as acidosis develops because the kidneys are not able to secrete hydrogen ions. Pulmonary edema often develops because of water and sodium ion retention. The likelihood of infection increases, as a result of pulmonary edema.
Digestive	Decreased appetite, nausea, and vomiting result from altered gastrointestinal functions due to the effects of ionic imbalances on the nervous system. The breath can have the odor of ammonia, and there can be a metallic taste in the mouth. These effects are the result of the accumulation of metabolic waste products in the gastrointestinal tract and the action of the normal gastrointestinal organisms on the waste products, which convert urea to ammonia. The ammonia and other metabolic waste products predispose the mouth to inflammation and infection.

Summary

The urinary system consists of the kidneys, ureters, urinary bladder, and urethra. The urinary system eliminates wastes, controls blood volume, regulates blood ion concentration and pH, and regulates red blood cell production.

Functions of the Urinary System

- The kidneys excrete waste products.
- The kidneys control blood volume by regulating the volume of urine produced.
- The kidneys help regulate the concentration of major ions in the body fluids.
- The kidneys help regulate pH of the body fluids.
- The kidneys regulate the concentration of red blood cells in the blood.
- The kidneys participate, with the skin and liver, in vitamin D synthesis.

Urinary System

Kidneys

- Each kidney is behind the peritoneum and surrounded by a renal capsule and a renal fat pad.
- The kidney is divided into an outer cortex and an inner medulla.
- Each renal pyramid has a base that extends into the cortex; the tip extends into the medulla and is surrounded by a calyx.
- Calyces are extensions of the renal pelvis, which is the expanded end of the ureter within the renal sinus.
- The functional unit of the kidney is the nephron. The parts of a nephron are the renal corpuscle, the proximal tubule, the loop of Henle, and the distal tubule.
- The filtration membrane is formed by the glomerular capillaries, the basement membrane, and the podocytes of Bowman's capsule.

Arteries and Veins

- Renal arteries give rise to branches that lead to afferent arterioles.
- Afferent arterioles supply the glomeruli.
- Efferent arterioles carry blood from the glomeruli to the peritubular capillaries.
- Blood from the peritubular capillaries flows to the renal veins.

Ureters, Urinary Bladder, and Urethra

- Ureters carry urine from the renal pelvis to the urinary bladder.
- The urethra carries urine from the urinary bladder to the outside of the body.
- The ureters and urinary bladder are lined with transitional epithelium and have smooth muscle in their walls.
- The internal and external urinary sphincter muscles regulate the flow of urine through the urethra.

Urine Production

- Urine is produced by the processes of filtration, reabsorption, and secretion.

Filtration

- The renal filtrate passes from the glomerulus into Bowman's capsule and contains no blood cells and few blood proteins.
- Filtration pressure is responsible for filtrate formation.

Reabsorption

- About 99% of the filtrate volume is reabsorbed; 1% becomes urine.
- Proteins; amino acids; glucose; fructose; and sodium, potassium, calcium, bicarbonate, and chloride ions are among the substances reabsorbed.
- About 80% of the volume is reabsorbed in the proximal tubule (65%) and descending limb of the loop of Henle (15%). Another 19% is reabsorbed in the distal tubule and collecting duct.

Secretion

- Hydrogen ions, some by-products of metabolism, and some drugs are actively secreted into the nephron.

Regulation of Urine Concentration and Volume

Hormonal Mechanisms

- ADH is secreted from the posterior pituitary when the concentration of blood increases or when blood pressure decreases. ADH increases the permeability to water of the distal convoluted tubule and collecting duct. It increases water reabsorption by the kidney.
- Renin is secreted from the kidney when the blood pressure decreases or when the concentration of sodium ions decreases in the blood. Renin converts angiotensinogen to angiotensin I which is then converted to angiotensin II by angiotensin-converting enzyme. Angiotensin II stimulates aldosterone secretion, and aldosterone increases the rate of sodium chloride reabsorption from the nephron.
- Atrial natriuretic hormone, secreted from the right atrium in response to increases in blood pressure, acts on the kidney to increase sodium and water loss in the urine.

Effect of Sympathetic Innervation on Kidney Function

- Increased sympathetic activity decreases blood flow to the kidney, decreases filtrate formation, and decreases urine formation.

Urine Movement

- Increased volume in the urinary bladder stretches its wall and activates the micturition reflex.
- Parasympathetic impulses cause contraction of the urinary bladder and relaxation of the internal urinary sphincter. Reduced somatic action potentials cause relaxation of the external urinary sphincter.
- Higher brain centers control the micturition reflex. Stretch of the urinary bladder stimulates ascending neurons that carry impulses to the brain and inform the brain of the need to urinate.

Body Fluid Compartments

- Water and ions dissolved in it are distributed in the intracellular and extracellular fluid compartments.
- Approximately 60% of the total body water is found within cells.
- Approximately 40% of the total body water is found outside cells, mainly in interstitial fluid, plasma of blood, and lymph.

Composition of the Fluid in the Body Fluid Compartments

- Intracellular fluid contains more potassium, calcium, magnesium, phosphate, sulfate ions, and protein than extracellular fluid.
- Extracellular fluid contains more sodium, chloride, and bicarbonate ions than intracellular fluid.

Exchange Between Body Fluid Compartments

- Water moves between compartments continually in response to hydrostatic pressure differences and osmotic differences between the compartments.

Regulation of Extracellular Fluid Composition

- The total amount of water and electrolytes in the body does not change unless the person is growing, gaining weight, or losing weight.

Thirst

- The sensation of thirst increases if extracellular fluid becomes more concentrated or if blood pressure decreases.

Ions

- Sodium ions are one of the dominant extracellular ions. Aldosterone increases sodium reabsorption from the filtrate. ADH increases water reabsorption from the nephron, and atrial natriuretic hormone increases sodium loss in the urine.
- Aldosterone increases potassium secretion in the urine. Increased blood levels of potassium stimulate, and decreased blood levels of potassium inhibit, aldosterone secretion.
- Parathyroid hormone secreted from the parathyroid glands increases extracellular calcium levels by causing bone resorption and increased calcium uptake in the kidney and small intestine. Parathyroid hormone increases vitamin D synthesis. Calcitonin, secreted by the thyroid gland, inhibits bone resorption and lowers blood calcium levels when they are too high.
- When phosphate and sulfate levels in the filtrate are low, nearly all phosphate and sulfate ions are reabsorbed. When levels are high, excess is lost in the urine.

Regulation of Acid–Base Balance

Buffers

- Three principal classes of buffers in the circulatory system resist changes in the pH: protein, phosphate, and bicarbonate buffers.

Respiratory System

- The respiratory system regulates pH. It responds rapidly. An increased respiratory rate raises the pH because the rate of carbon dioxide elimination is increased, and a reduced respiratory rate reduces the pH because the rate of carbon dioxide elimination is reduced.

Kidneys

- The kidneys excrete hydrogen ions in response to a decreasing blood pH, and they reabsorb hydrogen ions in response to an increasing blood pH.

Acidosis and Alkalosis

- Acidosis occurs when the pH of the blood falls below 7.35. The two major types are respiratory acidosis and metabolic acidosis.
- Alkalosis occurs when the pH of the blood increases above 7.45. The two major types are respiratory alkalosis and metabolic alkalosis.

Content Review

1. Name the structures that make up the urinary system. List the functions of the urinary system.
2. What structures surround the kidney?
3. Describe the relationships of the renal pyramids, calyces, renal pelvis, and ureter.
4. What is the functional unit of the kidney? Name its parts.
5. Describe the blood supply of the kidney.
6. What are the functions of the ureters, urinary bladder, and urethra? Describe their structure.
7. Name the three general processes that are involved in the production of urine.
8. Describe the filtration membrane. What substances do not pass through it?
9. How do changes in blood pressure in the glomerulus affect the volume of filtrate produced?
10. What substances are reabsorbed in the nephron? What happens to most of the filtrate volume that enters the nephron?
11. In what parts of the nephron are large volumes of filtrate reabsorbed? In what part of the nephron is no filtrate reabsorbed?
12. In general, what substances are secreted into the nephron?
13. What effect does ADH have on urine volume? Name the factors that cause an increase in ADH secretion.

14. Where is renin produced, and what stimulates its secretion?
15. Explain how renin controls the synthesis of angiotensin II. What enzyme regulates the conversion of antiotensin I to angiotensin II?
16. Describe the effect of angiotensin II on aldosterone secretion.
17. Where is aldosterone produced, and what effect does it have on urine volume? What factors stimulate aldosterone secretion?
18. Where is atrial natriuretic hormone produced, and what effect does it have on urine production?
19. What effect does sympathetic stimulation have on the kidneys?
20. Describe the micturition reflex. How is voluntary control of micturition accomplished?
21. What stimuli result in an increased sensation of thirst?
22. Describe how sodium levels are regulated in the body fluids.
23. Describe how potassium levels are regulated in the body fluids.
24. Describe how calcium levels are regulated in the body fluids.
25. Explain how buffers respond to changes in the pH of body fluids.
26. Explain how the respiratory system and the kidneys respond to changes in the pH of body fluids.
27. Define respiratory acidosis, metabolic acidosis, respiratory alkalosis, and metabolic alkalosis.

Develop Your Reasoning Skills

1. Mucho McPhee decided to do an experiment after reading the urinary system chapter in his favorite anatomy and physiology textbook. He drank 2 L of water in 15 min and then monitored the rate of urine production and urine concentration over the next 2 h. What did he observe? Explain the major mechanism involved.
2. A student ate a full bag of salty (sodium chloride) potato chips but drank no liquids. What effect did this have on urine concentration and the rate of urine production? Explain the mechanisms involved.
3. During severe exertion in a hot environment, a person can lose up to 4 L of sweat per hour (sweat is less concentrated than extracellular fluid in the body). What effect would this loss have on urine concentration and rate of production? Explain the mechanisms involved.
4. Which of the following symptoms are consistent with reduced secretion of aldosterone: excessive urine production, low

blood pressure, high plasma potassium levels, and high plasma sodium levels? Explain.
5. While doing hospital rounds, a nurse observed that one of the patients received a much larger volume of an IV saline solution than she was supposed to receive. A saline solution consists of sodium chloride but sometimes has other solutes such as small amounts of potassium chloride. Saline solutions are the same concentration as body fluids. Predict the effect of the large volume of IV saline solution on the rate of urine production, and describe the role of renin, atrial natriuretic hormone, and aldosterone in the control of the change in urine production.
6. Propose as many ways as you can to decrease the rate filtrate enters Bowman's capsule.
7. Swifty Trotts has an enteropathogenic *Escherichia coli* infection that produces severe diarrhea. Diarrhea causes the production of a large volume of mucus that contains high

concentrations of bicarbonate. What would this diarrhea do to his blood pH, urine pH, and respiration rate?

8. Spanky and his mother went to a grocery store where Spanky eyed some candy he wanted. His mother refused to buy it, so

Spanky became angry. He held his breath for 2 min. What effect did this have on his body fluid pH? After the 2 min, what mechanisms were most important in reestablishing the normal body fluid pH?

Answers to Predict Questions

1. p. 495 The female urinary bladder is more accessible to bacteria from the exterior because the urethra of a female is much shorter than that of a male. For this reason urinary bladder infections are more common in females than in males.

2. p. 498 If large amounts of glucose enter the nephron and are not reabsorbed, the glucose causes the concentration of solutes in the filtrate to increase. The glucose molecules attract water; and, because the glucose molecules are trapped in the nephron, the amount of water that remains in the nephron is increased. A large volume of urine that contains glucose is a symptom of diabetes mellitus.

3. p. 503 Without the normal active transport of sodium ions and chloride ions, their concentration within the nephron remains elevated. The normal movement of water out of the nephron cannot occur because of the osmotic effects of the sodium and chloride ions trapped in the nephron. The result is an increased urine volume.

4. p. 503 Because the solution was a saline solution, it had the same concentration of solutes as the body fluids. The excess IV solution did not therefore change the concentration of the body fluids, but it did increase the volume of the body fluids. An increased volume of saline solution

increases the blood volume and blood pressure. Increased blood pressure stimulates baroreceptors, which results in inhibition of ADH secretion. The reduced ADH secretion causes the kidneys to produce a large volume of urine. At the same time, the increased blood volume stretches the walls of the atria, especially the right atrium, and causes the release of atrial natriuretic hormone. Atrial natriuretic hormone acts on the kidneys to reduce sodium reabsorption. Because sodium reabsorption is decreased, both sodium ions and water are lost in the urine. Consequently, the urine volume and the amount of sodium chloride in the urine increase until the excess saline solution is eliminated.

5. p. 510 Hyperventilation results in a greater than normal rate of carbon dioxide loss from the circulatory system. Because carbon dioxide is lost from the circulatory system, hydrogen ion concentration decreases, and the pH of body fluids increases. Breathing into a paper bag corrects for the effects of hyperventilation because the person rebreathes air that has a higher concentration of carbon dioxide. The result is an increase in carbon dioxide in the body. Consequently, the hydrogen ion concentration increases, and pH decreases toward normal levels.

6. p. 514 After 7 days Mr. H.'s kidney's began to produce a large volume of urine with larger than normal sodium and potassium ion concentrations. The observations are consistent with Mr. H. becoming dehydrated by day 9. Dehydration results in reduced blood volume, and the manifestations were due, in part, to a reduced blood volume and blood pressure. His hematocrit was increased because the volume of his blood was decreased, but there was no decrease in the number of blood cells. The percentage of the blood made of blood cells therefore increased. The pale skin was the result of vasoconstriction, which was triggered by the reduced blood pressure. Dizziness resulted from reduced blood flow to the brain when Mr. H. tried to stand and walk. He was lethargic in part because of reduced blood volume, but also because of low blood levels of potassium and sodium ions, caused by the loss of these ions in the urine. Low blood levels of sodium and potassium alter the electrical activity of nerve and muscle cells and results in muscular weakness. The arrythmia of his heart was due to low blood levels of potassium ions and increased sympathetic stimulation, which was also triggered by low blood pressure.

Chapter Nineteen

The Reproductive System

estrogen
(es′trō-jen) A class of hormones secreted primarily by the ovaries and placenta; aids in growth and development of female secondary sexual characteristics; stimulates cell division and development of the endometrium of the uterus during the menstrual cycle.

menstrual cycle
(men′stroo-ăl) Series of changes that occur in sexually mature, nonpregnant females resulting in menses; specifically includes the cyclical changes that occur in the uterus and ovary.

oocyte
(ō′ō-sīt) Female gamete, or sex cell; a secondary oocyte and a polar body result from the first meiotic division, which occurs before the time of ovulation; a zygote and a polar body result from the second meiotic division, which occurs following union of the sperm cell with the secondary oocyte.

ovary
(ō′vă-rē) One of two female reproductive glands located in the pelvic cavity; produces the secondary oocyte, estrogen, and progesterone.

ovulation
(ov′ū-lā′shŭn) Release of a secondary oocyte from the mature follicle.

progesterone
(prō-jes′ter-ōn) Hormone secreted primarily by the corpus luteum and the placenta; aids in growth and development of female reproductive organs and secondary sexual characteristics; causes growth and maturation of the endometrium of the uterus during the menstrual cycle.

puberty
(pū′ber-tē) [L. *pubertas,* grown up] Series of events that transform a child into a sexually mature adult; involves an increase in the secretion of all reproductive hormones.

spermatogenesis
(sper′mă-tō-jen′ĕ-sis) Formation and development of sperm cells.

spermatozoon, pl. spermatozoa
(sper′mă-tō-zō′on, sper′mă-tō-zō′ă) [Gr. *sperma,* seed + *zoon,* animal] Sperm cell. Male gamete, or sex cell, composed of a head, midpiece, and tail. Spermatozoa contain the genetic information transmitted by the male.

testis, pl. testes
(tes′tis, tes′tēz) One of two male reproductive glands located in the scrotum; produces testosterone and sperm cells.

testosterone
(tes′tos′tĕ-rōn) Hormone secreted primarily by the testes; aids in spermatogenesis, controls maintenance and development of male reproductive organs and secondary sexual characteristics and influences sexual behavior.

Objectives

After reading this chapter, you should be able to:

1. Describe the scrotum and explain the role of the dartos and cremaster muscles in temperature regulation of the testes.
2. Describe the structure of the testes, name the specialized cells of the testes, and give their functions.
3. Describe the process of spermatogenesis.
4. Describe the route sperm cells follow from the site of their production to the outside of the body.
5. Describe the structure of the penis.
6. Name the male reproductive glands, state where they empty into the duct system, and describe their secretions.
7. List the hormones that influence the male reproductive system and describe their functions.
8. Explain the events that occur during the male sexual act.
9. Name the organs of the female reproductive system and describe their structure.
10. Describe the anatomy and histology of the ovaries.
11. Discuss the development of the follicle and the oocyte, and describe the processes of ovulation and fertilization.
12. Describe the changes that occur in the ovary and uterus during the menstrual cycle.
13. List the hormones of the female reproductive system and explain how their secretion is regulated.
14. Explain the events that occur in the female sexual act.
15. Define menopause and describe the changes that result from it.

A fully functional reproductive system, unlike a functional heart or kidney, is not essential for survival of the individual. Many people who are not able to reproduce live long and fulfilling lives. However, the reproductive system is responsible for the development of differences between males and females including sexual behavior. The attention given to these differences emphasizes the significance of the reproductive system.

Most organ systems of the body show little difference between males and females, but the male and female reproductive systems exhibit striking differences. They also share a number of similarities. Many reproductive organs of males and females are derived from the same embryological structures (see chapter 20), and some hormones are the same in males and females, even though they produce different responses.

Functions of the Reproductive System

The male reproductive system performs the following functions:

1. *Production of sperm cells.* The reproductive system produces sperm cells in the testes.
2. *Sustaining and transfer of the sperm cells to the female.* The duct system provides nutrients for the sex cells produced in the testes, provides an environment in which the sex cells mature, provides secretions that form most of volume of the semen transferred to the female, and transports the sex cells from the testes through the penis, which is a specialized organ that functions to deposit the sperm cells in the female reproductive system.
3. *Production of male sex hormones.* Hormones produced by the male reproductive system control the development not only of the reproductive system itself but also of the male body form. These hormones are also essential for the normal function of the reproductive system and reproductive behavior.

The female reproductive system performs the following functions:

1. *Production of female sex cells.* The reproductive system produces female sex cells in the ovaries.
2. *Reception of sperm cells from the male.* The female reproductive system includes structures that receive sperm cells from the male and transports the sperm cells to the site of fertilization.
3. *Nurturing the development of and providing nourishment for, the new individual.* The female reproductive system nurtures the development of a new individual in the uterus until birth and provides nourishment in the form of milk after birth.

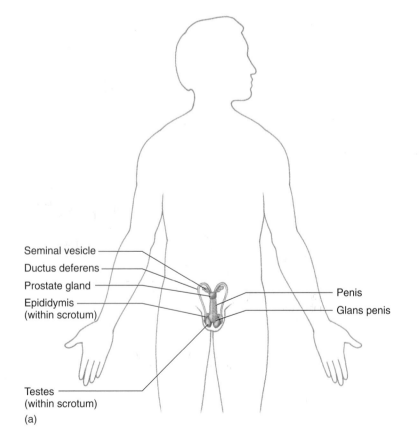

Seminal vesicle
Ductus deferens
Prostate gland
Epididymis
(within scrotum)
Penis
Glans penis
Testes
(within scrotum)
(a)

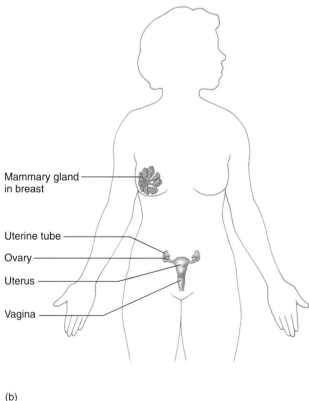

Mammary gland
in breast
Uterine tube
Ovary
Uterus
Vagina
(b)

Figure 19.1 Organs of the Reproductive System

(*a*) The male reproductive system: penis, testes, epididymis, ductus deferens, seminal vesicles, and prostate gland. (*b*) The female reproductive system: vagina, ovaries, uterine tubes, and uterus, and mammary glands.

4. *Production of female sex hormones.* Hormones produced by the female reproductive system control the development of the reproductive system itself and of the female body form. These hormones are also essential for the normal function of the reproductive system and reproductive behavior.

Formation of Sex Cells

The reproductive organs in males and females (figure 19.1) produce **sex cells**, or **gametes** (gam'ētz). The formation of sex cells in males and females occurs by a special type of cell division called **meiosis** (mī-ō'sis) (see Clinical Focus: Meiosis on p. 522). For both males and females, meiosis begins in cells that contain 23 pairs of chromosomes (46 chromosomes). Before the beginning of meiosis, the genetic material is duplicated. During meiosis, two cell divisions occur. In the male, for each cell that begins the process, four sex cells, called **sperm cells**, or **spermatozoa** (sper'mă-tō-zō'ă), are produced. Each sperm cell contains 23 chromosomes, with one chromo-

some coming from each of the original 23 pairs of chromosomes (figure 19.2*a*). In the female, during each of the meiotic divisions, distribution of the cytoplasm among the sex cells is unequal. In the first meiotic division, most of the cytoplasm remains with one of the resulting cells called a **secondary oocyte** (ō'ō-sīt). The cell receiving little cytoplasm is called a **polar body** (figure 19.2*b*). The polar body either degenerates or divides to form two polar bodies, which degenerate.

Fertilization results when a sperm cell penetrates into the cytoplasm of a secondary oocyte. This union occurs before the second meiotic division of the oocyte is complete. After fertilization, the secondary oocyte completes the second meiotic division to form two cells, each containing 23 chromosomes. One of these cells have very little cytoplasm and is another polar body, which degenerates. In the other, larger cell, the 23 chromosomes from the male join with the 23 from the female to form a **zygote** (zī'gōt), with 46 chromosomes (23 pairs of chromosomes; see chapter 20). All cells of the body contain 23 pairs of chromosomes, except for the male and female sex cells (see figure 19.2*b*).

(a)   Meiosis in the seminiferous tubules of testes results in the formation of sperm cell. Sperm cell production is a continuous process after males reach puberty. A primary spermatocyte undergoes the first meiotic division to produce secondary spermatocytes, which undergo the second meiotic division to produce spermatids. The spermatids undergo changes in structure to form sperm cells.

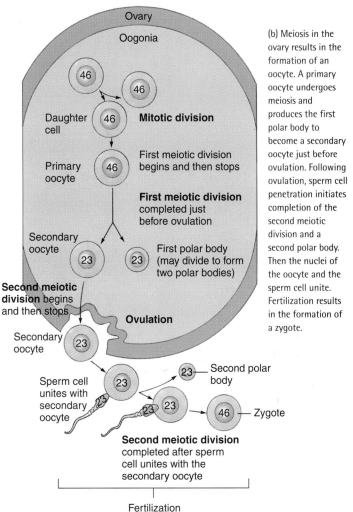

(b) Meiosis in the ovary results in the formation of an oocyte. A primary oocyte undergoes meiosis and produces the first polar body to become a secondary oocyte just before ovulation. Following ovulation, sperm cell penetration initiates completion of the second meiotic division and a second polar body. Then the nuclei of the oocyte and the sperm cell unite. Fertilization results in the formation of a zygote.

Figure 19.2   The Formation of Sex Cells

Clinical Focus Meiosis

The formation of sperm cells and female sex cells involves meiosis (see chapter 3). This kind of cell division occurs only in the testis and ovary. It consists of two consecutive cell divisions, and the production of four daughter cells, each having half as many chromosomes as the parent cell.

FIRST MEIOTIC DIVISION (MEIOSIS I)

Early prophase I
The duplicated chromosomes become visible chromatids (shown separated for emphasis, they actually are so close together that they appear as a single strand)

Chromatids — Chromosomes — Nucleus — Centrioles

Middle prophase I
Homologous chromosomes synapse to form tetrads

Crossing over may occur at this stage

Homologous chromosomes — Tetrad — Spindle fibers

Metaphase I
Tetrads align at the equatorial plane

Centromere — Equatorial plane

Anaphase I
Homologous chromosomes move apart to opposite sides of the cell

Telophase I
New nuclei form, and the cell divides; during interkinesis (not shown) there is no duplication of chromosomes

Cleavage furrow

Second Meiotic Division (top of next column)

SECOND MEIOTIC DIVISION (MEIOSIS II)

Prophase II
Each chromosome consists of two chromatids

Metaphase II
Chromosomes align at the equatorial plane

Anaphase II
Chromatids separate and each is now called a chromosome

Telophase II
New nuclei form around the chromosomes

Haploid cells
The chromosomes are about to unravel and become less distinct chromatin

Figure A Meiosis

The two divisions of meiosis are called meiosis I and meiosis II. Like mitosis, each division of meiosis has prophase, metaphase, anaphase, and telophase. Distinct differences exist between meiosis and mitosis, however.

Before meiosis begins, all the chromosomes are duplicated. At the beginning of meiosis, each of the 46 chromosomes consists of two chromatids connected by a centromere (figure A). The chromosomes align as pairs in a process called synapsis. Because each chromosome consists of two chromatids, the pairing of the chromosomes brings two chromatids of each chromosome close together. Occasionally, part of a chromatid of one chromosome will break off and be exchanged with part of another chromatid from the other chromosome. This exchange is called **crossing over**. Crossing over allows the exchange of genetic material between chromosomes.

The chromosomes align along the center of the cell, and then the pairs of chromosomes are separated to each side of the cell. As a consequence, when meiosis I is complete, each daughter cell has one chromosome from each of the pairs, or 23 chromosomes. Each of the 23 chromosomes in each daughter cell consists of two chromatids joined by a centromere.

It is during the first meiotic division that the chromosome number is reduced from 46 (23 pairs) to 23 chromosomes. The first meiotic division is therefore called a reduction division.

The second meiotic division is similar to mitosis. The chromosomes, each consisting of two chromatids, line up near the middle of the cell (see figure A). Then the chromatids separate at the centromere, and each daughter cell receives one of the chromatids from each chromosome. When the centromere separates, each of the chromatids is called a chromosome. Consequently, each of the four daughter cells produced by meiosis contains 23 chromosomes.

During fertilization, the zygote receives one chromosome of each pair of chromosomes from each parent. Although half of the genetic material of a zygote comes from each parent, the genetic makeup of the zygote is unique.

Figure 19.3   Sagittal View of the Male Pelvis
The reproductive tract and the urinary tract come together in the prostate.

Male Reproductive System

The male reproductive system consists of the **primary reproductive organs**, the testes, and the **secondary reproductive organs**, which include the scrotum, epididymis, ductus deferens, seminal vesicles, urethra, prostate gland, bulbourethral glands, and penis (figure 19.3). The sperm cells are very heat-sensitive and must develop at a temperature slightly less than normal body temperature. The testes, in which the sperm cells develop, are located outside the body cavity in the scrotum, where the temperature is lower. Sperm cells are transported from the testes to the epididymis, which lies on the external surface of each testis, and then through the ductus deferens into the pelvic cavity. Just before the ductus deferens enters the prostate gland, the ductus deferens increases in diameter to become the ampulla of the ductus deferens. A short duct of the seminal vesicle joins the ampulla of the ductus deferens to form the ejaculatory duct at the prostate, which then enters the prostate gland and empties into the urethra within the prostate gland. The urethra exits from the pelvis and passes through the penis to the outside of the body.

Scrotum

The **scrotum** (skrō'tum) contains the testes and is divided into right and left internal compartments by a connective tissue septum. Externally the scrotum consists of skin. Beneath the skin is a layer of loose connective tissue and a layer of smooth muscle, called the **dartos** (dar'tōs, to skin) muscle.

In cold temperatures, the dartos muscle contracts, causing the skin of the scrotum to become firm and wrinkled and reducing the overall size of the scrotum. At the same time, extensions of abdominal muscles into the scrotum, called **cremaster** (krē-mas'ter) muscles, contract. Consequently, the testes are pulled nearer to the body, and their temperature is raised. During warm weather or exercise, the dartos and cremaster muscles relax, the skin of the scrotum becomes loose and thin, and the testes descend away from the body, which lowers their temperature. The response of the dartos and cremaster muscles is important in the regulation of temperature in the testes. If the testes become too warm or too cold, normal sperm cell development does not occur.

Testes

The **testes** (tes'tēz) are oval organs, each about 4 to 5 cm long, within the scrotum (see figure 19.3). The outer part of each testis consists of a thick, white connective tissue capsule. Extensions of the capsule project into the interior of the testis and divide each testis into about 250 cone-shaped lobules (figure 19.4a). The lobules contain **seminiferous** (sem'ĭ-nif'er-ŭs, seed carriers) **tubules**, in which sperm cells develop. Delicate connective tissue surrounding the seminiferous tubules contains clusters of endocrine cells called **interstitial** (in-ter-stish'ăl) **cells**, or **cells of Leydig** (lī'dig, named after a German anatomist), which secrete testosterone.

Spermatogenesis

Spermatogenesis (sper'mă-tō-jen'ĕ-sis) is the formation of sperm cells. Before puberty, the testes remain relatively simple and unchanged from the time of their initial development. The interstitial cells are not prominent, and the semi-

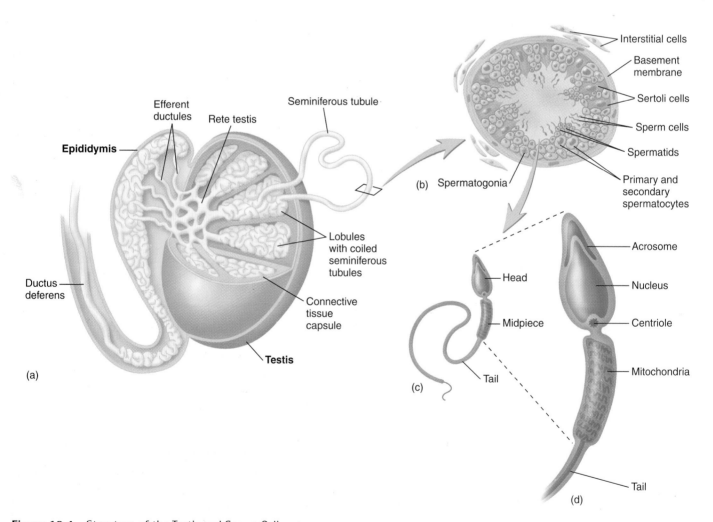

Figure 19.4 Structure of the Testis and Sperm Cell

(*a*) Gross anatomy of the testis with a section cut away to reveal internal structures. The epididymis is also shown. (*b*) Cross section of a seminiferous tubule. Spermatogonia are near the periphery, and mature sperm cells are near the lumen of the seminiferous tubule. (*c*) The head, midpiece, and tail of a sperm cell. (*d*) Enlargement of the head and midpiece of a sperm cell to show the nucleus and acrosome in the head and the mitochondria in the midpiece.

niferous tubules are small and not yet functional. At the time of puberty, the interstitial cells increase in number and size. The seminiferous tubules enlarge, and spermatogenesis begins.

The seminiferous tubules contain **germ cells** and **Sertoli** (ser-tō′lē, named for the Italian histologist, Enrico Sertoli) **cells** (figure 19.4b). Sertoli cells are large and extend from the periphery to the lumen of the seminiferous tubule. They nourish the germ cells and produce a number of hormones.

Germ cells are scattered between the Sertoli cells. The most peripheral cells are **spermatogonia** (sper′mă-tō-gō′nē-ă), which divide through mitosis. Some daughter cells produced from these mitotic divisions remain as spermatogonia and continue to divide by mitosis. Other daughter cells form **primary spermatocytes** (sper′mă-tō-sītz), which divide by meiosis.

A primary spermatocyte contains 46 chromosomes, each consisting of two chromatids. Each primary spermatocyte passes through the first meiotic division to produce two **secondary spermatocytes**. Each secondary spermatocyte undergoes a second meiotic division to produce two smaller sex cells called **spermatids** (sper′mă-tidz), each having 23 chromosomes. After the second meiotic division, the spermatids undergo major structural changes to form sperm cells. Much of the cytoplasm of the spermatids is eliminated, and each spermatid develops a head, midpiece, and flagellum (tail) to become a **sperm cell**, or **spermatozoon** (see figure 19.4b to d). The nucleus of the sperm cell is located in the head of the sperm cell. Just anterior to the nucleus is a vesicle called the **acrosome** (ak′rō-sōm), which contains enzymes that are released during the process of fertilization and are necessary for the sperm cell to penetrate the female sex cell.

At the end of spermatogenesis, the developing sperm cells gather around the lumen of the seminiferous tubules with their heads directed toward the surrounding Sertoli cells and their tails directed toward the center of the lumen (see figure 19.2a and figure 19.4b). Finally, sperm cells are released into the lumen of the seminiferous tubules.

Ducts

After their production, the sperm cells are transported through the seminiferous tubules and a series of ducts to reach the exterior of the body.

Epididymis

The seminiferous tubules of each testis empty into a tubular network called the **rete** (rē′tē, net) **testis** (see figure 19.4a). The rete testis empties into 15 to 20 tubules called the **efferent ductules** (ef′er-ent dŭk′toolz). The efferent ductules carry sperm cells from the testis to a tightly coiled series of thread-like tubules that form a comma-shaped structure on the posterior side of the testis called the **epididymis** (ep-i-did′i-mis, upon twins) (see figures 19.3, 19.4a, and figure 19.5). The sperm cells continue to mature within the epididymis. Within the epididymis, sperm cells develop the capacity to swim and the ability to bind to the secondary oocyte. Sperm cells taken directly from the testes are not capable of fertilizing the secondary oocyte, but after maturing for several days in the epididymis, the sperm cells develop the capacity to function as sex cells. Final changes in sperm cells, called **capacitation** (kă-pas′i-tā′shun) occur after ejaculation and prior to fertilization.

Ductus Deferens

The **ductus deferens** (dŭk′tŭs def′er-enz), or **vas deferens**, emerges from the epididymis and ascends along the posterior side of the testis to become associated with the blood vessels and nerves that supply the testis. These structures form the **spermatic cord** (see figure 19.5). Each spermatic cord consists of the ductus deferens, testicular artery and veins, lymphatic vessels, and testicular nerve. It is surrounded by the cremaster muscle, and a connective tissue sheath.

Each ductus deferens extends, in the spermatic cord, through the abdominal wall by way of the inguinal canal. Each ductus deferens then crosses the lateral wall of the pelvic cavity and loops behind the posterior surface of the urinary bladder to approach the prostate gland (see figures 19.3 and 19.5). The total length of the ductus deferens is about 45 cm. Just before reaching the prostate gland, the ductus deferens increases in diameter to become the **ampulla of the ductus deferens** (see figure 19.5). The wall of the ductus deferens contains smooth muscle. Peristaltic contractions of these smooth muscles propel the sperm cells from the epididymis through the ductus deferens.

Seminal Vesicle and Ejaculatory Duct

Near the ampulla of each ductus deferens is a sac-shaped gland called the **seminal vesicle** (sem′i-năl ves′i-kl). A short duct extends from the seminal vesicle to the ampulla of the ductus deferens. The duct from the seminal vesicle and the ampulla of the ductus deferens join at the prostate gland to form the **ejaculatory** (ē-jak′ū-lă-tōr-ē) **duct**. Each ejaculatory duct extends into the prostate gland and ends by joining the urethra within the prostate gland (see figure 19.5).

Figure 19.5 Frontal View of the Male Reproductive Organs

The testes, epididymis, ductus deferens, penis, and glands of the male reproductive system are illustrated. The testis is viewed in the scrotal sac with the smooth muscle and cremaster muscles on one side. The ductus deferens extends from the epididymis in the scrotal sac and passes through the inguinal canal and pelvic cavity to the prostate gland. Note that the ductus deferens joins the artery, vein, cremaster muscle, and nerves that supply the testis to form the spermatic cord.

Urethra

The male **urethra** (ū-rē′thră) extends from the urinary bladder to the distal end of the penis (see figures 19.3 and 19.5). The urethra can be divided into three parts: the prostatic part, which passes through the prostate gland; the membranous part, which passes through the floor of the pelvis and is surrounded by the external urinary sphincter; and the spongy, or penile, part, which extends the length of the penis and exits at its end. The urethra is a passageway for both urine and male reproductive fluids. Urine and the reproductive fluids, however, do not exit the urethra at the same time. While male reproductive fluids are passing through the urethra, a parasympathetic reflex prevents urine from passing from the urinary bladder through the urethra. Stimuli cause the internal urinary sphincter to contract and to keep semen from passing into the urinary bladder. Many minute mucus-secreting glands are located in the epithelial lining of the urethra.

Penis

The **penis** (pē′nis) contains three columns of erectile tissue (see figure 19.5). Engorgement of this erectile tissue with blood causes the penis to enlarge and become firm, a process called **erection** (ē-rek′shŭn). The penis is the male organ of copulation and functions in the transfer of sperm cells from the male to the female. Two columns of erectile tissue form the dorsal portion and the sides of the penis and are called the **corpora cavernosa** (kōr′pōr-ă kav-er-nōs′ă). The third and smaller erectile column occupies the ventral portion of the penis and is called the **corpus spongiosum** (kōr′pŭs spŭn-gē-ō′sŭm). It expands over the distal end of the penis to form a cap, the **glans penis**. The spongy, or penile, urethra passes through the corpus spongiosum, including the glans penis, and opens to the exterior as the **external urethral orifice**.

The shaft of the penis is covered by skin that is loosely attached to the connective tissue surrounding the penis. The skin is firmly attached at the base of the glans penis, and a thinner layer of skin tightly covers the glans penis. The skin of the penis, especially the glans penis, is well supplied with sensory receptors. A loose fold of skin, called the **prepuce** (prē′pūs), or **foreskin**, covers the glans penis.

Did You Know?

> **Circumcision** (ser-kŭm-sizh′ŭn) is the surgical removal of the prepuce, usually near the time of birth. There are few compelling medical reasons for circumcision. Uncircumcised males have a higher incidence of penile cancer, but the underlying cause appears to be related to chronic infections and poor hygiene. In those few cases in which the prepuce is "too tight" to be moved over the glans penis, circumcision can be necessary to avoid chronic infections and maintain normal circulation.

Glands

The **seminal vesicles** (sem′i-năl ves′i-klz) are glands consisting of many saclike structures located next to the ampulla of the ductus deferens (see figures 19.3 and 19.5). There are two seminal vesicles. Each is about 5 cm long and tapers into a short duct that joins the ampulla of the ductus deferens to form the ejaculatory duct.

The **prostate** (pros′tāt) **gland** consists of both glandular and muscular tissue and is about the size and shape of a walnut (see figures 19.3 and 19.5). The prostate gland surrounds the urethra and the two ejaculatory ducts. It consists of a capsule and numerous partitions. The cells lining the partitions secrete prostatic fluid. There are 10 to 20 short ducts that carry secretions of the prostate gland to the prostatic part of the urethra.

Did You Know?

> **Cancer of the prostate** is the second most common cause of male deaths from cancer in the United States, fewer than from lung cancer and more than from colon cancer. A **prostate-specific antigen (PSA)**

increases in the circulatory system of men who have prostatic cancer. A blood sample can be taken, and an assay performed for the antigen. If the concentration of the antigen in the blood has increased, an examination for prostatic cancer is highly recommended. A test result indicating an elevated concentration of the antigen does not confirm the presence of cancer, other tests are necessary. In some cases test results can show an increase in the antigen when no cancer is apparent. Because of the prevalence of prostatic cancer in men over 50 years of age, an annual or biannual analysis for prostatic cancer should be done. There is controversy concerning the treatment for prostatic cancer. Cancer of the prostate in relatively young men and large tumors in all men generally require treatment. Treatment of cancer of the prostate in elderly men, however, is controversial. Some evidence suggests that elderly men with small tumors in the prostate are likely to die of causes unrelated to prostatic cancer, even if they receive no treatment. Treatment for prostatic cancer includes radiation, chemotherapy, and surgery. Surgery generally results in the inability to sustain an erection, although new, more successful techniques have been developed.

1 ▏ PREDICT

Changes in the size and texture of the prostate gland can be an indication of developing prostate cancer. Suggest a way that the size and texture of the prostate gland can be examined by palpation without surgical techniques (see figure 19.3).

✔ *Answer on page 549*

The **bulbourethral** (bul′bō-ū-rē′thrăl) **glands** are a pair of small mucus-secreting glands located near the base of the penis (see figures 19.3 and 19.5). In young adults they are each about the size of a pea, but they decrease in size with age. A single duct from each gland enters the urethra.

Secretions

Semen (sē′men) is a mixture of sperm cells and secretions from the male reproductive glands. The seminal vesicles produce about 60% of the fluid, the prostate gland contributes approximately 30%, the testes contribute 5%, and the bulbourethral glands contribute 5%.

The bulbourethral glands and the mucous glands of the urethra produce a mucous secretion, which lubricates the urethra, helps neutralize the contents of the normally acidic urethra, provides a small amount of lubrication during intercourse, and helps reduce the acidity in the vagina.

Testicular secretions include sperm cells and a small amount of fluid. The thick, mucuslike secretion of the seminal vesicles contains the sugar fructose and other nutrients that provide nourishment to sperm cells. The seminal vesicle secretions also contain proteins that weakly coagulate after ejaculation and enzymes that are thought to help destroy abnormal sperm cells. Prostaglandins, which stimulate smooth muscle contractions, are present in high concentrations in the secretions of the seminal vesicles and can cause contractions of the female reproductive tract, which help transport sperm cells through the female reproductive tract.

The thin, milky secretions of the prostate have an alkaline pH and help neutralize the acidic urethra, as well as the acidic secretions of the testes, the seminal vesicles, and the vagina. The increased pH is important for normal sperm cell function. The movement of sperm cells is not optimal until the pH is increased to between 6.0 and 6.5. In contrast, the secretions of the vagina have a pH between 3.5 and 4.0. Prostatic secretions also contain proteolytic enzymes that break down the coagulated proteins of the seminal vesicles and make the semen more liquid. The normal volume of semen is 2 to 5 milliliters (mL). The normal sperm cell count is about 100 million sperm cells per milliliter of semen.

Physiology of Male Reproduction

The male reproductive system depends on both hormonal and neural mechanisms to function normally. Hormones control the development of reproductive structures, the development of secondary sexual characteristics, spermatogenesis, and, in part, sexual behavior. The mature neural mechanisms are primarily involved in controlling the sexual act and in the expression of sexual behavior.

Regulation of Sex Hormone Secretion

The hypothalamus of the brain, the anterior pituitary gland, and the testes (figure 19.6) produce hormones that influence the male reproductive system. **Gonadotropin-releasing** (gō′nad-ō-trō′pin) **hormone (GnRH)** is released from neurons in the hypothalamus and passes to the anterior pituitary gland (table 19.1). GnRH causes cells in the anterior pituitary gland to secrete two hormones, **luteinizing** (loo′tē-ĭ-nīz-ing) **hormone (LH)** and **follicle-stimulating hormone (FSH)**, into the blood (see table 19.1). LH and FSH are named for their functions in females, but they are also essential reproductive hormones in males.

LH binds to the interstitial cells in the testes and causes them to secrete testosterone. LH was once referred to as **interstitial cell-stimulating hormone (ICSH)** because it stimulates interstitial cells of the testes to secrete testosterone, but it was later discovered to be identical to LH found in the female. Consequently, it is now simply called LH. FSH binds primarily to Sertoli cells in the seminiferous tubules and promotes sperm cell development. It also increases the secretion of a hormone called **inhibin** (in-hib′in).

Testosterone has a negative-feedback effect on the secretion of GnRH from the hypothalamus, and on LH and FSH from the anterior pituitary gland. Inhibin has a negative-feedback effect on the secretion of FSH from the anterior pituitary gland.

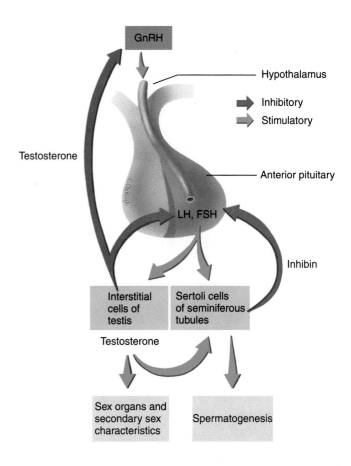

Figure 19.6 Regulation of Reproductive Hormone Secretion in Males

Gonadotropin-releasing hormone (GnRH) from the hypothalamus stimulates the secretion of luteinizing hormone (LH) and follicle-stimulating hormone (FSH) from the anterior pituitary. LH stimulates the interstitial cells of the testes to secrete testosterone. FSH binds to the Sertoli cells of the seminiferous tubules and stimulates spermatogenesis. Testosterone has a negative-feedback effect on the hypothalamus and pituitary gland to reduce LH and FSH secretion. Testosterone has a stimulatory effect on the sex organs and secondary sex characteristics, as well as on the Sertoli cells. Inhibin has a negative-feedback effect on FSH secretion.

Did You Know?

For GnRH to stimulate LH and FSH release, the pituitary gland must be exposed to a series of brief increases and decreases in GnRH. If GnRH is maintained at a high level in the circulatory system for days or weeks, the anterior pituitary cells become insensitive to it. GnRH can be produced synthetically and is useful in treating some people who are infertile. Synthetic GnRH must be administered in small amounts in frequent pulses or surges. GnRH can also inhibit reproduction, because long-term administration of GnRH can sufficiently reduce LH and FSH levels to prevent sperm cell production in males or ovulation in females.

Table 19.1 Major Reproductive Hormones in Males and Females

Hormone	Source	Target Tissue	Response
Male Reproductive System			
Gonadotropin-releasing hormone (GnRH)	Hypothalamus	Anterior pituitary	Stimulates secretion of LH and FSH
Luteinizing hormone (LH)	Anterior pituitary	Interstitial cells of the testes	Stimulates synthesis and secretion of testosterone
Follicle-stimulating hormone (FSH)	Anterior pituitary	Seminiferous tubules (Sertoli cells)	Supports spermatogenesis and inhibin secretion
Testosterone	Interstitial cells of the testes	Testes; body tissues	Development and maintenance of reproductive organs;
			Supports spermatogenesis; development and maintenance of secondary sexual characteristics
		Anterior pituitary and hypothalamus	Inhibits GnRH, LH, and FSH secretion through negative feedback
Inhibin	Sertoli cells	Anterior pituitary	Inhibits FSH secretion through negative feedback
Female Reproductive System			
Gonadotropin-releasing hormone (GnRH)	Hypothalamus	Anterior pituitary	Stimulates secretion of LH and FSH
Luteinizing hormone (LH)	Anterior pituitary	Ovaries	Causes follicles to complete maturation and undergo ovulation; causes ovulation; causes the ovulated follicle to become the corpus luteum
Follicle-stimulating hormone (FSH)	Anterior pituitary	Ovaries	Causes follicles to begin development
Estrogen	Follicles of ovaries and corpus luteum	Uterus	Proliferation of endometrial cells
		Breasts	Development of the mammary glands (especially duct systems)
		Anterior pituitary and hypothalamus	Positive feedback before ovulation, resulting in increased LH and FSH secretion; negative feedback with progesterone on the hypothalamus and anterior pituitary after ovulation, resulting in decreased LH and FSH secretion
		Other tissues	Development and maintenance of secondary sexual characteristics
Progesterone	Corpus luteum of ovaries	Uterus	Enlargement of endometrial cells and secretion of fluid from uterine glands
		Breasts	Development of the mammary glands (especially alveoli)
		Anterior pituitary	Negative feedback, with estrogen, on the hypothalamus and anterior pituitary after ovulation, resulting in decreased LH and FSH secretion
		Other tissues	Secondary sexual characteristics
Oxytocin	Posterior pituitary	Uterus and mammary glands	Contraction of uterine smooth muscle and contraction of cells in the breast, resulting in milk letdown in lactating women
Human chorionic gonadotropin	Placenta	Corpus luteum of ovaries	Maintains the corpus luteum and increases its rate of progesterone secretion during the first one-third (first trimester) of pregnancy

Puberty

Puberty (pū'ber-tē) is the sequence of events by which a child is transformed into a young adult. The reproductive system matures and assumes its adult functions, and the structural differences between adult males and females become more apparent. In boys, puberty commonly begins at ages 12 to 14 and is largely completed by age 18. Before puberty, small amounts of testosterone, secreted by the testes and the adrenal cortex, inhibit GnRH, LH, and FSH secretion. At puberty, developmental changes in the hypothalamus cause the hypothalamus and the anterior pituitary gland to become much less sensitive to the inhibitory effect of testosterone, and the rate of GnRH, LH, and FSH secretion increases. Consequently, elevated FSH levels promote spermatogenesis, and elevated LH levels cause the interstitial cells to secrete larger amounts of testosterone. Testosterone still has a negative-feedback effect on the hypothalamus and anterior pituitary gland, but it does not completely suppress GnRH, LH, and FSH secretion.

Effects of Testosterone

Testosterone (tes'tos'tě-rōn) is the major male hormone secreted by the testes. Testosterone influences reproductive organs and nonreproductive structures. During puberty, testosterone causes the enlargement and differentiation of the male genitals and reproductive duct system. It is necessary for spermatogenesis and for the development of male secondary sexual characteristics. The **secondary sexual characteristics** are those structural and behavioral changes, other than in the reproductive organs, that develop at puberty and distinguish males from females (table 19.2). Secondary sexual characteristics in males include hair distribution and growth, skin texture, fat distribution, skeletal muscle growth, and changes in the larynx. After puberty, testosterone maintains the adult structure of the male genitals, reproductive ducts, and secondary sex characteristics.

Did You Know?

Some athletes, especially those who depend on muscle strength, may either ingest or inject synthetic **androgens** (an'drō-jenz), which are hormones that have testosteronelike effects, such as stimulating the development of male sexual characteristics. The synthetic androgens are commonly called **anabolic steroids,** or simply **steroids,** and they are used in an attempt to increase muscle mass. Many of the synthetic androgens are structurally different from testosterone. Their effect on muscle is greater than their effect on the reproductive organs. They are often taken in large amounts, however, and they can influence the reproductive system. Large doses of synthetic androgens have a negative-feedback effect on the hypothalamus and pituitary, causing a reduction in GnRH, LH, and FSH levels. As a result, the testes can atrophy, and sterility can develop. Other side effects of large doses of synthetic androgens include kidney and liver damage, heart attack, and stroke. Taking synthetic androgens is highly discouraged by the medical profession, is a violation of the rules of most athletic organizations, and is illegal. For people who take anabolic steroids by injection, the risk of contacting hepatitis B or HIV (the AIDS virus) is increased if they share needles with other people.

Did You Know?

Some men have a genetic tendency called **male pattern baldness,** which develops in response to testosterone and other androgens. When testosterone levels increase at puberty, the density of hair on top of the head begins to decrease. Baldness usually reaches its maximum rate of development when the individual is in the third or fourth decade of life. Minoxidil (mi-noks'si-dil) is a drug which effectively prevents a decrease in hair growth in many men who exhibit male pattern baldness. Its effectiveness is increased in those who are young and starting to show evidence of baldness. The mechanism by which the drug works is unclear.

Table 19.2 Effects of Testosterone on Target Tissues

Target Tissue	Response
Penis and scrotum	Enlargement and differentiation
Hair follicles	Hair growth and coarser hair in pubic area, legs, chest, axillary region, the face, and occasionally the back; male pattern baldness on the head if the person has the appropriate genetic makeup
Skin	Coarser texture of skin; increased rate of secretion of sebaceous glands, frequently resulting in acne at the time of puberty; increased secretion of sweat glands in axillary regions
Larynx	Enlargement of larynx and deeper masculine voice
Most tissues	Increased rate of metabolism
Red blood cells	Increased rate of red blood cell production; red blood cell count increased by about 20% as a result of increased erythropoietin secretion
Kidney	Retention of sodium and water to a small degree, resulting in increased extracellular fluid volume
Skeletal muscle	Skeletal muscle mass increases at puberty; the average increase is greater in males than in females
Bone	Rapid bone growth resulting in increased rate of growth and in early cessation of bone growth; males who mature sexually at a later age do not exhibit a rapid period of growth, but they grow for a longer time and can become taller than men who mature earlier

Male Sexual Behavior and the Male Sexual Act

Testosterone is required for normal sexual behavior. Testosterone enters certain cells within the brain, especially within the hypothalamus, and influences their functions. The blood levels of testosterone remain relatively constant throughout the lifetime of a male, from puberty until about 40 years of age. Thereafter the levels slowly decline to approximately 20% of this value by 80 years of age, causing a slow decrease in sex drive and fertility.

The male sexual act is a complex series of reflexes that result in erection of the penis, secretion of mucus into the urethra, emission, and ejaculation. **Emission** (ē-mish′ŭn) is the movement of sperm cells, mucus, prostatic secretions, and seminal vesicle secretions into the prostatic and spongy part of the urethra. **Ejaculation** (ē-jak′ū-lā′shŭn) is the forceful expulsion of the secretions that have accumulated in the penis to the exterior. Sensations that are normally interpreted as pleasurable occur during the male sexual act and result in an intense sensation called an **orgasm** (ōr′gazm), or **climax**. In males, orgasm is closely associated with ejaculation, although they are separate functions and do not always occur simultaneously. A phase called **resolution** occurs after ejaculation. During resolution the penis becomes flaccid, an overall feeling of satisfaction exists, and the male is unable to achieve erection and a second ejaculation.

Afferent Impulses and Integration

Sensory action potentials from the genitals are carried to the sacral region of the spinal cord, in which reflexes that result in the male sexual act are integrated. Action potentials also travel from the spinal cord to the cerebrum to produce conscious sexual sensations.

Rhythmic massage of the penis, especially the glans, and surrounding tissues, such as the scrotal, anal, and pubic regions, provide important sources of sensory action potentials. Engorgement of the prostate gland and seminal vesicles with secretions or irritation of the urethra, urinary bladder, ductus deferens, and testes can also cause sexual sensations.

Psychic stimuli such as sight, sound, odor, or thoughts have a major effect on male sexual reflexes. Ejaculation while sleeping (nocturnal emission) is a relatively common event in young males and is thought to be triggered by psychic stimuli associated with dreaming. The inability to concentrate on sexual sensations can result in **impotence** (im′pŏ-tens), or the inability to achieve an erection of the penis. Impotence can also be caused by nervous system lesions or physical factors such as inability of the erectile tissue to fill with blood.

Erection, Emission, and Ejaculation

Erection is the first major component of the male sexual act. Parasympathetic action potentials from the sacral region of the spinal cord cause the arteries that supply blood to the erectile tissues to dilate. Blood then fills small venous sinuses called **sinusoids** in the erectile tissue and compresses the veins, which reduces blood flow from the penis. The increased blood pressure in the sinusoids causes the erectile tissue to become inflated and rigid. Parasympathetic action potentials also cause the mucous glands within the penile urethra and the bulbourethral glands to secrete mucus.

Before ejaculation, the ductus deferens begins to contract rhythmically, propelling sperm cells and testicular fluid from the epididymis through the ductus deferens. Contractions of the ductus deferens, seminal vesicles, and ejaculatory ducts cause the sperm cells, testicular secretions, and seminal fluid to move into the urethra, in which they mix with prostatic secretions released as a result of contraction of the prostate.

Emission is stimulated by sympathetic action potentials that originate in the lumbar region of the spinal cord. Action potentials cause contractions of the reproductive ducts and stimulate the seminal vesicles and prostate gland to release secretions. Consequently, semen accumulates in the urethra.

Ejaculation results from the contraction of smooth muscle in the wall of the urethra and skeletal muscles surrounding the base of the penis. Just before ejaculation, action potentials are sent to the skeletal muscles that surround the base of the penis. Rhythmic contractions are produced that force the semen out of the urethra, resulting in ejaculation. In addition, muscle tension increases throughout the body.

Decreased sperm cell count can occur because of damage to the testes as a result of trauma, radiation, cryptorchidism, or infections such as mumps, which block the ducts in the epididymis. Reduced sperm cell counts can result from inadequate secretion of luteinizing hormone and follicle-stimulating hormone, which can be caused by hypothyroidism, trauma to the hypothalamus, infarctions of the hypothalamus or anterior pituitary gland, or tumors. Decreased testosterone secretion also reduces the sperm cell count.

Fertility is reduced if the sperm cell count is normal but sperm cell structure is abnormal, such as chromosomal abnormalities caused by genetic factors. Reduced sperm cell motility also results in infertility. A major cause of reduced sperm cell motility is antisperm antibodies produced by the immune system, which bind to sperm cells.

Fertility can sometimes be achieved by collecting several ejaculations, concentrating the sperm cells, and inserting the sperm cells into the female's reproductive tract, a process called **artificial insemination** (in-sem-i-nā'shŭn).

Female Reproductive System

The female reproductive organs consist of the ovaries, uterine tubes (or fallopian tubes), uterus, vagina, external genitalia, and mammary glands. The internal reproductive organs of the female (figures 19.7 and 19.8) are located within the pelvis, be-tween the urinary bladder and the rectum. The uterus and the vagina are in the midline, with an ovary to each side of the uterus. The internal reproductive organs are held in place within the pelvis by a group of ligaments. The most conspicuous is the **broad ligament**, which spreads out on both sides of the uterus and to which the ovaries and uterine tubes attach.

Ovaries

The two **ovaries** (ō'vă-rēz) are small organs suspended in the pelvic cavity by ligaments. The **suspensory ligament** extends from each ovary to the lateral body wall, and the **ovarian ligament** attaches the ovary to the superior margin of the uterus (see figure 19.8). In addition, the ovaries are attached to the posterior surface of the broad ligament by folds of peritoneum called the **mesovarium** (mez'ō-vā'rē-ŭm, mesentery of the ovary). The ovarian arteries, veins, and nerves traverse the suspensory ligament and enter the ovary through the mesovarium.

A layer of visceral peritoneum covers the surface of the ovary. The outer part of the ovary is made up of dense connective tissue and contains **ovarian follicles** (figure 19.9). Each of the ovarian follicles contains an **oocyte** (ō'ō-sīt), the female germ cell. Loose connective tissue makes up the inner part of the ovary, where blood vessels, lymphatic vessels, and nerves are located.

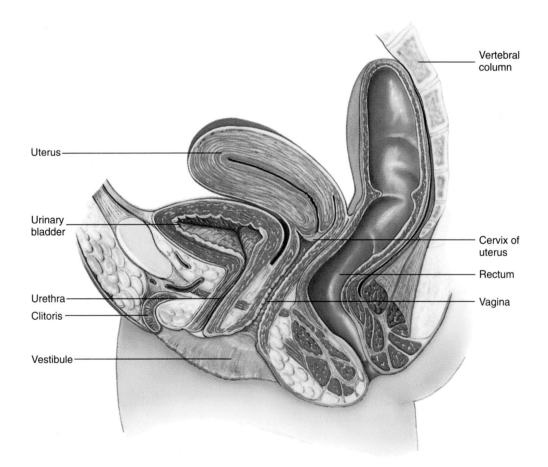

Uterus

Urinary bladder

Urethra

Clitoris

Vestibule

Vertebral column

Cervix of uterus

Rectum

Vagina

Figure 19.7 Sagittal View of the Female Pelvis

The female reproductive tract and the female urinary tract open separately to the exterior in the vestibule.

Figure 19.8 Frontal View of Female Reproductive Organs
The uterus, uterine tubes, and vagina are cut in frontal section to show the internal anatomy.

Follicle and Oocyte Development

During the second third of pregnancy, the developing ovaries of the fetus can contain 5 million **oogonia** (ō-ō-gō'nē-ă), the cells from which oocytes develop (see figure 19.2b). By the time of birth, many of the oogonia have degenerated, and those remaining have begun meiosis. Meiosis stops, however, during the first meiotic division at a stage called prophase I. The cell at this stage is called a **primary oocyte**, and at birth there are about 2 million of them. The primary oocyte is surrounded by a single layer of flat cells, called **granulosa cells**, and the structure is called a **primordial follicle**. From birth to puberty the number of primordial follicles declines to 300,000 to 400,000. Of these only about 400 reach the final stage of development. The primordial follicles are converted to **primary follicles** when the oocyte enlarges and the single layer of granulosa cells becomes enlarged and cuboidal. Subsequently, several layers of granulosa cells form, and a layer of clear material is deposited around the primary oocyte called the **zona pellucida** (zō'nă pel-lū'sid-dă) (see figure 19.9; figure 19.10).

Beginning during puberty, approximately every 28 days hormonal changes stimulate some of the primordial follicles to continue to develop (see figure 19.10). The primary follicle becomes a secondary follicle as small amounts of fluid accumulate among the granulosa cells in more than one location as the development of the antrum begins. The **antrum** (an'trŭm) is a fluid-filled chamber near the center of the fol-

licle. Tissue around the secondary follicle thickens to form the **theca** (thē'kă). The oocyte is pushed off to one side of the follicle and lies in a mass of follicular cells called the **cumulus mass**.

The secondary follicle continues to enlarge and becomes a **mature follicle**, or a **Graafian** (graf'ē-ăn) **follicle**, when the fluid-filled spaces combine to form the antrum. The mature follicle forms a lump on the surface of the ovary.

Follicles are stimulated to develop by FSH secreted by the anterior pituitary gland. FSH causes several follicles to begin developing during each menstrual cycle, but normally only one ovulates. The remainder of the developing follicles degenerate. Also, it takes more than one menstrual cycle for a follicle to undergo the transition from a primordial follicle to a mature follicle. Thus a follicle ovulated during one menstrual cycle started developing in response to FSH two or more menstrual cycles earlier.

The developing follicles secrete small amounts of a class of hormones called **estrogen** (es'trō-jen) (see table 19.1). Estrogen plays an important role in coordinating the menstrual cycle and preparing the uterus to receive the fertilized ovum.

Ovulation

The mature follicle expands and ruptures, a process called **ovulation** (ov'ū-lā'shŭn), forcing a small amount of blood, follicular fluid, and the oocyte, surrounded by the cumulus mass, out of the ruptured follicle and into the peritoneal cavity.

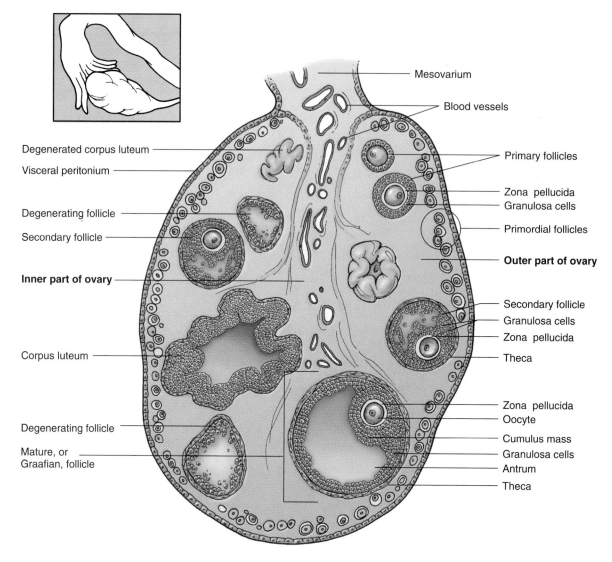

Mesovarium

Blood vessels

Degenerated corpus luteum

Visceral peritonium

Degenerating follicle

Secondary follicle

Inner part of ovary

Corpus luteum

Degenerating follicle

Mature, or
Graafian, follicle

Primary follicles

Zona pellucida
Granulosa cells

Primordial follicles

Outer part of ovary

Secondary follicle
Granulosa cells
Zona pellucida
Theca

Zona pellucida
Oocyte
Cumulus mass
Granulosa cells
Antrum
Theca

Figure 19.9 Structure of the Ovary

The ovary is sectioned to illustrate its internal structure (inset shows plane of section). Ovarian follicles from each major stage of development are presented, and a corpus luteum is also shown.

Ovulation occurs in response to LH secreted by the anterior pituitary gland.

Just before ovulation, the first meiotic division is completed, and the second meiotic division begins. The second meiotic division is stopped, however, and proceeds to completion only if fertilization occurs (see figure 19.2*b*).

After ovulation, the remaining cells of the ruptured follicle become transformed into a glandular structure called the **corpus luteum** (loo′tē-ŭm, yellow) (see figures 19.9 and 19.10). LH from the anterior pituitary causes cells of the ruptured follicle to divide and enlarge to form the corpus luteum. The cells of the corpus luteum secrete the hormone, **progesterone** (prō-jes′ter-ōn) and smaller amounts of estrogen.

If pregnancy occurs, the corpus luteum enlarges in response to a hormone secreted by the placenta of the developing embryo called **human chorionic gonadotropin hormone (HCG)** (kō-rē-on′ik gō′nad-ō-trō′pin) (see table 19.1). Maintenance of pregnancy depends on progesterone secreted

by the corpus luteum for about the first trimester (first third, or first 12 weeks) of pregnancy. After the first trimester of pregnancy, progesterone and estrogen are produced by the placenta, and the corpus luteum is no longer essential for the maintenance of pregnancy.

If pregnancy does not occur, the corpus luteum lasts for about 10 to 12 days and then begins to degenerate. Degeneration of the corpus luteum occurs unless HCG causes it to enlarge and remain functional.

Uterine Tubes

A **uterine tube**, also called a **fallopian** (fa-lō′pē-an) **tube**, or **oviduct** (ō′vi-dŭct), is associated with each ovary. The uterine tubes extend from the area of the ovaries to the uterus. They open directly into the peritoneal cavity near each ovary and receive the oocyte. The opening of each uterine tube is surrounded by long, thin processes called **fimbriae** (fim′brē-ă, fringe) (see figure 19.8).

1. The primordial follicle consists of an oocyte surrounded by a single layer of squamous granulosa cells.

2. A primordial follicle becomes a primary follicle as the granulosa cells become enlarged and cuboidal.

3. The primary follicle enlarges. Granulosa cells form more than one layer of cells.

4. A secondary follicle forms when fluid-filled spaces develop among the granulosa cells and a well developed theca becomes apparent around the granulosa cells.

5. A mature follicle forms when the fluid-filled spaces form a single antrum. When a follicle becomes fully mature, it is enlarged to its maximum size, a large antrum is present, and the oocyte is located in the cumulus mass.

6. During ovulation the oocyte is released from the follicle, along with some surrounding granulosa cells of the cumulus mass.

7. Following ovulation, the granulosa cells divide rapidly and enlarge to form the corpus luteum.

8. The corpus luteum degenerates.

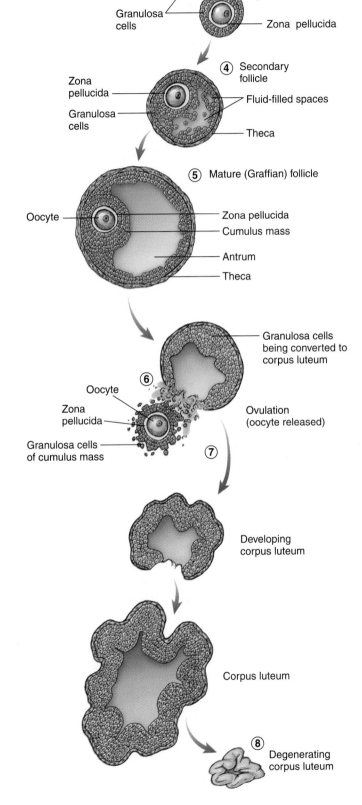

Figure 19.10   Maturation of the Follicle and Corpus Luteum

The fimbriae nearly surround the surface of the ovary. As a result, as soon as the oocyte is ovulated, it comes into contact with the surface of the fimbriae. Cilia on the fimbriae surface sweep the oocyte into the uterine tube. Fertilization usually occurs in the part of the uterine tube near the ovary.

Uterus

The **uterus** (ū′ter-ŭs) is as big as a medium-sized pear (see figures 19.7 and 19.8). It is oriented in the pelvic cavity with the larger, rounded part directed superiorly. The part of the uterus superior to the entrance of the uterine tubes is called the **fundus** (fŭn′dŭs). The main part of the uterus is called the **body**, and the narrower part, the **cervix** (ser′viks, neck), is directed inferiorly. Internally, the **uterine cavity** in the fundus and uterine body continues through the cervix as the **cervical canal**, which opens into the vagina. The cervical canal is lined by mucous glands.

> ## Did You Know?
>
> **Cancer of the cervix** is relatively common in females and fortunately can be detected and treated. A **Papanicolaou (Pap) smear** is a diagnostic test used to determine if a woman is suffering from cancer of the uterine cervix. A smear of epithelial cells is taken from the area of the cervix by inserting a swab through the vagina. Cells from the wall of the vagina are also included in the smear. The smear is placed on a glass slide and stained. The cells are then examined microscopically to determine whether some of them show signs of being cancerous. Early in the development of cervical cancer, the cells of the cervix change in a characteristic way. Cells that are cancerous appear to be less mature than the characteristic epithelial cells of the cervix or vaginal wall.

The uterine wall is composed of three layers: a serous layer, a muscular layer, and a layer of endometrium (see figure 19.8). The outer layer, called the **serous layer**, or **perimetrium** (per-i-mē′trē-ŭm), of the uterus, is formed from peritoneum. The middle layer, called the **muscular layer**, or **myometrium** (mī′ō-mē′trē-ŭm), consists of smooth muscle, is quite thick, and accounts for the bulk of the uterine wall. The innermost layer of the uterus is the **endometrium** (en′dō-mē′trē-ŭm). The endometrium consists of simple columnar epithelial cells with an underlying connective tissue layer. Simple tubular glands, called endometrial glands, are formed by folds of the endometrium. The superficial part of the endometrium is sloughed off during menstruation.

The uterus is supported by the broad ligament and the **round ligament**. In addition to these ligaments that support the uterus, much support is provided inferiorly to the uterus by skeletal muscles of the pelvic floor. If ligaments that support the uterus or muscles of the pelvic floor are weakened such as in childbirth, the uterus can extend inferiorly into the vagina, a condition called a **prolapsed uterus.** Severe cases require surgical correction.

> ## Did You Know?
>
> An **ectopic pregnancy** results if implantation occurs anywhere other than in the uterine cavity. The most common site of ectopic pregnancy is the uterine tube. Implantation in the uterine tube eventually is fatal to the fetus and can cause the tube to rupture. In some cases, implantation can occur in the mesenteries of the abdominal cavity, and the fetus can develop normally but must be delivered by cesarean section.

Vagina

The **vagina** (vă-jī′nă) is the female organ of copulation and functions to receive the penis during intercourse. It also allows menstrual flow and childbirth. The vagina extends from the uterus to the outside of the body (see figures 19.7 and 19.8). The superior portion of the vagina is attached to the sides of the cervix so that a part of the cervix extends into the vagina.

The wall of the vagina consists of an outer muscular layer and an inner mucous membrane. The muscular layer is smooth muscle and contains many elastic fibers. Thus the vagina can increase in size to accommodate the penis during intercourse, and it can stretch greatly during childbirth. The mucous membrane is moist stratified squamous epithelium that forms a protective surface layer. Lubricating fluid passes through the vaginal epithelium into the vagina.

In young females, the vaginal opening is covered by a thin mucous membrane called the **hymen** (hī′men). The hymen can completely close the vaginal orifice, in which case it must be removed to allow menstrual flow. More commonly, the hymen is perforated by one or several holes. The openings in the hymen are usually greatly enlarged during the first sexual intercourse. The hymen can also be perforated or torn at some earlier time in a young female's life during a variety of activities including strenuous exercise. The condition of the hymen is therefore not a reliable indicator of virginity.

External Genitalia

The external female genitalia, also called the **vulva** (vŭl′vă), or **pudendum** (pū-den′dŭm), consist of the vestibule and its surrounding structures (figure 19.11). The **vestibule** (ves′ti-bool) is the space into which the vagina and urethra open. The urethra opens just anterior to the vagina. The vestibule is bordered by a pair of thin, longitudinal skin folds called the **labia minora** (lā′bē-ă mī-nō′ră, lips). A small erectile structure called the **clitoris** (klit′ō-ris or klī′tŏ-ris) is located in the anterior margin of the vestibule. The two labia minora unite over the clitoris to form a fold of skin called the **prepuce** (prē′poos).

The clitoris consists of a shaft and a distal glans. Like the glans penis, the clitoris is well supplied with sensory receptors, and it is made up of erectile tissue. Additional erectile tissue is located on either side of the vaginal opening.

On each side of the vestibule, between the vaginal opening and the labia minora, are openings of the **greater vestibular glands.** They produce a lubricating fluid that helps maintain the moistness of the vestibule.

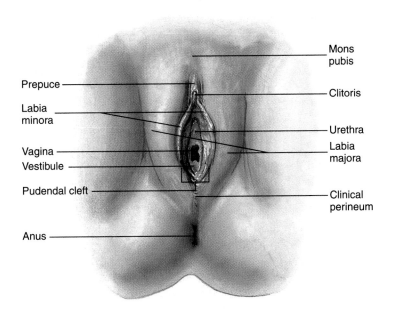

Figure 19.11   Female External Genitalia

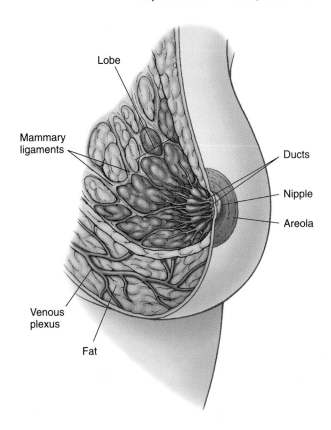

Figure 19.12   Anatomy of the Breast

A sagittal section through the breast illustrates the duct system and fat of the breast.

Lateral to the labia minora are two prominent, rounded folds of skin called the **labia majora** (mă-jō′ră). The two labia majora unite anteriorly in an elevation of tissue over the pubic symphysis called the **mons** (mound) **pubis** (monz pū′bis) (see figure 19.11). The lateral surfaces of the labia majora and the surface of the mons pubis are covered with coarse hair. The medial surfaces of the labia majora are covered with numerous sebaceous and sweat glands. The space between the labia majora is called the **pudendal** (pū-den′dal) **cleft**. Most of the time, the labia majora are in contact with each other across the midline, closing the pudendal cleft and covering the deeper structures within the vestibule.

The region between the vagina and the anus is the **clinical perineum** (per′i-nē′ŭm). The skin and muscle of this region can tear during childbirth. To prevent such tearing, an incision called an **episiotomy** (e-piz-ē-ot′ō-mē) is sometimes made in the clinical perineum. This clean, straight incision is easier to repair than a tear. Alternatively, allowing the perineum to stretch slowly during the delivery can prevent tearing, making an episiotomy unnecessary.

Mammary Glands

The **mammary** (mam′ă-rē) **glands** are the organs of milk production and are located in the **breasts**, or **mammae** (mam′ē) (figure 19.12). The mammary glands are modified sweat glands. Externally, each of the breasts of both males and females have a raised **nipple** surrounded by a circular, pigmented **areola** (ă-rē′ō-lă).

In prepubescent children, the general structure of the male and female breasts is similar, and both males and females possess a rudimentary duct system. The female breasts begin to enlarge during puberty, under the influence of estrogen and progesterone. Some males also experience a mi-

nor and temporary enlargement of the breasts at puberty. The breasts of a male can become permanently enlarged, however, a condition called **gynecomastia** (gī′nĕ-kō-mas′tē-ă). Causes of gynecomastia include hormonal imbalances and the abuse of anabolic steroids.

Each adult female breast contains mammary glands consisting of usually 15 to 20 glandular **lobes** covered by a considerable amount of fat tissue. It is primarily this superficial fat that gives the breast its form. Each lobe possesses a single duct which opens independently to the surface of the nipple. The duct of each lobe is formed as several smaller ducts that originate from lobules converge. Within a lobule, the ducts branch and become even smaller. In the milk-producing, or lactating, mammary gland, the ends of these small ducts expand to form secretory sacs called **alveoli**.

The breasts are supported by the mammary ligaments, which extend from the fascia over the pectoralis major muscles to the skin over the breasts and prevent them from excessive sagging. In older adults, the mammary ligaments can weaken and elongate, increasing the tendency for the breasts to sag.

The nipples are very sensitive to tactile stimulation and contain smooth muscle. When the smooth muscle contracts, the nipple becomes erect. The smooth muscle cells contract in response to stimuli such as touch, cold, and sexual arousal.

Did You Know?

Cancer of the breast is a serious, often fatal disease most often occurring in women. **Mammography** (ma-mog′ră-fē) uses low-intensity x-rays to detect tumors in the soft tissue of the breast. The use of mammography and regular self-examination of the breast can lead to early detection of breast cancer and effective treatment. With mammography, however, tumors can often be identified before they can be detected by palpation. Once a tumor is identified, a biopsy is normally performed to determine whether the tumor is benign or malignant. Most tumors of the mammary glands are benign. Those that are malignant have the potential to spread to other areas of the body and ultimately lead to death.

Physiology of Female Reproduction

As in the male, female reproduction is under hormonal and neural regulation.

Puberty

The first signs of puberty typically appear between 11 and 13 years of age in girls, and the process is largely completed by age 16. Puberty in females is marked by the first episode of menstrual bleeding, which is called **menarche** (me-nar′kē). During puberty, the vagina, uterus, uterine tubes, and external genitalia begin to enlarge. Fat is deposited in the breasts and around the hips, causing them to enlarge and assume an adult form. In addition, pubic and axillary hair grows. Development of sexual drive is also associated with puberty.

The changes associated with puberty are primarily the result of the increasing rate of estrogen and progesterone secretion by the ovaries. Before puberty, estrogen and progesterone are secreted in very small amounts. At puberty, the cyclical adult pattern of hormone secretion is gradually established.

Before puberty, the rate of GnRH secretion from the hypothalamus and the rate of LH and FSH secretion from the anterior pituitary are very low. Estrogen and progesterone from the ovaries also have a strong negative-feedback effect on the hypothalamus and pituitary. After the onset of puberty, the hypothalamus and anterior pituitary secrete larger amounts of GnRH, LH, and FSH. Estrogen and progesterone have less of a negative-feedback effect on the hypothalamus and pituitary, and a sustained increase in estrogen concentration has a positive-feedback effect. The normal cyclical pattern of reproductive hormone secretion that occurs during the menstrual cycle becomes established. The initial change that results in puberty appears to be maturation of the hypothalamus.

Menstrual Cycle

The term **menstrual** (men′stroo-ăl) **cycle** refers to the series of changes that occur in sexually mature, nonpregnant females and that culminate in menses. **Menses** (men′sēz) is derived from a Latin word meaning month, and is a period of mild hemorrhage during which part of the endometrium is sloughed and expelled from the uterus. Typically the menstrual cycle is about 28 days long, although it can be as short as 18 days or as long as 40 days (figure 19.13 and table 19.3). The menstrual cycle results from the cyclical changes that occur in the endometrium of the uterus. These changes result from the cyclical changes that occur in the ovary and are controlled by the secretions of FSH and LH from the anterior pituitary.

The first day of menstrual bleeding (menses) is considered to be day 1 of the menstrual cycle. Menses typically lasts 4 or 5 days. Ovulation occurs on about day 14 of the menstrual cycle, although the timing of ovulation varies from individual to individual and can vary within an individual from one menstrual cycle to the next. A small increase in FSH secretion occurs during menses as a result of the end of the previous menstrual cycle (see following discussion).

The time between the ending of menses and ovulation is called the **proliferative phase**, which refers to proliferation of the endometrium. During the proliferative phase, follicles in the ovary mature, and, as they do so, they secrete increasing amounts of estrogen. Estrogen acts on the uterus and causes the epithelial cells of the endometrium to divide rapidly. The endometrium thickens, and endometrial glands form.

The sustained increase of estrogen secreted by the developing follicles stimulates GnRH secretion from the hypothalamus, and GnRH triggers LH and FSH secretion from the anterior pituitary gland. FSH stimulates estrogen secretion at an increasing rate from the developing follicles. This positive-feedback loop produces a series of larger and larger surges of LH and FSH secretion. Ovulation occurs in response to the large increases in LH levels that normally occur on about day 14 of the menstrual cycle. This large increase in LH is also responsible for the development of the corpus luteum.

Following ovulation, the corpus luteum begins to secrete progesterone and smaller amounts of estrogen. Progesterone acts on the uterus, causing the cells of the endometrium to become larger and to secrete a small amount of fluid. Together, progesterone and estrogen act on the hypothalamus and anterior pituitary gland to inhibit LH and FSH secretion. Thus LH and FSH levels decline to low levels after ovulation.

The time between ovulation and the next menses is called the **secretory phase** of the menstrual cycle because of the small amount of fluid secreted by the cells of the endometrium. During the secretory phase, the lining of the uterus reaches its greatest degree of development.

If fertilization occurs, the zygote undergoes several cell divisions to produce a collection of cells called the **blastocyst** (blas′tō-sist). The blastocyst passes through the oviduct and arrives in the uterus by 7 or 8 days after ovulation. The endometrium is prepared to receive the blastocyst, which becomes implanted in the endometrium, where development continues. If the secondary oocyte is not fertilized, the endometrium sloughs away as a result of declining blood progesterone levels. Unless the secondary oocyte is fertilized, the corpus luteum begins to produce less progesterone by day 24 or 25 of the menstrual cycle. By day 28, the declining progesterone causes the endometrium to slough away to begin menses and the next menstrual cycle. The declining progesterone secretion results in a small increase in FSH secretion at the beginning of the next mensus.

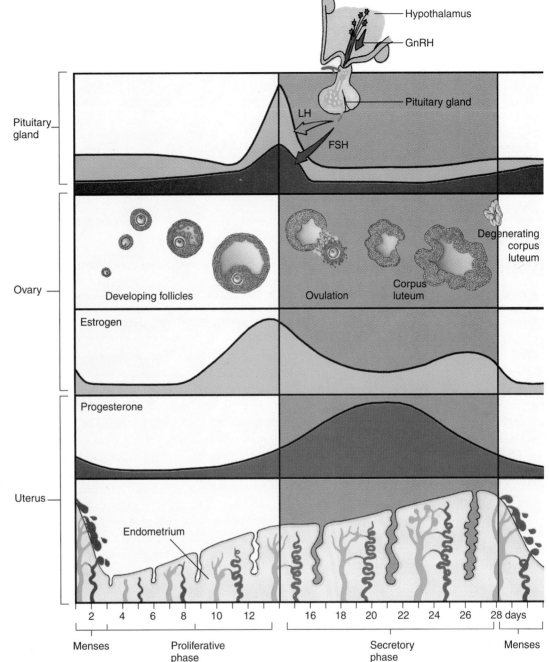

Figure 19.13   The Menstrual Cycle

The figure illustrates gonadotropin-releasing hormone (GnRH) and changes in follicle-stimulating hormone (FSH) and luteinizing hormone (LH) secretion from the anterior pituitary and changes in estrogen and progesterone secretion from the ovary. In addition, changes in the ovary and changes in the endometrium of the uterus are correlated with the changes in hormone secretion throughout the menstrual cycle.

3   P R E D I C T

Predict the effect of administering a relatively large amount of progesterone and estrogen just before the increase in LH that precedes ovulation.

✔ *Answer on page 549*

A topic of current research emphasis concerns a phenomenon called the **premenstrual syndrome (PMS)**. Some women suffer from severe changes in mood that can result in aggression and other socially unacceptable behaviors before menses. It has been hypothesized that hormonal changes associated with the menstrual cycle trigger these mood changes.

Women with severe cases of PMS can be treated with fluoxetine (Prozac). Although some women with PMS appear to have been successfully treated with progesteronelike hormones, and a variety of other drugs, these treatments do not appear to be effective for all people. Similarly, reduced caffeine, alcohol, sugar, or animal fat consumption helps some people. It is unclear how many women are affected by PMS. The definition of the premenstrual period is not well established, the symptoms of the condition are not easily monitored, and its precise cause and physiological mechanisms are unknown. In addition, it is not clear that all women diagnosed as having PMS are suffering from the same condition. Additional research is needed to resolve these uncertainties.

Table 19.3 Events During the Menstrual Cycle

Menses (Day 1 to Day 4 or 5 of the Menstrual Cycle)

Pituitary gland	The rate of FSH and LH secretion is low and the rate of FSH secretion increases as progesterone levels decline.
Ovary	The rate of estrogen and progesterone secretion is low after degeneration of the corpus luteum produced during the previous menstrual cycle.
Uterus	In response to declining progesterone levels, the endometrial lining of the uterus sloughs off, resulting in menses followed by repair of the endometrium.

Proliferative Phase (from Day 4 or 5 Until Ovulation on About Day 14)

Pituitary gland	The rate of FSH and LH secretion is only slightly elevated during most of the proliferative phase; FSH and LH secretion increase near the end of the proliferative phase in response to increasing estrogen secretion from the ovaries.
Ovary	Developing follicles secrete increasing amounts of estrogen, especially near the end of the proliferative phase; increasing FSH and LH cause additional estrogen secretion from the ovaries near the end of the proliferative phase.
Uterus	Estrogen causes endometrial cells of the uterus to divide. The endometrium of the uterus thickens and tubelike glands form. Estrogen causes the cells of the uterus to be more sensitive to progesterone by increasing the number of progesterone receptors in uterine tissues.

Ovulation (About Day 14)

Pituitary gland	The rate of FSH and LH secretion increases rapidly just before ovulation in response to increasing estrogen levels. Increasing FSH and LH levels stimulate estrogen secretion, resulting in a positive-feedback cycle.
Ovary	LH causes final maturation of a mature follicle and initiates the process of ovulation. FSH acts on immature follicles and causes several of them to begin to enlarge.
Uterus	The endometrium continues to divide in response to estrogen.

Secretory Phase (from About Day 14 to Day 28)

Pituitary gland	Estrogen and progesterone reach levels high enough to inhibit FSH and LH secretion from the pituitary gland.
Ovary	After ovulation, the follicle is converted to the corpus luteum; the corpus luteum secretes large amounts of progesterone and smaller amounts of estrogen from shortly after ovulation until about day 24 or 25. If fertilization does not occur, the corpus luteum degenerates after about day 25, and the rate of progesterone secretion rapidly declines to low levels.
Uterus	In response to progesterone, the endometrial cells enlarge, the endometrial layer thickens, and the glands of the endometrium reach their greatest degree of development; the endometrial cells secrete a small amount of fluid. After progesterone levels decline, the endometrium begins to degenerate.

Menses (Day 1 to Day 4 or 5 of the Next Menstrual Cycle)

Pituitary gland	The rate of LH remains low and the rate of FSH secretion increases as progesterone levels decline.
Ovary	The rate of estrogen and progesterone secretion is low.
Uterus	In response to declining progesterone levels, the endometrial lining of the uterus sloughs off, resulting in menses followed by repair of the endometrium.

Did You Know?

Menstrual cramps are the result of strong myometrial contractions that occur before and during menstruation. The cramps can result from excessive secretion of prostaglandins. Sloughing of the endometrium of the uterus results in an inflammation in the endometrial layer of the uterus, and prostaglandins are produced as part of the inflammation. Sloughing of the endometrium is inhibited by progesterone but stimulated by estrogen. In some women, menstrual cramps are extremely uncomfortable. Many women can alleviate painful menstruation by taking drugs, such as aspirinlike drugs, that inhibit prostaglandin biosynthesis just before the onset of menstruation. These treatments, however, are not effective in treating all painful menstruation, especially when the causes of pain,

such as those in some women who have tumors of the myometrium, differ from the ones caused by the inflammatory response.

The absence of a menstrual cycle is called **amenorrhea** (ă-men-ō-rē′ă). If the pituitary gland does not function properly because of abnormal development, the woman will not begin to menstruate at puberty. This condition is called **primary amenorrhea.** In contrast, if a woman has had normal menstrual cycles and later stops menstruating, the condition is called **secondary amenorrhea.** One cause of secondary amenorrhea is anorexia, a condition in which the lack of food causes the hypothalamus of the brain to decrease GnRH secretion to levels so low that the menstrual cycle cannot occur. Female athletes or ballet dancers who have rigorous training schedules often have secondary amenorrhea. The physical stress that can be coupled with an inadequate food intake also results in very low GnRH secretion. Increased food intake for anorexic women or reduced training for dancers and athletes generally restores normal hormone secretion and normal menstrual cycles.

Secondary amenorrhea can also be the result of pituitary tumors, which decrease FSH and LH secretion, or from a lack of GnRH secretion from the hypothalamus. Head trauma and tumors that affect the hypothalamus can result in lack of GnRH secretion.

Secondary amenorrhea can result from a lack of normal hormone secretion from the ovaries, which can result from autoimmune diseases that attack the ovary, or from **polycystic ovarian disease,** in which the cysts in the ovary produce large amounts of androgen that are converted to estrogen by other tissues in the body. The increased estrogen prevents the normal cycle of FSH and LH secretion required for ovulation to occur. Other hormone-secreting tumors of the ovary can also disrupt the normal menstrual cycle and result in amenorrhea.

Menopause

When a woman is 40 to 50 years old, the menstrual cycles become less regular, and ovulation does not consistently occur during each cycle. Eventually the cycles stop completely. The cessation of menstrual cycles is called **menopause** (men′ō-pawz), and the whole time period from the onset of irregular cycles to their complete cessation is called the **female climacteric** (klī-mak′ter-ik).

The major cause of menopause is age-related changes in the ovary. The number of follicles remaining in the ovaries of menopausal women is small. In addition, the follicles that remain become less sensitive to stimulation by FSH and LH. As the ovaries become less responsive to stimulation by FSH and LH, fewer mature follicles and corpora lutea are produced. Gradual

changes occur in women in response to the reduced amount of estrogen and progesterone produced by the ovaries (table 19.4).

During the climacteric, some women experience "hot flashes," irritability, fatigue, anxiety, temporary decrease in libido, and occasionally severe emotional disturbances. Many of these symptoms can be treated successfully by administering small amounts of estrogen and progesterone and then gradually decreasing the dosage, or by providing psychological counseling. A potential side effect of estrogen therapy is a slightly increased possibility of the development of breast and uterine cancer in some women. Recent reports suggest that the low dosage currently used in estrogen replacement therapy may not increase the probability of breast cancer, although there may not be enough data for the issue to be completely resolved. Estrogen replacement also slows the decrease in bone density that can become severe in some women after menopause.

Female Sexual Behavior and the Female Sex Act

Sexual drive in females, like sexual drive in males, is dependent on hormones. Testosteronelike hormones, and possibly estrogen, affect brain cells (especially in the area of the hypothalamus) and influence sexual behavior. Testosteronelike hormones are produced primarily in the adrenal cortex. Psychological factors also play a role in sexual behavior. The afferent and efferent neural pathways involved in controlling female sexual responses are similar to those found in the male.

Erectile tissue within the clitoris and around the vaginal opening becomes engorged with blood during sexual excitement. The mucous glands within the vestibule, especially the vestibular glands, secrete small amounts of mucus. Larger amounts of mucuslike fluid are also extruded into the

Table 19.4   Possible Changes in Postmenopausal Women Caused by Decreased Ovarian Hormone Secretion

	Changes
Menstrual cycle	5–7 years before menopause the cycle becomes irregular; the number of cycles in which ovulation does not occur and in which corpora lutea do not develop increases.
Uterus	Irregular menstruation gradually is followed by no menstruation; the endometrium finally atrophies, and the uterus becomes smaller.
Vagina and external genitalia	The epithelial lining becomes thinner; the external genitalia become thinner and less elastic; the labia majora becomes smaller; the pubic hair decreases; reduced secretion leads to dryness; the vagina is more easily inflamed and infected.
Skin	The epidermis becomes thinner.
Cardiovascular system	Hypertension and atherosclerosis occur more frequently.
Vasomotor instability	Hot flashes and increased sweating are correlated with vasodilation of cutaneous blood vessels; the hot flashes are related to decreased estrogen levels.
Libido	Temporary changes, usually a decrease in libido are associated with onset of menopause.
Fertility	Fertility begins to decline about 10 years before the onset of menopause; by age 50 almost all the oocytes and follicles have degenerated.
Pituitary function	Low levels of estrogen and progesterone produced by the ovaries cause the pituitary gland to secrete larger than normal amounts of LH and FSH; increased levels of these hormones have little effect on the postmenopausal ovaries.

Clinical Focus Reproductive Disorders

Infectious Diseases

Sexually Transmitted Diseases

Sexually transmitted diseases (STDs) are a class of infectious diseases spread by intimate sexual contact between individuals. These diseases include the major venereal diseases such as nongonococcal urethritis, trichomoniasis, gonorrhea, genital herpes, genital warts, syphilis, and acquired immunodeficiency syndrome (AIDS).

Nongonococcal urethritis (non-gon′ō-kok′ăl ū-rē-thrī′tis) refers to any inflammation of the urethra that is not caused by gonorrhea. Factors such as trauma or passage of a nonsterile catheter through the urethra can cause this condition, but many cases are acquired through sexual contact. In most cases, a bacterium such as *Chlamydia trachomatis* (kla-mid′ē-ă tra-kō′mă-tis) is responsible, but other bacteria can be involved. *C. trachomatis* infection is one of the most common sexually transmitted diseases. It is often unrecognized in people who have it, and it is responsible for many cases of pelvic inflammatory disease. It can also result in sterility. Antibiotics are usually effective in treating the condition.

Trichomonas (trik′ō-mō′nas) is a protozoan commonly found in the vagina of females and the urethra of males. If the normal acidity of the vagina is disturbed, *Trichomonas* can grow rapidly. **Trichomoniasis** (trik-ō-mō-nī′ă-sis) is more common in females than in males. The rapid growth of these organisms results in inflammation and a greenish yellow discharge characterized by a foul odor.

Gonorrhea (gon-ō-rē′ă) is caused by *Neisseria gonorrhoeae* (nī-sē′rē-ă gon-ō-rē′ē). The organisms attach to the epithelial cells of the vagina or to the male urethra. The invasion of bacteria establishes an inflammatory response in which pus is formed. Males become aware of a gonorrheal infection because of painful urination and the discharge of pus-containing material from the urethra. Symptoms appear within a few days to a week. Recovery can eventually occur without complication, but, when complications do occur, they can be serious. The urethra can become partially blocked, or sterility can result from scar tissue blocking the reproductive ducts. In some cases, other organ systems, such as the heart, meninges of the brain, or joints can become infected. In females, the early stages of infection may not be noticeable, but the infection can lead to pelvic inflammatory disease. Gonorrheal eye infections can occur in newborn children of women with gonorrheal infections. Antibiotics are usually effective in treating gonorrheal infections, and the immune system often successfully combats gonorrheal infections in untreated individuals.

Genital herpes (her′pēz) is a viral infection by herpes simplex type 2. Lesions appear after an incubation period of about 1 week and cause a burning sensation. After this, blister-like areas of inflammation appear. In males and females, urination can be painful, and walking or sitting can be unpleasant, depending on the location of the lesions. The blister-like areas heal in about 2 weeks. The lesions can recur. The viruses exist in a latent condition in the infected tissues and can initiate periods of inflammation in response to factors such as menstruation, emotional stress, or illness. If active lesions are present in the mother's vagina or external genitalia, a cesarean delivery should be performed to prevent newborns from becoming infected with the herpes virus. Because genital herpes is caused by a virus, there is no effective cure for the condition.

Genital warts (wōrtz) result from a viral infection and are quite contagious. Genital warts are common, and their frequency is increasing. Genital warts can also be transmitted from infected mothers to their infants. Genital warts vary from separate small warty growths to large cauliflowerlike clusters. The lesions are usually not painful, but they can cause painful intercourse and they bleed easily. Women who have genital warts have an increased risk of developing cervical cancer. Treatments for genital warts include topical agents, cryosurgery, or other surgical methods.

Syphilis (sif′i-lis) is caused by the bacterium *Treponema pallidum* (trep-ō-nē′mă pal′i-dŭm), which can be spread by sexual contact of all kinds. Syphilis exhibits an incubation period from 2 weeks to several months. The disease progresses through several recognized stages. In the primary stage, the initial symptom is a small, hard-based **chancre** (shang′ker) or sore, which usually appears at the site of infection. Several weeks after the primary stage, the disease enters the secondary stage, characterized mainly by skin rashes and mild fever. The symptoms of secondary syphilis usually subside after a few weeks, and the disease enters a latent period in which no symptoms are present. In less than half the cases, a tertiary stage develops after many years. In the tertiary stage, many neural lesions develop that can cause extensive tissue damage and can lead to paralysis, insanity, and even death. Syphilis can be passed on to newborns if the mother is infected. Damage to mental development and other neurological symptoms are among the more serious consequences. Females who have syphilis in the latent phase are most likely to have babies who are infected. Antibiotics are used to treat syphilis, although some strains are very resistant to certain antibiotics.

Acquired immunodeficiency syndrome (AIDS) is caused by infection with the human immunodeficiency virus (HIV), which appears to ultimately result in destruction of the immune system (see chapter 14). The most common mechanisms of transmission of the virus are through sexual contact with a person infected with HIV or through sharing needles with an infected person during the administration of illicit drugs. Screening techniques now implemented make the transmission of HIV through blood transfusions very rare. Some cases of transmission of HIV through accidental needlesticks in hospitals and other health care facilities have been documented, but the frequency is rare. There is no evidence that casual contact with a person who has AIDS or who is infected with HIV results in transmission of the disease. Transmission appears to require exposure to body fluids of an infected person in a way that allows HIV into the interior of another person. Normal casual contact, including touching an HIV-infected person, does not increase the risk of infection.

Other Infectious Diseases

Pelvic inflammatory disease (PID) is a bacterial infection of the female pelvic organs. It usually involves the uterus, uterine tubes, or ovaries. A vaginal or uterine infection can spread throughout the pelvis. PID is commonly caused by the gonorrhea or chlamydia bacteria, but other bacteria can be involved. Early symptoms of PID include increased vaginal discharge and pelvic pain. Early treatment with antibiotics can stop the spread of PID, but lack of treatment results in a life-threatening infection. PID can also lead to sterility.

vagina through its wall. These secretions provide lubrication to allow easy entry and movement of the penis in the vagina during intercourse. Tactile stimulation of the female's genitals, during sexual intercourse and psychological stimuli, normally trigger an **orgasm**, or **climax**. The vaginal and uterine smooth muscle, as well as the surrounding skeletal muscles contract rhythmically; and muscle tension increases throughout much of the body. After the sexual act, there is a period of **resolution**, which is characterized by an overall sense of satisfaction and relaxation. Females are sometimes receptive to further immediate stimulation, however, and can experience successive orgasms. Orgasm is not necessary for fertilization to occur. Ovulation occurs as a result of hormonal stimuli and is not dependent on the female sexual act.

Causes of infertility in females include malfunctions of the uterine tubes, reduced hormone secretion from the pituitary or ovary, and interruption of implantation. Adhesions from pelvic inflammatory conditions, caused by a variety of infections, can cause blockage of one or more uterine tubes and is a relatively common cause of infertility in women. Reduced ovulation can result from inadequate secretion of LH

and FSH, which can be caused by hypothyroidism, trauma to the hypothalamus, infarctions of the hypothalamus or anterior pituitary gland, and tumors.

Interruption of implantation can result from uterine tumors or conditions causing abnormal ovarian hormone secretion. For example, premature degeneration of the corpus luteum causes progesterone levels to decline and menses to occur. If the corpus luteum degenerates before the placenta begins to secrete progesterone, the endometrium and the developing embryonic mass will degenerate and be eliminated from the uterus. The conditions that result in secondary amenorrhea also reduce fertility

Endometriosis (en'dō-mē-trē-ō'sis), a condition in which endometrial tissue is found in abnormal locations, reduces fertility. Generally, endometriosis is thought to result from some endometrial cells passing from the uterus through the uterine tubes into the pelvic cavity. The endometrial cells invade the peritoneum of the pelvic cavity. Periodic inflammation of the areas where the endometrial cells implant occurs because the endometrium is sensitive to estrogen and progesterone. Endometriosis is a cause of painful menstruation and can reduce fertility.

Clinical Focus   Control of Pregnancy

Many methods are used to prevent or terminate pregnancy (figure B), including methods that prevent fertilization (contraception), prevent implantation of the developing embryo (IUDs), or remove the implanted embryo or fetus (abortion). Many of these techniques are quite effective when done properly (table A) and used consistently. Some disadvantages are associated with each of them, and the use of some of them is controversial.

Behavioral Methods

Abstinence, or refraining from sexual intercourse, is a sure way to prevent pregnancy when it is practiced consistently. It is not an effective method when used only occasionally.

Coitus interruptus (kō'i-tŭs int-ĕ-rŭp'tŭs) is removal of the penis from the vagina just before ejaculation. This is a very unreliable method of preventing pregnancy because it

requires perfect awareness and willingness to withdraw the penis at the correct time. It also ignores the fact that some sperm cells are found in preejaculatory emissions.

The **rhythm method** requires abstaining from sexual intercourse near the time of ovulation. A major factor in the success of this method is the ability to predict accurately the time of ovulation. Although the rhythm method provides some protection against

Table A Effectiveness of Various Methods for Preventing Pregnancy		
Technique	Effectiveness When Used Properly (%)	Actual Effectiveness (%)
Abortion	100	Unknown
Sterilization	100	99.9
Combination (estrogens and progesterones) pill	99.9	98
Intrauterine device	98	98
Pill (low dose of estrogens and progesterones)	99	97
Condom plus spermicide	99	96
Condom alone	97	90
Diaphragm plus spermicide	97	85
Foam	97	80
Rhythm	97	70

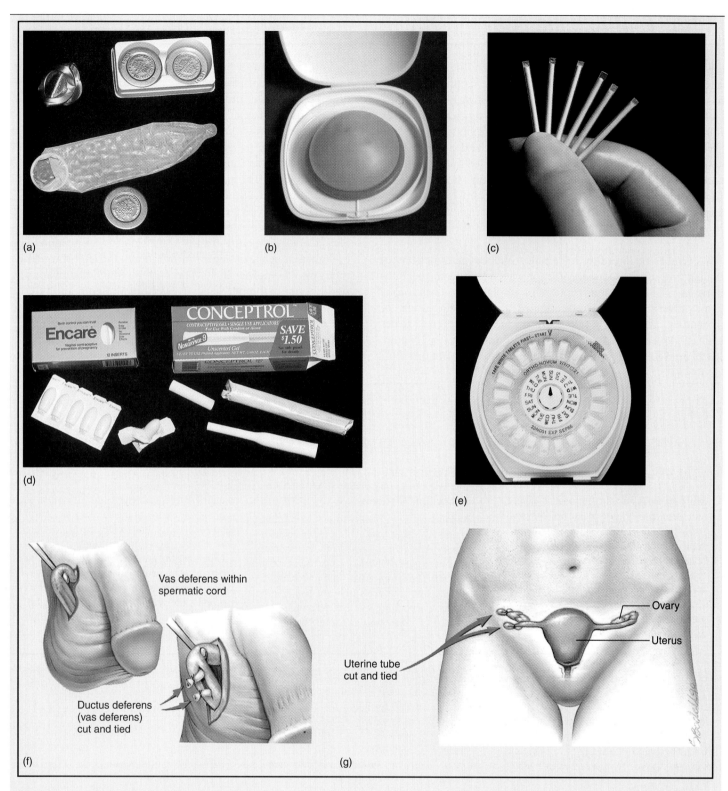

Figure B Contraceptive Devices and Techniques

(*a*) Condom. (*b*) Diaphragm. (*c*) Norplant system. (*d*) Spermicidal foam. (*e*) Oral contraceptives. (*f*) Vasectomy. (*g*) Tubal ligation.

becoming pregnant, it has a relatively high rate of failure because of both the inability to predict the time of ovulation and the failure to abstain from intercourse around the time of ovulation.

Barrier Methods

A **condom** (kon'dom) is a sheath of animal membrane, rubber, or plastic. A condom, placed over the erect penis, is a barrier device because the semen is collected within the condom instead of being released into the vagina. Condoms also provide some protection against sexually transmitted diseases.

A **vaginal condom** also acts as a barrier. The vaginal condom can be placed into the vagina by the female before sexual intercourse.

Methods to prevent sperm cells from reaching the oocyte once they are in the vagina include use of a diaphragm, spermicidal agents, and a vaginal sponge. A **diaphragm** is a flexible plastic or rubber dome that is placed over the cervix within the vagina, where it prevents passage of sperm cells from the vagina through the cervical canal of the uterus. The most commonly used **spermicidal agents** are foams or creams that kill sperm cells. They are inserted into the vagina before sexual intercourse. **Spermicidal douches** (dūsh'ez), which remove and kill sperm cells, are sometimes used. Spermicidal douches used alone are not very effective.

Lactation (lak-tā'shŭn) prevents the menstrual cycle for a few months after childbirth. Action potentials sent to the hypothalamus in response to suckling inhibit GnRH release from the hypothalamus. Reduced GnRH reduces LH, which prevents ovulation. Despite continual lactation, the ovarian and uterine cycles eventually resume. Because ovulation normally precedes menstruation, relying on lactation to prevent pregnancy is not consistently effective.

Chemical Methods

Synthetic estrogen and progesterone in **oral contraceptives** (birth control pills) effectively suppress fertility in females. These sub-stances can have more than one action, but they reduce LH and FSH release from the anterior pituitary. Estrogen and progesterone are present in high enough concentrations to have a negative-feedback effect on the pituitary, which prevents the large increase in LH and FSH secretion that triggers ovulation. Over the years, the dose of estrogen and progesterone in birth control pills has been reduced. The current lower dose birth control pills have fewer side effects than earlier dosages. There is an increased risk of heart attack or stroke in females using oral contraceptives who smoke or who have a history of hypertension or coagulation disorders. For most females, the pill is effective and has a minimum frequency of complications, until at least age 35.

Progesteronelike chemicals, such as medroxyprogesterone (Depo-Provera), which are injected intramuscularly and slowly released into the circulatory system, can act as effective contraceptives. Injected progesteronelike chemicals can provide protection from pregnancy for approximately 1 month, depending on the amount injected. A thin silastic tube containing progesteronelike chemicals, such as levonorgestrel (the Norplant system), can be implanted beneath the skin, usually of the upper arm. The progesteronelike chemicals are slowly released into the circulatory system. The implants can be effective for periods of up to 5 years. The advantage of these injected and implanted contraceptives over other chemical methods of birth control is that they do not require taking pills on a daily basis. The long-term effects of the injected and implanted progesteronelike chemicals are not as thoroughly studied as those of birth control pills, and they are still being evaluated.

A drug called **RU486 or mifepristone**, blocks the action of progesterone, causing the endometrium of the uterus to slough off as it does at the time of menstruation. It can, therefore, be used to induce menstruation and reduce the possibility of implantation when sexual intercourse has occurred near the time of ovulation. It can also be used to terminate pregnancies.

Surgical Methods

Vasectomy (va-sek'tō-mē) is a common method used to render males permanently incapable of fertilization without affecting the performance of the sexual act. Vasectomy is a surgical procedure in which the ductus deferens from each testis is cut and tied off within the scrotal sac. This procedure prevents sperm cells from passing through the ductus deferens and becoming part of the ejaculate. Because such a small volume of ejaculate comes from the testis and epididymis, vasectomy has little effect on the volume of the ejaculated semen. The sequestered sperm cells are reabsorbed in the epididymis.

A common method of permanent birth control in females is **tubal ligation** (lī-gā'shŭn), a procedure in which the uterine tubes are tied and cut or clamped by means of an incision made through the wall of the abdomen. This procedure closes off the path between the sperm cells and the oocyte. **Laparoscopy** (lap-ă-ros'kŏ-pē), in which a special instrument is inserted into the abdomen through a small incision, is commonly used so that only small openings are required to perform the operation.

In some cases, pregnancies are terminated by surgical procedures called **abortions** (ă-bōr'shŭnz). The most common method for performing abortions is the insertion of an instrument through the cervix into the uterus. The instrument scrapes the endometrial surface, and at the same time a strong suction is applied. The endometrium and the embedded embryo are disrupted and sucked out of the uterus. This techinque is normally used only in pregnancies that have progressed less than 3 months.

Prevention of Implantation

Intrauterine (in'tră-yū'ter-in) devices (IUDs) are inserted into the uterus through the cervix, and they prevent normal implantation of the developing embryo within the endometrium. Some early IUD designs produced serious side effects such as perforation of the uterus, and, as a result, many IUDs have been removed from the market. Data indicate, however, that IUDs are effective in preventing pregnancy.

Systems Pathology
benign uterine tumors

BENIGN UTERINE TUMORS

Mrs. M. had four children and was 43 years of age. She noticed that menstruation was becoming gradually more severe and lasting up to several days longer each time menstruation started. After Mrs. M. menstruated almost continuously for 2 months she made an appointment with her physician. The physician performed a pelvic examination on Mrs. M. (figure C), including tests to check for conditions such as cervical and uterine cancer. Palpation of the uterus indicated the presence of enlarged masses in Mrs. M.'s uterus. Dilation and curettage (D&C), which is dilation of the cervix and scraping (curettage) of the endometrium to remove growths or other abnormal tissues, was performed. The results of the D&C indicated that Mrs. M. suffered from leiomyomas.

Background Information

Leiomyomas (lī'ō-mī-ō'măz), also called uterine fibroids, are fibroid tumors of the uterus. They are one of the most common disorders of the uterus, and the most frequent tumor in women, affecting one of every four. Three-fourths of the women with this condition, however, experience no symptoms. The enlarged masses of smooth muscle tissue compresses the uterine lining (endometrium) resulting in ischemia and inflammation and results in frequent and severe menstruations. Abdominal cramping due to strong uterine contractions can be present. Constant menstruation is a frequent manifestation of these tumors, and it is one of the most common reasons why women elect to have the uterus removed, a procedure called a **hysterectomy** (his-ter-ek'tō-mē).

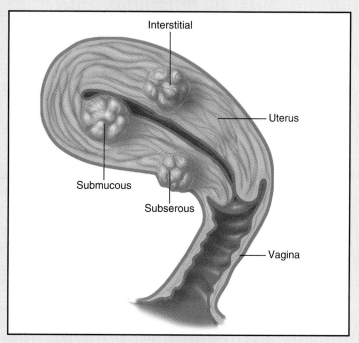

Figure 19C Leiomyomas, or fibroid tumors, are enlarged masses of smooth muscle. They are located near the mucosa (submucous), within the myometrian (interstitial) or near the serosa (subserous).

4   P R E D I C T

When discussing her condition with her mother, Mrs. M. discovered that her mother recalled frequent menstruations that were irregular and prolonged when she was in her late forties. Mrs. M.'s mother did not have a hysterectomy and in a few years, the frequency of menstruation began to gradually subside. Explain

✔ *Answer on page 549*

System Interactions: Effect of Benign Uterine Tumors on other Systems

System	Interactions
Integumentary	If anemia does not develop, skin appearance is normal. But if anemia does develop, the skin can appear pale because of the reduced hemoglobin in red blood cells.
Muscular	If anemia develops and is severe, muscle weakness results because of the reduced ability of the cardiovascular system to deliver adequate oxygen to muscles.
Skeletal	The rate of red blood cell synthesis in the red bone marrow increases.
Cardiovascular	A chronic loss of blood, as in prolonged menstruation over many months to years, frequently results in iron-deficiency anemia. Manifestations of anemia include pale skin, reduced hematocrit, reduced hemoglobin concentration, smaller than normal red blood cells (microcytic anemia), and increased heart rate.
Respiratory	Because of anemia, the oxygen-carrying capacity of the blood is reduced. Increased respiration during physical exertion and rapid fatigue are likely to occur if anemia develops.
Urinary	The kidney increases erythropoietin secretion in response to the reduced oxygen-carrying capacity of blood. The erythropoietin increases red blood cell synthesis in red bone marrow. An enlarged tumor can put pressure on the urinary bladder, resulting in increased frequency of and painful urination.

Summary

Functions of the Reproductive System

- The male reproductive system produces sperm cells, provides nutrients for the sperm cells and secretions, transfers the sperm cells to the female, and makes male sex hormones.
- The female reproductive system produces female sex cells, receives sex cells from the male, provides nourishment for the developing infant before and after birth, and produces female sex hormones.

Formation of Sex Cells

- The reproductive organs in males and females produce sex cells by meiosis.

Male Reproductive System

Scrotum

- The scrotum is a two-chambered sac that contains the testes.
- The dartos and cremaster muscles help to regulate testes temperature.

Testes

- The testes are divided into lobules containing the seminiferous tubules and interstitial cells.
- During development the testes pass from the abdominal cavity through the inguinal canal to the scrotum.

Spermatogenesis

- Spermatogenesis begins in the seminiferous tubules at the time of puberty.
- Sperm cells are produced in the seminiferous tubules.
  - Germ cells divide (mitosis) to form primary spermatocytes.
  - Primary spermatocytes divide by meiosis to produce sperm cells.
  - Sertoli cells nourish the sperm cells and produce small amounts of hormones.
- Spermatids develop a head, midpiece, and flagellum to become a sperm cell. The head contains the acrosome and the nucleus.

Ducts

- The epididymis is a coiled tube system, located on the testis, that is the site of sperm maturation.
- The seminiferous tubules lead to the rete testis.
- The rete testis opens into the efferent ductules that extend to the epididymis.
- The ductus deferens passes from the epididymis into the abdominal cavity.
- The ejaculatory duct is formed by the joining of the ductus deferens and the duct from the seminal vesicle.
- The ejaculatory ducts join the urethra in the prostate gland.
- The urethra extends from the urinary bladder through the penis to the outside of the body.

Penis

- The penis consists of erectile tissue.
  - The two corpora cavernosa form the dorsum and the sides.
  - The corpus spongiosum forms the ventral portion and the glans penis, and it encloses the spongy urethra. The prepuce covers the glans penis.

Glands

- The seminal vesicles empty into the ejaculatory duct.
- The prostate gland consists of glandular and muscular tissue and empties into the urethra.
- The bulbourethral glands are glands that empty into the urethra.

Secretions

- Semen is a mixture of gland secretions and sperm cells.
- The bulbourethral glands and the urethral mucous glands produce mucus that neutralizes the acidic pH of the urethra.
- The testicular secretions contain sperm cells.
- The seminal vesicle fluid contains nutrients, prostaglandins, and proteins that coagulate.
- The prostate fluid contains nutrients and proteolytic enzymes, and it neutralizes the pH of the vagina.

Physiology of Male Reproduction

Regulation of Sex Hormone Secretion

- GnRH is produced in the hypothalamus and is released in surges.
- GnRH stimulates release of LH and FSH from the anterior pituitary.
  - LH stimulates the interstitial cells to produce testosterone.
  - FSH binds to Sertoli cells and stimulates spermatogenesis.

Puberty

- Before puberty small amounts of testosterone inhibit GnRH release.
- During puberty testosterone does not completely suppress GnRH release, resulting in increased production of FSH, LH, and testosterone.

Effects of Testosterone

- Testosterone causes enlargement of the genitals and is necessary for spermatogenesis.
- Testosterone is responsible for the development of secondary sex characteristics.

Male Sexual Behavior and the Male Sex Act

- Testosterone is required for normal sex drive.
- Stimulation of the sexual act can be tactile or psychological.
- Afferent impulses pass to the sacral region of the spinal cord.
- Efferent stimulation causes erection, mucus production, emission, and ejaculation.
- The most common cause of infertility is a low sperm cell count.

Female Reproductive System

Ovaries

- The ovaries are covered by the visceral peritoneum.
- Follicles consist of an oocyte surrounded by granulosa cells and a thecal layer.
- As follicles mature in response to FSH they enlarge, an antrum forms, and the oocyte increases in size. Granulosa cells form a cumulus layer that surrounds the oocyte, and a zona pellucida (a thin noncellular layer) forms around the oocyte.

- About the time of ovulation the first meiotic division is completed.
- Ovulation is the release of the oocyte from the ovary.
  - In response to LH the follicle completes its growth and ruptures, and the oocyte is released from the ovary.
  - The second meiotic division is completed when the oocyte unites with a sperm cell to form a zygote.
- Fate of the follicle.
  - The ovulated follicle becomes the corpus luteum.
  - If fertilization occurs, the corpus luteum persists. If there is no fertilization, it degenerates.

Uterine Tubes

- The uterine tubes transport the oocyte or zygote from the ovary to the uterus.
- The ovarian end of the uterine tube is surrounded by fimbriae.
- Cilia on the fimbriae move the oocyte into the uterine tube.
- Fertilization usually occurs in the upper part of the uterine tube.

Uterus

- The uterus is a pear-shaped organ. The uterine cavity and the cervical canal are the spaces formed by the uterus.
- The wall of the uterus consists of the perimetrium or serous layer, the myometrium (smooth muscle), and the endometrium.

Vagina

- The vagina connects the uterus (cervix) to the vestibule.
- The vagina consists of a layer of smooth muscle and an inner lining of moist stratified squamous epithelium.
- The hymen covers the vestibular opening of the vagina.

External Genitalia

- The vestibule is a space into which the vagina and the urethra open.
- The clitoris is composed of erectile tissue and contains many sensory organs important in detecting sexual stimuli.
- The labia minora are folds that cover the vestibule and form the prepuce.
- The greater vestibular glands produce a mucous fluid, and lubricating fluid is produced by the wall of the vagina.
- The labia majora cover the labia minora, and the pudendal cleft is a space between the labia majora.
- The mons pubis is an elevated area superior to the labia majora.

Mammary Glands

- The mammary glands are modified sweat glands that consist of glandular lobes and adipose tissue.

- The lobes connect to the nipple through ducts. The nipple is surrounded by the areola.

Physiology of Female Reproduction

Puberty

- Puberty begins with the first menstrual bleeding (menarche).
- Puberty begins when GnRH, LH, and FSH levels increase.

Menstrual Cycle

- The cyclical changes in the uterus are controlled by estrogen and progesterone produced by the ovary.
- Cyclical changes in the uterus.
  - Menses (day 1 to days 4 or 5). Menstrual fluid is produced by degeneration of the endometrium.
  - Proliferative phase (day 5 to day of ovulation). Epithelial cells multiply and form glands.
  - Secretory phase (from day of ovulation to day 28). The endometrium becomes thicker, and endometrial glands secrete. The uterus is prepared for implantation of the developing blastocyst by day 21.
  - Estrogen stimulates proliferation of the endometrium, and progesterone causes thickening of the endometrium. Decreased progesterone causes menses.
- FSH initiates the development of the follicles.
- LH stimulates ovulation and formation of the corpus luteum.
- A positive-feedback mechanism causes FSH and LH levels to increase near the time of ovulation.
  - Estrogen produced by the follicles stimulates GnRH, FSH, and LH secretion.
  - FSH and LH stimulate more estrogen secretion, and the cycle repeats.

Menopause

- The cessation of the menstrual cycle is called menopause.

Female Sexual Behavior and the Female Sex Act

- Female sex drive is partially influenced by testosteronelike hormones (produced by the adrenal cortex) and estrogen produced by the ovary.
- Autonomic nerves cause erectile tissue to become engorged with blood, the vestibular glands to secrete mucus, and the vagina to produce a lubricating fluid.
- Causes of infertility in females include malfunctions of the uterine tubes, reduced hormone secretion from the pituitary or ovary, and interruption of implantation.

Content Review

1. What is the scrotum? Explain the function of the dartos and cremaster muscles.
2. Where, specifically, are sperm cells produced in the testes? Describe the process of spermatogenesis.
3. Name the ducts the sperm cells traverse to go from their site of production to the outside of the body.
4. Where do sperm cells develop their ability to fertilize?
5. Name the erectile tissues of the penis, and describe how it functions.
6. State where the seminal vesicles, prostate gland, and bulbourethral glands empty into the male reproductive duct system.
7. Define emission and ejaculation.
8. Define semen. What structures give rise to secretions that make up the semen?

9. Where are GnRH, FSH, LH, and testosterone produced?
10. Describe the effects of testosterone during puberty and on the adult male.
11. Describe the regulation of the male sexual act.
12. Describe the process of follicle development and ovulation.
13. What is the corpus luteum? What happens to the corpus luteum if fertilization occurs? If fertilization does not occur?
14. Describe the normal pathway followed by the oocyte after ovulation. Where does fertilization usually take place?
15. Describe the relationship between the uterus, vagina, vestibule, and external genitalia.

16. Describe the labia minora, the prepuce, the labia majora, the pudendal cleft, and the mons pubis.
17. What are the effects of estrogen and progesterone on the uterus?
18. Describe the hormonal changes that result in ovulation. Explain the sequence of events during each phase of the menstrual cycle.
19. Define menopause and female climacteric. What causes these changes?

Develop Your Reasoning Skills

1. If an adult male were castrated by having his testes removed, what would happen to the levels of GnRH, FSH, LH, and testosterone in his blood?
2. Birth control pills for women contain estrogen and progesterone compounds. Explain how these hormones can prevent pregnancy.
3. During the secretory phase of the menstrual cycle, you would normally expect:
   a. The highest levels of progesterone that occur during the menstrual cycle
   b. A follicle present in the ovary that is ready to undergo ovulation

   c. That the endometrium reaches its greatest degree of development
   d. a and b
   e. a and c
4. Predict the consequences if a drug that blocks the effect of progesterone is taken by a woman 2 or 3 days following ovulation or by a woman who is pregnant.
5. During menopause which reproductive hormones are reduced in the blood and which are increased?

Answers to Predict Questions

1. p. 527 The prostate gland is located just anterior to the rectum. It can be palpated through the wall of the rectum. A physician can insert a finger into the rectum and palpate the prostate through the wall of the rectum. The procedure does not require surgical procedures and involves relatively minor discomfort.
2. p. 531 Because secondary sexual characteristics, external genitalia, and sexual behavior develop in response to testosterone, if the testes fail to produce normal amounts of testosterone at puberty, they do not develop normally. Secondary sexual characteristics and external genitalia

remain juvenile, and normal adult sexual behavior does not develop.
3. p. 539 Administration of a large amount of progesterone and estrogen just before the preovulatory LH surge inhibits the release of GnRH, LH, and FSH. Consequently ovulation does not occur. A small amount of estrogen administered, without progesterone, before the preovulatory LH surge, however, could stimulate GnRH, LH, and FSH secretion.
4. p. 546 Mrs. M.'s mother could have had leiomyomas also, although, without direct data of medical examinations, one cannot be certain. If that was the cause of her irregular

menstruations they may have become less frequent as Mrs. M.'s mother experienced menopause. During menopause the uterus gradually becomes smaller, and eventually the cyclical changes in the endometrial lining ceases. If the condition was relatively mild, the onset of menopause could explain the gradual disappearance of the irregular and prolonged menstruations (Note: If the tumors are large, constant and severe menstruations are likely even if regular menstrual cycles stop due to menopause.)

Chapter Twenty

Development, Heredity, and Aging

blastocyst

(blas′tō-sist) [Gr. *blastos*, germ + *kystis*, bladder] Early stage of mammalian embryo development consisting of a hollow ball of cells with an inner cell mass and an outer trophoblast layer.

ectoderm

(ek′tō-derm) Outermost of the three germ layers of the embryo.

embryo

(em′brē-ō) In prenatal development, the developing human between approximately 14 and 56 days of development.

endoderm

(en′dō-derm) Innermost of the three germ layers of the embryo.

fertilization

(fer′til-i-zā′shŭn) Union of a sperm cell and secondary oocyte to form a zygote.

fetus

(fē′tŭs) In prenatal development, the developing human between approximately 56 days and birth.

genotype

(jen′ō-tīp, jēn′ō-tīp) Genetic makeup of the individual.

heterozygous

(het′er-ō-zī′gŭs) Having two different genes for a given trait.

homozygous

(hō-mō-zī′gŭs) Having two identical genes for a given trait.

lactation

(lak′tā′shŭn) [L. *lactatio*, suckle] Production of milk.

mesoderm

(mez′ō-derm) Middle of the three germ layers of the embryo.

neural tube

(noor′ăl) Tube formed from the neuroectoderm in the embryo by closure of the neural groove; develops into the brain and spinal cord.

parturition

(par-toor-ish′ŭn) [L. *parturio*, to be in labor] Childbirth; the delivery of a baby at the end of pregnancy.

phenotype

(fē′nō-tīp) [Gr. *phaino*, to display + *typos*, model] Characteristic observed in the individual resulting from expression of the genotype.

primitive streak

A shallow groove in the ectodermal surface of the embryonic disk; cells migrating through the streak become mesoderm.

zygote

(zī′gōt) [Gr. *zygotos*, yoked] The single diploid cell product of fertilization, resulting from the union of a sperm cell and a secondary oocyte.

Objectives

After reading this chapter, you should be able to:

1. List the prenatal periods and state the major developmental events associated with each.

2. Describe the process of fertilization.

3. Describe the blastocyst, the process of implantation, and placental formation.

4. List the three germ layers, describe their formation, and list the adult derivatives of each layer.

5. Describe the formation of the neural tube and neural crest cells.

6. Describe the formation of the gastrointestinal tract, the limbs, and the face.

7. Explain how the single heart tube is divided into four chambers.

8. Explain the events that occur during parturition and the process of lactation.

9. Discuss the respiratory, circulatory, and digestive changes that occur in the newborn at the time of birth.

10. List the stages of life and describe the major events that are associated with each stage. Describe the changes that occur during the aging process.

11. Define genetics and explain how chromosomes are related to genetics.

12. Describe the major types of inheritance.

The life span of a person is usually considered the time from birth to death. The 9 months before birth, however, constitute a critical part of an individual's existence, and the events that occur during that period have profound effects on the rest of the person's life. Most people develop normally and are born without defects. However, approximately 7 out of every 100 people are born with some type of birth defect, and 3 out of every 100 people are born with a birth defect so severe that it requires medical attention during the first year of life. Later in life, many more people discover previously unrecognized problems, such as the tendency to develop asthma, certain brain disorders, or cancer. About 15% of all birth defects have a known genetic basis. The causes for most of the remaining 85% of birth defects are unknown. Nevertheless, all of us are strongly affected by the genes we inherited from our parents. Everything about us, including the shape of our nose, the likelihood of developing certain diseases, or how long we will live, has genetic components.

Prenatal Development

The **prenatal** (prē-nā′tăl) **period**, the period from conception to birth, can be divided into three parts: (1) the germinal period—approximately the first 2 weeks of development, during which the primitive germ layers are formed; (2) the embryonic period—from about the second to the eighth week of development, during which the major organ systems come into existence; and (3) the fetal period—the last 7 months of the prenatal period, during which the organ systems grow and become more mature.

The medical community in general uses the **last menstrual** (men′stroo-ăl) **period (LMP)** to calculate the **clinical age** of the unborn child. An embryo or fetus is therefore considered to be a certain number of days post-LMP. Most embryologists, on the other hand, use **developmental age**, which begins with fertilization, to describe the timing of developmental events. Because fertilization is assumed to occur approximately 14 days after LMP, it is assumed that developmental age is 14 days less than clinical age. The times presented in this chapter are based on developmental age.

Fertilization

After **sperm cells** are ejaculated into the vagina, they are transported through the cervix, the body of the uterus, and the uterine tubes, where fertilization occurs. The swimming ability of the sperm cells and muscular contractions of the uterus and uterine tubes are responsible for the movement of sperm cells through the female reproductive tract. Oxytocin released by the female posterior pituitary and prostaglandins within the semen both stimulate contractions in the uterus and uterine tubes.

While passing through the uterus and the uterine tubes, the sperm cells undergo capacitation. **Capacitation** (kă-pas′i-tā′shŭn) makes the sperm cells capable of releasing enzymes contained in the acrosome, a region of concentrated enzymes located between the cell membrane and nuclear membrane within the leading edge of the sperm cell head. The enzymes

digest a pathway through the cumulus cells and the cell membrane of the **secondary oocyte** (ō′ō-sīt), allowing one sperm cell to enter the oocyte.

The secondary oocyte is capable of being fertilized for perhaps up to about 1 day after ovulation, and some sperm cells remain viable in the female reproductive tract for up to 7 days, although most of them degenerate before that time.

1   P R E D I C T

During what days of the menstrual cycle is sexual intercourse most likely to result in pregnancy?

✔ *Answer on page 579*

Hundreds of sperm cells reach the secondary oocyte, but normally a change occurs in the oocyte cell membrane that prevents more than one sperm cell from entering the secondary oocyte. The secondary oocyte undergoes the second meiotic division only after a sperm cell enters it. After the second meiotic division, the oocyte nucleus moves to the center of the cell, where it meets the nucleus of the sperm cell. Each of these nuclei has 23 chromosomes, each having one chromosome from each chromosome pair. Their fusion, which completes the process of fertilization, restores the number of chromosomes to 46 (see chapter 19).

Fertilization (fer′til-i-zā′shŭn) is defined as the union of the sperm cell and secondary oocyte, with the union of their genetic material, the chromosomes. The product of fertilization (figure 20.1*a*) is a single cell called the **zygote** (zī′gōt).

Early Cell Division

About 18 to 36 hours after fertilization, the zygote divides to form two cells. Those two cells divide to form four cells, which divide to form eight, and so on (figure 20.1*b* to *d*). Even though the number of cells increases, the size of each cell decreases, so that the total mass of cells remains about the same size as the zygote. The cells of this dividing embryonic mass have the ability to develop into a wide range of tissues. As a result, the total number of embryonic cells can be decreased, increased, or reorganized during this period without affecting the normal development of the embryo.

Did You Know?

In rare cases, following early cell divisions, the cells may separate and develop to form two individuals, called **"identical,"** or **monozygotic** (mon-ō-zī′got′ik), **twins.** Identical twins therefore have identical genetic information in their cells. Identical twins can also occur by other mechanisms, which occur a little later in development.

Occasionally a woman can ovulate two or more secondary oocytes at the same time. Fertilization of multiple oocytes by different sperm cells results in **"fraternal"** (fră-ter′năl), or **dizygotic** (dī′zī-got′ik), **twins.** Multiple ovulations can occur naturally or can be stimulated by injection of drugs that stimulate gonadotropin release. These drugs are sometimes used to treat certain forms of infertility.

Figure 20.1 Early Stages of Human Development

(a) Zygote (120 μm in diameter). (b)–(d) During the early cell divisions, the zygote divides, and then the embryonic mass divides into more and more cells, but the total size of the embryonic mass remains relatively constant. (b) Two cells. (c) Four cells. (d) Eight cells.

Blastocyst

About 3 or 4 days after fertilization, multiple cell divisions have produced an embryonic mass of about 32 cells, which is sometimes referred to as an embryo (e.g., see Clinical Focus: Embryo Transfer on p. 554). Most of the cells in the mass at this age, however, will not contribute to the embryo but will form support structures such as the placenta. An embryo doesn't technically exist until about 2 weeks after fertilization, when cells begin to be organized to form the individual.

When a cavity begins to appear within the mass of cells, the whole structure is then called a **blastocyst** (blas′tō-sist) (figure 20.2). The fluid-filled cavity is called the **blastocele** (blas′tō-sēl). Most of the blastocele is surrounded by a single layer of cells, but at one end of the blastocyst the cells are several layers thick. The thickened area is the **inner cell mass**. The embryo will develop from a few cells of the inner cell mass. The remaining cells of the blastocyst are called the **trophoblast** (trof′ō-blast, trō′fō-blast; feeding layer), which forms the embryonic part of the placenta and the membranes (chorion and amnion) surrounding the embryo.

Implantation of the Blastocyst and Development of the Placenta

All these early events, from the first cell division to formation of the blastocele, occur as the embryonic mass moves from the site of fertilization in the uterine tube to the site of implantation in the uterus. By 7 or 8 days after ovulation (day 21 or 22 post-LMP), the endometrium of the uterus is prepared for implantation. About 7 days after fertilization, the blastocyst attaches itself to the uterine wall and begins the process of **implantation** (im-plan-tā′shŭn). The trophoblast cells of the blastocyst digest the uterine tissues as the blastocyst burrows into the uterine wall.

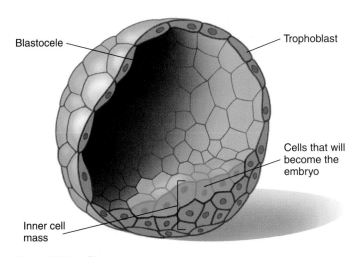

Blastocele

Trophoblast

Cells that will become the embryo

Inner cell mass

Figure 20.2   Blastocyst

The orange cells of the inner cell mass will become the embryo. All the green cells will become the embryonic part of the placenta and membranes (chorion and amnion).

As the blastocyst burrows into the uterine wall, trophoblast cells, now called the **chorion** (kō′rē-on), form the embryonic portion of the **placenta** (plă-sen′tă). Fingerlike projections, called **chorionic villi**, protrude into cavities formed within the maternal endometrium. Those cavities, called **lacunae** (lă-koo′nē), are filled with maternal blood (figure 20.3). In the mature placenta, the embryonic blood supply is separated from the maternal blood supply by the embryonic capillary wall, a basement membrane, and a thin layer of chorion. As a result, the embryonic and maternal blood do not mix. Nutrients and waste products must cross this semipermeable barrier between the two circulations.

The developing human between 14 and 56 days of development is called an **embryo** (em′brē-ō). Unlike the dividing mass of cells that exists before day 14, the embryo is developing a complex form, and the cells within the embryo are developing into tissues and organs. Initially the embryo is attached to the placenta by a connecting stalk. As the embryo matures, the connecting stalk elongates and becomes known as the **umbilical** (ŭm-bil′i-kăl) **cord** (see figure 20.3). Within

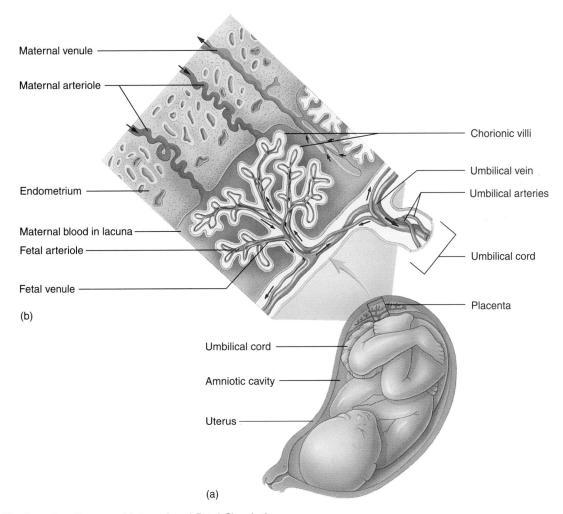

Maternal venule

Maternal arteriole

Endometrium

Maternal blood in lacuna

Fetal arteriole

Fetal venule

(b)

Chorionic villi

Umbilical vein

Umbilical arteries

Umbilical cord

Placenta

Umbilical cord

Amniotic cavity

Uterus

(a)

Figure 20.3   The Interface Between Maternal and Fetal Circulation

(a) Location of the placenta and umbilical cord. (b) As maternal blood vessels are encountered by the trophoblast (chorionic villi), lacunae (cavities) are formed and filled with maternal blood. In the mature placenta, the embryonic blood vessels and other tissue form chorionic villi, and nutrients are exchanged between embryonic and maternal blood. At no time, under normal conditions, do the maternal and fetal blood mix.

1. Human chorionic gonadotropin (HCG) increases until it reaches a maximum concentration near the end of the first trimester of pregnancy and then decreases to a low level thereafter.

2. Progesterone continues to increase until it levels off near the end of pregnancy. Early in pregnancy, progesterone is produced by the corpus luteum in the ovary, later production shifts to the placenta.

3. Estrogen levels increase slowly throughout pregnancy, but they increase more rapidly as the end of pregnancy approaches. Early in pregnancy, estrogen is produced only in the ovary, later production shifts to the placenta.

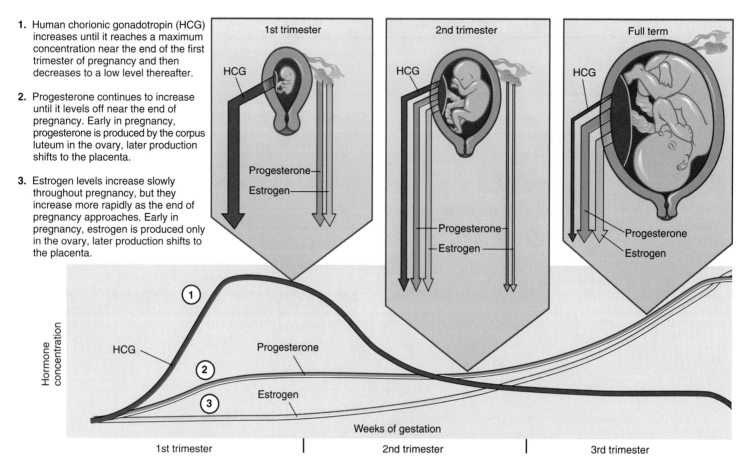

Figure 20.4 Levels of Hormones Released from the Ovary and Placenta During Pregnancy

The levels of human chorionic gonadotropin (HCG), which is produced in the placenta, decline during pregnancy. There is a shift in progesterone and estrogen synthesis from the corpus luteum in the ovary early in pregnancy to the placenta late in pregnancy. The level of each hormone is indicated by the size of the arrow.

Clinical Focus   Embryo Transfer

In a small number of women, normal pregnancy is not possible because of some anatomical or physiological condition. In 87% of these cases the uterine tubes are incapable of transporting the zygote to the uterus or of allowing sperm cells to reach the oocyte. In vitro fertilization and embryo transfer have made pregnancy possible in hundreds of such women since 1978. **In vitro fertilization** involves removal of secondary oocytes from a woman, placing the oocytes into a petri dish, and adding sperm cells to the dish, allowing fertilization and early development to occur in vitro, which means "in glass." **Embryo transfer** involves the removal of the developing embryonic mass (not actually an embryo at this age) from the petri dish and introduction of the mass into the uterus of a recipient female.

For in vitro fertilization and embryo transfer to be accomplished, a woman is first injected with an LH-like substance, which causes more than one follicle to ovulate at a time. Just before the follicles rupture, the secondary oocytes are surgically removed from the ovary. The oocytes are then incubated in a dish and maintained at body temperature for 6 hours. Then sperm cells are added to the dish.

After 24 to 48 hours, when the zygotes have divided to form two- to eight-cell embryonic masses, several of the embryonic masses are transferred to the uterus. Several embryonic masses are transferred, because only a few of them survive. Implantation and subsequent development then proceed in the uterus as they would for natural im-

plantation. The woman is usually required to lie perfectly still for several hours after the embryonic masses have been introduced into the uterus to prevent possible expulsion before implantation can occur. It is not fully understood why such expulsion does not occur in natural fertilization and implantation.

The success rate of embryo transfer varies from clinic to clinic but is increasing steadily (the success rate at the best U.S. clinic is about 27%). Multiple births have occurred frequently following embryo transfer because of the practice of introducing more than one embryo into the uterus in an attempt to increase the success rate as much as possible.

the umbilical cord, blood vessels carry blood from the embryo to the placenta and from the placenta to the embryo.

The chorion secretes **human chorionic gonadotropin** (gō′nad-ō-trō′pin) (HCG), which is transported in the blood to the maternal ovary and causes the corpus luteum to remain functional. The secretion of HCG begins shortly after implantation, increases rapidly, and reaches a peak about 8 or 9 weeks after fertilization. Subsequently, HCG levels decline to a lower level and are maintained at a low level throughout the remainder of the pregnancy (figure 20.4). Most pregnancy tests are designed to detect HCG in either urine or blood.

The estrogen and progesterone secreted by the corpus luteum (see chapter 19) are essential for the maintenance of the endometrium for the first 3 months of pregnancy. After the placenta forms, it also begins to secrete estrogens and progesterone. By the third month of pregnancy, the placenta has become an endocrine gland that secretes sufficient quantities of estrogen and progesterone to maintain pregnancy. Estrogen and progesterone levels increase in the mother's blood throughout pregnancy.

Formation of the Germ Layers

After implantation, a new cavity, called the **amniotic** (am-nē-ot′ik) **cavity**, forms inside the inner cell mass and causes the part of the inner cell mass nearest the blastocele to separate as a flat disk of tissue called the **embryonic disk** (figure 20.5). The amniotic cavity is bounded by a membrane called the **amniotic sac** and is filled with **amniotic fluid**. The embryo will grow into the amniotic cavity, where the amniotic fluid forms a protective cushion. The embryonic disk is composed of two layers of cells: an **ectoderm** (ek′tō-derm, outside layer) adjacent to the amniotic cavity and an **endoderm** (en′dō-derm, inside layer) on the side of the disk opposite the amniotic cavity. A third cavity, the **yolk sac**, forms inside the blastocele from the endoderm.

At about 14 days after fertilization, the embryonic disk has become a slightly elongated oval structure. Some of the ecto-

derm cells migrate toward the center of the disk, forming a thickened line called the **primitive streak**. The formation of the primitive streak establishes the **embryo**, marking the beginning of the embryonic period. Some of the ectoderm cells migrate through the primitive streak and emerge between the ectoderm and endoderm as a new germ layer, called the **mesoderm** (mez′ō-derm, middle layer) (figure 20.6). The embryo is now three-layered, having ectoderm, mesoderm, and endoderm. All tissues of the adult can be traced to these three germ layers (table 20.1).

A specialized group of cells at the cephalic end of the primitive streak moves from one end of the primitive streak to the other and, in some as yet unknown way, organizes the embryo. A cordlike structure called the **notochord** (nō′tō-kōrd) is formed by these cells as they move down the primitive streak. The notochord marks the central axis of the developing embryo (see figure 20.6).

2   PREDICT

Predict the result if two primitive streaks form in one embryonic disk. What if the two primitive streaks are touching each other?

✔ *Answer on page 579*

Neural Tube and Neural Crest Formation

At about 18 days after fertilization, the ectoderm overlying the notochord thickens to form the **neural plate** (figure 20.7). The lateral edges of the plate begin to rise like two ocean waves coming together. These edges are called the **neural folds**, and a **neural groove** lies between them. The neural folds begin to meet in the midline and fuse into a neural tube, which is completely closed by day 26. The cells of the **neural tube** are called **neuroectoderm** (noor-ō-ek′tō-derm) (see table 20.1). Neuroectoderm becomes the brain, the

Figure 20.5   Early Embryo and Surrounding Structures in the Placenta

The embryonic disk consisting of ectoderm and endoderm, with amniotic cavity and yolk sac. The connecting stalk, which attaches the embryo to the uterus, will become part of the umbilical cord.

Table 20.1	Major Cardiac Arrhythmias				
Endoderm	**Ectoderm**	**Mesoderm**
Lining of gastointestinal tract	Epidermis of skin	Dermis of skin
Lining of lungs	Tooth enamel	Circulatory system
Lining of hepatic, pancreatic, and other exocrine ducts	Lens and cornea of eye	Parenchyma (substance) of glands
Kidney ducts and bladder	Outer ear	Kidneys
Anterior pituitary	Nasal cavity	Gonads
Thymus gland	Neuroectoderm	Muscle
Thyroid gland	Brain and spinal cord	Bones (except facial)
Parathyroid gland	Somatic motor neurons	
Tonsils	Preganglionic autonomic neurons	
	Neural crest cells	
	Melanocytes	
	Sensory neurons	
	Postganglionic autonomic neurons	
	Adrenal medulla	
	Facial bones	
	Teeth: dentin and pulp	
	Skeletal muscles in head	

1. Cells in the surface ectoderm move toward the primitive streak and fold into the streak (blue arrow tails).

2. Cells that enter the primitive streak come out the other side of the streak as mesodermal cells (red arrows).

3. The mesoderm (red) lies between the ectoderm (blue) and endoderm (yellow).

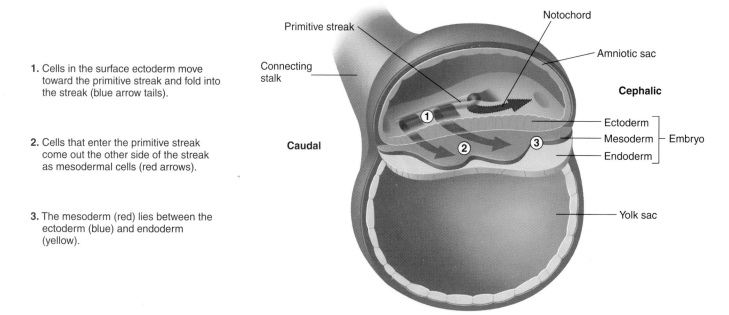

Figure 20.6 Embryonic Disk with a Primitive Streak
The head of the embryo will develop over the notochord.

spinal cord, and parts of the peripheral nervous system. If the neural tube fails to close, major defects of the central nervous system can result.

As the neural folds come together and fuse, a population of cells breaks away from the neuroectoderm all along the crests of the folds. Most of these **neural crest cells** become part of the peripheral nervous system or become melanocytes of the skin. In the head, neural crest cells also contribute to the skull, the dentin of teeth, blood vessels, and general connective tissue.

1. The neural plate is formed from ectoderm.

2. Neural folds form as parallel ridges along the embryo.

3. Neural crest cells break away from the crest of the neural folds.

4. The neural folds meet at the midline to form the neural tube.

(a)

Neural groove
Neural fold — Neural plate
Notochord

Neural groove
Crest of the neural fold
Neural fold

Crest of the neural fold
Neural crest cells

Skin
Neural crest cells
Neural tube
Notochord

(b)

Figure 20.7   Formation of the Neural Tube

The neural folds come together in the midline and fuse to form a neural tube. This fusion begins in the center and moves both cranially and caudally. (*a*) The embryo shown is about 21 days after fertilization. (*b*) The insets to the right show progressive closure of the neural tube.

> **Did You Know?**
>
> **Anencephaly** (an'en-sef'ă-lē, no brain) is a birth defect wherein much of the brain fails to form because the neural tube fails to close in the region of the head. A baby born with anencephaly cannot survive. **Spina bifida** (spī'nă bif'i-dă, split spine) is a general term describing defects of the spinal cord or vertebral column. Spina bifida can range from a simple defect with no clinical manifestation and with one or more vertebral spinous processes split or missing, to a more severe defect that can result in paralysis of the limbs or the bowels and bladder, depending on where the defect occurs.

Formation of the General Body Structure

Arms and legs first appear at about 28 days after fertilization as **limb buds** (figure 20.8) and quickly begin to elongate. At about 35 days, expansions called hand and foot plates form at the ends of the limb buds. Zones of cell death between the future fingers and toes of the hand and foot plates help sculpture the fingers and toes.

The face develops by fusion of five masses of tissue. One mass forms the forehead, nose, and center of the upper jaw and lip. Two masses form from the maxillae (upper lip and jaw) and two form the mandible (lower lip and jaw). The nose begins as two structures, one on each side of the forehead mass (figure 20.9).

As the brain enlarges and the face matures, the two parts of the nose approach each other in the midline and fuse (see figure 20.9). The two masses forming the upper jaw expand toward the midline and fuse with part of the nose to form the upper jaw and lip. A **cleft lip** results from failure of these structures to fuse.

The roof of the mouth, or palate, begins to form as vertical shelves of tissue that grow on the inside of the maxillary masses. These shelves swing to a horizontal position and

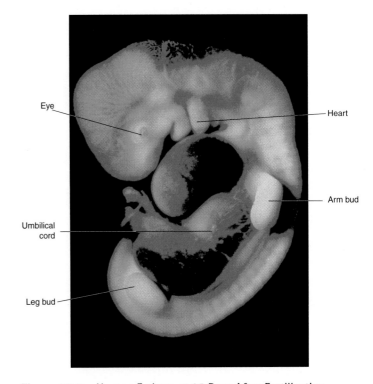

Eye
Heart
Arm bud
Umbilical cord
Leg bud

Figure 20.8   Human Embryo at 35 Days After Fertilization

begin to fuse with each other at about 56 days of development. If the palate does not fuse, a midline cleft in the roof of the mouth called a **cleft palate** results.

Development of the Organ Systems

The major organ systems appear and begin to develop during the embryonic period. This period is therefore also called the period of **organogenesis** (ōr'gă-nō-jen'ĕ-sis). The individual organ systems are not described in the text but are listed in table 20.2. Only general comments about a few select systems are presented in the text.

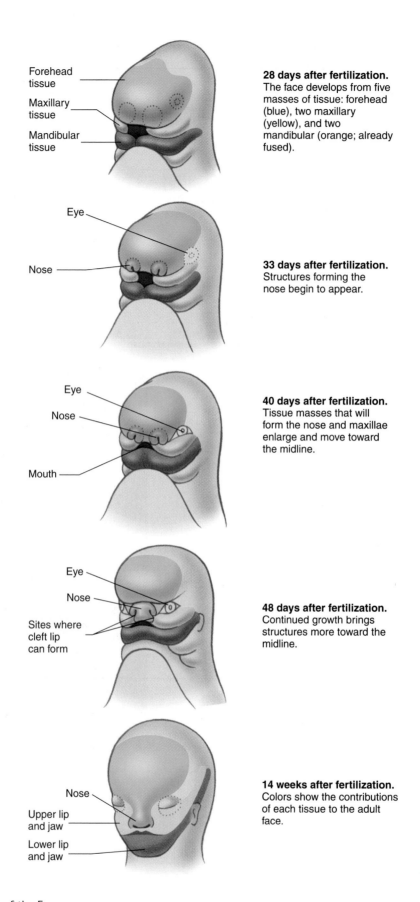

28 days after fertilization.
The face develops from five masses of tissue: forehead (blue), two maxillary (yellow), and two mandibular (orange; already fused).

33 days after fertilization.
Structures forming the nose begin to appear.

40 days after fertilization.
Tissue masses that will form the nose and maxillae enlarge and move toward the midline.

48 days after fertilization.
Continued growth brings structures more toward the midline.

14 weeks after fertilization.
Colors show the contributions of each tissue to the adult face.

Figure 20.9 Development of the Face

Ages indicate developmental days; colors show the contributions of each process to the adult face.

Table 20.2   Development of the Organ Systems

	Age (Days Since Fertilization)					
	1–5	6–10	11–15	16–20	21–25	26–30
General Features	Fertilization Blastocyst	Blastocyst implants	Primitive streak Three germ layers	Neural plate	Neural tube closed	Limb buds and other "buds" appear
Integumentary System			Ectoderm Mesoderm		Melanocytes from neural crest	
Skeletal System			Mesoderm		Neural crest cells	Limb buds
Muscular System			Mesoderm	Somites (body segments) begin to form		Somites all formed
Nervous System			Ectoderm	Neural plate	Neural tube complete Neural crest Eyes and ears begin to form	Lens appears
Endocrine System			Ectoderm Mesoderm Endoderm	Thyroid gland begins to develop		Parathyroid glands and pancreas appear
Cardiovascular System			Mesoderm	Blood islands form Two-tubed heart	Single-tubed heart begins to beat	Interatrial septum forms
Lymphatic System			Mesoderm			Thymus appears
Respiratory System			Mesoderm Endoderm		Diaphragm begins to form	Trachea Lung buds
Digestive System			Endoderm		Foregut and hindgut form	Liver and pancreas appear as buds
Urinary System			Mesoderm Endoderm		Embryonic kidneys appear	Embryonic kidneys elongate
Reproductive System			Mesoderm Endoderm	Primordial germ cells on yolk sac	Male reproductive ducts appear External genital structures begin to form	

Table 20.2 Development of the Organ Systems (continued)

Age (Days Since Fertilization)					
31–35	36–40	41–45	46–50	51–55	56–60
Hand and foot plates on limbs	Fingers and toes appear Lips formed Embryo 15 mm	External ear forming Embryo 20 mm	Embryo 25 mm	Limbs elongate to adult proportions Embryo 35 mm	Face is distinctly human in appearance
Sensory receptors appear in skin		Collagen fibers clearly present in skin		Extensive sensory nerve endings in skin	
Mesoderm condensation in areas of future bone	Cartilage in site of future humerus	Cartilage in site of future ulna and radius	Cartilage in site of future hand and fingers		Ossification begins in clavicle and then in other bones
Muscle precursor cells enter limb buds			Functional muscle		Nearly all muscles appear in adult form
Nerve processes enter limb buds		External ear forming Olfactory nerve begins to form		Semicircular canals in inner ear complete	Eyelids form Cochlea in inner ear complete
Pituitary appears as evaginations from brain and mouth	Gonads begin to form Adrenal glands form		Pineal body appears	Thyroid gland in adult position	Anterior pituitary loses its connection to mouth
Interventricular septum begins to form		Interventricular septum complete	Interatrial septum complete but foramen ovale remains until birth		
Large lymphatic vessels form in neck	Spleen appears			Adult lymph pattern formed	
Secondary bronchi to lobes form	Tertiary bronchi to lobules form		Tracheal cartilage begins to form		
Mouth opens to outside		Palate begins to form Tooth buds begin to form			Palate begins to fuse (fusion complete by 90 days); anus opens
Adult kidneys begin to develop				Embryonic kidneys degenerate	
	Gonads begin to form	Primordial germ cells enter gonads	Female reproductive ducts appear		Uterus forming External genitalia begins to differentiate in male and female

(a)   (b)

Figure 20.10   Development of the Digestive Tract
The digestive tract develops along the dorsal side of the yolk sac (yellow) as the body folds into a tube (blue arrows). The figures in back are shown in sagittal section. The figures in front are shown in cross section. The dashed line on the figures in back shows the plane of section in the figures in front. (*a*) An early embryo. (*b*) A slightly older embryo.

At the same time the neural tube is forming (18–26 days), the remainder of the embryo is folding to form a tube along the upper part of the yolk sac (figure 20.10). Another tube, which will form the gastrointestinal (GI) tract, develops inside the embryo from the upper part of the yolk sac.

A considerable number of outpocketings appear at about 28 days after fertilization along the entire length of the GI tract (figure 20.11). A surprisingly large number of important internal organs develops from those outpocketings, including the auditory tubes, tonsils, thymus gland, anterior pituitary gland, thyroid gland, parathyroid glands, lungs, liver, pancreas, and urinary bladder.

The heart develops from two blood vessels, lying side by side in the early embryo, which fuse about 21 days after fertilization into a single, midline heart. At about this time, the primitive heart begins to beat. Blood vessels form from "blood islands" on the surface of the yolk sac and inside the embryo. These islands expand and fuse to form the circulatory system.

The major chambers of the heart, the atrium and ventricle, expand rapidly. The single ventricle is subdivided into two chambers by the development of an **interventricular** (in-ter-ven-trik′ū-lăr) **septum** (figure 20.12). If the interventricular septum does not grow enough to completely separate the ventricles, a ventricular septal defect results.

An **interatrial** (in-ter-ā′trē-ăl) **septum** forms to separate the two atria. An opening in the interatrial septum called the **foramen ovale** (ō-val′ē) connects the two atria and allows blood to flow from the right to the left atrium in the fetus. Because of the

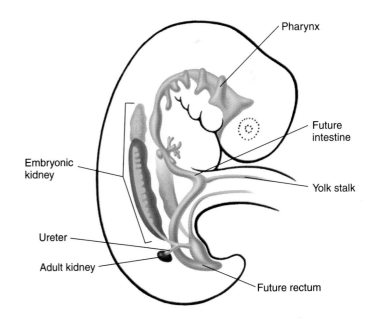

Figure 20.11   The Embryonic Digestive and Urinary Systems
Outpocketings of the digestive tract (yellow), which will form many adult structures such as the lungs and glands, are depicted. The embryonic and adult kidneys are also shown (purple).

presence of the foramen ovale, most of the blood in the fetus passes from the right atrium to the left atrium and bypasses the right ventricle and the lungs. The foramen ovale normally closes off at the time of birth, and blood then circulates through

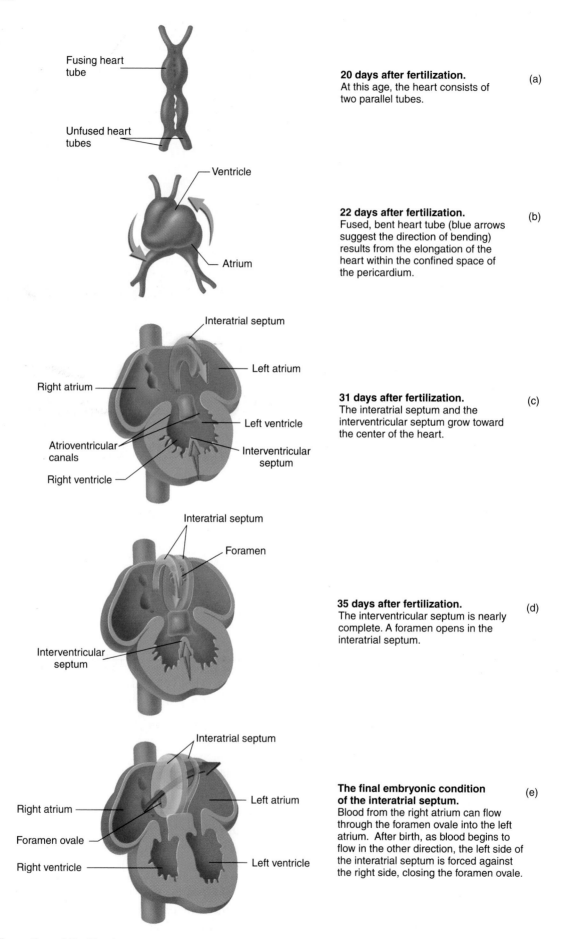

Fusing heart tube

Unfused heart tubes

20 days after fertilization. (a)
At this age, the heart consists of two parallel tubes.

Ventricle

Atrium

22 days after fertilization. (b)
Fused, bent heart tube (blue arrows suggest the direction of bending) results from the elongation of the heart within the confined space of the pericardium.

Interatrial septum

Left atrium

Right atrium

Left ventricle

Atrioventricular canals

Interventricular septum

Right ventricle

31 days after fertilization. (c)
The interatrial septum and the interventricular septum grow toward the center of the heart.

Interatrial septum

Foramen

Interventricular septum

35 days after fertilization. (d)
The interventricular septum is nearly complete. A foramen opens in the interatrial septum.

Interatrial septum

Right atrium

Left atrium

Foramen ovale

Right ventricle

Left ventricle

The final embryonic condition (e)
of the interatrial septum.
Blood from the right atrium can flow through the foramen ovale into the left atrium. After birth, as blood begins to flow in the other direction, the left side of the interatrial septum is forced against the right side, closing the foramen ovale.

Figure 20.12 Formation of the Heart

the right ventricle and the lungs. If this does not occur, an interatrial septal defect occurs. An interatrial septal defect or a ventricular septal defect usually results in a heart murmur.

The kidneys develop from mesoderm located along the lateral wall of the body cavity (see figure 20.11). The embryonic kidney is much more extensive than the adult kidney, extending the entire length of the body cavity. It is closely associated with internal reproductive organs such as the ovaries or testes and reproductive ducts such as the uterine tubes or vas deferens. Most of the embryonic kidney degenerates, with only a very small part forming the adult kidney.

Growth of the Fetus

The embryo becomes a fetus about 56 days after fertilization (figure 20.13). The beginning of the fetal period is marked by the beginning of bone ossification. In the embryo, most of the organ systems are developing, whereas in the fetus the organs are present. During the fetal period, the organ systems enlarge and mature. The fetus grows on average from about 3 cm and 2.5 g (0.09 oz) at 56 days to 50 cm and 3300 g (7 lb, 4 oz) at the end of pregnancy. The growth during the fetal period represents more than a 15-fold increase in length and a 1400-fold increase in weight.

Fine, soft hair called **lanugo** (lă-noo′gō) covers the fetus, and a waxy coat of loose epithelial cells called **vernix caseosa** (ver′niks kā′sē-ō′să) forms a protective layer between the fetus and the amniotic fluid. The amniotic fluid contains toxic waste products from the digestive tract and kidneys of the fetus.

Subcutaneous fat that accumulates in the fetus provides a nutrient reserve, helps insulate, and aids the newborn in sucking by strengthening and supporting the cheeks so that a small vacuum can be developed in the oral cavity.

Peak body growth occurs late in gestation, but as placental size reaches a maximum, the oxygen and nutrient supply to the fetus becomes limited. Growth of the placenta essentially stops at about 35 weeks, limiting fetal growth.

At approximately 38 weeks of development, the fetus has progressed to the point at which it is ready to be delivered. The average weight at this point is 3250 g (7 lb, 2 oz) for a female fetus and 3300 g (7 lb, 4 oz) for a male fetus.

Parturition

Physicians usually calculate the **gestation** (jes-tā′shŭn) **period** (length of pregnancy) as 280 days (40 weeks or 10 lunar months) from the LMP to the date of delivery of the fetus. **Parturition** (par-toor-ish′ŭn) refers to the process by which the baby is born (figure 20.14). Near the end of pregnancy, the uterus becomes progressively more irritable and usually exhibits occasional contractions that become stronger and more frequent until parturition is initiated. The cervix gradually dilates, and strong uterine contractions help expel the fetus from the uterus through the vagina. Just before expulsion of the fetus from the uterus, the amniotic sac surrounding the fetus ruptures, and amniotic fluid flows through the vagina to the exterior. This event is commonly referred to as the woman's "water breaking."

Labor is the period during which uterine contractions occur that result in expulsion of the fetus. Although labor may

Figure 20.13 Fetus
(a) At 50 days of development. (b) At 3 months of development.

3 **P R E D I C T**

How many days (developmental time) does it take an infant to develop from fertilization to parturition?

✔ *Answer on page 579*

differ greatly from woman to woman, it can usually be divided into three stages.

1. The **first stage** begins with the onset of regular uterine contractions and extends until the cervix dilates to a diameter about the size of the fetus' head (10 cm) (see figure 20.14). This stage takes approximately 24 hours, but it may be as short as a few minutes in some women who have had more than one child.
2. The **second stage** of labor lasts from the time of maximum cervical dilation until the time that the baby exits the vagina. This stage may last from 1 minute to up to 1 hour. During this stage, contraction of the woman's abdominal muscles assists the uterine contractions.

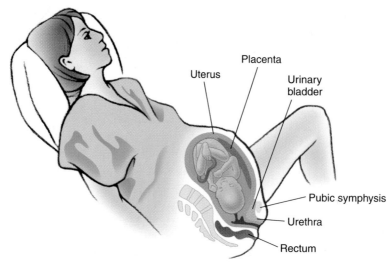

1. The position of the fetus before parturition.

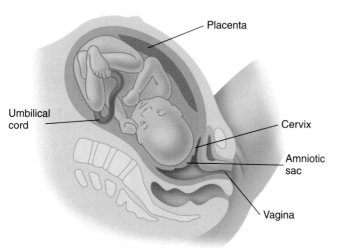

2. The cervix begins to dilate.

3. Further dilation of the cervix and rupture of the amniotic sac occur.

4. The fetus is expelled from the uterus.

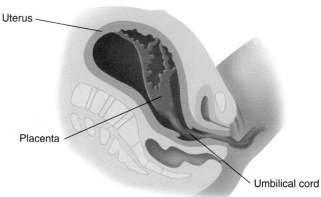

5. The placenta is then expelled.

Figure 20.14 Parturition

3. The **third stage** of labor involves the expulsion of the placenta from the uterus. Contractions of the uterus cause the placenta to tear away from the wall of the uterus. Some bleeding from the wall of the uterus occurs because of the intimate contact between the placenta and the uterus. Bleeding is normally limited, however, because uterine smooth muscle contractions compress the blood vessels.

During the 4 or 5 weeks following parturition, the uterus becomes much smaller, but it remains somewhat larger than it was before pregnancy. A vaginal discharge composed of small amounts of blood and degenerating endometrium can persist for several days after parturition.

The precise signal that triggers parturition is unknown, but many factors that support it have been identified (figure 20.15). Before parturition, the progesterone concentration in the mother's blood has reached its highest level. Progesterone has an inhibitory effect on uterine smooth muscle cells. Estrogen levels rapidly increase in the maternal circulation, however, exciting uterine smooth muscle. The inhibitory influence of progesterone on smooth muscle can be overcome by the stimulatory effect of estrogens near the end of pregnancy.

The fetus also plays a role in stimulating parturition. Stress on the fetus triggers the secretion of a releasing hormone from the fetal hypothalamus, which, in turn, causes adrenocorticotropic hormone (ACTH) release from the fetal anterior pituitary. ACTH stimulates the fetal adrenal gland to secrete cortical steroids that reduce progesterone secretion, increase estrogen secretion, and increase prostaglandin production by the placenta. Prostaglandins strongly stimulate uterine contractions.

During parturition, oxytocin is released from the mother's posterior pituitary. Stretching of the cervix produces action potentials that are sent to the hypothalamus and cause the release of oxytocin. Oxytocin also stimulates uterine contractions.

The Newborn

The newborn, or **neonate** (nē′ō-nāt), experiences several dramatic changes at the time of birth. The major and earliest changes are the separation of the infant from the maternal circulation and the transfer from a fluid to a gaseous environment.

Respiratory and Circulatory Changes

The large, forced gasps of air that occur when the infant cries at the time of delivery help to inflate the lungs. The fetal lungs produce a substance called **surfactant** (ser-fak′tănt), which coats the inner surface of the alveoli, reduces surface tension in the lungs, and allows the newborn lungs to inflate.

Did You Know?

Surfactant is not manufactured in the fetal lungs before about 6 months after fertilization. If a fetus is born before the lungs can produce surfactant, the surface tension inside the lungs is too great for the lungs to inflate. Under these conditions, the newborn may die of respiratory distress.

1. The fetal hypothalamus secretes a releasing hormone that stimulates adrenocorticotropic hormone (ACTH) secretion from the pituitary. The fetal pituitary secretes ACTH in greater amounts near parturition.

2. ACTH causes the fetal adrenal gland to secrete greater quantities of adrenal cortical steroids.

3. Adrenal cortical steroids travel in the umbilical blood to the placenta.

4. In the placenta the adrenal cortical steroids cause progesterone synthesis to level off and estrogen and prostaglandin synthesis to increase, making the uterus more irritable.

5. The stretching of the uterus produces action potentials that are transmitted to the brain through ascending pathways.

6. Action potentials stimulate the secretion of oxytocin by the posterior pituitary.

7. Oxytocin causes the uterine smooth muscle to contract.

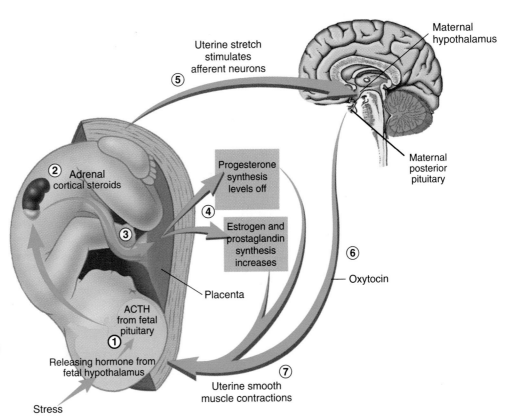

Figure 20.15 Factors That Influence the Process of Parturition

1. Blood bypasses the lungs by flowing through the ductus arteriosus.

2. Blood also bypasses the lungs by flowing through the foramen ovale.

3. Oxygen-rich blood is carried to the fetus from the placenta by the umbilical vein.

4. Blood bypasses the liver sinusoids by flowing through the ductus venosus.

5. Oxygen-poor blood returns to the placenta through the umbilical arteries.

Superior vena cava
Aortic arch
Ductus arteriosus
Ascending aorta
Pulmonary trunk
Foramen ovale
Inferior vena cava
Ductus venosus
Liver
Hepatic portal vein
Umbilical vein
Fetal umbilicus
Umbilical cord
Umbilical arteries
Abdominal aorta
Kidney
Common iliac artery
Internal iliac arteries

(a)

Figure 20.16 Circulatory Changes at the Time of Birth
(*a*) Before birth.

The initial inflation of the lungs causes important changes in the circulatory system (figure 20.16). Expansion of the lungs reduces the resistance to blood flow through the lungs, resulting in increased blood flow from the right ventricle of the heart through the pulmonary arteries. Consequently, an increased amount of blood flows from the right atrium to the right ventricle and into the pulmonary arteries, and less blood flows from the right atrium through the foramen ovale to the left atrium. The reduced resistance to blood flow through the lungs and the increasing volume of blood returning from the lungs through the pulmonary veins to the left atrium makes the pressure in the left atrium greater than that in the right atrium. This pressure difference forces blood against the interatrial septum, closing a flap of tissue that develops in that region over the foramen ovale. This action completes the separation of the heart into two pumps: the right side and the left side of the heart. A short artery, the **ductus arteriosus** (ar-tēr′ē-ō-sŭs), connects the pulmonary trunk to the aorta. Before birth, the ductus arteriosus carries blood from the pulmonary trunk to the aorta, bypassing the fetal lungs. This artery closes off shortly after birth, forcing blood to flow through the lungs.

The fetal blood supply passes to the placenta through **umbilical** (ŭm-bil′i-kăl) **arteries**, which originate in the internal iliac arteries, and returns through an **umbilical vein**. The umbilical vein passes through the liver but bypasses the sinusoids of the liver by way of the **ductus venosus** (vē-nō′sŭs) and joins the inferior vena cava. When the umbilical cord is tied and cut, no more blood flows through the umbilical vein and arteries, and they degenerate. The remnant of the umbilical vein becomes the round ligament of the liver.

Digestive Changes

The fetus swallows amniotic fluid from time to time late in gestation. Shortly after birth, this swallowed fluid plus cells sloughed from the mucosal lining of the GI tract, mucus produced by intestinal mucous glands, and bile from the liver are

1. When air enters the lungs, the ductus arteriosus closes.

2. The foramen ovale closes.

3. The umbilical arteries and vein are cut. The umbilical vein becomes the round ligament of the liver.

4. The ductus venosus degenerates.

5. The umbilical arteries also degenerate.

Superior vena cava

Ascending aorta

Foramen ovale closed

Inferior vena cava

Liver

Degenerated ductus venosus

Hepatic portal vein

Round ligament of liver (degenerated umbilical vein)

Umbilicus

Degenerated umbilical arteries

Aortic arch

Closed ductus arteriosus

Pulmonary trunk

Abdominal aorta

Kidney

Common iliac artery

Internal iliac arteries

(b)

Figure 20.16   (continued)

(b) After birth.

eliminated as a greenish anal discharge called **meconium** (mē-kō′nē-ŭm).

After birth, the neonate is suddenly separated from its source of nutrients provided by the maternal circulation. Because of this separation and the shock of birth, the neonate usually loses 5% to 10% of its total body weight during the first few days of life. Although the digestive system of the fetus becomes somewhat functional late in development, it is still very immature in comparison with that of the adult, and only a limited number of food types can be digested.

The newborn digestive system is capable of digesting lactose (milk sugar) from the time of birth. The pancreatic secretions are sufficiently mature for a milk diet, but the digestive system only gradually develops the ability to digest more solid foods over the first year or two. New foods should therefore be introduced gradually during the first 2 years. It is also advised that only one new food at a time be introduced into the infant's diet so that, if an allergic reaction occurs, the cause is more easily determined.

Amylase secretion by the salivary glands and the pancreas remains low until after the first year. Lactase activity in the small intestine is high at birth but declines during infancy, although the levels still exceed those in adults. In many adults, lactase activity is lost, and an intolerance to milk can develop.

Lactation

Lactation (lak-tā′shŭn) is the production of milk by the mammary glands (figure 20.17). It normally occurs in women following parturition and may continue for up to 2 or 3 years.

During pregnancy, the high concentration and continuous presence of estrogen and progesterone cause development of the duct system and the secretory units within the breast. Other hormones, including a prolactinlike hormone produced by the placenta, help support the development of the breasts. Also, additional adipose tissue is deposited; thus

Clinical Focus   Disorders of Pregnancy and Birth

Ectopic Pregnancy

The term **ectopic** (ek-top'ik) means out of place, and an ectopic pregnancy is one that occurs outside the uterus. The most common site of an ectopic pregnancy, the uterine tube, produces a tubal pregnancy. The blastocyst may not have reached the uterine cavity by the time it is ready to implant and may implant into the wall of the uterine tube. The uterine tube cannot expand enough to accommodate the growing fetus, and, if the fetus is not removed, the tube eventually ruptures. The ruptured uterine tube causes life-threatening internal bleeding.

Miscarriage

It is estimated that as many as 50% of all zygotes are lost before delivery. Most are lost before implantation. Approximately 15% of all pregnancies end in **miscarriage** (mis-kar'ij), or **spontaneous abortion** (ă-bōr'shŭn), which results from the death or early delivery of the fetus. Before about 24 weeks post-LMP the fetus is not viable outside the uterus. After 24 weeks, but before 37 weeks post-LMP, the infant is referred to as **premature**.

Although there is a higher incidence of birth defects among aborted fetuses, the vast majority of miscarried fetuses appear to be normal. Many factors can cause a miscarriage, many of which do not directly involve the fetus, and many of which are unknown. One common cause of miscarriage is improper implantation of the blastocyst in the uterus. In most cases, the blastocyst implants in the upper part of the uterus, but occasionally a blastocyst can implant near the opening into the cervical canal, a condition called **placenta previa** (prē'vē-ă). As the fetus grows and the uterus stretches, the previa placenta may tear away from the uterine wall, a condition called **placental abruption** (ab-rŭp'shŭn). When this occurs, the fetus often dies. The associated hemorrhaging can be life-threatening to the mother as well.

Pregnancy-Induced Hypertension

One reason the mother's weight is carefully monitored during pregnancy is that a sudden weight gain associated with edema and high blood pressure can be a sign of **pregnancy-induced hypertension**, or **toxemia** (tok-sē'mē-ă) of **pregnancy**. The cause of the disorder is unknown, but it can result in convulsions, kidney failure, and death of both the mother and the fetus.

Teratogens

Teratogens (ter'ă-tō-jenz) are drugs or other chemicals that can cross the placenta and cause birth defects in the developing embryo. The most famous teratogen is thalidomide (thă-lid'ō-mīd), an over-the-counter drug that was given to thousands of pregnant women in the early 1960s. The drug inhibited normal limb development and resulted in several thousand children being born, mostly in Germany and England, with severely reduced or even absent arms or legs. Thalidomide has been recently discovered effective in treating a variety of diseases, including leprosy, rheumatoid arthritis, tuberculosis, and some complications of AIDS. So although thalidomide was withdrawn from the market in the early 1960s, its return to the market for limited use is now being considered.

Fetal alcohol syndrome (FAS) is a major concern today. This syndrome, which consists of brain dysfunction, growth retardation, and facial peculiarities, is seen in children of women who consumed substantial amounts of alcohol while they were pregnant. It has been estimated that FAS may occur as often as 1 in 350 births and may account for as much as 33% of all mental retardation. **Fetal alcohol effect** includes brain dysfunction without the facial characteristics and may be three times as common as FAS.

Cocaine addiction can occur in babies whose mothers were cocaine users during pregnancy. A fetus can also suffer strokelike symptoms if the mother ingests cocaine during the latter part of pregnancy.

Infections

Infections can occur in the mother or infant, or both. Maternal death associated with childbirth can result from infections. Cleanliness associated with childbirth procedures can reduce the rate of infection, and antibiotics have greatly reduced the number of fatal infections.

If a pregnant woman contracts **German measles** (mē'zlz), or **rubella** (rū-bel'ă), during pregnancy, the fetus may be severely affected. These effects can occur even if the mother suffers only a mild case of measles. Defects in the newborn can include visual and hearing defects, as well as mental retardation.

Neonatal gonorrheal ophthalmia (of-thal'mē-ă) is a severe form of conjunctivitis that is contracted by an infant as it passes through the birth canal of a mother with gonorrhea. This infection carries a high risk of blindness. The treatment of newborn eyes with silver nitrate or antibiotics is effective in preventing the disease.

Chlamydial conjunctivitis (kon-jŭnk-ti-vī'tis) is also contracted as an infant passes through the birth canal if the mother has a chlamydial infection. This infection is not affected by silver nitrate eyedrops; thus in many places newborns are treated with antibiotics against both chlamydia and gonorrhea.

If a woman has **genital herpes** (her'pēz) and has open lesions in the birth canal near the time of parturition, the baby can be removed by cesarean section to prevent the infection spreading to the baby.

Human immunodeficiency virus (HIV), the virus that causes **acquired immune deficiency syndrome (AIDS)**, can cross the placenta and infect the fetus in utero, can infect the infant during parturition, or can infect the infant during breast-feeding. Approximately 30% to 50% of the infants born to HIV-infected mothers are infected. About 20% of those infected die of AIDS within the first 18 postnatal months. Azidothymidine (az'i-dō-thi'mi-dēn) (AZT) is a drug that inhibits HIV replication. The number of infants who contract AIDS from their mothers can be dramatically reduced by giving AZT to HIV-infected women and to their newborn infants.

---

the size of the breasts increases substantially throughout pregnancy. Estrogen and progesterone prevent the secretory part of the breast from producing milk during pregnancy.

Blood levels of estrogen and progesterone fall dramatically after parturition. Once the placenta has been dislodged from the uterus, the source of these hormones is gone. After parturition, in the absence of estrogen and progesterone, prolactin produced by the anterior pituitary stimulates milk production. During suckling, sensory action potentials are sent from the nipple to the brain and result in the release of prolactin from the anterior pituitary (see figure 20.17). For the first few days following parturition, the mammary glands secrete **colostrum** (kō-los'trŭm), which contains little fat and less lactose than milk. Eventually, more nutritious milk is produced. Colostrum and milk provide nutrition and antibodies that help protect the nursing baby from infections.

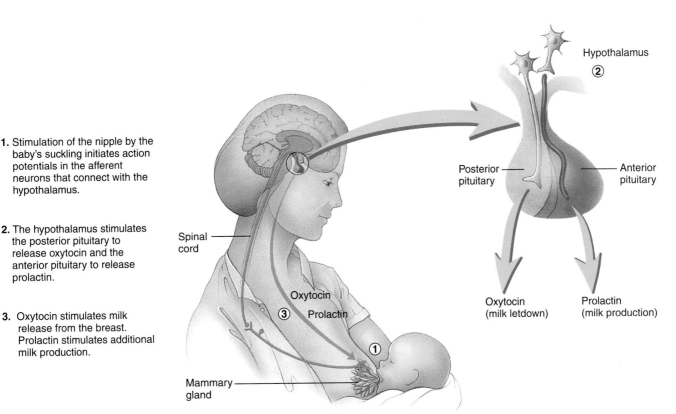

1. Stimulation of the nipple by the baby's suckling initiates action potentials in the afferent neurons that connect with the hypothalamus.

2. The hypothalamus stimulates the posterior pituitary to release oxytocin and the anterior pituitary to release prolactin.

3. Oxytocin stimulates milk release from the breast. Prolactin stimulates additional milk production.

Hypothalamus
②

Posterior pituitary   Anterior pituitary

Spinal cord

Oxytocin
③ Prolactin

①

Mammary gland

Oxytocin (milk letdown)   Prolactin (milk production)

Figure 20.17 Hormonal Activities During Lactation

Repeated stimulation of prolactin release makes nursing possible for several years. If nursing is stopped, within a few days the ability of the breast to respond to prolactin is lost, and milk production ceases.

At the time of nursing, milk contained in the alveoli and ducts of the breast is forced out of the breast by contractions of cells surrounding the alveoli. Mechanical stimulation of the breasts produces action potentials that are carried to the hypothalamus, where they cause the release of oxytocin from the posterior pituitary (see figure 20.17). Oxytocin stimulates cells surrounding the alveoli to contract. As a result, milk flows from the breasts, a process that is called milk "**letdown**." Higher brain centers can cause the release of oxytocin in response to such things as hearing an infant cry or thinking about breastfeeding.

4   P R E D I C T

While nursing her baby, a woman noticed that she developed cramps in her abdomen. Explain what was happening.

✔ *Answer on page 579*

The First Year Following Birth

A great number of changes occur in the infant from the time of birth until 1 year of age. The time when these changes occur may vary considerably from child to child, and the dates given are only rough estimates. The brain is still developing at this time, and much of what the infant can accomplish depends on the amount of brain development achieved. It is estimated that the total adult number of neurons is present in the central nervous system at birth, but subsequent growth and maturation of the brain involves the addition of new neuroglial cells, myelin sheaths, and new connections between neurons, which may continue throughout life.

By 6 weeks, the baby is usually able to hold up his or her head when placed in a prone position and begins to smile in response to people or objects. At 3 months of age, the infant's limbs are exercised aimlessly. The arms and hands are controlled enough, however, that voluntary thumb-sucking can occur. The infant can follow a moving person with his eyes. At 4 months the infant begins to do push-ups, that is, raises himself by the arms. The infant can begin to grasp things placed in his hands, coo and gurgle, roll from back to side, listen quietly when hearing a person's voice or music, hold the head erect, and play with his hands. At 5 months the infant can usually laugh out loud, reach for objects, turn the head to follow an object, lift the head and shoulders, sit with support, and roll over. At 8 months the infant can recognize familiar people, sit up without support, and reach for specific objects. At 12 months the infant may pull herself to a standing position and may be able to walk without support. The child can pick up objects in her hands and examine them carefully. A 12-month-old child can understand much of what is said and may say several words.

Life Stages

The stages of life from fertilization to death are as follows: (1) the **germinal** (jer'mi-năl) **period**—fertilization to 14 days; (2) the **embryo**—14 to 56 days after fertilization; (3) the **fetus**—56 days after fertilization to birth; (4) **neonate**—birth to 1 month after birth; (5) **infant** (in'fănt)—1 month to 1 or 2 years after birth (the end of infancy is sometimes set at the time that the child begins to walk); (6) **child**—1 or 2 years old to puberty (about 11 to 14 years); (7) **adolescent** (ad-ō-les'ent)—teenage years, from puberty to 20 years old; (8) **adult**—20 years old to death. Adulthood is sometimes divided into three periods: **young adult**, 20 to 40 years old; **middle age**, 40 to 65 years old; and **older adult**, or **senior citizen**, 65 years old to death. Much of this designation is associated more with social norms than with physiology.

During childhood the individual grows in size and develops considerably. Many of the emotional characteristics that a person possesses throughout life are formed during early childhood.

Major physical and physiological changes occur during adolescence, and many of these changes also affect the emotions and behavior of the individual. Other emotional changes occur as the adolescent attempts to fit into an adult world. **Puberty** (pū'ber-tē) is the time when maturation of reproductive cells begins and when gonadal hormones are first secreted in substantial amounts. These hormones stimulate the development and maturation of secondary sex characteristics, such as enlargement of the female breasts and growth of body hair in both sexes. Puberty usually occurs in females who are about 11 to 13 years old and usually begins in males who are about 12 to 14 years old. The onset of puberty is usually accompanied by a growth spurt, followed by a period of slower growth. Full adult stature is usually achieved before age 17 or 18 in females and before age 19 or 20 in males.

Aging

Development of a new human being begins at fertilization, as does the process of aging. Cell division occurs at an extremely rapid rate during early development and then begins to slow as various cells become committed to specific functions within the body.

Many cells of the body continue to divide throughout life, replacing dead or damaged tissue; but other cells, such as the neurons in the brain, cease to divide once they have reached a certain number. Dead neurons are not replaced. After the number of neurons reaches a peak (at approximately the time of birth), the number begins to decline. Neuronal loss is most rapid early in life and decreases to a slower, steady rate.

Young embryonic tissue is very flexible and elastic. It has relatively small amounts of collagen, and the collagen that is present is not highly cross-linked. Many of the collagen fibers produced during development, however, are permanent components of the individual. As the individual ages, more and more cross-links form between the collagen molecules, rendering the tissues more rigid and less flexible.

The tissues with the highest collagen content and the greatest dependency on collagen for their function are the most severely affected by the collagen cross-linking and tissue rigidity associated with aging. The lens of the eye is one of the first structures to exhibit pathological changes as a result of this increased rigidity. Vision of close objects becomes more difficult with advancing age until most middle-aged people require reading glasses. Loss of elasticity also affects other tissues, including the joints, kidneys, lungs, and heart, and greatly reduces the functional ability of these organs.

As with nervous tissue, the number of skeletal muscle fibers declines with age. The strength of skeletal muscle reaches a peak between 20 to 35 years of life and usually declines steadily thereafter. Skeletal muscle strength depends primarily on the size of the muscle fibers, but the total number of fibers is probably also important to muscle strength. As most people age, both the number of fibers and the size of each tend to decline. The decline in muscle fiber size may be more related to a general decrease in activity, rather than to any specific age-related changes. Like the collagen of connective tissue, however, the macromolecules of skeletal muscle cells undergo biochemical changes during aging, rendering the muscle tissue less functional. A good exercise program can slow or even partly reverse the process of muscular aging.

Cardiac muscle cells also do not normally divide after birth. Age-related changes in cardiac muscle cell function probably contribute to a decline in cardiac function with advancing age. The heart loses elastic recoil ability and muscular contractility. As a result, total cardiac output declines, and less oxygen and nutrients reach the cells of the body supplied by the cardiovascular system. This decline in nutrition can be particularly harmful to cells that require high oxygen levels, such as neurons of the brain, and cells that are already compromised, such as cartilage cells of the joints, contributing to the general decline in these tissues.

Reduced cardiac function also can result in decreased blood flow to the kidneys, contributing to decreases in the filtration ability of the kidney. Degeneration of the connective tissues as a result of collagen cross-linking and other factors also decreases the filtration efficiency of the glomerular basement membrane.

Atherosclerosis (ath'er-ō-skler-ō'sis) is the deposit of lipids in the tunica intima of large and medium-sized arteries (see figure 13.5). These deposits then become fibrotic and calcified, resulting in **arteriosclerosis** (ar-tēr'ē-ō-skler-ō'sis, hardening of the arteries). Arteriosclerosis interferes with normal blood flow and may result in a **thrombosis** (throm-bō'sis), which is a clot or plaque formed inside a vessel. An **embolus** (em'bō-lŭs) is a piece of the clot that has broken loose and floats through the circulation. An embolus can lodge in smaller arteries to cause heart attacks or strokes. Although atherosclerosis occurs to some extent in all middle-aged and elderly people and can occur even in certain young people, some people appear more at risk because of high blood cholesterol levels. This condition seems to have a hereditary component, and blood tests are available to screen people for high blood cholesterol levels.

Many other organs, such as the liver, pancreas, stomach, and colon, undergo degenerative changes with age. The ingestion of harmful agents can accelerate such changes. Examples include the degenerative changes induced in the lungs (aside from lung cancer) by cigarette smoke and sclerotic changes in the liver as a result of excessive alcohol consumption.

In addition to the previously described changes associated with aging, cellular wear and tear, or cellular aging, is another factor that contributes to aging. Progressive damage from many sources such as radiation and toxic substances can result in irreversible cellular insults and may be one of the major factors leading to aging. It has been suggested that ingestion of moderate amounts of vitamins E and C in combination may help slow aging due to cellular insult by stimulating cell repair. Vitamin C also stimulates collagen production and may slow the loss of tissue elasticity associated with aging collagen.

According to the **free radical theory of aging**, free radicals, which are atoms or molecules with an unpaired electron, can react with and alter the structure of molecules that are critical for normal cell function. Alteration of these molecules can result in cell dysfunction, cancer, or other types of cellular damage. Free radicals are produced as a normal part of metabolism and are introduced into the body from the environment through the air we breathe and the food we eat. The damage caused by free radicals may accumulate with age. Antioxidants, such as beta carotene (provitamin A), vitamin C, and vitamin E, can donate electrons to free radicals, without themselves becoming harmful. Thus antioxidants may prevent the damage caused by the free radicals and may ward off age-related disorders, ranging from wrinkles to cancer.

One characteristic of aging is an overall decrease in ATP production. This decline in ATP production is associated with a decrease in oxidative phosphorylation. This decline in oxidation has been shown in many cases to be associated with **mitochondrial DNA mutations**. Such mutations are often associated with Alzheimer's disease. There are also genes in the nuclear DNA associated with Alzheimer's.

Immune system changes may also be a major contributing factor to aging. The aging immune system loses its ability to respond to outside antigens and begins to be more sensitive to the body's own antigens. Immune responses to one's own tissues can result in the degeneration of the tissues and may be responsible for such things as arthritic joint disorders, chronic glomerular nephritis, and hyperthyroidism. In addition, T lymphocytes tend to lose their functional capacity with aging and cannot destroy abnormal cells as efficiently. This change may be one reason that certain types of cancer occur more frequently in older people.

One of the greatest disadvantages of aging is the increasing lack of ability to adjust to stress. Elderly people have a far more precarious homeostatic balance than younger people, and eventually some stress is encountered that is so great that the body's ability to recover is surpassed and death results.

Death

Death is usually not attributed to old age. Some other problem such as heart failure, renal failure, or stroke is usually listed as the cause of death.

Death was once defined as the loss of heartbeat and respiration. In recent years, however, more precise definitions of death have been developed, because both the heart and the lungs can be kept working artificially, such as during cardiopulmonary resuscitation, and the heart can even temporarily be replaced by an artificial device. Modern definitions of death are based on the permanent cessation of life functions and the cessation of integrated tissue and organ function. The most widely accepted indication of death in humans is whole brain death, which is manifested clinically by the absence of response to stimulation, the absence of natural respiration and heart function, and an isoelectric ("flat") electroencephalogram for at least 30 minutes, in the absence of known central nervous system poisoning or hypothermia. Some central nervous system poisons can cause a flat electroencephalogram, but the patient can be revived if the effects of the poison are eliminated. Hypothermia slows down all chemical reactions, including those involved in degenerative changes that begin at the time of death. As a result, a person suffering from hypothermia can exhibit no response to stimulation, exhibit no respiration or heart beat, and have a flat electroencephalogram for more than 30 minutes and still be revived.

Did You Know?

Neocortical (nē-ō-kōr'ti-kăl) **death** is a condition in which major portions of the cerebrum are no longer functioning. Under these conditions, the patient is comatose and incapable of responding to stimuli. Heartbeat and respiration still continue, however, because of some relatively unimpaired brainstem functions. Also, because some brainstem function still occurs, the electroencephalogram is not flat but exhibits some level of activity. Some state laws require that under these conditions the patient be kept alive by intravenous feeding and by other support equipment. The patient may have previously stated in a "living will" that, if neocortical death occurs and the patient cannot be returned to a reasonably normal level of function, no artificial support should be applied in an attempt to keep the patient's body alive.

Genetics

Genetics is the study of heredity, that is, those characteristics inherited by children from their parents. Many of a person's abilities, susceptibility to disease, and even life span are influenced by heredity.

Chromosomes

Deoxyribonucleic (dē-oks'ē-rī'bō-noo-klē'ic) **acid (DNA)** molecules and their associated proteins become visible as densely stained bodies, called **chromosomes** (krō'mō-sōmz,

Figure 20.18 Human Karyotype

The chromosome pairs are numbered in order from the largest to smallest. The 23 pairs of chromosomes in humans consist of 22 pairs of autosomal chromosomes (numbered 1 to 22) and 1 pair of sex chromosomes. This karyotype is of a male and has an X and a Y sex chromosome. A female karyotype would have two X chromosomes.

colored bodies), during cell division (see chapter 3). **Somatic** (sō-mat'ik) **cells,** all the cells of the body except the sex cells, contain 23 pairs of chromosomes, or 46 total chromosomes. The sex cells, or the **gametes** (gam'ētz) contain 23 unpaired chromosomes.

A **karyotype** (kar'ē-ō-tīp) is a display of the chromosomes in a somatic cell (figure 20.18; see chapter 3). There are 22 pairs of **autosomal** (aw-tō-sō'măl) **chromosomes,** all the chromosomes but the sex chromosomes, and one pair of **sex chromosomes.** A normal female has two **X chromosomes** (XX) in each somatic cell, whereas a normal male has one X and one **Y chromosome** (XY).

> ### Did You Know?
>
> There is a wide range of sex chromosome abnormalities. The presence of a Y chromosome makes a person male, and the absence of a Y chromosome makes a person female, regardless of the number of X chromosomes. The following combinations, therefore, are female: XO (Turner's syndrome), XX, XXX, or XXXX. Any combinations that include a Y are male: XY, XXY, XXXY, or XYY. A YO condition is lethal, because the genes on the X chromosome are necessary for survival. Secondary sexual characteristics are usually underdeveloped in both the XXX female and the XXY male (called Klinefelter's syndrome), and additional X chromosomes (XXXX or XXXY) are often associated with some degree of mental retardation.

Gametes are derived by **meiosis** (mī-ō'sis) (see figure 3.23). Meiosis is called a reduction division because the number of chromosomes in the gametes is half the number in the somatic cells. When a sperm cell and an oocyte fuse during

fertilization, each contributes one-half of the chromosomes necessary to produce new somatic cells. Half of an individual's genetic makeup therefore comes from the father, and half comes from the mother.

During meiosis, the chromosomes are distributed in such a way that each gamete receives only one chromosome from each **homologous** (hŏ-mol'ō-gŭs) pair of chromosomes (see chapters 3 and 19). Homologous chromosomes contain the same compliment of genetic information. The inheritance of sex illustrates, in part, how chromosomes are distributed during gamete formation and fertilization. During meiosis and gamete formation, the pair of sex chromosomes separates so that each oocyte receives one of a homologous pair of X chromosomes, whereas each sperm cell receives either an X chromosome or a Y chromosome (figure 20.19). When a sperm cell fertilizes an oocyte to form a single cell, the sex of the individual is determined randomly. If the oocyte is fertilized by a sperm cell with a Y chromosome, a male results, but if the oocyte is fertilized by a sperm cell with an X chromosome, a female results. Estimating the probability of any given zygote being male or female is much like flipping a coin. When all the possible combinations of sperm cells with oocytes are considered, half the individuals should be female and the other half should be male.

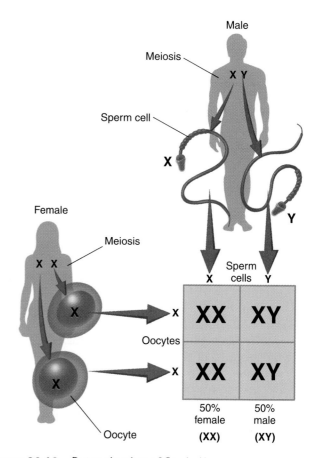

Figure 20.19 Determination of Sex in Humans

The female produces oocytes containing one X chromosome, whereas the male produces sperm cells with either an X or a Y chromosome. There are four possible combinations of an oocyte with a sperm cell, half of which produce females and half of which produce males.

Genes

The functional unit of heredity is the gene. Each **gene** consists of a certain portion of a DNA molecule but not necessarily a continuous stretch of DNA. Each chromosome contains thousands of genes. Both chromosomes of a given pair contain similar but not necessarily identical genes. Similar genes on homologous chromosomes are called **alleles** (ă-lēlz′). If the two allelic genes are identical, the person is **homozygous** (hō-mō-zī′gŭs) for the trait specified by that gene. If the two alleles are slightly different, the person is **heterozygous** (het′er-ō-zī′gŭs) for the trait. All the genes in one homologous set of 23 chromosomes in one individual, taken together is called the **genome**.

Did You Know?

The importance of genes is dramatically illustrated by situations in which the alteration of a single gene results in a genetic disorder. For example, in **phenylketonuria** (fen′il-kē′tō-nū′rē-ă) **(PKU)** the gene responsible for producing an enzyme that converts the amino acid phenylalanine to the amino acid tyrosine is defective. Phenylalanine therefore accumulates in the blood and is eventually converted to harmful substances that can cause mental retardation.

Through the processes of meiosis, gamete formation, and fertilization the distribution of genes received from each parent is essentially random. This random distribution is influenced by several factors, however. For example, all of the genes on a given chromosome are **linked**, that is, they tend to be inherited as a set rather than as individual genes because chromosomes, not individual genes segregate during meiosis. Also during meiosis, however, homologous chromosomes may exchange genetic information by **crossing over**.

Furthermore, segregation errors can occur during meiosis. As the chromosomes separate during meiosis, the two members of a homologous pair may not segregate. As a result, one of the daughter cells receives both chromosome pairs and the other daughter cell receives none. When the gametes are fertilized, the resulting zygote has either 47 chromosomes or 45 chromosomes rather than the normal 46. This condition is usually, but not always, lethal and is one reason for a high rate of early embryo loss. The sex chromosome abnormalities described in the section dealing with chromosomes are not always lethal. Another example is **Down syndrome**, or **trisomy 21**, in which there are three #21 chromosomes.

Dominant and Recessive Genes

Most human genetic traits are recognized because defective alleles for those traits exist in the population. For example, on chromosome 11 is a gene that produces an enzyme necessary for the synthesis of melanin, the pigment responsible for skin, hair, and eye color (see chapter 5). An abnormal allele, however, produces a defective enzyme not capable of catalyzing one of the steps in melanin synthesis. If a given person inherits two defective alleles, a homozygous condition, the person is unable to produce melanin, and therefore lacks normal pigment. This condition is referred to as **albinism** (al′bi-nizm).

For many genetic traits, the effects of one allele for that trait can mask the effect of another allele for that same trait. For example, a person who is heterozygous for the melanin-producing enzyme gene has one normal gene for melanin production and one defective gene for melanin production. One copy of the gene and its resulting enzymes are enough to make normal melanin. As a result, the person who is heterozygous produces melanin and appears normal. In this case, the allele that produces the normal enzyme is said to be **dominant**, whereas the allele producing the abnormal enzyme is **recessive**. By convention, dominant traits are indicated by uppercase letters and recessive traits are indicated by lowercase letters. In this example, the letter "*A*" designates the dominant normal, pigmented condition, and the letter "*a*" the recessive albino condition. It is important to note that not all dominant traits are the normal condition and that not all recessive traits are abnormal. Many examples exist of abnormal dominant traits.

The possible combinations of dominant and recessive alleles for normal melanin production versus albanism are *AA* (homozygous dominant, normal), *Aa* (heterozygous, normal), and *aa* (homozygous recessive, albino). The alleles a person has for a given trait is called the **genotype** (jen′ō-tīp). The person's appearance is called the **phenotype** (fē′nō-tīp). A person with the genotype *AA* or *Aa* would have the phenotype of normal pigmentation, whereas a person with the genotype *aa* would have the phenotype of albinism. Note that the recessive trait is expressed only when it is not masked by the dominant trait.

---

5   P R E D I C T

Polydactyly (pol-ē-dak′ti-lē) is a condition in which a person has extra fingers or toes. Given that polydactyly is a dominant trait, list all the possible genotypes and phenotypes for polydactyly. Use the letters "*D*" and "*d*" for the genotypes.

✔ *Answer on page 000*

The inheritance of dominant and recessive traits can be determined if the genotypes of the parents are known. For example, if an albino person (*aa*) mates with a heterozygous normal person (*Aa*), the probability is that half of the children will be albino (*aa*), and half will be normal heterozygous carriers (*Aa*). If two carriers (*Aa*) mate, the probability is that 1/4 will be homozygous dominant (*AA*), 1/4 will be homozygous recessive (*aa*), and 1/2 will be heterozygous (*Aa*). Such a probability can be easily determined by the use of a table called a **Punnett square** (figure 20.20). A **carrier** is a heterozygous person with an abnormal recessive gene, but with a normal phenotype because they also have a normal dominant allele for that gene.

Sex-Linked Traits

Traits affected by genes on the sex chromosomes are called **sex-linked traits**. Most sex-linked traits are **X-linked**, that is, they are on the X chromosome, whereas, only a few **Y-linked** traits exist, largely because the Y chromosome is very small. An example of an X-linked trait is **hemophilia A** (classic hemophilia) in which the person is unable to produce one of the

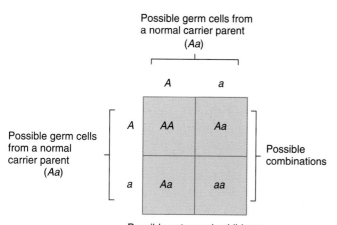

Possible germ cells from
a normal carrier parent
(*Aa*)

Possible germ cells
from a normal
carrier parent
(*Aa*)

Possible combinations

Possible outcome in children:
$\frac{1}{4}$ *AA* (normal) : $\frac{1}{2}$ *Aa* (normal carrier) : $\frac{1}{4}$ *aa* (albino)

Figure 20.20 Inheritance of a Recessive Trait: Albinism

A represents the normal pigmented condition, and *a* represents the recessive unpigmented condition. The figure shows a Punnett square of a mating between two normal carriers.

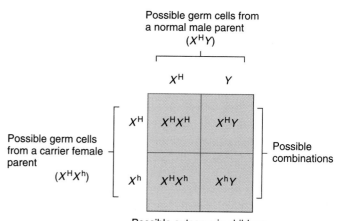

Possible germ cells from
a normal male parent
($X^H Y$)

Possible germ cells
from a carrier female
parent
($X^H X^h$)

Possible combinations

Possible outcome in children:
$\frac{1}{4}$ $X^H X^H$ (normal female) : $\frac{1}{4}$ $X^H X^h$ (carrier female) :

$\frac{1}{4}$ $X^H Y$ (normal male) : $\frac{1}{4}$ $X^h Y$ (male with hemophilia)

Figure 20.21 Inheritance of an X-Linked Trait: Hemophilia

X^H represents the normal X chromosome condition with all clotting factors, and X^h represents the X chromosome lacking a gene for one clotting factor. The figure shows a Punnett square of a mating between a normal male and a normal carrier female.

clotting factors (see chapter 11). Consequently, clotting is impaired and persistent bleeding can occur either spontaneously or as a result of an injury. Hemophilia A is a recessive trait located on the X chromosome. The possible genotypes and phenotypes (in parentheses) are therefore $X^H X^H$ (normal homozygous female), $X^H X^b$ (normal heterozygous female), $X^b X^b$ (hemophiliac homozygous female), $X^H Y$ (normal male), and $X^b Y$ (hemophiliac male). Note that a female must have both recessive genes to exhibit hemophilia, whereas a male, because he has only one X chromosome, has hemophilia if he has only one of the recessive genes. An example of the inheritance of hemophilia is illustrated in figure 20.21. If a woman who is a carrier for hemophilia mates with a man who does not have hemophilia, none of their daughters but half of their sons will have hemophilia.

6 PREDICT

Predict the probability of a girl with Turner's syndrome (refer to the "Did You Know?" box on sex chromosome abnormalities on p. 572) having hemophilia if her mother is a carrier for hemophilia.

✔ *Answer on page 579*

Other Types of Gene Expression

In some cases the dominant gene does not completely mask the effects of the recessive gene. This is called **incomplete dominance**. An example of incomplete dominance is **sickle-cell anemia**, in which the hemoglobin produced by the gene is abnormal. The result is sickle-shaped red blood cells, which are likely to stick in capillaries and tend to rupture more easily than normal red blood cells. The normal hemoglobin allele (*S*) is dominant over the sickle-cell allele (*s*). A normal person (*SS*) has normal hemoglobin, and person with sickle-cell anemia (*ss*) has abnormal hemoglobin. A person who is heterozygous (*Ss*) has half normal hemoglobin and half abnormal

hemoglobin, and usually has only a few sickle-shaped red blood cells. This condition is called **sickle-cell trait**.

In another type of gene expression, called **codominance** (kō-dom′i-năns), two alleles can combine to produce an effect without either of them being dominant or recessive. For example, a person with type AB blood has A antigens and B antigens on the surface of his red blood cells (see chapter 11). The antigens result from a gene that causes the production of the A antigen and a different gene that causes the production of the B antigen, and neither gene is dominant or recessive in relation to each other.

Many traits, called **polygenic** (pol-ē-jen′ik) **traits**, are determined by the expression of multiple genes on different chromosomes. Examples are a person's height, intelligence, eye color, and skin color. Polygenic traits typically are characterized by having a great amount of variability. For example, there are many different shades of eye color and skin color (figure 20.22).

Genetic Disorders

Genetic disorders are caused by abnormalities in a person's genetic makeup, that is, in his or her DNA. They may involve a single gene or an entire chromosome. Some genetic disorders result from a **mutation** (mū-tā′shŭn), a change in a gene that usually involves a change in the nucleotides composing the DNA (see chapter 2). Mutations occur by chance or can be caused by chemicals, radiation, or viruses. Once a mutation has occurred, the abnormal trait can be passed from one generation to the next.

Cancer is a tumor resulting from uncontrolled cell divisions. **Oncogenes** (ong′kō-jēnz) are genes associated with cancer. Many oncogenes are actually control genes involved in regulating cell division and differentiation in the embryo and fetus.

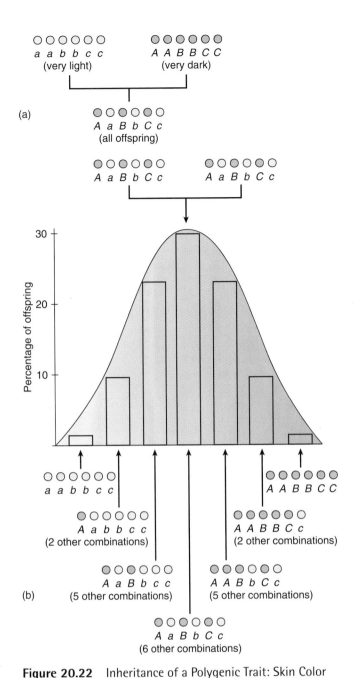

Figure 20.22   Inheritance of a Polygenic Trait: Skin Color

In this example, three genes for skin color are shown. The dominant alleles (*A*, *B*, *C*), each of which contributes one "unit of dark color" to the offspring (indicated by a dark dot), are incompletely dominant over the recessive alleles (*a*, *b*, *c*), each of which contributes one "unit of light color" to the offspring (indicated by a light dot). (*a*) A mating between a very light-skinned person (*aabbcc*) and a very dark-skinned person (*AABBCC*) is shown. All the offspring are of intermediate color. (*b*) A mating between two people of intermediate skin color (*AaBbCc*). The possible offspring skin color falls within a normal distribution in which a very low percentage (less than 2%) are either very light or very dark, and most of the offspring are of intermediate color.

A change in an oncogene or in the regulation of an oncogene can result in uncontrolled cell division and the development of cancerous tumors. The normal control of oncogenes involves other genes, called **tumor suppressor genes**. Cancer can occur when a mutation activates an oncogene or inactivates a tumor

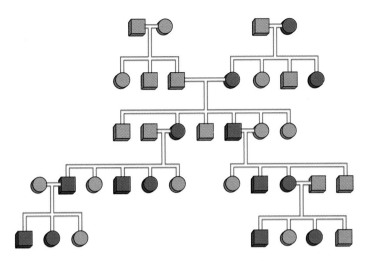

Figure 20.23   Pedigree of a Simple Dominant Trait

Males are indicated by squares, females by circles. Affected people are indicated in purple. The horizontal line between symbols represents a mating. The symbols connected to the mating line by vertical and horizontal lines represent the children resulting from the mating in order of birth from left to right. Matings not related to the pedigree are not shown.

suppressor gene. An accumulation of several mutations is necessary for cancer to occur. It is believed that certain chemicals called **carcinogens** (kar-sin′ō-jenz) can induce such mutations and thereby initiate the development of cancer. For example, chemicals in cigarette smoke are known to cause lung cancer.

A change in cells that results in cancer is not usually inherited. Nonetheless, there may be a genetic basis that allows cancer development, especially under the right environmental conditions. In this sense, the inheritance of cancer and other abnormalities has been described as **genetic susceptibility**, or **genetic predisposition**. For example, if a woman's close relatives, such as her mother or sister, have breast cancer, she has a greater than average risk of developing it herself. Similar genetic susceptibilities have been found for diabetes mellitus, schizophrenia, and other disorders.

Genetic Counseling

Genetic counseling includes predicting the possible results of matings involving carriers of harmful genes and talking to parents or prospective parents about the possible outcomes and treatments of a genetic disorder. With this knowledge, prospective parents can make informed decisions about having children.

A first step in genetic counseling is to attempt to determine the genotype of the individuals involved. A family tree, or **pedigree**, provides historical information about family members (figure 20.23). Sometimes by knowing the phenotypes of relatives it is possible to determine a person's genotype. As part of the process of collecting information, a karyotype can be prepared. For some genetic disorders, the amount of a given substance, such as an enzyme, produced by a carrier can be tested. For example, carriers for cystic fibrosis produce more salt in their sweat than is normal.

Clinical Focus The Human Genome Project

The **human genome** (jē'nōm) is all of the genes found in one homologous set of human chromosomes. It is estimated that humans have 50,000 to 100,000 genes. A **genomic** (jĕ-nom'ik or je-nōm'ik) **map** is a description of the DNA nucleotide sequences of the genes and their locations on the chromosomes (figure A). To date, approximately 10,000 genes have been mapped at least to their location on chromosomes. The goal of the **Human Genome Project** is to completely map all the human genes by the year 2005.

Chromosome Pairs

1. a. Gaucher disease
   b. Prostate cancer
   c. Glaucoma
   d. Alzheimer disease*
2. a. Familial colon cancer*
   b. Waardenburg syndrome
3. a. Lung cancer
   b. Retinitis pigmentosa*
4. a. Huntington chorea
   b. Parkinson disease
5. a. Cockayne syndrome
   b. Familial polyposis of the colon
   c. Asthma
6. a. Spinocerebellar ataxia
   b. Diabetes*
   c. Epilepsy*

7. a. Diabetes*
   b. Cystic fibrosis
   c. Obesity*
8. a. Werner syndrome
   b. Burkitt lymphoma
9. a. Malignant melanoma
   b. Friedreich ataxia
   c. Tuberous sclerosis
10. a. Multiple endocrine neoplasia, type 2
    b. Gyrate atrophy
11. a. Sickle-cell anemia
    b. Multiple endocrine neoplasia
12. a. Zellweger syndrome
    b. Phenylketonuria (PKU)

13. a. Breast cancer*
    b. Retinoblastoma
    c. Wilson disease
14. a. Alzheimer disease*
15. a. Marfan syndrome
    b. Tay-Sachs disease
16. a. Polycystic kidney disease
    b. Crohn disease*
17. a. Peroneal muscular atrophy
    b. Breast cancer*
18. a. Amyloidosis
    b. Pancreatic cancer*
19 a. Familial hypercholesterolemia
    b. Myotonic dystrophy

20. a. Severe combined immunodeficiency
21. a. Amyotrophic lateral sclerosis*
22. a. DiGeorge syndrome
    b. Neurofibromatosis, type 2
X a. Duchenne dystrophy
   b. Menkes syndrome
   c. X-linked severe combined immunodeficiency
   d. Factor VIII deficiency (hemophilia A)

*Gene responsible for only some cases.

Figure A Human Genome Map

Representative genetic defects mapped to date are listed and their positions on the chromosomes are indicated by circles.

Summary

Prenatal development is an important part of an individual's life. About 7 of every 100 people are born with some type of birth defect.

Prenatal Development

- Prenatal development is divided into the germinal, embryonic, and fetal periods.
- Developmental age is 14 days less than clinical age.

Fertilization

- Fertilization, the union of the oocyte and sperm cell, results in a zygote.

Early Cell Division

- The zygote undergoes divisions until it becomes an embryonic mass of cells.

Blastocyst

- The embryonic mass develops a cavity and is known as the blastocyst.
- The blastocyst consists of a trophoblast and an inner cell mass, where the embryo forms.

Implantation of the Blastocyst and Development of the Placenta

- The blastocyst implants into the uterus about 7 days after fertilization.
- The embryonic portion of the placenta is derived from the trophoblast of the blastocyst.

Formation of the Germ Layers

- The embryo forms around the primitive streak, which forms about 14 days after fertilization.
- All tissues of the body are derived from three primary germ layers: ectoderm, mesoderm, and endoderm.

Neural Tube and Neural Crest Formation

- The nervous system develops from a neural tube that forms in the ectodermal surface of the embryo and from neural crest cells derived from the developing neural tube.

Formation of the General Body Structure

- The limbs develop as outgrowths called limb buds.
- The face develops by the fusion of five tissue masses.

Development of the Organ Systems

- The GI tract develops as the developing embryo closes off part of the yolk sac.
- The heart develops as two tubes fuse into a single tube that develops septa to form four chambers.
- The kidneys and reproductive system are closely related in their development.

Growth of the Fetus

- The fetus increases 15-fold in length and 1400-fold in weight.

Parturition

- Uterine contractions force the baby out of the uterus during labor.
- Increased estrogens, decreasing progesterone levels, and secretions from the fetal adrenal cortex initiate parturition.
- Stretching of the uterus stimulates oxytocin secretion, which stimulates uterine contractions.

The Newborn

Respiratory and Circulatory Changes

- Inflation of the lungs at birth results in closure of the foramen ovale and the ductus arteriosus.
- When the umbilical cord is cut, blood no longer flows through the umbilical vessels.

Digestive Changes

- The newborn digestive system only gradually develops the ability to digest a variety of foods.

Lactation

- Estrogens and progesterone help stimulate the growth of the breasts during pregnancy.
- Suckling stimulates prolactin and oxytocin synthesis. Prolactin stimulates milk production, and oxytocin stimulates milk "letdown."

The First Year Following Birth

- Many important changes occur during the first year after birth. Many of these changes are linked to continued development of the brain.

Life Stages

- The eight stages of life are: germinal period (fertilization to 14 days), embryo (14–56 days after fertilization), fetus (56 days after fertilization to birth), neonate (birth–1 month), infant (1 month–1 or 2 years), child (1 or 2 years–puberty), adolescent (puberty–20 years), adult (20 years–death).

Aging

- Aging occurs as irreplaceable cells wear out and the tissue becomes more brittle and less able to repair damage.
- Atherosclerosis is the deposit of lipids in the arteries. Arteriosclerosis is hardening of the arteries.

Death

- Death is defined as the absence of brain response to stimulation, the absence of natural respiration and heart function, and a flat electroencephalogram for 30 minutes.

Genetics

Chromosomes

- Humans have 46 chromosomes in 23 pairs.
- Males have the sex chromosomes XY and females have XX.
- During gamete formation, the chromosomes of each pair of chromosomes separate; therefore half of a person's genetic makeup comes from the father and half from the mother.

Genes

- A gene is a portion of a DNA molecule. Genes determine the proteins in a cell.
- Genes are paired (located on the paired chromosomes).
- Dominant genes mask the effects of recessive genes.
- Sex-linked traits result from genes on the sex chromosomes.
- In incomplete dominance, the heterozygote expresses a trait that is intermediate between the two homozygous traits.
- In codominance, neither gene is dominant or recessive, but both are fully expressed.
- Polygenic traits result from the expression of multiple genes.

Genetic Disorders

- A mutation is a change in the DNA.
- Some genetic disorders result from an abnormal distribution of chromosomes during gamete formation.
- Oncogenes are genes associated with cancer.
- Genetic predisposition makes it more likely a person will develop a disorder.

Genetic Counseling

- A pedigree (family history) can be used to determine the risk of having children with a genetic disorder.
- Specific chemical tests or examination of a person's karyotype can be used to determine a person's genotype.

Content Review

1. Define clinical age and developmental age, and state the difference between the two in number of days.
2. What are the events during the first week after fertilization? Define zygote and blastocyst.
3. How does the placenta develop?
4. Describe the formation of the germ layers and the role of the primitive streak.
5. How are the neural tube and neural crest cells formed? What do they become?
6. Describe the formation of the limbs and face.
7. Describe the formation of the digestive tract.
8. How does the single heart tube become four-chambered?
9. What major events distinguish embryonic and fetal development?
10. Describe the hormonal changes that take place before and during parturition.
11. What changes take place in the newborn's circulatory system and digestive system shortly after birth?
12. What hormones are involved in preparing the breasts for lactation? What hormones are involved in milk production and milk "letdown"?
13. Describe the changes in motor and language skills that take place during the first year of life.
14. List the different life stages.
15. How does the loss of cells that are not replaced affect the aging process? Give examples.
16. How does the loss of tissue elasticity affect the aging process? Give examples.
17. How does aging affect the immune system?
18. Define death.
19. Give the number and type of chromosomes in the karyotype of a human somatic cell. How do the chromosomes of a male and female differ from each other?
20. How do the chromosomes in somatic cells and gametes differ from each other?
21. What is a gene, and how are genes responsible for the structure and function of cells?
22. Define homozygous dominant, heterozygous, and homozygous recessive.
23. What is a sex-linked trait? Give an example.
24. How does sickle-cell anemia, type AB blood, and a person's height result from the expression of genes?
25. What is a mutation?
26. What is the cause of the genetic disorder called Down syndrome?
27. What are oncogenes?
28. What is genetic susceptibility?
29. How are pedigrees, karyotypes, and chemical tests used in genetic counseling?

Develop Your Reasoning Skills

1. A woman is told by her physician that her pregnancy has progressed 44 days since her last menstrual period (LMP). How many days has the embryo been developing, and what developmental events are occurring?
2. A high fever can prevent neural tube closure. If a woman has a high fever about 35 to 45 days post-LMP, what kinds of birth defects may be seen in the developing embryo?
3. A drug that would stop the production of milk in the breast after a few days probably has which effect?
   a. Inhibits prolactin secretion
   b. Inhibits oxytocin secretion
   c. Increases estrogen secretion
   d. Increases progesterone secretion
   e. Increases prolactin secretion
4. Dimpled cheeks are inherited as a dominant trait. Is it possible for two parents, each of whom have dimpled cheeks, to have a child without dimpled cheeks? Explain.
5. The ability to roll the tongue to form a "tube" results from a dominant gene. Suppose that a woman and her son can both roll their tongues, but her husband cannot. Is it possible to determine if the husband is the father of her son?
6. A woman who does not have hemophilia marries a man who has the disorder. Determine the genotype of both parents if half of their children have hemophilia.

Answers to Predict Questions

1. p. 551 Because some sperm cells remain viable in the female reproductive tract for up to 7 days, and the secondary oocyte is capable of being fertilized for up to 1 day after ovulation, fertilization could occur if sexual intercourse occurred between 7 days before ovulation and 1 day following ovulation. That will be between 7 days and 15 days post-LMP. Data indicate, however, that the most fertile period during the menstrual cycle is the 5 days just before ovulation.

2. p. 555 Two primitive streaks forming in one embryonic disk can result in identical twins, because one embryo is formed in association with each primitive streak. If the two streaks are touching, the twins will be conjoined (Siamese), or attached to each other. This attachment can be fairly simple, and the twins can be separated fairly easily by surgery; or the attachment can be extensive, involving internal organs and may not be corrected easily.

3. p. 563 266 days (280 days minus 14 days).

4. p. 569 Suckling causes a reflex release of oxytocin from the mother's posterior pituitary. Oxytocin causes expulsion of milk from the breast, but it also causes contraction of the uterus. Contraction of the uterus is responsible for the sensation of cramps.

5. p. 573 Genotype DD (homozygous dominant) has the polydactyly phenotype, genotype Dd (heterozygous) has the polydactyly phenotype, and genotype dd (homozygous recessive) has the normal phenotype.

6. p. 574 The probability of a girl with Turner's syndrome (XO; that is, with one X chromosome and no other sex chromosome) having hemophilia if her mother is a carrier for hemophilia is the same as for a male because she has only one X chromosome. If her mother is a carrier for hemophilia ($X^H X^b$), the daughter will be either $X^H O$ (normal), or $X^b O$ (hemophiliac). The probability is 1/2, or 50%.

Appendix A

Table of Measurements

Appendix A	Table of Measurements		
Unit	**Metric Equivalent**	**Symbol**	**U.S. Equivalent**
Measures of Length			
1 kilometer	= 1000 meters	km	0.62137 mile
1 meter	= 10 decimeters or 100 centimeters	m	39.37 inches
1 decimeter	= 10 centimeters	dm	3.937 inches
1 centimeter	= 10 millimeters	cm	0.3937 inch
1 millimeter	= 1000 micrometers	mm	
1 micrometer*	= 1/1000 millimeter or 1000 nanometers	μm	
1 nanometer*	= 10 angstroms or 1000 picometers	nm	No U.S. equivalent
1 angstrom	= 1/10,000,000 millimeter	Å	
1 picometer	= 1/1,000,000,000 millimeter	pm	
Measures of Volume			
1 cubic meter	= 1000 cubic decimeters	m^3	1.308 cubic yards
1 cubic decimeter	= 1000 cubic centimeters	dm^3	0.03531 cubic foot
1 cubic centimeter	= 1000 cubic millimeters or 1 milliliter	cm^3 (cc)	0.06102 cubic inch
Measures of Capacity			
1 kiloliter	= 1000 liters	kL	264.18 gallons
1 liter	= 10 deciliters	L	1.0567 quarts
1 deciliter	= 100 milliliters	dL	0.4227 cup
1 milliliter	= volume of 1 gram of water at standard temperature and pressure	mL	0.3381 ounces
Measures of Mass			
1 kilogram	= 1000 grams	kg	2.2046 pounds
1 gram	= 100 centigrams or 1000 milligrams	g	0.0353 ounces
1 centigram	= 10 milligrams	cg	0.1543 grain
1 milligram	= 1/1000 gram	mg	

*Note that a micrometer was formerly called a micron (μm), and a nanometer was formerly called a millimicron (mμ).

Comparative Temperature Scales

Appendix B

Some Reference Laboratory Values

Table B.1 Blood, Plasma, or Serum Values

Test	Normal Values	Clinical Significance
Acetoacetate plus acetone	0.32–2 mg/100 mL	Values increase in diabetic acidosis, fasting, high-fat diet, and toxemia of pregnancy
Ammonia	80–110 μmg/100 mL	Values decrease with proteinuria and as a result of severe burns and increase in multiple myeloma
Amylase	4–25 U/mL*	Values increase in acute pancreatitis, intestinal obstruction, and mumps; values decrease in cirrhosis of the liver, toxemia of pregnancy, and chronic pancreatitis
Barbiturate	0	Coma level: phenobarbital, approximately 10 mg/100 mL; most other drugs, 1–3 mg/100 mL
Bilirubin	0.4 mg/100 mL	Values increase in conditions causing red blood cell destruction or biliary obstruction or liver inflammation
Blood volume	8.5 %–9% of body weight in kilograms	
Calcium	8.5–10.5 mg/mL	Values increase in hyperparathyroidism, vitamin D hypervitaminosis; values decrease in hypoparathyroidism, malnutrition, and severe diarrhea
Carbon dioxide content	24–30 mEq/L 20–26 mEq/L in infants (as $HCO_3{}^-$)	Values increase in respiratory diseases, vomiting, and intestinal obstruction; they decrease in acidosis, nephritis, and diarrhea
Carbon monoxide	0	Symptoms with over 20% saturation
Chloride	100–106 mEq/L	Values increase in Cushing's syndrome, nephritis, and hyperventilation; they decrease in diabetic acidosis, Addison's disease, and diarrhea and after severe burns
Creatine phosphokinase (CPK)	Female 5–35 mU/mL Male 5–55 mU/mL	Values increase in myocardial infarction and skeletal muscle diseases such as muscular dystrophy
Creatinine	0.6–1.5 mg/100 mL	Values increase in certain kidney diseases
Ethanol	0	0.3%–0.4%, marked intoxication 0.4%–0.5%, alcoholic stupor 0.5% or over, alcoholic coma
Glucose	Fasting 70–110 mg/100 mL	Values increase in diabetes mellitus, liver diseases, nephritis, hyperthyroidism, and pregnancy; they decrease in hyperinsulinsim, hypothyroidism, and Addison's disease
Iron	50–150 μg/100 mL	Values increase in various anemias and liver disease; they decrease in iron deficiency anemia
Lactic acid	0.6–1.8 mEq/L	Values increase with muscular activity and in congestive heart failure, severe hemorrhage, shock, and anaerobic exercise
Lactic dehydrogenase	60–120 U/mL	Values increase in pernicious anemia, myocardial infarction, liver diseases, acute leukemia, and widespread carcinoma

continued next page

*A unit (U) is the quantity of a substance that has a physiological effect.

Table B.1 Blood, Plasma, or Serum Values (continued)

Test	Normal Values	Clinical Significance
Lipids	Cholesterol 120–220 mg/100 mL; Cholesterol esters 60%–75% of cholesterol; Phospholipids 9–16 mg/100 mL as lipid phosphorus; Total fatty acids 190–420 mg/100 mL; Total lipids; 450–1000 mg/100 mL; Triglycerides 40–150 mg/100 mL	Increased values for cholesterol and triglycerides are connected with increased risk of cardiovascular disease, such as heart attack and stroke
Lithium	Toxic levels 2 mEq/L	
Osmolality	285–295 mOsm/kg water	
Oxygen saturation (arterial) (see PO_2)	96%–100%	
PCO_2	35–43 mm Hg	Values decrease in acidosis, nephritis, and diarrhea; they increase in respiratory diseases, intestinal obstruction, and vomiting
pH	7.35–7.45	Values decrease as a result of hypoventilation, severe diarrhea, Addison's disease, and diabetic acidosis; values increase due to hyperventilation, Cushing's syndrome, and vomiting
PO_2	75–100 mm Hg (breathing room air)	Values increase in polycythemia and decrease in anemia and obstructive pulmonary diseases
Phosphatase (acid)	Male: total 0.13–0.63 U/mL Female: total 0.01–0.56 U/mL	Values increase in cancer of the prostate gland, hyperparathyroidism, some liver diseases, myocardial infarction, and pulmonary embolism
Phosphatase (alkaline)	13–39 IU/L* (infants and adolescents up to 104 IU/L)	Values increase in hyperparathyroidism, some liver diseases, and pregnancy
Phosphorus (inorganic)	3–4.5 mg/100 ml (infants in first year up to 6 mg/100 mL)	Values increase in hypoparathyroidism, acromegaly, vitamin D hypervitaminosis, and kidney diseases; they decrease in hyperparathyroidism
Potassium	3.5–5 mEq/100 mL	
Protein	Total 6–8.4 g/100 mL Albumin 3.5–5 g/100 mL Globulin 2.3–3.5 g/100 mL	Total protein values increase in severe dehydration and shock; they decrease in severe malnutrition and hemorrhage
Salicylate		
Therapeutic	0	20–25 mg/100 mL
Toxic		Over 30 mg/100 mL Over 20 mg/100 mL after age 60
Sodium	135–145 mEq/L	Values increase in nephritis and severe dehydration; they decrease in Addison's disease, myxedema, kidney disease, and diarrhea
Sulfonamide		
Therapeutic	0	5–15 mg/100 mL
Urea nitrogen	8–25 mg/100 mL	Values increase in response to increased dietary protein intake; values decrease in impaired renal function
Uric acid	3–7 mg/100 mL	Values increase in gout and toxemia of pregnancy and as a result of tissue damage

*A unit (U) is the quantity of a substance that has a physiological effect.

Table B.2 Blood Count Values

Test	Normal Values	Clinical Significance
Clotting (coagulation) time	5–10 minutes	Values increase in afibrinogenemia and hyperheparinemia, severe liver damage
Fetal hemoglobin	Newborns: 60%–90% Before age 2: 0%–4% Adults: 0%–2%	Values increase in thalassemia, sickle-cell anemia, and leakage of fetal blood into maternal bloodstream during pregnancy
Hemoglobin	Male: 14–16.5 g/100 mL Female: 12–15 g/100 mL Newborn: 14–20 g/100 mL	Values decrease in anemia, hyperthyroidism, cirrhosis of the liver, and severe hemorrhage; values increase in polycythemia, congestive heart failure, obstructive pulmonary disease high altitudes
Hematocrit	Male: 40%–54% Female: 38%–47%	Values increase in polycythemia, severe dehydration, and shock; values decrease in anemia, leukemia, cirrhosis, and hyperthyroidism
Ketone bodies	0.3–2 mg/100 mL Toxic level: 20 mg/100 mL	Values increase in ketoacidosis, fever, anorexia, fasting, starvation, high-fat diet
Platelet count	250,000–400,000/mm^3	Values decrease in anemias and allergic conditions and during cancer chemotherapy; values increase in cancer, trauma, heart disease and cirrhosis
Prothrombin time	11–15 s	Values increase in prothrombin and vitamin deficiency, liver disease, and hypervitaminosis A
Red blood cell count	Males: 4.6–6.2 million/mm^3 Females: 4.2–5.4 million/mm^3	Values decrease in systemic lupus erythematosus, anemias, and Addison's disease; values increase in polycythemia and dehydration and following hemorrhage
Reticulocyte count	1%–3%	Values decrease in iron-deficiency and pernicious anemia and radiation therapy; values increase in hemolytic anemia, leukemia, and metastatic carcinoma
White blood cell count, differential	Neutrophils 60%–70% Eosinophils 2%–4% Basophils 0.5%–1% Lymphocytes 20%–25% Monocytes 3%–8%	Neutrophils increase in acute infections; eosinophils and basophils increase in allergic reactions; monocytes increase in chronic infections; lymphocytes increase during antigen–antibody reactions
White blood cell count, total	5000–9000/mm^3	Values decrease in diabetes mellitus, anemias, and following cancer chemotherapy; values increase in acute infections, trauma, some malignant diseases, and some cardiovascular diseases

Table B.3 Urine Values

Test	Normal Values	Clinical Significance
Acetone and acetoacetate	0	Values increase in diabetic acidosis and during fasting
Albumin	0 to trace	Values increase in glomerular nephritis and hypertension
Ammonia	20–70 mEq/L	Values increase in diabetes mellitus and liver disease
Bacterial count	Under 10,000/mL	Values increase in urinary tract infection
Bile and bilirubin	0	Values increase in biliary tract obstruction
Calcium	Under 250 mg/24 h	Values increase in hyperparathyroidism and decrease in hypoparathyroidism
Chloride	110–254 mEq/24 h	Values decrease in pyloric obstruction, diarrhea; values increase in Addison's disease and dehydration
Potassium	25–100 mEq/L	Values decrease in diarrhea, malabsorption syndrome, and adrenal cortical insufficiency; values increase in chronic renal failure, dehydration, and Cushing's syndrome
Sodium	75–200 mg/24 h	Values decrease in diarrhea, acute renal failure, and Cushing's syndrome; values increase in dehydration, starvation, and diabetic acidosis
Creatinine clearance	100–140 mL/minute	Values increase in renal diseases
Creatinine	1–2 g/24 h	Values increase in infections and decrease in muscular atrophy, anemia, and certain kidney diseases
Glucose	0	Values increase in diabetes mellitus and certain pituitary gland disorders
Urea clearance	Over 40 mL of blood cleared of urea per minute	Values increase in certain kidney diseases
Urea	25–35 g/24 h	Values decrease in complete biliary obstruction and severe diarrhea; values increase in liver diseases and hemolytic anemia
Uric acid	0.6–1 g/24 h	Values increase in gout and decrease in certain kidney diseases
Casts		
Epithelial	Occasional	Increase in nephrosis and heavy metal poisoning
Granular	Occasional	Increase in nephritis and pyelonephritis
Hyaline	Occasional	Increase in glomerular membrane damage and fever
Red blood cell	Occasional	Values increase in pyelonephritis; blood cells appear in urine in response to kidney stones and cystitis
White blood cell	Occasional	Values increase in kidney infections
Color	Amber, straw, transparent yellow	Varies with hydration, diet, and disease states
Odor	Aromatic	Becomes acetonelike in diabetic ketosis
Osmolality	500–800 mOsm/kg water	Values decrease in aldosteronism and diabetes insipidus; values increase in high protein diets, heart failure, and dehydration
pH	4.6–8	Values decrease in acidosis, emphysema, starvation, and dehydration; values increase in urinary tract infections and severe alkalosis

Table B.4 Hormone Levels

Test	Normal Values
Steroid hormones	
Aldosterone	Excretion: 5–19 µg/24 h*
Fasting at rest, 210 mEq sodium diet	Supine: 48 ± 29 pg/mL†
	Upright: 65 ± 23 pg/mL
Fasting at rest, 10 mEq sodium diet	Supine: 175 ± 75 pg/mL
	Upright: 532 ± 228 pg/mL
Cortisol	
Fasting	8 AM: 5–25 µg/100 mL
At rest	8 PM: Below 10 µg/100 mL
Testosterone	Adult male: 300–1100 ng/100 mL†
	Adolescent male: over 100 ng/100 mL
	Female: 25–90 ng/100 mL
Peptide hormones	
Adrenocorticotropin (ACTH)	15–170 pg/mL
Calcitonin	Undetectable in normals
Growth hormone (GH)	
Fasting, at rest	Below 5 ng/mL
After exercise	Children: over 10 ng/mL
	Male: below 5 ng/mL
	Female: up to 30 ng/mL
Insulin	
Fasting	6–26 µU/mL
During hypoglycemia	Below 20 µU/mL
After glucose	Up to 150 µU/mL
Luteinizing hormone (LH)	Male: 6–18 mU/mL
	Preovulatory or postovulatory female: 5–22 mU/mL
	Midcycle peak 30–250 mU/mL
Parathyroid hormone	Less than 10 µEq/L§
Prolactin	2–15 ng/mL
Renin activity	
Normal diet	
Supine	1.1 ± 0.8 ng/mL/h
Upright	1.9 ± 1.7 ng/mL/h
Low-sodium diet	
Supine	2.7 ± 1.8 ng/mL/h
Upright	6.6 ± 2.5 ng/mL/h
Thyroid-stimulating hormone (TSH)	0.5–3.5 µU/mL
Thyroxine-binding globulin	15.25 µg T_4/100 mL
Total thyroxine	4–12 µg/100 mL

*1 microgram (1 µg) is equal to 10^{-6} g.
†1 picogram (1 pg) is equal to 10^{-12} g.
‡1 nanogram (1 ng) is equal to 10^{-9} g.
§µEq = microequivalent; 1/1000 m Eq, which is defined in Appendix D.

Appendix C

Scientific Notation

Very large numbers with many zeros such as 1,000,000,000,000,000 or very small numbers such as 0.0000000000000001 are very cumbersome to work with. Consequently, the numbers are expressed in a kind of mathematical shorthand known as scientific notation. Scientific notation has the following form:

$$M \times 10^n$$

where n specifies how many times the number M is raised to the power of 10. The exponent n has two meanings, depending on its sign. If n is positive, M is multiplied by 10 n times. For example, if $n = 2$ and $M = 1.2$, then

$$1.2 \times 10^2 = 1.2 \times 10 \times 10 = 120$$

In other words, if n is positive, the decimal point of M is moved to the right n times. In this case the decimal point of 1.2 is moved two places to the right.

1.20.

If n is negative, M is divided by 10 n times.

$$1.2 \times 10^{-2} = \frac{1.2}{(10 \times 10)} = \frac{1.2}{100} = 0.012$$

In other words, if n is negative, the decimal point of M is moved to the left n times. In this case the decimal point of 1.2 is moved two places to the left.

0.01.2

If M is the number 1.0, it is often not expressed in scientific notation. For example, 1.0×10^2 is the same thing as 10^2, and 1.0×10^{-2} is the same thing as 10^{-2}.

Two common examples of the use of scientific notation in chemistry are Avogadro's number and pH. Avogadro's number, 6.023×10^{23}, is the number of atoms in 1 mole. Just as a grocer sells eggs in lots of 12 (a dozen), a chemist groups atoms or molecules in lots of 6.023×10^{23} (Avogadro's number). Thus

$$6.023 \times 10^{23} =$$
$$602,300,000,000,000,000,000,000$$

which is a very large number.

The pH scale is a measure of the concentration of hydrogen ions in a solution. A neutral solution has 10^{-7} moles of hydrogen ions per liter. In other words.

$$10^{-7} = 0.0000001$$

which is a very small amount (1 ten-millionth of a gram) of hydrogen ions.

Appendix D

Solution Concentrations

Physiologists often express solution concentration in terms of percent, molarity, molality, and equivalents.

Percent

The weight-volume method of expressing percent concentrations states the weight of a solute in a given volume of solvent. For example, to prepare a 10% solution of sodium chloride, 10 g of sodium chloride is dissolved in a small amount of water (solvent) to form a salt solution. Then additional water is added to the salt solution to form 100 mL of salt solution. Note that the sodium chloride was dissolved in water and then diluted to the required volume. The sodium chloride was not dissolved directly in 100 mL of water.

Molarity

Molarity determines the number of moles of solute dissolved in a given volume of solvent. A **mole** (mol) of a substance contains 6.023×10^{23} number (Avogadro's number) of particles, such as atoms, ions, compounds, or molecules. A 1 molar (1 M) solution is made by dissolving 1 mol of a substance in enough water to make 1 L of solution. For example, 1 mol of sodium chloride solution is made by dissolving 58.44 g of sodium chloride in enough water to make 1 L of solution. One mole of glucose solution is made by dissolving 180.2 g of glucose in enough water to make 1 L of solution. Both solutions have the same number (Avogadro's number) of sodium chloride or glucose compounds in solution.

Molality

Although 1 M solutions have the same number of solute particles, they do not have the same number of solvent (water) molecules. Because 58.5 g of sodium chloride occupies less volume then 180 g of glucose, the sodium chloride solution has more water molecules. **Molality** is a method of calculating concentrations that takes into account the number of solute and solvent molecules. A 1-molal solution (1 m) is 1 mol of a substance dissolved in 1 kg of water. Thus a 1 m solution of sodium chloride and a 1 m solution of glucose contain the same number of sodium chloride and glucose compounds dissolved in the same amount of water.

When sodium chloride (NaCl) is dissolved in water it dissociates, or separates, to form two ions: a Na^+ ion and a Cl^- ion. Glucose, however, does not dissociate when dissolved in water. Although 1 m solutions of sodium chloride and of glucose have the same number of sodium chloride and glucose compounds, because of dissociation the sodium chloride solution contains twice as many particles as the glucose solution (one Na^+ ion and one Cl^- ion for each glucose molecule). To report the concentration of these substances in a way that reflects the number of particles in a given mass of solvent the concept of **osmolality** is used. The osmolality of a solution is the molality of the solution times the number of particles into which the solute dissociates in 1 kg of solvent. Thus 1 mol of sodium chloride in 1 kg of water is a 2-osmolal (2-osm) solution because sodium chloride dissociates to form two ions.

The osmolality of a solution is a reflection of the number, not the type, of particles in a solution. Thus a 1-osm solution contains 1 osm of particles per kilogram of solvent, but the particles may be all one type or a complex mixture of different types.

The concentration of particles in body fluids is so low that the measurement milliosmole (mOsm), 1/1000 of an osmole, is used. Most body fluids have an osmotic concentration of approximately 300 mOsm and consist of many different ions and molecules. The osmotic concentration of body fluids is important because it influences the movement of water into or out of cells (see chapter 3).

Equivalents

Equivalents are a measure of the concentrations of ionized substances. One equivalent (Eq) is 1 mol of an ionized substance multiplied by the absolute value of its charge. For example, 1 mol of NaCl dissociates into 1 mol of Na^+ and 1 mol of Cl^-. Thus there is 1 Eq of Na^+ (1 mol $\times$ 1) and 1 Eq of Cl^- (1 mol $\times$ 1). One mole of $CaCl_2$ dissociates into 1 mol of Ca^{2+} and 2 mol of Cl^-. Thus there are 2 Eq of Ca^{2+} (1 mol $\times$ 2) and 2 Eq of Cl^- (2 mol $\times$ 1). In an electrically neutral solution the equivalent concentration of positively charged ions is equal to the equivalent concentration of the negatively charged ions. One milliequivalent (mEq) is 1/1000 of an equivalent.

Appendix E

pH

Pure water weakly dissociates to form small numbers of hydrogen and hydroxide ions:

$$H_2O \rightleftharpoons H^+ + OH^-$$

At 25°C the concentration of both hydrogen ions and hydroxide ions is 10^{-7} mol/L. Any solution that has equal concentrations of hydrogen and hydroxide ions is considered **neutral**. A solution is an **acid** if it has a higher concentration of hydrogen ions than hydroxide ions, and a solution is a **base** if it has a lower concentration of hydrogen ions than hydroxide ions. In any aqueous solution (at 25°C) the hydrogen ion concentration $[H^+]$ times the hydroxide ion concentration $[OH^-]$ is a constant that is equal to 10^{-14}.

$$[H^+] \times [OH^-] = 10^{-14}$$

Consequently, as the hydrogen ion concentration decreases, the hydroxide ion concentration increases, and vice versa. For example:

	$[H^+]$	$[OH^-]$
Acidic solution	10^{-3}	10^{-11}
Neutral solution	10^{-7}	10^{-7}
Basic solution	10^{-12}	10^{-2}

Although the acidity of basicity of a solution could be expressed in terms of either hydrogen or hydroxide ion concentration, it is customary to use hydrogen ion concentration. The pH of a solution is defined as

$$pH = -\log_{10}(H^+)$$

Thus a neutral solution with 10^{-7} mol of hydrogen ions per liter has a pH of 7

$$
\begin{aligned}
pH &= -\log_{10}(H^+) \\
&= -\log_{10}(10^{-7}) \\
&= -(-7) \\
&= 7
\end{aligned}
$$

In simple terms, to convert the hydrogen ion concentration to the pH scale, the exponent of the concentration (e.g., -7) is used, and it is changed from a negative to a positive number. Thus an acidic solution with 10^{-3} mol of hydrogen ions/L has a pH of 3, whereas a basic solution with 10^{-12} hydrogen ions/L has a pH of 12.

Glossary

Page numbers indicate where entries can be found in the text. Many of the words in this glossary and throughout the text are followed by a simplified phonetic spelling showing pronunciation. The pronunciation key reflects standard clinical usage, with minor modifications, as presented in *Stedman's Medical Dictionary* (27th edition), which has long been a leading reference volume in the health sciences.

ā as in day, ate, way
a as in mat, hat, act
ă as in alone, abortion, media
ah as in father
ar as in far
aw as in fall (fawl)
ē as in be, bee, meet
ĕ as in taken, genesis
er as in term, earn, learn
ī as in pie, pine, side
i as in pit, tip, fit
ĭ as in pencil
ō as in no, note, toe
o as in not, box, cot
ŏ as in occult, lemon, son
oo as in food, to, tool
ow as in cow, brow, plow, now
oy as in boy, toy, oil
u as in wood, foot, took
ŭ as in but, sun, bud, cup, up
ū as in pure, unit, union, future

A

abdomen (ab-dō'men, ab'dō-men) Belly, between the thorax and the pelvis. (p. 12)

abdominal cavity (ab-dom'i-năl) Space bounded by the diaphragm, the abdominal wall, and the pelvis. (p. 12)

abdominopelvic cavity (ab-dom'i-nō-pel'vik) The abdominal and pelvic cavities considered together. (p. 12)

abduction (ab-dŭk'shun) Movement away from the midline. (p. 145)

absorption (ab-sōrp'shŭn) The taking in or reception of gases, liquids, light, heat, or solutes, such as the movement of digested molecules across the intestinal wall and into the bloodstream, the movement of substances through the skin, and the movement of fluid into the lymphatics from the interstitial fluid. (p. 443)

accommodation (ă-kom'ŏ-dā'shŭn) The act or state of adjustment or adaptation such as the increase in the thickness and convexity of the lens in order to focus an object on the retina as the object moves closer to the eyes (p. 242); decreasing sensitivity of a nerve cell to a stimulus of constant strength. (p. 246)

acetabulum (as-ĕ-tab'ū-lŭm) [L., shallow vinegar vessel or cup] Cup-shaped depression on the lateral surface of the coxa, where the head of the femur articulates. (p. 133)

acetylcholine (as-e-til-kō'lēn) Neurotransmitter substance released from motor neurons that innervate skeletal muscle fibers, all autonomic preganglionic neurons, all postganglionic parasympathetic neurons, some postganglionic sympathetic neurons, and some central nervous system neurons. (p. 156)

acetylcholinesterase (as'e-til-kō-lin-es'ter-ās) An enzyme that breaks down acetylcholine to acetic acid and choline. (p. 156)

acetyl–CoA (as'e-til) Acetyl-coenzyme A; formed by the combination of the two-carbon acetyl group with coenzyme A; the molecule that combines with a four-carbon molecule to enter the citric acid cycle. (p. 468)

Achilles tendon (ă-kil'ēz) Common tendon of the calf muscles that attaches to the heel (calcaneus); named after a mythical Greek warrior who was vulnerable only in the heel. (p. 182)

acid (as'id) Any substance that is a proton donor; or any substance that releases hydrogen ions. (p. 29)

acidic solution Solution with more hydrogen ions than hydroxide ions; has a pH of less than 7. (p. 29)

acidosis (as-i-dō'sis) Condition characterized by a lower than normal blood pH (pH of 7.35 or lower). (p. 276)

acinus (as'i-nŭs), pl. **acini** (as'i-nī) [L., berry, grape] Grape-shaped secretory portion of a gland. (p. 78)

acromegaly (ak-rō-meg'ă-lē) [Gr. *acro; megas,* large] Disorder marked by progressive enlargement of the bones of the head, face, hands, feet, and thorax as a result of excessive secretion of growth hormone by the anterior pituitary gland. (p. 268)

actin myofilament (ak'tin mī-ō-fil'ă-ment) One of the two major kinds of protein fibers that make up a sarcomere; thin filaments; resemble two minute strands of pearls twisted together. (p. 151)

action potential All-or-none change in membrane potential in an excitable tissue that is propagated as an electrical signal. (p. 83)

activation energy Energy that must be added to atoms or molecules to start a chemical reaction. (p. 34)

active transport Carrier-mediated process that requires ATP and can move substances into or out of cells from a lower to a higher concentration. (p. 54)

adaptive immunity Immune system response in which there is an ability to recognize, remember, and destroy a specific antigen. (p. 372)

adduction (ă-dŭk'shun) [L. *adductus,* to bring toward] Movement toward the midline. (p. 145)

adductor (a-dŭk'ter, -tōr) [L. *adductus,* to bring toward] A muscle causing movement toward the midline. (p. 181)

adenoid (ad'ĕ-noyd) Enlarged pharyngeal tonsil. (p. 370)

adenosine triphosphate (ă-den'ō-sēn trī-fos'fāt) **(ATP)** Adenosine, an organic base, with three phosphate groups attached to it; energy stored in adenosine triphosphate is used in nearly all the energy-requiring reactions in the body. (p. 465)

ADH See *antidiuretic hormone.*

adipose (ad'i-pōs) [L. *adeps,* fat] Fat; relating to fat tissue. (p. 79)

adrenal cortex (ă-drē'năl kōr'teks) The outer part of the adrenal gland, which secretes the following steroid hormones: glucocorticoids, mainly cortisol; mineralocorticoids, mainly aldosterone; and androgens. (p. 274)

adrenal gland (ă-drē′năl) [L. *ad*, to; *ren*, kidney] One of two endocrine glands located on the superior pole of each kidney; secretes the hormones epinephrine, norepinephrine, aldosterone, cortisol, and androgens. (p. 273)

adrenal medulla (ă-drē′năl me-dool′ă) The inner part of the adrenal gland, which secretes mainly epinephrine but also small amounts of norepinephrine. (p. 273)

adrenalin (ă-dren′ă-lin) Synonym for epinephrine. (p. 274)

adrenocorticotropic hormone (ă-drē′nō-kōr′ti-kō-trō′pik) **(ACTH)** Hormone of the anterior pituitary gland that stimulates the adrenal cortex to secrete cortisol. (p. 269)

adventitia (ad-ven-tish′ă) [L. *adventicius*, coming from abroad, foreign] Outermost covering of an organ that is continuous with the surrounding connective tissue. (p. 426)

aerobic respiration (ār-ō′bik) Breakdown of glucose in the presence of oxygen to produce carbon dioxide, water, and approximately 38 ATP molecules; includes glycolysis, the citric acid cycle, and the electron-transport chain. (p. 161)

afferent (af′er-ent) [L. *afferens*, to bring to] Inflowing; conducting toward a center, denoting certain arteries, veins, lymphatics, and nerves. Opposite of efferent. (p. 192)

afferent arteriole (ar-tēr′ē-ōl) A small artery in the renal cortex that supplies blood to the glomerulus. (p. 485)

afferent fiber Nerve fiber going from the peripheral to the central nervous system; sensory or afferent fiber. (p. 192)

afterload The resistance against which the ventricles must pump blood, it is increased in people who have hypertension. (p. 324)

agglutination (ă-gloo′ti-nā′shŭn) [L. *ad*, to; *gluten*, glue] The process by which cells stick together to form clumps. (p. 296)

agranulocyte (ă-gran′ū-lō-sīt) White blood cells with very small cytoplasmic granules that cannot be easily seen with the light microscope; lymphocytes and monocytes. (p. 291)

aldosterone (al-dos′ter-ōn) Steroid hormone produced by the adrenal cortex that facilitates potassium exchange for sodium in the distal tubule and collecting duct, causing sodium ion reabsorption and potassium and hydrogen ion secretion. (p. 276)

alkaline solution (al′kă-līn) See *basic solution*. (p. 29)

alkalosis (al-kă-lō′sis) Condition characterized by a higher than normal blood pH (pH of 7.45 or above). (p. 30)

alveolar duct (al-vē′ō-lăr) Part of the respiratory passages beyond a respiratory bronchiole; from it arise alveolar sacs and alveoli. (p. 400)

alveolar sac Two or more alveoli that share a common opening. (p. 400)

alveolus (al-vē′ō-lŭs), pl. **alveoli** (al-vē′ō-lī) [L., cavity] Cavity; examples include the sockets into which the teeth fit (p. 427) and the ends of the respiratory system. (p. 400)

amino acid (ă-mē′nō) Class of organic acids containing an amine group (NH_2) that makes up the building blocks of proteins. (p. 34)

amniotic cavity (am-nē-ot′ik) Fluid-filled cavity surrounding and protecting the developing embryo. (p. 545)

amylase (am′il-ās) One of a group of starch-splitting enzymes that cleave starch, glycogen, and related polysaccharides. (p. 447)

anabolism (ă-nab′ō-lizm) [Gr. *anabole*, a raising up] All the synthesis reactions that occur within the body; requires energy. (p. 465)

anaerobic respiration (an-ār-ō′bik) Breakdown of glucose in the absence of oxygen to produce lactic acid and two ATP molecules; consists of glycolysis and the reduction of pyruvic acid to lactic acid. (p. 161)

anatomical position (an′ă-tom′i-kăl) Position in which a person is standing erect with the feet facing forward, arms hanging to the sides, and the palms of the hands facing forward. (p. 9)

anatomy (ă-nat′ŏ-mē) [Gr. *ana*, apart; *tome*, a cutting] Scientific discipline that investigates the structure of the body. (p. 2)

androgen (an′drō-jen) [Gr. *aner*, male] Hormone that stimulates the development of male sexual characteristics, includes testosterone. (p. 276)

anemia (ă-nē′mē-ă) [Gr. *an*, without; *haima*, blood] Any condition that results in less than normal hemoglobin in the blood or a lower than normal number of red blood cells. (p. 299)

anencephaly (an′en-sef′ă-lē) Defective development of the brain with absence of the cerebral and cerebellar hemispheres, and with only a rudimentary brainstem. (p. 546)

angina pectoris (an′ji-nă pek′tō-ris, an-jī′nă) Pain resulting from a reduced blood supply to cardiac muscle. (p. 311)

angioplasty (an′jē-ō-plas-tē) A technique used to dilate the coronary arteries by threading a small balloonlike device into a partially blocked coronary artery and then inflating the balloon to enlarge the diameter of the vessel. (p. 311)

angiotensin (an-jē-ō-ten′sin) Angiotensin I is a peptide derived when renin acts on angiotensinogen; angiotensin II is formed from angiotensin I when angiotensin-converting enzyme acts on angiotensin I; angiotensin II is a potent vasoconstrictor, and it stimulates the secretion of aldosterone from the adrenal cortex. (p. 276)

angiotensinogen (an′jē-ō-ten-sin′ō-jen) A protein found in the blood that gives rise to angiotensin I after renin, an enzyme secreted from the kidney, acts on it. (p. 276)

ANH See *atrial natriuretic hormone.*

antagonist (an-tag′ŏ-nist) A muscle that works in opposition to another muscle. (p. 165)

anterior (an-tēr′ē-ōr) [L., *to go* before] That which goes first; in humans, toward the belly or front. (p. 9)

anterior horn The part of the spinal cord gray matter containing motor neurons; also called the ventral horn or motor horn. (p. 211)

anterior pituitary gland Portion of the pituitary gland derived from the oral epithelium. (p. 265)

antibody (an′tē-bod-ē) Protein found in the plasma that is responsible for antibody-mediated (humoral) immunity; binds specifically to an antigen. (p. 296)

antibody-mediated immunity Immunity resulting from B cells and the production of antibodies. (p. 375)

anticoagulant (an′tē-kō-ag′ū-lant) Chemical that prevents coagulation or blood clotting; an example is antithrombin. (p. 295)

antidiuretic hormone (an′tē-dī-ū-ret′ik) **(ADH)** Hormone secreted from the posterior pituitary gland that acts on the kidney to reduce the output of urine; also called vasopressin. (p. 270)

antigen (an′ti-jen) Any substance that induces a state of sensitivity or resistance to microorganisms or toxic substances after a latent period; substance that stimulates the adaptive immune system; self-antigens are produced by the body, and foreign antigens are introduced into the body. (p. 296)

antigen-binding receptor Molecule on the surface of lymphocytes that specifically binds antigens. (p. 376)

aorta (ā-ōr′tă) [Gr. *aorte*, from; *aeiro*, to lift up] Large elastic artery that is the main trunk of the systemic arterial system, which carries blood from the left ventricle of the heart and passes through the thorax and abdomen. (p. 310)

aortic semilunar valve The semilunar valve consisting of three cusps of tissue located at the base of the aorta where it arises from the left ventricle; the cusps overlap during ventricular diastole to prevent leakage of blood from the aorta into the left ventricle. (p. 312)

apex (ā′peks) [L., tip] Extremity of a conical or pyramidal structure; the apex of the heart is the rounded tip directed anteriorly and slightly inferiorly. (p. 306)

aphasia (ă-fā′zē-ă) [Gr., speechlessness] Impaired or absent communication by speech, writing, or signs, because of dysfunction of brain centers in the dominant cerebral hemisphere. (p. 208)

apocrine (ap′ō-krin) [Gr. *apo*, away from; *krino*, to separate] Gland whose cells contribute cytoplasm to its secretion; sweat glands that produce organic secretions traditionally are called apocrine. These sweat glands now are known, however, to be merocrine glands; see *merocrine* and *holocrine*, see page 591. (p. 99)

aponeurosis (ap′ō-noo-rō′sis) [Gr., end of a muscle where it becomes a tendon] A sheet of fibrous connective tissue, or an expanded tendon, serving as the origin or insertion of a flat muscle. (p. 165)

appendicular (ap′en-dik′ū-lăr) [L. *appendo*, to hang something on] Relating to an appendage, such as the limbs and their associated girdles. (p. 130)

appendix (ă-pen′diks), pl. **appendices** (ă-pen′di-sēs) [L. *appendo*, to hang something on] Smaller structure usually attached by one end to a larger structure; a small blind extension of the colon attached to the cecum. (p. 434)

appositional growth (ap-ō-zish′ŭn-ăl) [L. *ap* + *pono*, to place at or to] To place one layer of bone, cartilage, or other connective tissue against an existing layer; increases the width or diameter of bones. (p. 118)

aqueous humor (ak′wē-ŭs, ā′kwē-ŭs) Watery, clear fluid that fills the anterior compartment of the eye. (p. 242)

arachnoid mater (ă-rak′noyd ma′ter) [Gr. *arachne*, spiderlike, cobweb] Thin, cobweblike meningeal layer surrounding the brain and spinal cord; the middle of three layers. (p. 214)

areola (ă-rē′ō-lă, -ē), pl. **areolae** (ă-rē′ō-lē) A pigmented area surrounding the nipple of a mammary gland. (p. 527)

areolar (ă-rē′ō-lăr) Relating to connective tissue with small spaces within it; loose connective tissue. (p. 79)

arrector pili (ă-rek′tōr pī′lī) [L., that which raises hair] Smooth muscle attached to the hair follicle and dermis that raises the hair when it contracts. (p. 99)

arteriosclerosis (ar-tēr′ē-ō-skler-ō′sis) [L. *arterio-*; Gr., *sklerosis*, hardness] Hardness of the arteries. (p. 339)

arteriosclerotic lesion (ar-tēr′ē-ō-skler-ot′ik) A lesion or growth in arteries that narrows the lumen, or passage, and makes the walls of the arteries less elastic.

artery (ar′ter-ē) Blood vessel that carries blood away from the heart. (p. 336)

articulation (ar-tik-ū-lā′shŭn) [L. *articulatio*, a forming of vines] The place where two bones come together; a joint. (p. 137)

artificial heart A mechanical pump used to replace a diseased heart. (p. 328)

artificial pacemaker An electronic device implanted beneath the skin with an electrode that extends to the heart; provides periodic electrical stimuli to the heart and substitutes for a faulty SA node. (p. 327)

astrocyte (as′trō-sīt) [Gr. *astron*, star; *kytos*, a cell] Star-shaped neuroglial cell that helps regulate the composition of fluid around the neurons of the central nervous system. (p. 196)

atherosclerosis (ath′er-ō-skler-ō′sis) [Gr. *athere*, gruel or soft, pasty material; *sklerosis*, hardness] Lipid deposits (plaques) in the tunica intima of large and medium-sized arteries. (p. 339)

atom (at′ŏm) [Gr. *atomos*, indivisible, uncut] Smallest particle into which an element can be divided using chemical methods; composed of neutrons, protons, and electrons. (p. 20)

atomic number (ă-tom′ik) The number of protons in an element. (p. 20)

ATP See *adenosine triphosphate.*

atrial natriuretic hormone (ANH) (ā′trē-ăl nā′tre-yū-ret′ik) Hormone released from cells in the atrial wall of the heart when atrial blood pressure is increased; acts to lower blood pressure by increasing the rate of urine production. (p. 359)

atrioventricular (AV) bundle (ā-trē-ō-ven-trik′ū-lar) Bundle of modified cardiac muscle fibers that projects from the AV node through the interventricular septum; conducts action potentials from the AV node rapidly through the interventricular septum; also called the bundle of His. (p. 317)

atrioventricular (AV) node Small collection of specialized cardiac muscle fibers located in the inferior part of the right atrium; functions to delay action potential transmission to the atrioventricular bundle. (p. 317)

atrioventricular valve Valve located between the atrium and the ventricle of the heart, the tricuspid valve between the right atrium and right ventricle and the bicuspid (or mitral valve) between the left atrium and left ventricle. (p. 312)

atrium (ā′trē-ŭm), pl. **atria** (ā′trē-ă) [L., entrance chamber] One of the two chambers of the heart that collect blood during ventricular contraction and pump blood into the ventricles to complete ventricular filling at the end of ventricular relaxation; the right atrium receives blood from the inferior and superior venae cavae and from the coronary sinus, and delivers blood to the right ventricle; the left atrium receives blood from the pulmonary veins and delivers blood to the left ventricle. (p. 309)

auditory (aw′di-tōr-ē) Relating to hearing. (p. 243)

auditory ossicles (os′i-klz) Bones of the middle ear; the malleus, incus, and stapes. (p. 243)

auditory tube Air-filled passageway between the middle ear and pharynx. (p. 243)

auricle (aw′ri-kl) [L. *auris*, ear] The fleshy part of the external ear on the outside of the head; a small conical pouch projecting from the upper anterior part of each atrium of the heart. (p. 243)

auscultatory (aws-kŭl′tă-tō-rē) [L. *ausculto*, to listen] To listen to the sounds made by the various body structures, especially to Korotkoff sounds when determining blood pressure. (p. 350)

autoimmune disease (aw-tō-i-mūn′) Disorder resulting from a specific immune system reaction against self-antigens. (p. 375)

autonomic nervous system (ANS) (aw-tō-nom′ik) That part of the peripheral nervous system composed of efferent fibers that reach from the central nervous system to smooth muscle, cardiac muscle, and glands. (p. 192)

autosome (aw′tō-sōm) [Gr. *auto-* self; *soma*, body] Any chromosome other than a sex chromosome; normally occurs in pairs in somatic cells and singly in gametes. (p. 59)

AV See *atrioventricular.*

axial (ak′sē-ăl) [L. *axle*, axis] Head, neck, and trunk as distinguished from the extremities. (p. 120)

axon (ak′son) [Gr., axis] Main process of a neuron; usually conducts action potentials away from the neuron cell body. (p. 83)

B

baroreceptor (bar′ō-rē-sep′ter) Sensory nerve endings in the walls of the atria of the heart, aortic arch, and carotid sinuses;

sensitive to stretching of the wall caused by increased blood pressure; also called a pressoreceptor. (p. 324)

baroreceptor reflex   Process in which baroreceptors detect changes in blood pressure and produce changes in heart rate, force of heart contraction, and blood vessel diameter that return blood pressure toward normal levels. (p. 324)

basal nuclei   Nuclei at the base of the cerebrum, diencephalon, and midbrain involved in controlling motor functions. (p. 210)

base   Any substance that is a proton acceptor; or any substance that binds to hydrogen ions (p. 29); lower part or bottom of a structure; the base of the heart is the flat portion directed posteriorly and superiorly; veins and arteries project into and out of the base, respectively. (p. 306)

basement membrane   The structure that attaches most epithelia (exceptions include lymph vessels and the liver sinusoids) to underlying tissue; consists of carbohydrates and proteins secreted by the epithelia and the underlying connective tissue. (p. 72)

basic solution   (bā′sik) Solution with fewer hydrogen ions than hydroxide ions; has a pH greater than 7. (p. 29)

basilar membrane   (bas′i-lăr) One of two membranes forming the cochlear duct; supports the spiral organ. (p. 246)

basophil   (bā′sō-fil) [Gr. *basis*, base; *phileo*, to love] White blood cell with granules that stain purple with basic dyes; promotes inflammation and prevents clot formation. (p. 292)

belly   The largest part of a muscle, between the origin and insertion. (p. 165)

benign   (bē-nīn′) [L. *benignus*, kind] Mild in character or nonmalignant; does not spread to distant sites. (p. 89)

beta-adrenergic   (bā′tă ad-rĕ-ner′jik) **blocking agent** Drug that binds to and prevents adrenergic receptors from responding to adrenergic compounds that normally bind to beta-adrenergic receptors and cause them to function; beta-adrenergic blocking agents are used to treat certain arrhythmias in the heart and to treat tachycardia (rapid heart rate). (p. 327)

biceps brachii   (bī′seps brā′kē-ī) Muscle in the anterior arm with two heads or origins on the scapula and an insertion onto the radius; flexes and supinates the forearm. (p. 174)

bicuspid valve   (bī-kŭs′pid) Valve closing the opening between the left atrium and left ventricle of the heart; has two cusps; also called the mitral valve. (p. 312)

bile   (bīl) Fluid secreted from the liver, stored in the gallbladder, and released into the duodenum; consists of bile salts, bile pigments, bicarbonate ions, fats, and other materials. (p. 443)

bile salt   Organic salt secreted by the liver that functions to emulsify lipids. (p. 443)

bilirubin   (bil-i-roo′bin) A bile pigment formed from the heme in hemoglobin during the destruction of red blood cells by macrophages. (p. 291)

biopsy   (bī′op-sē) The process of removing tissue from living patients for diagnostic examination, or a specimen obtained by biopsy. (p. 89)

blastocele   (blas′tō-sēl) [Gr. *blastos*, germ; *koilos*, hollow] Cavity in the blastocyst. (p. 542)

blastocyst   (blas′tō-sist) [Gr. *blastos*, germ; *kystis*, bladder] Early stage of mammalian embryo development consisting of a hollow ball of cells with an inner cell mass and an outer trophoblast layer. (p. 528)

blood–brain barrier   Cellular and matrix barrier made up primarily of blood vessel endothelium, with some help from the surrounding astrocytes; it allows some (usually small) substances to pass from the circulation into the brain, but does not allow other (larger) substances to pass. (p. 196)

blood group   A category of red blood cells based on the type of antigen on the surface of the red blood cell; for example, the ABO blood group is involved with transfusion reactions. (p. 296)

blood pressure   [L. *pressus*, to press] The force blood exerts against the blood vessel walls; expressed relative to atmospheric pressure and reported in the form of millimeters of mercury (mm Hg) of pressure. (p. 350)

bony labyrinth   (lab′i-rinth) The interconnecting tunnels and chambers within the temporal bone in which the inner ear is located. (p. 243)

Bowman's capsule   The enlarged end of the nephron; Bowman's capsule and the glomerulus make up the renal corpuscle. (p. 481)

brachialis   (brā′kē-ăl-is) Muscle of the anterior arm that originates on the humerus and inserts onto the ulna; flexes the forearm. (p. 174)

brachial plexus   (brā′kē-ăl) [L. *brachium*, arm] The nerve plexus to the upper limb; originates from spinal nerves C5 to T1. (p. 223)

brainstem   Portion of the brain consisting of the midbrain, pons, and medulla oblongata. (p. 203)

breathing   (brēthin) Movement of air into and out of the lung, see *ventilation*. (p. 405)

bronchiole   (brong′kē-ōl) One of the finer subdivisions of the bronchial tubes, less than 1 mm in diameter, that has no cartilage in its wall, but has relatively more smooth muscle and elastic fibers than do larger bronchial tubes. (p. 400)

bronchus   (brong′kŭs), pl. **bronchi** (brong′kī) [Gr. *bronchos*, windpipe] Any one of the air ducts conducting air from the trachea to the bronchioles. (p. 400)

buccinator   (buk′si-nā′tōr) Muscle making up the lateral sides of the oral cavity; flattens the cheeks. (p. 168)

buffer   (bŭf′er) Chemical that resists changes in pH when either an acid or a base is added to a solution containing the buffer. (p. 30)

bundle of His   See *atrioventricular bundle*.

burn   A lesion caused by heat, acid, or other agents; a partial-thickness burn of the skin damages only the epidermis (first-degree burn) or the epidermis and part of the dermis (second-degree burn); a full-thickness (third-degree) burn destroys the epidermis and the dermis and sometimes the underlying tissue as well. (p. 101)

bursa   (ber′să) [L., purse] Closed sac or pocket containing synovial fluid, usually found in areas where friction occurs. (p. 139)

C

calcaneus   (kal-kā′nē-ŭs) [L., the heel] The largest tarsal bone, forming the heel. (p. 136)

calcitonin   (kal-si-tō′nin) Hormone released from cells of the thyroid gland that acts on tissues, especially bone, to cause a decrease in blood levels of calcium ions. (p. 271)

calcium channel blocker   (kal′sē-ŭm) A class of drugs that specifically block channels in cell membranes through which calcium ions pass; calcium channel blockers are used to treat some kinds of cardiac arrhythmias. (p. 327)

callus   (kal′ŭs) [L., hard skin] Thickening of the stratum corneum of skin in response to friction. The zone of tissue repair between fragments of a broken bone. (pp. 96; 117)

calorie   (kal′ō-rē) [L. *calor*, heat] Unit of heat or energy content; the quantity of energy required to raise the temperature of 1 gram of water 1°C. A Calorie (Cal), or kilocalorie (kcal), is the amount of heat or energy required to raise the temperature of 1000 grams of water from 14°C to 15°C. (p. 459)

calyx (kā′liks), pl. **calyces** (kal′i-sēz, flower petal) The small containers into which urine flows as it leaves the collecting ducts at the tip of the renal pyramids; the calyces come together to form the renal pelvis. (p. 480)

canaliculus (kan-ă-lik′ū-lŭs) Tiny canal in bone between osteocytes containing osteocyte cell processes (p. 112); a cleftlike lumen between the cells of each hepatic cord (p. 431), connects medial corner of eye to the lacrimal sac. (p. 238)

cancellous bone (kan′sĕ-lŭs) [L., grating or lattice] Bone with latticelike appearance; spongy bone. (pp. 112, 115)

capacitation (kă-pas′i-tā′shŭn) The process whereby the sperm cells develop the ability to fertilize oocytes. (p. 541)

capillary (kap′i-lār-ē) Minute blood vessel consisting only of simple squamous epithelium and a basement membrane; major site for the exchange of substances between the blood and tissues. (p. 336)

carbohydrate (kar-bō-hī′drāt) Organic molecule made up of one or more monosaccharides chemically bound together; sugars and starches. (p. 32)

carbonic anhydrase (kar-bon′ik an-hī′drās) An enzyme that increases the rate at which carbon dioxide reacts with water to form hydrogen ions and bicarbonate ions. (p. 290)

carcinoma (kar-si-nō′mă) [Gr. *karkinoma*, cancer; *oma*, tumor] A malignant tumor derived from epithelial tissue. (p. 103)

cardiac cycle (kar′dē-ak) One complete sequence of cardiac systole and diastole. (p. 319)

cardiac output Volume of blood pumped by either ventricle of the heart per minute; about 5 L/min for the heart of a healthy adult at rest. (p. 321)

cardioregulatory center Specialized area within the medulla oblongata of the brain that receives sensory input and functions to control parasympathetic and sympathetic stimulation of the heart. (p. 324)

carotene (kar′ō-tēn) A yellow pigment found in plants such as squash and carrots; accumulates in the lipids of the stratum corneum and in the fat cells of the dermis and hypodermis and used as a source of vitamin A. (p. 97)

carotid bodies (ka-rot′id) Small organ near the carotid sinuses that detects changes in blood oxygen, carbon dioxide, and pH. (p. 357)

carotid sinus Enlargement of the internal carotid artery near the point where the internal carotid artery branches from the common carotid artery; contains baroreceptors. (p. 340)

carpal (kar′păl) [Gr. *karpos*, wrist] Associated with the wrist; bones of the wrist. (p. 132)

carrier molecule Protein that extends from one side of the plasma membrane to the other; binds to molecules to be transported and moves them from one side of the membrane to the other. (p. 50)

cartilage (kar′ti-lij) [L., *cartilage*, gristle] Firm, smooth, resilient, nonvascular connective tissue. (p. 83)

catabolism (kă-tab′ō-lizm) [Gr. *katabole*, a casting down] All the decomposition reactions that occur in the body; releases energy. (p. 465)

catalyst (kat′ă-list) A substance that increases the rate of a chemical reaction; in the process the catalyst is not permanently changed or used up. (p. 29)

cecum (sē′kŭm) [L. *caecus*, blind] A blind sac forming the beginning of the large intestine. (p. 432)

cell (sel) [L. *cella*, chamber] Basic living unit of all plants and animals. (p. 3)

cell-mediated immunity Immunity resulting from the actions of T cells. (p. 375)

cell membrane Plasma membrane; outermost component of the cell, surrounding and binding the rest of the cell contents. (p. 42)

central canal A small canal containing blood vessels, nerves, and loose connective tissue and running parallel to the long axis of a bone. Also called a Haversian canal (p. 112).

central nervous system (CNS) The brain and spinal cord. (p. 192)

centriole (sen′trē-ōl) Small organelle that divides and migrates to each pole of the nucleus; spindle fibers extend from the centromeres to the centrioles during mitosis. (p. 63)

centromere (sen′trō-mēr) A specialized region where chromatids are linked together in a chromosome. (p. 63)

cerebellum (ser-e-bel′ŭm) [L., little brain] A part of the brain attached to the brainstem; important in maintaining muscle tone, balance, and coordination of movements. (p. 211)

cerebral aqueduct (ser′ĕ-brăl, sĕ-rē′brăl) A small connecting tube through the midbrain between the third and fourth ventricles. (p. 215)

cerebrospinal fluid (ser′ĕ-brō-spī′năl, sĕ-rē′brō-spī′năl) Fluid filling the ventricles and surrounding the brain and spinal cord. (p. 215)

cerebrum (ser′ĕ-brŭm, sĕ-rē′brŭm) [L., brain] The largest part of the brain, consisting of two hemispheres and including the cortex, nerve tracts, and basal nuclei. (p. 207)

cerumen (sĕ-roo′men) A specific type of sebum produced in the external auditory meatus; earwax. (p. 243)

cervical (ser′vĭ-kal) Neck. (p. 125)

cervical plexus The nerve plexus of the neck; originates from spinal nerves C1 to C4. (p. 223)

cervix (ser′viks) [L., neck] Lower part of the uterus extending to the vagina. (p. 526)

chemical (kem′i-kăl) Relating to chemistry, especially to the characteristics of atoms and molecules and to their interactions. (p. 3)

chemical bond An association between two atoms formed when the outermost electrons are transferred or shared between atoms. (p. 21)

chemical reaction Process by which atoms or molecules interact to form or break chemical bonds. (p. 25)

chemistry (kem′is-trē) [Gr. *chemeia*, alchemy] Science dealing with the atomic composition of substances and the reactions they undergo. (p. 20)

chemoreceptor reflex (kem′ō-rē-sep′tŏr) Process in which chemoreceptors detect changes in oxygen levels, carbon dioxide levels, and pH in the blood and produce changes in heart rate, force of heart contraction, and blood vessel diameter that return these values toward their normal levels. (p. 358)

cholecystokinin (kō′lē-sis-tō-kī′nin) Hormone released from the duodenum; inhibits gastric acid secretion and stimulates contraction of the gallbladder. (p. 440)

chondrocyte (kon′drō-sīt) [G. *chondrion*, gristle; cyte] Cartilage cell. (p. 83)

chordae tendineae (kōr′dē ten′di-nē-ē) [L., cord] Tendinous strands running from the papillary muscles to the free margin of the cusps that make up the tricuspid and bicuspid valves; prevent the cusps of these valves from extending up into the atria during ventricular contraction. (p. 312)

choroid (kō′royd) [Gr. *chorioeides*, membranelike] Portion of the vascular tunic associated with the sclera of the eye; functions to prevent scattering of light. (p. 239)

choroid plexus Specialized group of ependymal cells in the ventricles; secretes cerebrospinal fluid. (p. 215)

chromatid (krō′mă-tid) [Gr. *chroma*, color] One of a pair of duplicated chromosomes, joined by the centromere, which separates from its partner during cell division. (p. 61)

chromatin (krō′ma-tin) [Gr. *chroma*, color] The genetic material of the nucleus consisting of deoxyribonucleic acid (DNA) associated with proteins. (p. 44)

chromosome (krō′mō-sōm) [Gr. *chroma*, color; *soma*, body] One of the bodies (normally 46 in humans) in the cell nucleus that carry the cell's genetic information. (p. 44)

chyle (kīl) [Gr. *chylos*, juice] Milky colored lymph with a high fat content. (p. 368)

chyme (kīm) [Gr. *chymos*, juice] Semifluid mass of partly digested food passed from the stomach into the duodenum. (p. 438)

ciliary body (sil′ē-ar-ē) Structure continuous with the choroid layer of the eye at its anterior margin that contains smooth muscle cells and is attached to the lens by suspensory ligaments; regulates the thickness of the lens and produces aqueous humor. (p. 239)

cilium (sil′ē-ŭm), pl. **cilia** (sil′ē-ă) [L., eyelid] A mobile extension of a cell surface, varies from one to thousands per cell, and contains specialized microtubules enclosed by the cell membrane. (pp. 48, 77)

citric acid cycle (sit′rik) Series of chemical reactions in which citric acid (six-carbon molecule) is converted into a four-carbon molecule, carbon dioxide is formed, and energy is released; the released energy is used to form ATP; the four-carbon molecule can combine with acetyl-CoA (two-carbon) to form citric acid and start the cycle again. (p. 468)

clavicle (klav′i-kl) [L., a small key] The bone between the sternum and shoulder; the collarbone. (p. 130)

climacteric (klī-mak′ter-ik, klī-mak-ter′ik) [Gr., the rung of a ladder] The period of endocrine, somatic, and transitory psychological changes occuring in the transition to menopause. (p. 531)

clitoris (klit′ō-ris) A small erectile structure located in the anterior margin of the vestibule. (p. 526)

clot (klot) To coagulate; a soft insoluble mass formed when blood coagulates. (p. 87)

clot retraction Condensation of the clot into a denser, more compact structure. (p. 295)

clotting factor One of many proteins found in the blood in an inactive state; activated in a series of chemical reactions that result in the formation of a blood clot. (p. 294)

coagulation (kō-ag-ū-lā′shŭn) The process of changing from a liquid to a solid, especially blood. (p. 294)

cochlea (kok′lē-ă) The portion of the inner ear involved in hearing; shaped like a snail shell. (p. 246)

codon (kō′don) Sequence of three nucleotides in mRNA that codes for a specific amino acid in a protein. (p. 59)

coenzyme (kō-en′zīm) A substance that enhances or is necessary for the function of an enzyme. (p. 463)

collagen (kol′lă-jen) [Gr. *koila*, glue; *gen*, producing] Ropelike protein of the extracellular matrix. (p. 78)

collecting duct Straight tubule that extends from the cortex of the kidney to the tip of the renal pyramid; filtrate from the distal tubules enter the collecting duct and is carried to the calyces. (p. 481)

colliculus (ko-lik′ū-lŭs) [L. *collis*, hill] One of four small mounds on the dorsal side of the midbrain; the superior two are involved in visual reflexes, and the inferior two are involved in hearing. (p. 205)

colon (kō′lon) Division of the large intestine that extends from the cecum to the rectum. (p. 434)

commissure (kom′ĭ-shūr) [L., a joining together] A bundle of nerve fibers passing from one side to the other in the brain or spinal cord. (p. 210)

common bile duct Duct formed by the union of the common hepatic and cystic ducts; it joins the pancreatic duct and empties into the duodenum. (p. 431)

common hepatic duct Duct formed by union of the right and left hepatic ducts; it joins the cystic duct to form the common bile duct. (p. 431)

compact bone Bone that is denser and has fewer spaces than cancellous bone. (p. 112)

complement (kom′plĕ-ment) Group of serum proteins that stimulates phagocytosis, inflammation, and lysis of cells. (p. 373)

compound (kom′pound) A substance containing two or more different kinds of atoms that are chemically combined. (p. 24)

concha (kon′kă) [L., shell] Structure resembling a shell in shape; the three bony ridges on the lateral wall of the nasal cavity. (p. 394)

condyle (kon′dīl) [Gr. *kondyles*, knuckle] Rounded articulating surface of a joint. (p. 120)

cone Photoreceptor cell in the retina of the eye with cone-shaped photoreceptive process; important in color vision and visual acuity. (p. 239)

conjunctiva (kon-jŭnk-tī′vă) [L. *conjungo*, to bind together] Mucous membrane covering the anterior surface of the eye and the inner lining of the eyelids. (p. 238)

connective tissue One of the four major tissue types; consists of cells usually surrounded by large amounts of

extracellular material; functions to hold other tissues together and provides a supporting framework for the body. (p. 78)

constant region Part of an antibody that does not combine with an antigen and is the same in different antibodies; responsible for activation of complement and binding the antibody to cells such as macrophages, basophils, and mast cells. (p. 378)

corn [L. *cornu*, horn] Thickening of the stratum corneum of the skin over a bony projection in response to friction or pressure. (p. 96)

cornea (kōr′nē-ă) Transparent, anterior part of the fibrous tunic of the eye through which light enters the eye. (p. 238)

corneum (kōr′nē-ŭm) See stratum corneum.

coronal plane (kōr′ō-năl) [Gr. *korone*, crown] Plane separating the body into anterior and posterior portions; also called a frontal plane. (p. 12)

coronary artery (kōr′o-nār-ē) An artery that carries blood to the muscles of the heart; the left and right coronary arteries arise from the aorta. (p. 310)

coronary bypass Surgery in which a vein from some other part of the body is grafted to a coronary artery in such a way as to allow blood flow past a blockage in the coronary artery. (p. 311)

coronary vein Vein that carries blood from the heart muscle primarily to the right atrium. (p. 315)

corpus callosum (kōr′pus kă-lō′sŭm) [L., body; callous] A large, thick nerve fiber tract connecting the two cerebral hemispheres. (p. 210)

corpus luteum (loo′tē′ŭm) Yellow endocrine body formed in the ovary in the site of a ruptured follicle immediately after ovulation; secretes progesterone and estrogen. (p. 524)

cortex (kōr′teks), pl. **cortices** (kōr′ti-sēz) [L., bark] The outer part of an organ such as the brain (p. 196), kidney (p. 480), adrenal gland (p. 274), or hair. (p. 97)

cortisol (kōr′ti-sol) Steroid hormone released by the adrenal cortex; increases blood glucose and inhibits inflammation; it is a glucocorticoid. (p. 269)

cotransport (kō-trans′pōrt) The transport of one substance across a plasma membrane, coupled with the simultaneous transport of another substance across the same membrane in the same direction.

covalent bond (kō-vāl′ent) Chemical bond that is formed when two atoms share one or more pairs of electrons. (p. 22)

coxa (kok′să), pl. **coxae** (kok′sē) [L., hip] The bone of the hip. (p. 133)

cranial nerve (krā′nē-ăl) Peripheral nerve originating in the brain. (p. 217)

cranial vault Eight skull bones that surround and protect the brain; braincase. (p. 120)

cremaster muscle (krē-mas′ter) Extension of abdominal muscles; in the male it raises the testis. (p. 514)

crenation (krē-nā′shŭn) Cell shrinkage which occurs when water moves by osmosis from a cell into a hypertonic solution. (p. 52)

cretinism (krē′tin-izm) Hypothyroidism in an infant; appears during the first years of life and results in stunting of bodily growth and of mental development; hypothyroid dwarfism. (p. 270)

cricoid cartilage (krī′koyd) Most inferior laryngeal cartilage. (p. 396)

cricothyrotomy (krī′kō-thī-rot′ō-mē) Formation of an artificial opening in a victim's air passageway through the membrane between the cricoid and thyroid cartilage. (p. 399)

crown That part of the tooth that is formed of and covered by enamel. (p. 427)

crypt (kript) [Gr. *kryptos*, hidden] A pitlike depression. (p. 434)

cryptorchidism (krip-tōr′ki-dizm) Failure of the testes to descend into the scrotal sac. (p. 515)

cupula (koo′poo-lă) [L. *cupa*, a tub] Gelatinous mass that overlies the hair cells of the cristae ampullares of the semicircular canals; responds to fluid movement. (p. 249)

cyanosis (sī-ă-nō′sis) [Gr., dark blue color] Blue coloration of the skin and mucous membranes caused by insufficient oxygenation of blood. (p. 101)

cystic duct (sis′tik) Duct from the gallbladder; it joins the common hepatic duct to form the common bile duct. (p. 431)

cytoplasm (sī′tō-plazm) Cellular material surrounding the nucleus. (p. 42)

cytoskeleton (sī-tō-skel′ĕ-ton) The collection of microtubules, microfilaments, and intermediate filaments that support the cytoplasm and organelles; also involved with cell movements. (p. 47)

D

dartos muscle (dar′tōs) [Fr. *dero*, to skin] The layer of smooth muscle beneath the skin of the scrotum. (p. 514)

deciduous teeth (dē-sid′ū-ŭs) [L. *deciduus*, falling off] The primary teeth that fall out to be replaced by the permanent teeth. (p. 427)

decomposition reaction (dē′kom-pō-zish′ŭn) The breakdown of a larger molecule into smaller molecules, ions, or atoms. (p. 26)

deep [O.E. deop, deep] Away from the surface, internal. (p. 10)

defecation (def-ĕ-kā′shŭn) [L. *defaeco*, to purify] Discharge of feces from the rectum. (p. 445)

deglutition (dē-gloo-tish′ŭn) [L. *de-*, from, away; *glutio*, to swallow] The act of swallowing. (p. 438)

deltoid (del′toyd) Triangular muscle over the shoulder; inserts onto the humerus; abducts the arm. (p. 174)

denaturation (dē-na-tū-rā′shŭn) The change in shape of a protein caused by breaking hydrogen bonds; agents that cause denaturation include heat and changes in pH. (p. 34)

dendrite (den′drīt) [Gr. *dendrite*, tree] Short, treelike cell process of a neuron; receives stimuli. (p. 83)

dentin (den′tin) Bonelike material forming the mass of the tooth. (p. 427)

deoxyribonucleic (dē-oks′ē-rī′bō-noo-klē′ic) **acid (DNA)** Type of nucleic acid containing the sugar deoxyribose; the genetic material of cells; DNA. (p. 34)

dermis (der′mis) [Gr. *derma*, skin] Dense connective tissue that forms the deep layer of the skin; responsible for the structural strength of the skin. (p. 94)

desmosome (dez′mō-sōm) A point of adhesion between two cells. (p. 77)

diabetes mellitus (dī-ă-bē′tēz me-lī′tŭs) A condition resulting from too little insulin secreted from the pancreatic islets, insufficient numbers of insulin receptors on target cells, or defective receptors that do not respond to insulin. (p. 277)

diaphragm (dī′ă-fram) Muscular separation between the thoracic and abdominal cavities; its contraction results in inspiration. (p. 172)

diaphysis (dī-af′i-sis) [Gr., growing between] Shaft of a long bone. (p. 112)

diastole (dī-as′tō-lē) [Gr. *diastole*, dilation] Relaxation of the heart chambers during which they fill with blood; usually refers to ventricular relaxation. (p. 321)

diastolic pressure The minimum arterial blood pressure achieved during ventricular diastole. (p. 350)

diencephalon (dī-en-sef′ă-lon) [Gr. *dia*, through; *enkephalos*, brain] Part of the brain inferior to and nearly surrounded by the cerebrum, and connecting posteriorly and inferiorly to the brainstem. (p. 206)

diffusion (di-fū′zhŭn) [L. *diffundo*, to pour in different directions] Tendency for solute molecules to move from an area of higher concentration to an area of lower concentration in a solution; the product of the constant random motion of all atoms, ions, or molecules, in a solution. (p. 50)

digestion (di-jes′chŭn, dī-jes′chŭn) The breakdown of carbohydrates, lipids, proteins, and other large molecules to their component parts. (p. 446)

digestive tract (di-jes′tiv, dī-jes′tiv) The tract from the mouth to the anus, including the stomach and intestines, where food is taken in, broken down, and absorbed. (p. 425)

digitalis (dij′i-tal′is) [L., relating to fingerlike flowers] A steroid used in the treatment of heart diseases such as heart failure; increases the force of contraction of the heart; extracted from the foxglove plant (*Digitalis purpura*). (p. 327)

diploid (dip′loyd) The condition in which there are two copies of each autosome and two sex chromosomes (46 total chromosomes in humans). (p. 59)

disaccharidase (dī-sak′ă-rid-ās) An enzyme that breaks disaccharides down to monosaccharides; commonly found in the microvilli of the intestinal epithelium. (p. 442)

disaccharide (dī-sak′ă-rīd) Two monosaccharides chemically bound together; glucose and fructose chemically join to form sucrose. (p. 32)

dissociate (di-sō-sē-āt′) [L. *dis-* + *socio*, to disjoin, separate] The separation of positive and negative ions when they dissolve in water and are surrounded by water molecules. (p. 24)

distal (dis′tăl) [L. *di-* + *sto*, to be distant] Farther from the point of attachment to the body than another structure. (p. 10)

distal tubule Convoluted tubule of the nephron that extends from the ascending limb of the loop of Henle and ends in a collecting duct. (p. 480)

DNA See *deoxyribonucleic acid.*

dominant (dom′i-nant) [L. *dominus*, a master] In genetics, a gene that is expressed phenotypically to the exclusion of a contrasting recessive trait. (p. 563)

dorsal (dōr′săl) [L. *dorsum*, back] Back surface of the body; in humans, synonymous with posterior. (p. 10)

dorsal root Sensory (afferent) root of a spinal nerve. (p. 212)

ductus arteriosus (dŭk′tŭs ar-tēr′ē-ō-sŭs) A short artery that extends from the pulmonary trunk to the aorta; in the fetus blood flows through the ductus arteriosus from the pulmonary trunk into the aorta and bypasses the lungs. (p. 322)

ductus deferens (dŭk′tŭs def′er-enz) Duct of the testis, running from the epididymis to the ejaculatory duct; also called the vas deferens. (p. 515)

duodenum (doo-ō-dē′nŭm, doo-od′ĕ-nŭm) [L. *duodeni*, twelve] First division of the small intestine; connects to the stomach. (p. 429)

dura mater (doo′ră mā′ter) [L., tough mother] Tough, fibrous membrane forming the outermost meningeal covering of the brain and spinal cord. (p. 214)

E

eardrum See *tympanic membrane*.

eccrine (ek′rin) [Gr. *ek*, out; *krino*, to separate] Exocrine; refers to water-producing sweat glands; see *merocrine*.

ECG See *electrocardiogram*.

ectoderm (ek′tō-derm) Outermost of the three germ layers of the embryo. (p. 545)

ectopic beat (ek-top′ik) A heart beat that originates from an area of the heart other than the SA node. (p. 318)

edema (e-dē′mă) [Gr. *oidema*, a swelling] Excessive accumulation of fluid, usually causing swelling. (p. 86)

efferent (ef′er-ent) [L. *efferens*, to bring out] Conducting outward from a given organ or part, denoting certain arteries, veins, lymphatics, and nerves. Opposite of afferent. (p. 192)

efferent arteriole (ar-tēr′ē-ōl) Vessel that carries blood from the glomerulus to the peritubular capillaries. (p. 485)

efferent ductule (dŭk′tool) Small duct that leads from the testis to the epididymis. (p. 515)

efferent fiber Nerve fiber going from the central nervous system toward the peripheral nervous system; motor fiber. (p. 192)

ejaculation (ē-jak′ū-lā′shŭn) Reflexive expulsion of semen from the penis. (p. 521)

ejaculatory duct (ē-jak′ū-lă-tōr-ē) Duct formed by the union of the ductus deferens and the excretory duct of the seminal vesicle, which opens into the urethra. (p. 515)

electrocardiogram (ē-lek-trō-kar′dē-ō-gram) **(ECG)** Graphic record of the heart's electrical currents obtained with an electronic recording instrument. (p. 318)

electrolyte (ē-lek′trō-līt) [Gr. *electro*, + *lytos*, soluble] Positive and negative ions that conduct electricity in solution. (p. 25)

electron (ē-lek′tron) Negatively charged particle found around the nucleus of atoms. (p. 20)

electron–transport chain Series of energy transfer molecules in the inner mitochondrial membrane; they receive

energy and use it in the formation of ATP and water. (p. 468)

element (el′ĕ-ment) [L. *elementum*, a rudiment] The simplist type of matter with unique chemical properties. (p. 20)

embolus (em′bō-lŭs) [Gr. *embolos*, a plug] A detached clot or other foreign body that occludes a blood vessel. (p. 295)

embryo (em′brē-ō) In prenatal development, the developing human between 14 and 56 days of development. (p. 543)

emission (ē-mish′ŭn) [L. *emissio*, to send out] Discharge; formation and accumulation of semen prior to ejaculation. (p. 521)

emulsification (ē-mŭl′si-fi-kā-shŭn) The dispersal of one liquid, or very small globules of the liquid, within another liquid. (p. 447)

emulsify (ē-mŭl′si-fī) To form an emulsion, which is one liquid dispersed in another liquid. (p. 447)

enamel (ē-nam′ĕl) Hard substance covering the exposed portion of the tooth. (p. 427)

endocardium (en-dō-kar′dē-ŭm) [Gr. *endon*, within; Gr. *kardia*, heart] Innermost layer of the heart, including endothelium and connective tissue. (p. 314)

endochondral (en-dō-kon′drăl) [*endo* + Gr. *chondrion*, gristle] Growth of cartilage, which is then replaced by bone. (p. 114)

endochondral ossification (en-dō-kon′drăl os′i-fi-kā′shŭn) Bone formation within cartilage. (p. 114)

endocrine (en′dō-krin) [*endo* + Gr. *krino*, to separate] Ductless gland that secretes internally, usually into the circulatory system. (p. 78)

endocytosis (en′dō-sī-tō′sis) [*endo* + Gr. *kytos*, cell; *-osis*, condition] Bulk uptake of material through the cell membrane by taking it into a vesicle. (p. 56)

endoderm (en′dō-derm) [*endo* + Gr. *derma*, skin] Innermost of the three germ layers of the embryo. (p. 545)

endolymph (en′dō-limf) [*endo* + Gr. *lympha*, clear fluid] The fluid inside the membranous labyrinth of the inner ear. (p. 246)

endometrium (en′dō-mē′trē-ŭm) [*endo* + Gr. *mētra*, uterus] Mucous membrane that constitutes the inner layer of the uterine wall; consists of a simple columnar epithelium and a lamina propria that contains simple tubular uterine glands. (p. 526)

endomysium (en′dō-mis′ē-ŭm, en′dō-miz′ē-ŭm,) [*endo-* + Gr. *mys*, muscle]

The fine connective tissue sheath surrounding a muscle fiber. (p. 151)

endoplasmic reticulum (en′dō-plas′mik re-tik′ū-lŭm) [*endo* + Gr. *plastos*, formed] Membranous network inside the cytoplasm; rough endoplasmic reticulum has ribosomes attached to the surface; smooth endoplasmic reticulum does not have ribosomes attached. (p. 44)

endosteum (en-dos′tē-ŭm) [*endo* + Gr. *osteon*, bone] Membranous lining of the medullary cavity and the cavities of spongy bone. (p. 112)

enzyme (en′zīm) [Gr. *en*, in; *zyme*, leaven] A protein molecule that increases the rate of a chemical reaction without being permanently altered; an organic catalyst. (p. 34)

eosinophil (ē-ō-sin′ō-fil) [Gr. *eos*, dawn; *phileo*, to love] White blood cell with granules that stain red with acidic dyes; inhibits inflammation. (p. 292)

ependymal (ep-en′di-măl) The neuroglial cell layer lining the ventricles of the brain. (p. 196)

epicardium (ep-i-kar′dē-ŭm) [Gr. *epi-*, upon; *kardia*, heart] Serous membrane covering the surface of the heart; also called the visceral pericardium. (p. 309)

epicondyle (ep′i-kon′dīl) [*epi* + Gr. *kondyles*, knuckle] Projection on (usually to the side of) a condyle. (p. 132)

epidermis (ep-i-derm′is) [*epi* + Gr. *derma*, skin] Outer portion of the skin formed of epithelial tissue that rests on the dermis; resists abrasion and forms a permeability barrier. (p. 94)

epididymis (ep-i-did′i-mis) [*epi* + Gr. *didymos*, twin] Elongated structure connected to the posterior surface of the testis; site of storage and maturation of the sperm cells. (p. 515)

epiglottis (ep-i-glot′is) [*epi* + Gr. *glottis*, the mouth of the windpipe] Plate of elastic cartilage, covered with mucous membrane, that serves as a valve over the opening of the larynx during swallowing to prevent materials from entering the larynx. (p. 396)

epimysium (ep-i-mis′ē-ŭm, -miz′ē-ŭm) [*epi* + Gr. *mys*, muscle] The fibrous connective tissue layer surrounding a skeletal muscle. (p. 151)

epinephrine (ep′i-nef′rin) [*epi* + Gr. *nephros*, kidney] Hormone similar in structure to the neurotransmitter norepinephrine; major hormone released from the adrenal medulla; increases cardiac output and blood glucose levels. (p. 274)

epiphyseal line (ep-i-fiz′ē-ăl) Dense plate of bone in a bone that is no longer growing, indicating the former site of the epiphyseal plate. (p. 112)

epiphyseal plate   Site at which bone growth in length occurs; located between the epiphysis and diaphysis of a long bone; area of cartilage where cartilage growth is followed by ossification; also called the growth plate. (p. 112)

epiphysis   (e-pif'-i-sis) [*epi*, on; Gr. *physis*, growth] The end of a bone; separated from the remainder of the bone by the epiphyseal plate or epiphyseal line. (p. 112)

epiploic appendage   (ep'i-plō'ik) One of a number of little, fat-filled processes of peritoneum projecting from the serous coat of the large intestine.

episiotomy   (e-piz-ē-ot'ō-mē, e-pis-e-ot'ō-mē) An incision in the clinical perineum, performed sometimes during childbirth. (p. 527)

epithelial tissue   (ep-i-thē'lē-ăl) One of the four major tissue types consisting of cells with a basement membrane (exceptions are lymph vessels and liver sinusoids), little extracellular material, and no blood vessels; covers the surfaces of the body and forms glands. (p. 72)

epithelium   (ep-i-thē'lē-ŭm), pl. **epithelia** (ep-i-thē'lē-ă) See *epithelial tissue.*

eponychium   (ep-ō-nik'ē-ŭm) The thin skin that attaches to the proximal part of the nail. (p. 99)

equilibrium   (ē-kwi-lib'rē-ŭm) [Gr. *aequus*, equal; *libra*, a balance] A state created by a chemical reaction proceeding in opposite directions (e.g., from reactants to products and from products to reactants) at equal speed. (p. 27)

erection   (ē-rek'shŭn) Engorgement of erectile tissue with blood such as in the erectile tissues of the penis causing the penis to enlarge and become firm. (p. 517)

erector spinae   (ē-rek'tōr spī'nē) Common name of the muscle group of the back; holds the back erect. (p. 172)

erythroblastosis fetalis   (ĕ-rith'rō-blas-tō'sis fē-tă'lis) [erythroblast + Gr. *-osis*, condition] See *hemolytic disease of the newborn.*

erythrocyte   (ĕ-rith'rō-sīt) [Gr. *erythro*, red; *kytos*, cell] Red blood cell (RBC); biconcave disk that contains hemoglobin, which transports oxygen and carbon dioxide; erythrocyte does not have a nucleus. (p. 286)

erythropoietin   (ĕ-rith'rō-poy'ĕ-tin) Protein hormone that stimulates red blood cell formation in red bone marrow. (p. 279)

esophagus   (ē-sof'ă-gŭs) [Gr. *oisophagos*, gullet] The part of the digestive tract between the pharynx and stomach. (p. 428)

estrogen   (es'trō-jen) Steroid hormone secreted primarily by the ovaries; involved in the maintenance and development of female reproductive organs, secondary sexual characteristics, and the menstrual cycle. (p. 278)

eustachian tube   (ū-stā'shŭn) See *auditory tube.*

exchange reaction   A combination of a decomposition reaction, in which molecules are broken down, and a synthesis reaction, in which the products of the decomposition reaction are combined to form new molecules. (p. 27)

exocrine   (ek'sō-krin) [Gr. *exo-*, outside; *krino*, to separate] Gland that secretes to a surface or outward through a duct. (p. 78)

exocytosis   (ek'sō-sī-to'sis) Elimination of material from a cell through the formation of vesicles. (p. 56)

exophthalmia   (ek-sof-thal'mē-ă) Bulging of the eyes that frequently accompanies Graves' disease, due to accumulation of a type of connective tissue behind the eye. (p. 270)

expiration   (eks-pi-rā'shŭn) To breathe out, to move air out of the lungs. (p. 401)

extension   [L. *extensio*] To stretch out; usually to straighten out a joint. (p. 140)

extracellular   (eks-tră-sel'ū-lăr) Refers to the outside of the cell. (p. 42)

extracellular matrix   (mā'triks) Nonliving chemical substances located between cells; often consisting of protein fibers, ground substance, and fluid. (p. 78)

extrinsic muscle   (eks-trin'sik) Muscle located outside of the structure on which it acts. (p. 168)

extrinsic regulation   Regulation of the heart that involves mechanisms outside the heart, including nervous and hormonal regulation. (p. 324)

F

facet   (fas'et) [Fr., little face] A small, smooth articular surface. (p. 126)

facilitated diffusion   (fă-sil'i-tā-tĭd di-fū'zhŭn) Carrier-mediated process that does not require ATP and moves substances into or out of cells from a higher to a lower concentration. (p. 53)

fascia   (fash'ē-ă) [L., band or fillet] Loose areolar connective tissue found beneath the skin (hypodermis), or dense connective tissue that encloses and separates muscles. (p. 151)

fasciculus   (fă-sik'ū-lus) [L. *fascis*, bundle] Band or bundle of nerve or muscle fibers bound together by connective tissue. (p. 151)

fat   Greasy, soft-solid lipid found in animal tissues and many plants; composed of glycerol and fatty acids. (p. 33)

fatty acid   Straight chain of carbon atoms with a carboxyl group (–COOH) attached at one end; a building block of fats. (p. 33)

feces   (fē'sēz) Matter discharged from the digestive tract during defecation, consisting of the undigested residue of food, epithelial cells, intestinal mucus, bacteria, and waste material. (p. 445)

fertilization   (fer'til-i-zā'shŭn) Union of the sperm cell and oocyte to form a zygote. (p. 511)

fetus   (fē'tŭs) In prenatal development, the developing human between approximately 56 days and birth. (p. 560)

fibrillation   (fī-bri-lā'shŭn, fib-rĭ-lā'shŭn) Very rapid contraction of cardiac muscle fibers, but not of the muscle as a whole, results in dramatically reduced pumping action of the heart. (p. 318)

fibrin   (fī'brin) [L. *fibra*, fiber] A threadlike protein fiber derived from fibrinogen by the action of thrombin; forms a clot, that is, a network of fibers that traps blood cells, platelets, and fluid, which stops bleeding. (p. 294)

fibrinogen   (fī-brin'ō-jen) A protein in plasma that gives rise to fibrin when acted on by thrombin to form a clot. (p. 286)

fibrinolysis   (fī-bri-nol'i-sis) [L. *fibra*, fiber; Gr. *lysis*, dissolution] The breakdown of a clot by plasmin. (p. 295)

fibroblast   (fī'brō-blast) Cell in connective tissue responsible for the production of collagen. (p. 79)

filtration   (fil-trā'shŭn) Movement, resulting from a pressure difference, of a liquid through a filter, which prevents some or all of the substances in the liquid from passing. (p. 52)

filtration membrane   Membrane formed by the glomerular capillary endothelium, the basement membrane, and the podocytes of Bowman's capsule. (p. 482)

fimbria   (fim'brē-ă), pl. **fimbriae** (fim'brē-ē) Long thin process that surrounds the opening of the uterine tube. (p. 524)

first heart sound   The heart sound that results from the simultaneous closure of the tricuspid and bicuspid valves. (p. 321)

flagellum   (flă-jel'ŭm), pl. **flagella** (flă-jel'ă) [L., whip] Whiplike locomotor organelle similar to cilia except longer, and there is usually one per sperm cell. (p. 48)

flexion   (flek'shŭn) [L. *flectus*] To bend. (p. 140)

focal point   The point at which light rays cross after passing through a concave lens. (p. 242)

follicle–stimulating hormone (fol'i-kl) **(FSH)** Hormone of the anterior pituitary gland that, in the female, stimulates the follicles of the ovary, assists in maturation of the follicle, and causes secretion of estrogen from the follicle; in the male, stimulates the epithelium of the seminiferous tubules and is partially responsible for inducing spermatogenesis. (p. 270)

fontanel (fon'tă-nel') [Fr., fountain] One of several membranous gaps between bones of the skull. (p. 137)

foramen (fō-rā'men) A hole; referring to a hole or opening in a bone. (p. 118)

foramen ovale (ō-val'ē) In the fetal heart, the oval opening in the interatrial septum with a valve that allows blood to flow from the right to left atrium but not in the opposite direction; becomes the fossa ovalis after birth. (p. 548)

formed element A cell, such as a red blood cell or white blood cell, or cell fragments, such as a platelet, in blood. (p. 286)

fossa (fos'ă) A depression, usually more or less longitudinal in shape below the level of the surface of a bone. (p. 118)

fovea centralis (fō'vē-ă) Depression in the center of the macula of the eye, which has the greatest visual acuity and where there are only cones. (p. 241)

free energy Total amount of energy that can be liberated by the complete catabolism of food. (p. 474)

frenulum (fren'ū-lŭm) [L. *frenum, bridle*] Fold extending from the floor of the mouth to the middle of the under surface of the tongue. (p. 426)

frontal plane Plane separating the body into anterior and posterior portions; also called a coronal plane. (p. 12)

FSH See *follicle-stimulating hormone.*

full–thickness burn Burn that destroys the epidermis and the dermis and sometimes the underlying tissue as well; sometimes called a third-degree burn. (p. 102)

fundus (fŭn'dŭs) [L., bottom] The bottom, or area farthest from the opening, of a hollow organ such as the stomach (p. 429), uterus (p. 526).

G

gamete (gam'ēt) Germ cell such as an oocyte or sperm cell. (p. 63)

gamma globulin (gam'ă glob'ū-lin) A family of proteins found in plasma. (p. 378)

ganglion (gang'glē-on), pl. **ganglia** (gang'glē-ă) [Gr., knot] A group of neuron cell bodies in the peripheral nervous system. (p. 196)

gap junction Small channels that allow materials to pass from one cell to an adjacent cell; provides a means of intercellular communication. (p. 78)

gastric gland (gas'trik) A gland within the stomach. (p. 429)

gastric inhibitory polypeptide Hormone released from the duodenum; inhibits gastric acid secretion. (p. 440)

gastrin (gas'trin) Hormone secreted in the mucosa of the stomach and duodenum that stimulates secretion of hydrochloric acid by the gastric glands. (p. 440)

gastrointestinal tract (gas'trō-in-tes'tin-ăl) Technically only the stomach and intestines. Often used as a synonym for digestive tract, which extends from the mouth to the anus. (p. 425)

gene A sequence of nucleotides in DNA that is a chemical set of instructions for making a specific protein. (p. 563)

genetics (jĕ-net'iks) The branch of science that deals with heredity. (p. 561)

genotype (jen'ō-tīp) Genetic makeup of an individual. (p. 563)

GH See *growth hormone.*

giantism (jī'an-tizm) Abnormal growth in young people because of hypersecretion of growth hormone by the pituitary gland. (p. 268)

gingiva (jin'ji-vă) Dense fibrous tissue, covered by mucous membrane, that covers the alveolar processes of the upper and lower jaws and surrounds the necks of the teeth. (p. 427)

girdle (ger'dl) A bony ring or belt that attaches a limb to the body such as the pectoral (shoulder) (p. 130) and pelvic girdles. (p. 133)

gland A single cell or a multicellular structure that secretes substances into the blood, into a cavity, or onto a surface. (p. 78)

glia (glī'ă) See *neuroglia.*

glomerulus (glō-mār'ū-lŭs) [L. *glomus,* ball of yarn] Mass of capillary loops at the beginning of each nephron, nearly surrounded by Bowman's capsule. (p. 481)

glucagon (gloo'kă-gon) Hormone secreted from the pancreatic islets of the pancreas that acts primarily on the liver to release glucose into the circulatory system. (p. 277)

glucocorticoid (gloo-kō-kōr'ti-koyd) Hormones from the adrenal cortex capable of increasing the rate at which lipids are broken down to fatty acids and proteins are broken down to amino acids; elevates blood glucose levels, and acts as an anti-inflammatory substance. (p. 274)

glycerol (glis'er-ol) A three-carbon molecule with a hydroxyl group attached to each carbon; a building block of fats. (p. 33)

glycogen (glī'kō-jen) Animal starch; composed of many glucose molecules bound together in chains that are highly branched; functions as a carbohydrate reserve, stored glucose molecules, in animal cells. (p. 466)

glycolysis (glī-kol'i-sis) [Gr. *glykys,* sweet; *lysis,* a loosening] Anaerobic process during which one glucose molecule is converted to two pyruvic acid molecules; a net of two ATP molecules is produced during glycolysis. (p. 467)

glycoprotein (glī-kō-prō'tēn) An organic molecule composed of a protein and a carbohydrate.

GnRH See *gonadotropin-releasing hormone.*

goblet cell Epithelial cell that has the end of the cell at the free surface distended with mucin. (p. 77)

goiter (goy'ter) [L. *guttur,* throat] An enlargement of the thyroid gland, not due to a neoplasm, usually caused by a lack of iodine in the diet. (p. 270)

Golgi apparatus (gol'jē) Named for Camillo Golgi, Italian histologist and Nobel laureate, 1843–1926; stacks of flattened sacks, formed by membranes, that collect, modify, package, and distribute proteins and lipids. (p. 45)

gonadotropin (gō'nad-ō-trō'pin) Hormone capable of promoting gonadal growth and function; two major gonadotropins are luteinizing hormone (LH) and follicle-stimulating hormone (FSH). (p. 269)

gonadotropin–releasing hormone (GnRH) Hypothalamic hormone that stimulates the secretion of LH and FSH from the anterior pituitary gland. (p. 518)

granulation tissue (gran'ū-lā'shŭn) Vascular connective tissue formed in wounds. (p. 87)

granulocyte (gran'ū-lō-sīt) White blood cell named according to the appearance, in stained preparations, of large cytoplasmic granules; neutrophils, basophils, and eosinophils. (p. 291)

Graves' disease A type of hyperthyroidism resulting from abnormal proteins produced by the immune system that are similar in structure and function to thyroid-stimulating hormone, often accompanied by exophthalmia. (p. 270)

growth hormone (GH) Protein hormone of the anterior pituitary gland; it promotes body growth, increases fat mobilization, increases blood glucose levels because it inhibits glucose utilization. (p. 267)

gynecomastia (gĭ'nĕ-kō-mas'tē-ă) Enlarged breasts in males. (p. 527)

gyrus (jī'rŭs) [L. *gyros*, circle] Rounded elevation or fold on the surface of the brain. (p. 207)

H

hair A threadlike outgrowth of the skin consisting of columns of dead keratinized epithelial cells. (p. 97)

hair cell Cell of the inner ear containing hairlike processes (microvilli) that respond to bending of the hairs by depolarizing. (p. 246)

hamstring muscle One of the three major muscles of the posterior thigh. (p. 181)

haploid (hap'loyd) The condition in which a cell has one copy of each autosome and one sex chromosome (23 total chromosomes in humans); characteristic of gametes. (p. 63)

haustra (haw'stră) Sacs of the colon, formed by the teniae coli, which are slightly shorter than the gut, so that the gut is thrown into pouches.

Haversian canal (ha-ver'shan) Named for 17th-century English anatomist, Clopton Havers (1650–1702); see *central canal*. (p. 112)

haversian system See *osteon*.

hCG See *human chorionic gonadotropin*.

heart–lung machine A machine that pumps blood and carries out the process of gas exchange; it substitutes for the heart and lungs during heart surgery. (p. 327)

heart rate The number of complete cardiac cycles (heartbeats) per minute. (p. 323)

heart transplant The process of taking a healthy heart from a recently deceased donor and transplanting it into a recipient who has a diseased heart. (p. 328)

hematocrit (hē'mă-tō-krit, hem'a-tō-krit) [Gr. *hemato*, blood; *krino*, to separate] The percentage of total blood volume composed of red blood cells. (p. 299)

hematopoiesis (hē'mă-tō-poy-ē'sis) [Gr. *haima*, blood; *poiesis*, a making] Production of blood cells. (p. 286)

hemidesmosome (hem-ē-des'mō-sōm) Half desmosome that occurs on the basal surface epithelial cells that rest on the basement membrane. (p. 77)

hemoglobin (hē-mō-glō'bin) Red protein of red blood cells consisting of four globin proteins with an iron-containing red pigment, heme, bound to each globin protein; transports oxygen and carbon dioxide. (p. 290)

hemolysis (hē-mol'i-sis) [Gr. *hemo*, blood; *lysis*, destruction] The rupture of red blood cells. (p. 296)

hemolytic (hē-mō-lit'ik) **disease of the newborn** Destruction of red blood cells in the fetus or newborn caused by antibodies produced in the Rh-negative mother acting on the Rh-positive blood of the fetus or newborn. (p. 299)

hemorrhage (hem'ŏ-rij) [Gr. *haima*, blood; *rhegnymi*, to burst forth] Rupture or leaking of blood from vessels. (p. 301)

hepatic (he-pat'ik) [Gr. *hepar*, liver] Associated with the liver. (p. 349)

hepatic portal system [L. *porta*, gate] Blood flow through the veins that begin as capillary beds in the small intestine, spleen, pancreas, and stomach and carry blood to the liver, where they end as a capillary bed. (p. 349)

hepatic portal vein The vein that carries blood from the intestines, stomach, spleen, and pancreas to the liver. (p. 349)

Hering–Breuer reflex Named for the Austrian internist, Josef Breuer (1842–1914), and the German physiologist, Heinrich E. Hering (1866–1948). Process in which action potentials from stretch receptors in the lungs arrest inspiration, expiration then occurs. (p. 413)

heterozygous (het'er-ō-zī'gŭs) Having two different genes for a given trait. (p. 563)

hilum (hī'lŭm) [L., a small amount or trifle] Part of an organ where the nerves and vessels enter and leave. (p. 400)

histology (his-tol'ō-jē) [Gr. *histo*, web (tissue); *logos*, study] The science that deals with the structure of cells, tissues, and organs in relation to their function. (p. 72)

holocrine (hol'ō-krin) [G. *holo*, whale + G. *krinō*, to separate] Gland whose secretion consists of disintegrated cells of the gland. An example is a sebaceous gland.

homeostasis (ho'mē-ō-stā'sis) [Gr. *homoio*, like; *stasis*, a standing] Existence and maintenance of a relatively constant environment within the body with respect to functions and the composition of fluids and tissues. (p. 7)

homeotherm (hō'mē-ō-therm) [Gr. *homoiois*, like; *thermos*, warm] Any animal, including mammals and birds, that tends to maintain a constant body temperature; also referred to as warm-blooded. (p. 473)

homozygous (hō-mō-zī'gŭs) Having two identical genes for a given trait. (p. 563)

hormone (hōr'mōn) [Gr. *hormon*, to set into motion] Substance secreted by endocrine tissues into the blood that acts on a target tissue to produce a specific response. (p. 264)

human chorionic gonadotropin (hCG) (kō-rē-on'ik gō'nad-ō-trō'pin) A hormone similar to LH secreted from the placenta and is essential for the maintenance of pregnancy for the first three months, functions to prevent the corpus luteum from degenerating. (p. 279)

humerus (hū'mer-ŭs) [L., shoulder] The bone of the arm. (p. 132)

humoral immunity (hū'-mōr-ăl i-mū'ni-tē) See *antibody-mediated immunity*.

hydrogen bond (hī'drō-jen) The weak attraction between the oppositely charged ends of two polar covalent molecules; the weak attraction between the end of a polar covalent molecule and an ion. (p. 23)

hydroxyapatite (hī-drok'sē-ap-ă-tīt) The complex crystal structure that makes up the mineral portion of bones and teeth. (p. 112)

hymen (hī'men) [Gr. *hymēn*, membrane] A thin membranous fold highly variable in appearance which partly occludes the opening of the vagina prior to its rupture, which may occur for a variety of reasons, and is frequently absent. (p. 526)

hyoid (hī'oyd) [Gr., shaped like the letter epsilon, ϵ] The U-shaped bone in the throat. (p. 120)

hypertension (hī'per-ten'shŭn) [Gr. *hyper*, above; *tensio*, tension] High blood pressure; generally blood pressure greater than 140/90 is considered to be too high. (p. 351)

hyperthyroidism (hī-per-thī'royd-izm) An abnormality of the thyroid gland in which thyroid hormone secretion is increased. (p. 270)

hypertonic (hī-per-ton'ik) [Gr. *hyper*, above; *tonos*, tension] Solution that causes cells to shrink. (p. 52)

hypodermis (hī-pō-der'mis) [Gr. *hypo*, under; *dermis*, skin] Loose connective tissue under the dermis that attaches the skin to muscle and bone. (p. 94)

hypophysis (hī-pof'i-sis) [*hypo* + Gr., an undergrowth] Endocrine gland attached to the hypothalamus by the infundibulum; the pituitary gland. (p. 265)

hypothalamic–pituitary portal system (hī'pō-thal'ă-mĭk-pi-too'i-tār-ē) Series of blood vessels that carry blood from the area of the hypothalamus to the anterior pituitary gland; originates from capillary beds in the hypothalamus and terminates as a capillary bed in the anterior pituitary gland. (p. 267)

hypothalamus (hī'pō-thal'ă-mŭs) [*hypo* + Gr. *thalamus*, bedroom] Important autonomical and endocrine control center of the brain located beneath the thalamus of the brain. (p. 207)

hypothyroidism   (hī′pō-thī′royd-izm) Reduced secretion of thyroid hormones from the thyroid gland, leading to cretinism in infants and symptoms of inadequate thyroid hormone secretion in adults. (p. 270)

hypotonic   (hī-pō-ton′ik) [*hypo* + Gr. *tonos,* tension] Solution that causes cells to swell. (p. 52)

I

ICSH   See *interstitial cell-stimulating hormone.*

Ig   See *immunoglobulin.*

ileocecal junction   (il′ē-ō-se′kăl) The junction of the ileum of the small intestine and the cecum of the large intestine. (p. 429)

ileum   (il′ē-ŭm) [L. *eileo,* to roll up, twist] The third portion of the small intestine, about 3.5 meters in length; extends from the jejunum to the ileocecal opening. (p. 429)

ilium   (il′ē-ŭm) the broad, flaring portion of the hipbone, becomes fused with the ischium and pubis. (p. 133).

immunity   (i-mū′ni-tē) The ability to resist damage from foreign substances such as microorganisms and harmful chemicals such as toxins released by microorganisms. (p. 372)

immunoglobulin   (im′ū-nō-glob-ū-lin) **(Ig)** Refers to antibodies. (p. 378)

implantation   (im-plan-tā′shŭn) Attachment of the blastocyst to the endometrium of the uterus; occurring 6 or 7 days after fertilization of the oocyte. (p. 542)

impotence   (im′pŏ-tens) Inability of the male to achieve or maintain an erection and thus engage in sexual intercourse. (p. 521)

incompetent valve   A leaky valve; usually refers to a leaky valve in the heart that allows blood to flow through it when it is closed. (p. 321)

incus   (ing′kus) [L. anvil] The middle bone of the middle ear; the anvil. (p. 243)

infarct   (in′farkt) Area of necrosis resulting from a sudden insufficiency of arterial blood supply. (p. 311)

inferior   (in-fē′rē-ōr) [L., lower] Down, or lower, with reference to the anatomical position. (p. 9)

inferior vena cava   (vē′nă kā′vă) Receives blood from the lower limbs, pelvis, and abdominal organs and empties into the right atrium of the heart. (p. 310)

inflammatory   (in-flam′ă-tōr-ē) **response** Complex sequence of events involving chemicals and immune system cells that results in the isolation and destruction of foreign substances such as bacteria;

symptoms include redness, heat, swelling, pain, and disturbance of function. (p. 86)

infundibulum   (in-fŭn-dib′ū-lŭm) [L., funnel] Funnel-shaped structure or passage, for example, the infundibulum that attaches the pituitary gland to the hypothalamus; funnellike expansion of the uterine tube near the ovary. (p. 207)

inguinal canal   (ing′gwi-năl) The passageway through which a testis passes as it descends from the abdominopelvic cavity to the scrotum. (p. 515)

inguinal hernia   (her′nē-ă) A rupture which allows the potential protrusion of abdominal organs such as the small intestine through the inguinal canal. (p. 515)

innate immunity   (i′nāt, i-nāt′) Immune system response that is the same on each exposure to an antigen; there is no ability to remember a previous exposure to a specific antigen. (p. 372)

inner cell mass   Group of cells at one end of the blastocyst from which the embryo develops. (p. 542)

inorganic   (in-ōr-gan′ik) Molecules that do not contain carbon atoms; originally defined as molecules that came from nonliving sources; the original definition is no longer valid, because carbon dioxide produced by living organisms is considered an inorganic molecule. (p. 30)

insertion   (in-ser′shŭn) The more movable attachment point of a muscle. (p. 165)

inspiration   (in-spi-rā′shŭn) To breathe in, to move air into the lungs, or inhale. (p. 401)

insulin   (in′sŭ-lin) Protein hormone secreted from the pancreas that increases the uptake of glucose and amino acids by most tissues. (p. 277)

interatrial septum   (in-ter-ā′trē-ăl) The cardiac muscle partition separating the right and left atria. (p. 312)

intercalated disk   (in-ter′kă-lā-ted) Connection between cardiac muscle cells; important in coordinating the contractions of cardiac muscle cells; contains gap junctions that allow action potentials to pass from one cardiac muscle cell to adjacent cardiac muscle cells. (p. 83)

intercostal muscle   (in-ter-kos′tăl) Muscle located between ribs. (p. 172)

interferon   (in-ter-fēr′on) A protein released by virally infected cells that binds to other cells and stimulates them to produce antiviral proteins that inhibit viral replication. (p. 373)

interkinesis   (in′ter-ki-nē′sis) The short time period between the formation of the

daughter cells of the first meiotic division and the second meiotic division. (p. 63)

interstitial cell   (in-ter-stish′ăl) Cell between the seminiferous tubules of the testes; secretes testosterone; also called cell of Leydig. (p. 514)

interstitial cell-stimulating hormone (ICSH) A term sometimes used to refer to luteinizing hormone in males. Hormone of the anterior pituitary gland that stimulates the secretion of testosterone in the testes. See *luteinizing hormone.* (p. 270)

interventricular septum   (in-ter-ven-trik′ū-lăr) The cardiac muscle partition separating the right and left ventricles. (p. 312)

intestinal glands   (in-tes′ti-năl) Tubular glands in the mucous membrane of the small intestine. (p. 429)

intracellular   (in-tră-sel′ū-lăr) Refers to the inside of the cell. (p. 42)

intramembranous ossification   (in′tră-mem′bră-nŭs os′i-fi-kā′shŭn) Bone formation within connective tissue membranes. (p. 114)

intramural plexus   (in′tră-mū′răl plek′sŭs) [L., within the wall] A nerve plexus within the walls of the gastrointestinal tract; involved in local and autonomic control of digestion. (p. 425)

intrinsic factor   (in-trin′sik) Factor secreted by the gastric glands and required for adequate absorption of vitamin B$_{12}$. (p. 440)

intrinsic muscle   Muscle located within the structure on which it acts. (p. 168)

ion   (ī′on) Atom or group of atoms carrying an electrical charge because of a loss or gain of one or more electrons. (p. 21)

ionic bond   (ī-on′ik) Chemical bond resulting from the attraction between ions of opposite charge. (p. 22)

iris   (ī′ris) Specialized part of the vascular tunic of the eye; the "colored" part of the eye that can be seen through the cornea; consists of smooth muscles that regulate the amount of light entering the eye. (p. 239)

isometric contraction   (ī-sō-met′rik) Muscle contraction in which the length of the muscle does not change but the amount of tension increases. (p. 162)

isotonic   (ī′sō-ton′ik) [Gr. *iso,* equal; *tonos,* tension] Solution that causes cells to neither shrink nor swell. (p. 52)

isotonic contraction   Muscle contraction in which the amount of tension is constant and the muscle shortens. (p. 163)

isotope   (ī′sō-tōp) One of two or more elements that have the same number of protons and electrons, but a different number of neutrons. (p. 26)

J

jaundice (jawn′dis) [Fr. *jaune,* yellow] Yellowish staining of the skin, sclerae, and deeper tissues and excretions with bile pigments. (p. 101)

jejunum (jĕ-joo′nŭm) [L. *jejunus,* empty] A portion of the small intestine, about 2.5 meters in length, between the duodenum and ileum. (p. 429)

juxtaglomerular apparatus (jŭks′tă-glŏ-mer′ū-lăr) Specialized wall of the distal tubule and afferent arteriole that secretes renin. (p. 485)

K

keratin (ker′ă-tin) A protein that accumulates in cells of nails, hair, and the superficial layers of the epidermis of the skin. (p. 95)

keratinization (ker′ă-tin-i-ză′shŭn) Production of keratin and changes in the structure and shape of epithelial cells as they move to the skin surface. (p. 95)

Korotkoff sound (kō-rot′kof) Named for the Russian physician Nickolai Korotkoff (1874–1920). Sound heard over an artery when blood pressure is determined by the auscultatory method. (p. 350)

kyphosis (kī-fō′sis) [Gr., hump-back] Abnormal posterior curvature, or flexion, of the spine. (p. 126)

L

labia majora (lā′bē-a) Two rounded folds of skin surrounding the labia minora and vestibule. (p. 526)

labia minora Two narrow longitudinal folds of mucous membrane enclosed by the labia majora; anteriorly they unite to form the prepuce. (p. 526)

labyrinth (lab′i-rinth) A series of membranous and bony tunnels in the temporal bone; part of the inner ear involved in hearing and balance. (p. 243)

lacrimal (lak′ri-măl) [L., a tear] Relating to tears or tear production. (p. 124)

lactation (lak′tā′shŭn) [L. *lactatio,* suckle] Period following childbirth during which milk is formed in the breasts. (p. 556)

lacteal (lak′tē-ăl) Lymphatic vessel in the wall of the small intestine that carries chyle from the intestine and absorbs fat. (p. 368)

lactic acid (lak′tik) Three-carbon molecule derived from pyruvic acid as a product of anaerobic respiration. (p. 468)

lacuna (lă-koo′nă), pl. **lacunae** (lă-koo′nē) [L., a pit] A small space, cavity, or depression; a space in cartilage in which a condrocyte is located (p. 83); a

space in bone matrix in which an osteocyte is located (p. 112); cavity containing maternal blood in the placenta. (p. 543)

lamella (lă-mel′ă), pl. **lamellae** (lă-mel′ē) [L. *lamina,* plate, leaf] A thin sheet or layer of bone. (p. 112)

lamina (lam′i-nă), pl. **laminoe** (lam′i-nē) [L. *lamina,* plate, leaf] A layer; a portion of the vertebra that extends from the transverse process to the spinous process. (p. 126)

lamina propria (prō′prē-ă) Layer of connective tissue underlying the epithelium of a mucous membrane. (p. 425)

lanugo (lă-noo′gō) [L. *lana,* wool] Fine, soft, fetal or embryonic hair. (p. 548)

laryngitis (lar-in-jī′tis) Inflammation of the mucous membrane of the larynx. (p. 397)

laryngopharynx (lă-ring′gō-far-ingks) Part of the pharynx lying below the tip of the epiglottis extending to the level of the cricoid cartilage of the larynx. (p. 396)

larynx (lar′ingks) Organ of voice production located between the pharynx and the trachea; it consists of a framework of cartilages and elastic membranes housing the vocal folds (true vocal cords) and the muscles that control the position and tension of these elements. (p. 396)

lateral [L. *latus,* side] Away from the middle or midline of the body. (p. 10)

lateral horn The small, lateral extension of spinal cord gray matter; located only in spinal cord regions T1–L2; containing preganglionic sympathetic neuron cell bodies. (p. 211)

lens The biconvex structure in the anterior part of the eye capable of being flattened or thickened to adjust the focus of light entering the eye. (p. 239)

leukemia (loo-kē′mē-ă) [Gr. *leukos,* white; *haima,* blood] A tumor of the red bone marrow that results in the production of large numbers of abnormal white blood cells; often accompanied by decreased production of red blood cells and platelets. (p. 300)

leukocyte (loo′kō-sīt) [Gr. *leukos,* white; *kytos,* cell] White blood cell; round, nucleated cell involved in immunity; the five types of leukocytes are neutrophils, eosinophils, basophils, lymphocytes, and monocytes. (p. 286)

leukocytosis (loo′kō-sī-tō′sis) [leukocyte + Gr. *-osis,* a condition] A higher than normal number of white blood cells. (p. 300)

leukopenia (loo-kō-pē′nē-ă) [leukocyte + Gr. *penia,* poverty] A lower than normal number of white blood cells. (p. 300)

Leydig cell (lī′dig) Named for the German anatomist, Franz von Leydig (1821–1908). See *interstitial cell.*

LH See *luteinizing hormone.*

ligament (lig′ă-ment) A tough connective tissue band usually connecting bone to bone. (p. 111)

limbic system (lim′bik) [L. *limbus,* a border] A primitive part of the brain involved in visceral and emotional response and in the response to odor. (p. 211)

linea alba (lin′ē-ă al′bă) White line in the center of the abdomen where muscles of the abdominal wall insert. (p. 172)

lipase (lip′ās) An enzyme that breaks down lipids. (p. 444)

lipid (lip′ĭd) [Gr. *lipos,* fat] Substance composed principally of carbon, oxygen, and hydrogen; generally soluble in nonpolar solvents; fats and cholesterol. (p. 32)

local inflammation Inflammation confined to a specific area of the body; symptoms include redness, heat, swelling, pain, and loss of function. (p. 375)

longitudinal section A cut made through the long axis of an organ. (p. 12)

loop of Henle U-shaped part of the nephron extending from the proximal to the distal tubule and consisting of descending and ascending limbs; many of the loops of Henle extend into the renal pyramids. (p. 481)

lordosis (lōr-dō′sis) [Gr., a bending backward; swayback] An abnormal anterior curvature of the spine, usually in the lumbar region; saddle back or swayback. (p. 126)

lower motor neuron A motor neuron located in the brainstem or spinal cord, as opposed to the cerebral cortex. (p. 214)

lumbosacral plexus (lŭm′bō-sā′krăl) The nerve plexus that innervates the lower limbs; originates from spinal nerves L1 to S4. (p. 223)

lunula (loo′noo-lă) [L. *luna,* moon] White, crescent-shaped portion of the nail matrix visible through the proximal end of the nail. (p. 99)

luteinizing hormone (LH) (loo′tē-ĭ-nīz-ing) Hormone of the anterior pituitary gland that, in the female, initiates final maturation of the follicles, their rupture to release the oocyte, the conversion of the ruptured follicle into the corpus luteum, and the secretion of progesterone; in the male, stimulates the secretion of testosterone in the testes and is sometimes referred to as interstitial cell-stimulating hormone (ICSH). (p. 269)

lymph (limf) [L. *lympha,* clear spring water] Clear or yellowish fluid derived from interstitial fluid and found in lymphatic vessels. (p. 368)

lymph node Encapsulated mass of lymphatic tissue found along lymphatic vessels; functions to filter lymph and produce lymphocytes. (p. 370)

lymphocyte (lim′fō-sīt) Nongranulocytic white blood cell involved in the immune system; there are several types of lymphocytes with diverse functions, including antibody production, allergic reactions, graft rejections, tumor control, and regulation of the immune system. (p. 292)

lymphokine (lim′fō-kīn) A class of chemicals produced by T cells that activate macrophages and other immune cells; promote phagocytosis and inflammation. (p. 387)

lymphoma (lim-fō′mă) A neoplasm (tumor) of lymphatic tissue that is almost always malignant. (p. 372)

lysis (lī′sis) [Gr., dissolution or loosening] The rupturing or breaking of the cell membrane of a cell. (p. 52)

lysosome (lī′sō-sōm) [Gr. *lysis,* a loosening; *soma,* body] Membrane-bound vesicle containing intracellular digestive enzymes. (p. 45)

M

macrophage (mak′rō-fāj) [Gr. *makros,* large; *phagein,* to eat] Any large mononuclear, phagocytic cell. (p. 79)

macula (mak′ū-lă) One of the sensory structures in the vestibule, consisting of hair cells and a gelatinous mass embedded with otoliths; responds to gravity. (p. 248)

macula lutea (loo′tē-ă) [L., a yellow spot] Small yellow spot in the posterior retina of the eye where the cones are concentrated; has no red tint because it is devoid of blood vessels. (p. 241)

malignant (mă-lig′nănt) [L. *maligno,* to do anything malicious] In reference to a neoplasm, the property of locally spreading and spreading to distant sites. (p. 89)

malleus (mal′ē-ŭs) [L., hammer] The most lateral of the middle ear bones, attached to the tympanic membrane; the hammer. (p. 243)

mamma (mam′ă) pl. **mammae** (mam′ē) See *mammary gland.*

mammary gland (mam′ă-rē) The organ of milk secretion, located in the breast or mamma. (p. 527)

mastication (mas-ti-kā′shŭn) [L. *mastico,* to chew] Process of chewing. (p. 168)

matrix (mā′triks) The substance between the cells of a tissue. (p. 111)

matter Anything that occupies space. (p. 20)

mean arterial blood pressure The average of the arterial blood pressure; it is slightly less than the average of the systolic and diastolic blood pressure, because diastole lasts longer than systole. (p. 355)

meatus (mē-ā′tŭs) [L., to go, pass] Passageway or tunnel. (p. 118)

meconium (mē-kō′nē-ŭm) Greenish anal discharge from the fetus; consists of fluid swallowed, epithelial cells from the mucosa of the gut, mucus from the intestinal glands, and bile from the liver. (p. 556)

medial (mē′dē-ăl) [L. *medialis,* middle] Toward the middle or midline of the body. (p. 10)

mediastinum (me′dē-as-tī′nŭm) [L., middle septum] The middle wall of the thorax consisting of the trachea, esophagus, thymus, heart, and other structures. (p. 12)

mediator of inflammation Chemical released or activated by injured tissues and adjacent blood vessels; produces vasodilation, increases vascular permeability, and attracts blood cells; includes histamine, kinins, prostaglandins, and leukotrienes. (p. 86)

medulla (me-dool′ă) [L. *medius,* middle, marrow] The center or core of an organ such as the adrenal gland, kidney, or hair. (p. 97)

medulla oblongata (ob-long-gah′tă) Inferior portion of the brainstem that connects the spinal cord with the brain; contains nuclei of cranial nerves plus autonomic control centers for heart rate, respiration, and so forth. (p. 203)

medullary cavity (med′ŭl-er-ē) Large, marrow-filled cavity in the diaphysis of a long bone. (p. 112)

medullary respiratory center (res′pi-ră-tōr-ē, rĕ-spīr′ă-tōr-ē) Nerve cells in the medulla oblongata and pons of the brain that control inspiration and expiration. (p. 411)

megakaryocyte (meg-ă-kar′ē-ō-sīt) Large cell in red bone marrow that gives rise to platelets. (p. 293)

meiosis (mī-ō′sis) [Gr., a lessening] Process of cell division that results in gametes. Consists of two cell divisions that result in four cells, each of which contains half the number of chromosomes as the parent cell; occur in the testes and ovaries. (p. 63)

melanin (mel′ă-nin) [Gr. *melas,* black] Brown to black pigment responsible for skin and hair color. (p. 96)

melanocyte (mel′ă-nō-sīt) [Gr. *melas,* black; *kytos,* cell] Cells found mainly in the stratum basale of skin that produce the brown or black pigment melanin. (p. 96)

melanocyte–stimulating hormone (MSH) Peptide hormone secreted by the anterior pituitary gland; increases melanin production by melanocytes, making the skin darker in color. (p. 270)

melanoma (mel′ă-nō′mă) [Gr. *melas,* black; *oma,* tumor] A malignant tumor derived from melanocytes. (p. 103)

melatonin (mel-ă-tōn′in) Hormone secreted by the pineal body; may inhibit gonadotropin-releasing hormone secretion from the hypothalamus. (p. 279)

membranous labyrinth (mem′bră-nŭs lab′i-rinth) The membrane-bound set of tunnels and chambers of the inner ear. (p. 243)

memory cell Lymphocyte derived from a B cell or T cell that has been exposed to an antigen; when exposed to the same antigen a second time, the memory cell rapidly responds to provide immunity. (p. 381)

memory response Immune response that occurs when the immune system is exposed to an antigen against which it has already had a primary response; results in the production of large amounts of antibodies and memory cells; also called a secondary response. (p. 381)

menarche (me-nar′kē) The time of the first menstrual period or flow. (p. 528)

meninges (mĕ-nin′jēz) [Gr., membrane] A series of three connective tissue membranes; the dura mater, arachnoid mater, and pia mater; surround and protect the brain and spinal cord. (p. 214)

menopause (men′ō-pawz) [Gr. *mensis,* month; *pausis,* cessation] Permanent cessation of the menstrual cycle. (p. 531)

menses (men′sēz) [L. *mensis,* month] Loss of blood and tissue as the endometrium of the uterus sloughs away at the end of the menstrual cycle; occurring at about 28-day intervals in the nonpregnant female of reproductive age. (p. 528)

menstrual cycle (men′stroo-ăl) Series of changes that occur in sexually mature, nonpregnant females and result in menses; specifically includes the cyclical changes that occur in the uterus and ovary. (p. 528)

merocrine (mer′ō-krin) [Gr. *meros,* part; *krino,* to separate] Gland that secretes products with no loss of cellular material; an example is water-producing sweat glands; see *apocrine* and *holocrine.* (p. 99)

mesentery (mes′en-ter-ē) [Gr. *mesos,* middle; *enteron,* intestine] Double layer of peritoneum extending from the abdominal wall to the abdominopelvic organs; conveys blood vessels and nerves to abdominopelvic organs; holds and supports abdominopelvic organs. (p. 436)

mesoderm (mez′ō-derm) Middle of the three germ layers of the embryo. (p. 545)

mesovarium (mez′ō-vā′rē-ŭm) Mesentery of the ovary; mesentery that attaches the ovary to the posterior surface of the broad ligament. (p. 522)

metabolic rate The total amount of energy produced and used by the body per unit of time. (p. 472)

metabolism (mĕ-tab′ō-lizm) [Gr. *metabole,* change] Sum of the chemical changes that occur in tissues, consisting of the breakdown of molecules (catabolism) to produce energy and the buildup of molecules (anabolism), which requires energy. (p. 465)

metastasis (mĕ-tas′tă-sis) The shifting of a disease or a neoplasm from one part of the body to another remote from the original location. (p. 89)

micelle (mi-sel′, mī-sel′) [L. *micella,* small morsel] Droplet of digested lipid surrounded by bile salts in the small intestine. (p. 448)

microglia (mī-krog′lē-ă) [Gr. *micro,* small; *glia,* glue] Small neuroglial cells that become phagocytic and mobile in response to inflammation; considered to be macrophages of the central nervous system. (p. 196)

microtubule (mī-krō-too′būl) Hollow tube composed of tubulin; microtubules help provide support to the cytoplasm of the cell and are components of certain cell organelles such as cilia and flagella. (p. 47)

microvillus (mī′krō-vil′ŭs), pl. **microvilli** (mī′krō-vil′ī) One of the minute projections of the cell membrane that greatly increase the surface area of the cell membrane. (pp. 77)

micturition reflex (mik-choo-rish′ŭn) Contraction of the urinary bladder stimulated by stretching of the urinary bladder wall; results in emptying of the urinary bladder. (p. 494)

midbrain The superior end of the brainstem; located between the pons and diencephalon; contains fibers crossing from the brain to the spinal cord and vice versa, as well as nuclei and visual reflex centers. (p. 205)

midsagittal (mid′saj′i-tăl) Plane running vertically through the body and dividing it into equal right and left parts. (p. 12)

mineral (min′er-ăl) Inorganic nutrient necessary for normal metabolic functions. (p. 465)

mineralocorticoid (min′er-al-ō-kōr′ti-koyd) A steroid hormone released from the adrenal cortex; acts on the kidney to increase the rate of sodium ion reabsorption from the nephron and potassium and hydrogen ion secretion into the nephron of the kidney; an example is aldosterone. (p. 276)

mitochondrion (mī-tō-kon′drē-on), pl. **mitochondria** (mī-tō-kon′drē-ă) [Gr. *mitos,* thread; *chandros,* granule] Small, spherical, rod-shaped or thin filamentous structure in the cytoplasm that is a major site of ATP production. (p. 47)

mitosis (mī-tō′sis) [Gr., thread] Division of the nucleus. Process of cell division that results in two daughter cells with exactly the same number and type of chromosomes as the parent cell. (p. 59)

mitral valve (mī′trăl) See *bicuspid valve.*

molecule (mol′ĕ-kūl) Two or more atoms chemically combined to form a structure that behaves as an independent unit. (p. 24)

monocyte (mon′ō-sīt) A type of white blood cell that transforms to become a macrophage. (p. 292)

mononuclear phagocytic system (mon-ō-noo′klē-ăr fag-ō-sit′ik) Phagocytic cells with a single nucleus, derived from monocytes; the cells either enter a tissue by chemotaxis in response to infection or tissue damage, or are positioned to intercept microorganisms entering tissues. (p. 373)

monosaccharide (mon-ō-sak′ă-rīd) The basic building block from which more complex carbohydrates are constructed; for example, glucose and fructose. (p. 32)

mons pubis (monz pū′bis) [L., mountain] Prominence formed by a pad of fatty tissue over the symphysis pubis in the female. (p. 526)

motor unit A single motor neuron and all the skeletal muscle fibers it innervates. (p. 156)

MSH See *melanocyte-stimulating hormone.*

mucin (mū′sin) Secretion containing mucopolysaccharides (proteoglycans), produced by mucous gland cells. (p. 438)

mucosa (mū-kō′să) Mucous membrane consisting of the epithelium and connective tissue; in the digestive tract there is also a layer of smooth muscle. (p. 425)

mucous membrane (mū′kŭs) Thin sheet consisting of epithelium and connective tissue that lines cavities opening to the outside of the body; many contain mucous glands, which secrete mucus. (p. 86)

mucus (mū′kŭs) Viscous secretion produced by and covering mucous membranes; lubricates and protects the mucous membrane, and traps foreign substances. (p. 77)

murmur (mer′mer) An abnormal sound produced within the heart. (p. 321)

muscle fiber (mŭs′ĕl) Muscle cell. (p. 83)

muscle tissue One of the four major tissue types; consists of cells with the ability to contract; includes skeletal, cardiac, and smooth muscle. (p. 83)

muscle twitch Contraction of an entire muscle in response to a stimulus that causes an action potential in one or more muscle fibers. (p. 159)

muscularis (mŭs-kū-lā′ris) The outermost smooth muscle coat of a hollow organ. (p. 425)

muscularis mucosa The inner, thin layer of smooth muscle found in most parts of the digestive tube outside the lamina propria. (p. 425)

myelinated (mī′ĕ-li-nāt-ed) [Gr. *myelos,* marrow] Nerve fibers having a myelin sheath. (p. 196)

myelin sheath (mī′ĕ-lin) A lipoprotein envelope made by wrappings of the cell membrane of a Schwann cell or oligodendrocyte around an axon. (p. 196)

myocardium (mī-ō-kar′dē-ŭm) [*myo-* + Gr. *kordin,* heart] Middle layer of the heart, consisting of cardiac muscle. (p. 314)

myofibril (mī-ō-fī′bril) A fine longitudinal fibril within a skeletal muscle fiber; consisting of sarcomeres composed of thick (myosin) and thin (actin) myofilaments, placed end to end. (p. 151)

myofilament (mī-ō-fil′ă-ment) An ultramicroscopic protein thread helping to form myofibrils in skeletal muscle; thin myofilaments are composed of actin, and thick myofilaments are composed of myosin. (p. 152)

myometrium (mī′ō-mē′trē-ŭm) Muscular wall of the uterus, composed of smooth muscle. (p. 526)

myosin myofilament (mī′ō-sin) One of the two major kinds of protein fibers of a sarcomere; thick filament, resembles bundles of golf clubs. (p. 152)

myxedema (mik-se-dē′mă) Hypothyroidism characterized by edema beneath the skin due to a change in the structure of the subcutaneous connective tissue. (p. 270)

N

NADH See *nicotinamide adenine dinucleotide.*

nail (nāl) A thin, horny plate at the ends of the fingers and toes, consisting of several layers of dead epithelial cells containing a hard keratin. (p. 99)

naris (nā'ris), pl. **nares** (nā'res) Nostril, the opening into the nasal cavity. (p. 394)

nasal cavity (nā'zăl) Cavity divided by the nasal septum, and extending from the external nares anteriorly to the nasopharynx posteriorly; bounded inferiorly by the hard palate. (p. 123)

nasolacrimal duct (nā-zō-lak'ri-măl) Duct that leads from the lacrimal sac to the nasal cavity. (p. 238)

nasopharynx (nā'zō-far'ingks) Part of the pharynx that lies above the soft palate; anteriorly it opens into the nasal cavity. (p. 396)

negative feedback Mechanisms by which any deviation from an ideal normal value or set point is resisted or negated; returns a parameter to its normal range and thereby maintains homeostasis. (p. 7)

neonate (nē'ō-nāt) [Gr. *neos,* new; L. *natalis,* relating to birth] Newborn, from birth to 1 month. (p. 554)

neoplasm (nē'ō-plazm) [*neo* + Gr. *plasma,* thing formed] New growth, an abnormal tissue growth that grows by cellular proliferation; may be benign or malignant. (p. 89)

nephron (nef'ron) [Gr. *nephros,* kidney] Functional unit of the kidney, consisting of the renal corpuscle, the proximal tubule, the loop of Henle, and the distal tubule. (p. 480)

nerve (nerv) A collection of axons in the peripheral nervous system; functions to conduct action potentials to and from the central nervous system. (p. 196)

nerve cell A cell capable of receiving a stimulus and propagating an action potential; a neuron. (p. 83)

nerve tract Bundle of axons, their sheaths, and accompanying connective tissues located in the central nervous system. (p. 196)

nervous tissue (ner'vŭs) One of the four major tissue types; consists of neurons, which have the ability to conduct action potentials, and neuroglia, which are support cells. (p. 83)

neural crest cell (noor'ăl) Cell derived during embryonic development from the crests of the neural folds; gives rise to facial structures, pigment cells, and peripheral nerve ganglia. (p. 546)

neural tube Tube formed from the neuroectoderm in the embryo by closure of the neural groove; develops into the brain and spinal cord. (p. 546)

neuroectoderm (noor-ō-ek'tō-derm) That part of the ectoderm that forms the neural tube and neural crest. (p. 546)

neuroglia (noo-rog'lē-ă) [Gr. *neuro,* nerve; *glia,* glue] Cells of the nervous system other than neurons; play a support role in the nervous system; include astrocytes, ependymal cells, microglia, oligodendrocytes, and Schwann cells; also called glia. (p. 84)

neuromuscular junction (noor-rō-mŭs'kū-lăr) The synaptic junction between a nerve axon and a muscle fiber. (p. 156)

neuron (noor'on) [Gr., nerve] A nerve cell. (p. 83)

neurotransmitter (noor'ō-trans-mit'er) [Gr. *neuro,* nerve; L. *tramitto,* to send across] A chemical that is released by a presynaptic cell into the synaptic cleft and that acts up on the postsynaptic cell to cause a response. (p. 156)

neutral solution (noo'trăl) Solution with equal numbers of hydrogen and hydroxide ions; has a pH of 7.0. (p. 29)

neutron (noo'tron) [L. *neuter,* neither] Electrically neutral particle found in the nucleus of atoms. (p. 20)

neutrophil (noo'trō-fil) [L. *neuter,* neither; Gr. *phileo,* to love] White blood cell with granules that stains equally with either basic or acidic dyes; phagocytic white blood cell. (p. 86)

nevus (nē'vŭs), pl. **nevi** (nē'vī) A benign localized overgrowth of the melanin-forming cells of the skin present at birth or appearing early in life, a mole. (p. 89)

nicotinamide adenine dinucleotide (NADH) (nik-ō-tin'ă-mīd ad'ě-nēn dī-noo'klē-ō-tīd) A base-containing organic molecule capable of accepting hydrogen atoms and of transferring energy from glycolysis and the citric acid cycle to the electron-transport chain. (p. 467)

nitroglycerin (nī-trō-glis'er-in) Glyceryl trinitrate used as a vasodilator, especially in angina pectoris. (p. 327)

node of Ranvier (ron'vē-ā) The unmyelinated area of an axon, every 0.1–1.0 mm, between adjacent oligodentrocytes of an axon in the central nervous system and between individual Schwann cells of the peripheral nervous system. (p. 196)

norepinephrine (nōr'ep-i-nef'rin) Neurotransmitter substance released from most of the postganglionic neurons of the sympathetic division; hormone released from the adrenal cortex that increases cardiac output and blood glucose levels. (p. 202)

notochord (nō'tō-kōrd) [Gr. *notor,* back; *chords,* cord] Small rod of tissue lying ventral to the neural tube; characteristic of all vertebrates; in humans it becomes the nucleus pulposus of the intervertebral disks. (p. 545)

nuclear pore (noo'klē-er) Point where the inner and outer membranes of the nuclear envelope come together to form a hole. (p. 44)

nuclease (noo'klē-ās) An enzyme that breaks down nucleic acids. (p. 444)

nucleic acid (noo-klē'ik, -klā'ik) Molecule consisting of many nucleotides chemically bound together; deoxyribonucleic acid and ribonucleic acid. (p. 34)

nucleolus (noo-klē'ō-lŭs), pl. **nucleoli** (noo-klē'ō-lī) Rounded, dense, well-defined nuclear bodies with no surrounding membrane; subunits of ribosomes are manufactured within the nucleolus. (p. 44)

nucleotide (noo'klē-ō-tīd) Basic building block of nucleic acids consisting of a sugar molecule (either ribose or deoxyribose), one of several types of organic bases, and a phosphate group. (p. 34)

nucleus (noo'klē-ŭs), pl. **nuclei** (noo'klē-ī) [L., inside of a thing] Cell organelle containing most of the genetic material of the cell; center of an atom consisting of protons and neutrons; collection of neuron cell bodies in the central nervous system. (pp. 20, 44)

nutrient (noo'trē-ent) [L. *nutriens,* to nourish] Chemical taken into the body that is used to produce energy, provide building blocks for new molecules, or function in other chemical reactions. (p. 459)

nutrition (noo-trish'ŭn) Process by which nutrients are obtained and used in the body. (p. 459)

O

oblique section (ob-lēk') A cut made at other than a right angle to the long axis of an organ. (p. 12)

obturator (ob'toor-ā-tōr) [L., to occlude or stop up] Any occluding structure or a foramen so occluded, as with the obturator foramen of the hip. (p. 133)

occipital (ok-sip'i-tăl) The back of the head. (p. 122)

olecranon (ō-lek'ră-non) The point of the elbow. (p. 132)

olfaction (ol-fak'shŭn) [L., to smell] The sense of smell. (p. 235)

olfactory (ol-fak'tō-rē) Relating to the sense of smell. (p. 235)

oligodendrocyte (ol'i-gō-den'drō-sīt) Neuroglial cells with multiple cell processes that form myelin sheaths around axons in the central nervous system. (p. 196)

omental bursa (ō-men'tăl ber'să) The pocketlike sac inside the fold of the greater omentum. (p. 436)

omentum (ō-men'tŭm) A fold of peritoneum extending from the stomach to another organ. (p. 436)

oncology (ong-kol'ō-jē) [Gr. *onco,* a tumor; *logos,* to study] The study of cancer and its associated problems. (p. 89)

oocyte (ō'ō-sīt) [Gr. *oon,* egg; *kytos,* cell] Female gamete, or sex cell; a secondary oocyte and a polar body result from the first meiotic division, which occurs prior to the time of ovulation; a zygote and a polar body result from the second meiotic division, which occurs following union of the sperm cell with the secondary oocyte. (p. 522)

oogonium (ō-ō-gō'nē-ŭm), pl. **oogonia** (ō-ō-gō'nē-ă) Cells that give rise to oocytes; have a diploid number of chromosomes. (p. 523)

optic (op'tik) Relating to vision. (p. 243)

optic disc The region in the posterior wall of the eye where the optic nerve exits the eye; the blind spot. (p. 241)

optic nerve Nerve that leaves the eye and exits the orbit through the optic foramen to enter the cranial vault. (p. 241)

oral cavity (ōr'ăl) Mouth; the first portion of the digestive tract. (p. 426)

orbit (ōr'bit) Seven skull bones that surround and protect the eye; eye socket. (p. 123)

organ (ōr'găn) [Gr. *organon,* tool] Part of the body composed of two or more tissue types and performing one or more specific functions. (p. 3)

organ of Corti Specialized region of the cochlear duct consisting of hair cells; produces action potentials in response to sound waves. (p. 246)

organ system Group of organs classified as a unit because of a common function or set of functions. (p. 3)

organelle (or'gă-nel) Specialized part of a cell performing one or more specific functions. (p. 42)

organic (ōr-gan'ik) Molecules that contain a carbon atom (carbon dioxide is an exception); originally defined as molecules extracted from living organisms; the original definition became obsolete when it became possible to manufacture these molecules in the laboratory. (p. 30)

organism (ōr'gă-nizm) Any living thing considered as a whole, whether composed of one cell or many. (p. 3)

organogenesis (ōr'gă-nō-jen'ĕ-sis) The formation of organs during embryonic development. (p. 546)

orgasm (ōr'gazm) [Gr. *orgao,* to swell, be excited] Climax of the sexual act, often associated with a pleasurable sensation. (p. 521)

origin (ōr'i-jin) The less movable attachment point of a muscle. (p. 165)

oropharynx (ōr'ō-far'ingks) Portion of the pharynx that lies posterior to the mouth; it is continuous above with the nasopharynx and below with the laryngopharynx. (p. 396)

osmosis (os-mō'sis) [Gr. *osmos,* thrusting or an impulsion] Diffusion of solvent (water) through a selectively permeable membrane from a region of higher water concentration to one of lower water concentration. (p. 53)

osmotic pressure (os-mot'ik) Force required to prevent the movement of water across a selectively permeable membrane. (p. 53)

ossification (os'i-fi-kā'shŭn) [L. *os,* bone; *facio,* to make] Bone formation. (p. 112)

osteoblast (os'tē-ō-blast) A cell that makes bone. (p. 112)

osteoclast (os'tē-ō-klast) A cell that digests and removes bone. (p. 114)

osteocyte (os'tē-ō-sīt) [Gr. *osteon,* bone; *kytos,* cell] Mature bone cell surrounded by bone matrix. (p. 112)

osteon (os'tē-on) A single central canal, with its contents, and the associated lamellae and osteocytes surrounding it. Also called a Haversian system. (p. 112)

otolith (ō'tō-lith) [Gr. *ous,* ear; *lithos,* stone] Small protein and calcium carbonate weights in the maculae of the vestibule. (p. 249)

ovary (ō'vă-rē) One of two female reproductive glands located in the pelvic cavity; produces the oocyte, estrogen, and progesterone. (p. 522)

ovulation (ov'ū-lā'shŭn) Release of an oocyte from the mature follicle. (p. 523)

oxidative metabolism (ok-si-dā'tiv mĕ-tab'ō-lizm) Metabolism in which oxygen is required to produce ATP. (p. 49)

oxygen debt (ok'sē-jen) The amount of oxygen required to convert the lactic acid produced during anaerobic respiration to glucose and to replenish creatine phosphate stores. (p. 162)

oxytocin (ok'sĭ-tō'sin) Peptide hormone secreted by the posterior pituitary gland that increases uterine contraction and stimulates milk ejection from the mammary glands. (p. 270)

P

palate (pal'ăt) The roof of the oral cavity; consists of the anterior bony part, the hard palate, and the posterior soft palate that consists mainly of skeletal muscle and connective tissue. (p. 427)

pancreas (pan'krē-as) An elongated gland extending from the duodenum to the spleen; consists of a head, body, and a tail. There is an exocrine portion, which secretes digestive enzymes that are carried by the pancreatic duct to the duodenum, and pancreatic islets, which secrete insulin and glucagon. (p. 276)

pancreatic duct (pan-krē'at'ik) The duct of the pancreas; it joins the common bile duct to empty into the duodenum. (p. 429)

pancreatic islet (i'let) Cellular mass in the tissue of the pancreas; composed of different cell types that constitute the endocrine portion of the pancreas and are the source of insulin and glucagon. (p. 276)

papilla (pă-pil'ă), pl. **papillae** (pă-pil'ē) [L., nipple] A small, nipplelike process; projection of the dermis, containing blood vessels and nerves, into the epidermis; projections on the surface of the tongue. (pp. 95, 235)

papillary muscle (pap'i-l-ār-ē) A raised area of cardiac muscle in the ventricle to which the chordae tendineae attach. (p. 312)

parafollicular cell (par-ă-fo-lik'ū-lăr) A cell type scattered in a network of loose connective tissue between the thyroid follicles of the thyroid gland; secretes calcitonin. (p. 270)

paranasal sinus (par-ă-nā'săl) Air-filled cavity within certain skull bones that connects to the nasal cavity; the four sets of paranasal sinuses are the frontal, maxillary, sphenoidal, and ethmoidal. (p. 124)

parasympathetic (par-ă-sim-pa-thet'ik) Subdivision of the autonomic nervous system with preganglionic neurons in the brainstem and sacral part of the spinal cord; involved in involuntary functions such as digestion, defecation, and urination. (p. 192)

parathyroid gland (par-ă-thī'royd) One of four glandular masses embedded in the posterior surface of the thyroid gland; secretes parathyroid hormone. (p. 271)

parathyroid hormone (PTH) (hōr'mōn) Hormone produced by the parathyroid gland; increases bone breakdown and blood calcium levels. (p. 271)

parietal (pă-rī'ĕ-tăl) [L. *paries,* wall] Relating to the wall of any cavity; parietal serous membranes are in contact with the walls of cavities. The parietal bones form part of the skull. (p. 122)

parietal peritoneum (pĕ'rĭ-tō-nē'ŭm) [L., wall] That portion of the serous membranes of the abdominal cavity lining the inner surface of the body wall. (p. 436)

parotid gland (pă-rot'id) The largest of the salivary glands; one of a pair of salivary glands located anterior and inferior to each ear. (p. 427)

partial pressure   Pressure exerted by a single gas in a mixture of gases. (p. 408)

partial-thickness burn   Burn that damages only the epidermis (first-degree burn) or the epidermis and part of the dermis (also called a second-degree burn). (p. 101)

parturition   (par-toor-ish′ŭn) [L. *parturio,* to be in labor] Childbirth; the delivery of a baby at the end of pregnancy. (p. 548)

patella   (pa-tel′ă) [L. *patina,* shallow disk] Kneecap. (p. 134)

pectoral   (pek′tŏ-răl) [L. *pectoralis,* breastbone] Relating to the chest. (p. 130)

pedicle   (ped′ĭ-kl) [L. *pedicellus,* foot] Portion of a vertebra that extends from the body to the transverse process. (p. 126)

pelvic cavity   (pel′vik) Space completely surrounded by the pelvic bones. (p. 12)

pepsin   (pep′sin) [Gr. *pepsis,* digestion] Principal digestive enzyme produced by the stomach; digests proteins into smaller peptide chains. (p. 429)

peptidase   (pep′ti-dās) An enzyme capable of breaking peptide chains into smaller chains and amino acids. (p. 442)

peptide bond   (pep′tīd) A covalent chemical bond between adjacent amino acids in a polypeptide chain. (p. 59)

pericardial cavity   (per-i-kar′dē-ăl) [Gr. *peri-,* around; Gr. *kardia,* the heart] Space between the visceral and parietal pericardium, filled with pericardial fluid; a cavity that surrounds the heart. (p. 13)

pericardial fluid   The serous fluid found within the pericardial cavity. (p. 309)

pericardial membrane   Serous membranes associated with the heart. (p. 86)

pericardium   (per-i-kar′dē-ŭm) [Gr. *pericardion,* the membrane around the heart] The membrane consisting of the epicardium and parietal pericardium (of the serous layers) and the outer fibrous pericardium; also called the pericardial sac. (p. 309)

perilymph   (per′i-limf) [*peri* + Gr. *lympha,* clear fluid] Fluid contained between the bony labyrinth and the membranous labyrinth of the inner ear. (p. 246)

perimetrium   (per-i-mē′trē-ŭm) The outer layer of the uterus, also called the serous layer. (p. 526)

perimysium   (per′-i-mis′ē-ŭm, per′-i-miz′ē-ŭm) [*peri-* + Gr. *mys,* muscle] The fibrous sheath enveloping each of the skeletal muscle fascicles. (p. 151)

perineum   (per′-i-nē′ŭm) Area inferior to the pelvic diaphragm between the thighs; extends from the coccyx to the pubis. (p. 172)

periodontal   (per′ē-ō-don′tăl) [*peri-* + Gr. *odous,* tooth] Referring to structures surrounding the tooth, primarily in the alveolus. (p. 427)

periosteum   (per-ē-os′tē-ŭm) [*peri-* + ˙Gr. *osteon,* bone] Thick, double-layered connective tissue sheath covering the entire surface of a bone except the articular surface, which is covered with cartilage. (p. 112)

peripheral circulation   (pĕ-rif′ĕ-răl) Blood flow through all blood vessels that carry blood away from the heart (arteries), the capillaries, and all vessels that carry blood back to the heart (veins); consists of the pulmonary circulation and the systemic circulation; includes all blood flow except that through the heart tissue itself. (p. 336)

peripheral nervous system   The part of the nervous system not surrounded by the skull or vertebral column; consisting of nerves and ganglia. (p. 192)

peristaltic waves   (per-i-stal′tik) Waves of relaxation followed by waves of contraction moving along a tube; propels food along the digestive tube. (p. 438)

peritoneal cavity   (per′i-tō-nē′ăl) Space between the visceral and parietal peritoneum, filled with peritoneal fluid; cavity that surrounds many abdominopelvic organs. (p. 13)

peritoneal membrane   Serous membrane associated with the peritoneal cavity. (p. 86)

peritubular capillary   (per′ĭ-too′bū-lăr) The capillary network located in the cortex of the kidney; associated with the distal and proximal convoluted tubules. (p. 485)

peroxisome   (per-ok′si-sōm) Membrane bound body similar to a lysosome in appearance but often smaller and irregular in shape; contains enzymes that either decompose or synthesize hydrogen peroxide.

Peyer's patch   Named for the Swiss anatomist, Johann Peyer (1653–1712). Collection of lymph nodules found in the distal half of the small intestine and in the appendix. (p. 429)

pH scale   A measure of the hydrogen ion concentration of a solution; the scale extends from 0 to 14.0. A pH of 7.0 being neutral, a pH of less than 7 acidic, and a pH of greater than 7 basic. (p. 29)

phagocytosis   (fag′ō-sī-tō′sis) [Gr. *phagein,* to eat; *kytos,* cell; *osis,* condition] Process of ingestion and digestion by cells of substances such as other cells, bacteria, cell debris, and foreign particles. (p. 56)

pharynx   (far′ingks) [Gr. *pharynx,* throat] The joint openings of the digestive tract and the windpipe. The part of the digestive and respiratory tubes superior to the larynx and esophagus and inferior and posterior to the oral and nasal cavities. (p. 396)

phenotype   (fē′nō-tīp) [Gr. *phaino,* to display; *typos,* model] Characteristic observed in the individual resulting from expression of the genotype. (p. 563)

phlebitis   (fle-bī′tis) Inflammation of a vein. (p. 339)

phospholipid   (fos-fō-lip′id) Lipid with phosphorus resulting in a molecule with a polar and a nonpolar end; main component of cell membranes. (p. 33)

physiology   (fiz-ē-ol′ō-jē) [Gr. *physis,* nature; *logos,* study] Scientific discipline that deals with the processes or functions of living things. (p. 2)

pia mater   (pī′ă mā′ter, pē′ă ma′ter) [L., affectionate mother] The innermost meningeal layer; tightly attached to the brain and spinal cord. (p. 214)

pineal body   (pin′ē-ăl) [L. *pineus,* pine cone-shaped] A small endocrine gland attached to the dorsal surface of the diencephalon; may influence the onset of puberty and may play a role in some long-term cycles. (p. 206)

pinocytosis   (pī′nō-sī-tō′sis, pī′nō-sī-tō′sis) [Gr. *pineo,* to drink; *kytos,* cell; *osis,* condition] Cell drinking; uptake of liquid by a cell. (p. 56)

pituitary dwarf   (dwŏrf) An individual of short stature, of relatively normal proportion, as the result of insufficient growth hormone secreted from the anterior pituitary gland. (p. 267)

pituitary gland   (pi-too′i-tār-rē) Endocrine gland attached to the hypothalamus by the infundibulum; secretes hormones that influence the function of several other glands and tissues. (p. 265)

placenta   (plă-sen′tă) Structure derived from embryonic and maternal tissues by which the embryo and fetus are attached to the uterus. (p. 543)

plasma   (plaz′mă) Fluid portion of blood; blood minus the formed elements. (p. 286)

plasma membrane   Cell membrane; outermost component of the cell, surrounding and binding the rest of the cell contents. (p. 42)

plasmin   (plaz′min) An enzyme that breaks down the fibrin in blood clots; derived from plasminogen. (p. 295)

platelet   (plāt′let) Minute fragments of cells derived from megakaryocytes; play an important role in preventing blood loss. (p. 286)

platelet plug   Accumulation of platelets that stick to connective tissue and to one another and prevent blood loss from damaged blood vessels. (p. 293)

pleural (ploor′ăl) **cavity**   Space between the visceral and parietal pleura, filled with pleural fluid; a cavity that surrounds each lung. (p. 13)

pleural membrane Serous membranes associated with the lungs. (p. 86)

plexus (plek'sŭs) [L., a braid] An intertwining of nerves or blood vessels. (p. 221)

PMS See *premenstrual syndrome.*

pneumothorax (noo-mō-thōr'aks) The presence of air in the pleural cavity. (p. 404)

podocyte (pod'ō-sīt) [Fr. *pous, podos,* foot; *kytos,* a hollow (cell)] Epithelial cell of Bowman's capsule attached to the outer surface of the glomerular capillary basement membrane; forms part of the filtration membrane. (p. 481)

polar body The oocyte receiving little cytoplasm, which results from the first and the second meiotic division. (p. 511)

polar covalent bond Chemical bond in which electrons are shared unequally between two atoms. (p. 23)

polycythemia (pol'ē-sī-thē'mē-ă) [Gr. *polys,* many; *kytos,* cell] Increase in red blood cell numbers above the normal value. (p. 299)

polysaccharide (pol-ē-sak'ă-rīd) Many monosaccharides chemically bound together, such as glycogen and starch. (p. 32)

pons (ponz) [L., bridge] The part of the brainstem between the medulla oblongata and midbrain; contains nerve tracts between the cerebrum and cerebellum, as well as ascending and descending tracts. (p. 205)

portal system (pōr'tăl) System of vessels in which blood, after passing through one capillary bed, is conveyed through a second capillary network. (p. 348)

positive feedback Mechanism by which any deviation from an ideal normal value or set point is made greater. (p. 8)

posterior (pos-tēr'ē-ŏr) [L. *posterus,* following] That which follows; in humans, toward the back. (p. 9)

posterior horn The posterior extension of spinal cord gray matter; contains neuron cell bodies that receive input from primary sensory neurons and relay that input to the brain; also called the dorsal horn. (p. 211)

posterior pituitary gland The posterior portion of the pituitary gland, which consists of processes of nerve cells that have their cell bodies located in the hypothalamus; secretes oxytocin and antidiuretic hormone. (p. 265)

postganglionic (pōst'gang-glē-on'ik) Autonomic neurons whose cell bodies are located outside the central nervous system and that receive synaptic stimulation from preganglionic autonomic neurons. (p. 223)

preganglionic (prē'gang-glē-on'ik) Autonomic neurons whose cell bodies are located in the central nervous system and that synapse with postganglionic neurons. (p. 223)

preload (prē'lōd) The degree to which the ventricular wall is stretched at the end of diastole; increases as the venous return increases. (p. 323)

premenstrual syndrome (PMS) (prē-men'stroo-al sin'drōm) In some women of reproductive age, the regular monthly experience of physiological and emotional distress, usually during the few days preceding menses, typically involving fatigue, edema, irritability, tension, anxiety, and depression. (p. 528)

prenatal period (prē-nā'tăl) [L. *prae,* before; *natalis,* relating to birth] The period before birth. (p. 541)

prepuce (prē'poos) In the male, a free fold of skin that almost completely covers the glans penis; the foreskin; in the female, a fold of mucous membrane that covers the clitoris. (p. 517)

primary response Immune response that occurs as a result of the first exposure to an antigen; results in the production of antibodies and memory cells. (p. 380)

prime mover Muscle that plays the principal role in accomplishing a movement. (p. 165)

primitive streak A shallow groove in the ectodermal surface of the embryonic disk; cells migrating through the streak become mesoderm. (p. 545)

process (pros'es, prō'ses) Projection on a bone. (p. 120)

product (prod'ŭkt) Substance produced in a chemical reaction. (p. 25)

progesterone (prō-jes'ter-ōn) Hormone secreted primarily by the corpus luteum and the placenta; aids in growth and development of female reproductive organs and secondary sexual characteristics; causes growth and maturation of the endometrium of the uterus during the menstrual cycle. (p. 278)

prolactin (prō-lak'tin) Hormone of the anterior pituitary gland that stimulates the secretion of milk. (p. 270)

pronation (prō-nā'shŭn) [L. *pronare,* to bend forward] Rotation, as of the forearm, starting in the anatomical position, so that the anterior surface faces posteriorly. (p. 145)

proprioceptive neurons (prō'prē-ō-sep'tiv) [L. *proprius,* one's own; *capio,* to take] Nerves that innervate the joints and tendons and provide information about the position of the body and its various parts. (p. 211)

prostaglandin (pros-tă-glan'din) Class of physiologically active substances present in many tissues; effects include vasodilation, stimulation and contraction of uterine smooth muscle, and promotion of inflammation and pain. (p. 265)

prostate gland (pros'tāt) [Gr. *prostates,* one standing before] Gland that surrounds the beginning of the urethra in the male. The secretion of the gland is a milky fluid that is discharged into the urethra as part of the semen. (p. 517)

protein (prō'tēn) [Gr. *proteios,* primary] Large molecule consisting of long sequences of amino acids (polypeptides) linked by peptide bonds. (p. 34)

proteoglycan (prō'tē-ō-glī'kan) Macromolecule consisting of numerous polysaccharides attached to a common protein core, attract and retain large amounts of water. (p. 111)

proteolytic (prō'tē-ō-lit'ik) An enzyme capable of digesting proteins or polypeptides. (p. 454)

proton (prō'ton) [Gr. *protos,* first] Positively charged particle found in the nuclei of atoms. (p. 20)

provitamin (prō-vīt'ă-min) Substance that can be converted into a vitamin. (p. 463)

proximal (prok'si-măl) [L. *proximus,* nearest] Closer to the point of attachment to the body than another structure. (p. 10)

proximal tubule Convoluted portion of the nephron that extends from Bowman's capsule to the descending limb of Henle's loop. (p. 480)

pterygoid (ter'ĭ-goyd) [Gr. *pteryx,* wing] Wing-shaped structure; two of the muscles of mastication, attached to wing-shaped bony projections. (p. 168)

PTH See *parathyroid hormone.*

puberty (pū'ber-tē) [L. *pubertas,* grown up] Series of events that transform a child into a sexually mature adult; involves an increase in the secretion of all reproductive hormones. (p. 520)

pudendal cleft (pū-den'dal) Cleft between the labia majora. (p. 526)

pudendum (pū-den'dŭm), pl. **pudenda** (pū-den'da) The external genitals, especially the female genitals. See *vulva.* (p. 526)

pulmonary capacity (pŭl'mō-nār-ē) The sum of two or more pulmonary volumes. (p. 406)

pulmonary circulation Blood flow through the system of blood vessels that carry blood from the right ventricle of the heart to the lungs and back from the lungs to the left atrium. (p. 306)

pulmonary semilunar valve The semilunar valve found at the base of the pulmonary trunk where it exits from the right ventricle. (p. 312)

pulmonary trunk   Large elastic artery that carries blood from the right ventricle of the heart to the right and left pulmonary arteries. (p. 310)

pulmonary volume   Lung volume, measured by spirometry; deviations from a normal value can be used to diagnose certain lung diseases; the pulmonary volumes are the tidal volume, inspiratory reserve volume, expiratory reserve volume, and residual volume. (p. 405)

pulp   (pŭlp) [L. *pulpa,* flesh] The soft tissue inside a tooth, consisting of connective tissue, blood vessels, nerves, and lymphatic vessels. (p. 427)

pulse   (pŭls) A pressure wave that travels rapidly along the arteries when blood is ejected from the left ventricle into the aorta. (p. 353)

pulse pressure   The difference between systolic and diastolic pressure. (p. 353)

pupil   (pū′pĭl) [L. *pupa,* a doll, because you can see a little reflection or doll in the pupil of another person's eye] Opening in the iris of the eye through which light enters. (p. 239)

Purkinje fiber   (pŭr-kĭn′jē) Named for the Bohemian anatomist/physiologist, Johannes Purkinje (1787–1869). A specialized cardiac muscle fiber that conducts action potentials through cardiac muscle; forms part of the conduction system of the heart. (p. 317)

pus   (pŭs) Product of inflammation consisting of a liquid containing white blood cells, dead cells, and cell fragments. (p. 86)

pyloric sphincter   (pī-lōr′ik) [Gr., gatekeeper] A thickened ring of smooth muscle at the distal end of the stomach. (p. 429)

pyrogen   (pī′rō-jen) Chemical released by microorganisms, neutrophils, monocytes, and other cells that stimulates fever production by acting on the hypothalamus. (p. 375)

pyruvic acid   (pī-roo′vik) Three-carbon end product of glycolysis; two pyruvic acid molecules are produced from each glucose molecule. (p. 467)

Q

quadrant   (kwăh′drant) [L. *quadrans,* a quarter] One-quarter of a circle; the abdomen is divided into right upper, right lower, left upper, and left lower quadrants by a horizontal and a vertical line intersecting at the umbilicus. (p. 12)

R

RBC   See *erythrocyte.*

reactant   (rē-ak′tant) Substance taking part in a chemical reaction. (p. 25)

receptor   (rē-sep′tŏr, rē-sep′-tōr) A molecule that is located in the membrane or cytoplasm of cells of a target tissue to which a hormone binds; each receptor binds to a specific type of hormone, neurotransmitter, or other substance. (p. 44)

recessive   (rē-ses′iv) In genetics, a gene that may not be expressed phenotypically because of the expression of a contrasting dominant gene. (p. 563)

rectum   (rek′tŭm) [L. *rectus,* straight] The last, straight part of the large intestine; between the colon and the anal canal. (p. 434)

rectus   (rek′tŭs) Straight. (p. 165)

reflex   (rē′fleks) Automatical responses to stimuli; does not require conscious thought. (p. 202)

reflex arc   Consists of a sensory receptor, afferent (sensory) neuron, association neuron, efferent (motor) neuron, and effector organ. (p. 202)

regeneration   (rē′jen-er-ā′shŭn) Tissue repair in which the damaged cells are replaced by cells of the same type as those damaged. (p. 86)

releasing hormone   Hormone that is released from neurons in the hypothalamus and flows through the hypothalamic–pituitary portal system to the anterior pituitary gland; functions to regulate the secretion of hormones from the cells of the anterior pituitary gland. (p. 265)

renal capsule   (rē′năl) The connective tissue capsule that surrounds each kidney. (p. 480)

renal corpuscle   (kōr′pŭs-l) The structure composed of a Bowman's capsule and its glomerulus. (p. 481)

renal fat pad   The layer of adipose tissue that surrounds each kidney. (p. 480)

renal pyramid   (pir′ă-mid) Cone-shaped structure that extends from the renal sinus, where the apex is located, into the cortex of the kidney, where the base is located. (p. 480)

renal sinus   (sī′nŭs) The cavity central to the medulla of the kidney that is filled with adipose tissue and contains the renal pelvis. (p. 480)

renin   (rē′nin, ren′in) Enzyme secreted by the kidney that converts the plasma protein, angiotensinogen to angiotensin I. (p. 276)

replacement   Tissue repair in which the damaged cells are replaced by cells of a type different from those damaged. (p. 87)

respiration   (res-pi-rā′shŭn) [L. *respiratio,* to breathe] Process in which oxygen is used to oxidize organic fuel molecules, providing a source of energy

as well as carbon dioxide and water; includes ventilation, gas exchange, transport of oxygen and carbon dioxide in the blood, gas exchange between the blood and the tissues, and cell metabolism. (p. 394)

respiratory membrane   (res′pi-ră-tōr-ē, rĕ-spīr′ă-tōr-ē) Membrane in the lungs across which gas exchange occurs with blood; consists of a thin layer of fluid, the alveolar epithelium, a basement membrane of the alveolar epithelium, interstitial space, the basement membrane of the capillary endothelium, and the capillary endothelium. (p. 406)

respiratory system   Includes the nose, nasal cavity, pharynx, larynx, trachea, bronchi, and lungs. (p. 394)

resting membrane potential   The charge difference across the membrane of a resting cell (i.e., a cell that has not been stimulated to produce an action potential). (p. 154)

rete testis   (rē′tē) The network of canals at the termination of the straight portion of the seminiferous tubules. (p. 515)

reticular formation   (rē-tik′ū-lăr) [L. *rete,* net] A loose network of neuron cell bodies scattered throughout the brainstem; involved in the regulation of cycles such as the sleep–wake cycle. (p. 205)

retina   (ret′i-nă) [L. *rete,* a net] The inner, light-sensitive tunic of the eye; nervous tunic. (p. 239

retinaculum   (ret-i-nak′ū-lŭm) [L., band, halter, to hold back] Dense, regular connective tissue sheath holding down the tendons at the wrist, ankle, or other sites. (p. 178)

retroperitoneal   (re′trō-per′i-tō-nē′ăl) Located behind the parietal peritoneum; includes the kidneys, adrenal glands, pancreas, portions of the intestines, and urinary bladder. (p. 436)

reversible reaction   (rē-verŝi-bl) Chemical reaction in which the reaction can proceed from reactants to products, or from products to reactants; the amount of reactants relative to products is constant at equilibrium. (p. 27)

ribonucleic acid   (rī′bō-noo-klē′ik) **(RNA)** Type of nucleic acid containing the sugar ribose; involved in protein synthesis. (p. 34)

ribosomal RNA (rRNA)   (ri′bō-sōm-ăl) RNA that is associated with certain proteins to form ribosomes. (p. 44)

ribosome   (ri′bō-sōm) Small, spherical, cytoplasmic organelle where protein synthesis occurs. (p. 44)

right lymphatic duct   Lymphatic duct that empties into the right subclavian vein; drains the right side of the head and neck, the right upper thorax, and the right upper limb. (p. 368)

RNA   See *ribonucleic acid.*

rod   Photoreceptor cell in the retina of the eye with a rod-shaped photoreceptive process; very light-sensitive cell that is important in dim light. (p. 243)

rotator cuff   (rō-tā′tŏr, rō-tā′tōr) Four deep muscles that attach the humerus to the scapula. (p. 174)

rRNA   See *ribosomal RNA.*

ruga   (roo′gă) Ridge or fold in the mucous membrane of the stomach. (p. 429)

S

SA   See *sinoatrial.*

sagittal plane   (saj′i-tăl) [L. *sagitta,* the flight of an arrow] Plane running vertically through the body and dividing it into right and left parts. (p. 9)

saliva   (să-lī′vă) A fluid containing enzymes and mucus, produced by the salivary glands and released into the oral cavity. (p. 427)

salivary gland   (sal′i-vār-rē) Gland opening into the mouth and producing saliva. (p. 427)

salt   Molecule consisting of a positively charged ion other than hydrogen, and a negatively charged ion other than hydroxide. (p. 30)

sarcolemma   (sar′kō-lem′ă) [Gr. *sarx,* flesh, means muscle; *lemma,* husk] The cell membrane of a muscle fiber. (p. 154)

sarcomere   (sar′kō-mēr) [*sarco-* + Gr. *meros,* part] The part of a myofibril formed of actin and myosin myofilaments, extending from Z disk to Z disk; the structural and functional unit of a muscle. (p. 152)

sarcoplasm   (sar′kō-plazm) [*sarco-* + *plasma,* a thing formed] The cytoplasm of a muscle fiber. (p. 151)

sarcoplasmic reticulum   (sar′kō-plaz′mik re-tik′ū-lŭm) The endoplasmic reticulum of a muscle fiber. (p. 154)

scapula   (skap′ū-lă) The shoulder blade. (p. 130)

Schwann cell   Named for the German histologist/physiologist, Theodor Schwann (1810–1882). Neuroglial cell forming myelin sheaths around axons in the peripheral nervous system. (p. 196)

sclera   (sklēr′ă) [L. *skleros,* hard] The dense, white, opaque posterior four-fifths of the fibrous tunic of the eye; white of the eye. (p. 238)

scoliosis   (skō-lē-ō′sis) [Gr., a crookedness] An abnormal lateral curvature of the spine. (p. 126)

scrotum   (skrō′tum) Musculocutaneous sac containing the testes. (p. 514)

sebaceous gland   (sē-bā′shŭs) [L. *sebum,* tallow] Gland of the skin that produces sebum; usually associated with a hair follicle. (p. 99)

sebum   (sē′bŭm) [L., tallow] Oily, white, fatty substance produced by the sebaceous glands; oils hair and the surface of the skin. (p. 99)

secondary response   See *memory response.*

secretin   (se-krē′tin) Hormone release from the epithelium of the duodenum; inhibits gastric secretion. (p. 440)

sella turcica   (sel′ătŭr′sĭ-kă) [L., saddle, Turkish] The saddle-shaped depression in the inner surface of the skull where the pituitary gland is located. (p. 125)

semen   (sē′men) [L., seed] Penile ejaculate; thick, yellowish white, viscous fluid containing sperm cells and secretions of the testes, seminal vesicles, prostate gland, and bulbourethral glands. (p. 517)

semicircular canal   (sem′ē-sir′kū-lăr) One of three canals in each temporal bone; involved in the detection of motion. (p. 249)

semilunar valve   (sem-ē-loo′năr) One of two valves in the heart composed of three crescent-shaped cusps that prevent flow of blood into the ventricles following ejection; located at the beginning of the aorta and pulmonary trunk. (p. 312)

seminal vesicle   (sem′i-năl ves′i-kl) One of two glandular structures that empty into the ejaculatory ducts; its secretion is one of the components of semen. (p. 515)

seminiferous tubule   (sem′i-nif′er-ŭs) Tubule in the testis in which sperm cells develop. (p. 514)

serosa   (se-rō′să) The smooth, outermost covering of an organ where it faces a cavity and is not surrounded by connective tissue. (p. 425)

serous membrane   (sēr′ŭs) Thin sheet consisting of epithelium and connective tissue that lines cavities not opening to the outside of the body; does not contain glands but does secrete serous fluid. (p. 86)

Sertoli cell   (ser-tō′lē) Named for the Italian histologist, Enrico Sertoli (1842–1910). Cell in the wall of the seminiferous tubules to which spermatogonia and spermatids are attached. (p. 515)

serum   (sēr′ŭm) Fluid portion of blood after the removal of fibrin and formed elements. (p. 295)

sex chromosome   A chromosome other than an autosome; responsible for sex determination. (p. 562)

sinoatrial (SA) node   (sī′nō-ā′trē-ăl) Mass of specialized cardiac muscle fibers located in the right atrium near the opening of the superior vena cava that acts as the "pacemaker" of the cardiac conduction system. (p. 316)

sliding filament mechanism   Mechanism by which actin and myosin myofilaments slide over one another during muscle contraction. (p. 156)

solute   (sol′ūt, sō′loot) [L. *solutus,* dissolved] Dissolved substance in a solution. (p. 50)

solution   (sō-loo′shŭn) Homogeneous mixture formed when a solute dissolves in a solvent (liquid). (p. 50)

solvent   (sol′vent) [L. *solvens,* dissolve] Liquid that holds another substance in solution. (p. 50)

somatic motor   (sō-mat′ik) [Gr. *soma,* body] A type of motor (efferent) neuron of the peripheral nervous system that innervates skeletal muscle. (p. 220)

somesthetic   (sō′mes-thet′ik) [Gr. *soma,* body; *aisthesis,* sensation] Consciously perceived body sensations. (p. 210)

somesthetic cortex   That part of the cerebral cortex involved with the conscious perception and localization of general body sensations. (p. 210)

spermatid   (sper′mă-tid) A cell in the late stage of the development of the sperm cell (male sex cell). It is haploid and is derived from the secondary spermatocyte. (p. 515)

spermatocyte   (sper′mă-tō′sīt) Cell arising from a spermatogonium and destined to give rise to spermatozoa. (p. 515)

spermatogenesis   (sper′mă-tō-jen′ĕ-sis) Formation and development of sperm cells. (p. 514)

spermatogonium   (sper′mă-tō-gō′nē-ŭm), pl. **spermatogonia** (sper′mă-tō-gō′nē-ă) The most peripheral germ cells in the seminiferous tubules scattered between the Sertoli cells; divide by mitosis and some form primary spermatocytes. (p. 515)

spermatozoon   (sper′mă-tō-zō′on), pl. **spermatazoa** (sper′mă-tō-zō′ă) [Gr. *sperma,* seed; *zoon,* animal] Male gamete, or sex cell, composed of a head, midpiece, and tail; contains the genetic information transmitted by the male; sperm cell. (p. 511)

sperm cell   [Gr. *sperma,* seed] Male reproductive cell; see *spermatozoon.*

sphygmomanometer   (sfig′mō-mă-nom′ĕ-ter) [Gr. *sphygmos,* pulse; *manos* + *metron,* measure] An instrument for measuring blood pressure consisting of an arm sleeve and inflating bulb with a device attached for measuring pressure in the arm sleeve. (p. 350)

spina bifida (spī′nă bif′ĭ-dă, bī′fĭ-dă) A defect in the spinal column, consisting in absence of the vertebral arches, through which the spinal membranes, with or without spinal cord tissue, may protrude. (p. 546)

spinal cord Portion of the central nervous system extending from the foramen magnum at the base of the skull to the second lumbar vertebra; consists of a central gray portion and a peripheral white portion. (p. 211)

spinal nerve Peripheral nerve exiting from the spinal cord. (p. 217)

spirometer (spī-rom′ĕ-ter) [L. *spiro,* to breathe; Gr. *metron,* measure] Meter used for measuring the volume of respiratory gases; usually consisting of a counterbalanced cylindrical bell sealed by dipping into a circular trough of water. (p. 405)

spirometry (spī-rom′ĕ-trē) Process of making pulmonary measurements with a spirometer. (p. 405)

spleen (splēn) Large lymphatic organ in the left upper part of the abdominal cavity, between the stomach and diaphragm; composed of white and red pulp; responds to foreign substances in the blood, destroys worn out red blood cells, and is a reservoir for blood. (p. 370)

squamous (skwā′mŭs) [L. *squama,* a scale] Scalelike, flat. (p. 73)

stapes (stā′pēz) [L., stirrup] The third of the three middle ear bones; attached to the oval window; the stirrup. (p. 243)

Starling's law of the heart Named for the English physiologist, Ernest Starling (1866–1927). Force of contraction of cardiac muscle is a function of the length of its muscle fibers at the end of diastole; the greater the degree of filling of the heart (the greater the venous return), the greater the force of contraction of the cardiac muscle. (p. 323)

stem cell Single population of cells that differentiate to give rise to the formed elements of blood. (p. 288)

stenosed valve (sten′ōzd) A valve that has its opening narrowed or partially closed. (p. 321)

sternum (ster′nŭm) [L. *sternon,* chest] Breastbone. (p. 129)

steroid (stēr′oyd, ster′oyd) Large family of lipids, including some hormones, vitamins, and cholesterol. (p. 520)

stethoscope (steth′ō-skōp) [Gr. *stetho-,* chest; *skopeo,* to view] An instrument originally devised for aid in hearing the respiratory and cardiac sounds in the chest and now used in hearing other sounds in the body as well. (p. 321)

strabismus (stra-biz′mŭs) [Gr. *strabismos,* a squinting] Lack of parallelism of the visual axes of the eyes. (p. 246)

stratum (strat′ŭm), pl. **strata** (strat′tă) [L., bed cover, layer] Layer of tissue. (p. 95)

stratum basale (bā-sāl′ē) The deepest layer of the epidermis; consists of columnar cells that undergo mitotic divisions. (p. 95)

stratum corneum (kōr′nē-ŭm) The most superficial layer of the epidermis; consists of dead, squamous cornified cells that have undergone keratinization. (p. 96)

stroke volume The volume of blood ejected from either the right or left ventricle during each heartbeat. (p. 321)

styloid (stī′loyd) [Gr. *stylos,* a stake or pen] A slender, pencil-shaped process. (p. 125)

subarachnoid space (sŭb-ă-rak′noyd) The fluid-filled space below the arachnoid layer covering the brain and spinal cord; contains cerebrospinal fluid. (p. 214)

subcutaneous (sŭb-koo-tā′nē-ŭs) [L. *sub,* under; *cutis,* skin] Under the skin; same tissue as the hypodermis. (p. 94)

sublingual gland (sŭb-ling′gwăl) One of a pair of salivary glands located below the tongue. (p. 427)

submandibular gland (sŭb-man-dib′ū-lăr) One of a pair of salivary glands located below the mandible. (p. 427)

submucosa (sŭb-moo-kō′să) The layer of connective tissue deep to the mucous membrane. (p. 425)

sulcus (soo′kŭs), pl. **sulci** (sŭl′sī) [L., ditch] A groove on the surface of the brain between gyri. (p. 207)

superficial (soo-per-fish′ăl) [L. *superficialis,* surface] Toward or on the surface. (p. 10)

superior (soo-pēr′ē-ōr) [L., higher] Up, or higher, with reference to the anatomical position. (p. 9)

superior vena cava (vē′nă kā′vă) Receives blood from the head, neck, and upper limbs and empties into the right atrium of the heart. (p. 310)

supination (soo′pi-nā′shŭn) [L. *supino,* to place something on its back] Rotation of the forearm so that the anterior surface is anterior, that is, the forearm is in the anatomical position. (p. 145)

surfactant (ser-fak′tănt) A mixture of lipoprotein molecules produced by the secretory cells of the alveolar epithelium of the lung; reduces water surface tension. (p. 404)

suture (soo′choor) [L. *surtura,* a seam] Fibrous joint between flat bones of the skull. (p. 137)

sweat gland (swet) Usually a secretory organ that produces a watery secretion called sweat that is released onto the surface of the skin; some sweat glands, however, produce an organic secretion. (p. 99)

sympathetic (sim-pă-thet′ik) Subdivision of the autonomic nervous system with preganglionic nerve cell bodies located in the thoracic and lumbar regions of the spinal cord; generally involved in preparing the body for immediate physical activity. (p. 192)

synapse (sin′aps) [Gr. *syn,* together; *haptein,* to clasp] Junction between a nerve cell and another nerve cell, muscle cell, or gland cell; in a chemical synapse, chemicals are released from the nerve cell as a result of an action potential in the nerve cell, the chemicals cross the cleft between the cells, and they cause some response in the postsynaptic cell. (p. 156)

synapsis (si-nap′sis) The pairing of homologous chromosomes during prophase of the first meiotic division. (p. 513)

synergist (sin′er-jist) A muscle that works with another muscle to cause a movement. (p. 165)

synovial cavity (si-nō′vē-ăl) [Gr. *syn,* coming together; *ovia,* resembling egg albumin] Cavity surrounding articulating bones of a freely movable or synovial joint; contains synovial fluid. (p. 141)

synovial fluid A somewhat viscous substance serving as a lubricant in movable joints, tendon sheaths, and bursae. (p. 139)

synovial joint Freely movable joint. (p. 139)

synovial membrane Lines the inside of a joint cavity; produces synovial fluid. (p. 139)

synthesis reaction (sin′thě-sis) The combination of atoms, ions, or molecules to form a new and larger molecule. (p. 35)

systemic circulation (sis-tem′ik) Blood flow through the system of blood vessels that carry blood from the left ventricle of the heart to the tissues of the body and back from the body to the right atrium. (p. 306)

systemic inflammation Inflammation that occurs in many areas of the body; in addition to the symptoms of local inflammation, can include increased neutrophil numbers in the blood, fever, and shock. (p. 375)

systole (sis′tō-lē) [Gr., a contracting] Contraction of the heart chambers during which blood leaves the chambers; usually refers to ventricular contraction. (p. 321)

systolic pressure (sis-tol′ik) The maximum arterial blood pressure reached during ventricular systole. (p. 350)

T

target tissue Tissue on which a hormone acts. (p. 264)

tarsal (tar′săl) [Gr. *tarsos*, sole of foot] Bone of the instep of the foot. (p. 136)

taste bud Sensory structure that is found mostly on the tongue and functions as a taste receptor. (p. 235)

tectorial membrane (tek-tŏr′ē-ăl) Membrane attached to the spiral lamina and extending over the hair cells; hairs of the hair cells have their tips embedded in the membrane. (p. 246)

temporal (tem′pŏ-răl) [L. *tempus*, time] Indicating the temple; the temple of the head is so named because it is there that the hair first begins turning white, indicating the passage of time. (p. 122)

tendinous intersection (ten′di-nŭs) One of the bands of connective tissue crossing the rectus abdominus muscle subdividing it and attaching it to adjacent connective tissue. (p. 172)

tendon (ten′dŏn) A tough connective tissue band connecting a muscle to bone. (p. 165)

teniae coli (tē′nē-ē kō′lī) [Gr. *tainia*, band, tapeworm; *coli*, colon] The segmented, longitudinal smooth muscle layer of the colon. (p. 434)

testis (tes′tis), pl. **testes** (test′tēz) One of two male reproductive glands located in the scrotum; produces testosterone and sperm cells. (p. 514)

testosterone (tes′tos′tě-rōn) Steroid hormone secreted primarily by the testes; aids in spermatogenesis, controls maintenance and development of male reproductive organs and secondary sexual characteristics, and influences sexual behavior. (p. 278)

tetany (tet′ă-nē) A condition in muscle contraction in which there is no relaxation between muscle twitches. (p. 159)

tetraiodothyronine (tet′ră-ī-ō-dō-thī′rō-nēn) **(T4)** One of the thyroid hormones that contains four iodine atoms; also called thyroxine. (p. 270)

thalamus (thal′ă-mŭs) [Gr., a bedroom] A large mass of gray matter making up the bulk of the diencephalon; involved in the relay of sensory input to the cerebrum. (p. 206)

thoracic cavity (thō-ras′ik) Space bounded by the neck, the thoracic wall, and the diaphragm. (p. 12)

thoracic duct Largest lymph vessel in the body; drains the left side of the head and neck, the left upper thorax, the left upper limb, and the inferior half of the body into the left subclavian vein. (p. 368)

thorax (thō′raks) [Gr., breastplate] The chest; the upper part of the trunk between the neck and the abdomen. (p. 12)

thrombocyte (throm′bō-sīt) [*thrombo-* + Gr. *kytos*, cell] A cell fragment involved in platelet plug and clot formation; also called a platelet. (p. 286)

thrombosis (throm′bō′sis) [Gr. *thrombos*, clot] The formation or presence of a clot (thrombus) inside of a blood vessel. (p. 339)

thrombus (throm′bŭs) [Gr. *thrombos*, clot] A clot within the cardiovascular system. (p. 295)

thymosin (thī′mō-sin) A hormone secreted from the thymus gland that helps activate the immune system. (p. 279)

thymus (thī′mŭs) [Gr. *thymos*, sweetbread] Bilobed lymphatic organ located in the inferior neck and superior mediastinum; involved with the maturation of T cells. (p. 372)

thyroid cartilage (thī′royd) [Gr. *thyreoeides*, shield] Largest laryngeal cartilage; forms the laryngeal prominence, or Adam's apple. (p. 396)

thyroid follicle One of many small spheres with walls consisting of cuboidal epithelial cells in the thyroid gland, and which is filled with proteins to which thyroid hormones are attached until they are secreted. (p. 270)

thyroid gland Endocrine gland located inferior to the larynx and consisting of two lobes connected by a narrow band; secretes the thyroid hormones. (p. 270)

thyroid hormone Any hormone secreted by the thyroid gland; especially those such as thyroxine that contain iodine and function to regulate metabolism and maturation of tissues. (p. 270)

thyroid–stimulating hormone (TSH) Hormone released from the hypothalamus that stimulates thyroid hormone secretion from the thyroid gland. (p. 269)

thyroxine (thī-rok′sēn, thī-rok′sin) See *tetraiodothyronine* (*T4*).

tissue (tish′ū) [L. *texo*, to weave] Collection of cells with similar structure and function and the substances between the cells. (p. 3)

tissue repair Substitution of viable cells for damaged or dead cells by regeneration or replacement. (p. 86)

tonsil (ton′sil) Any collection of lymphoid tissue; usually refers to large collections of lymphoid tissue beneath mucous membranes of the oral cavity and pharynx; lingual, pharyngeal, and palatine tonsils. (p. 368)

trabecula (tră-bek′ū-lă) [L. *trabs*, beam] A beam or plate of cancellous bone or other tissue. (p. 112)

trachea (tră′kē-ă) [Gr. *tracheia arteria*, rough artery] Air tube extending from the larynx into the thorax, where it divides to form bronchi; has 16–20 C-shaped pieces of cartilage in its walls. (p. 398)

tracheostomy (tră′kē-os′tō-mē) An incision into the trachea. (p. 399)

tract (trakt) Nerve tract; a bundle of neuron cell processes (axons) in the central nervous system, usually sharing a common function. (p. 196)

transfer RNA (tRNA) RNA that attaches to individual amino acids and transports them to the ribosomes, where they are connected to form a protein polypeptide chain. (p. 58)

transverse plane (trans-vers′) Plane separating the body into superior and inferior parts. (p. 12)

transverse section A cut made at right angles to the long axis of an organ. (p. 10)

trapezius (tra-pē′zē-ŭs) Back muscle, shaped like a trapezium (a four-sided geometric figure in which no two sides are parallel), that rotates the scapula. (p. 173)

triacylglycerol (trī-as′il-glis′er-ol) A common type of lipid, or fat, with three fatty acids bound to a glycerol molecule; also called a triglyceride. (p. 33)

triceps brachii (trī′seps brā′kē-ī) A three-headed muscle in the posterior arm that extends the forearm. (p. 174)

tricuspid valve (trī-kŭs′pid) Valve closing the opening between the right atrium and right ventricle of the heart. (p. 312)

triglyceride (trī-glis′er-īd) See *triacylglycerol*.

triiodothyronine (trī-ī′ō-dō-thī′rō-nēn) **(T3)** One of the thyroid hormones that contains three iodine atoms. (p. 270)

tRNA See *transfer RNA*.

trochanter (trō′kanter) [Gr., a runner] One of the large tubercles of the proximal femur. (p. 134)

trophoblast (trō′fō-blast) [Gr. *trophe*, nourishment; *blastos*, germ] The outer part of the blastocyst; enters the uterus and becomes the embryonic portion of the placenta. (p. 542)

trypsin (trip′sin) An enzyme released from the pancreas that digests proteins. (p. 444)

TSH See *thyroid-stimulating hormone*.

tubercle (too′ber-kl) Lump on a bone. (p. 120)

tuberosity (too′ber-os′i-tē) Lump on a bone, usually larger than a tubercle. (p. 120)

tubular reabsorption Movement of materials, by means of diffusion or active transport, from the filtrate within a nephron into the blood. (p. 487)

tubular secretion   Movement of materials, by means of active transport, from the blood into the filtrate of a nephron. (p. 487)

tumor   (too′mŏr) Any swelling, one of the cardinal signs of inflammation, or a new growth of tissue in which the multiplication of cells is uncontrolled and progressive (see *neoplasm*). (p. 89)

tunic   (too′nik) [L., coat] A layer or coat; one of the three enveloping layers of the wall of the eye; the three tunics are the fibrous, vascular, and nervous tunics; one of the three layers of blood vessels: tunica intimima, tunica media, and tunica adventitia. (p. 238)

tunica adventitia   (too′ni-kă ad-ven-tish′ă) Outermost fibrous coat of a vessel or an organ that is derived from the surrounding connective tissue. (p. 336)

tunica intima   (in′ti-mă) Innermost layer of a blood or lymphatic vessel; consists of endothelium and a small amount of connective tissue. (p. 336)

tunica media   Middle, usually muscular, coat of an artery or other tubular structure. (p. 336)

tympanic membrane   (tim-pan′ik) Cellular membrane that covers the inner opening of the external auditory meatus and separates the middle and external ears; vibrates in response to sound waves; the eardrum. (p. 243)

U

ulcer   (ŭl′ser) [L. *ulcus*, a sore] A lesion on the surface of the skin or a mucous membrane such as in the stomach or intestine caused by a superficial loss of tissue, usually with inflammation. (pp. 104, 451)

umbilical cord   (ŭm-bil′i-kăl) [L., naval] Cord connecting the fetus to the placenta; contains two umbilical arteries, which originate from the embryo's internal iliac arteries, that carry blood from the embryo to the placenta, and one umbilical vein that carries blood back to the fetus. (p. 543)

umbilical vein   Vein in the umbilical cord of the fetus by which the fetus receives nourishment from the placenta; becomes the round ligament of the liver in the adult. (p. 554)

upper motor neuron   A motor neuron located in the cerebral cortex and synapsing with a lower motor neuron in the brainstem or spinal cord. (p. 214)

ureter   (ū-rē′ter, ū′re-ter) [Gr. *oureter*, urinary canal] Tube conducting urine from the kidney to the urinary bladder. (p. 480)

urethra   (ū-rē′thră) A duct leading from the bladder, discharging the urine externally. (p. 486)

uterus   (ū′ter-ŭs) Hollow muscular organ in which the fertilized oocyte develops into a fetus. (p. 524)

uvula   (ū′vū-lă) [L. *uva*, grape] Small grapelike appendage at the posterior margin of the soft palate. (p. 396)

V

vaccine   (vak′sēn, vak-sēn′) Preparation of killed microorganisms, altered microorganisms, or derivatives of microorganisms intended to produce immunity; usually administered by injection, but sometimes ingestion is preferred. (p. 385)

vagina   (vă-jī′nă) [L., sheath] Genital canal in the female, extending from the uterus to the vulva. (p. 526)

variable region   Part of an antibody that combines with an antigen; responsible for the specificity of the antibody. (p. 378)

varicose (văr′ĭ-kōs) **vein**   A vein that is so dilated that the cusps of the valves are no longer capable of preventing backflow of blood; usually the veins in the lower legs or the hemorrhoidal veins. (p. 339)

vasoconstriction   (vă′sō-kon-strik′shŭn) Decreased diameter of blood vessels. (p. 336)

vasodilation   (vă′sō-dī-lā′shŭn) Increased diameter of blood vessels. (p. 336)

vasomotor center   (vă-sō-mō′ter) An area of the lower pons and upper medulla oblongata that continually transmits a low frequency of action potentials through sympathetic neurons to smooth muscle in blood vessels; can cause vasoconstriction and vasodilation. (p. 355)

vasomotor tone   Partial constriction of blood vessels in the periphery, which results from relatively constant sympathetic stimulation (p. 355)

vein   (vān) Blood vessel that carries blood toward the heart. (p. 336)

venous return   (vē′nŭs) Volume of blood returning to the heart. (p. 323)

ventilation   (ven-ti-lā′shŭn) Movement of air in and out of the lungs. (p. 401)

ventral   (ven′trăl) [L. *venter*, belly] In humans, synonymous with anterior. (p. 10)

ventral root   Motor (efferent) root of a spinal nerve. (p. 212)

ventricle   (ven′tri-kl) [L. *venter*, belly] A cavity; in the brain, one of four cavities filled with cerebrospinal fluid; one of two chambers of the heart that pump blood into arteries; there is a left and a right ventricle. (p. 309)

vernix caseosa   (ver′niks kā′sē-ō′să) Epithelial cells and sebaceous matter that covers the skin of the fetus. (p. 548)

vesicle   (ves′i-kl) [L. *vesicula*, blister] A small, membrane-bound sac containing material to be transported across the cell membrane. (p. 45)

vestibular fold   (ves-tib′ū-lăr) A false vocal fold. (p. 397)

vestibule   (ves′ti-bool) A small cavity or a space at the entrance of a canal (see also *vulva*). (p. 248)

villus   (vil′ŭs), pl. **villi** (vil′ī) [L., shaggy hair] Projection of the mucous membrane in the small intestine that increases surface area. (p. 429)

visceral   (vis′er-ăl) [L. *viscus*, the soft parts, internal organs] Relating to the internal organs. (p. 13)

visceral peritoneum   (per′i-tō-nē′ŭm) [L., organ] That part of the serous membrane in the abdominal cavity covering the surface of some abdominal organs. (p. 436)

vitamin   (vīt′ă-min) [L. *vita*, life; *amine*, from ammonia] One of a group of organic substances, present in minute amounts in natural foods, that are essential to normal metabolism; insufficient amounts in the diet may cause deficiency diseases. (p. 463)

vitamin D   Fat-soluble vitamin produced from a precursor molecule in skin exposed to ultraviolet light; increases calcium and phosphate uptake in the intestine. (p. 100)

vitreous humor   (vit′rē-ŭs) Transparent jellylike substance that fills the posterior compartment of the eye; helps maintain pressure within the eye and holds the lens and retina in place. (p. 242)

vocal fold   (vō′kăl) One of the ligaments that extends from the posterior surface of the thyroid cartilage to the paired cartilages of the larynx; the superior pair are the false vocal folds, and the inferior pair are the true vocal folds. (p. 397)

vulva   (vŭl′vă) [L. a wrapper or covering, seed covering, womb] The external genitalia of the female; the mons pubis, labia majora and minora, the clitoris, the vestibule and its glands, the opening of the urethra, and the opening of the vagina. (p. 526)

W

WBC   See *white blood cell*.

white blood cell (WBC)   A leukocyte in the blood; includes neutrophils, basophils, eosinophils, lymphocytes, and monocytes. (p. 286)

X

X-linked   A trait caused by a gene on the X chromosome. (p. 563)

Y

yolk sac   (yōk, yōlk) Highly vascular endodermal layer surrounding the yolk of an embryo. (p. 545)

Z

zygomatic   (zī′gō-mat′ik) [Gr. *zygon,* yoke] Referring to the zygomatic, or cheek, bone; the zygomatic arch is a bony arch created by the junction of the zygomatic and temporal bones. (p. 122)

zygomaticus muscle   (zī′gō-mat′i-kŭs) A muscle originating on the zygomatic bone and inserting onto the corner of the mouth, involved in smiling. (p. 168)

zygote   (zī′gōt) [Gr. *zygotos,* yoked] The single-celled, diploid cell product of fertilization, resulting from the union of the sperm cell and an oocyte. (p. 511)

Credits

Photographs

Chapter 1

1.1: © Pat Watson; **1.2a-m, 1.6a-b, 1.7a:** © Terry Cockerham/ Cynthia Alexander/Synapse Media Productions; **1.7b:** © Robert A. Chase, M.D./Videosurgery; **1.7c-d:** © R.T. Hutchings; **1.9:** © Terry Cockerham/Cynthia Alexander/Synapse Media Productions.

Chapter 2

2.3c: © Pat Watson; **2A:** © Howard Sochurek/Woodfin Camp; **2B:** © Phillipe Plailly/Photo Researchers, Inc.; **2.11b:** © Barry King/Tom Stack and Associates.

Chapter 3

3.3b: © Don Fawcett/Science Source/Photo Researchers, Inc.; **3.3c:** © Bernard Gilula/Photo Researchers, Inc.; **3.7b:** © Don Fawcett/Visuals Unlimited; **3.8b:** Fawcett/Heuser/Photo Researchers, Inc.; **3.16b:** © Dr. Birgit H. Satir.

Chapter 4

4.2b, 4.2d: © Ed Reschke; **4.2f:** © Trent Stephens; **4.2h:** © Victor Eroschenko; **4.2j:** © Ed Reschke; **4.21:** © R. Calentine/Visuals Unlimited; **4.5b, 4.5d:** © Trent Stephens;

4.5f, 4.5h: © Ed Reschke; **4.5j:** © Carolina Biological Supply/Phototake; **4.5l, 4.5n:** © Victor Eroschenko; **4.5p:** © Trent Stephens; **4.5r, 4.6b, 4.6d, 4.6f:** © Ed Reschke; **4.7b:** © Trent Stephens

Chapter 5

5.3b: © John Cunningham/Visuals Unlimited; **5.10a-c:** © Thomas B. Habif; **5.Aa:** © James Stevenson/SPL/Photo Researchers, Inc.; **5.Ab:** © Stan Levy/Photo Researchers, Inc.

Chapter 6

6.7b: © Biophoto Associates/Photo Researchers, Inc.; **6.B:** © Ewing Galloway; **6.11b:** © Synapse Media Productions; **6.16b, 6.20b:** © Trent Stephens; **6.21, 6.25, 6.32, 6.37a, 6.37b, 6.37c, 6.37d, 6.37e, 6.37f, 6.37g:** © Synapse Media Productions; **6.Ca-b:** © CNRI/SPL/ Photo Researchers, Inc.; **6.Da:** © Princess Margaret Rose Orthopedic Hospital/SPL/Photo Researchers, Inc.; **6.Db:** © Dr. Michael Klein/Peter Arnold, Inc.

Chapter 7

7.3a: © Ed Reschke; **7.3b:** © Richard Rodewald; **7.5b:** © Fred Hossler/Visuals Unlimited: **7.14:**

© Duomo/Paul J. Sutton; **7.24, 7.27a-b:** © Synapse Media Production; **7.A:** © Phillipe Plailly/SPL/Photo Researchers, Inc.

Chapter 8

8.18: Courtesy Branislav Vidic; **8.21a-b:** © R.T. Hutchings; **8.23a:** © Deep Light Productions/SPL/Photo Researchers, Inc.; **8.A:** © M. Bernsau/The Image Works

Chapter 9

9.5a: © Terry Cockerham/Cynthia Alexander/Synapse Media Productions; **9.10:** © A.L. Blum/Visuals Unlimited; **9.17b-c:** © Erica Stone/Peter Arnold, Inc.; **9.19a:** © Jerry Wachter/Photo Researchers, Inc.

Chapter 10

10.13b: © Victor Eroschenko; **10Aa-b:** © Ken Greer/Visuals Unlimited.

Chapter 11

11.3: © National Cancer Institute/SPL/Photo Researchers, Inc.; **11.6:** © Ed Reschke.

Chapter 12

12.5b: © R.T. Hutchings; **12.8:** © McMinn & Hutchings, *Color Atlas of Human Anatomy/*

Mosby; **12.13b:** © Ed Reschke; **12.18:** © Sam Collins/Art and Science, Inc.; **12.A:** © Hank Morgan/Photo Researchers, Inc.

Chapter 13

13.2: © Visuals Unlimited

Chapter 14

14.A: © Ken Greer/Visuals Unlimited.

Chapter 15

15.14b: © Custom Medical Stock Photo; **15.19a:** © Beebe/Custome Medical Stock Photo;

Chapter 16

16.3a-b: © Trent Stephens; **16.8b:** © David M. Phillips/Visuals Unlimited; **16.13b:** © Scott Camazine/Brian Camazine/Photo Researchers, Inc.; **16.A:** © Larry Dale Gordon/The Image Bank.

Chapter 17

17.11: Rothenberg Pacific/Pacific Stock

Chapter 18

18.3b: © R.T. Hutchings.

Chapter 19

19.C: © Blair Seitz/Photo Researchers, Inc.

Chapter 20

20.1a-d: © Dr. Yorgus Nikas/Jason Burns/Phototake; **20.8:** © John Giannicchi/Science Source/Photo Researchers, Inc.; **20.13a-b:** © Petit Format/Nestle/Photo Researchers, Inc.; **20.18:** © Phototake/CNRI/Photo Researchers, Inc.

Index

M

MRI. *See* Magnetic resonance
  imaging
mRNA. *See* Messenger ribonucleic
  acid
Mucin, 442
Mucosa, 430, 431, 432, 435
Mucous cells, 435
Mucous epithelium, 431
Mucous membrane, 71, 87–88
Mucous neck cells, 435, 436
Mucus, 77, 401, 443, 445
Multiple sclerosis, 222
Multipolar neurons, 197
Mumps, 434
Murmurs, 328
Muscle, 101. *See also* Cardiac
  muscle; Skeletal muscle;
  Smooth muscle; *specific
  muscles*
Muscle cells, 154
Muscle contractions, 160–66
  energy requirements for,
  163–65
  types of, 165–66
Muscle disorders, 166
Muscle fasciculi, 154
Muscle fatigue, 164–65
Muscle fiber, 85, 154, 158, 165
Muscles of expiration, 407, 408
Muscles of inspiration, 407, 408
Muscles of respiration, 407, 408
Muscle tissue, 71, 85–87, 94
Muscle tone, 165
Muscle twitch, 152, 160–63, 163
Muscular arteries, 342
Muscular dystrophy, 166
Muscularis, 431, 432, 435
Muscularis mucosa, 431
Muscular layer, of uterus, 536
Muscular system, 4, 152–92. *See
  also specific muscles*
  acute renal failure and, 515
  asthma and, 425
  benign uterine tumors and, 546
  burns and, 108
  development of, 559–60
  diarrhea and, 460
  functions of, 153
  hyperthyroidism and, 287
  malignant melanoma and, 92
  myocardial infarction and, 336
  osteoarthritis and, 149
  stroke and, 232
  systemic lupus erythematosus
  and, 395
Musculocutaneous nerve, 227
Myasthenia gravis, 166, 230
Myelinated axons, 198, 200
Myelin sheath, 196, 198, 199, 200
Myeloblasts, 295
Myelocytes, 295
Myelograph, 220
Myocardial infarction, 329, 335–36

Myocarditis, 329
Myocardium, 320, 321
Myofibril, 152, 154, 155,
  156, 321
Myofilament, 152, 154
Myometrium, 533, 536
Myopia, 249
Myosin, 154
Myosin molecule, 155
Myosin myofilament, 155
Myotonic dystrophy, 230
Myotonic muscular dystrophy,
  166
Myxedema, 276

N

NADH. *See* Nicotinamide adenine
  dinucleotide
Nail, 95, 101, 102
Nail bed, 101
Nail body, 101, 102
Nail matrix, 101, 102
Nail root, 101, 102
Nares, 400
Nasal bone, 122, 124, 125, 126
Nasal cavity, 4, 125, 240, 399,
  400–401, 401
Nasal conchae, 125, 126, 400, 401
Nasal retina, 248
Nasal septum, 11, 125, 126
Nasolacrimal canal, 124, 126
Nasolacrimal duct, 241, 242, 401
Nasopharynx, 401, 402
Natural immunity, 391
Natural killer (NK) cells, 380
Navicular, 138, 140
Nearsightedness, 249
Neck, 12
  arteries of, 349–50
  of bone, 124
  of femur, 138
  of humerus, 133
  muscles of, 173
  of tooth, 433
  veins of, 351
Necrosis, 345
Negative feedback, 1, 7, 8–9
Neisseria gonorrhoeae, 542
Neocortical death, 571
Neonatal gonorrheal ophthalmia,
  249, 568
Neonate, 565–67, 570
  first year, 569
Neoplasm, 91
Nephron, 487, 488, 491
Nerve cells. *See* Neurons
Nerve pathways, 215
Nerves, 5, 198
Nerve tracts, 198, 215

Nervous system, 5, 193–235, 283
  acute renal failure and, 515
  asthma and, 425
  burns and, 108
  cells of, 195–98
  control of ventilation, 419
  cystic fibrosis and, 67
  development of, 559–60
  diarrhea and, 460
  disorders of, 418
  divisions of, 194, 195
  functions of, 194
  hyperthyroidism and, 287
  malignant melanoma and, 92
  muscular dystrophy and, 190
  and osteoarthritis, 149
  systemic lupus erythematosus
  and, 395
Nervous system poisoning,
  571
Nervous tissue, 71, 87
  organization of, 198
Nervous tunic, 243–45
Neural crest, 555–56
Neural crest cells, 556, 557
Neural folds, 555, 557
Neuralgia, 230
Neural groove, 555, 557
Neural plate, 555, 557
Neural tube, 550, 555–56, 557
Neuritis, 230
Neuroectoderm, 555
Neurofibromatosis, 230
Neurofilaments, 196
Neurogenic shock, 369
Neuroglia, 87, 193, 197, 198, 199
Neurohormones, 262, 268
Neurolemmocytes, 198
Neuromodulators, 261, 262
Neuromuscular junction, 152, 158
Neuron, 87, 193
Neuronal circuits, 206–7
Neuronal loss, 570
Neuron cell body, 196, 199
Neurons, 87, 195–98
Neurotransmitters, 158, 159, 193,
  203, 204, 261, 262
Neutrons, 19, 20, 21, 26
Neutrophil, 88
Neutrophilic band cell, 295
Neutrophilic myelocyte, 295
Neutrophils, 293, 294, 295, 297–98,
  298, 379
Nevus, 91
Newborn. *See* Neonate
Niacin, 470
Nicotinamide adenine dinucleotide
  (NADH), 474
Night blindness, 245
Nipples, 537
Nissl bodies, 195, 196
Nitrogen, 21t
Nitrogen parital pressure, 414

Upper limb, 12, 135
  arteries of, 347, 351
  bones of, 122, 132–35
  muscles of, 178–81
  surface anatomy of, 182
  veins of, 352, 353
Upper motor neurons, 218
Upper respiratory tract, 400
  infections of, 423
Ureters, 5, 6, 488, 489, 490, 494–95, 513, 523, 526
Urethra, 5, 6, 177, 488, 489, 494–95, 523, 526, 532, 537
Urinary bladder, 5, 6, 488, 489, 494–95, 513, 523, 526, 532
Urinary sphincter, 494, 495
Urinary system, 5, 488–95
  arteries of, 493
  asthma and, 425
  benign uterine tumors and, 546
  burns and, 108
  development of, 559–60, 561
  diarrhea and, 460
  disorders of, 512–13
  functions of, 488
  malignant melanoma and, 92
  muscular dystrophy and, 190
  myocardial infarction and, 336
  stroke and, 232
  systemic lupus erythematosus and, 395
  veins of, 493
Urine
  concentration, regulation of, 500–504
  movement of, 504
  production of, 495–500
  substances in, 495
  values of, 586
  volume, regulation of, 500–504
Uterine cavity, 533, 536
Uterine tube, 5, 520, 533, 534–36
Uterine tumors, benign, 546
Uterus, 5, 520, 532, 536
  hormones of, 271
  during menopause, 541
Utricle, 252, 254
Utricular macula, 254
Uvula, 401, 402, 433, 434

V

Vaccination, 391
Vaccine, 373, 391
Vagina, 5, 177, 520, 532, 536, 537, 541
Vaginal condom, 545
Vagus nerve (X), 224, 225
Valves, 345. *See also* Heart valves

Variable, 7
Variable region, of antibodies, 384
Varicose veins, 345
  hemorrhoidal, 441
Vasa recta, 493
Vascular tunic, 242–43
Vas deferens, 525. *See also* Ductus deferens
Vasectomy, 545
Vasoconstriction, 341, 342
Vasodilation, 341, 343
Vasomotor center, 361
Vasomotor instability, during menopause, 541
Vasomotor tone, 361
Vasopressin mechanism, 365–67, 367, 368
Vasospasm, 223
Vastus intermedius muscle, 168, 185
Vastus lateralis muscle, 168, 185, 186, 188
Vastus medialis muscle, 168, 185, 186, 188
Vein, 341, 342, 344–45, 351–55, 493
Vena cava
  inferior, 5, 312, 314, 315, 318, 320, 351, 352, 354, 355, 356, 438, 489
  superior, 5, 312, 314, 315, 316, 318, 320, 351, 352, 353, 354
Venous return, 330, 341
Venous thrombosis, 108
Ventilation, 407–12
  chemical control of, 419–21
  effects of exercise on, 422
  modification of, 419–22
  nervous control of, 419
  rhythmic, 416–19
Ventral, 10
Ventral cavity, 12
Ventral respiratory groups, 417
Ventral root, 216, 217
Ventricle
  of brain, 220
  of heart, 311, 314, 315, 316, 317
Ventricular diastole, 326
Ventricular systole, 327
Ventricular tachycardia, 325
Venule, 344–45
Vernix caseosa, 563
Vertebra, 11, 129, 131
  regional differences in, 128–31, 130
Vertebral arch, 128, 129
Vertebral artery, 349
Vertebral canal, 128, 131
Vertebral column, 4, 11, 113, 122, 123, 127–31, 133, 174
Vertebral foramen, 129, 130
Vesicle, 43, 45, 49
Vestibular fold, 401, 403

Vestibular gland, 536
Vestibular membrane, 250, 252, 253
Vestibule, 251, 252, 254, 401, 532, 536, 537
Vestibulocochlear nerve (VIII), 223, 224, 250, 251
Vibrio cholerae, 457
Viral hepatitis, 456–57
Viral infection, 106
Visceral artery, 351
Visceral pericardium, 15, 313, 315, 320, 321
Visceral peritoneum, 15, 430, 441–42, 534
Visceral pleura, 15, 404, 405, 407
Visceral serous membrane, 13
Vision, 240–47, 246
Vision testing, 247
Visual association area, 212
Visual cortex, 212, 247, 248
Visual field, 247, 248
Visual pathways, 248
Vital capacity, 411, 412
Vitamin, 464, 465, 469, 470–71
Vitamin A (retinol), 469, 470
  deficiency, 243–45
Vitamin B$_1$ (thiamine), 470
Vitamin B$_2$ (riboflavin), 470
Vitamin B$_3$ (niacin), 470
Vitamin B$_6$ (pyridoxine), 470
Vitamin B$_{12}$ (cobalamin), 470
Vitamin C (ascorbic acid), 470
Vitamin D (cholecalciferol ergosterol), 95, 102, 277, 470
Vitamin K, 301
Vitreous humor, 243, 246
Vocal cord, 401
Vocal folds, 403
Voltage-gated potassium ion channels, 323
Voltage-gated sodium ion channels, 323
Volume, 252
Voluntary phase, of deglutition, 443–45
Vomer bone, 122, 125, 126, 128
Vomiting, 456
Von Willebrand's disease, 307
Von Willebrand's factor, 299
Vulva, 536

W

Warfarin (Coumadin), 301
Warm-blooded animals, 481
Warm receptors, 237
Warts, 106
  genital, 542